HANDBOOK OF PHYSIOLOGY

SECTION 6: Alimentary Canal, VOLUME V

HANDBOOK EDITORIAL COMMITTEE

HANDBOOK OF PHYSIOLOGY

Section 6: Alimentary Canal

HANDBOOK OF PHYSIOLOGY

A critical, comprehensive presentation

of physiological knowledge and concepts

SECTION 6:   # Alimentary Canal

VOLUME V. *Bile; Digestion; Ruminal Physiology*

Section Editor: CHARLES F. CODE

Editorial Committee
    JOHN R. BROBECK
    ROBERT K. CRANE
    HORACE W. DAVENPORT
    MORTON I. GROSSMAN
    HENRY D. JANOWITZ
    C. LADD PROSSER
    THOMAS H. WILSON

Executive Editor: WERNER HEIDEL

American Physiological Society, WASHINGTON, D. C., 1968

Contents*

* Most of the manuscripts of the chapters in this volume were received for publication between September 1966 and February 1967.

BILE; DIGESTION; RUMINAL PHYSIOLOGY

CHAPTER 110

Formation of bile pigment[1]

IRWIN M. ARIAS | *Department of Medicine, Albert Einstein College of Medicine, and The Bronx Municipal Hospital Center, New York City*

CHAPTER CONTENTS

FROM ANTIQUITY TO ABOUT 1850, little was known about bile pigments, although jaundice had been clinically associated with various types of liver disease since the time of Hippocrates. In the latter half of the nineteenth century, bilirubin was crystallized and physiological studies of its formation were begun. The introduction, in 1916, of Ehrlich's diazo reaction for estimation of bilirubin in biological specimens and description of direct- and indirect-reacting bilirubin began forty years of study and speculation into the role of the liver in bile pigment excretion. Identification of direct-reacting bilirubin as bilirubin diglucuronide in 1956, and its subsequent biosynthesis, has resulted in partial elucidation of the metabolic pathway of bilirubin formation and excretion by the liver and the pathogenesis of jaundice, particularly in congenital and inheritable disorders. Present experimental inquiry concerns the molecular basis of the formation of bile pigment and its hepatic uptake, conjugation, and excretion; the biological regulation and interdependence of these processes, and their association with cellular ultrastructures. This chapter reviews the development of present concepts of bile pigment formation and excretion, emphasizing unresolved problems.

BILE PIGMENT FORMATION FROM HEMOGLOBIN

Although Hippocrates associated jaundice with anemia (1) and Maimonides wrote that the pigment in bile stones probably came from blood pigment (175), not until 1847 was this postulate supported experimentally, when Virchow isolated bilirubin crystals from ecchymotic areas in skin and other tissues (263). Tarchanoff later injected blood into dogs with bile fistulas and observed increased bile pigment excretion (254). These observations were confirmed, and a relationship between bile pigment excretion and the degree of anemia experimentally

[1] The work performed in the author's laboratory was supported by Public Health Service Research Grant AM-02019 from the National Institute of Arthritis and Metabolic Diseases, Bethesda, Md., and The New York Heart Association and Heart Fund, Inc.

produced in dogs was observed (180). In 1937, Fischer and associates provided further evidence that bilirubin is derived from the heme group of hemoglobin by demonstrating the closely related tetrapyrrole structures of heme and bilirubin (83).

Based on the survival in the circulation of newly formed erythrocytes containing labeled hemoglobin after administration of glycine-^{15}N, the estimate is that the average life span of the mature, circulating red blood cell is approximately 120 days (171). The normal human erythrocyte is destroyed as a function of its age and not in a random fashion as occurs in other species (169). The site of sequestration and subsequent degradation of senescent red blood cells is the reticuloendothelial system, particularly of the spleen, liver, and bone marrow, but other organs also participate (208). Aschoff (25) was probably the first to suggest this possibility based on morphologic studies following injections of blood in various animals. The classic studies of Bollman and Mann revealed that bilirubin formation occurs after hepatectomy (178). Their observations corrected earlier conclusions of Minkowski & Naunyn (183) who observed that hemolysis in hepatectomized geese failed to produce jaundice. According to Schmid, the latter observation was correct and is clarified by the finding that in the goose virtually all reticuloendothelial cells are located in the liver (223).

The end products of erythrocyte destruction are bilirubin, iron, and globin (208). Bilirubin is released into the circulation and ultimately excreted by the liver. By contrast, iron is reutilized. Some iron is stored locally as hemosiderin, a ferric hydroxide polymer, whereas the remainder reenters the plasma where it combines with siderophilin, a β_1-globulin, and is transported to other tissues for storage as hemosiderin or as ferritin, which is a ferrous iron-protein complex (184). The fate of globin is unknown; however, it has been suggested that globin is hydrolyzed to its substituent amino acids, which enter a labile protein pool (123). Before 1956, some investigators believed that globin left the reticuloendothelial system firmly bound to bilirubin and was ultimately separated from it in the liver (180, 182), and the globin-bilirubin complex was thought to be responsible for the indirect van den Bergh reaction. Subsequent electrophoretic studies showed that bilirubin in serum is associated with albumin and not globin (105, 201). Globin is probably removed at a stage of hemoglobin degradation within the reticuloendothelial system, although its subsequent metabolism is uncertain.

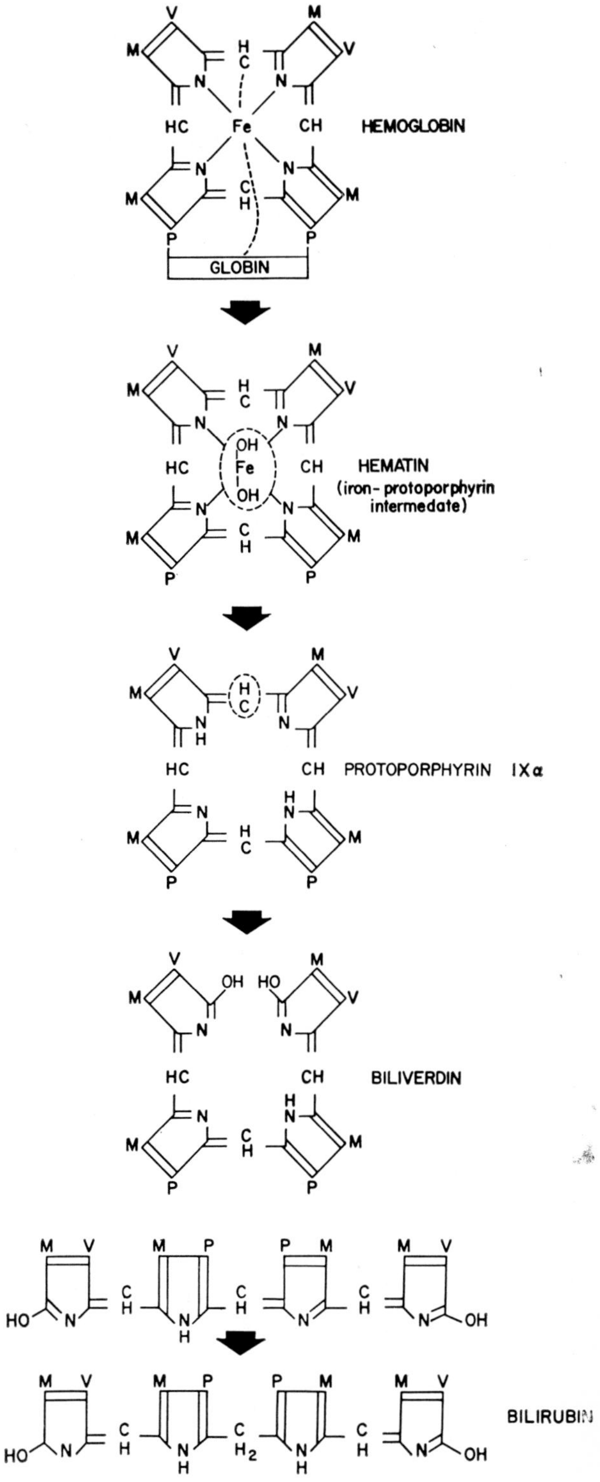

M = − CH$_3$ (Methyl)

V = − CH = CH$_2$ (Vinyl)

P = − CH$_2$ − CH$_2$ − COOH (Proprionic Acid)

FIG. 1. Bile pigment formation from hemoglobin. Hemoglobin degradation to form hematin and globin.

Possibly globin leaves the reticuloendothelial system and is metabolized elsewhere.

The precise biochemical sequence whereby the hemoglobin of senescent erythrocytes is catabolized into bile pigment is uncertain. Experimental evidence has suggested two possible cellular mechanisms.

Hemoglobin Degradation
To Form Hematin and Globin

According to some investigators, the initial step involves splitting of hemoglobin to form globin and hematin, a hydroxide of the trivalent-iron derivative of heme [(171); Fig. 1]. Hematin is then converted to protoporphyrin IXa by removal of iron, following which oxidation of the α-methene bridge occurs; a carbon atom is lost, the porphyrin ring opens to form a straight-chain tetrapyrrole, biliverdin, and on reduction of the central methene bond, bilirubin is formed. Endogenous formation of carbon monoxide is dependent on the degradation of hemoglobin; one molecule of hemoglobin results in the formation of four molecules of carbon monoxide (238). Carbon monoxide combines with hemoglobin to form carbon monoxyhemoglobin and is subsequently eliminated in the expired air. Endogenous carbon monoxide formation has been found to provide a reliable estimate of hemoglobin degradation (44).

Despite several experimental studies, there is no evidence that hematin is actually an intermediate in hemoglobin catabolism. London (168) administered hematin-^{15}N to a dog and recovered 18 % of the isotope in stercobilin which was excreted in the feces during the subsequent nine days. Hematin has been converted into bilirubin in vitro (149). Hematin-^{14}C injected into rats with bile fistulas was converted into bilirubin-^{14}C with an efficiency of approximately 60 % (239). Conversion of hematin to bilirubin has been regarded as the cause of the increased bilirubin production that occurs with intravascular hemolysis (33) or severe liver disease (230) and after extravasation of blood into tissues (263). These pathologic conditions are associated with the formation of hematin which may be present in plasma bound to albumin (methemalbumin) (81). Hematin is not normally present in blood but is presumably present in reticuloendothelial cells.

It was formerly suggested that bilirubin is formed from hematin through an intermediate such as protoporphyrin IXa. London et al. (173) injected protoporphyrin-^{15}N and recovered a small fraction of the label in stercobilin; however, the possibility was not

M= $-CH_3$ (Methyl)

V= $-CH=CH_2$ (Vinyl)

P= $-CH_2-CH_2-COOH$ (Proprionic Acid)

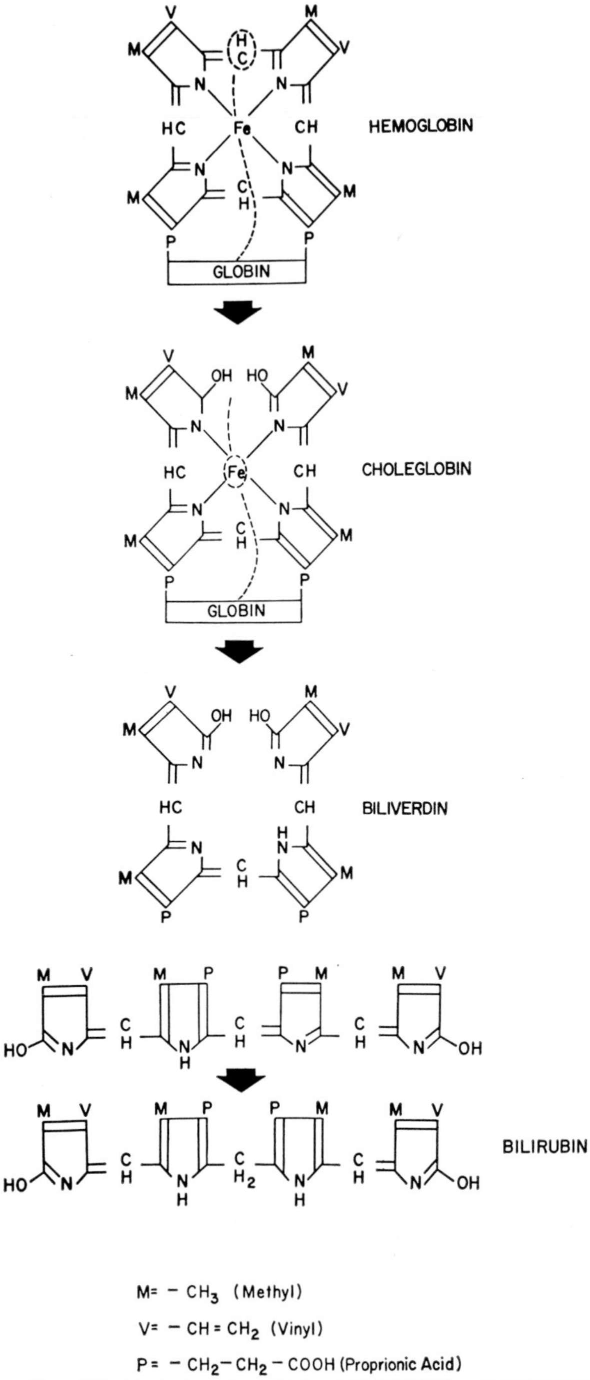

FIG. 2. Bile pigment formation from hemoglobin. Hemoglobin degradation to form choleglobin.

excluded that iron was introduced into protoporphyrin to form heme before its conversion to bile pigment (162). Protoporphyrin can spontaneously combine with ferrous iron to form heme (128). Kench et al. (149) formed bile pigment in vitro by coupled oxidation of l-ascorbic acid and hematin, methemalbumin, hemoglobin, or methemoglobin, but failed to do so with protoporphyrin. These observations and those of Lemberg & Legge (162) indicate that divalent or trivalent iron must be within the porphyrin molecule before cleavage of its ring structure can occur. Although the data are inconclusive, current evidence suggests that protoporphyrin is not an intermediate in bile pigment production from hematin.

Hemoglobin Degradation To Form Choleglobin

A more widely accepted alternative pathway for hemoglobin degradation has been proposed by Lemberg and associates (162). According to these investigators, the initial step involves oxidative removal of the carbon atom in the α-methene bridge, resulting in the opening of the porphyrin ring to yield choleglobin, a green, iron-containing pigment-protein complex (Fig. 2). The precise structure of choleglobin is unknown, for it has never been isolated. Several possible structures have been suggested, including the one shown in Figure 2. In this scheme, iron and globin are subsequently removed and biliverdin is formed. The choleglobin complex has a well-defined absorption band at 629 mμ in the reduced form and a maximum at 670 mμ in the unreduced form (109). The chemical properties of choleglobin and hemoglobin are so similar that it has not been possible to separate the former pigment from the excess of hemoglobin always present. Lemberg suggested that the conversion of hemoglobin to choleglobin involves coupled oxidation with ascorbic acid and glutathione because this reaction occurs in vitro under physiological conditions of pH, temperature, and oxygen tension. By contrast, the conversion of hematin or methemalbumin to bile pigment in vitro requires ascorbic acid concentrations and oxygen tensions that are never attained in the tissues (162). Choleglobin and biliverdin have been found in rabbit erythrocytes, and after production of hemolysis with phenylhydrazine their concentrations increased significantly (161). Other investigators have been unable to confirm this, so the importance of hemoglobin degradation within erythrocytes is uncertain (94, 95). More recently Petryka and associates demonstrated that hematin in Lemberg's in vitro system is cleaved at positions other than the α-methene bridge (204), whereas under physiological conditions cleavage of the porphyrin ring occurs exclusively at the α-methene bridge (83).

The specificity of the cleavage of the porphyrin ring which occurs physiologically suggests that an enzymatic mechanism may be present. Nakajima and associates (186) have isolated and characterized an enzyme, heme α-methenyl oxygenase, which is responsible for oxidative cleavage of heme at the α-methenyl bridge. The enzyme is found in the supernatant fraction of homogenates of beef and guinea pig liver, and requires NADH, ferrous iron, and an activator from the nuclear fraction for activity. The compound formed in the reaction with heme was partially identified and is analogous to the verdochrome pigment of Lemberg & Legge (162) which is formed nonenzymatically. The pigment has an open tetrapyrrole structure with a formyl group at the site of ring cleavage and one atom of iron (185). It is easily converted to biliverdin by a second enzyme, heme α-methenyl formylase, with concomitant liberation of iron and formaldehyde. It is of considerable physiological interest that the enzymatic conversion of hemoglobin to bile pigment is accelerated with addition of haptoglobin. The biological role of haptoglobin is uncertain (159). These studies suggest that haptoglobin may function in the enzymatic conversion of hemoglobin in vivo as well as in the transfer of hemin from plasma to the liver cell.

At present it is impossible to decide whether hemoglobin catabolism in vivo involves the formation of hematin, choleglobin, or both; however, it is agreed that biliverdin is the principal bile pigment initially formed. A minor hemoglobin fraction may be converted into metabolites other than bilirubin. In rats after injection of ^{14}C-labeled antibody-sensitized erythrocytes, only 63–80% of the sequestered heme pigment appeared in the bile as bilirubin-[14]C (200). The production of monopyrrolic or dipyrrolic compounds, undetectable by current methods, is believed responsible for this observation. Dipyrrolic compounds of the bilifuscin, mesobilifuscin, and pentdyopent groups have been identified and isolated from the feces of healthy subjects (103, 234, 235), and pentdyopent has been found in the urine of jaundiced patients (34, 134); however, their origin and significance are unknown.

The normal production of bile pigment from hemoglobin may be quantitatively estimated. One gram of hemoglobin (mol wt 68,000) yields approximately 34 mg of bilirubin (mol wt 572) on degradation. Assuming that an average adult has a blood volume of 5 liters, a hemoglobin concentration of 15 g per 100 ml, and that 1% of mature, circulating erythrocytes are destroyed per day, approximately 7.5 g of hemoglobin are destroyed per day, and this results in production of approximately 250 mg of bile pigment (150). The capacity of the reticuloendothelial system to convert hemoglobin to bile pigment was studied by Crosby in healthy subjects (63). Increasing amounts of hemoglobin were infused intravenously and the concentrations of bilirubin and hemoglobin were estimated. The maximal capacity of the reticuloendothelial system to convert hemoglobin to bile pigment was between 45 and 50 g of hemoglobin per day, which is equivalent to a daily production of approximately 1.5 g of bilirubin.

Conversion of Biliverdin to Bilirubin

The first bile pigment formed in the reticuloendothelial system is biliverdin, which must be rapidly converted to bilirubin since no biliverdin is found in normal serum (154), although biliverdin glucuronides are found in human, rabbit, and snake bile (93, 190). Lemberg, studying the enzymatic reduction of biliverdin by washings of guinea pig liver mince, observed that several intermediary metabolites of carbohydrate metabolism stimulated the conversion, and postulated that biliverdin was a nonspecific acceptor of electrons (162). Recently Singleton & Laster (237) have purified bilirubin reductase from guinea pig liver and spleen and from human liver. Highly purified preparations of alcohol, lactate, or malate dehydrogenases failed to catalyze biliverdin reduction. Conversion of biliverdin to bilirubin in vivo was demonstrated by Goldstein & Lester (105), who prepared biliverdin-^{14}C by oxidation of bilirubin-^{14}C, administered 200 μg of biliverdin-^{14}C intravenously to rats with bile fistulas, and recovered 60–80 % of the radioactive dose in bile as bilirubin-^{14}C (106).

BILE PIGMENT FORMATION FROM SOURCES OTHER THAN MATURE CIRCULATING ERYTHROCYTES

The view that bile pigment is derived to a significant extent from sources other than the hemoglobin of circulating erythrocytes was originally proposed by Whipple (271a) in 1922. Subsequently, the studies of London and colleagues (171) and of Gray et al. (109) clearly demonstrated that normally 10–30 % of bilirubin formed is derived from such sources. After administration of glycine-^{15}N to normal subjects for 2–4 days, ^{15}N was demonstrable in stercobilin isolated from feces before any of the newly formed, circulating erythrocytes containing ^{15}N-labeled hemoglobin had been destroyed. This component was referred to as the "early labeled pigment" and several possible sources were suggested (171): *1)* heme or porphyrins not utilized during the synthesis of hemoglobin; *2)* intracorpuscular degradation of hemoglobin during erythrocyte maturation in the bone marrow; *3)* destruction of newly formed erythrocytes in the bone marrow before they reach the circulation; *4)* direct synthesis of bile pigment from porphyrins without degradation of a porphyrin ring, and *5)* turnover of other heme proteins such as myoglobin, catalase, peroxidase, and the cytochromes.

Recent studies indicate that the early labeled pigment fraction has at least two components, one originating from the bone marrow, the other originating in the liver. Yamamoto and associates (276) studied the rapid phase of bilirubin labeling in plasma and bile in humans after the intravenous administration of glycine-2-^{14}C and ALA-^{14}C.[2] After glycine administration the isolated plasma bilirubin exhibited peaks of radioactivity at 12–24 hours and at 3–5 days, whereas after ALA administration a single peak of bilirubin radioactivity was observed at 1.5–6 hours (276). The initial peak originates in the liver and the second peak is associated with erythropoiesis. The conversion of ALA-^{14}C to bilirubin is too rapid to be erythropoietic in origin. In rats, the rate and magnitude of bilirubin-^{14}C production by isolated perfused liver following administration of glycine-2-^{14}C are comparable to that observed for the early labeled pigment in the whole animal (210). The source of the hepatic component of the early labeled pigment is unknown, but recent observations suggest that heme compounds are involved. Schwartz and associates administered glycine-2-^{14}C, ALA-^{14}C, and protoporphyrin-^{14}C to dogs with bile fistulas and studied the incorporation of ^{14}C into bilirubin in bile, hemoglobin protoporphyrin, and nonhemoglobin hemes of liver and other tissues (231). The nonerythropoietic component of bilirubin-^{14}C formation was limited to 2 days, and over 99 % of ALA or protoporphyrin converted into bilirubin-^{14}C resulted from nonhemoglobin heme turnover in liver and other tissues. The rapid turnover of hepatic catalase (66, 205), tryptophan pyrrolase (221), or perhaps the hepatic P-450 microsomal enzyme (207) makes these heme enzymes possible sources for the hepatic component of the early labeled pigment. The

[2] These abbreviations are used throughout this chapter: ALA (delta-aminolevulinic acid); ATP (adenosine triphosphate); BSP (sulfobromophthalein sodium); CB (conjugated bilirubin); NAD and NADH (nicotinamide adenine dinucleotide and reduced form); PP (inorganic pyrophosphate); UCB (unconjugated bilirubin); UDP (uridine diphosphate); UDPG (uridine diphosphate glucose); UDPGA (uridine diphosphate glucuronic acid); UTP (uridine triphosphate), and EDTA (ethylene diaminetetraacetate).

quantitative contribution of hepatic bilirubin synthesis to the early labeled pigment is uncertain and may differ in different species. Although unconjugated hyperbilirubinemia is associated with many disorders of erthropoiesis in which the erythropoietic component of the early labeled pigment is greatly increased, no clinical disorder is known in which jaundice results from exaggeration of hepatic bilirubin synthesis.

The early labeled pigment is responsible for a major portion of the bile pigment excreted in patients with pernicious anemia (170), sickle cell anemia (272), and congenital porphyria (109, 172). The association of the early labeled pigment with erythrocyte formation is further supported by an increase in this fraction in other disorders of erythropoiesis such as thalassemia (209) and after hemorrhage (110). James & Abbot (142) suggest that the early labeled pigment may arise partly from nonerythroid sources after studying patients with complete erythroid aplasia who demonstrated this fraction. Israels and associates (137–139) have described cases in which the early labeled pigment accounted for at least 65% of total bile pigment formed and was associated with mild unconjugated hyperbilirubinemia not accounted for by increased destruction of mature, circulating erythrocytes. Although the term "shunt hyperbilirubinemia" was used to describe this disorder, there is no evidence for a true shunt of porphyrins to bile pigment without heme as an intermediate, and in this regard the terminology is misleading. Similar cases have been described by others, and evidence suggests selective destruction of young erythrocytes in the bone marrow (8, 31).

The above discussion indicates that the recognized bile pigment has several sources, the most important of which is the hemoglobin of mature, circulating erythrocytes. However, there are other sources of bile pigment, and additional pathways of bilirubin metabolism may exist which result in formation of metabolites not detectable by current methods.

VAN DEN BERGH REACTION AND
BILIRUBIN CONJUGATES

The coupling of bilirubin with diazotized sulfanilic acid involves splitting of the bilirubin molecule with the formation of two relatively stable dipyrrole azopigment molecules (75). This reaction was first described by Ehrlich, in 1883, who used chloroform as a solvent for bilirubin and added alcohol to permit solution of the otherwise immiscible aqueous reagent (75). Fifty years later, van den Bergh & Snapper (260) used this reaction to estimate bilirubin quantitatively in body fluids and included alcohol in the reaction mixture. In 1916, van den Bergh & Muller (259) discovered that alcohol could be omitted in performing the reaction when using bile or sera from patients with obstructive jaundice, but not with alkaline solutions of crystalline bilirubin or sera from patients with hemolytic jaundice. To these two reactions they applied the terms "direct" and "indirect," respectively. Many theories were subsequently advanced to account for the different behavior of bilirubin in the van den Bergh reaction (108). The two major theories were 1) that differences in binding of bilirubin to protein were responsible for the two types of reactions, and 2) that two chemically distinct forms of bilirubin exist, one requiring alcohol to couple with diazotized sulfanilic acid and the other not.

Pigments I and II

In 1953, Cole & Lathe (55) proved that protein binding is not essential for the two reactions. They separated protein-free preparations of directly and indirectly reacting bilirubin by reverse-phase chromatography on silicone-treated kieselguhr using a solvent system of chloroform, methanol, carbon tetrachloride, and phosphate buffer at pH 6. The direct-reacting pigment migrated rapidly down the column and was water soluble at an acid pH; however, the indirect-reacting pigment moved more slowly and was soluble in organic solvents. Subsequently, in collaboration with Billing, it was demonstrated that the direct-reacting pigment could be partitioned in a solvent system of *n*-butanol and phosphate buffer at pH 6 into two fractions, both of which gave a direct van den Bergh reaction and were subsequently designated "pigments I and II" (37, 56). Extracts of bile yielded predominantly pigment II with lesser amounts of pigment I and traces of bilirubin. The pattern was similar in jaundiced urine; however, pigment I was the major component. The serum bile pigment in hemolytic jaundice was bilirubin, and in obstructive jaundice the serum bile pigment was a mixture of pigment I and pigment II. Basing judgment on these observations, Billing suggested that pigment I is an intermediate in the conversion of bilirubin to pigment II (36, 56). Pigment I is found in the serum of hepatectomized dogs (46) and is converted into pigment II by isolated perfused rat liver (228). These observations suggested that pigment I is formed in extrahepatic tissues and is converted into pigment II exclusively in the liver. The view that pigment I is a single chemical compound was widely accepted, and its measurement has influenced clinical conclusions regarding the pathogenesis of various forms of jaundice (228, 278); however, there is evidence that pigment I may be a complex of bilirubin and pigment II (112, 191, 266). Gregory subjected pigment I to additional chromatographic analysis and found that by slight alteration of the chromatographic system, pigment I is readily resolved into two zones behaving as free bilirubin and pigment II (112). Similar treatment of pigment II yielded only minute amounts of free bilirubin. Weber & Schalm (266) mixed increasing amounts of bilirubin with equal amounts of pigment II in serum and observed increased formation of a pigment I complex. The nature of pigment I needs further study although evidence is accumulating that it probably is a complex.

The instability of pigments I and II made it difficult to establish their structural differences. The problem was solved by the discovery that on diazotization they yielded different azopigments which are stable and can be separated chromatographically (35, 222). Using a silicone-treated kieselguhr column and a solvent system of n-butanol, water, and citrate buffer at pH 4, Billing showed that the diazotization product of bilirubin (azopigment A) is insoluble in water, whereas the corresponding product of pigment II (azopigment B) is water soluble (35). The azo derivative of pigment I behaved as a mixture of azopigments A and B. Because of the asymmetric arrangements of the methyl and vinyl side chains in the bile pigments, each of the azopigments consists of a mixture of two isomers differing only in the position of the side chains. Although the isomers can be separated chromatographically, their behavior is so similar that they may be considered together as if they were identical (41).

Bilirubin Glucuronide and Other Conjugates

In 1956, three groups of investigators independently established that the direct-reacting bile pigment is a glucuronide conjugate of bilirubin (39, 222, 253). Billing et al. (39) isolated a pure preparation of azopigment B from diazotized human bile by countercurrent distribution and showed that with alkaline or β-glucuronidase hydrolysis it was converted to azopigment A with the concomitant release of one mole of glucuronic acid. This observation indicated that the original azopigment B was a monoglu-

curonide. Since one mole of bilirubin yields two moles of azopigment after diazotization, it was concluded that pigment II is a diglucuronide of bilirubin and that pigment I, which yields approximately equal amounts of azopigments A and B, is bilirubin monoglucuronide. Because the conjugates were hydrolyzed by mild alkali, it was suggested that glucuronic acid is in ester linkage to the propionic acid substituents of the bilirubin molecule rather than in glycosidic linkage to the hydroxyl groups of the first and fourth pyrrole rings. Schachter substantiated this impression by demonstrating that the direct-reacting pigment in the urine of patients with obstructive jaundice and the azopigment B derived from it yield hydroxamic acids on treatment with hydroxylamine (214). This reaction is characteristic of ester or acyl glucuronides.

Schmid isolated azopigments A and B from diazotized samples of jaundiced serum, urine, and bile by ascending paper chromatography using a solvent system of ethyl methyl ketone, n-propionic acid, and water (222). Hydrolysis of azopigment B with acid or β-glucuronidase yielded equimolar amounts of azopigment A and glucuronic acid. Talafant also suggested that the direct-reacting bile pigment is a glucuronide conjugate after observing on paper electrophoresis of partially purified dog bile that the direct-reacting fraction was associated with glucuronic acid in a molar ratio of approximately 1:2 (253).

Billing observed that 10–15% of the direct-reacting pigment in human bile was alkali stable and suggested that this fraction is not a glucuronide conjugate of bilirubin (39). This was confirmed by Isselbacher & McCarthy (141), who showed chromatographically that approximately 24% of the total azopigment derivatives of bilirubin in human bile resist β-glucuronidase hydrolysis and that nearly 14% is an ethereal sulfate conjugate. Watson subsequently observed that, on treatment of bilirubin with acetic anhydride and sulfuric acid, a water-soluble, direct-reacting bilirubin sulfate is formed (265). Isselbacher & McCarthy (141) suggested that this reaction involved a change in bilirubin structure and that synthetic bilirubin sulfate had little relationship to the naturally occurring sulfate conjugate which they found in the bile of rats, cats, and man. Recently the biological importance of bilirubin sulfate has been questioned (113, 267). Gregory & Watson (113) were unable to confirm the presence of bilirubin sulfate in human bile. Using radioactive inorganic sulfate, they separated the bilirubin azoderivative prepared from human and dog bile from radioactive sulfate. Bilirubin sulfate formation in the rat has been confirmed (113). Weber & Schalm

(267) did not detect free sulfate formation after acid hydrolysis of the alkali-stable bilirubin fraction in bilirubin fraction in bile; they found that alkali-stable pigment formation was greatly influenced by addition of serum to pigment II, and emphasized that the alkali-stable bilirubin has never been shown to be directly equatable with bilirubin sulfate, and the latter has not been isolated as a chemical entity and analyzed. Presently it is uncertain whether nonglucuronide conjugates of bilirubin are of functional significance in mammals. In several inheritable disorders in which glucuronide formation is deficient, compensatory increases in nonglucuronide conjugates of bilirubin are not observed.

Because chromatographic methods for analysis of bilirubin fractions are too complex for clinical use, the van den Bergh reaction is still generally used to estimate the concentration of conjugated bilirubin in biological tissues and fluids. Despite the fact that the results are influenced by such factors as time for coupling (152), the concentration of unconjugated bilirubin (202), pH (156), protein concentration (156), and the amount of diazotized sulfanilic acid used (156), the van den Bergh reaction provides a reasonable estimate of the concentration of conjugated bilirubin.

TRANSPORT OF BILIRUBIN IN BLOOD

In human plasma most, if not all, UCB is tightly bound to albumin (151, 201). Electrophoretic study of human icteric plasma reveals a small but constant amount of bilirubin bound to α-globulin. On separation of the plasma proteins (Cohn method) in alcohol-water mixtures at subzero temperatures under varying conditions of pH, salt, and protein concentrations, the only bilirubin-protein complex that survives is in the α_1-globulin fraction V-I (54). Because of its stability, Cohn regarded it as the only bile pigment-protein complex in native plasma (54); however, its concentration is such that it cannot account for more than 0.05 mg of bound bilirubin per 100 ml of plasma (150). Approximately 2 moles of UCB can be bound per mole of human albumin, and this corresponds to a maximal plasma UCB concentration of 60–80 mg per 100 ml (196, 201). Albumin binds 1 mole of UCB more tightly than 2 moles (196). Whether both moles of UCB are bound by albumin with the same intrinsic affinity or whether UCB already bound interferes with the binding of a second mole by electrostatic as well as statistical factors is unknown. The specific molecular sites of UCB and albumin responsible for binding are not definitely known but probably involve the cationic amino groups of albumin and the carboxyl groups of the propionic acid side chain of UCB (196, 197). Rat plasma albumin binds UCB less well (201), and in elasmobranchs, which lack serum albumin, UCB is bound to other plasma proteins (10). In man, CB is less bound to albumin than is UCB (42) and may also be bound to a dialyzable substance, of low molecular weight, which may be a bile salt (91).

The physicochemical nature of the bond between UCB and albumin is unknown; however, it is sufficiently stable to prevent passage of UCB through a semipermeable membrane unless the pH is below 5 (38). Certain organic anions used as drugs, such as salicylate, sulfonamides, and bile and fatty acids can displace bilirubin from albumin and render it ultrafiltrable (67, 145, 197). Administration of these organic anions can displace UCB from albumin and permit its entrance into brain, liver, and other tissues in vivo (67, 145). Increasing plasma albumin concentration in patients and rats with unconjugated hyperbilirubinemia results in transfer of UCB from brain (67, 89, 196), and presumably other tissues, to plasma.

The concentration of UCB in plasma is determined by the relative rates at which it enters and leaves the circulation, the plasma albumin concentration, and the availability of binding sites on albumin. The normal bilirubin concentration lies between 0.5 and 1.0 mg per 100 ml; however, the upper limit of normality is uncertain, for the distribution curve of values obtained from allegedly normal adults is asymmetrical. Based on a statistical analysis of a large population, the upper limit of normal has been designated as 1.5 mg per 100 ml (277). In other species, such as the dog, rat, and sheep, the plasma is virtually devoid of bilirubin (273); however, in horses the plasma bilirubin concentration is considerably higher than in man (273).

Most investigators accept that nearly all bilirubin in normal human plasma is unconjugated; however, none of the techniques for analysis of bilirubin fractions permits meaningful detection of small amounts of CB.

TRANSFER OF UNCONJUGATED BILIRUBIN FROM PLASMA INTO THE LIVER

The fundamental mechanism of this transfer is unknown. Studies of the hepatic uptake of UCB are hampered by the use of cumulative and nonsequential measurements, uncertainty that the injected pigment is entirely in parenchymal and not phagocytic cells, and the functional heterogeneity of the liver.

In the normal adult rat, UCB in plasma enters the liver preferentially with respect to other tissues. Although tissue distributions of bilirubin and albumin are generally similar (148), UCB is transferred from albumin in plasma into the liver much faster than the comparable transfer rate for albumin (32, 48, 270). The relative specificity of the parenchymal liver cell to remove UCB from plasma could be accounted for by the two following largely theoretical considerations.

Role of Plasma Membrane

The lateral extension of the plasma membrane facing the hepatic sinusoid may have this unique functional property because of a specific molecular composition as compared with plasma membranes of other cells and with other portions of the plasma membrane of the parenchymal liver cell itself. A plasma membrane fraction of considerable purity has been isolated by differential centrifugation of liver homogenates (188). Its protein, lipid, and fatty acid composition is remarkably similar to that observed in similar membranes isolated from polymorphonuclear and red blood cells (77, 78, 242, 252, 258); however, considerable heterogeneity in enzymatic activity is noted by enzyme cytochemistry in different portions of the hepatic cell plasma membrane (194, 195). With respect to liver homogenates, isolated hepatic plasma membranes have greatly increased activities of magnesium-stimulated adenosine triphosphatase; sodium-, potassium-, and magnesium-stimulated, ouabain-inhibited adenosine triphosphatase; 5'-nucleotidase; and cobalt-stimulated cytidine monophosphatase (78, 194, 258). Rat liver plasma membranes bind various organic anions in vitro, and the kinetics of BSP binding has been described (59). Equimolar amounts of organic anions such as taurocholate, UCB, and fluorescein, which do not compete for hepatic uptake with BSP when simultaneously injected in vivo (2, 5, 119), show little or no interference with BSP binding by plasma membranes in vitro. By contrast, other organic anions, such as indocyanine green, flavaspidic acid glucaminate, and iodipamide methyl glucamine, which compete with BSP for hepatic uptake in vivo (51, 192, 193, 233), significantly reduce BSP binding by isolated plasma membranes in vitro. This suggests that the plasma membrane of the liver cell is not molecularly homogeneous and is consistent with the postulate that specific receptor sites for various

organic anions may be located in the lateral extension of the plasma membrane facing the sinusoid. This possibility may be open to experimental investigation because of the rediscovery of mutant Southdown sheep with an apparent functional defect in the transfer of several organic anions from plasma into the liver cell (60). Electron-microscopic studies of liver reveal no ultrastructural differences between normal and mutant sheep (60).

Role of a Cytoplasmic-Acceptor Protein

The second theory is that UCB may be dissociated from albumin at the plasma membrane, which is generally permeable for nonpolar molecules, and that an intracellular acceptor with a considerable affinity for UCB maintains a concentration gradient for the pigment across the plasma membrane. Such an acceptor has been suggested by several investigators (32, 48, 165, 198), and evidence to support its existence has been presented [(32, 198); L. H. Bernstein and I. M. Arias, unpublished observations]. One to sixty minutes following the intravenous administration of UCB-^{3}H to normal rats, approximately 80 % of liver homogenates (32). This bilirubin is unconjugated (32). Odell and associates (198) studied the distribution of UCB in liver and kidneys in jaundiced rats, found evidence in support of a nonalbumin cytoplasmic receptor protein, and showed that the intravenous administration of albumin resulted in transfer of UCB from the liver into the circulation. Lack of such a cytoplasmic-receptor protein in nonhepatic tissues could account for the specificity in hepatic uptake of UCB, and hepatic deficiency of the receptor may be postulated in certain types of unconjugated hyperbilirubinemia associated with normal enzymatic capacity to form bilirubin glucuronide, for example, certain forms of the Gilbert syndrome (9, 86).

At present there is too little information to pursue discussion of these two theoretical concepts for the hepatic uptake of UCB. To the reviewer, it seems reasonable that unique characteristics of the plasma membrane as well as cytoplasmic-acceptor proteins may be important in the mechanism and control of hepatic uptake of organic anions such as UCB.

CONJUGATION OF BILIRUBIN
WITH GLUCURONIC ACID

Mammalian liver contains an enzyme system referred to as "glucuronyl transferase" or "uridine diphosphate transglucuronylase" which catalyzes the transfer of glucuronic acid from UDPGA to various phenolic, carboxylic, and amine receptors. After the identification of bilirubin glucuronide, several groups of investigators described its biosynthesis based on the classic glucuronide pathway presented below (21, 74, 114, 157, 227, 248).

$$\text{Glucose} + \text{ATP} \xleftrightarrow{\text{hexokinase}} \text{glucose-6-P} \qquad (1)$$

$$\text{Glucose-6-P} \xleftrightarrow{\text{phosphoglucomutase}} \text{glucose-1-P} \qquad (2)$$

$$\text{Glucose-1-P} + \text{UTP} \xleftrightarrow[\text{pyrophosphorylase}]{\text{UDPG}} \text{UDPG} + \text{PP} \quad (3)$$

$$\text{UDPG} + 2\text{ NAD} \xleftrightarrow[\text{dehydrogenase}]{\text{UDPG}} \text{UDPGA} + \\ 2\text{ NADH} + 2\text{ H}^+ \qquad (4)$$

$$\text{UDPGA} + \text{bilirubin} \xrightarrow{\text{glucuronyl transferase}} \text{bilirubin} \\ \text{glucuronide} + \text{UDP} \qquad (5)$$

In this scheme glucose serves as the source of glucuronide acid. This mechanism represents the major, and possibly the only, pathway for glucuronide formation in mammals.

Although glucuronyl transferase activity is found in skin (243), kidney (114), intestinal mucosa (15, 72), synovial membrane (45), adrenal gland (114), testes (114), and ovary (72), the greatest activity occurs in liver. Bilirubin glucuronide formation in mammals has not been shown with tissues other than liver, although homogenates and slices of kidney (114) and intestine (255) form direct-reacting bilirubin in vitro. Glucuronyl transferase activity is primarily found in the microsomal fraction of liver homogenates [(3, 21, 114, 157, 227); Table 1]. Ultrastructural examination of this fraction reveals primarily smooth and rough membranes of the endoplasmic reticulum (88) which may be partly separated by appropriate differential centrifugation (64, 211). The glucuronyl transferase catalyzing the formation of several ethereal glucuronides is primarily associated in the smooth endoplasmic reticulum fraction (J. Weiss and I. M. Arias, unpublished observations). This fraction also contains several oxidative enzymes involved in drug metabolism (79, 87).

The direct van den Bergh reaction has been widely used to estimate the formation of bilirubin glucuronide in vitro, and variable rates of formation have been observed (21, 114, 157, 227). Recent modifications using bilirubin-^{14}C (181), sulfanilic acid-^{35}S (182), and partition separation (266) may overcome previous

TABLE 1. *Conjugated Bilirubin Production by Rat Liver Fractions and Homogenates*

Fraction	Method for Cell Fractionation, μg/Fraction from 1 g Wet Wt Liver	
	Novikoff et al. (195a)	Schneider & Hogeboom (227a)
Nuclei	0.0	0.3
Mitochondria	0.0	1.1
"Mixed"	0.5	
Microsomes	6.4	5.6
Supernatant	0.0	1.0
Homogenate	8.8	9.1

From Arias (3).

objections which have been partly circumvented by using different glucuronide receptors in place of UCB.

Multiplicity of Glucuronyl Transferases

It was first suggested that a single enzyme catalyzes the formation of ethereal, ester, and amine-linked glucuronides because various receptors reversibly inhibited glucuronide formation in vitro (26, 114). However, because of the following observations, it is not known whether the observed differences in glucuronide formation with various receptors are due to different glucuronyl transferases or whether there is varied affinity of the several receptors for a single enzyme. *a*) Lathe & Walker (157) observed no parallel between the capacity of liver from different animal species to form bilirubin glucuronide (an ester glucuronide) and *o*-aminophenol glucuronide (an ethereal glucuronide) in vitro. *b*) Humans and rats (Gunn) with inherited glucuronyl transferase deficiency demonstrate defective formation of the ester glucuronide of bilirubin and the ethereal glucuronides of *o*-aminophenol, 4-methyl umbelliferone, and menthol in vitro (9, 22, 50); however, in Gunn rats, similar preparations form ethereal glucuronides of *p*-nitrophenol and tetrahydrocortisone at a normal rate (68, 158). In Gunn rats, the biliary excretion of the ethereal glucuronide of phenol-3,6-dibromphthalein and the ester glucuronide of diphenylacetic acid is comparable to that observed in normal rats (143), although biliary excretion of ethereal thyroxin glucuronides is reduced in mutant rats (85). Infusion of N-acetyl-*p*-aminophenol, which forms an ethereal glucuronide, into heterozygous Gunn rats does not inhibit the conjugation and biliary excretion of bilirubin (19). *c*) Recent inhibition studies by Storey indicate that various phenols may attach to different glucuronyl transferases although sharing them with other substrates (246, 247). *d*) Different rates of development of hepatic glucuronyl transferase activity have been described in different species, with different glucuronide receptors used (73, 96, 246). In neonatal mouse liver, glucuronyl transferase activity with *p*-nitrophenol as substrate developed more rapidly than transferase with *o*-aminophenol as substrate (246). Homogenates of liver from newborn rats have reduced capacity to form conjugated bilirubin when compared with the capacity of homogenates of adult rat liver; however, the neonatal liver homogenates form greater amounts of *o*-aminophenol glucuronide than do homogenates of adult liver (96). *e*) *o*-Aminophenol glucuronide formation by homogenates of liver from hypophysectomized rats is greatly reduced, but bilirubin glucuronide formation by the same liver homogenates is not significantly different from that of normal rat liver in vitro (97).

Comparative rates of glucuronide formation have not been well studied in vitro and in vivo in the same animal, and analogies may be misleading. For example, ethereal glucuronide formation by slices and homogenates of intestine from Gunn rats was virtually zero in vitro when a sensitive fluorescent method was used with 4-methyl umbelliferone as a glucuronide receptor; however, formation and transport of the ethereal glucuronides of monoiodotyrosine, triiodothyroacetic acid, and testosterone by everted gut sacs were reduced by only about 50% (15).

Solution of the problem requires solubilization, purification, and characterization of glucuronyl transferase. This has been difficult because of instability of the enzymatic activity. Pogell & Leloir (205) solubilized glucuronyl transferase with digitonin and noted enzymatic activation by UDP-*n*-acetyl glucosamine, ATP, an extract of liver supernatant, and bovine serum albumin (206). Halac & Bonevardi (118) observed a twentyfold increase in glucuronyl transferase activity following treatment of liver microsomes with EDTA. Isselbacher solubilized and partly purified glucuronyl transferase from rabbit liver microsomes using a heat-treated snake venom preparation (140). The enzyme catalyzing the formation of amine-lined glucuronides was not solubilized by this treatment; this suggests that the glucuronyl transferase catalyzing the formation of N-glucuronides is different from that catalyzing the formation of ester and ethereal glucuronides. Supporting this is the observation that N-glucuronides are formed normally in vitro and in vivo in jaundiced mutant rats (7). The solubilized glucuronyl transferase described by Isselbacher catalyzed the formation of ester and ethereal glucuronides; however, further purification of the enzyme with regard to ethereal glucuronide formation did not increase ester glucuronide formation in vitro (140).

From present evidence, therefore, it seems probable that N-glucuronides are formed by a different glucuronyl transferase from that involved in the formation of ester and ethereal glucuronides. Enzymes catalyzing the formation of ester and ethereal glucuronides have not been separated, and the observed data are consistent with greatly varied affinity of different phenolic and carboxylic receptors for a single enzyme.

Glucuronyl Transferase Deficiency

Bilirubin must be conjugated to be excreted by the mammalian liver (20, 224). Glucuronyl transferase deficiency results in failure to form bilirubin glucuronide; and because there is no adaptive formation of other bilirubin conjugates, UCB accumulates in the plasma and tissues. Unconjugated bilirubin is not excreted by the mammalian kidney, and therefore the clinical state is characterized as chronic, nonhemolytic, acholuric, unconjugated hyperbilirubinemia. Not all clinical disorders characterized by chronic jaundice of this type result from demonstrable glucuronyl transferase deficiency (9, 86); however, transient unconjugated hyperbilirubinemia in newborn infants is related to delayed development of the hepatic glucuronide conjugating system, and chronic jaundice of this type occurs in rats and humans with inheritable disorders of bilirubin conjugation.

NEONATAL UNCONJUGATED HYPERBILIRUBINEMIA. Virtually every full-term newborn infant develops mild unconjugated hyperbilirubinemia during the first three to five days of life. Various factors, including prematurity, hemolysis, infection, drugs, and inhibitors, may convert physiological jaundice of the newborn into a serious disorder with kernicterus (4, 99). The benign clinical disorder is believed to result from delayed development of the hepatic glucuronide conjugating system (47, 72, 115, 125, 197, 257), particularly glucuronyl transferase (174), although reduced UDPG dehydrogenase activity has also been demonstrated in guinea pig liver (47, 115). Similar investigations have not been extensively performed in human infants. Available data are consistent with these observations in animals (72, 197, 262); however, there are potential hazards in direct extrapolations from the animal studies. For example, *o*-aminophenol glucuronide formation is significantly greater in slices of newborn rat liver than in comparable preparations from older rats (197), and an active UDPGA pyrophosphatase is present in neonatal rat liver (197); so the rat is unsuitable as a general model for the study of the pathogenesis of neonatal jaundice.

In 1958, Lathe suggested that the functional immaturity of the liver with regard to glucuronide formation may represent delayed development of the entire "microsomal" structure (155). Later studies showed that the developmental pattern of various enzymes associated with this subcellular fraction varied considerably, and the original concept was largely discarded (84). Recent high-resolution electron-microscopic studies of fetal and newborn liver reveal a marked reduction in smooth endoplasmic reticulum compared with adult liver (66, 131), and biochemical studies demonstrated a delayed developmental pattern for other drug-metabolizing enzymes associated with the smooth endoplasmic reticulum (65, 89). This may explain the reduced ability observed clinically of newborn infants to tolerate various drugs that are metabolized by these systems (179). Since the smooth endoplasmic reticulum is a major component of the microsomal fraction isolated by differential centrifugation, it seems that Lathe's concept is largely correct. Activity of drug-metabolizing enzymes associated with the smooth endoplasmic reticulum is virtually nil in preparations of fetal liver; however, within an hour after birth functional activity is easily detectable but at a reduced rate when compared with adult liver. The mechanism for this rapid appearance of enzymatic activity is unknown. Possibly the appropriate proteins are synthesized within such a short time, but it is also possible that the enzymes are in an inactive form in fetal liver and that with increased hepatic oxygenation or reduced plasma concentrations of naturally occurring steroidal inhibitors, activation ensues.

HEREDITARY UNCONJUGATED HYPERBILIRUBINEMIA IN RATS (GUNN). In 1938 a spontaneous mutation occurred in the Wistar rat colony at the Connaught Laboratory in Toronto. Mutant rats were characterized by acholuric jaundice, and Gunn reported that the defect is transmitted with the characteristics of an autosomal recessive gene (117). Bilirubin in serum gave an indirect van den Bergh reaction; after ligation of the common bile duct, the serum bilirubin increased but was still "indirectly reacting," and a

defect involving the formation of "direct-reacting" bilirubin was postulated (176). It is remarkable that no further study of these animals was performed until 1957, and they probably would have been lost had it not been for the late Professor William E. Castle, who kept a colony of Gunn rats for about 19 years. Since 1957, studies using the Gunn rat have provided much of the information summarized in this chapter. As was discussed in a previous section, homozygous Gunn rats have chronic nonhemolytic unconjugated hyperbilirubinemia due to an inherited defect in the conjugation of bilirubin with glucuronic acid. Activity of UDPGA dehydrogenase is comparable to that in the liver of normal rats (Table 2). Heterozygous Gunn rats appear normal and are not jaundiced, and glucuronide formation in vivo and in vitro is intermediate between that observed in genetically normal and homozygous jaundiced littermates (3, 156). After intravenous injection of UCB, the pigment disappears from the plasma of heterozygotes at a significantly lower rate than in genetically normal rats (19). The enzymatic defect in heterozygous Gunn rats is not severe enough to result in retention of UCB in their plasma.

Homozygous Gunn rats born of a homozygous mating do not manifest hyperbilirubinemia immediately at birth, probably because of transfer of UCB across the placenta and its subsequent conjugation and excretion by the maternal liver (116, 146, 163, 217). Shortly after birth the serum bilirubin concentration in the neonate rises to a maximal level of approximately 15–20 mg per 100 ml; functional and structural impairment of the central nervous system (i.e., kernicterus) frequently occurs; bilirubinuria is absent, and, if the animal survives the neonatal period, unconjugated hyperbilirubinemia persists throughout life. There is no evidence of hemolysis, and isolated perfused Gunn rat liver forms an early labeled pigment which appears quantitatively similar to that observed with normal rat liver after administration of ALA-^{14}C. Light-microscopic examination

TABLE 2. *Enzymatic Synthesis of UDPGA, o-Aminophenol Glucuronide, and Bilirubin Glucuronide by Liver from Male Normal and Gunn Rats In Vitro*

Genetic Type	UDPGA Formed	o-Amino-phenol Glucuronide	Bilirubin Glucuronide
Homozygous Gunn	4.9	0.008	0.0
Heterozygous	4.3	0.034	0.011–0.039
Homozygous normal	5.8	0.061	0.056–0.089

Results are expressed as micromoles per gram of liver. [From Schmid et al. (224) and Arias (3).]

of liver is normal (195), and electron-microscopic examination reveals large areas of agranular endoplasmic reticulum (195). The maximal rates for biliary excretion of injected BSP or CB are similar in jaundiced and normal rats (20, 224); however, intravenous administration of UCB to homozygous Gunn rats does not increase biliary excretion of the pigment (20, 224). Bile obtained from jaundiced Gunn rats is almost colorless, lacks bilirubin glucuronide, and contains only a trace of UCB as well as diazo-negative bilirubin derivatives of unknown structure (224, 226). Total urinary excretion of glucuronic acid and glucuronides in icteric rats is about half that in control animals (224). After administration of menthol or o-aminobenzoate, but not aniline (7), icteric rats excrete smaller fractions of the test compound as a glucuronide (224). The deficiency in glucuronyl transferase activity involves intestine and kidney as well as liver (15, 50). The variable results regarding hepatic glucuronyl transferase activity in vitro are presented earlier in this chapter.

Homozygous Gunn rats maintain normal production of bile pigment, a relatively constant serum and tissue UCB concentration, and acholuria, despite the inability of the liver to conjugate bilirubin. This suggests that alternate pathways of pigment disposition are present in mutant rats. Schmid and Hammaker studied this in icteric rats following injection with bilirubin-^{14}C. The following patterns of bile pigment excretion were observed: a) the major portion is catabolized to diazo-negative, polar bilirubin derivatives which are excreted in the bile and urine; b) a small amount of UCB is excreted in the bile; and c) a substantial amount of UCB is transferred across the intestinal mucosa into the intestine (226). Presumably these combined excretory rates balance the rate of UCB formation and a steady state in pigment turnover is attained. Five-sixths of the total pool of UCB is in the extravascular compartments of liver, kidney, and other tissues (226); and after intravenous injection of human albumin, which has a stronger binding capacity for UCB than does rat albumin (201), the plasma UCB concentration increased threefold (223). This is analogous to results obtained by Odell, who injected human albumin into jaundiced newborn infants with hemolytic disease before performing exchange transfusion for the purpose of removing UCB and preventing kernicterus (196).

HEREDITARY UNCONJUGATED HYPERBILIRUBINEMIA IN MAN. In 1952, Crigler & Najjar (62) described severe nonhemolytic acholuric jaundice associated with kernicterus in six infants from three related families [see also Childs & Naggar (52)]. In each infant jaundice was first noted on about the third day and persisted throughout life, although five infants died of kernicterus within the first 15 months. The sixth child remained well for 15 years, when, for unapparent reasons, he manifested signs of central nervous system damage and died of kernicterus. Since the original report, approximately 20 additional patients with the Crigler-Najjar syndrome have been reported [(223); I. M. Arias, unpublished data], 14 of whom died in infancy as a result of kernicterus. The characteristic features of the syndrome are severe unconjugated hyperbilirubinemia with serum bilirubin concentrations ranging from approximately 14 to 45 mg per 100 ml. There is no evidence of hemolysis, the early labeled pigment is normal (40), conventional tests of liver function give normal results, the extrahepatic biliary system is patent, light-microscopic examination of liver is normal, electron-microscopic examination of liver reveals increased smooth endoplasmic reticulum (195), and there is no bilirubin in the urine. Fecal urobilinogen excretion is much less than in normal subjects. Bile aspirated from the gallbladder or the duodenum is almost colorless (222). Bilirubin glucuronide has never been demonstrated chromatographically in bile, although small amounts of direct-reacting bile pigment have been described (222, 249, 251). Studies of bilirubin-^{14}C metabolism reveal that more of the pigment pool is limited to the vascular compartment than in the Gunn rat (226); this is consistent with the species differences in albumin-UCB interaction (201). As in the murine mutant, alternate pathways of pigment disposition establish a steady state between bilirubin formation and removal at greatly increased plasma bilirubin concentrations (226).

Glucuronide formation of menthol (251), chloral hydrate (53), trichlorethanol (53), salicylate (53, 90), N-acetyl-p-aminophenol (223), and tetrahydrocortisol (203) in vivo are reduced but not absent in affected individuals. Glucuronyl transferase activity is absent when studied in vitro with bilirubin as receptor [(251); I. M. Arias, unpublished observations].

The defect is transmitted with the characteristics of an autosomal recessive gene (53, 249). Nonicteric heterozygotes have glucuronide excretion in vivo which is intermediate between that observed in normal and icteric family members (53, 249). Four families having the classic syndrome have one or more individuals with chronic asymptomatic unconjugated hyperbilirubinemia with serum bilirubin concentrations ranging from 2 to 5 mg per 100 ml. Studies of glucuronide formation in vivo and in vitro in these individuals are consistently normal (9, 160, 238a). Either this is fortuitous, or present methods for study of glucuronide formation are not sufficiently specific or sensitive to demonstrate an enzymatic defect. The variability noted when different receptors are used to study glucuronide formation in vivo may represent differences in their absorption, distribution, metabolism, and margin of safety (9). For example, the father of a child with the Crigler-Najjar syndrome had normal urinary excretion of N-acetyl-*p*-aminophenol glucuronide (225) but much less excretion of other ethereal glucuronides after administration of the appropriate glucuronide receptor (53).

In 1962, a form of unconjugated hyperbilirubinemia possibly related to the Crigler-Najjar syndrome was described in eight patients (9), and additional cases have subsequently been studied (223). The following differences from the Crigler-Najjar syndrome are noted: *a*) the serum bilirubin is unconjugated, and its concentration ranges from about 5 to 20 mg per 100 ml; *b*) jaundice is first observed either shortly after birth or near puberty; *c*) although one adult had pathological evidence of kernicterus following her death at age 44 (144), the other patients have not shown clinical evidence of neurological damage; and *d*) in the 11 cases studied to date, bile aspirated from the gallbladder or duodenum had abundant amounts of bilirubin glucuronide (9, 223, 238a). Similarities with the Crigler-Najjar syndrome include normal erythrocyte survival, patent extrahepatic biliary system, normal light-microscopic examination of liver, increased smooth endoplasmic reticulum on electron-microscopic examination of liver (194), slightly to moderately reduced fecal urobilinogen excretion, reduced glucuronide excretion in vivo when menthol (9) and tetrahydrocortisone (69) are used as receptors, and deficient hepatic glucuronyl transferase activity in vitro when bilirubin, *o*-aminophenol, or 4-methyl umbelliferone is used as the glucuronide receptor (9, 223). In one family study (9), three icteric patients were siblings, but defective conjugation was demonstrable in only two. In the third patient, unconjugated hyperbilirubinemia was mild and studies of glucuronide formation were normal. Defective conjugation and delayed bilirubin clearance from plasma were demonstrated in an anicteric father and paternal uncle. Similar observations have been made in another large family which includes two siblings with chronic unconjugated hyperbilirubinemia and a demonstrable defect

in glucuronide formation in vivo and in vitro (238a). In both these families the hereditary pattern suggests an autosomal dominant gene.

The relationship of this syndrome to the Crigler-Najjar syndrome is uncertain. A partial deficiency of bilirubin conjugation has been suggested (223); but, if this were so, one might expect to observe siblings with demonstrable defective glucuronide formation and less pronounced hyperbilirubinemia in families having members with the classic Crigler-Najjar syndrome. Since glucuronyl transferase has not been isolated and studied for structural and kinetic characteristics, the existence of several glucuronyl transferases, isozymes, or repressor genes cannot be excluded from consideration.

Chronic unconjugated hyperbilirubinemia of mild degree without overt signs of hemolysis occurs in adolescents and adults and is usually called "Gilbert's syndrome" (9, 86). Etiologic heterogeneity results from the following recognized factors. *a*) Defective glucuronide formation has been demonstrated in vivo and in vitro in patients with serum bilirubin concentrations ranging from 8 to 20 mg per 100 ml (9, 223). *b*) Compensated hemolytic diseases may occur without overt evidence of hemolysis (9, 58, 223). *c*) Increased production of bile pigment from sources other than mature, circulating erythrocytes is associated with various disorders of erythropoiesis (8, 31, 137–139). *d*) Mild jaundice of this type occurs after viral hepatitis (9, 86) and with a wide variety of infectious and metabolic disorders (166). Studies of glucuronide formation are usually normal (9, 27, 86, 225, 264) although sometimes reduced hepatic glucuronyl transferase activity (182) and abnormal menthol excretion have been demonstrated (28). Impaired hepatic uptake of UCB has been postulated (225); but this has been only indirectly supported (43, 92). *e*) Chronic unconjugated hyperbilirubinemia of unknown etiology has also been found associated with thyrotoxicosis (111) and living at high altitude (30, 244), and after portal-caval shunt surgery for relief of portal hypertension (236).

Unconjugated hyperbilirubinemia of brief duration occurs in association with several drugs. Male fern extract produces hyperbilirubinemia and BSP retention possibly by affecting hepatic uptake mechanisms (192). Patients receiving bunamiodol, an organic anion used for radiological studies of the gallbladder, demonstrate mild jaundice on the following day (42). Bunamiodol inhibits glucuronyl transferase activity in vitro and hepatic excretion of CB in vivo (42, 106). Similar observations have been made with novobiocin, which produces unconjugated hyper-bilirubinemia in neonates and adults (168).

Stimulation of Glucuronyl Transferase Activity

Administration of various drugs metabolized by enzymes in the endoplasmic reticulum results in proliferation of the smooth endoplasmic reticulum (87, 88, 207) and induction of various drug-metabolizing enzymes, including glucuronyl transferase, which are associated with this structure (24, 57, 87, 88). The process involves protein synthesis (14a, 101). The newly formed membranes are associated with ribosomes (i.e., rough endoplasmic reticulum) which are later detached, the result being the appearance of membranes lacking RNA particles (i.e., smooth endoplasmic reticulum) (65).

Hepatic glucuronyl transferase activity is increased in vitro in neonatal rats and guinea pigs treated with benzpyrene (17, 136) and is less in female than in male rats (136). Administration of androgens to female rats increases glucuronyl transferase activity to levels seen in males, and administration of estrogens reduces the activity to levels observed in females (136). Administration of benzpyrene, chloroquine, pamaquine, or chlorcyclizine to three-day old Wistar rats or to pregnant rats increases hepatic glucuronide formation of bilirubin and o-aminophenol in vitro (17). Treatment of pregnant women with chloroquine did not, however, alter the course or severity of neonatal unconjugated hyperbilirubinemia in their infants (17). Giving phenobarbital to mice stimulated hepatic glucuronyl transferase activity (275), and prolonged administration of phenobarbital to patients with chronic unconjugated hyperbilirubinemia resulting from glucuronyl transferase deficiency was associated with sustained reduction in the serum UCB concentration (61, 275). There are apparently species differences in the induction response to phenobarbital because administration of the drug to Gunn rats for three months increased barbiturate metabolism in vitro and in vivo, but neither increased hepatic glucuronide formation nor reduced the chronic unconjugated hyperbilirubinemia (66a).

Stimulation of glucuronyl transferase activity by drugs has been used to study the role of the enzyme in intracellular transport of UCB. Recent evidence suggests that glucuronyl transferase may be an intracellular binding site for UCB and may be important in the transfer of UCB from a cytoplasmic acceptor protein to the site of conjugation on the endoplasmic reticulum (32, 48). After administration of physiological amounts of UCB-^{3}H to normal and Gunn rats, a significant difference in the hepatic subcellular distribution of the labeled bile pigment is observed [(32); Fig. 3]. After injection of UCB-^{3}H in Gunn rats or its addition in vitro, the distribution of radioactivity is significantly reduced in the microsomal fraction and correspondingly increased in the supernatant fraction. Infusion of unlabeled UCB to normal rats for one hour produced hepatic bilirubin concentrations similar to those observed in Gunn rats; however, the subcellular distribution of injected UCB-^{3}H did not differ from that of normal rats without prior bilirubin infusions. Thus reduced distribution of UCB-^{3}H in the microsomal fraction in Gunn rats does not result from significant amounts of unlabeled UCB bound to the microsomal fraction which thereby limits further binding of UCB-^{3}H. Further evidence that glucuronyl transferase may be a binding site of UCB and influences its transfer from the cytoplasm to the smooth endoplasmic reticulum where conjugation occurs is provided by recent studies (J. Weiss and I. M. Arias, unpublished observations). These investigators found that treatment of normal or Gunn rats with phenobarbital fails to increase glucuronyl transferase activity, although smooth endoplasmic reticulum proliferation occurs morphologically and biochemically; however, benzpyrene administration to normal or Gunn rats enhances glucuronyl transferase activity and formation of smooth endoplasmic reticulum. After treatment of normal and Gunn rats with phenobarbital or benzpyrene, distribution of UCB-^{3}H in submicrosomal fractions and induction of glucuronyl

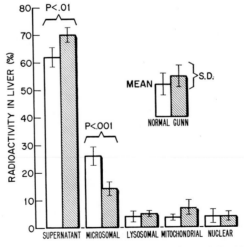

FIG. 3. Subcellular distribution of radiobilirubin 1–60 min after administration of UCB-^{3}H to normal and Gunn rats. [From Bernstein et al. (32).]

transferase activity and the barbiturate oxidizing enzyme which is also associated primarily with smooth endoplasmic reticulum (87) were studied. In each experiment the distribution of UCB-³H in the smooth endoplasmic reticulum fraction correlated with glucuronyl transferase activity in this fraction and was independent of changes in barbiturate oxidizing activity or electron-microscopic evaluation of the proliferation of smooth endoplasmic reticulum. A role for glucuronyl transferase in regulation of intracellular transport of UCB would provide an attractive explanation for the subcellular distribution of physiological amounts of radiobilirubin as observed in normal (32, 48) and mutant rats (32).

Inhibition of Glucuronyl Transferase Activity

In 1958 Lathe & Walker (157) found that pregnancy serum inhibited the formation of direct-reacting bilirubin by rat liver slices in vitro. The titer of inhibitor increased in maternal blood to term and was also observed with cord blood. Bilirubin conjugation was also inhibited by a variety of steroid hormones. Pregnanediol and etiocholanolone were active, but a number of characteristics, including 11-oxidation as in the cortisol series, blocked the inhibitory effect. Hsia and associates isolated pregnane-3(α),20(α)-diol from human pregnancy serum (132) and demonstrated that it competitively inhibits glucuronyl transferase activity in vitro (133). Holton & Lathe (130) later isolated four substances from human newborn serum: pregnane-3(α),20(α)-diol; pregnanolone; and two unknown substances. One of the unknown

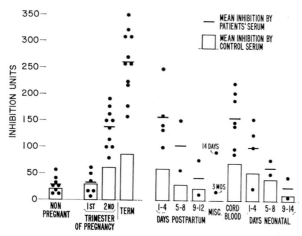

FIG. 4. Inhibition of o-aminophenol glucuronide formation by rat liver homogenates by control serum and by serum from infants with transient familial neonatal hyperbilirubinemia and their pregnant mothers. [From Arias et al. (23).]

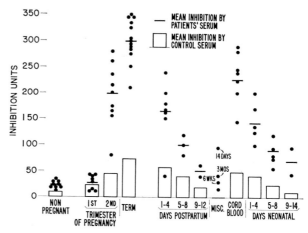

FIG. 5. Inhibition of direct-reacting bilirubin formation by rat liver slices by control serum and by serum from infants with transient familial neonatal hyperbilirubinemia and their pregnant mothers. [From Arias et al. (23).]

steroids inhibited direct-reacting bilirubin formation by slices of human liver, whereas the other steroids did not inhibit in this system.

The role of serum inhibitors of glucuronyl transferase in the production of jaundice is uncertain, particularly in newborns in whom the capacity to conjugate bilirubin is limited. That neonatal jaundice may be influenced by inhibitors is suggested by studies of two syndromes:

1. The Lucey-Driscoll syndrome (transient familial neonatal hyperbilirubinemia) is a form of intense but transient unconjugated hyperbilirubinemia affecting all newborn infants of a group of unrelated mothers who appear normal in other respects (22). None of the factors known to predispose to severe neonatal jaundice has been implicated. Serum from affected infants and their anicteric pregnant mothers inhibits bilirubin and o-aminophenol glucuronide formation by rat liver slices three to five times as effectively as does serum from normal pregnant women and their newborn infants (Figs. 4, 5). The association of such inhibition with pregnancy suggests that the unidentified factor may be a maternal steroid that influences bilirubin metabolism in the neonate.

2. A syndrome of severe and prolonged unconjugated hyperbilirubinemia related to breast-feeding has been described (18, 98, 189, 245). In one study, six newborn infants were investigated (18). In five cases, withdrawal of breast milk was associated with rapid amelioration of unconjugated hyperbilirubinemia and jaundice. In one case, alternating breast-feeding and bottle-feeding led to more gradual reduction of jaundice. Milk from the mother of breast-fed

the ill-defined group of lipofuscins and was differentiated from that found in normal liver (71, 241). Ehrlich and associates (76) suggested that the Dubin-Johnson pigment has different staining characteristics and electron-microscopic appearance from conventional lipofuscin, showed its association with abnormal lysosomes, and postulated a storage phenomenon. Consistent with this interpretation is the report of a patient with the Dubin-Johnson syndrome who developed viral hepatitis, at which time hepatic pigment was released from damaged parenchymal cells, engulfed by phagocytic cells, and slowly reaccumulated in regenerating parenchymal liver cells (135). The presence of normal lipfuscin in some livers is probably responsible for reports of hybrids of the various syndromes represented as cases of unconjugated hyperbilirubinemia with hepatic pigmentation (129, 213) or hepatic pigmentation without hyperbilirubinemia (58). Basing their hypothesis on staining reactions and physicochemical studies, Wegmann and associates (269) suggest that the pigment in the Dubin-Johnson syndrome is an atypical melanin. Further knowledge of the structure of the pigment has come from studies of mutant Corriedale sheep which have a functional and morphological defect similar to that of the Dubin-Johnson syndrome in man (13, 14). The hepatic pigment was isolated from livers of mutant sheep and patients with the Dubin-Johnson syndrome by sucrose-density-gradient centrifugation and organic extraction. Studies of the isolated pigments gave identical results with regard to solubility in organic solvents, ultraviolet absorption spectra, elemental analysis, and electron-spin resonance characteristics (13, 14). The results of these studies suggest that the isolated pigments are melanins possibly arising from defective hepatic excretion of metabolites of tyrosine, phenylalanine, or tryptophan. After intravenous administration of epinephrine-7-^{3}H, mutant sheep excreted less tritiated metabolites in bile than did normal sheep (13). Radioactivity was incorporated into the hepatic pigment by the third day, and subsequent turnover was slow (13). Hepatic pigmentation in mutant sheep, therefore, is postulated to result, at least in part, from impaired hepatic excretion of metabolites of epinephrine which are oxidized in the liver to insoluble melanin polymers and subsequently stored in lysosomes.

The author gratefully acknowledges the capable assistance of Shirley Nichol, Louise Laube, and Linda Arias in the preparation of this review.

REFERENCES

1. ADAMS, F. *The Genuine Works of Hippocrates*. Baltimore: Williams & Wilkins, 1939, p. 284.

2. ANDREWS, W. H. H., AND I. DEL RIO LOZANO. Some factors affecting the passage of BSP into and out of hepatic parenchymal cells. *Quart. J. Exptl. Physiol.* 46: 238–256, 1961.

3. ARIAS, I. M. A defect in microsomal function in nonhemolytic acholuric jaundice. *J. Histochem. Cytochem.* 7: 250–253, 1959.

4. ARIAS, I. M. The biochemical basis of kernicterus. *Advan. Clin. Chem.* 3: 45–84, 1960.

5. ARIAS, I. M. The transport of bilirubin in the liver. *Progress in Liver Disease*. New York: Grune & Stratton, 1961, p. 187–201.

6. ARIAS, I. M. Studies of chronic familial nonhemolytic jaundice with conjugated bilirubin in the serum with and without an unidentified pigment in the liver cells. *Am. J. Med.* 31: 510–518, 1961.

7. ARIAS, I. M. Ethereal and N-linked glucuronide formation by normal and Gunn rats *in vitro* and *in vivo*. *Biochem. Biophys. Res. Commun.* 6: 81–84, 1961.

8. ARIAS, I. M. Chronic unconjugated hyperbilirubinemia with increased production of bile pigment not derived from the hemoglobin of mature, circulating erythrocytes. *J. Clin. Invest.* 41: 1341, 1962.

9. ARIAS, I. M. Chronic unconjugated hyperbilirubinemia without overt signs of hemolysis in adolescents and adults. *J. Clin. Invest.* 41: 2233–2245, 1962.

10. ARIAS, I. M. Hepatic metabolism of bilirubin in the dogfish (*Squalus acanthias*). *Federation Proc.* 22: 398, 1963.

11. ARIAS, I. M. Effects of a plant acid (icterogenin) and certain anabolic steroids on the hepatic metabolism of bilirubin and sulfobromphthalein (BSP). *Ann. N.Y. Acad. Sci.* 104: 1014–1025, 1963.

12. ARIAS, I. M. Further studies of the mechanism of prolonged neonatal jaundice associated with breast feeding. *Proc. Intern. Congr. Steroid Metabolism, 2nd, Milan, 1966*.

13. ARIAS, I. M., L. BERNSTEIN, R. TOFFLER, AND J. BEN EZZER. Black liver disease in Corriedale sheep: metabolism of tritiated epinephrine and incorporation of isotope into the hepatic pigment in vivo. *J. Clin. Invest.* 44: 1026, 1965.

14. ARIAS, I. M., L. BERNSTEIN, R. TOFFLER, C. E. CORNELIUS, A. B. NOVIKOFF, AND E. ESSNER. Black liver disease in Corriedale sheep: a new mutation affecting hepatic excretory function. *J. Clin. Invest.* 43: 1249, 1964.

14a. ARIAS, I. M., AND A. DELEON. Estimation of the turnover rate of barbiturate side-chain oxidation enzyme in rat liver. *Mol. Pharmacol.* 3: 216–218, 1967.

15. ARIAS, I. M., M. FURMAN, D. F. TAPLEY, AND J. E. ROSS. Glucuronide formation and transport of various compounds by Gunn rat intestine in vitro. *Nature* 197: 1109–1110, 1963.

16. ARIAS, I. M., AND L. M. CARTNER. Production of unconjugated hyperbilirubinemia in fullterm newborn infants

following administration of pregnane-3 (α), 20 (β)-diol. *Nature* 203: 1292, 1964.

17. ARIAS, I. M., L. GARTNER, M. FURMAN, AND S. WOLFSON. Effect of several drugs and chemicals on hepatic glucuronide formation in newborn rats. *Proc. Soc. Exptl. Biol. Med.* 112: 1037–1040, 1963.

18. ARIAS, I. M., L. M. GARTNER, S. SEIFTER, AND M. FURMAN. Prolonged neonatal unconjugated hyperbilirubinemia associated with breast feeding and a steroid, pregnane-3 (α), 20 (β)-diol, in maternal milk which inhibits glucuronide formation *in vitro*. *J. Clin. Invest.* 43: 2037–2047, 1964.

19. ARIAS, I. M., AND L. JOHNSON. Studies of bilirubin excretion in normal and Gunn rats. *Clin. Res.* 7: 291, 1959.

20. ARIAS, I. M., L. JOHNSON, AND S. WOLFSON. Biliary excretion of injected conjugated and unconjugated bilirubin by normal and Gunn rats. *Am. J. Physiol.* 200: 1091–1094, 1961.

21. ARIAS, I. M., AND I. M. LONDON. Bilirubin glucuronide formation *in vitro*: demonstration of a defect in Gilbert's disease. *Science* 126: 563, 1957.

22. ARIAS, I. M., B. A. AND I. M. LONDON. Studies of glucuronide synthesis and of glucuronyl transferase in liver and serum. *J. Clin. Invest.* 37: 875, 1958.

23. ARIAS, I. M., S. WOLFSON, J. F. LUCEY, AND R. J. McKAY. Transient familial neonatal hyperbilirubinemia. *J. Clin. Invest.* 44: 1442–1450, 1965.

24. ARCOS, J. C., A. H. CONNEY, AND NG. PH. BUU-HOI. Induction of microsomal enzyme synthesis by polycyclic aromatic hydrocarbons of different molecular sizes. *J. Biol. Chem.* 236: 1291–1296, 1961.

25. ASCHOFF, L. Das reticulo-endotheliale System und seine Beziehungen zur Gallenfarbstoffbildung. *Muench. Med. Wochschr.* 69: 1352–1356, 1922.

26. AXELROD, J., J. K. INSCOE, AND G. M. TOMKINS. Enzymatic synthesis of N-glucosyluronic acid conjugates. *J. Biol. Chem.* 232: 835–841, 1958.

27. BARNIVILLE, H. T. F., AND R. MISK. Urinary glucuronic acid excretion in liver disease and the effect of a salicylamide load. *Brit. Med. J.* 1: 337–342, 1959.

28. BECK, K., AND H. A. KUHN. Beitrag zuv Pathoegnese der funktionellen Hyperbilirubinamie. *Z. Klin. Med.* 155: 547–567, 1959.

29. BEKER, S., AND A. E. READ. Familial Dubin-Johnson syndrome. *Gastroenterology* 35: 387–389, 1958.

30. BERENDSOHN, S. Hepatic function at high altitude. *Arch. Internal Med.* 109: 256–264, 1962.

31. BERENDSOHN, S., J. LOWMAN, D. SUNDBERG, AND C. J. WATSON. Idiopathic dyserythropoietic jaundice. *Blood* 24: 1–18, 1964.

32. BERNSTEIN, L. H., J. BEN EZZER, L. GARTNER, AND I. M. ARIAS. Hepatic intracellular distribution of tritium-labeled unconjugated and conjugated bilirubin in normal and Gunn rats. *J. Clin. Invest.* 45: 1194–1201, 1966.

33. BINGOLD, K. Haemolyse, Blutfarbstoffabbau, Haematinaemie und Ikterus. *Arch. Klin. Med.* 97: 257–264, 1923.

34. BINGOLD, K. Eigenschaften und physiologische bedeutung des pentdyopents. *Klin. Wochschr.* 17: 289–295, 1938.

35. BILLING, B. H. Quantitative determination of bile pigment in serum using reverse phase partition chromatography. *Biochem. J.* 56: 1954.

36. BILLING, B. H. Chromatographic method for the determination of the three bile pigments in serum. *J. Clin. Pathol.* 8: 126–129, 1955.

37. BILLING, B. H. The three serum bile pigments in obstructive jaundice and hepatitis. *J. Clin. Pathol.* 8: 130–131, 1955.

38. BILLING, B. H. Bile pigments in jaundice. *Advan. Clin. Chem.* 2: 268–293, 1959.

39. BILLING, B. H., P. G. COLE, AND G. H. LATHE. Excretion of bilirubin as di-glucuronide giving direct van den Bergh reaction. *Biochem. J.* 65: 774–784, 1957.

40. BILLING, B. H., C. H. GRAY, A. KULCZYCKA, P. MANFIELD, AND D. C. NICHOLSON. The metabolism of ^{14}C-bilirubin in congenital non-haemolytic hyperbilirubinemia. *Clin. Sci.* 27: 163–170, 1964.

41. BILLING, B. H., AND G. H. LATHE. Bilirubin metabolism in jaundice. *Am. J. Med.* 24: 111–121, 1958.

42. BILLING, B. H., Q. MAGGIORE, AND M. A. CARTER. Hepatic transport of bilirubin. *Ann. N.Y. Acad. Sci.* 111: 319–325, 1963.

43. BILLING, B. H., R. WILLIAMS, AND T. G. RICHARDS. Hepatic transport of bilirubin in familial hyperbilirubinemia. *Clin. Sci.* 27: 245–257, 1964.

44. BJURE, J., AND S. P. FALLSTROM. Endogenous formation of carbon dioxide in newborn infants. *Acta Pediat.* 52: 361–366, 1963.

45. BOLLET, A. J., J. F. GOODWIN, AND A. K. BROWN. Metabolism of mucopolysaccharides in connective tissues. *J. Clin. Invest.* 38: 451–455, 1959.

46. BOLLMAN, J. L. Bilirubin metabolism. *Gastroenterology* 36: 1313–1331, 1959.

47. BROWN, A. K., AND W. W. ZUELZER. Studies on the neonatal development of the glucuronide conjugating system. *J. Clin. Invest.* 37: 332–340, 1958.

48. BROWN, W. R., G. M. GRODSKY, AND J. V. CARBONE. Intracellular distribution of tritiated bilirubin during hepatic uptake and excretion. *Am. J. Physiol.* 207: 1237–1241, 1965.

49. BURKA, E. R., I. B. BRICK, AND H. R. WOLFE. Lipochrome hepatosis without jaundice: a variant of the Dubin-Johnson syndrome. *Am. J. Med. Sci.* 242: 746–749, 1961.

50. CARBONE, J. V., AND G. M. GRODSKY. Constitutional nonhemolytic hyperbilirubinemia in the rat: defect of bilirubin conjugation. *Proc. Soc. Exptl. Biol. Med.* 94: 461–463, 1957.

51. CHERRICK, G. R., S. W. STEIN, C. M. LEEVY, AND C. S. DAVIDSON. Indocyanine green: observations on its properties, plasma decay, and hepatic extraction. *J. Clin. Invest.* 39: 592–600, 1960.

52. CHILDS, B., AND V. A. NAJJAR. Familial nonhemolytic jaundice with kernicterus: report of two cases without neurologic disease. *Pediatrics* 18: 369–377, 1956.

53. CHILDS, B., J. B. SIDBURY, AND C. J. MIGEON. Glucuronic acid conjugation by patients with familial non-hemolytic jaundice and their relatives. *Pediatrics* 23: 903–913, 1959.

54. COHN, E. J. The chemical specificity of the interaction of diverse human plasma proteins. *Blood* 3: 471–485, 1948.

55. COLE, P. G., AND G. H. LATHE. The separation of serum pigments giving the direct and indirect van den Bergh reaction. *J. Clin. Pathol.* 6: 99–104, 1953.

56. COLE, P. G., AND G. H. LATHE. Separation of the bile pigments of serum, bile and urine. *Biochem. J.* 57: 514–518, 1954.

57. CONNEY, A. H. Enzyme induction and drug toxicity. *Drugs and Enzymes*, edited by B. Brodie and J. Gilette. New York: Pergamon, 1965, p. 277–307.

58. CONRAD, M., W. CROSBY, AND D. HOWIE. Hereditary nonspherocytic disease. *Am. J. Med.* 29:811–819, 1960.

59. CORNELIUS, C. E., J. BEN EZZER, AND I. M. ARIAS. Binding of organic anions by rat liver plasma membranes in vitro. *Proc. Soc. Exptl. Biol.* 124:665–667, 1967.

60. CORNELIUS, C. E., AND R. R. GRONWALL. A mutation in Southdown sheep affecting the hepatic uptake of BSP, indocyanine green, rose bengal, sodium cholate and phylloerythrin from blood. *Federation. Proc.* 24:144, 1965.

61. CRIGLER, J. Sodium phenobarbital-induced decrease in serum bilirubin in an infant with congenital nonhemolytic jaundice and kernicterus. *J. Clin. Invest.* 45:998–999, 1966.

62. CRIGLER, J. F., AND V. A. NAJJAR. Congenital familial nonhemolytic jaundice with kernicterus. *Pediatrics* 10:169–180, 1952.

63. CROSBY, W. H. Capacity for bilirubin production as reflected in the concentration of plasma bilirubin. *J. Clin. Invest.* 37:887–888, 1958.

64. DALLNER, G., S. ORRENIUS, AND A. BERGSTRAND. Isolation and properties of rough and smooth vesicles from rat liver. *J. Cell Biol.* 16:426–430, 1963.

65. DALLNER, G., P. SIEKEVITZ, AND G. E. PALADE. Biogenesis of endoplasmic reticulum membranes. *J. Cell Biol.* 30:73–117, 1966.

66. DE DUVE, C. The separation and characterization of subcellular particles. *Harvey Lectures* 59:49–87, 1963–64.

66a.DELEON, A., L. M. GARTNER, AND I. M. ARIAS. The effect of phenobarbital on hyperbilirubinemia in glucuronyl transferase deficient rats. *J. Lab. Clin. Med.* 70:273–278, 1967.

67. DIAMOND, I., AND R. SCHMID. Experimental bilirubin encephalopathy. *J. Clin. Invest.* 45:678–689, 1966.

68. DRUCKER, W. D. Glucosiduronidation of tetrahydrocortisone in normal and Gunn rats. *Bull. N.Y. Acad. Med.* 41:277, 1965.

69. DRUCKER, W. D., A. SFIKAKIS, A. BORKOWSKI, AND N. P. CHRISTY. On the rate of formation of steroidal glucuronosides in patients with familial and acquired jaundice. *J. Clin. Invest.* 43:1952–1967, 1964.

70. DUBIN, I. N. Chronic idiopathic jaundice: review of fifty cases. *Am. J. Med.* 24:268–292, 1958.

71. DUBIN, I. N., AND F. B. JOHNSON. Chronic idiopathic jaundice with unidentified pigment in liver cells: a new clinicopathologic entity with report of 12 cases. *Medicine* 33:155–197, 1954.

72. DUTTON, G. J. Glucuronide synthesis in foetal liver and tissues. *Biochem. J.* 61:141–148, 1959.

73. DUTTON, G. J. Comparison of glucuronide synthesis in developing mammalian and avian liver. *Ann. N.Y. Acad. Sci.* 111:259–273, 1963.

74. DUTTON, G. J., AND I. D. E. STOREY. Uridine compounds in glucuronic acid metabolism. *Biochem. J.* 57:275, 1954.

75. EHRLICH, P. Sulfodiazolenzol, em reagen auf bilirubin. *Centr. Klin. Med.* 4:721–723, 1883.

76. EHRLICH, J., A. B. NOVIKOFF, R. PLATT, AND E. ESSNER. Hepatocellular lipofuscin and the pigment of chronic idiopathic jaundice. *Bull. N.Y. Acad. Med.* 36:488–491, 1960.

77. EMMELOT, P., AND C. J. BOS. Adenosine triphosphatase in the cell membrane fraction from rat liver. *Biochim. Biophys. Acta* 58:374–375, 1962.

78. EMMELOT, P., C. J. BOS, E. L. BENEDETTI, AND P. H. RUMKE. Studies on plasma membranes. *Biochim. Biophys. Acta* 90:126–145, 1964.

79. ERNSTER, L., AND S. ORRENIUS. Substrate-induced synthesis of the hydroxylating enzyme system of liver microsomes. *Federation Proc.* 5:1190–1199, 1965.

80. ESSNER, E., AND A. B. NOVIKOFF. Human hepatocellular pigments and lysosomes. *J. Ultrastruct. Res.* 3:374–391, 1960.

81. FAIRLEY, N. H. Methaemalbumin: clinical aspects. *Quart. J. Med.* 10:95–114, 1941.

82. FIESSINGER, N., A. GAYDOS, AND M. POLONOVSKI. Le rôle de la globine dans la réaction indirecte de diazotation de la bilirubine. *Compt. Rend. Soc. Biol.* 135:1572–1579, 1941.

83. FISCHER, H., AND H. ORTH. *Die Chemie des Pyrrols*. Leipzig: Akad. Verlagsges. m.b.H., 1937, p. 764.

84. FLINT, M., G. H. LATHE, T. R. RICKETTS, AND G. SILMAN. Development of glucuronyl transferase and other enzyme systems in the newborn rabbit. *Quart. J. Exptl. Physiol.* 49:66–73, 1964.

85. FLOCK, E. V., AND J. L. BOLLMAN. Altered thyroxine conjugation in Gunn rats. *Federation Proc.* 18:227, 1959.

86. FOULK, W. T., H. R. BUTT, C. A. OWEN, F. F. WHITCOMB, AND H. L. MASON. Constitutional hepatic dysfunction (Gilbert's disease). *Medicine* 38:25–53, 1959.

87. FOUTS, J. R. The metabolism of drugs by subfractions of hepatic microsomes. *Biochem. Biophys. Res. Commun.* 6:373–378, 1961.

88. FOUTS, J. R. Interaction of drugs and hepatic microsomes. *Federation Proc.* 21:1107–1111, 1962.

89. FOUTS, J. R., AND R. H. ADAMSON. Drug metabolism in the newborn rabbit. *Science* 129:897, 1959.

90. FRANCOIS, R., M. A. BERTHOLON, J. BERTRAND, AND A. QUINCY. La maladie de Crigler-Najjar. *Rev. Intern. Hepatol.* 12:753–764, 1962.

91. FULOP, M., J. SANDSON, AND P. BRAZEAU. Dialyzability, protein binding and renal excretion of plasma conjugated bilirubin. *J. Clin. Invest.* 44:666–680, 1965.

92. GALAMBOS, J. T., AND G. R. MCLAREN. Hepatic uptake defect in patients with Gilbert's disease. *Arch. Internal Med.* 111:214–218, 1963.

93. GARAY, E. R., B. NOIR, AND M. ROYER. Biliverdin pigments in green biles. *Biochim. Biophys. Aeta* 100:411–417, 1965.

94. GARDIKAS, C., J. E. KENCH, AND J. F. WILKINSON. Choleglobin formation in the erythrocyte. *Nature* 161:607, 1948.

95. GARDIKAS, C., J. E. KENCH, AND J. F. WILKINSON. Bile pigment precursors in normal human erythrocytes. *Biochem. J.* 46:85–88, 1950.

96. GARTNER, L., AND I. M. ARIAS. Developmental pattern of glucuronide formation in rat and guinea pig liver. *Am. J. Physiol.* 205:663–670, 1963.

97. GARTNER, L., AND I. M. ARIAS. Pituitary regulation of hepatic excretory function. *J. Clin. Invest.* 45:1011, 1966.

98. GARTNER, L. M., AND I. M. ARIAS. Studies of prolonged neonatal jaundice in the breast fed infant. *J. Pediat.* 68:54–66, 1966.

99. GARTNER, L. M., AND I. M. ARIAS. Pharmacologic and

genetic determinants of disordered bilirubin transport and metabolism in the liver. *N. Y. Acad. Sci.* In press.

100. GARTNER, L., AND I. M. ARIAS. The hormonal regulation of hepatic bilirubin excretion. In: *Bilirubin Metabolism*, edited by I. A. D. Bouchier and B. H. Billing. Oxford: Blackwell, 1967, p. 175–182.

101. GELBOIN, H. V., AND L. SOKOLOFF. Effects of 3-methylcholanthrene and phenobarbital on amino acid incorporation into protein. *Science* 134: 611–612, 1961.

102. GILBERTSEN, A. S., I. BOSSENMAIER, AND R. CARDINAL. Enterohepatic circulation of unconjugated bilirubin in man. *Nature* 196: 141, 1962.

103. GILBERTSEN, A. S., P. T. LOWRY, V. HAWKINSIN, AND C. J. WATSON. Studies of dipyrrlmethene ("fuscin") pigments. I. The anabolic significance of the fecal mesobilifuscin. *J. Clin. Invest.* 38: 1166–1174, 1959.

104. GOLDFISCHER, S., I. M. ARIAS, E. ESSNER, AND A. B. NOVIKOFF. Cytochemical and electron microscopic studies of rat liver with reduced capacity to transport conjugated bilirubin. *J. Exptl. Med.* 115: 467–474, 1962.

105. GOLDSTEIN, G. W., AND R. LESTER. Reduction of biliverdin-C^{14} to bilirubin-C^{14} *in vivo*. *Proc. Soc. Exptl. Biol. Med.* 117: 681–683, 1964.

106. GOULIS, G., AND B. H. BILLING. Studies of hepatic excretory function. *Maladie Foie* 4: 49–54, 1963.

107. GRAY, C. H. *The Bile Pigments*. London: Methuen, 1953, p. 37–50.

108. GRAY, C. H., AND R. A. KELWICK. Bilirubin-serum protein complexes and the van den Bergh reaction. *Nature* 161: 274, 1948.

109. GRAY, C. H., A. NEUBERGER, AND P. H. A. SNEATH. Incorporation of N in the stercobilin in the normal and the porphyric. *Biochem. J.* 47: 87–92, 1950.

110. GRAY, C. H., AND J. J. SCOTT. The effect of hemorrhage on the incorporation of glycine-2-C^{14} into stercobilin. *Biochem. J.* 71: 38–42, 1959.

111. GREENBERGER, N. J., F. D. MILLIGAN, L. J. DEGROOT, AND K. J. ISSELBACHER. Jaundice and thyrotoxicosis in the absence of congestive heart failure. *Am. J. Med.* 36: 840–846, 1964

112. GREGORY, C. H. Studies of conjugated bilirubin. III. Pigment I, a complex of conjugated and free bilirubin. *J. Lab. Clin. Med.* 61: 917–925, 1963.

113. GREGORY, C. H., AND C. J. WATSON. Studies of conjugated bilirubin. II. Problems of sulfates of bilirubin *in vivo* and *in vitro*. *J. Lab. Clin. Med.* 60: 17–30, 1962.

114. GRODSKY, G. M., AND J. V. CARBONE. The synthesis of bilirubin glucuronide by tissue homogenates. *J. Biol. Chem.* 226: 449–458, 1957.

115. GRODSKY, G. M., J. V. CARBONE, AND R. FANSKA. Enzymatic defect in metabolism of bilirubin in fetal and newborn rat. *Proc. Soc. Exptl. Biol. Med.* 97: 291–294, 1958.

116. GRODSKY, G. M., A. N. CONTOPOULUS, R. FANSKA, AND J. V. CARBONE. Distribution of bilirubin-H^3 in the fetal and maternal rat. *Am. J. Physiol.* 204: 837–841, 1963.

117. GUNN, C. K. Hereditary acholuric jaundice. *J. Heredity* 29: 137–139, 1938.

118. HALAC, E., AND E. BONEVARDI. Solubilization and activation of liver UDP glucuronyl transferase by EDTA. *Biochim. Biophys. Acta* 67: 498–500, 1963.

119. HANZON, V. Liver cell secretion under normal and pathologic conditions studied by fluorescence microscopy on living rats. *Acta Physiol. Scand.* 28, Suppl. 101: 267, 1952.

120. HARGREAVES, T. Cholestatic drugs and bilirubin metabolism. *Nature* 206: 154–156, 1965.

121. HARGREAVES, T., AND J. B. HOLTON. Jaundice of the newborn due to novobiocin. *Lancet* 1: 839, 1962.

122. HARGREAVES, T., AND G. H. LATHE. Inhibitory aspects of bile secretion. *Nature* 200: 1172–1176, 1963.

123. HARRIS, J. W. *The Red Cell: Production, Metabolism, Destruction: Normal and Abnormal*. Cambridge, Mass.: Harvard Press, 1963, p. 482.

124. HARRIS, L. E., F. J. FARRELL, R. G. SHORTER, E. A. BANNER, AND D. R. MATTHIESON. Conjugated serum bilirubin in erythroblastosis fetalis: an analysis of 38 cases. *Proc. Staff Meetings Mayo Clinic* 37: 574–581, 1962.

125. HARTIALA, K. J. V., AND M. PULKKINEN. Studies on detoxification mechanisms. IV. Glucuronide synthesis in the fetal rabbit. *Ann. Med. Exptl. Biol. Fenniae, Helsinki* 33: 246–248, 1955.

126. HAVERBACK, B. J., AND S. K. WIRTSCHAFTER. Familial nonhemolytic jaundice with normal liver histology and conjugated bilirubin. *New Engl. J. Med.* 262: 113–117, 1960.

127. HEIKEL, T., B. C. KNIGHT, C. RIMINGTON, H. D. RITCHIE, AND E. J. WILLIAMS. Studies on biliary excretion in the rabbit. I. *Proc. Roy. Soc., London, Ser. B* 153: 47–79, 1960.

128. HEIKEL, T., W. H. LOCKWOOD, AND C. RIMINGTON. Formation of non-enzymatic haem. *Nature* 182: 313, 1958.

129. HERMAN, J. D., E. B. COOPER, A. TAKEUCHI, AND H. SPRINZ. Constitutional hyperbilirubinemia with unconjugated bilirubin in the serum and pigment deposition in the liver. *Am. J. Digest. Diseases* 9: 160–169, 1964.

130. HOLTON, J. B., AND G. H. LATHE. Inhibitors of bilirubin conjugation in newborn infant serum and male urine. *Clin. Sci.* 25: 499–509, 1963.

131. HOWATSON, A. F., AND A. W. HAM. Electron microscope study of sections of two rat liver tumors. *Cancer Res.* 15: 62–69, 1955.

132. HSIA, D. Y., R. M. DOWBEN, R. SHAW, AND A. GROSSMAN. Inhibition of glucuronyl transferase by progestational agents from serum of pregnant women. *Nature* 187: 693, 1960.

133. HSIA, D. Y., S. RIABOV, AND R. M. DOWBEN. Inhibition of glucuronyl transferase by steroid hormones. *Arch. Biochem.* 103: 181–185, 1963.

134. HULST, L. A., AND W. GROTEPASS. Ueber das pentdyopent von Bingold. *Klin. Wochschr.* 15: 201–203, 1936.

135. HUNTER, F. M., R. D. SPARKS, AND R. L. FLINNER. Hepatitis with resulting mobilization of hepatic pigment in a patient with Dubin-Johnson syndrome. *Gastroenterology* 47: 631–635, 1964.

136. INSCOE, J. K., AND J. AXELROD. Some factors affecting glucuronide formation *in vitro*. *J. Pharmacol. Exptl. Therap.* 129: 128–131, 1960.

137. ISRAELS, L. G., H. J. SUDERMAN, AND S. E. RITZMAN. Hyperbilirubinemia due to an alternate path of bilirubin production. *Am. J. Med.* 27: 693–702, 1959.

138. ISRAELS, L. G., AND A. ZIPURSKY. Primary shunt hyperbilirubinemia. *Nature* 193: 73, 1962.

139. ISRAELS, L. G., T. YAMAMOTO, J. SKANDERBEG, AND A.

ZIPURSKY. Shunt bilirubin: evidence for two components. *Science* 139: 1054, 1963.

140. ISSELBACHER, K. J., M. F. CHRABAS, AND R. C. QUINN. The solubilization and partial purification of a glucuronyl transferase from rabbit liver microsomes. *J. Biol. Chem.* 237: 3033–3036, 1962.

141. ISSELBACHER, K. J., AND E. A. McCARTHY. Studies on bilirubin sulphate and other nonglucuronide conjugates of bilirubin. *J. Clin. Invest.* 38: 645–651, 1959.

142. JAMES, G. W., AND L. ABBOT. Stercobilin N¹⁵ excretion in refractory anemia. *Am. Clin. Climatol. Assoc.* 73: 110–114, 1961.

143. JAVITT, N. B. Ethereal and acylglucuronide formation in the homozygous Gunn rat. *Am. J. Physiol.* 210: 424–428, 1966.

144. JERVIS, G. A. Constitutional nonhemolytic hyperbilirubinemia with findings resembling kernicterus. *AMA Arch Neurol. Psychiat.* 81: 55–60, 1959.

145. JOHNSON, L. The effect of certain substances on bilirubin levels and occurrence of kernicterus in genetically jaundiced rats. In: *Kernicterus*, edited by A. Sass-Kortsak. Toronto: Univ. of Toronto Press, 1961, p. 208–218.

146. JOHNSON, L., F. SARMIENTO, W. A. BLANC, AND R. DAY. Kernicterus in rats with an inherited defect of glucuronyl transferase. *A.M.A. J. Diseases Children* 99: 591–608, 1959.

147. KARUNAIRATNAM, M. C., L. M. H. KERR, AND G. A. LEVVY. Glucuronide-synthesizing system in mouse and its relationship to β-glucuronidase. *Biochem. J.* 45: 496–499, 1949.

148. KATZ, J. S., S. ROSENFELD, AND A. L. SELLERS. Sites of plasma albumin catabolism in the rat. *Am. J. Physiol.* 200: 1301–1306, 1961.

149. KENCH, J. E., C. GARDIKAS, AND J. F. WILKINSON. Bile pigment formation *in vitro* from haematin and other haem derivatives. *Biochem. J.* 47: 129–134, 1950.

150. KLATSKIN, G. Bile pigment metabolism. *Ann. Rev. Med.* 12: 211–250, 1961.

151. KLATSKIN, G., AND L. BUNGARDS. Bilirubin-protein linkages in serum and their relationship to the van den Bergh reaction. *J. Clin. Invest.* 35: 537–551, 1956.

152. KLATSKIN, G., AND V. A. DRILL. Significance of the "one minute" (prompt direct reacting) bilirubin in serum. *J. Clin. Invest.* 29: 660–676, 1950.

153. KLEINER, G., L. KRESCH, AND I. M. ARIAS. Studies of hepatic excretory function. II. The effect of norethynodrel and mestranol on bromsulfalein sodium metabolism in women of childbearing age. *New Engl. J. Med.* 273: 420–423, 1965.

154. LARSON, E. A., G. T. EVANS, AND C. J. WATSON. A study of the serum biliverdin concentration in various types of jaundice. *J. Lab. Clin. Med.* 32: 481–488, 1947.

155. LATHE, G. H. Bile pigment metabolism and liver function in premature infants. In: *Physiology of Prematurity*, edited by J. T. Lanman. New York: Josiah Macy Jr. Found., 1958, p. 59–76.

156. LATHE, G. H., AND C. R. J. RUTVEN. Factors affecting the rate of coupling of bilirubin and conjugated bilirubin in the van den Bergh reaction. *J. Clin. Pathol.* 11: 155–161, 1958.

157. LATHE, G. H., AND M. WALKER. The synthesis of bili-

rubin glucuronide in animal and human liver. *Biochem. J.* 70: 705–712, 1958.

158. LATHE, G. H., AND M. WALKER. Inhibition of bilirubin conjugation in rat liver slices by human pregnancy and neonatal serum and steroids. *Quart. J. Exptl. Physiol.* 43: 257–265, 1958.

159. LAURELL, C. B., AND C. GRONVALL. Haptoglobins. *Advan. Clin. Chem.* 5: 135–172, 1962.

160. LELONG, M., J. COLIN, D. ALAGILLE, C. GENTIL, J. BRETAGNE, AND L. HOULLEMARE. Ictère familial non hèmolytique avec ictère nucléaire (maladie de Crigler-Najjar). *Arch. Franc. Pediat.* 18: 272–275, 1961.

161. LEMBERG, R. Bile pigments from normal erythrocytes. *Nature* 163: 97, 1949.

162. LEMBERG, R., AND J. W. LEGGE. *Hematin Compounds and Bile Pigments*. New York: Interscience, 1949, p. 748.

163. LESTER, R., R. E. BEHRMAN, AND J. F. LUCEY. Transfer of bilirubin-C¹⁴ across monkey placenta. *Pediatrics* 32: 416–419, 1963.

164. LESTER, R., AND R. SCHMID. Intestinal absorption of bile pigments. II. Bilirubin absorption in man. *New Engl. J. Med.* 269: 178–182, 1963.

165. LESTER, R., AND R. SCHMID. Bilirubin metabolism. *New Engl. J. Med.* 270: 779–786, 1964.

166. LEVINE, R., AND G. KLATSKIN. Unconjugated hyperbilirubinemia in the absence of overt hemolysis. *Am. J. Med.* 36: 541–552, 1964.

167. LOKIETZ, H., R. M. DOWBEN, AND D. Y. HSIA. Studies on the effect of novobiocin on glucuronyl transferase. *Pediatrics* 32: 47–51, 1963.

168. LONDON, I. M. The conversion of hematin to bile pigment. *J. Biol. Chem.* 184: 373–376, 1950.

169. LONDON, I. M. The metabolism of the erythrocyte. *Harvey Lectures Ser. 56* 151–190, 1961.

170. LONDON, I. M., AND R. WEST. The formation of bile pigment in pernicious anemia. *J. Biol. Chem.* 184: 359–364, 1950.

171. LONDON, I. M., R. WEST, D. SHEMIN, AND D. RITTENBERG. On the origin of bile pigment in normal man. *J. Biol. Chem.* 184: 351–358, 1950.

172. LONDON, I. M., R. WEST, D. SHEMIN, AND D. RITTENBERG. Porphyrin formation and hemoglobin metabolism in congenital porphyria. *J. Biol. Chem.* 184: 365–371, 1950.

173. LONDON, I. M., M. YAMASAKI, AND A. G. SABELLA. Conversion of protoporphyrin to bile pigment. *Federation Proc.* 10: 217, 1951.

174. LUCEY, J. F., AND C. A. VILLEE. Studies of glucuronide formation *in vitro*. *Proc. Intern. Congr. Pediat., 10th, Lisbon, 1962*.

175. MAIMONIDES, M. *Commentary on the Aphorisms of Hippocrates*, translated by R. Moshe Ibn Tibbon. Jerusalem: Mossad Harav Kook and Israel Med. Assoc., 1961, p. 1–158.

176. MALLOY, H. T., AND L. LOEWENSTEIN. Hereditary jaundice in the rat. *Can. Med. Assoc. J.* 42: 122–125, 1940.

177. MANDEMA, E., W. H. DE FRAITURE, H. O. NIEWEG, AND A. ARENDS. Familial chronic idiopathic jaundice (Dubin-Sprinz disease), with a note on bromsulphalein metabolism in this disease. *Am. J. Med.* 28: 42–50, 1960.

178. MANN, F. C., C. SHEARD, J. L. BOLLMAN, AND E. J. BLADES. The formation of bile pigment from hemoglobin. *Am. J. Physiol.* 76: 306–315, 1926.

179. McKay, R. J., and J. F. Lucey. Neonatology. *New. Engl. J. Med.* 270: 1292–1299, 1964.

180. McNee, J. W. Jaundice: a review of recent work. *Quart. J. Med.* 16: 390–420, 1923.

181. Menken, M., P. Barret, and N. Berlin. Conjugation of bilirubin-C14 by rat liver homogenate *in vitro*. *Federation Proc.* 24: 135, 1965.

182. Metge, W. R., C. A. Owen, W. T. Foulk, and N. H. Hoffman. Bilirubin glucuronyl transferase activity in liver disease. *J. Lab. Clin. Med.* 64: 89–98, 1964.

183. Minkowski, O., and B. Naunyn. Beitrage zur Pathologie der und des Ikterus. *Arch. Exptl. Pathol. Pharmakol.* 21: 1–33, 1886.

184. Moore, C. V., and R. Dubach. Metabolism and requirements of iron in man. *J. Am. Med. Assoc.* 162: 197–204, 1956.

185. Nakajima, H. Studies on heme alpha-methenyl oxygenase. II. The isolation and characterization of the final reaction product, a possible precursor of biliverdin. *J. Biol. Chem.* 238: 3797–3801, 1963.

186. Nakajima, H., T. Takemura, O. Nakajima, and K. Yamaoka. Studies on heme α-methenyl oxygenase. I. enzymatic conversion of pyridine hemichromogen and hemoglobin-haptoglobin into a possible precursor of biliverdin. *J. Biol. Chem.* 238: 3784–3796, 1963.

187. Natschka, J. C., and G. B. Odell. The influence of albumin on the distribution and excretion of bilirubin in jaundiced rats. *Pediatrics* 37: 51–61, 1966.

188. Neville, D. N. The isolation of a cell membrane fraction from liver. *J. Biophys. Biochem. Cytol.* 8: 413–422, 1960.

189. Newman, A. J., and S. Gross. Hyperbilirubinemia in breast-fed infants. *Pediatrics* 32: 995–1001, 1963.

190. Noir, B. A., E. R. Garay, and M. Royer. Separation and properties of conjugated biliverdin. *Biochim. Biophys. Acta* 100: 403–410, 1965.

191. Nosslin, B. The direct diazo reaction of bile pigments in serum: experimental and clinical studies. *Scand. J. Clin. Lab.* 49, Suppl. 3: 1–176, 1960.

192. Nosslin, B. Bromsulfalein retention and jaundice with unconjugated bilirubin following treatment with male fern extract. *Scand. J. Clin. Lab. Invest.* 15, Suppl. 69: 206–212, 1963.

193. Nosslin, B., and E. H. Morgan. The effect of phloroglucinol derivatives from male fern or dye excretion by the liver in the rabbit and rat. *J. Lab. Clin. Med.* 65: 891–902, 1965.

194. Novikoff, A. B. Studies of nucleoside-phosphatase in isolated cell membranes. *Proc. Intern. Congr. Biochem., 6th, New York City*, 1964.

195. Novikoff, A. B., and E. Essner. The liver cell. *Am. J. Med.* 29: 102–131, 1960.

195a. Novikoff, A. B. Biochemical heterogeneity of the cytoplasmic particles isolated from rat liver homogenate. *J. Histochem. Cytochem.* 1: 27–46, 1953.

196. Odell, G. B. The dissociation of bilirubin from albumin and its clinical implications. *J. Pediat.* 55: 268–279, 1959.

197. Odell, G. B. Studies in kernicterus. I. The protein binding of bilirubin. *J. Clin. Invest.* 38: 823–833, 1959.

198. Odell, G. B., J. C. Natschka, and B. Storey. The distribution of bilirubin in liver and kidney in jaundiced rats. *Pediatrics* 37: 51–61, 1966.

199. Ostrow, J. D. Biliary reabsorption of C14-bilirubin. *J. Lab. Clin. Med.* 62: 998, 1963.

200. Ostrow, J. D., J. H. Jandl, and R. Schmid. The formation of bilirubin from hemoglobin *in vivo*. *J. Clin. Invest.* 41: 1628–1637, 1962.

201. Ostrow, J. D., and R. Schmid. The protein-binding of C14-bilirubin in human and murine serum. *J. Clin. Invest.* 42: 1286–1299, 1963.

202. Overbeek, J. T. G., C. L. J. Vink, and H. Deenstra. The solubility of bilirubin. *Rec. Trav. Chim.* 74: 85–89, 1955.

203. Peterson, R. E., and R. Schmid. A clinical syndrome associated with a defect in steroid glucuronide formation. *J. Clin. Endocrinol.* 17: 1485–1488, 1957.

204. Petryka, Z., D. C. Nicholson, and C. H. Gray. Isomeric bile pigments as products of the *in vitro* fission of haemin. *Nature* 194: 1047, 1962.

205. Pogell, B. M., and L. Leloir. Nucleotide activation of liver microsomal glucuronidation. *J. Biol. Chem.* 236: 293–298, 1961.

206. Price, V. E., W. R. Sterling, V. A. Tarantola, R. W. Hartley, and M. Rechiegl. The kinetics of catalase synthesis and destruction *in vivo*. *J. Biol. Chem.* 237: 3468–3475, 1962.

207. Remmer, H., and H. J. Merker. Drug-induced changes in the liver endoplasmic reticulum: association with drug metabolizing enzymes. *Science* 142: 1657–1658, 1963.

208. Rich, A. R. The formation of bile pigment. *Physiol. Rev.* 5: 182–224, 1925.

209. Robinson, S., T. Vanier, J. F. Desforges, and R. Schmid. Jaundice in thalassemia minor. *New Engl. J. Med.* 267: 523–529, 1962.

210. Robinson, S. H., C. A. Owen, E. V. Flock, and R. Schmid. Bilirubin formation in the liver from nonhemoglobin sources. *Blood.* 26: 823–829, 1965.

210a. Rosenfeld, R. S., I. M. Arias, L. M. Gartner, L. Hellman, and T. F. Gallagher. Studies of urinary pregnane-3α,20β-diol during pregnancy, post-partum, lactation and progesterone ingestion. *J. Clin. Endocrinol. Metab.* 27: 1705–1710, 1967.

211. Rothschild, J. A. The isolation of microsomal membranes. *Biochem. Soc. Symp., Cambridge, Engl.* 22: 4–31, 1963.

212. Rotor, A. B., L. Manahan, and A. Florentin. Familial nonhemolytic jaundice with direct van den Bergh reaction. *Acta Med. Phillipina* 5: 37–49, 1948.

213. Sagild, V., O. Z. Dalgaard, and N. Tygstrup. Constitutional hyperbilirubinemia with unconjugated bilirubin in the serum and lipochrome-like pigment granules in the liver. *Ann. Internal Med.* 56: 308–314, 1962.

214. Schachter, D. Nature of the glucuronide in direct-reacting bilirubin. *Science* 126: 507–508, 1957.

215. Schallner, F., H. Popper, and V. Perez. Changes in bile canaliculi produced by norethandrolone: electron microscopic study of human and rat liver. *J. Lab. Clin. Med.* 56: 623–628, 1960.

216. Schalm, L., and A. P. Weber. Jaundice with conjugated bilirubin in hyperhemolysis. *Acta Med. Scand.* 176: 549–553, 1964.

217. Schenker, S., N. H. Dawber, and R. Schmid. Bilirubin metabolism in the fetus. *J. Clin. Invest.* 43: 32–39, 1964.

218. Schenker, S., and R. Schmid. Excretion of C14-bilirubin in newborn guinea pigs. *Proc. Soc. Exptl. Biol. Med.* 115: 446–448, 1964.

219. Scherb, J., M. Kirschner, and I. M. Arias. Studies of hepatic excretory function. The effect of 17-ethyl-19-

nortestosterone on sulfobromophthalein sodium (BSP) metabolism in man. *J. Clin. Invest.* 42 : 404–410, 1963.

220. SCHIFF, L., B. H. BILLING, AND Y. OIKAWA. Familial non-hemolytic jaundice with conjugated bilirubin in the serum. *New Engl. J. Med.* 260 : 1315–1318, 1959.

221. SCHIMKE, R. T., E. W. SWEENEY, AND C. M. BERLIN. The roles of synthesis and degradation in the control of rat liver tryptophan pyrrolase. *J. Biol. Chem.* 240 : 322–331, 1965.

222. SCHMID, R. Identification of "direct-reacting" bilirubin as bilirubin glucuronide. *J. Biol. Chem.* 229 : 881–888, 1957.

223. SCHMID, R. *The Metabolic Basis of Inherited Disease.* New York : McGraw-Hill, 1966, p. 871–902.

224. SCHMID, R., J. AXELROD, L. HAMMAKER, AND R. L. SWARM. Congenital jaundice in rats due to a defect in glucuronide formation. *J. Clin. Invest.* 37 : 1123–1130, 1958.

225. SCHMID, R., AND L. HAMMAKER. Glucuronide formation in patients with constitutional hepatic dysfunction (Gilbert's disease). *New Engl. J. Med.* 260 : 1310–1314, 1959.

226. SCHMID, R., AND L. HAMMAKER. Metabolism and disposition of C^{14}-bilirubin in congenital nonhemolytic jaundice. *J. Clin. Invest.* 42 : 1720–1734, 1963.

227. SCHMID, R., L. HAMMAKER, AND J. AXELROD. The enzymic formation of bilirubin glucuronide. *Arch. Biochem. Biophys.* 70 : 285–287, 1957.

227a. SCHNEIDER, W. C., AND W. M. HOGEBOOM. Fractionation of cell components of animal tissues. In : *Methods in Enzymology,* edited by S. P. Colowick and N. Kaplan. New York : Acad. Press, 1955, p. 16–19.

228. SCHOENFIELD, L. J., J. H. GRINDLAY, W. T. FOULK, AND J. L. BOLLMAN. Identification of intrahepatic bilirubin monoglucuronide and its conversion to pigments by isolated liver (26362). *Proc. Soc. Exptl. Biol. Med.* 106 : 438–441, 1961.

229. SCHOENFIELD, L. J., D. B. MCGILL, D. B. HUNTON, W. T. FOULK, AND H. R. BUTT. Studies of chronic idiopathic jaundice (Dubin-Johnson syndrome). I. Demonstration of excretory defect. *Gastroenterology* 44 : 101–111, 1963.

230. SCHUMM, O. Haematin als pathologischer Besandteil des Blutes. *Z. Physiol. Chem.* 97 : 32–38, 1916.

231. SCHWARTZ, S., G. IBRAHIM, AND C. J. WASTON. The contribution of nonhemoglobin hemes to the early labeling of bile pigment. *J. Lab. Clin. Med.* 64 : 73, 1964.

232. SHANKER, L. S., AND H. M. SOLOMON. Active transport of quaternary ammonium compounds into bile. *Am. J. Physiol.* 204 : 829–832, 1963.

233. SHOTTON, D., M. CARPENTER, AND W. B. RINEHART. Bromsulfalein retention due to administration of bunamiodyl. *New Engl. J. Med.* 264 : 550–552, 1961.

234. SIEDEL, W., W. V. POELNITZ, AND F. EISENREICHE. Bilifuscin und Mesobilifuscin als natuerliche Abbauprodukte des Blutfarbstoffes; ueber Vorkommen und Bildung. *Naturwissenschaften* 34 : 314–318, 1947.

235. SIEDEL, W., W. STICH, AND F. EISENREICH. Promesobilifuscin, ein neues physiologische Abbauprodukt des Blufarbstoffes. *Naturwissenschaften* 35 : 316–324, 1948.

236. SILVA, L. C. DA., F. GODOY, F. MENDES, G. LEITE, AND J. PONTES. Indirect reacting hyperbilirubinemia after porto-systemic shunt. *Gastroenterology* 39 : 605–614, 1960.

237. SINGLETON, J. W., AND L. LASTER. Biliverdin reductase of guinea pig liver. *J. Biol. Chem.* 12 : 4780–4789, 1965.

238. SJOSTRAND, T. The formation of carbon monoxide by the decomposition of haemoglobin in vivo. *Acta Physiol. Scand.* 26 : 338–344, 1952.

238a. SLEISENGER, M. H., I. KAHN, H. BARNIVILLE, W. RUBIN, J. BEN EZZER, AND I. M. ARIAS. Nonhemolytic unconjugated hyperbilirubinemia with hepatic glucuronyl transferase deficiency : a genetic study in four generations. *Trans. Am. Assoc. Physiol.* 80 : 259–266, 1967.

239. SNYDER, A. L., AND R. SCHMID. The conversion of hematin to bile pigments in the rat. *J. Lab. Clin. Med.* 65 : 817–824, 1965.

240. SPERBER, I. Secretion of organic anions in formation of urine and bile. *Pharmacol. Rev.* 11 : 109–134, 1959.

241. SPRINZ, H., AND R. S. NELSON. Persistent nonhemolytic hyperbilirubinemia associated with lipochrome-like pigment in liver cells : report of 4 cases. *Ann. Internal Med.* 41 : 952–962, 1954.

242. SKIPSKI, V. P., M. BARCLAY, F. M. ARCHIBALD, O. Terebus-Kekish, E. S. REICHMAN, AND J. J. GOOD. Lipid composition of rat liver cell membranes. *Life Sci.* 4 : 1673–1680, 1965.

243. STEVENSON, I. H., AND G. J. DUTTON. Mechanism of glucuronide synthesis in skin. *Biochem. J.* 7 : 19P, 1960.

244. STICKNEY, J. C., P. S. STEWART, AND J. L. COLLINS. Plasma bilirubin and bromsulfophthalein clearance during simulated high altitude in unanesthetized rats. *Proc. Soc. Exptl. Biol. Med.* 118 : 433–435, 1965.

245. STIEHM, E. R., AND J. RYAN. Breast-milk jaundice. *Am. J. Diseases Children* 109 : 212–216, 1965.

246. STOREY, I. D. E. The inhibition of the uridine diphosphatetransglucuronylase activity of mouse-liver homogenates by thiol reagents. *Biochem. J.* 95 : 201–208, 1965.

247. STOREY, I. D. E. Some differences in the conjugation of o-aminophenol and p-nitrophenol by the uridine diphosphatetransglucuronylase of mouse-liver homogenate. *Biochem. J.* 95 : 209–214, 1965.

248. STOREY, I. D. E., AND G. J. DUTTON. Uridine compounds in glucuronic acid metabolism. *Biochem. J.* 59 : 279–288, 1955.

249. SUGAR, P. Familial nonhemolytic jaundice, congenital with kernicterus. *Arch. Internal Med.* 108 : 121–127, 1961.

250. SZABO, L., AND P. EBREY. Studies on the inheritance of Crigler-Najjar's syndrome by the menthol test. *Acta Pediat. Hung.* 4 : 153–156, 1963.

251. SZABO, L., Z. KOVACS, AND P. B. EBREY. Crigler-Najjar syndrome. *Acta Pediat. Hung.* 3 : 49–70, 1962.

252. TAKEUCHI, M., AND H. TERAYAMA. Preparation and chemical composition of rat liver cell membranes. *Exptl. Cell Res.* 40 : 32–44, 1965.

253. TALAFANT, E. The nature of direct and indirect bilirubin. *Collection Trav. Chim. Tchecoslov.* 22 : 661–663, 1957.

254. TARCHANOFF, J. F. Ueber die Bildung von Gallenpigment aus Blutfarbstoff im Tierkoerper. *Arch. Ges. Physiol.* 9 : 53–65, 1874.

255. TENHUNEN, J., AND H. TORSTI. Synthesis of bilirubin glucuronide. *Scand. J. Clin. Lab. Invest.* 11 : 162–165, 1954.

256. TISDALE, W., G. KLATSKIN, AND E. KINSELLA. Significance of direct-reacting fraction of serum bilirubin in hemolytic jaundice. *Am. J. Med.* 26 : 214–227, 1959.

257. TOMLINSON, G. A., AND S. J. YAFFE. The formation of bilirubin and p-nitrophenyl glucuronides by rabbit liver. *Biochem. J.* 99 : 507–512, 1966.

258. TRIA, E., AND O. BARNABEI. Presence of a phosphatidopeptide fraction in liver cell membrane and its possible role in the active transport of amino-acids. *Nature* 197 : 598–599, 1963.

259. VAN DEN BERGH, A. A. H., AND P. MULLER. Über eine directe und eine indirekte Diazoreaktion auf Bilirubin. *Biochem. Z.* 77: 90–103, 1916.

260. VAN DEN BERGH, A. A. H., AND I. SNAPPER. Dic farbstoffe des blutserums. *Deut. Arch. Klin. Med.* 110: 540–561, 1913.

261. VAN LEUSDEN, H. A. I. M., J. A. J. M. BAKKEREN, F. ZILLIKEN, AND C. A. M. STOLTE. p-Nitrophenylglucuronide formation by homozygous adult Gunn rats. *Biochem. Biophys. Res. Commun.* 7: 67–69, 1962.

262. VEST, M. Insufficient glucuronide formation in the newborn and its relationship to the pathogenesis of icterus neonatorum. *Arch. Disease Childhood* 33: 473–481, 1958.

263. VIRCHOW, R. Die pathologische pigmente. *Arch. Pathol. Anat. Physiol.* 1: 379–404, 1847.

264. WAKISAKA, G. Clinical and enzymological observations on cases with Gilbert's disease. *Japan. Arch. Internal Med.* 8: 634–648, 1961.

265. WATSON, C. J. Color reaction of bilirubin with sulfuric acid, a direct diazo-reacting bilirubin sulfate. *Science* 128: 142, 1958.

266. WEBER, A. P., AND L. SCHALM. Quantitative separation and determination of bilirubin and conjugated bilirubin in human serum. *Clin. Chim. Acta* 7: 805–810, 1962.

267. WEBER, A. P., AND L. SCHALM. Evidence against "bilirubin sulphate." *Acta Med. Scand.* 177: 519–526, 1965.

268. WEBER, A. P., L. SCHALM, AND J. WITMANS. Bilirubin monoglucuronide (pigment I): complex. *Acta Med. Scand.* 173: 19–24, 1963.

269. WEGMAN, R., M. RANGIER, J. ETEVE, A. CHARBONNIER, AND J. CAROLI. Melanose hepatosplenique avec ictère chronique à bilirubine directe. *Semaine Hop. Paris* 36: 1761–1781, 1960.

270. WEINBREN, K., AND B. H. BILLING. Hepatic clearance of bilirubin as an index of cellular function in the regenerating rat liver. *Brit. J. Exptl. Pathol.* 37: 199–204, 1956.

271. WHEELER, H. O., J. I. MELTZER, AND S. E. BRADLEY. Biliary transport and hepatic storage of sulfobromphthalein sodium in the unanesthetized dog, in normal man, and in patients with hepatic disease. *J. Clin. Invest.* 39: 1131–1144, 1960.

271a. WHIPPLE, G. Pigment metabolism and regeneration of hemoglobin in the body. *Harvey Lecture* 17: 95–121, 1921.

272. WINTROBE, M. M., E. MATTHEWS, R. POLLACK, AND B. M. DOBYNS. A familial hemopoietic disorder in Italian adolescents and adults. *J. Am. Med. Assoc.* 114: 1530–1540, 1940.

273. WITH, T. K. *Biology of Bile Pigments.* Copenhagen: Arne Forst-Hansen, 1954, p. 334.

274. WOLF, R. L., M. PIZETTE, A. RICHMAN, D. DREILING, W. JACOBS, C. FERNANDEZ, AND H. POPPER. Chronic idiopathic jaundice. *Am. J. Med.* 28: 32–41, 1960.

275. YAFFE, S., AND C. CATZ. Pharmacological modification of bilirubin conjugation in the newborn. *Am. J. Diseases Children* 104: 516–517, 1962.

276. YAMAMOTO, T., J. SKANDERBEG, A. ZIPURSKY, AND L. G. ISRAELS. The early appearing bilirubin: evidence for two components. *J. Clin. Invest.* 44: 31–41, 1965.

277. ZIEVE, L., E. HILL, M. C. L. HANSON, A. B. FALCONE, AND C. J. WATSON. Normal and abnormal variations and clinical significance of the one-minute and total serum bilirubin determinations. *J. Lab. Clin. Med.* 38: 446–469, 1951.

278. ZUELZER, W. W., L. E. REISMAN, AND A. K. BROWN. Studies in hyperbilirubinemia. *Am. J. Diseases Children* 102: 815–842, 1961.

CHAPTER 111

Evolution and bile salts

G. A. D. HASLEWOOD | *Department of Biochemistry, Guy's Hospital Medical School, London, England*

CHAPTER CONTENTS

THE COURSE OF BIOSYNTHESIS of cholic acid in rats and mice appears to include the steps set out in Figure 1. The steps may not occur entirely in the order given; the subject is discussed in Chapter 112; see also reference 11. However, it seems clear *a*) that the changes that convert the ring system of cholesterol [Fig. 1 (1)] to that of cholic acid [Fig. 1 (9)] are completed before carbon atoms are lost from the side chain, *b*) that an almost completely stereospecific reduction takes place to give the C-5β configuration found in cholic acid [step (4) → (5) in Fig. 1], and *c*) that another stereospecific reduction leads to a 3α-hydroxyl group at C-3 [step (5) → (6) in Fig. 1]. In chenodeoxycholic acid biosynthesis, the step in which —OH is added at C-12 is missing or suppressed, and there may be other differences also in the stages of biogenesis of this acid.

The biosynthesis as it exists today in advanced mammals may be regarded as being, like any physiological or anatomical characteristic, the result of evolution. It is the purpose of this article to inquire whether animals more primitive and having a lower level of organization than mammals also have bile salts less highly evolved, and whether a study of bile salt differences can be expected to throw new light on evolutionary processes and on adaptations to environmental conditions. With these aims, and with the biosynthetic scheme outlined in Figure 1 in mind, it will be convenient to discuss the bile salts that have been isolated from representatives of various animal groups. References to the species mentioned are cited by Haslewood (8–11).

INVERTEBRATES

Although invertebrates do not have a separate liver and biliary system, there is in some a hepatopancreas which produces a digestive fluid containing substances

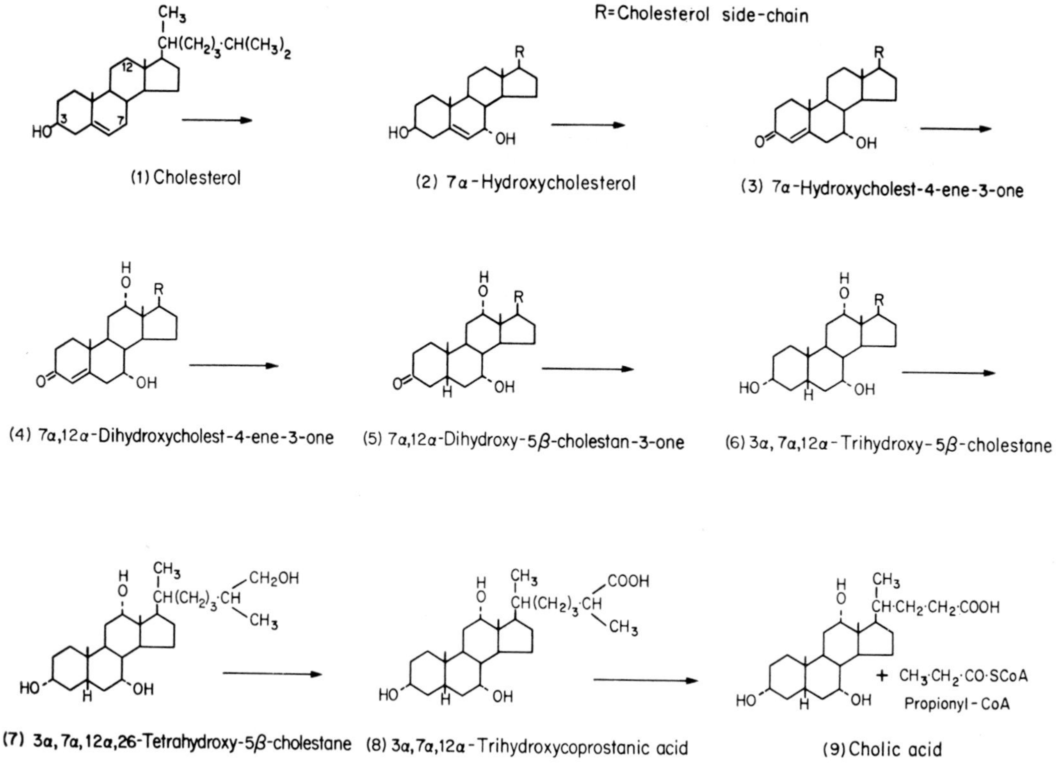

FIG. 1. Biosynthesis of cholic acid in mammals (see Chapter 112).

with surface-tension-lowering or "detergent" properties (21). These compounds were at first thought to be bile acid conjugates of the kind to be discussed later, but recent chemical work has failed to substantiate this idea. The digestive juices of the crayfish *Procanbarus clarkii* apparently contain no bile acids, and from the edible crab *Cancer pagurus* compounds were isolated which, after hydrolysis, yielded fatty acids, taurine ($NH_2 \cdot CH_2 \cdot CH_2 \cdot SO_3H$) and sarcosine ($CH_3NH \cdot CH_2 \cdot COOH$). The fatty acids included decanoic acid, $CH_3(CH_2)_8COOH$, and 5-dodecenoic acid, $CH_3(CH_2)_5CH{=}CH(CH_2)_3COOH$. These substances may be combined in the digestive fluid as, for example, in decanoylsarcosyltaurine shown as the ion:

$$CH_3(CH_2)_8CO \cdot N \cdot CH_2 \cdot CO \cdot NH \cdot CH_2 \cdot CH_2 \cdot SO_3{}^-$$
$$\mid$$
$$CH_3$$

decanoylsarcosyltaurate

A molecule like this is similar in general properties to the alcohol sulfates and taurine conjugates found in vertebrate biles and like these must exist at any biological hydrogen ion concentration as the anion, as shown. It may be concluded that the evolutionary step of converting cholesterol to steroid bile salts has

not been taken in the invertebrates so far examined for this feature. This is not the result of their not having cholesterol available, for although invertebrate animals have not been convincingly shown to be able to perform cholesterol biosynthesis to any great extent (6), they do contain cholesterol and sometimes other sterols in abundance (1).

VERTEBRATES

General

All vertebrates examined secrete a separate bile, and all below the evolutionary level of birds also have a gallbladder. The bile salts have always been found to be steroids, and there is reason to believe that they are made by biosynthesis from cholesterol. The administration of ^{14}C-labeled cholesterol has been followed by the recovery of radioactive bile salts in the following animals: Carp, *Cyprinus carpio;* frog, *Rana catesbeiana;* toad, *Bufo vulgaris japonicus* (= *Bufo b. formosus*); *Alligator mississipiensis;* boa constrictor; domestic fowl, pig, rabbit, and dog; laboratory rat, mouse, and guinea pig, and man himself. In the carp, frog, and toad, intact animals were used; the radioactive cholesterol was given intraperitoneally, and bile was obtained from the gallbladder. Thus the experiments did not exclude the enterohepatic circulation. It is possible, therefore, although unlikely, that intestinal microorganisms played some part in the biogenesis of the bile salts in these cases. The point is important, for at least one of the major bile acids (deoxycholic acid) in certain mammals is an artifact made by the intestinal microflora, and, before phylogenetic and other general conclusions can be safely drawn about bile salt differences, this possible intestinal intervention must be taken into account. Such intervention may itself be of zoological interest and its consideration must take its proper place in assessing the significance of bile salt differences among vertebrate forms.

As remarked above, it is only in a few species (man; laboratory rat, mouse, rabbit, and guinea pig; domestic dog, pig, sheep, and fowl; alligator and python) that germ-free animals have been used or biliary fistulas made and the bile salts identified so as to exclude the influence of the intestine. The results of these and other in vitro experiments may, however, be used to suggest whether bile salts obtained from gallbladder bile are, on the basis of their chemical structure alone, likely to be the result of intestinal microbial intervention. Such suggestions contain, of course, an element of doubt that can be resolved only experimentally.

In what follows, it will generally be assumed that the isolated bile salts are "primary," that is, those made by the liver from cholesterol, unless there is some reason to suppose or suspect that they are "secondary" products resulting from the action of intestinal microorganisms on the primary bile salts. The significance of these secondary bile salts is further discussed later in this article. It is convenient now to give an account of bile salts found in different vertebrate groups, with some discussion of their possible evolutionary significance.

FISHES

Agnatha: Cyclostomata; Myxinidae (Hagfishes); Petromyzontidae (Lampreys)

The hagfishes are commonly regarded as the most primitive living vertebrates. They have a cartilaginous "skeleton," a very simple type of brain, unmyelinated nerves, an innervated heart, and a chemically primitive type of hemoglobin; their inorganic ionic composition is close to that of sea water (5). The course of

their descent from early fossil fishes is unclear, but there is no evidence of a fresh-water history. They are specialized as scavengers, feeding chiefly on dead or moribund fishes whose tissues they ingest after a rasping action of the horny plates constituting the hagfish "jaw." Hagfishes have a very large liver, containing cholesterol in free and esterified form, and a relatively enormous gallbladder. The bile salts, present in high concentration in the bile, contain at least two substances, of which the chief has been isolated from two species and has been called "myxinol disulfate." This compound is shown in formula 10 as the disodium salt.

(10) Disodium myxinol disulfate

It is common to find bile alcohol sulfate esters in primitive fishes and amphibians, but the hagfish is the only animal so far discovered that has a bile alcohol esterified with two sulfate groups. Myxinol, the parent alcohol $C_{27}H_{48}O_4$, is also the only bile alcohol occurring as a principal constituent of the bile salts that has only four OH groups in the molecule, and it may be suggested that a C_{27}-tetrol like this must have two sulfate ester groups to confer sufficient detergent properties for the ester to act adequately as a bile salt.

In myxinol, the —OH group at C-3 is in the β position as in cholesterol (formula 1, Fig. 1); if this state of affairs is not a secondary one (in the sense discussed above), it may be that the Myxinidae and their ancestors never evolved the enzymes (at least three in the scheme shown in Fig. 1) necessary to bring about the inversion of this group to C-3α.

The myxinol structure has the 7α-OH group that would be expected if its biogenesis from cholesterol included steps (1)→(2) (Fig. 1), but the presence of the 16α-OH group is unique in bile alcohols.

A Stuart type of molecular model does not show myxinol disulfate as a very efficient detergent type as compared with more "modern" bile salts. The hydrophilic sulfate ester and —OH groups are not very sharply separated from the lipophilic ring structure and side chain (11). As the purest speculation, it may be suggested that it is because of its relative inefficiency as a detergent that myxinol disulfate is required in such large amounts in hagfish bile.

In summary, myxinol disulfate is a bile salt whose chemical structure agrees with the view that it comes from a primitive animal that has not evolved the enzymic mechanisms necessary to produce from cholesterol the molecular patterns found in more advanced forms.

The only other family of the Cyclostomata, the lampreys (Petromyzontidae), apparently have bile only in the larval (ammocoete) stage. The chief or sole bile salt in *Petromyzon marinus* is the 24-sulfate of 3α, $7\alpha,12\alpha,24$-tetrahydroxy-5α-cholane [petromyzonol sulfate; formula 10a; (12)]. This remarkable structure

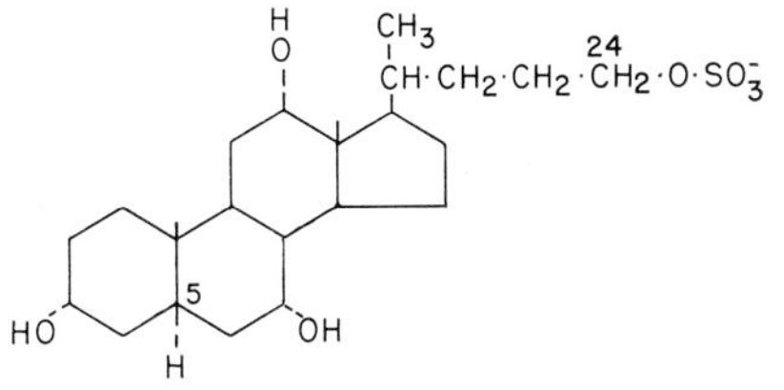

(10a) Petromyzonol sulfate

shows that some very primitive organisms can degrade cholesterol to C_{24} bile salts, although one would suppose that the biochemical steps of side-chain shortening must be quite different from those leading to C_{24} bile acids (Fig. 1). The structure of petromyzonol sulfate also suggests that the 5α configuration is the primitive condition in bile salts and that lampreys and hagfish are indeed not closely related.

Chondrichthyes: Holocephali

This group of marine cartilaginous fishes, of which the "rabbit fishes" (family Chimaeridae) are living representatives, has been carefully discussed by Patterson (20), who suggests that the morphological evidence favors the view that the chimaeras shared a common ancestor with a primarily marine stock, the fossil arthrodires. On the other hand, other systematists [e.g., Moy-Thomas (18)] have suggested that the chimaeras are to be regarded as descendants of primitive elasmorbanchs.

The bile salts of one species, *Chimaera monstrosa*, have been examined, and the principal bile salt is the sulfate of an alcohol, chimaerol, which probably has formula 11.

Chimaerol differs from myxinol in that it has the C-3, C-7, and C-12 pattern of ring hydroxylation found in all bile alcohols (except myxinol) so far discovered; this pattern was evidently selected at an

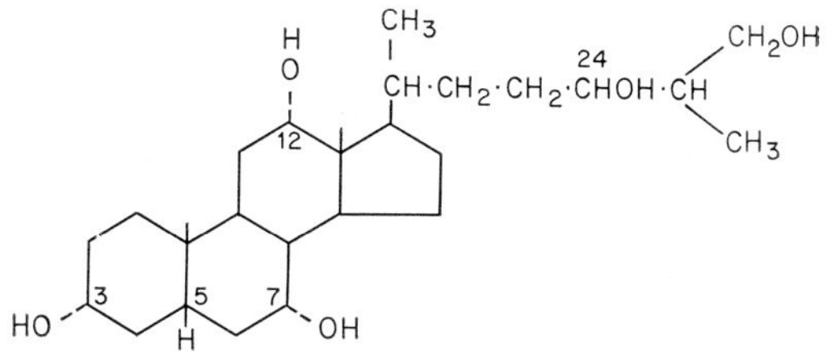

(11) Chimaerol

early stage in vertebrate evolution and is found also in the majority of bile acids. Chimaerol has the C-5β configuration, with extra side-chain hydroxylation at C-24.

Chondrichthyes: Elasmobranchii

About a dozen species of sharks and rays of several families have been shown to have as their principal bile salt the substance scymnol sulfate, formula 12. Scymnol, the alcohol of which (12) is the sulfate ester,

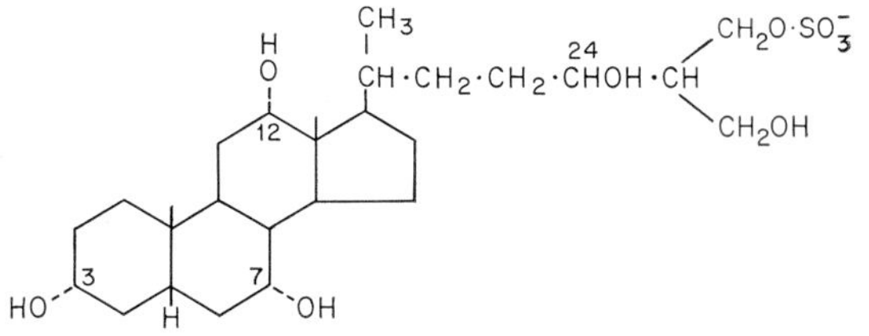

(12) Scymnol sulfate

differs from chimaerol (formula 11) only in that an extra side chain —OH group is present, at C-26 or C-27.[1] Thus scymnol could have arisen by evolution from chimaerol by the elaboration of a single enzyme (a C-26 or C-27 hydroxylase). Such a simple biochemical relationship supports the view that the chimaeras and elasmobranchs are closely related [as Patterson (20) says, ". . .they share much genetic material"], and this idea is confirmed by the finding of chimaerol in a ray (*Dasayatis akajei*) having scymnol

[1] In numbering C_{27} steroids, C-26 is regarded as the carbon atom corresponding to the methyl group at C-26 in cholesterol. This methyl group is the one derived in the biosynthesis of cholesterol from the β methyl group in mevalonic acid; i.e.,

α CH₂COOH
|
β C(CH₃)(OH). It is not known for any C_{27} bile alcohol or bile
|
  CH₂OH

acid which of the carbon atoms (C-26 or C-27) is in —CH₂OH or —COOH, although biosynthesis experiments in mammals suggest that it may be C-26 (17).

as its chief bile salt and also by the observation that *Chimaera* probably contains some scymnol.

Scymnol is a poor precursor of cholic acid (formula 9, Fig. 1) in rats having a biliary fistula and may thus be an evolutionary end point in elasmobranchs. The cholic acid isolated in small amounts from the bile of these fishes is probably endogenous, at least in some cases; in others, it could perhaps have been derived from the diet.

No other bile alcohol or acid has been identified in elasmobranch bile; the evidence so far thus supports the idea that the primarily marine cartilaginous fishes have only the C-5β type of bile salt.

Osteichthyes: Crossopterygii; Dipnoi

It has proved possible to examine the bile salts of the only known surviving coelacanth, *Latimeria chalumnae* Smith. No bile acids could be identified, and the principal bile salt was found to be latimerol sulfate (formula 13).

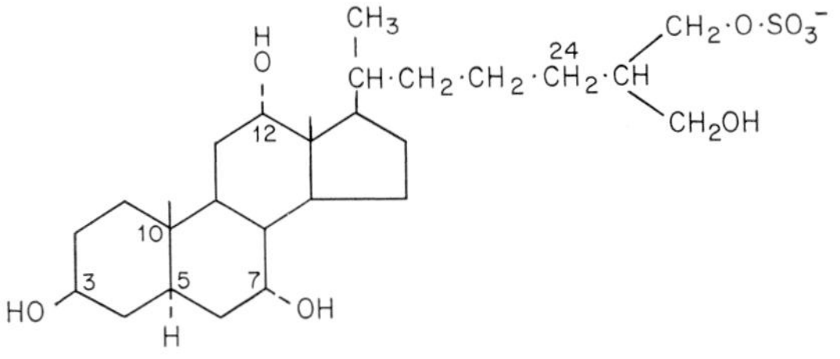

(13) Latimerol sulfate

The parent alcohol, latimerol, is quite different from those of chondrichthyans in that the configuration of the hydrogen at C-5 is α. This is the so-called allo structure, in which the C-5 hydrogen atom and the —CH_3 group at C-10 are in the trans relationship. It produces a rather flat ring nucleus, in contrast to the fist-shaped molecule formed when the —H at C-5 is in the β position. Allo bile salts were discovered only recently; their existence came as a surprise to investigators in the field, who had perhaps assumed that such a structure would be unlikely to function very effectively as a detergent.

Latimerol, like myxinol, has the 3β-OH configuration of cholesterol itself, and since *Latimeria* is a very primitive fish it is tempting to suggest that it also cannot invert the —OH group at C-3. This statement is not entirely true, for *Latimeria* bile contains a minor proportion of 5α-cyprinol sulfate (formula 14), the molecule of which is identical with latimerol sulfate except that the C-3 OH group is in the α-configuration.

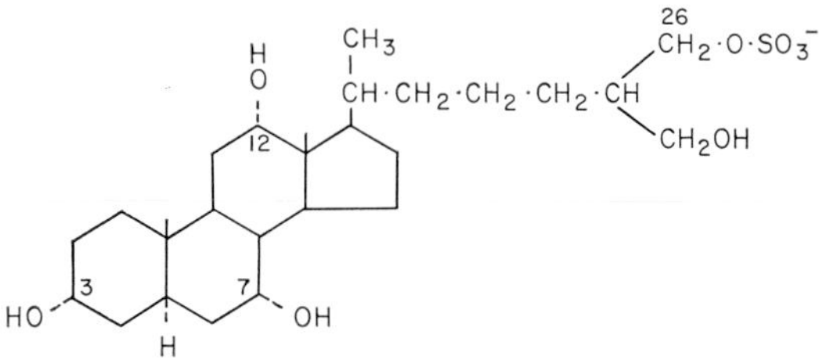

(14) 5α-Cyprinol sulfate

5α-Cyprinol sulfate has been found as the principal bile salt in 12 species of fishes of the family Cyprinidae and also in the American sucker *Catostomus commersoni* (family Catostomidae). All these fishes belong to the teleostean order Ostariophysi, a very large group that appears, according to the fossil record, to have had a history entirely in fresh water. Thus it is a fair inference that the latimerol/5α-cyprinol type of bile alcohol is a fresh-water form, and this entirely accords with the known history of *Latimeria*, for, although the living coelacanth is now marine, its fossil ancestors are found in fresh-water deposits.

5α-Cyprinol sulfate is also one of the bile salts in the lungfishes (Dipnoi), which are also primitive fresh-water species.

Osteichthyes: Chondrostei

This curious group of fishes comprises the sturgeons (Acipenseridae) and the American paddlefish of the genus *Polyodon*. Three species of sturgeons and one of paddlefish have a similar mixture of bile salts. The principal component of these is taurine-conjugated cholic acid, and there is a minor proportion of allo-cholic acid (formula 17). However, bile alcohols are present also and constitute perhaps 1–4% by weight of the bile salts. These alcohols occur as their sulfates and a chief component, at least in the sturgeon *Huso huso*, is the sulfate of 5β-cyprinol (formula 15). The

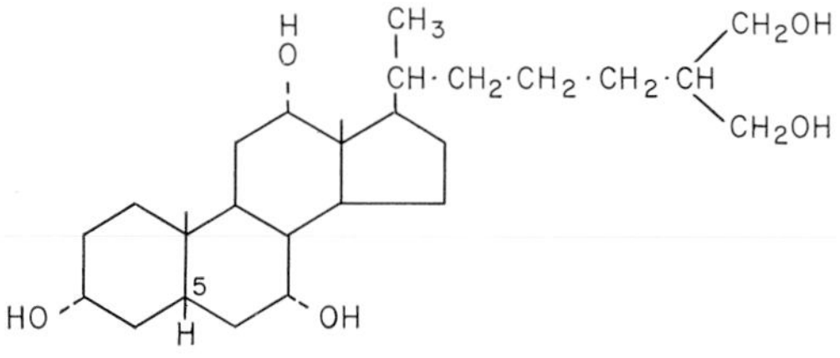

(15) 5β-Cyprinol

other substances in the bile alcohol mixture from chondrosteans include both 5α- and 5β-compounds with the properties of tetrols. It is difficult to believe that if most of the bile salts consisted of substances of this kind they could act effectively in their physiological role, and perhaps it is not too fanciful to suggest that the bile alcohols are in the process of disappearing during chondrostean evolution, so that their chemical nature makes no more functional "sense" than do, say, the limb remnants in primitive snakes.

Apart from these speculative conclusions, it is difficult to assess the significance of the chemical nature of chondrostean bile salts; perhaps the presence of allo substances can be taken as indicative of a freshwater ancestry, but it seems impossible at present to speculate reasonably about the meaning of the distribution of 5β-cyprinol.

Osteichthyes: Holostei

The bowfin *Amia calva* has taurocholate as almost its only bile salt; no bile alcohols and no allocholic acid (formula 17) could be found. As mentioned below, the holosteans are sometimes regarded as ancestral to teleostean fishes. If the bowfin evolved from a holostean form having 5α-cyprinol as its chief bile alcohol, one might perhaps have expected to find some allocholic acid in its bile.

Osteichthyes: Teleostei; Ostariophysi

As mentioned above, the cyprinids have 5α-cyprinol as their chief bile salt. As well as the Cyprinidae and closely related families, the Ostariophysi include the family Siluridae (catfishes) and allied forms. The silurids examined contain chiefly taurine-conjugated cholic acid, and this suggests that they may be more advanced than the cyprinids. The Cyprinidae themselves are apparently still evolving, for minor amounts of cholic acid (which can hardly be a dietary artifact in these fishes) have been found in the bile, and the common carp *Cyprinus carpio* makes radioactive cholic acid in small amounts after injection with ^{14}C-4-cholesterol.

Does the possession of 5α-cyprinol indicate that the cyprinids represent primitive teleostean fishes? This question may be considered in the light of the opinions of some taxonomists; for example, Newman (19) remarks as follows: "The carps are often cited as being the most generalized or most nearly ancestral of all surviving teleosts." On the other hand, Greenwood et al. (7) have published a new classification of teleostean fishes which, though it describes the ostariophysans as "relatively primitive teleosts," does not place this group nearest to the supposed holostean ancestors. The bile salt evidence separates the

cyprinids examined from the other teleosts and must be regarded as indicating a primitive level of organization in bile salt biosynthesis. It is for the taxonomist, taking this into account, to assess its weight as a character in conjunction with all other evidence of relationships. Before this is done, it will be important to know the bile salt composition in other ostariophysans, especially the gymnotids and characins. One characin, the piranha, *Serrasalmus ternetzi*, certainly has little but cholic acid. It may well be that carnivorous habits in some of the Ostariophysi have led to modernization of their bile salts.

It has been reported that carp bile contains a small amount of the tetrol $3\alpha,7\alpha,12\alpha,27$-tetrahydroxy-$5\alpha$-cholestane, i.e., 26 (or 27)-deoxy-5α-cyprinol (formula 22). As remarked previously, no tetrol other than myxinol and its disulfate has been found functioning as a principal bile salt and it is possible that the deoxy-5α-cyprinol in carp bile is an intermediate in the biosynthesis of 5α-cyprinol itself, since it is the 5α epimer of the substance of formula 7 (Fig. 1).

Osteichthyes: Other Teleostean Fishes

Most teleosts other than cyprinids that have been examined contain taurine conjugates of cholic acid (formula 9), with varying amounts also of taurochenodeoxycholic ($3\alpha,7\alpha$-dihydroxy-5β-cholanoic) acid shown as its ion in formula 16. Chenodeoxycholic acid

(16) Taurochenodeoxycholate

differs from cholic acid in not having the 12α-OH group, and, as remarked above, its biosynthesis from cholesterol may be somewhat different. It is the most abundant bile acid except cholic acid in vertebrates. In teleostean fishes it has been found to be present in lesser amounts than cholic acid, although in one instance, that of a gray mullet, *Mugil* species, the bile salts consisted almost entirely of taurochenodeoxycholate. This situation is perhaps the result of adaptation to the vegetarian type of diet of the fishes, and an analogous state of affairs is also frequently found in mammals.

The bile of many teleostean fish contains also small

amounts of allocholic ($3\alpha,7\alpha,12\alpha$-trihydroxy-5α-cholanoic) acid (formula 17), and it was indeed from

(17) Allocholic acid

such an animal, the Japanese gigi fish, *Pelteobagrus nudiceps* Sauvage (family Cobitidae), that this acid was first obtained as a mixture with cholic acid in 1939; its chemical nature remained unknown for more than 20 years. As mentioned above, allocholic acid with its 5α configuration might indeed be expected in the bile of a fish of the order Ostariophysi, since the (presumably) more primitive members of this order have 5α-cyprinol; however, it has also been found in other teleosts of different Orders.

From the eel *Anguilla japonica* [order Anguilliformes, division I of Greenwood et al. (7)], there have been obtained (in addition to cholic acid) two bile acids of formula $C_{27}H_{46}O_6$. These contain the ring nucleus of cholic acid and hence must presumably be $3\alpha,7\alpha,12\alpha$,x-tetrahydroxycoprostanic acids (formula 8 with an extra —OH group in the side chain). Such acids are found also in reptiles, and a consideration of the possibly biological significance of those in *Anguilla* bile must await further information.

Another eel, *Conger myriaster*, has 5β-cyprinol (formula 15) in its bile.

AMPHIBIANS

Although only a few species of amphibia have been investigated, it is clear that the bile salts of these animals contain substances apparently not found in other classes. However, 5α- and 5β-cyprinol, $3\alpha,7\alpha,12\alpha$-trihydroxycoprostanic acid, allocholic acid, and cholic acid have been found in the bile of various species, and the presence of these substances emphasizes the relationships of the amphibia on the one hand to crossopterygian fishes and on the other to crocodilians, saurians, and more advanced tetrapods.

Urodela

The giant salamander *Megalobatrachus japonicus* has the taurine conjugate of allocholic acid (formula 17)

as a chief bile salt, although a C-27 (probably trihydroxycoprostanic) acid was also found. A principal bile alcohol is 5α-cyprinol, present as its sulfate (formula 14). The common European fire salamander *Salamandra salamandra* also has taurine-conjugated allocholic acid as a large proportion of its bile salts.

The presence of 5α-cyprinol relates the giant salamander to the fishes (Crossopterygii, Dipnoi, Ostariophysi), mentioned above as also having this bile alcohol and fits in well with one supposed origin of amphibia, i.e., the ancestral crossopterygians.

The taurine conjugate of allocholic acid is the chief bile salt in some lizards of the family Iguanidae and perhaps of many other advanced lizards; thus its occurrence in the bile of salamanders agrees with the idea of the relationship of these urodeles to large groups of lizards.

On the other hand, another salamander, *Diemyctylus pyrrhogaster*, has as a bile alcohol the 5α epimer of 5β-bufol (formula 18), and this is a substance of a quite different side-chain pattern from cyprinol. 5β-Bufol is the characteristic bile alcohol of the toads (Bufonidae) examined, and the existence of its 5α epimer in a urodele might indicate an ancestral relationship between *Diemyctylus* and *Bufo*. Does it also, taken together with the different chemical picture in *Megalobatrachus* and *Salamandra*, indicate at least two evolutionary transitions of fishes to amphibians? Clarification of this question can await further chemical and biochemical information about amphibian bile salts.

Anura: Bufonidae

As mentioned above, the chief bile alcohol in toads seems to be 5β-bufol (formula 18). This substance has

(18) 5 β -Bufol

an —OH group at C-25, found so far in no other bile alcohol or acid except the 5α-bufol of *Diemyctylus*. It is difficult to see how the bufols could have arisen, biochemically, from any other known principal bile alcohol, and on the basis of our present understanding, their existence emphasizes the isolation of the groups of amphibians containing them. Toad bile contains C-25-deoxy-5α- and -5β-bufol and also a $3\alpha,7\alpha,12\alpha$-trihydroxycoprostanic acid (formula 8, with a double bond, probably at C_{23-24}); these substances, as well as 5α-bufol, have been shown to be made by the toad *Bufo b. formosus* (*Bufo vulgaris japonicus*) from cholesterol. It has not been shown that any toad can make cholic acid.

It had long been thought by the Japanese school of biochemists, to whom we owe most of our knowledge of toad bile salts, that toad bile contained a C_{28} alcohol (pentahydroxybufostane) and two unsaturated C_{28} acids (trihydroxybufosterocholenic and trihydroxyisosterocholenic acids), all having the ring structure of cholic acid. However, pentahydroxybufostane is apparently a methylated 5β-bufol arising as an artifact during the early methods of hydrolysis of toad bile, in which methanol was used, and there seems to be, in fact, only one C_{28} bile acid. This trihydroxybufosterocholenic acid has been shown to be probably a 3α,-7α,12α-trihydroxy-5β-cholest-22-ene-24-carboxylic acid (13). Its origin is a mystery, for it did not become labeled in the experiments in which radioactive cholesterol was shown to be a source of the other toad bile alcohols and acids (14). It was asserted by Hüttel & Behringer (15) that toad skin and liver contained C_{28} sterols. Their findings have now been reexamined with modern methods of separation and identification; the results might be relevant to the origin of trihydroxybufosterocholenic acid (11).

Some of the toad bile acids are apparently unconjugated, even in fresh bile from specimens not visibly parasitized in the liver. It is often claimed that unconjugated bile acids occur in lower vertebrates, and I have a specimen of bile salts from a teleost (piranha, *Serrasalmus ternetzi*) that contain little but sodium cholate. Unless bile from a freshly dead animal is put at once into excess of alcohol, or some other fixative, it is quite likely that microorganisms will deconjugate the bile salts and perhaps cause other changes. Thus, any report of free bile alcohols or acids in more than trace amounts must be treated with reserve, at least until the possible influence of microorganisms and other parasites has been considered. Of course it is biochemically quite plausible that some sterol other than cholesterol might be degraded by the enzymic systems responsible for the formation of bile salts; the "odd" product might then be unsuitable as a substrate for the conjugating enzymes. Whether there could actually be an evolutionary stage at which free bile alcohols or acids existed is a more open question. Free bile alcohols would certainly be useless as bile salts and unconjugated bile acids probably inferior, at least as "detergent" types, to the conjugates.

Anura: Ranidae

Two sharply distinguished groups have been found in frogs of the genus *Rana*. One group, containing *Rana catesbeiana*, *R. temporaria*, and probably *R. pipiens*, has the ranol sulfates (formula 19) as principal bile

(19) Ranol sulfates

salts. Both epimers at C-5 occur. *Rana temporaria* bile has chiefly 5α-ranol; in the others mentioned, 5β-ranol is the chief bile alcohol. These bile alcohols contain only 26 of the 27 carbon atoms of cholesterol (from which the 5β epimer at least has been shown to be derived), and their biosynthesis presumably involves the loss of a carbon atom from the side chain. The fact that the sulfate ester group is on the —OH at C-24 is also curious; indeed, the whole chemical picture is one suggesting that the ranol sulfates are bile salts standing apart from others known.

It is all the more remarkable, therefore, to find that other Ranidae, for example *Rana nigromaculata* and (probably) *R. esculenta*, do not have the ranols but instead the C_{27} 5β-cyprinol (formula 15) as a bile alcohol.

The bile alcohol situation in ranids is thus heterogeneous and both biochemically and taxonomically of great interest. 3α,7α,12α-Trihydroxycoprostanic acid (formula 8) was first isolated from *Rana catesbeiana* bile. It is the chief bile acid in crocodilians and occurs as a stage in cholic acid biosynthesis in rats and men. Frog bile also contains a little cholic acid, and this, like (8), has been shown to be derived from cholesterol in *R. catesbeiana*. There may also be Ranidae in which 3α,7α,12α-trihydroxycoprostanic acid, as its taurine conjugate, is the principal bile salt.

It is very clear that results of the greatest interest must follow from further investigations of amphibian bile.

REPTILES

General

No bile alcohols have been found above the evolutionary level of the amphibians; the attainment of this level appears to have been accompanied by a complete abandonment of the alcohol-sulfate type of bile salt. The chemical nature of their bile salts (all C_{27} or C_{24} acids as taurine conjugates) agrees with the division of reptiles into at least four major groups, as indicated below.

Testudines

This group is thought by some paleontologists to have been separated from the rest of the reptiles at a very early date, and the bile salt picture in turtles and tortoises agrees with this view. So far, no bile acid has been found in common between chelonians and any other vertebrate group. A bile acid isolated from the soft-shelled turtle *Trionyx sinensis* (= *japonica, Amyda*), the European pond tortoise *Emys orbicularis*, and the green turtle *Chelonia mydas* is very probably $3\alpha,7\alpha,12\alpha,22\xi$-tetrahydroxycoprostanic acid (formula 20). This substance seems to be peculiar to

(20) $3\alpha,7\alpha,12\alpha,22\,\xi$-Tetrahydroxycoprostanic acid

chelonians, but it is by no means certain that it occurs in the bile of them all. A so-far unidentified "heterocholic" acid was found in *Trionyx sinensis* bile; there are no reports of the C_{27} or C_{24} acids already discovered elsewhere.

It will be of great interest to discover whether any chelonian has the ability to make cholic acid or its biosynthetic precursor $3\alpha,7\alpha,12\alpha$-trihydroxycoprostanic acid (formula 8) from cholesterol, for there is at present no evidence for "modernization" in the bile salts of any of these animals.

Sauria: Diploglossa

The lizard genera *Varanus* and *Heloderma* have a bile acid not yet discovered in other animals. All the Varanidae (monitors) examined seem to have varanic acid (taurine-conjugated) as a chief bile salt, although there may be cholic (or allocholic) acid and perhaps other bile acids also. Varanic acid is probably a 3α, $7\alpha,12\alpha,24\xi$-tetrahydroxycoprostanic acid (formula 21). This acid or substances isomeric with it at C-24 or

(21) Varanic acid

C-25 may, like (8), be an intermediate in cholic acid biosynthesis in mammals (16). It represents a β-oxidation of the side chain of (8) thus:

$$\overset{\text{24}}{} \quad \overset{\alpha}{}$$
$$R\cdot CH(CH_3)CH_2\cdot CH_2\cdot CH_2\cdot CH(CH_3)COOH$$
$$(8)$$
$$\Big| \;\beta\text{-oxidation}$$
$$\overset{\alpha}{}$$
$$R\cdot CH(CH_3)CH_2\cdot CH_2\cdot CHOH\cdot CH(CH_3)COOH$$
$$(21)$$

(R = cholic acid nucleus)

This oxidation might well be part of the usual sequence of events in fatty acid degradation, which would result finally in the loss of a 3-carbon fragment as propionyl-CoA and the production of the cholyl-CoA necessary for conjugation with taurine or glycine. If all this is the case in mammals, then presumably varanic acid represents a "frozen" stage in cholic acid biosynthesis in monitors, just as (8) does in crocodilians, the monitors being a stage further along the route to C_{24} bile acids.

The beaded poisonous lizard *Heloderma horridum* has a bile acid that closely resembles but is not identical with varanic acid, and perhaps this is a C_{24}/C_{25} epimer.

Sauria: Other Lizards

Apart from those mentioned above, the lizards examined contain taurine conjugates of allocholic acid with small amounts of other bile acids, including cholic acid. Thus, modern C_{24} bile acids predominate, but these are of the 5α (allo) rather than the 5β configuration. These animals therefore differ sharply from the Diploglossa discussed, which already have 5β-compounds at the C_{27} stage of evolution. On the assumption that the overall tendency in bile salt evolution is toward $5\beta, C_{24}$ bile acids, the course of events can be depicted as

Amphibians	$5\alpha,\ C_{27}$ bile alcohols
	↓
? Early lizards	$5\alpha,\ C_{27}$ bile acids (undescribed)
	↓
Existing lizards	allocholic acid $(5\alpha, C_{24})$

for the lizards, except the diploglossans mentioned, and

Amphibians   5α or 5β, C$_{27}$ bile alcohols
                                          ↓
   Varanus: Heloderma   5β, C$_{27}$ bile acids (varanic acid, etc.)

for the monitors and *Heloderma*.

Thus, the stock ancestral to *Varanus* and *Heloderma* could have been a group of early lizards that (perhaps because of flesh-eating habits) changed from 5α to 5β, C$_{27}$ acids, leaving animals having the unchanged 5α, C$_{27}$ acids to give rise to the non-diploglossan lizards. Alternatively, the bile salt evidence points to the possibility that the *Varanus-Heloderma* groups arose from amphibians having a 5β, C$_{27}$ bile alcohol. The bile alcohols concerned could have been of the 26-(or 27) deoxycyprinol type (formulas 7 and 22) which

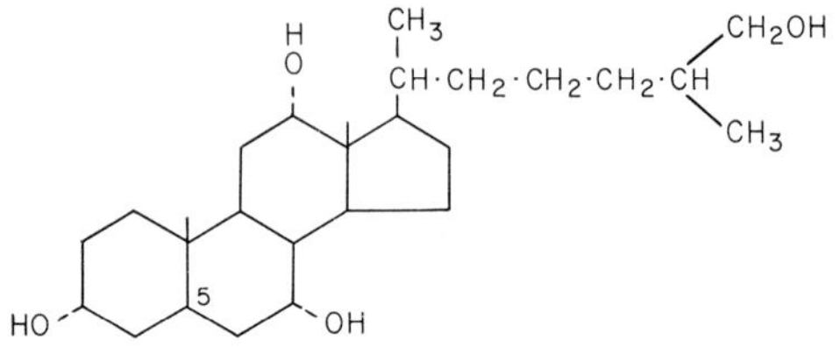

(22) 26(or 27) Deoxycyprinol (5α or 5β)

is found today in minor amounts in the bile of some amphibians and also in cyprinid fishes. All this argument assumes that no ancestral reptile had bile alcohols, an untestable assumption.

The living snakes, which have no more than traces of 5α bile salts, could have reached this position after departing from lizards that have 5α, C$_{27}$ or 5α, C$_{24}$ bile acids, and it might have been the persistence of carnivorous habits that brought about the virtual disappearance of 5α bile salts in snakes. Alternatively, the snakes could have arisen from a lizard group (say, ancestral to *Varanus*) that had already evolved to C$_{27}$, 5β bile acids.

Serpentes

Numerous snakes have been examined; all have C$_{24}$ bile acids, with no more than traces of allocholic or any other 5α compound.

Almost all the Boidae (boas and pythons) examined have a bile acid found nowhere else in vertebrates except probably in *Cylindrophis rufus*, also a primitive snake. This is pythocholic acid, 3α, 12α, 16α-trihydroxy-5β-cholanoic acid (formula 23). Pythocholic acid has been shown to be partly secondary, that is, partly an artifact of the enterohepatic circulation. Snakes having this compound make it by 16α-hy-

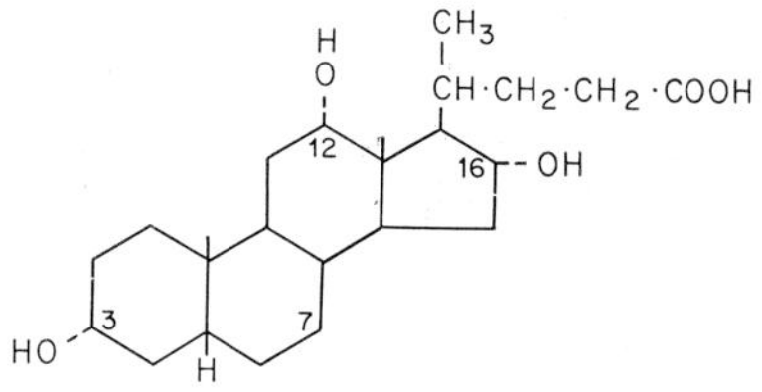

(23) Pythocholic acid

droxylation of deoxycholic (3α, 12α-dihydroxy-5β-cholanoic) acid (formula 24), which in turn is made

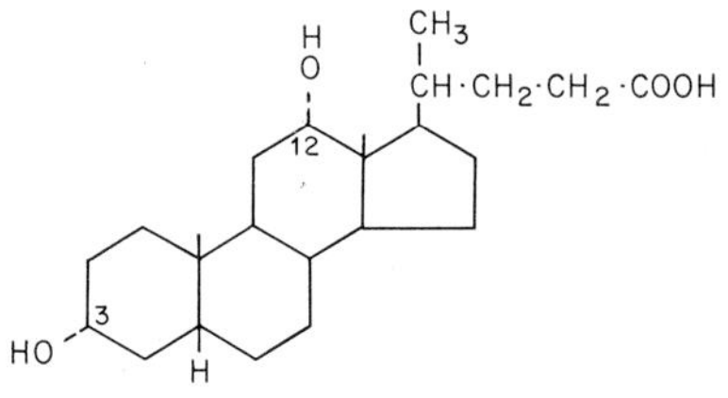

(24) Deoxycholic acid

by intestinal microorganisms from the primary cholic acid. Thus the sequence is: liver cholesterol $\xrightarrow{\text{biogenesis}}$

cholic acid $\xrightarrow[\text{microorganisms}]{\text{intestinal}}$ deoxycholic acid

$\xrightarrow[\text{16α-hydroxylase}]{\text{liver}}$ pythocholic acid (2).

It is possible that other snakes can rehydroxylate deoxycholic acid in the 7α-position, as rats and mice do (see below), to re-form cholic acid, but 16α-hydroxy bile acids have not been found except in the animals mentioned. This response to deoxycholic acid is thus the special feature of certain primitive snakes and it would be of great interest if it were found in any lizard. At least one boid snake (*Corallus enhydris*) contained, apparently, cholic but no pythocholic acid; this could mean that it is able to cause 7α-hydroxylation of deoxycholic acid or that the microorganisms making this acid were not present in the intestine.

Another group of snakes, including most of the Viperinae examined, have 3α, 7α, 12α, 23ξ-tetrahydroxy-5β-cholanoic acid (formula 25). This bile acid can be regarded as possibly incidental to the formation

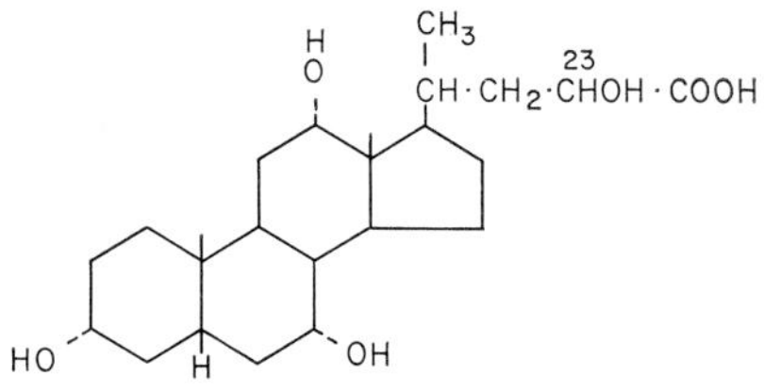

(25) 3α, 7α, 12α, 23ξ —Tetrahydroxy-5β-cholanoic acid

of bitocholic acid, $3\alpha,12\alpha,23\xi$-trihydroxy-5β-cholanoic acid (formula 26), first isolated from snakes of

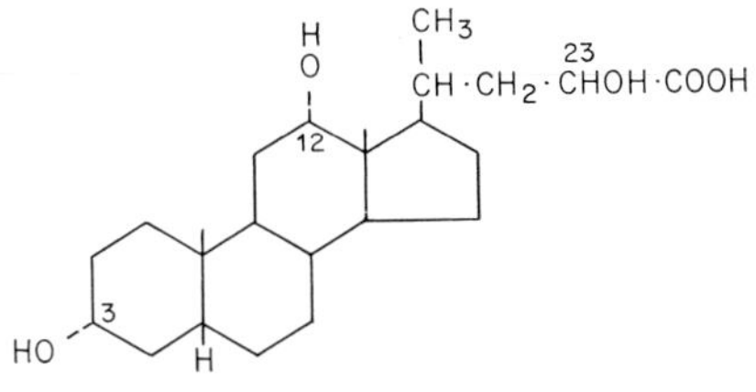

(26) Bitocholic acid

the genus *Bitis* and possibly a response, like pythocholic acid, to deoxycholic acid. C-23 hydroxylation is not not confined to the Viperinae but occurs also in a few colubrid snakes; some vipers do not show this feature. By the arguments given above, the absence of C-23 hydroxylation might mean the existence of 7α-hydroxylation or the absence of intestinally formed deoxycholic acid.

All other snakes examined, including the primitive *Typhlops*, have taurocholate as the chief bile salt.

Crocodilia

The chief bile salt in the archosaurs is the taurine conjugate of $3\alpha,7\alpha,12\alpha$-trihydroxycoprostanic acid (formula 8); thus evolution of biosynthesis to cholic acid has apparently halted at this point. Experimentally, attempts to demonstrate the formation of cholic acid in a specimen of *Alligator mississipiensis* having a biliary fistula were unsuccessful. The chenodeoxycholic analogue of (8), namely $3\alpha,7\alpha$-dihydroxycoprostanic acid (formula 27), has been found in alligator bile in minor amounts. A substance of formula 27 may well be a biosynthetic precursor of

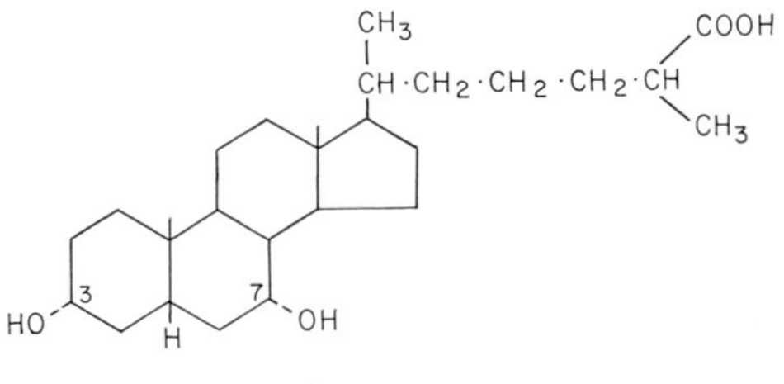

(27) $3\alpha,7\alpha$ – Dihydroxycoprostanic acid

chenodeoxycholic acid (see formula 16) in man and other mammals.

BIRDS

At one time taurochenodeoxycholate (formula 16) was regarded as the characteristic bile salt of birds,

since the parent chenodeoxycholic acid had been found in large amounts in the domestic goose and fowl. In these and other Galliformes, it does seem that chenodeoxycholic acid is the chief bile acid, but detailed study of flesh-eating birds such as penguins and birds of prey has shown that cholic and allocholic acids as their taurine conjugates predominate in these animals. It seems probable that the usual association with dietary habits will be found: granivorous and gerbivorous birds tending to dihydroxy and carnivorous birds to trihydroxy bile acids.

All bile acids so far found in birds are apparently C_{24} compounds. Allocholic, cholic, and chenodeoxycholic seem to be primary bile acids (having been isolated from the bile of germ-free chicks), and 3α-hydroxy-7-oxo-5β-cholanoic acid (formula 28) is prob-

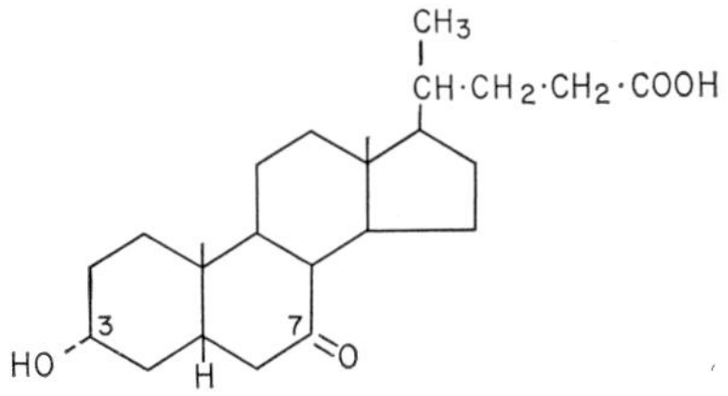

(28) 3α-Hydroxy-7-oxo-5β-cholanoic acid

ably secondarily derived from chenodeoxycholic acid. Some other bile acids found in small amounts in domestic fowl bile may also be intestinal artifacts, but the common deoxycholic acid of mammalian bile has not been detected; it is not known whether any birds can rehydroxylate this to cholic acid, but there seems no zoological reason why it should be of advantage, at least to the Galliformes, to do this.

3-Oxo-chola-4:6-dienoic acid was found in domestic fowl bile, and it could have arisen during the isolation procedure by dehydration of 7α-hydroxy-3-oxochol-4-enoic acid (formula 29). This substance has the ring

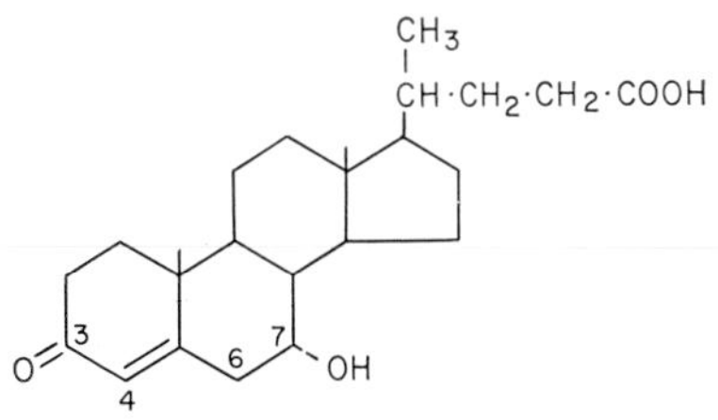

(29) 7α-Hydroxy-3-oxochol-4-enoic acid

structure of a biosynthetic precursor of chenodeoxycholic acid (see Fig. 1), but the side chain has been shortened to the C_{24} pattern.

There are a number of unidentified bile acids in bird bile, and knowledge of the pattern in these animals is still too fragmentary for detailed consideration.

MAMMALS

General

In mammals, all the principal bile acids are 5β, C_{24} compounds, although traces of $3\alpha,7\alpha,12\alpha$-trihydroxycoprostanic (formula 8, Fig. 1) were found and shown to be made from cholesterol and converted into cholic acid in human patients with biliary fistulas (10). $3\alpha,7\alpha$-Dihydroxycoprostanic acid (formula 27) may also occur in human fistula bile (J. B. Carey, Jr., personal communication). Pig bile may contain a C_{27} acid. Several mammalian species, including man, have small amounts of allocholic acid.

In mammals a very obvious correlation exists between bile salt type and diet. Except for bovids, a herbivorous diet goes with dihydroxy or mono-hydroxy-mono-keto bile acids and often, in eutherians, with glycine conjugates, whereas carnivores have trihydroxy bile acids and taurine conjugates. Omnivores have good proportions of all these types, and this is also the case in bovids. "Unique" bile acids are found in some groups and are discussed below.

Mammalian bile contains a number of secondary acids made during the enterohepatic circulation. Perhaps this circulation affords greater opportunities for reabsorption than it does in other vertebrate groups, and some mammals appear to have come to rely on their intestinal microflora to provide bile salts suitable to their habits.

Prototheria: Monotremata

The egg-laying mammals comprise the platypus and two species of spiny anteater. The platypus and one echidna species contain cholic, chenodeoxycholic, and probably deoxycholic acids, all as taurine conjugates. Deoxycholic acid (formula 24) has been shown to be a secondary bile acid in all cases in which the question has been investigated (3) and may be assumed to be of this nature in monotremes.

Metatheria: Marsupalia

The bile salts of the opossum *Didelphis marsupialis virginiana* and of three kangaroo species contain the mixture of cholic, chenodeoxycholic, and deoxycholic acids so commonly found in mammalian bile, but there is no convincing evidence of glycine conjugates, in spite of the mainly vegetarian habits of these marsupials. An even more striking case is that of the koala *Phascolarctos cinereus*, an animal specialized for a diet of certain eucalyptus plants. Koala bile salts contain little but taurine-conjugated 3α-hydroxy-7-oxo-5β-cholanoic acid (formula 28), and glycine conjugates could not be detected. Thus the general nature of the bile salts is what would be expected in a strictly vegetarian member of a group that could not make glycine conjugates. Similar cases do occur among eutherian mammals and are discussed later, but if marsupials could make glycine conjugates, one might perhaps have expected to find them in the koala. Of course, it is possible that traces of glycine conjugates are present in vertebrate groups other than eutherians, and if this were so, it would be another example of the evolution of small amounts of an advanced type of bile salt in animals still having mainly more primitive substances of this kind.

It will be interesting to discover whether the 3α-hydroxy-7-oxo-5β-cholanoic acid of koala bile is made from cholesterol in the liver or whether it is intestinally derived from chenodeoxycholic acid, which does occur in small amounts in the gallbladder.

Eutheria: General

Except for the unique bile acids mentioned later, eutherian mammals have varying proportions of cholic and chenodeoxycholic acids as primary bile acids. Considerable amounts of the secondary deoxycholic acid occur in some species; in others 3α-hydroxy-7-oxo-5β-cholanoic acid and ursodeoxycholic acid (formula 35) may be primary or secondary. Glycine conjugates are easily detected and in some mammals are predominant.

The unique bile acids are hyocholic acid (formula

(30) Hyocholic acid

30) of pigs, α-muricholic and β-muricholic acids (formulas 31 and 32) of rats and mice (Murinae), and

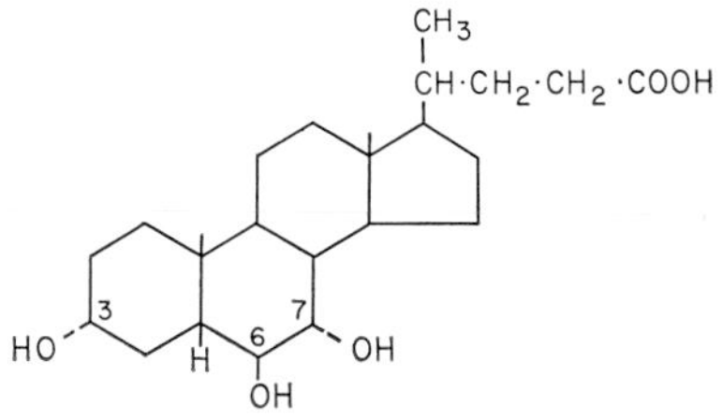

CH_3
$CH \cdot CH_2 \cdot CH_2 \cdot COOH$

HO 3   6 7 OH
OH

(31) α−Muricholic acid

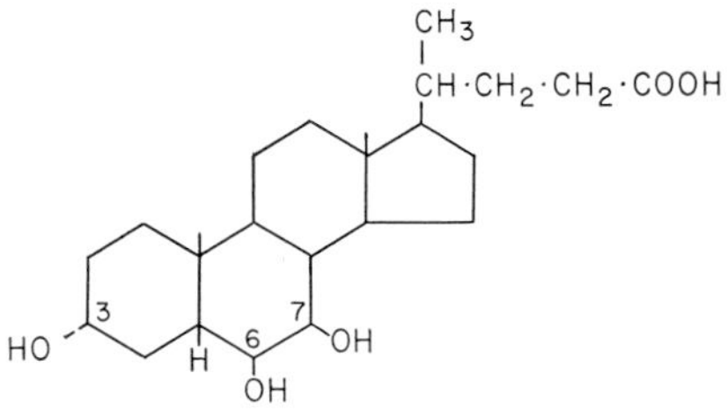

CH_3
$CH \cdot CH_2 \cdot CH_2 \cdot COOH$

HO 3   6 7 OH
OH

(32) β−Muricholic acid

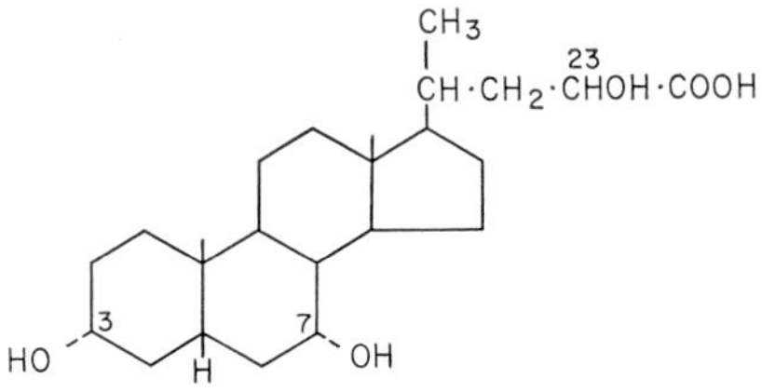

CH_3 23
$CH \cdot CH_2 \cdot CHOH \cdot COOH$

HO 3   7 OH

(33) Phocaecholic acid

phocaecholic acid (formula 33) of Pinnepedia (seals, sea lions, and walruses).

A general hypothesis that explains the existence of all these acids is that they arose by hydroxylation of chenodeoxycholic acid, in groups of mammals that became more carnivorous. The ancestral pigs, murinids, and pinnipeds might have evolved to have mainly chenodeoxycholic acid as a result of a vegetarian diet. Then, a group of each of these animals became more carnivorous. The resulting selection pressures were toward trihydroxy bile acids, and it was biochemically more feasible to hydroxylate chenodeoxycholic acid rather than re-evolve the production of more cholic acid. Hydroxylation at C-6α, C-6β, and C-23 would form acids of formulas 30, 31, and 33, respectively, from chenodeoxycholic acid; this is known to be the course of biogenesis of acids 30 and 31. Acid (32) is made in vivo from (31).

Eutheria: Primates

There is nothing remarkable about the bile salts of the several species of monkeys, the chimpanzee, and man. Deoxycholic acid is common, and lithocholic (3α-hydroxy-5β-cholanoic) acid (formula 34) is similarly derived by intestinal microorganisms

CH_3
$CH \cdot CH_2 \cdot CH_2 \cdot COOH$

HO 3
H

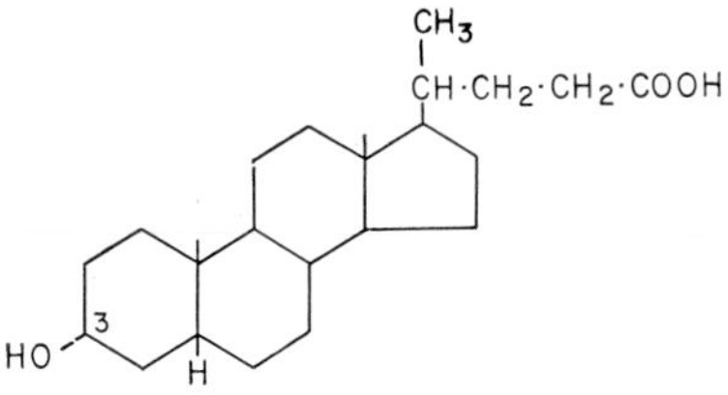

(34) Lithocholic acid

by deoxygenation at C-7 of chenodeoxycholic acid. Human bile salts are taurine and glycine conjugates of cholic, chenodeoxycholic, and deoxycholic acids with traces of allocholic, lithocholic, and 3α,7α,12α-trihydroxycoprostanic acids. Ursodeoxycholic (3α,7β-dihydroxy-5β-cholanoic) acid (formula 35) is also

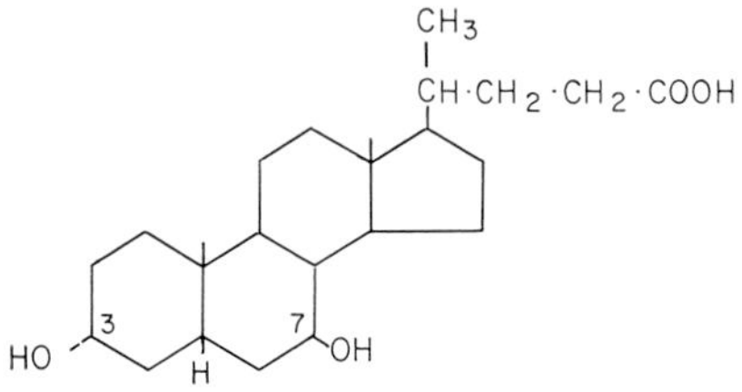

CH_3
$CH \cdot CH_2 \cdot CH_2 \cdot COOH$

HO 3   7 OH
H

(35) Ursodeoxycholic acid

found in human bile; it may be primary or secondary. Like other primate bile salts, those of man consist of high proportions of both glycine and taurine conjugates of both dihydroxy and trihydroxy bile acids. This is an "omnivorous" type of bile salt mixture and it has been suggested that man is eating like a carnivore with the bile of an omnivore; cholesterol gallstones may be one unfortunate result of this situation (10).

Eutheria: Lagomorpha

The laboratory rabbit, which has been carefully investigated in studies of cholesterol metabolism, is a domesticated form of the European *Oryctolagus cuniculus*. As a herbivore it might be expected to have dihydroxy bile acids, but apparently it has minimal ability to make chenodeoxycholic acid. Cholic acid is almost completely converted by intestinal microorganisms during the enterohepatic circulation to deoxycholic acid and this, conjugated almost entirely with glycine, serves as the chief bile salt. A little lithocholic and allodeoxycholic (3α,12α-dihydroxy-5α-cholanoic) acid is found in rabbit bile, and it has been shown that when rabbits are fed cholestanol (5α-cholestan-3β-ol, formula 36), they form gallstones consisting of allodeoxycholic acid. Presumably (36) is first converted into allocholic acid (formula 17), and

(36)Cholestanol

this becomes allodeoxycholic acid through the action of intestinal microorganisms. This interesting experiment shows that the —OH group at C-3 can be inverted ($3\beta \to 3\alpha$) even in the absence of the C_{5-6} double bond of cholesterol.

The almost complete adherence to glycine conjugation in the domestic rabbit extends to the microsomal fraction of the liver, which cannot, apparently, form taurine conjugates in more than small amounts (4).

Other rabbit and hare species do not seem so specialized in their conjugation, but few have been examined.

Eutheria: Rodentia

This enormous group presents many taxonomic problems, some of which might be clarified by consideration of the bile salts. For example, the extent of the occurrence of the muricholic acids (formulas 31 and 32), formed after 6β-hydroxylation of chenodeoxycholic acid, would perhaps be worth further study. The ability of the liver of rodents to form either chenodeoxycholic (7α-OH) or ursodeoxycholic (7β-OH) acids by reduction of 3α-hydroxy-7-oxo-5β-cholanoic acid (formula 28) varies: laboratory rats reduce the 7-keto group chiefly to the β hydroxyl and guinea pigs to the α epimer.

In one case, the type of conjugation was the striking difference between two rodent species put by some taxonomists in the same superfamily. The South American coypu, *Myocastor coypus*, and the cutting-grass, *Thryonomys swinderianus*, were compared as examples of rodents whose similarities might be due to convergent evolution or, alternatively, to close relationship. It was found that the bile salts (largely conjugated chenodeoxycholic acid) of these two herbivores were very similar, except that the coypu contained 3α-hydroxy-7-oxo-5β-cholanoic acid (primary or secondary). However, no glycine conjugates could be detected in *Thryonomys* bile, whereas *Myocastor* contained principally these conjugates. It was thought that this difference argued against a close

hereditary relationship between these forms. Glycine conjugates seem specially common in South American rodents (for example, coypu, guinea pig, *Proechimys*), and this group of mammals is certainly worth further exploration. It seems, perhaps, unlikely that specialization in glycine conjugation arose once only in evolution, but its distribution might be informative about the radiation of different mammalian forms.

In the guinea pig, at least, 3α-hydroxy-7-oxo-5β-cholanoic acid is primary, being found in fistula animals.

Eutheria: Cetacea

Nothing has been found in whale bile that promises to throw light on the origin of these animals from terrestrial forms.

Eutheria: Carnivora

The truly carnivorous members of this order have chiefly taurocholate, but some of the more omnivorous forms (for example, some bears) have considerable proportions of both dihydroxy bile acids and glycine conjugates. Ursodeoxycholic acid (formula 35) was at one time thought to be characteristic of bear's bile, but it has not been found in the bile of some bears, and is also present in other mammals, for example rats, coypus, and men.

The Pinnipedia differ from all other known mammals in that, as well as cholic and chenodeoxycholic acids, they have phocaecholic ($3\alpha,7\alpha,23\xi$-trihydroxy-5β-cholanoic) acid (formula 33) conjugated chiefly with taurine. This substance has been isolated from the bile of all pinnipeds (three sea lions, seven seals, and a walrus) examined; the evidence thus points to its being a primary bile acid. If this is so, and if the hypothesis about unique primary bile acids put forward on page 2387 is correct, the pinnipeds arose from a group having principally chenodeoxycholic acid, that is, from a group of vegetarian mammals.

Eutheria: Artiodactyla

One group of these, the pigs (Suidae), have no cholic acid but a unique bile acid, namely hyocholic ($3\alpha,6\alpha,7\alpha$-trihydroxy-5β-cholanoic) acid, formula 30. This substance has been shown to be made by 6α-hydroxylation of chenodeoxycholic acid, and it is converted (3) by intestinal microorganisms during the enterohepatic circulation to hyodeoxycholic ($3\alpha,6\alpha$-dihydroxy-5β-cholanoic) acid (formula 37). Pig bile also

(37) Hyodeoxycholic acid

contains 3α-hydroxy-6-oxo-5α- or -5β-cholanoic acid, probably also an intestinal artifact derived from acid (37). Pig bile salts are chiefly glycine conjugates, and it may be supposed that these animals, like the rabbit *Oryctolagus*, rely on their attendant microorganisms for bile acids adapted to their dietary habits. Pigs of other families (including the New World peccary) ought to be examined to investigate the extent of 6α-hydroxylation; it seems to occur to a small extent in the warthog, *Phacochoerus aethiopicus*, which has mainly cholic acid and both taurine and glycine conjugates. No 6α-hydroxy bile acids could be found in hippopotamus bile.

The Bovidae have bile salts much more like those of omnivorous than herbivorous mammals, with good proportions of trihydroxy and dihydroxy bile acids and also of taurine and glycine conjugates. The small amounts of various keto acids found in ox bile are probably intestinal artifacts.

GENERAL CONCLUSIONS

It is obvious that bile salt differences can be used in various vertebrate groups for taxonomic purposes. The weight to be given to a characteristic such as this must clearly be decided by the taxonomist himself, but more needs to be discovered about the biochemical mechanisms that have led to and that maintain the bile salt differences before their importance for taxonomy and systematists can be properly assessed. Little or nothing is known about bile salt biosynthesis in vertebrates other than a few common eutherian mammals, and even in these cases the enzymatic processes concerned are still largely obscure.

In the writer's opinion, the greatest interest in the study of bile salt differences is not as an aid to systematics but rather lies in the possibility that such differences might indicate something about the nature of the evolutionary process itself in a way not so far explored, at least biochemically. For example, there are now a number of examples of animals having mainly primitive bile salts but also small amounts of more advanced substances; such animals can be said to have set foot on the road to bile salt modernization. What are the forces by which such small amounts of advanced bile salts come finally to replace the more primitive types? One can appreciate that the superior physiological properties of advanced substances might have selective value when they had come to constitute a certain proportion of the bile salts; but this argument is unconvincing for the very small amounts found in some of the examples (e.g., Ranidae, Cyprinidae). Again, why has this sort of modernization apparently begun in some forms, but not in others? What prevents, say, the carnivorous crocodilians' advance from C_{27} to C_{24} bile acids? Perhaps the concepts of "vigor" and "senescence" in evolution can, via bile salt studies, be translated into biochemical terms.

It is clear that, as one would expect, diet plays a major role in determining the kind of bile salts an animal has, and possibly the response to diet has become more marked as evolution has proceeded. In some mammalian species, intestinal microorganisms have apparently been called on to play their part in this response, and in eutherian mammals generally there seem to be larger differences associated with dietary habits than in other groups (except, perhaps, birds). However, it would be premature to conclude that the selective pressures concerned in all the variations discussed above are dietary; we badly need more knowledge about the physiological functions of bile salts, and not only in man and the common laboratory animals.

REFERENCES

1. BERGMANN, W. Sterols: their structure and distribution. In: *Comparative Biochemistry*, edited by M. Florkin and H. S. Mason. New York: Acad. Press, 1962, vol. IIIA, p. 103–162.
2. BERGSTRÖM, S. H. DANIELSSON, AND T. KAZUNO. Bile acids and steroids 98. The metabolism of bile acids in python and constrictor snakes. *J. Biol. Chem.* 235: 983–988, 1960.
3. BERGSTRÖM, S., H. DANIELSSON, AND B. SAMUELSSON. For-mation and metabolism of bile acids. In: *Lipide Metabolism*, edited by K. Bloch. New York: Wiley, 1960, p. 291–336.
4. BREMER, J. Species difference in the conjugation of free bile acids with taurine and glycine. *Biochem. J.* 63: 507–513, 1956.
5. BRÖDAL, A., AND R. FÄNGE. *The Biology of Myxine.* Oslo: Universitetsforlaget. 1963.

6. CLAYTON, R. B. The utilization of sterols by insects. *J. Lipid Res.* 5: 3–19, 1964.

7. GREENWOOD, P. H., D. H. ROSEN, S. H. WEITZMANN, AND G. S. MYERS. Phyletic studies of teleostean fishes, with a provisional classification of living forms. *Bull. Am. Museum Nat. Hist.* 131: 339–456, 1966.

8. HASLEWOOD, G. A. D. Bile salts: structure, distribution, and possible biological significance as a species character. In: *Comparative Biochemistry*, edited by M. Florkin and H. S. Mason. New York: Acad. Press, 1962, vol. IIIA, p. 203–229.

9. HASLEWOOD, G. A. D. The biological significance of chemical differences in bile salts. *Biol. Rev. Cambridge Phil. Soc.* 39: 537–574, 1964.

10. HASLEWOOD, G. A. D. *Bile Salts*. London: Methuen, 1967.

11. HASLEWOOD, G. A. D. Bile salt evolution. *J. Lipid Res.* 8: 535–550, 1967.

12. HASLEWOOD, G. A. D. Petromyzonol sulfate, a bile salt of lampreys. *Biochem. J.* 107: 6P, 1968.

13. HOSHITA, T., K. OKUDA, AND T. KAZUNO. Stero-bile acids and bile alcohols. XCV. Synthesis of $3\alpha,7\alpha,12\alpha$-trihydroxy-5β-cholestane-24-carboxylic acid and the chemical structure of trihydroxybufosterocholenic acid isolated from toad bile. *J. Biochem., Tokyo* 61: 756–759, 1967.

14. HOSHITA, T., T. SASAKI, Y. TANAKA, S. BETSUKI, AND T. KAZUNO. Stero bile acids and bile sterols 74. Biosynthesis of bile acids and bile alcohols in toad. *J. Biochem., Tokyo* 57: 57: 751–757, 1965.

15. HÜTTEL, R., AND H. BEHRINGER. Über das Vorkommen von Pflanzersterinen in Kröten. *Z. Physiol. Chem.* 245: 175–180, 1937.

16. MASUI, T., AND E. STAPLE. The formation of bile acids from cholesterol. The conversion of 5β-cholestane-$3\alpha,7\alpha,12\alpha$-triol-26-oic acid to cholic acid via 5β-cholestane-$3\alpha,7\alpha$ $12\alpha,24\xi$-tetraol-26-oic acid I by rat liver. *J. Biol. Chem.* 241: 3889–3893, 1966.

17. MITROPOULOS, K. A., AND N. B. MYANT. Evidence that the oxidation of the side chain of cholesterol by liver mitochondria is stereospecific, and that the immediate product of cleavage is propionate. *Biochem. J.* 97: 26–28c, 1965.

18. MOY-THOMAS, J. A. The early evolution and relationships of the elasmobranchs. *Biol. Rev. Cambridge Phil. Soc.* 14: 1–26, 1939.

19. NEWMAN, W. H. *The Phylum Chordata*. New York: Macmillan, 1939, p. 187.

20. PATTERSON, C. The phylogeny of the chimaeroids. *Phil. Trans. Roy. Soc. London, Ser. B* 249: 101–219, 1965.

21. VONK, H. J. Emulgators in the digestive fluids of invertebrates. *Arch. Internal Physiol.* 70: 67–85, 1962.

CHAPTER 112

Formation and metabolism of bile acids

SUNE BERGSTRÖM

HENRY DANIELSSON

Department of Chemistry, Karolinska Institutet, Stockholm, Sweden

CHAPTER CONTENTS

ATTEMPT IS MADE in this chapter to summarize present knowledge of the formation and metabolism of bile acids in mammals. Discussion as well as documentation of references emphasizes the more recent developments. Several reviews of the conversion of cholesterol to bile acids as well as of the intermediary metabolism of bile acids have appeared in recent years, and the reader is directed to these articles for many of the references to the original literature (8, 26, 31, 49). These reviews also contain a discussion of the formation and metabolism of bile salts in species other than mammalian. In the preceding chapter the structures of a number of naturally occurring bile salts are given, and a separate discussion of the chemistry of bile salts is, therefore, not included in this chapter.

I. FORMATION OF PRIMARY BILE ACIDS

The primary bile acids are those that are formed from cholesterol by action of liver enzymes. Secondary bile acids arise from the primary bile acids during the enterohepatic circulation of bile. They are formed initially by the action of intestinal microorganisms on the primary bile acids, but after absorption from the intestinal tract they can be further modified by the action of liver enzymes. The main primary bile acids in most mammalian species are cholic acid ($3\alpha,7\alpha,12\alpha$-trihydroxy-5β-cholanoic acid) and chenodeoxycholic acid ($3\alpha,7\alpha$-dihydroxy-5β-cholanoic acid) (Fig. 1). In the mammalian species studied, chenodeoxycholic acid is not a precursor of cholic acid. Changes of the cholesterol molecule that occur in its conversion to chenodeoxycholic acid and cholic acid include saturation of the Δ^5 double bond, transformation of the 3β-hydroxyl group into the 3α-position, introduction of hydroxyl groups in the C-7 position and in the C-12 position (only in the case of cholic acid), and degradation of the side chain to form a carboxyl group at C-24. Finally, the bile acids are conjugated with taurine or glycine.

The mechanisms of formation of chenodeoxycholic acid and cholic acid from cholesterol have been studied in several mammalian species including man. The main information has been obtained from studies of the metabolism of cholesterol and other C_{27} steroids in bile fistula rats and in homogenates of mouse and rat liver. Early work on the metabolism of cholesterol and other C_{27} steroids in rats provided with a bile fistula indicated that the major part of the changes in the steroid nucleus precedes the oxidation of the C_{27} side chain during the conversion of cholesterol to cholic acid (8, 26). Of the considerable number of compounds studied in these investigations, cholest-5-ene-$3\beta,7\alpha$-diol, 5β-cholestane-$3\alpha,7\alpha,12\alpha$-

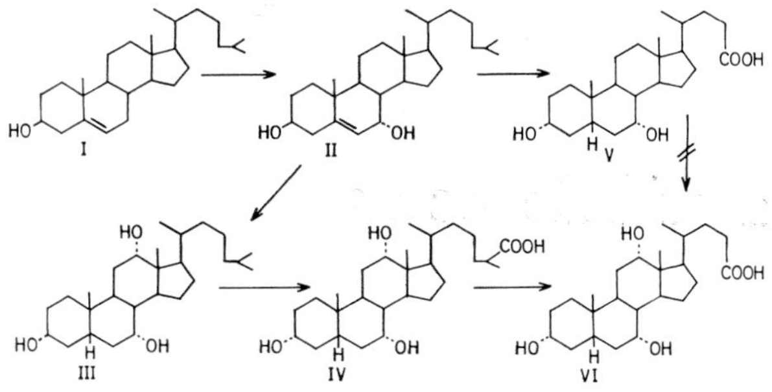

FIG. 1. Some intermediates in the conversion of cholesterol to chenodeoxycholic acid and cholic acid. I, Cholesterol; II, cholest-5-ene-3β,7α-diol; III, 5β-cholestane-3α,7α,12α-triol; IV, 3α,7α,12α-trihydroxy-5β-cholestan-26-oic acid; V, chenodeoxycholic acid; VI, cholic acid.

triol, and 3α,7α,12α-trihydroxy-5β-cholestanoic acid appeared most probable as intermediates in the formation of cholic acid (Fig. 1). More detailed information on the sequence of reactions in cholic acid formation has been obtained from studies in vitro carried out during the last few years. Of particular importance to the studies of the sequence of changes of the steroid nucleus has been the work of Mendelsohn & Staple (81), who were the first to describe an enzyme system capable of catalyzing the conversion of cholesterol to 5β-cholestane-3α,7α,12α-triol.

A. Sequence of Changes in Steroid Nucleus in Cholic Acid Formation

The long-standing notion that hydroxylation at the C-7 position is the first step in the conversion of cholesterol to bile acids has been confirmed by the isolation of labeled cholest-5-ene-3β,7α-diol after incubation of labeled cholesterol with the 20,000 × g supernatant fluid of rat liver homogenates (27, 78). The 7α-hydroxylase has not yet been studied in detail. Mitton & Boyd (88) have reported in preliminary form that cholesterol is converted to cholest-5-ene-3β,7α-diol in the presence of microsomes fortified by addition of NADPH and 6,7-dimethyltetrahydropteridine. In cholic acid formation there appear to be two pathways for the further metabolism of cholest-5-ene-3β,7α-diol (Fig. 2). One pathway entails hydroxylation at C-12 to yield cholest-5-ene-3β-,7α,12α-triol (12). This compound is converted to 7α,12α-dihydroxycholest-4-en-3-one in the presence of microsomal fraction fortified by addition of NAD (12). Another pathway involves oxidation of cholest-5-ene-3β,7α-diol to 7α-hydroxycholest-4-en-3-one. This reaction was observed originally in the mitochondrial and the 100,000 × g supernatant

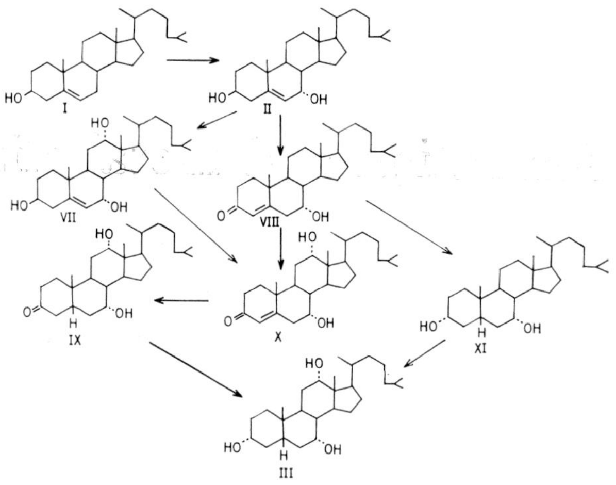

FIG. 2. Conversion of cholesterol to 5β-cholestane-3α,7α,12α-triol. I, Cholesterol; II, cholest-5-ene-3β,7α-diol; III, 5β-cholestane-3α,7α,12α-triol; VII, cholest-5-ene-3β,7α,12α-triol; VIII, 7α-hydroxycholest-4-en-3-one; IX, 7α,12α-dihydroxy-5β-cholestan-3-one; X, 7α,12α-dihydroxycholest-4-en-3-one; XI, 5β-cholestane-3α,7α-diol.

fractions of mouse and rat liver homogenates (25, 111) but has since been shown to be catalyzed mainly by the microsomal fraction (14, 61). Although not yet demonstrated experimentally, it is likely that, in analogy with the mechanism of formation of the Δ⁴-3-ketosteroids in the steroid hormone series, cholest-5-ene-3β,7α-diol and cholest-5-ene-3β,7α,12α-triol are converted to 7α-hydroxycholest-4-en-3-one and 7α,12α-dihydroxycholest-4-en-3-one, respectively, by means of the intermediate formation of 7α-hydroxycholest-5-en-3-one and 7α,12α-dihydroxycholest-5-en-3-one, respectively. Oleinick & Koritz (95) have reported recently that the conversion of androst-5-ene-3,17-dione to androst-4-ene-3,17-dione catalyzed by rat adrenal small particles is stimulated greatly by the addition of NAD or NADH. These authors have also presented evidence that this stimulation is allosteric in nature. There are indications that NAD and NADH exert a similar effect on the formation of 7α-hydroxycholest-4-en-3-one and 7α,12α-dihydroxycholest-4-en-3-one catalyzed by the microsomal fraction of a rat liver homogenate (12, 14). However, due to lack of the appropriate substrates for the microsomal isomerase, that is, 7α-hydroxycholest-5-en-3-one and 7α,12α-dihydroxycholest-5-en-3-one, it has not yet been possible to obtain conclusive evidence.

The further metabolism of 7α-hydroxycholest-4-en-3-one in cholic acid biogenesis appears to follow more than one pathway (Fig. 2). One pathway, suggested by Mendelsohn et al. (80), entails the conversion of 7α-hydroxycholest-4-en-3-one to 5β-cholestane-3α,7α-diol, which in turn is hydroxylated in the 12α-position to yield 5β-cholestane-3α,7α,12α-triol. Thus, these authors (79) isolated 5β-cholestane-3α,7α-diol as a major metabolite of cholesterol in incubations of 4-¹⁴C-cholesterol with the 20,000 × g supernatant fluid of rat liver homogenates. As only small amounts of radioactivity were present in 7α-hydroxy-5β-cholestan-3-one after incubation with 4-¹⁴C-cholesterol (80), it was suggested that 5β-cholestane-3α,7α-diol was formed by means of the intermediate formation of cholest-4-ene-3α,7α-diol (cf. Fig. 2). Another pathway entails the hydroxylation of 7α-hydroxycholest-4-en-3-one at C-12 to yield 7α,12α-dihydroxycholest-4-en-3-one (27). This reaction is catalyzed by the microsomal fraction in the presence of NADPH. 7α,12α-Dihydroxycholest-4-en-3-one is converted to 7α,12α-dihydroxy-5β-cholestan-3-one by a soluble 5β-steroid reductase which requires NADPH (13). The enzyme has been purified about tenfold from the 100,000 × g supernatant fluid of rat liver homogenates (11). The enzyme preparation is active also on Δ⁴-3-ketosteroids in the C_{19}, C_{21}, and C_{24} series. 7α,12α-Dihydroxy-5β-cholestan-3-one is reduced to 5β-cholestane-3α,7α,12α-triol by a soluble 3α-hydroxysteroid dehydrogenase (13). The enzyme has been purified about 70-fold and requires reduced pyridine nucleotides (11). NADPH is about 10 times more efficient than NADH. The enzyme preparation catalyzes the reduction of 3-keto groups in C_{19} and C_{21} steroids as well as in C_{24} bile acids. The rate of reaction is about 40 times faster with C_{19} 3-ketosteroids, about 20–80 times faster with C_{21} 3-ketosteroids, and about 10 times faster with C_{24} 3-ketosteroids than with 7α,12α-dihydroxy-5β-cholestan-3-one. It is interesting that the reaction rate is also about 10 times faster with 7α-hydroxy-5β-cholestan-3-one than with 7α,12α-dihydroxy-5β-cholestan-3-one.

Three pathways for the conversion of cholesterol to 5β-cholestane-3α,7α,12α-triol have been discussed above (Fig. 2): cholesterol→cholest-5-ene-3β,7α-diol→cholest-5-ene-3β,7α,12α-triol→7α,12α-dihydroxycholest-4-en-3-one→7α,12α-dihydroxy-5β-cholestan-3-one→5β-cholestane-3α,7α,12α-triol (pathway 1); cholesterol→cholest-5-ene-3β,7α-diol→7α-hydroxycholest-4-en-3-one→cholest-4-ene-3α,7α-diol→5β-cholestane-3α,7α-diol→5β-cholestane-3α,7α,12α-triol (pathway 2); cholesterol→cholest-5-ene-3β,7α-diol→7α-hydroxycholest-4-en-3-one→7α-,12α-dihydroxycholest-4-en-3-one→7α,12α-dihydroxy-5β-cholestan-3-one→5β-cholestane-3α,7α,-

12α-triol (pathway 3). At present it is difficult to assess the relative importance of the different pathways, but some experimental evidence bearing on this question is available. In a comparison of the three pathways it is seen that they separate either at the stage of cholest-5-ene-3β,7α-diol or at the stage of 7α-dihydroxycholest-4-en-3-one. Cholest-5-ene-3β,7α-diol can be metabolized to cholest-5-ene-3β,7α,12α-triol (pathway 1) or to 7α-hydroxycholest-4-en-3-one (pathways 2 and 3), and 7α-hydroxycholest-4-en-3-one can be metabolized to cholest-4-ene-3α,7α-diol (pathway 2) or to 7α,12α-dihydroxycholest-4-en-3-one (pathway 3). Thus, the two points to consider are the metabolic role of cholest-5-ene-3β,7α,12α-triol and that of cholest-4-ene-3α,7α-diol. In incubations of cholesterol and cholest-5-ene-3β,7α-diol with the 20,000 × g supernatant fluid of rat liver homogenates cholest-5-ene-3β,7α,12α-triol is a major metabolite (12). The microsomal fraction fortified with NADPH catalyzes to a varying extent the 12α-hydroxylation of cholest-5-ene-3β,7α-diol, 7α-hydroxycholest-4-en-3-one, 7α-hydroxy-5β-cholestan-3-one, and 5β-cholestane-3α,7α-diol (12, 27, 36). Of these substrates 7α-hydroxycholest-4-en-3-one is hydroxylated at C-12 most efficiently and cholest-5-ene-3β,7α-diol least efficiently. This finding might indicate that a pathway involving cholest-5-ene-3β,7α,12α-triol as an intermediate is less important, quantitatively. However, it is possible that a suitably fortified microsomal fraction might catalyze an efficient 12α-hydroxylation of cholest-5-ene-3β,7α-diol. Hydroxylation of cholesterol at C-7 requires not only the microsomal fraction and NADPH but also other factors (88). With respect to the role of cholest-4-ene-3α,7α-diol, it appears that a reduction of 7α-hydroxycholest-4-en-3-one to cholest-4-ene-3α,7α-diol is a side reaction. Hutton & Boyd (62) have shown that small amounts of cholest-4-ene-3α,7α-diol are formed from 7α-hydroxycholest-4-en-3-one in the presence of the 100,000 × g supernatant fluid of a rat liver homogenate. The main metabolite was 5β-cholestane-3α,7α-diol, and evidence was presented that cholest-4-ene-3α,7α-diol was not an important intermediate in the conversion of 7α-hydroxycholest-4-en-3-one to 5β-cholestane-3α,7α-diol. Similar conclusions were reached from studies of the formation and metabolism of cholest-4-ene-3α,7α-diol in fractions of guinea pig and rat liver homogenates (16, 17). The investigations discussed seem to indicate that the major pathway from cholesterol to 5β-cholestane-3α,7α,12α-triol is the one with 7α-hydroxycholest-4-en-3-one and 7α,12α-dihydroxycholest-4-en-3-one as intermediates (pathway 3). However, much more information is needed to define more closely the sequence of reactions in the formation of 5β-cholestane-3α,7α, 12α-triol, and such information will be of importance to studies of the mechanisms of regulation of bile acid formation.

Boyd (19) has suggested that fatty acid esters of cholesterol and of some of the early intermediates may be involved in the conversion of cholesterol to bile acids. Small amounts of an ester of cholest-5-ene-3β,7α-diol have been isolated from liver and a similar compound is formed in incubations of cholest-5-ene-3β,7α-diol with the soluble fraction of a rat liver homogenate (61). The metabolic role of such compounds in the catabolism of cholesterol remains to be established. Another derivative of cholesterol, cholesteryl sulfate, has recently attracted considerable attention, especially in view of its capacity to serve as precursor in the biosynthesis of steroid hormones. The possibility that cholesteryl sulfate might be involved in the biosynthesis of bile acids seems excluded by some recent experiments by Raggatt et al. (101).

B. Oxidation of Side Chain

The mechanisms of the oxidation of the side chain of cholesterol in bile acid formation have been elucidated to a large extent (Fig. 3). The main pathway in the degradation of the side chain entails an ω-oxidation followed by a β-oxidation yielding the three

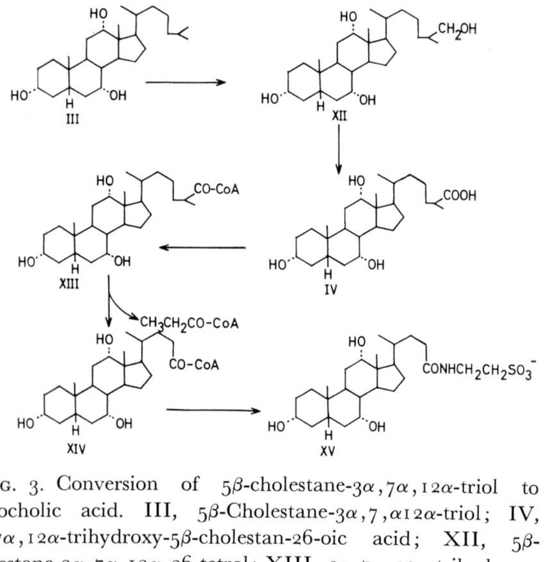

FIG. 3. Conversion of 5β-cholestane-3α,7α,12α-triol to taurocholic acid. III, 5β-Cholestane-3α,7,α12α-triol; IV, 3α,7α,12α-trihydroxy-5β-cholestan-26-oic acid; XII, 5β-cholestane-3α,7α,12α,26-tetrol; XIII, 3α,7α,12α-trihydroxy-5β-cholestan-26-oyl CoA; XIV, cholyl CoA; XV, taurocholic acid.

terminal carbon atoms of a C27 steroid in the form of propionic acid. The first studies on the mechanisms of side chain oxidation were performed with 5β-cholestane-3α,7α,12α-triol and before the key role of this compound in cholic acid biogenesis had been firmly established. In the presence of the mitochondrial fraction of rat or mouse liver homogenates, 5β-cholestane-3α,7α,12α-triol was found to be hydroxylated at C-26 to yield 5β-cholestane-3α,7α, 12α,26-tetrol (24, 109). This compound was transformed into 3α,7α,12α-trihydroxy-5β-cholestan-26-oic acid by the mitochondrial or the soluble fraction (24, 107). The conversion of 3α,7α,12α-trihydroxy-5β-cholestanoic acid to cholic acid (likely cholyl-CoA) was shown by Suld and co-workers (109) to occur with the concomitant release of propionyl-CoA. The formation of propionic acid also from cholesterol under similar conditions has been recently demonstrated by Mitropoulos & Myant (84, 85).

The first step in the degradation of the side chain, the 26-hydroxylation, has been shown to be stereospecific (9, 85). The conversion of 5β-cholestane-3α,7α,12α,26-tetrol to 3α,7α,12α-trihydroxy-5β-cholestanoic acid occurs by means of the intermediate formation of 3α,7α,12α-trihydroxy-5β-cholestan-26-al (76). The formation of the aldehyde from the tetrahydroxy compound as well as the conversion of the aldehyde to the acid has been demonstrated, and the reactions can be catalyzed by NAD-dependent enzyme(s) present in the 100,000 × g supernatant fluid of a rat liver homogenate (76, 94). The β-oxidation of 3α,7α,12α-trihydroxy-5β-cholestanoic acid is carried out by the mitochondrial fraction fortified with the 100,000 × g supernatant fluid (77). One of the intermediates in this reaction sequence, 3α,7α, 12α,24-tetrahydroxy-5β-cholestanoic acid, has been synthesized and shown to be formed from 3α,7α,12α-trihydroxy-5β-cholestanoic acid and to be converted to cholic acid (77). In this connection it should be mentioned that 3α,7α,12α-trihydroxy-5β-cholestanoic acid is present in human bile and becomes labeled after administration of labeled cholesterol (20, 21, 105).

It is likely that compounds analogous to those discussed above are intermediates in the oxidation of the side chains in chenodeoxycholic acid formation. The key intermediates would then be 5β-cholestane-3α,7α-diol and 3α,7α-dihydroxy-5β-cholestanoic acid. However, conclusive evidence for this contention has not yet been presented.

The enzymes that catalyze the β-oxidation of the C27 steroid side chain appear to be confined to liver and are probably different from those involved in β-oxidation of fatty acids (32).

C. Sequence of Reactions in Chenodeoxycholic Acid Formation

The detailed sequence of reactions in chenodeoxycholic acid formation has not been definitely established. One reason is that many different C_{27} steroids have been found to be metabolized into chenodeoxycholic acid (8, 26). Early work showed that 26-hydroxylation of a C_{27} steroid prior to 12α-hydroxylation leads to compounds that are metabolized predominantly into chenodeoxycholic acid and its metabolites, α- and β-muricholic acids. Thus, cholest-5-ene-3β,26-diol, cholest-5-ene-3β,7α,26-triol, 7α,26-dihydroxycholest-4-en-3-one, and 5β-cholestane-3α,7α,26-triol are all converted to chenodeoxycholic acid and its metabolites in the bile fistula rat, and only small amounts of cholic acid are formed [(8, 26); Fig. 4]. The formation of the above-mentioned 26-hydroxylated C_{27} steroids has been demonstrated in a mitochondrial system (26). One feature of this system is that it catalyzes very efficiently the 26-hydroxylation of a number of C_{27} steroids as well as the further oxidation of the side chain. The results obtained with this system may not permit definite

conclusions regarding the biological substrate for the 26-hydroxylase in chenodeoxycholic acid formation, especially since it has been shown that the reactions concerned with changes in the steroid nucleus are catalyzed mainly by microsomal and soluble enzymes. Some recent studies indicate that in chenodeoxycholic acid formation also the reactions concerned with changes in the steroid nucleus are catalyzed by microsomal and soluble enzymes (17). From experiments with homogenates of liver from strains of guinea pigs that have chenodeoxycholic acid as the main primary bile acid, it was concluded that a probable sequence of reactions in chenodeoxycholic acid formation is cholesterol→cholest-5-ene-3β,7α-diol→7α-hydroxycholest-4-en-3-one→7α-hydroxy-5β-cholestan-3-one→5β-cholestane-3α,7α-diol (Fig. 4). As mentioned in the preceding section, 5β-cholestane-3α,7α-diol can be expected to be transformed by mitochondrial and soluble enzymes into 3α,7α-dihydroxy-5β-cholestanoic acid, which is cleaved by β-oxidation to chenodeoxycholyl-CoA and propionyl-CoA.

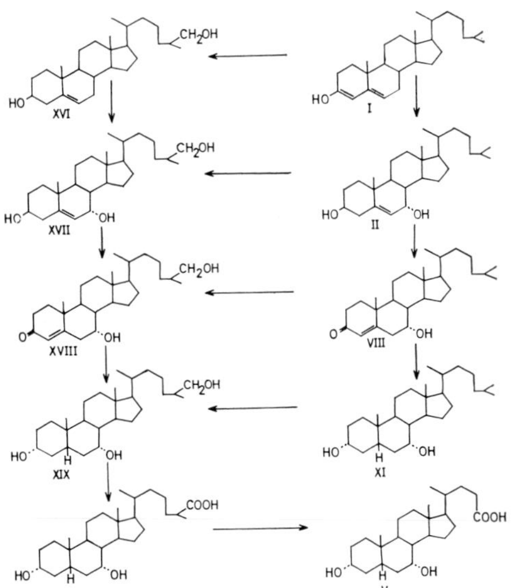

D. Conjugation of Bile Acids

Bile acids are present in bile as conjugates with taurine or glycine. The conjugation of bile acids is catalyzed mainly by the microsomal fraction and requires ATP, CoA, and Mg^{++} (8, 26). Recent work by Scherstén (103) indicates that the activation of the carboxyl group of a bile acid is catalyzed by the microsomal fraction in the presence of ATP, CoA, and Mg^{++}, whereas the conjugation proper is catalyzed by the lysosomal fraction.

The ratio of glycine to taurine conjugates in human bile is influenced by diet, hormones, and by different diseases (8, 26). The mechanisms of these effects are little known. The formation of conjugates of bile acids with ornithine was originally demonstrated in guinea pigs that had received parenteral injections of a capsular polysaccharide from *Klebsiella pneumoniae* or that had been subjected to hepatic injury of nonspecific nature (98). Since then, ornithocholanoic acids have been detected in human bile (44, 99), and further studies of the conditions for the appearance of these acids will be of interest.

FIG. 4. Conversion of cholesterol to chenodeoxycholic acid. I, Cholesterol; II, cholest-5-ene-3β,7α-diol; V, chenodeoxycholic acid; VIII, 7α-hydroxycholest-4-en-3-one; XI, 5β-cholestane-3α,7α-diol; XVI, cholest-5-ene-3β,26-diol; XVII, cholest-5-ene-3β,7α,26-triol; XVIII, 7α,26-dihydroxycholest-4-en-3-one; XIX, 5β-cholestane-3α,7α,26-triol; XX, 3α,7α-dihydroxy-5β-cholestan-26-oic acid.

II. METABOLISM OF BILE ACIDS

Of the two main primary bile acids, chenodeoxycholic acid can be metabolized further by the liver in some species. These metabolites are also, by defini-

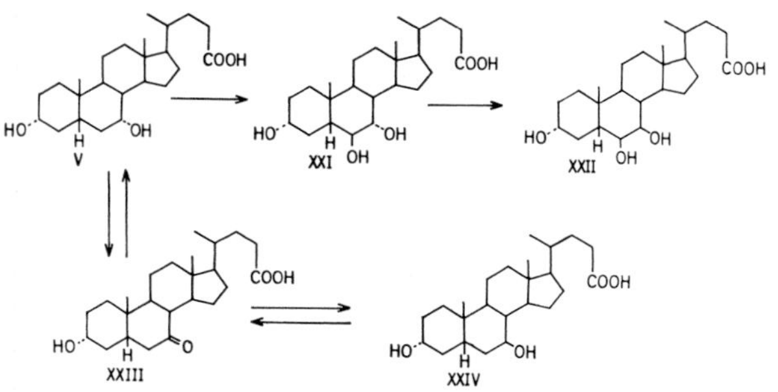

FIG. 5. Some metabolites of chenodeoxycholic acid. V, Chenodeoxycholic acid; XXI, α-muricholic acid; XXII, β-muricholic acid; XXIII, 3α-hydroxy-7-keto-5β-cholanoic acid; XXIV, ursodeoxycholic acid.

tion, primary bile acids. Such metabolites of chenodeoxycholic acid are 3α-hydroxy-7-keto-5β-cholanoic acid, ursodeoxycholic acid (3α,7β-dihydroxy-5β-cholanoic acid), α-muricholic acid (3α,6β,7α-trihydroxy-5β-cholanoic acid), β-muricholic acid (3α,6β,7β-trihydroxy-5β-cholanoic acid), ω-muricholic acid (3α,6α,7β-trihydroxy-5β-cholanoic acid), and hyocholic acid (3α,6α,7α-trihydroxy-5β-cholanoic acid) (Fig. 5). The formation of these acids is discussed below. It is possible that 3α-hydroxy-7-keto-5β-cholanoic acid and ursodeoxycholic acid might be formed, to some extent, from cholesterol without the intermediate formation of chenodeoxycholic acid. Possible precursors of these acids are 3β-hydroxycholest-5-en-7-one and cholest-5-ene-3β,7β-diol, both of which have been shown to be formed from cholesterol in vitro (18, 78, 88). Mitropoulos & Myant (86, 87) have found that a mitochondrial system from rat liver catalyzes the conversion of cholesterol to lithocholic acid (3α-hydroxy-5β-cholanoic acid), possibly by means of the intermediate formation of 3β-hydroxy-chol-5-enoic acid. Apparently, lithocholic acid can be, in part, a primary bile acid. As will be discussed below, lithocholic acid is further metabolized by liver to, among other acids, chenodeoxycholic acid. The importance of a pathway to chenodeoxycholic acid by means of the intermediate formation of lithocholic acid cannot be assessed at present.

The primary bile acids are further metabolized by intestinal microorganisms, and the products are partially reabsorbed and transported to the liver, where they may undergo further structural modifications. The most important types of reactions that are carried out by intestinal microorganisms are hydrolysis of the conjugates, removal of the 7α-hydroxyl group, and oxidation-reduction of the 3-, 7-, and 12-hydroxyl groups.

A. Metabolism of Chenodeoxycholic Acid in Liver

In the rat and mouse, chenodeoxycholic acid is transformed into α-muricholic acid, which in turn is converted to β-muricholic acid, likely by means of the intermediate formation of the 7-keto acid [(8); Fig. 5]. In addition to these acids, small amounts of 3α-hydroxy-7-keto-5β-cholanoic acid are formed (8). This acid is transformed, in part, to ursodeoxycholic acid. In the guinea pig, 3α-hydroxy-7-keto-5β-cholanoic acid is reduced predominantly to the 7α-hydroxy-epimer, i.e., chenodeoxycholic acid (8).

One of the major bile acids in guinea pig bile is 3α-hydroxy-7-keto-5β-cholanoic acid. It has been shown that this acid is formed from cholesterol in the liver, possibly by means of the intermediate formation of chenodeoxycholic acid, as well as by microbial oxidation of chenodeoxycholic acid during the enterohepatic circulation of bile (31).

Small amounts of ursodeoxycholic acid are present in human bile and can be assumed to have been formed, at least in part, by reduction of 3α-hydroxy-7-keto-5β-cholanoic acid [(8, 31); Fig. 5]. However, 3α-hydroxy-7-keto-5β-cholanoic acid and ursodeoxycholic acid could conceivably be primary bile acids, formed from 3β-hydroxycholest-5-en-7-one and cholest-5-ene-3β,7β-diol.

In the pig, chenodeoxycholic acid is hydroxylated in the 6α-position to yield hyocholic acid, which is a major primary bile acid in this species [(8, 49); Fig. 5]. Under abnormal conditions, surgical jaundice by ligation of the bile duct, chenodeoxycholic acid is converted, in part, to ω-muricholic acid in the mouse (112).

B. Metabolism of Bile Acids in Intestinal Tract

When the bile acids reach the lower part of the small intestine, they become subjected to the action of intestinal microorganisms, a process that continues throughout the large intestine. The conjugated bile acids are hydrolyzed to free bile acids. An extensive study by Midtvedt & Norman (82) has shown that bile acid conjugates can be split by a number of microorganisms normally present in human and rat intestinal contents, including strains of *Bacteroides*, *Clostridium*, *Enterococcus*, and *Lactobacillus*.

One of the main microbial reactions is the removal of the 7α-hydroxyl group from cholic acid and chenodeoxycholic acid, yielding deoxycholic acid (3α,12α-dihydroxy-5β-cholanoic acid) and lithocholic acid, respectively (Fig. 6). It is not known to what extent this reaction or the other microbial reactions discussed

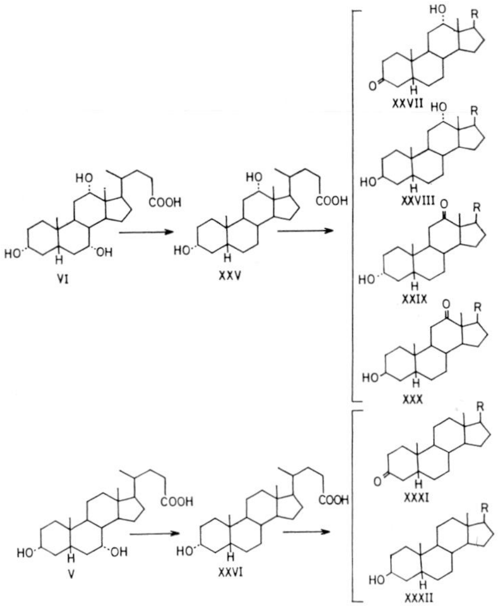

FIG. 6. The main metabolites of the primary bile acids formed by the action of intestinal microorganisms. V, Chenodeoxycholic acid; VI, cholic acid; XXV, deoxycholic acid; XXVI, lithocholic acid; XXVII, 12α-hydroxy-3-keto-5β-cholanoic acid; XXVIII, 3β,12α-dihydroxy-5β-cholanoic acid; XXIX, 3α-hydroxy-12-keto-5β-cholanoic acid; XXX, 3β-hydroxy-12-keto-5β-cholanoic acid; XXXI, 3-keto-5β-cholanoic acid; XXXII, 3β-hydroxy-5β-cholanoic acid.

below occur with conjugated bile acids as substrates. An anaerobic *Lactobacillus* has been isolated from rat intestinal contents that is able to carry out the 7α-dehydroxylation of cholic acid and chenodeoxycholic acid (47). The mechanisms of this reaction have been studied with the aid of specifically tritium-labeled cholic acid and it has been shown to proceed by means of a trans elimination of the elements of water yielding an unsaturated acid, 3α,12α-dihydroxy-5β-chol-6-enoic acid, which is subsequently reduced by a trans hydrogenation (8). It is probable that chenodeoxycholic acid is converted to lithocholic acid by the same reaction mechanisms (8). Evidence has been obtained showing that the microbial conversion of hyocholic acid into hyodeoxycholic acid (3α,6α-dihydroxy-5β-cholanoic acid) in the pig also occurs in the same manner (8). The microbial formation of deoxycholic acid from 3α,7β,12α-trihydroxy-5β-cholanoic acid and 3α,12α-dihydroxy-7-keto-5β-cholanoic acid and of lithocholic acid from ursodeoxycholic acid has been demonstrated in the rat (8, 31). It is not known whether these transformations occur by means of the intermediate formation of the 7α-hydroxylated derivatives, i.e., cholic acid and chenodeoxycholic acid. The microbial removal of a

7α-hydroxyl group is a reaction of widespread occurrence and has been demonstrated in a number of mammals.

The other transformations of bile acids carried out by intestinal microorganisms include oxidation of the hydroxyl groups at C-3, C-7, and C-12 and reduction of the keto bile acids formed, yielding both the α-hydroxy and the β-hydroxy epimers. Midtvedt & Norman (82) have studied these reactions also in cultures of a number of different microorganisms and have found that strains of *Bacteroides, Clostridium, Escherichia,* and *Lactobacillus* can carry out many of these reactions. The main keto bile acid formed from cholic acid is 3α,12α-dihydroxy-7-keto-5β-cholanoic acid. Deoxycholic acid is converted to 3α-hydroxy-12-keto-5β-cholanoic acid, 12α-hydroxy-3-keto-5β-cholanoic acid, and 3β-hydroxy-12-keto-5β-cholanoic acid (2, 29). The last-mentioned acid is formed by reduction of the corresponding diketo bile acid or by oxidation of 3β,12α-dihydroxy-5β-cholanoic acid. Chenodeoxycholic acid is oxidized to 3α-hydroxy-7-keto-5β-cholanoic acid and 7α-hydroxy-3-keto-5β-cholanoic acid, and lithocholic acid is converted to 3-keto-5β-cholanoic acid (Fig. 6). All above-mentioned keto bile acids have been isolated from human feces (2, 37, 38). Several of the acids have been identified in rat cecal contents and in rat and rabbit feces (8, 30, 31). However, it is probable that all of them can be present, though many in very low concentrations.

In the microbial reduction of the keto bile acids, both α-hydroxy and β-hydroxy epimers are formed. The main β-hydroxylated bile acids formed are 3α,7β,12α-trihydroxy-5β-cholanoic acid, 3β,12α-dihydroxy-5β-cholanoic acid, 3α,12β-dihydroxy-5β-cholanoic acid, 3β,12β-dihydroxy-5β-cholanoic acid, and 3β-hydroxy-12-keto-5β-cholanoic acid, 3β,7α-dihydroxy-5β-cholanoic acid, and 3β-hydroxy-5β-cholanoic acid (2, 37, 38). Again, all these acids have been isolated from human feces and some of them from rat and rabbit feces. Evidence has been obtained that an equilibrium exists between the oxidized and the reduced form of the bile acid metabolites, at least with respect to the oxygen function at C-3. Thus, Kallner (64) found that in the rat 3β-³H-24-¹⁴C-deoxycholic acid rapidly lost its tritium label when exposed to the intestinal microorganisms in vivo.

Some of the above-mentioned bile acids become esterified with what appears to be long-chain fatty acids. Such esterified bile acids have been demonstrated by Norman (90) in rat intestinal contents and feces. Thus, deoxycholic acid, 3β,12α-dihydroxy-5β-cholanoic acid, lithocholic acid, and 3β-hydroxy-5β-cholanoic acid are excreted, in part, in the form of esters.

The presence in human, rat, and rabbit feces of bile acids having the 5α configuration (allo configuration) has been recently demonstrated (30, 38, 64). Two such bile acids have been isolated so far: $3\alpha,7\alpha,12\alpha$-trihydroxy-5α-cholanoic acid (allocholic acid) from human feces and $3\alpha,12\alpha$-dihydroxy-5α-cholanoic acid (allodeoxycholic acid) from rat and rabbit feces. $3\alpha,12\alpha$-Dihydroxy-5α-cholanoic acid is also present in rabbit bile. 5α-Cholanoic acids can be either primary or secondary bile acids. The conversion by rat liver of 5α-cholestan-3β-ol to $3\alpha,7\alpha,12\alpha$-trihydroxy-5α-cholanoic acid and an acid tentatively identified as $3\alpha,7\alpha$-dihydroxy-5α-cholanoic acid (allochenodeoxycholic acid) has been demonstrated (68). Thus, these two acids are primary bile acids; 5α-cholestan-3β-ol is formed from cholesterol in the liver (31). On the other hand, $3\alpha,12\alpha$-dihydroxy-5α-cholanoic acid is a secondary bile acid. The microbial conversion of deoxycholic acid into $3\alpha,12\alpha$-dihydroxy-5α-cholanoic acid has been demonstrated in the rat and the rabbit (30, 64). It is probable that, in analogy with the formation of deoxycholic acid from cholic acid, $3\alpha,12\alpha$-dihydroxy-5α-cholanoic acid also can be formed by microbial 7α-dehydroxylation of $3\alpha,7\alpha,12\alpha$-trihydroxy-5α-cholanoic acid. Such a pathway would explain the finding of Hofmann & Mosbach (57) that feeding 5α-cholestan-3β-ol to rabbits leads to the accumulation of $3\alpha,12\alpha$-dihydroxy-5α-cholanoic acid, partly in the form of gallstones. However, the possibility has not been completely excluded that deoxycholic acid as well as $3\alpha,12\alpha$-dihydroxy-5α-cholanoic acid to some extent might be formed from cholesterol in the liver. The mechanism of the conversion of deoxycholic acid into $3\alpha,12\alpha$-dihydroxy-5α-cholanoic acid has not been definitely established. The reaction has been found to be reversible (65). A probable mechanism is oxidation of the 3α-hydroxyl group to the 3-keto bile acid, which in turn is dehydrogenated to the Δ^4-3-keto bile acid. This acid can then be hydrogenated to yield a 3-keto-5α- or a 3-keto-5β-cholanoic acid that again is reduced to the 3α-hydroxy acid. The experiments performed do not exclude the possibility of a direct dehydrogenation of deoxycholic acid and $3\alpha,12\alpha$-dihydroxy-5α-cholanoic acid to $3\alpha,12\alpha$-dihydroxy-chol-4-enoic acid, which could be hydrogenated to the 5α- or the 5β-cholanoic acid (65). It has been demonstrated recently that, in the rat, intestinal microorganisms are able to transform $3\alpha,7\alpha$-dihydroxy-5α-cholanoic acid and $3\alpha,7\alpha,12\alpha$-trihydroxy-5α-cho-

lanoic acid into bile acids having the 5β configuration (66).

It should be pointed out that the extent to which the primary bile acids are transformed into the above-mentioned microbial metabolites can be expected to vary considerably between species as well as between animals of the same species. The composition of bile acids in the lower part of the intestinal tract and in the feces varies also with diet. The effects of diet are probably due not only to changes in the composition of the intestinal flora but also to changes in the rate of passage of intestinal contents through the intestinal tract.

C. *Intestinal Absorption of Bile Acids and Metabolism of Reabsorbed Bile Acids*

The main site of absorption of bile acids is the lower part of the ileum (26, 31). In the rat, the cecum is also an important site of absorption (26, 31). In a detailed analysis of the absorption of cholic acid and taurocholic acid in the rat, Dietschy and colleagues (33) found three mechanisms of absorption, the relative quantitative importance of which was measured. The three processes are passive ionic diffusion, passive non-ionic diffusion, and active transport. The specificity of the absorption processes with regard to bile acid structure has not been completely established. In studies of taurocholic acid and cholic acid absorption in slices of rat ileum, Holt (59) found a competitive inhibition by dihydroxycholanoic acids. Similar results were obtained by Lack & Weiner (71) using everted sacs of guinea pig ileum. These authors found that the transport of a given bile acid is depressed in the presence of another bile acid and that dihydroxycholanoic acids are more inhibitory than trihydroxycholanoic acids. They also presented evidence that the rate of active transport depends on bile acid structure; for example, trihydroxycholanoic acids were absorbed better than dihydroxycholanoic acids and conjugated acids better than free acids. On the other hand, Cronholm & Sjövall (23) found no evidence of differences, in vivo, between the extent of absorption of trihydroxycholanoic acids and that of dihydroxycholanoic acids.

From studies of the composition of bile acids in portal blood and in bile, it is apparent that only a limited number of all the bile acid metabolites formed in the intestinal tract are absorbed. Thus, the main bile acids that reach the liver are, in most mammalian species, deoxycholic acid and the primary bile acids, that is, cholic acid and chenodeoxycholic acid, partly in the form of conjugates. (In the pig, the corresponding acids are hyodeoxycholic acid, hyocholic acid, and chenodeoxycholic acid; in some strains of guinea pig, 3α-hydroxy-7-keto-5β-cholanoic acid and chenodeoxycholic acid; in the rabbit, deoxycholic acid and cholic acid.) Practically no 3β-hydroxylated bile acids are present in bile (small amounts of $3\beta,7\alpha$-dihydroxy-5β-cholanoic acid are present in pig bile), and the concentration of bile acids with a keto group is usually very low (31, 49). However, in the bile of some species, e.g., guinea pig, 3α-hydroxy-7-keto-5β-cholanoic acid is a major component, and in pig bile 3α-hydroxy-6-keto-5β-cholanoic acid is present (31, 49). In a recent study of bile acids in rat portal blood, Cronholm & Sjövall (23) found the major bile acids to be cholic acid, β-muricholic acid, chenodeoxycholic acid, deoxycholic acid, and hyodeoxycholic acid, present partly in the form of conjugates. The presence of small amounts of several other bile acids was not excluded.

There are several possible reasons for the absence from bile of a number of the bile acid metabolites formed in the lower part of the intestinal tract. Many of the metabolites might be formed in segments of the intestine distal to the main sites of absorption; they might be taken up by or bound to the intestinal microorganisms and thus be prevented from being absorbed; the low solubility of some of the microbial metabolites, for example, lithocholic acid, might be a factor of importance with regard to extent of absorption; the absorption processes might be selective with regard to bile acid structure; enzymes in liver might rapidly transform metabolites into the bile acids normally present in bile. At present, information is not sufficient to warrant a detailed discussion of these alternatives. A few points may be made, however. Norman & Shorb (92) have shown that some metabolites, notably lithocholic acid, become tightly bound to intestinal microorganisms. Concerning the influence of bile acid structure on extent of absorption, the above-mentioned studies in vitro indicate the presence of such an influence, but the work so far carried out does not provide sufficient information with respect to conditions in vivo. In a number of metabolic studies in the rat, keto bile acids have been found to be absorbed when injected into the cecum, but the significance of these findings in terms of absorption of keto bile acids under physiological conditions cannot be assessed. Absorption of 3β-hydroxylated bile acids or of esterified bile acids has not been studied. The presence in liver of enzymes capable of oxidizing 3α-hydroxy and 3β-hydroxy bile acids to 3-keto bile acids as well as of reducing 3-keto bile acids to 3α-hydroxy and 3β-hydroxy acids is well documented (67). Thus, if 3β-hydroxy bile acids are absorbed from the intestinal tract, they could be transformed into 3α-hydroxy acids in the liver. Similarly, keto bile acids might be efficiently reduced to hydroxy acids in the liver, as has been demonstrated in the case of 3α-hydroxy-7-keto-5β-cholanoic acid.

The bile acids reaching the liver with the portal blood undergo some metabolic reactions that to some extent vary with species. Free bile acids are conjugated with glycine or taurine. In many mammalian species, deoxycholic acid is not further metabolized except for conjugation and is a major bile acid in bile under physiological conditions, that is, in animals with uninterrupted enterohepatic circulation of bile (8, 49). In the mouse and the rat, taurodeoxycholic acid is rapidly hydroxylated in the 7α-position to yield taurocholic acid (8, 31).

Although lithocholic acid is absorbed only to a limited extent and is present in bile only in small amounts, the further metabolism of this acid deserves mention. In man, lithocholic acid is not transformed into more polar metabolites. It becomes conjugated not only with taurine and glycine but also with as yet unidentified compounds to yield conjugates that are more stable to hydrolysis than taurine or glycine conjugates (22, 91). In the rat, lithocholic acid is metabolized extensively into more polar products. The main metabolites are α- and β-muricholic acids, chenodeoxycholic acid, and $3\alpha,6\beta$-dihydroxy-5β-cholanoic acid (8, 110). In this connection it is worth mentioning that $3\alpha,6\beta$-dihydroxy-5β-cholanoic acid is the precursor of hyodeoxycholic acid, which is present in small amounts in rat bile (35). The conversion of $3\alpha,6\beta$-dihydroxy-5β-cholanoic acid to hyodeoxycholic acid proceeds by means of the intermediate formation of 3α-hydroxy-6-keto-5β-cholanoic acid, and the reactions are catalyzed by microbial enzymes. In the rabbit, lithocholic acid is metabolized to a limited extent and gives rise to only small amounts of more polar products (63).

In man, lithocholic acid in small doses causes a pyrogenic and an inflammatory reaction (96). In several species, including rabbit and rat, lithocholic acid produces liver damage (58, 60, 106). The formation of gallstones with the administration of lithocholic acid has been observed in rats (97). The resistance to lithocholic acid administration has been shown to vary with species. Thus rats are much more resistant than are rabbits. This difference between species might depend on the manner in which lithocholic acid is metabolized by liver. As mentioned above, rat liver is able to transform lithocholic acid into several more polar metabolites, whereas rabbit liver has a low capacity to metabolize lithocholic acid into more polar metabolites. We then assume that the more polar products are less toxic than lithocholic acid itself (which, however, has not been demonstrated).

D. Excretion of Bile Acids

Bile acids are excreted mainly with the feces. The excretion with urine is usually of little importance, quantitatively, and constitutes less than 5 % of the total amount excreted daily (26). In the rabbit, however, the urinary excretion of bile acids is somewhat more significant and can reach values of about 10 % of total daily excretion of bile acids (26).

Under normal conditions, the bile acids excreted with the feces constitute a complex mixture of compounds most of which have been formed by microbial action on the primary bile acids. The composition of fecal bile acids has been studied in detail in man (2, 26, 31, 37, 38), and the structures of most of these bile acids were discussed in the foregoing section. It should be mentioned that many of these acids either have been identified or can be assumed to be present in feces of other species. At this point it appears sufficient to enumerate only the major fecal bile acids: cholic acid, 3α, 7β, 12α-trihydroxy-5β-cholanoic acid, 3α,12α-dihydroxy-7-keto-5β-cholanoic acid, deoxycholic acid, 3β, 12α-dihydroxy-5β-cholanoic acid, 3α,12β-dihydroxy-5β-cholanoic acid, 3α-hydroxy-12-keto-5β-cholanoic acid, 3β-hydroxy-12-keto-5β-cholanoic acid, 12α-hydroxy-3-keto-5β-cholanoic acid, 3,12-diketo-5β-cholanoic acid, chenodeoxycholic acid, ursodeoxycholic acid, 3β,7α-dihydroxy-5β-cholanoic acid, 3α-hydroxy-7-keto-5β-cholanoic acid, 7α-hydroxy-3-keto-5β-cholanoic acid, lithocholic acid, 3β-hydroxy-5β-cholanoic acid, and 3-keto-5β-cholanoic acid (Fig. 6). The relative proportion of these acids and of others that have not been enumerated varies from subject to subject and with diet and other factors that can influence the intestinal flora. It should be pointed out that such changes may not only lead to changes in the relative proportions of the different bile acids but also to the appearance of other bile acids than those normally present. The complexity of the mixture of fecal bile acids makes quantitative determination of fecal excretion of bile acids difficult and has not always been fully realized in studies of steroid balance in animals and man (26).

Recently Ahrens (1) has obtained evidence indi-cating that intestinal microorganisms might be able to degrade the steroid skeleton or the side chain of steroids, or both. The substrates for these reactions, whether they are bile acids or neutral steroids, or both, have not been defined, nor has the quantitative importance of these reactions been established. The presence of such reactions adds new difficulties to measurements of steroid balance, and more detailed information on this matter is of great importance.

E. Regulation of Bile Acid Formation

The mechanisms by which the formation of bile acids in the liver is regulated are not known in detail. Early work (7) indicates that the synthesis of bile acids was regulated homeostatically by the amount of bile acids returned to the liver with the portal blood. This conclusion is based on the effect of infusion of taurochenodeoxycholic acid on the synthesis of cholic acid in the bile fistula rat. If bile is continuously drained by preparation of a bile fistula, the synthesis of bile acids increases manyfold; in the rat, the increase in synthesis is about ten- to fifteenfold. When taurochenodeoxycholic acid, 5–10 mg per hour, was infused intraduodenally into a bile fistula rat, the synthesis of bile acids, as measured by cholic acid formation, was brought back to about the same level as in the intact rat. Recently, similar experiments were performed by Lee et al. (72), who measured the conversion of labeled cholesterol into bile acids in bile fistula rats receiving continuous infusions of bile salts. These authors obtained the same effect with taurochenode-oxycholic acid, as described above, but found, interestingly enough, that taurocholic acid was much less inhibitory. Taurochenodeoxycholic acid constitutes only about 20 % of total bile acids in rat bile and much less than 20 % in portal blood (8, 23). However, the amount of taurochenodeoxycholic acid needed daily to suppress bile acid synthesis in the bile fistula rat can be calculated to correspond to the total amount of bile acids daily reaching the liver in the intact rat. Thus, the difference in effect on bile acid synthesis between taurocholic acid and taurochenode-oxycholic acid indicates that taurochenodeoxycholic acid might have an effect on bile acid formation that is not related to the physiological regulation of bile acid formation. This effect might be ascribable, at least in part, to the more pronounced inhibition of mitochondrial ATP formation and NADH oxidation exerted by taurochenodeoxycholic acid than by, e.g., taurocholic acid (73). Yet, it appears that the role of bile acids in the regulation of their synthesis is not, at present, entirely defined.

Studies by Beher and associates (4, 5) on the formation and metabolism of cholesterol in rats, mice, and other rodents fed different bile acids also indicate that bile acids influence the rate of their synthesis. These authors have suggested that the synthesis of bile acids is regulated by a "double feedback" mechanism: bile acids inhibit the conversion of cholesterol to bile acids; this leads to an increase in liver cholesterol; and this, in turn, leads to a decreased cholesterol synthesis. Myant & Eder (89) studied the synthesis of cholesterol in liver from bile fistula rats and found an increase in rate of incorporation of acetate but not mevalonate into cholesterol. The increase in cholesterol synthesis preceded the increase in bile acid synthesis; this indicated that the regulation of bile acid synthesis might be exerted primarily on the rate of cholesterol synthesis. Dietschy & Siperstein (34) found that cholesterol synthesis in the intestinal mucosa, though insensitive to fasting and cholesterol feeding in contrast to liver, was inhibited by bile and was increased manyfold when bile was diverted from the intestinal tract. The factor(s) in bile responsible for this effect was not further studied. Fimognari & Rodwell (42) have reported recently that the synthesis of mevalonate from acetate in liver homogenates is inhibited by addition of various bile salts. The possibility of a partly nonspecific effect of bile acids, since they are powerful detergents, cannot be entirely excluded. The isolation from bile of a protein of low molecular weight capable of inhibiting incorporation of acetate into cholesterol in liver homogenates has been reported by Ogilvie & Kaplan (93). It was estimated that this protein was responsible, in large part, for the inhibitory action of bile on cholesterol synthesis in vitro.

The control of cholesterol biosynthesis has been shown to be exerted on the conversion of β-hydroxy-β-methylglutarate into mevalonate (26, 31). The site of control of bile acid biosynthesis has been suggested to be the first step in the conversion of cholesterol to bile acids, the 7α-hydroxylation (6). Some recent experiments (28) provide support for this contention. Examination of a number of isolated reactions in the formation of bile acids has shown that the rate of 7α-hydroxylation of cholesterol is several times faster in homogenates from bile fistula rats than in homogenates from control rats, whereas other reactions occur at about the same rate in control and bile fistula rats. It is possible that additional information on the regulation of bile acid formation might be gained from studies of the 7α-hydroxylase system under various conditions.

III. QUANTITATIVE ASPECTS OF FORMATION AND METABOLISM OF BILE ACIDS

The half-life and turnover of bile acids have been measured in man, rat, and rabbit. On a normal diet the half-life of cholic acid in healthy subjects was 2–3 days, and the daily synthesis of cholic acid was about 350 mg (26, 74). Simultaneous determination of the half-life periods of cholic acid and chenodeoxycholic acid in two subjects fed a standardized diet with 40% of the calories as butterfat gave values of 2–4 days and 4–6 days, respectively. The total daily synthesis of bile acids was 500–600 mg (29). The excretion of bile acids in feces has been measured by a number of investigators. The values reported vary within a wide range—from 100 mg to over 1,000 mg per day (26). The differences between the reported values can be ascribed, in part, to differences in methodology. The possible inadequacies of many of the methods used were discussed in some detail in a recent review (26). In more recent investigations (2, 3, 39–41, 45, 50, 83, 102, 104), a combination of isotopic methods and chromatographic methods, mainly gas and thin-layer chromatography, has been utilized for measurements of fecal excretion of bile acids and neutral steroids. With these methods the values obtained by different groups of investigators agree well.

Ever since it became clear that the serum cholesterol level is influenced by the degree of unsaturation of the dietary fat, much interest and effort have been devoted to measurements of steroid balance under different dietary regimens. Only the investigations using isotopic or chromatographic (or both) methods have apparently yielded accurate information about bile acid and neutral steroid excretion. The results obtained by different groups of investigators using such methods are, on the whole, corroborative. The studies have been performed with standardized diets containing either saturated or unsaturated fat. Measuring isotope excretion in feces after administration of 4-^{14}C-cholesterol, Rosenfeld & Hellman (102) found an average excretion of 290 mg of bile acids per day. Ahrens and collaborators (45, 104) found the daily excretion of bile acids to be about 100 mg on a steroid-free diet containing saturated fat and about 130 mg on the same diet with unsaturated fat. When the diet contained steroids, the corresponding figures were 250 and 270 mg, respectively. Avigan & Steinberg (3) found values of about 800 and 500 mg for excretion of bile acids on a diet containing 60% of the calories as saturated and unsaturated fat, respectively. Ali et al. (2) obtained values ranging from 130 to 650 mg for daily excretion of bile acids in feces in subjects fed a fat-free diet. Eneroth and colleagues (41) found values ranging between 100 and 500 mg per day in healthy subjects on a solid-food diet with 40% of the calories as fat. No significant change in the amount of bile acids excreted upon substitution of saturated fat by unsaturated fat was observed (P. Eneroth, K. Hellström, and S. Lindstedt, unpublished observations). In the above-mentioned studies, the excretion of neutral steroids in feces was, in most instances, measured simultaneously, and this thereby provided figures for total steroid balance. The values for neutral steroid excretion obtained by the different groups of investigators were again in good agreement—500–750 mg per day. From these careful studies it was concluded that there is no consistent difference in bile acid and neutral steroid excretion on diets with saturated fat or with unsaturated fat. The reduction in serum cholesterol level that follows a change from saturated to unsaturated fat is not accompanied by any corresponding changes in the excretion of bile acids and neutral steroids. It should be pointed out that, in the investigations referred to, significant reductions in serum cholesterol level were obtained on changing from saturated fat to unsaturated fat; and the changes were such that, if the cholesterol removed from the serum were excreted as bile acids and neutral steroids in feces, it should have been easily detected. Measuring cholic acid turnover in humans on formula diets with saturated or unsaturated fat, Lindstedt et al. (75) found no consistent changes with changes in diet. Similar results were obtained by Hellström & Lindstedt (52) in a study of turnover of cholic acid in healthy subjects and hypercholesterolemic subjects fed a standardized solid-food diet containing either saturated or unsaturated fat. All these investigations indicate that the main initial event in the reduction in serum cholesterol level induced by intake of unsaturated fat is a redistribution of cholesterol from blood to the tissues. Evidence for this concept has also been obtained in studies with rabbits and rats (15, 43, 55). It is possible that a small but prolonged increase in excretion of bile acids and neutral steroids on unsaturated fat might be difficult to detect. It is conceivable that, after the initial redistribution of cholesterol with change from saturated to unsaturated fat, such an increase in excretion may occur, perhaps over periods of months.

The turnover of deoxycholic acid has been studied in rabbits in connection with investigations of the effect of dietary fat on bile acid metabolism (54, 55). On a chow diet with low content of fat, the half-life of deoxycholic acid was about 7 days and the daily production about 70 mg. It should be pointed out that the main bile acid synthesized in rabbit liver is cholic acid, which is rapidly dehydroxylated to deoxycholic acid by microbial enzymes. The total daily synthesis of bile acids—small amounts of chenodeoxycholic acid are formed in addition to cholic acid—was calculated to be about 80 mg. Substitution of the chow diet by a semisynthetic diet containing corn oil or hydrogenated coconut oil led to an increase in half-life of deoxycholic acid from 7 days to 24–27 days and to a decrease in daily synthesis of bile acids from about 80 mg to about 30 mg. No significant difference in bile acid metabolism was observed between a corn-oil and a coconut-oil diet; this indicated a redistribution of cholesterol when changing from saturated to unsaturated fat. A recent report by Bieberdorf & Wilson (15) lends additional support to this contention.

The half-life periods of bile acids have been measured in the rat under various conditions. On a chow diet the half-life of cholic acid and chenodeoxycholic acid was 2–3 days and the total daily synthesis of bile acids was about 5 mg (8, 26). The influence of diet on bile acid turnover has been studied by Portman & Murphy (100), who found an increase in half-life and a decrease in daily production of bile acids with change from a chow diet to a semisynthetic diet containing sucrose or starch. Addition of indigestible material to the sucrose diet led to a substantial decrease in half-life. In germ-free rats the half-life of cholic acid was found to be three to five times longer than in conventional rats (46). Further studies have shown that the half-life of bile acids in germ-free rats can be substantially decreased by addition of indigestible material to the diet (48).

IV. FACTORS INFLUENCING FORMATION AND METABOLISM OF BILE ACIDS

A. Diet

As is apparent from the discussion in the preceding section, diet has a pronounced influence on the formation and metabolism of bile acids. A more detailed review of this subject, including references to investigations on effects of carbohydrates, steroids, bile acids, vitamins, and minerals, has appeared recently (26). The importance of detailed knowledge about the influence of amount and type of dietary fat on steroid and bile acid metabolism is apparent. As mentioned, present information strongly indicates that unsaturated fat primarily induces a redistribution of cholesterol from blood to the tissues. Further studies of steroid and bile acid metabolism will certainly supply additional information relevant to the fundamental question concerning the influence of diet on cardiovascular diseases.

In general, a change from a regular diet—ad libitum diet in humans, commercial chow diet in rabbits and rats—to a semisynthetic diet leads to an increase in half-life of bile acids and a decrease in bile acid production (26). Addition of indigestible material to such diets causes a more or less complete reversal of the effects (26). It is not known in detail what role the intestinal microorganisms play in connection with the changes in bile acid metabolism induced by different diets. It is conceivable that the dietary effects are mediated by changes in intestinal flora as well as by changes in the rate of passage of content through the intestinal tract.

B. Hormones

Studies on the influence of hormones on the formation and metabolism of bile acids have dealt mainly with the effects of thyroid hormones (26, 31). It has long been known that a relationship exists between the level of serum cholesterol and the state of thyroid activity. It has been shown that the rate of synthesis of cholesterol is higher than normal in the hyperthyroid state and lower than normal in the hypothyroid state (69). The hypothesis has been advanced that the drop in serum cholesterol observed in the hyperthyroid state could be due to an increase in catabolism and excretion of cholesterol greater than the increase in cholesterol synthesis; conversely, the decrease in degradation and elimination of cholesterol in the hypothyroid state would be more pronounced than the decrease in cholesterol synthesis (69). Investigations on the influence of thyroid activity on the rate of synthesis of bile acids have been carried out in man and in the rat. In man, the half-life of cholic acid was longer and the daily production lower than normal in hypothyroid patients. After treatment, there was a decrease in the half-life of cholic acid and an increase in daily synthesis of bile acids (51). Hyperthyroidism was associated with an increase in bile acid production. Hellström & Sjövall (53) found that the pattern of conjugation of bile acids is influenced by the state of thyroid activity. In hypothyroid patients there was a preponderance of bile acids conjugated with glycine. With treatment, the ratio of glycine-conjugated to taurine-conjugated bile acids decreased to normal values.

In rats with bile fistulas, the excretion of bile acids was lower in the hypothyroid state than in the euthyroid state. The total excretion of bile acids in hyperthyroid bile fistula rats was about the same as in euthyroid bile fistula rats. However, there was a reversal of the normal ratio of 3 between cholic acid and chenodeoxycholic acid (8). Similar effects on the pattern of bile acids excreted in bile fistula rats were induced by noncalorigenic doses of D-triiodothyronine (107). In intact rats, the hyperthyroid state was associated with the same reversal of the ratio of cholic acid to chenodeoxycholic acid and with an increase in daily production of bile acids and a decrease in half-life (108). The half-life and daily synthesis of bile acids in hypothyroid rats were about the same as in euthyroid rats. Noncalorigenic doses of D-triiodothyronine induced the same effects on bile acid metabolism in intact rats as observed in hyperthyroidism. The influence of thyroid activity on bile acid formation has also been studied in vitro. Mitropoulos & Myant (84) found an increase in formation of propionic acid from cholesterol in liver homogenates from hyperthyroid rats as compared with those from euthyroid rats and a decrease in those from hypothyroid rats. The same effects were observed by Berséus (10) in a study of the oxidation of 5β-cholestane-3α,7α,12α-triol. The reversal of the ratio of cholic acid to chenodeoxycholic acid associated with the administration of thyroid hormones as well as D-triiodothyronine to rats indicates that thyroid hormones might have an effect on bile acid formation not entirely explicable by a general stimulation of metabolic reactions.

Little is known about the effect of other hormones on bile acid metabolism. It has been shown that in adrenalectomized rats the ratio of glycine-conjugated to taurine-conjugated bile acids is about 1.0 as compared with a normal ratio of 0.1 (56). Cortisone treatment of adrenalectomized rats leads to a normal pattern of bile acid conjugation (56). Kritchevsky and co-workers (70) have found that the extent of oxidation of the cholesterol side chain to carbon dioxide is considerably greater in the presence of liver mitochondria from female rats than in the presence of those from male rats. Of interest in this connection is that administration of estrogens leads to a decrease in serum cholesterol level (19, 26).

REFERENCES

1. AHRENS, E. H., JR. Fecal bile acids and neutral steroids: significance of steroid balance studies. Presented at the 50th Annual Meeting of Federation of American Societies for Experimental Biology, Atlantic City, N.J., April 1966.

2. ALI, S. S., A. KUKSIS, AND J. M. R. BEVERIDGE. Excretion of bile acids by three men on a fat-free diet. Can. J. Biochem. 44: 957–969, 1966.

3. AVIGAN, J., AND D. STEINBERG. Steroid and bile acid excretion in man and the effect of dietary fat. J. Clin. Invest. 44: 1845–1856, 1965.

4. BEHER, W. T., G. D. BAKER, AND W. L. ANTHONY. Feedback control of cholesterol biosynthesis in the mouse. Proc. Soc. Exptl. Biol. Med. 109: 863–868, 1962.

5. BEHER, W. T., G. D. BAKER, AND D. G. PENNEY. A comparative study of the effects of bile acids and cholesterol on cholesterol metabolism in the mouse, rat, hamster, and guinea pig. J. Nutr. 79: 523–530, 1963.

6. BERGSTRÖM, S. Bile acids: formation and metabolism. In: Ciba Foundation Symposium, Biosynthesis of Terpenes and Sterols, edited by G. E. W. Wolstenholme and C. M. O'Connor. Boston: Little, Brown, 1959, p. 185–203.

7. BERGSTRÖM, S., AND H. DANIELSSON. On the regulation of bile acid formation in the rat liver. Acta Physiol. Scand. 43: 1–7, 1958.

8. BERGSTRÖM, S., H. DANIELSSON, AND B. SAMUELSSON. Formation and metabolism of bile acids. In: Lipide Metabolism, edited by K. Bloch. New York: Wiley, 1960, p. 291–336.

9. BERSÉUS, O. On the stereospecificity of 26-hydroxylation of cholesterol. Acta Chem. Scand. 19: 325–328, 1965.

10. BERSÉUS, O. On the effect of thyroid hormones on the oxidation of 5β-cholestane-3α,7α,12α-triol. Acta Chem. Scand. 19: 2131–2135, 1965.

11. BERSÉUS, O. Conversion of cholesterol to bile acids in rat: purification and properties of a Δ⁴-3-ketosteroid 5β-reductase and a 3α-hydroxysteroid dehydrogenase. Eur. J. Biochem. 2: 493–502, 1967.

12. BERSÉUS, O., H. DANIELSSON, AND K. EINARSSON. Synthesis and metabolism of cholest-5-ene-3β,7α,12α-triol. J. Biol. Chem. 242: 1211–1219, 1967.

13. BERSÉUS, O., H. DANIELSSON, AND A. KALLNER. Synthesis and metabolism of cholest-4-ene-7α,12α-diol-3-one and 5β-cholestane-7α,12α-diol-3-one. J. Biol. Chem. 240: 2396–2401, 1965.

14. BERSÉUS, O., AND K. EINARSSON. On the conversion of cholest-5-ene-3β,7α-diol to 7α-hydroxycholest-4-en-3-one in rat liver homogenates. Acta Chem. Scand. 21: 1105–1108, 1967.

15. BIEBERDORF, F., AND J. D. WILSON. Studies on the mechanism of action of unsaturated fats on cholesterol metabolism in the rabbit. J. Clin. Invest. 44: 1834–1844, 1965.

16. BJÖRKHEM, I., AND H. DANIELSSON. Formation and metabolism of some Δ⁴-cholestenols in the rat. Eur. J. Biochem. 2: 403–413, 1967.

17. BJÖRKHEM, I., H. DANIELSSON, AND K. EINARSSON. On the conversion of cholesterol to 5β-cholestane-3α,7α-diol in guinea pig liver homogenates. Eur. J. Biochem. 2: 294–302, 1967.

18. BJÖRKHEM, I., K. EINARSSON, AND G. JOHANSSON. Formation and metabolism of 3β-hydroxycholest-5-en-7-one and cholest-5-ene-3β,7β-diol. Acta Chem. Scand. 22: in press, 1968.

19. BOYD, G. S. Effect of linoleate and estrogen on cholesterol metabolism. Federation Proc. 21, Suppl. 11:86–92, 1962.

20. CAREY, J. B., JR. Conversion of cholesterol to trihydroxycoprostanic acid and cholic acid in man. J. Clin. Invest. 43: 1443–1448, 1964.

21. CAREY, J. B., JR., AND G. A. D. HASLEWOOD. Crystallization of trihydroxycoprostanic acid from human bile. J. Biol. Chem. 238: PC 855–856, 1963.

22. CAREY, J. B., JR., AND G. WILLIAMS. Metabolism of lithocholic acid in bile fistula patients. J. Clin. Invest. 42: 450–455, 1963.

23. CRONHOLM, T., AND J. SJÖVALL. Bile acids in portal blood of rats fed different diets and cholestyramine. Eur. J. Biochem. 2: 375–383, 1967.

24. DANIELSSON, H. On the oxidation of 3α,7α,12α-trihydroxycoprostane by mouse and rat liver homogenates. Acta Chem. Scand. 14: 348–352, 1960.

25. DANIELSSON, H. On the metabolism of 7α-hydroxycholesterol in mouse liver homogenates. Arkiv Kemi 17: 363–372, 1961.

26. DANIELSSON, H. Present status of research on catabolism and excretion of cholesterol. Advan. Lipid Res. 1: 335–385, 1963.

27. DANIELSSON, H., AND K. EINARSSON. On the conversion of cholesterol to 7α,12α-dihydroxycholest-4-en-3-one. J. Biol. Chem. 241: 1449–1454, 1966.

28. DANIELSSON, H., K. EINARSSON, AND G. JOHANSSON. Effect of biliary drainage on individual reactions in the conversion of cholesterol to taurocholic acid. Eur. J. Biochem. 2: 44–49, 1967.

29. DANIELSSON, H., P. ENEROTH, K. HELLSTRÖM, S. LINDSTEDT, AND J. SJÖVALL. On the turnover and excretory products of cholic and chenodeoxycholic acid in man. J. Biol. Chem. 238: 2299–2304, 1963.

30. DANIELSSON, H., A. KALLNER, AND J. SJÖVALL. On the composition of the bile acid fraction of rabbit feces and the isolation of a new bile acid: 3α,12α-dihydroxy-5α-cholanic acid. J. Biol. Chem. 238: 3846–3852, 1963.

31. DANIELSSON, H., AND T. T. TCHEN. Steroid metabolism. In: Metabolic Pathways, edited by D. M. Greenberg. New York: Acad. Press, 1968, vol. II, p. 117–168.

32. DEAN, P. D. G., AND M. W. WHITEHOUSE. Catabolism of 2-methyloctanoic acid and 3β-hydroxycholest-5-en-26-oic acid. Biochem. J. 101: 632–635, 1966.

33. DIETSCHY, J. M., H. S. SALOMON, AND M. D. SIPERSTEIN. Bile acid metabolism. I. Studies on the mechanisms of intestinal transport. J. Clin. Invest. 45: 832–846, 1966.

34. DIETSCHY, J. M., AND M. D. SIPERSTEIN. Cholesterol synthesis by the gastrointestinal tract: localization and mechanisms of control. J. Clin. Invest. 44: 1311–1327, 1965.

35. EINARSSON, K. On the formation of hyodeoxycholic acid in the rat. J. Biol. Chem. 241: 534–539, 1966.

36. EINARSSON, K. On the properties of the 12α-hydroxylase in cholic acid biosynthesis. Eur. J. Biochem. In press.

37. ENEROTH, P., B. GORDON, R. RYHAGE, AND J. SJÖVALL. Identification of mono- and dihydroxy bile acids in hu-

man feces by gas-liquid chromatography and mass spectrometry. *J. Lipid Res.* 7: 511–523, 1966.

38. ENEROTH, P., B. GORDON, AND J. SJÖVALL. Characterization of trisubstituted cholanoic acids in human feces. *J. Lipid Res.* 7: 524–530, 1966.

40. ENEROTH, P., K. HELLSTRÖM, AND R. RYHAGE. Identification and quantification of netural fecal steroids by gas-liquid chromatography and mass spectrometry: studies of human excretion during two dietary regimens. *J. Lipid Res.* 5: 245–262, 1964.

41. ENEROTH, P., K. HELLSTRÖM, AND J. SJÖVALL. A method for quantitative determination of bile acids in human feces. *Acta Chem. Scand.* 22: in press, 1968.

42. FIMOGNARI, G. M., AND V. W. RODWELL. Cholesterol biosynthesis: mevalonate synthesis inhibited by bile salts. *Science* 147: 1038, 1965.

43. GERSON, T., F. B. SHORLAND, AND Y. ADAMS. The effects of corn oil on the amounts of cholesterol and the excretion of sterol in the rat. *Biochem. J.* 81: 584–591, 1961.

44. GORDON, B. A., A. KUKSIS, AND J. M. R. BEVERIDGE. Separation of bile acid conjugates by ion exchange chromatography. *Can. J. Biochem. Physiol.* 41: 77–89, 1963.

45. GRUNDY, S. M., E. H. AHRENS, JR., AND T. A. MIETTINEN. Quantitative isolation and gas-liquid chromatographic analysis of total fecal bile acids. *J. Lipid Res.* 6: 397–410, 1965.

46. GUSTAFSSON, B. E., S. BERGSTRÖM, S. LINDSTEDT, AND A. NORMAN. Turnover and nature of fecal bile acids in germfree and infected rats fed cholic acid-24-C^{14}. *Proc. Soc. Exptl. Biol. Med.* 94: 467–471, 1957.

47. GUSTAFSSON, B. E., T. MIDTVEDT, AND A. NORMAN. Isolated fecal microorganisms capable of 7α-dehydroxylating bile acids. *J. Exptl. Med.* 123: 413–432, 1966.

48. GUSTAFSSON, B. E., AND A. NORMAN. Dietary influence on the turnover of bile acids in germfree and conventional rats. *Brit. J. Nutr.* In press.

49. HASLEWOOD, G. A. D. The biological significance of chemical differences in bile salts. *Biol. Rev.* 39: 537–574, 1964.

50. HELLMAN, L., AND R. S. ROSENFELD. Isotopic studies of cholesterol metabolism in man. In: *Hormones and Atherosclerosis*, edited by G. Pincus. New York: Acad. Press, 1959, p. 157–172.

51. HELLSTRÖM, K., AND S. LINDSTEDT. Cholic-acid turnover and biliary bile-acid composition in humans with abnormal thyroid function. *J. Lab. Clin. Med.* 63: 666–679, 1964.

52. HELLSTRÖM, K., AND S. LINDSTEDT. Studies on the formation of cholic acid in subjects given standardized diet with butter or corn oil as dietary fat. *Am. J. Clin. Nutr.* 18: 46–59, 1966.

53. HELLSTRÖM, K., AND J. SJÖVALL. Conjugation of bile acids in patients with hypothyroidism. *J. Atherosclerosis Res.* 1: 205–210, 1961.

54. HELLSTRÖM, K., AND J. SJÖVALL. Turnover of deoxycholic acid in the rabbit. *J. Lipid Res.* 3: 397–404, 1962.

55. HELLSTRÖM, K., J. SJÖVALL, AND G. WIGAND. Influence of semisynthetic diet and type of fat on the turnover of deoxycholic acid in the rabbit. *J. Lipid Res.* 3: 405–412, 1962.

56. HELLSTRÖM, K., AND O. STRAND. Effects of adrenalectomy and corticoid replacement on bile acid conjugation in bile fistula rats. *Acta Endocrinol.* 43: 305–310, 1963.

57. HOFMANN, A. F., AND E. H. MOSBACH. Identification of allodeoxycholic acid as the major component of gallstones induced in the rabbit by 5α-cholestan-3β-ol. *J. Biol. Chem.* 239: 2813–2821, 1964.

58. HOLSTI, P. Cirrhosis of the liver induced in rabbits by gastric instillation of 3-monohydroxycholanic acid. *Nature* 186: 250, 1960.

59. HOLT, P. R. Competitive inhibition of intestinal bile salt absorption in the rat. *Am. J. Physiol.* 210: 635–639, 1966.

60. HUNT, R. D., G. A. LEVEILLE, AND H. E. SAUBERLICH. Dietary bile acids and lipid metabolism III. Effects of lithocholic acid in mammalian species. *Proc. Soc. Exptl. Biol. Med.* 115: 277–280, 1964.

61. HUTTON, H. R. B., AND G. S. BOYD. The metabolism of cholest-5-en-3β,7α-diol by rat-liver cell fractions. *Biochim. Biophys. Acta* 116: 336–361, 1966.

62. HUTTON, H. R. B., AND G. S. BOYD. The metabolism of cholest-4-en-3-one-7α-ol by rat-liver cell fractions. *Biochim. Biophys. Acta* 116: 362–378, 1966.

63. JOHANSSON, G. On the metabolism of lithocholic acid in chicken and rabbit. *Acta Chem. Scand.* 20: 240–244, 1966.

64. KALLNER, A. The transformation of deoxycholic acid into allodeoxycholic acid in the rat. *Acta Chem. Scand.* 21: 87–92, 1967.

65. KALLNER, A. On the biosynthesis and metabolism of allodeoxycholic acid in the rat. *Acta Chem. Scand.* 21: 315–321, 1967.

66. KALLNER, A. The metabolism of allocholic, allochenodeoxycholic, and allolithocholic acids in the rat. *Arkiv Kemi* 26: 567–576, 1967.

67. KALLNER, A. On the reduction of 3-keto bile acids *in vitro. Arkiv Kemi* 26: 533–565, 1967.

68. KARAVOLAS, H. J., W. H. ELLIOTT, S. L. HSIA, E. A. DOISY, JR., J. T. MATSCHINER, S. A. THAYER, AND E. A. DOISY. Bile acids. XXII. Allocholic acid, a metabolite of 5α-cholestan-3β-ol in the rat. *J. Biol. Chem.* 240: 1568–1572, 1965.

69. KRITCHEVSKY, D. Influence of thyroid hormones and related compounds on cholesterol biosynthesis and degradation: a review. *Metab. Clin. Exptl.* 9: 984–994, 1960.

70. KRITCHEVSKY, D., E. STAPLE, J. L. RABINOWITZ, AND M. W. WHITEHOUSE. Differences in cholesterol oxidation and biosynthesis in liver of male and female rats. *Am. J. Physiol.* 200: 519–526, 1961.

71. LACK, L., AND I. M. WEINER. Intestinal bile salt transport: structure-activity relationships and other properties. *Am. J. Physiol.* 210: 1142–1152, 1966.

72. LEE, M. J., D. V. PARKE, AND M. W. WHITEHOUSE. Regulation of cholesterol catabolism by bile salts and glycyrrhetic acid *in vivo. Proc. Soc. Exptl. Biol. Med.* 120: 6–8, 1965.

73. LEE, M. J., AND M. W. WHITEHOUSE. Inhibition of electron transport and coupled phosphorylation in liver mitochondria by cholanic acids and their conjugates. *Biochim. Biophys. Acta* 100: 317–328, 1965.

74. LINDSTEDT, S. The turnover of cholic acid in man. *Acta Physiol. Scand.* 40: 1–9, 1957.

75. LINDSTEDT, S., J. AVIGAN, DeW. S. GOODMAN, J. SJÖVALL, AND D. STEINBERG. The effect of dietary fat on the turn-

over of cholic acid and on the composition of the biliary bile acids in man. *J. Clin. Invest.* 44: 1754–1765, 1965.

76. MASUI, T., R. HERMAN, AND E. STAPLE. The oxidation of 5β-cholestane-3α,7α,12α,26-tetraol to 5β-cholestane-3α,7α,12α-triol-26-oic acid *via* 5β-cholestane-3α,7α,12α-triol-26-al by rat liver. *Biochim. Biophys. Acta* 117: 266–268, 1966.

77. MASUI, T., AND E. STAPLE. The formation of bile acids from cholesterol. The conversion of 5β-cholestane-3α,7α,12α-triol-26-oic acid to cholic acid *via* 5β-cholestane-3α,7α,12α,24-tetraol-26-oic acid I by rat liver. *J. Biol. Chem.* 241: 3889–3893, 1966.

78. MENDELSOHN, D., L. MENDELSOHN, AND E. STAPLE. The catabolism *in vitro* of cholesterol: formation of the 7-epimeric hydroxycholesterols from cholesterol in rat liver. *Biochim. Biophys. Acta* 97: 379–381, 1965.

79. MENDELSOHN, D., L. MENDELSOHN, AND E. STAPLE. The *in vitro* catabolism of cholesterol: formation of 5β-cholestane-3α,7α-diol and 5β-cholestane-3α,12α-diol from cholesterol in rat liver. *Biochemistry* 4: 441–444, 1965.

80. MENDELSOHN, D., L. MENDELSOHN, AND E. STAPLE. The *in vitro* catabolism of cholesterol: a comparison of the formation of cholest-4-en-7α-ol-3-one and 5β-cho-lestan-7α-ol-3-one from cholesterol in rat liver. *Biochemistry* 5: 1286–1290, 1966.

81. MENDELSOHN, D., AND E. STAPLE. The *in vitro* catabolism of cholesterol: formation of 3α,7α,12α-trihydroxycoprostane from cholesterol in rat liver. *Biochemistry* 2: 577–579, 1963.

82. MIDTVEDT, T., AND A. NORMAN. Bile acid transformations by microbial strains belonging to genera found in intestinal contents. *Acta Pathol. Microbiol. Scand.* 71: 629–638, 1967.

83. MIETTINEN, T. A., E. H. AHRENS, JR., AND S. M. GRUNDY. Quantitative isolation and gas-liquid chromatographic analysis of total dietary and fecal neutral steroids. *J. Lipid Res.* 6: 411–424, 1965.

84. MITROPOULOS, K. A., AND N. B. MYANT. The metabolism of cholesterol in the presence of liver mitochondria from from normal and thyroxine-treated rats. *Biochem. J.* 94: 594–603, 1965.

85. MITROPOULOS, K. A., AND N. B. MYANT. Evidence that the oxidation of the side chain of cholesterol by liver mitochondria is stereospecific and that the immediate product of cleavage is propionate. *Biochem. J.* 97: 26–28c, 1965.

86. MITROPOULOS, K. A., AND N. B. MYANT. The formation of naturally occurring bile acids from cholesterol by rat-liver mitochondria *in vitro*. *Biochem. J.* 99: 51P, 1966.

87. MITROPOULOS, K. A., AND N. B. MYANT. Conversion of 3β-hydroxycholenoic acid into bile acid *in vivo* and *in vitro*. *Biochem. J.* 101: 38P, 1966.

88. MITTON, J. R., AND G. S. BOYD. The hydroxylation of cholesterol by liver microsomes. *Biochem. J.* 96: 60P, 1965.

89. MYANT, N. B., AND H. A. EDER. The effect of biliary drainage upon the synthesis of cholesterol in the liver. *J. Lipid Res.* 2: 363–368, 1961.

90. NORMAN, A. Action of intestinal microorganisms on bile acids. *Proc. Soc. Exptl. Biol. Med.* In press 1968.

91. NORMAN, A., AND R. H. PALMER. Metabolites of lithocholic acid-24-C14 in human bile and feces. *J. Lab. Clin. Med.* 63: 986–1001, 1964.

92. NORMAN, A., AND M. S. SHORB. *In vitro* formation of deoxycholic and lithocholic acid by human intestinal microorganisms. *Proc. Soc. Exptl. Biol. Med.* 110: 552–555, 1962.

93. OGILVIE, J. W., AND B. H. KAPLAN. The inhibition of sterol biosynthesis in rat liver homogenates by bile. *J. Biol. Chem.* 241: 4722–4730, 1966.

94. OKUDA, K., AND H. DANIELSSON. Synthesis and metabolism of 5β-cholestane-3α,7α,12α-triol-26-al. *Acta Chem. Scand.* 19: 2160–2165, 1966.

95. OLEINICK, N. L., AND S. B. KORITZ. The activation of the Δ5-3-keto steroid isomerase in rat adrenal small particles by diphosphopyridine nucleotides. *Biochemistry* 5: 715–724, 1966.

96. PALMER, R. H., P. B. GLICKMAN, AND A. KAPPAS. Pyrogenic and inflammatory properties of certain bile acids in man. *J. Clin. Invest.* 41: 1573–1577, 1962.

97. PALMER, R. H., AND Z. HRUBAN. Production of bile duct hyperplasia and gallstones by lithocholic acid. *J. Clin. Invest.* 45: 1255–1267, 1966.

98. PERIC-GOLIA, L., AND R. S. JONES. Ornithocholanic acids—abnormal conjugates of bile acids. *Proc. Soc. Exptl. Biol. Med.* 110: 327–331, 1962.

99. PERIC-GOLIA, L., AND R. S. JONES. Ornithocholanic acids and cholelithiasis in man. *Science* 142: 245–246, 1963.

100. PORTMAN, O. W., AND P. MURPHY. Excretion of bile acids and β-hydroxysterols by rats. *Arch. Biochem. Biophys.* 76: 367–376, 1958.

101. RAGGATT, P. R., P. D. G. DEAN, AND M. W. WHITEHOUSE. Some metabolic properties of cholesteryl sulphate and cholest-4-en-3-one. *Biochem. J.* 96: 26P, 1965.

102. ROSENFELD, R. S., AND L. HELLMAN. Excretion of steroid acids in man. *Arch. Biochem. Biophys.* 97: 406–410, 1962.

103. SCHERSTÉN, T. Conjugation of cholic acid in human liver homogenates. *Biochim. Biophys. Acta* 141: 144–163, 1967.

104. SPRITZ, N., E. H. AHRENS, JR., AND S. M. GRUNDY. Sterol balance in man as plasma cholesterol concentrations are altered by exchanges of dietary fats. *J. Clin. Invest.* 44: 1482–1493, 1965.

105. STAPLE, E., AND J. L. RABINOWITZ. Formation of trihydroxycoprostanic acid from cholesterol in man. *Biochim. Biophys. Acta* 59: 735–736, 1962.

106. STOLK, A. Induction of hepatic cirrhosis in *Iguana iguana* by 3-monohydroxycholanic acid treatment. *Experientia* 16: 507–508, 1960.

107. STRAND, O. Influence of propylthiouracil and D- and L-triiodothyronine on excretion of bile acids in bile fistula rats. *Proc. Soc. Exptl. Biol. Med.* 109: 668–672, 1962.

108. STRAND, O. Effects of D- and L-triiodothyronine and of propylthiouracil on the production of bile acids in the rat. *J. Lipid Res.* 4: 305–311, 1963.

109. SULD, H. M., E. STAPLE, AND S. GURIN. Mechanism of formation of bile acids from cholesterol: oxidation of 5β-cholestane-3α,7α,12α-triol and formation of propionic

acid from the side chain by rat liver mitochondria. *J. Biol. Chem.* 237: 338–344, 1962.

110. THOMAS, P. J., S. L. HSIA, J. T. MATSCHINER, E. A. DOISY, JR., W. H. ELLIOTT, S. A. THAYER, AND E. A. DOISY. Bile acids XIX. Metabolism of lithocholic acid-24-^{14}C in the rat. *J. Biol. Chem.* 239: 102–105, 1964.

111. YAMASAKI, K., F. NODA, AND K. SHIMIZU. Metabolic studies of bile acids. XX. 3β-Hydroxysterol dehydrogenase in rat liver. *J. Biochem., Tokyo* 46: 739–755, 1959.

112. ZIBOH, V. A., S. L. HSIA, J. T. MATSCHINER, E. A. DOISY, JR., W. H. ELLIOTT, S. A. THAYER, AND E. A. DOISY. Bile acids, XVIII. Further studies on the metabolism of chenodeoxycholic acid-24-^{14}C in surgically jaundiced mice. *J. Biol. Chem.* 238: 3588–3590, 1963.

CHAPTER 113

Water and electrolytes in bile

HENRY O. WHEELER | *Columbia University College of Physicians and Surgeons, New York City*

CHAPTER CONTENTS

THE BILIARY EXCRETION of water and electrolytes involves a number of complex and probably sequential operations within the liver cells and in the epithelium of the biliary tract. Much of the experimental data on electrolyte excretion is empirical, and comparison of the results of different investigations is difficult because of the variety of species and experimental techniques employed. It is possible, nevertheless, to present a general picture of the nature of some of the processes responsible for bile formation and to point the way toward investigations of the intimate electrochemical and mechanical steps involved in the initiation and modification of bile water and electrolyte excretion.

For a detailed review of earlier work in this field the reader is referred to Sobotka's classic monograph (118). A more recent excellent review is that of Bizard & Vanlerenberghe (16). For discussion of many areas of recent investigation the proceedings of the 1963 NATO Symposium (128) should be consulted.

STRUCTURE OF THE BILIARY SYSTEM

A detailed anatomical description of the biliary tract is not within the scope of this article. Nevertheless it is germane to consider the general arrangement of the structures through which water and electrolytes must move to gain access to the biliary tract.

The bile canalicular system is an elaborate network of minute channels whose relationship to the hepatic parenchymal cell laminae has been evaluated and presented in detail by Elias (43, 44). In essence, mammalian parenchymal cells appear to be arranged in a system of anastomosing cribriform plates. The bile canaliculi lie within these plates, situated in grooves between adjacent liver cells, and connected in such a way that each liver cell is ringed by canaliculi as shown diagrammatically in Figure 1. Thus the canalicular network could be compared to a labyrinth constructed from sheets of chicken-wire mesh. At no point do the canaliculi come in contact with the surfaces of the cells that face the sinusoids.

The canaliculi have no obvious membranous walls of their own but consist, rather, of a separation between the membranes of adjoining liver cells (103, 104, 122). On each side of this separation, however,

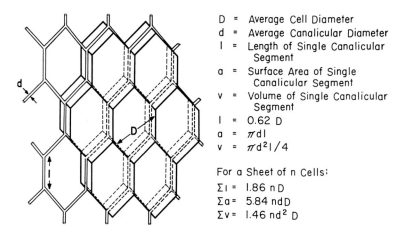

FIG. 1. Schematic representation of sheet of liver cells and canalicular network. Calculation of total canalicular length is based on a regular hexagonal arrangement and is therefore the shortest possible length for closely packed cells of given volume and thickness. Diameter D is the square root of the area of a single cell face and is also the average diameter one would obtain on random sections perpendicular to the sheet of cells.

D = Average Cell Diameter
d = Average Canalicular Diameter
l = Length of Single Canalicular Segment
a = Surface Area of Single Canalicular Segment
v = Volume of Single Canalicular Segment

$l = 0.62 D$
$a = \pi d l$
$v = \pi d^2 l / 4$

For a Sheet of n Cells:
$\Sigma l = 1.86 n D$
$\Sigma a = 5.84 n d D$
$\Sigma v = 1.46 n d^2 D$

the membranes are tightly joined, and this obviates leakage of luminal contents; the liver cell cytoplasm immediately surrounding the canaliculi appears to be unusually dense. Thus the canalicular system, which is but a specialized arrangement of parenchymal cell membranes, appears to have a mechanical integrity of its own, as has been shown by the observation that fragments of canalicular network can be obtained intact from teased or crushed pieces of liver (43). The existence of occasional direct communications between the bile canaliculi and the perisinusoidal space (space of Disse) suggested by some authors (5, 103, 111) has not been confirmed in the normal mammalian liver by other observers (56, 86, 122). It seems almost certain, therefore, that movement of most if not all solute and water from blood to canalicular bile must occur through the liver cells and, specifically, must traverse the canalicular membrane.

It is possible to carry out a rough calculation of the surface area of the canalicular system—the area available for movement of solute and solvent into the canalicular bile. If the average diameter of hepatic parenchymal cells is approximately 30 μ (94), the volume of an individual cell would be about 27,000 μ^3 (2.7 $\times$ 10^{-8} cm^3). One gram of liver cells would therefore contain approximately 4 $\times$ 10^7 cells, and if these were arranged as a single sheet of hexagons with canaliculi surrounding each cell the total canalicular length within this 1-g sheet would be approximately 2 $\times$ 10^5 cm (see Fig. 1 for details of calculation). Assuming an average canalicular diameter of 1 μ (111, 112), the total surface area of the canaliculi in a 1-g sheet of liver cells would be about 70 cm^2 (or 7,000 cm^2/100 g of liver cells). This figure might represent an overestimation because it fails to take

into account the fact that some canalicular segments are shared by three or more cells where sheets of liver cells adjoin, because canaliculi are absent from the edges of perforations in the sheet, and also because some canaliculi appear to have a diameter of less than 1 μ in many electron micrographs. However, the actual surface available for transport is almost certainly much greater than the value obtained by this calculation, because of the elaborate system of microvilli which project into the canalicular lumen (5, 86, 103, 104, 111, 112, 122). The calculated volume of bile in the same canaliculi would be only about 2 $\times$ 10^{-3} cm^3 per g of liver cells (0.2 cm^3/100 g of liver cells), and the actual volume may be considerably smaller because of the space occupied by microvilli projecting into the lumen.

Although the distribution of hydrostatic pressures and flows within the canalicular network must be complex and probably erratic, it may not be an unreasonable approximation to regard the canalicular system as a single blind compartment with a very large ratio of surface area to volume, whose only access to the exterior is by way of the bile ductules.

The bile ductules have a structural complexity that suggests that their function may not be limited simply to conducting bile toward the duodenum (122). Specifically, the interdigitation of the lateral walls of ductular cells and the appearance of lateral lacunae between cells (123) are reminiscent of the specialized structural arrangements that appear to be associated with reabsorptive activity in the gallbladder (39, 73). Moreover, the elaborate blood supply of the small bile ducts within the portal tracts suggests that these ducts may play an active role in modification of bile by secretion or absorption (4, 55, 130).

TABLE 1. *Bile Electrolyte Composition**

Species	Source	Na$^+$	K$^+$	Ca^{++}	Mg^{++}	Cl$^-$	HCO$_3^-$	SO$_4^-$	HPO$_4^-$	Bile Salt	Refs
Man	Chronic CD fistula	148–152	4.0–4.4	2.7–3.2		114–117	25–32			<4	46
Man	T-tube	146–165	2.7 4.9	2.5–4.8	1.4–3.0	88–115	27–55			3–45	132
Man	T-tube			2.0–4.7							21
Man	Gallbladder	100†–236	6.3–17.6	8.0–30.0		18–84				40–160	77
Dog	CD fistula	Total base 174–192		3.1–9.9		55–107	22–65			16–66	98
Dog	CD fistula	141–203	4.6–8.8	5.5–13.8	2.2–5.5	31–104	14–61		0–trace	17–125	100
Dog	CD fistula	221±117	6.1±3.5			66±30					31
Dog	CD‡ catheter	160–230	4.5–11.9			38–95	11–57			61–187	95, 141
Dog	Gallbladder	Total base 284–305		23–31		1.1–10.3	0.9			189–334	98
Rabbit	CD fistula	142–157	5.2–6.7	2.7–6.7	0.3–0.7	77–89	44–49	4.0–4.7	1.4–1.7		125
Rabbit	CD fistula	144	3.6			82	48				116
Cat	CD fistula	138	5.1			91	31				116
Sheep	CD fistula§	154–179	6.7–7.6			83–122					58
Sheep	Gallbladder	197	8.0			74					58

* All concentrations (including bile salt) expressed in milliequivalents per liter.

† A sodium concentration of 100 mEq/liter is inconsistent with normal tonicity. This value, obtained in a single bile specimen, is the only reported biliary sodium concentration significantly lower than serum sodium.

‡ Cholecystectomy and Thomas duodenal cannula (131) with intravenous sodium taurocholate infusion.

§ Common duct ligated distal to cystic duct (CD) and bile diverted through gallbladder to exterior.

BILIARY ELECTROLYTE COMPOSITION

Electrolyte Concentrations

The reported electrolyte composition of bile varies widely among different species and is also quite variable in a given species at different times or under different conditions of collection. Some of the representative data are shown in Table 1. In general, despite the marked variability it can be seen that the distribution of cations in bile is roughly similar to that in plasma in that the dominant cation is always sodium. The biliary distribution of anions, on the other hand, is often very different from the anion distribution in plasma. Chloride concentrations ranging from 30 to 120 mEq per liter and bicarbonate concentrations from 11 to 65 mEq per liter have been reported in hepatic bile, and much lower values for both anions may be found in highly concentrated specimens of gallbladder bile. In all mammalian species the naturally occurring bile acids are conjugated with either glycine or taurine and hence have pK values appreciably lower than the lowest physiological pH. Consequently these compounds appear in the bile as monovalent anions and usually constitute an appreciable if not the dominant fraction of the anions, making up most of the deficit between inorganic cations and anions. Pigments, lipids, and other compounds need not be discussed in detail in this section since they do not constitute an appreciable fraction of undissociated ions or even a very great fraction of the total osmotically active solute in bile. It must be emphasized, nevertheless, that certain lipid constituents (notably lecithin and cholesterol) form mixed micelles with the bile salts and may have a profound influence on the size, structure, and stability of these micellar aggregates. Consequently their influence on the electrochemical and osmotic properties of bile may be of considerable importance (62, 85).

Consistent with the wide variation in bicarbonate concentration, the pH of bile may vary from 5.9 to 7.8 (58, 95, 100, 132, 141) in specimens collected anaerobically and analyzed promptly to avoid loss of carbon dioxide. Although direct measurements of Pco$_2$ have not been reported, data available on bicarbonate concentration and pH appear, in general, to support the view that biliary Pco$_2$ is roughly comparable to plasma Pco$_2$. Since the concentration of buffers other than the bicarbonate-carbonic acid system is low, it is evident that measurements of biliary pH are meaningful only if care is taken to avoid loss of carbon dioxide.

Osmolality

Numerous observers have reported (28, 118, 141) that both hepatic and gallbladder bile are isotonic when compared with plasma in many species. Most of these measurements have been based on freezing-point determinations. Gilman & Cowgill (51) used a vapor-pressure method and reported that the osmolality of canine bile was identical with that of plasma as the latter was varied by infusion of hypotonic or hypertonic solutions. Recently, however, it has been found that the osmolality of canine bile may occasionally deviate from that of plasma, as shown in Figure 2 (95). This deviation is rarely more than 15% of total plasma osmolality and is least evident at the lower rates of bile flow which would be encountered in most random collections. During choleresis produced by infusion of sodium taurocholate, bile osmolality tends to be lower than that of plasma, whereas during secretin choleresis (at any rate of taurocholate infusion) the osmolality tends to be higher. The possible significance of these deviations is discussed in later sections. The values shown in Figure 2 were obtained by freezing-point determination, but comparable deviations in osmolality have also been observed by the vapor-pressure method (H. O. Wheeler, unpublished observations).

*Relationship Between Bile Salt Concentration
and Electrolyte Composition*

It will be noted in Table 1 that the sum of all ions including bile salts is often much higher than the

total ionic concentration of plasma, despite the fact that bile is a virtually isotonic solution. The concentration of sodium alone may be as high as 330 mEq per liter in occasional specimens of isotonic gallbladder bile (40), and values as high as 230 mEq per liter have been observed in canine hepatic bile. The apparent discrepancy between ionic concentration and osmotic activity is attributable to the fact that the conjugated bile salt anions form large aggregates or micelles whose osmotic activity is very low (42). Indeed, the total osmotic activity of bile has been found, empirically, to be accounted for by ignoring the bile acids altogether and taking the sum of the major inorganic ion concentrations (i.e., Na + K + Cl + HCO_3). This relationship was pointed out in 1932 by Ravdin et al. (98), and the probable explanation was first stated by Rheinhold & Wilson (100).

At this point it might be useful to consider the consequences of the micellar behavior and high molecular weight of bile salts on the overall electrolyte composition and "total solid" content of bile. In the illustrative (and deliberately oversimplified) schema shown in Figure 3, two isotonic solutions, one of sodium taurocholate and one of sodium chloride, are mixed in varying proportions. Assuming the bile salt anions have no osmotic activity (owing to their aggregated state), but that all other ions are fully dissociated and exhibit "ideal" osmotic behavior, the consequences of this admixture are shown below each bar graph.

Although the osmolality of all the four solutions in Figure 3 is the same, it is evident that wide variations in sodium concentration may occur and that there is an approximately linear relationship between sodium concentration and bile salt concentration. Such a relationship is apparent in actual observations on bile. For example, in the data of Rheinhold and Wilson (sixth entry in Table 1), the highest and lowest sodium concentrations (203 and 141 mEq/liter, respectively) correspond to the highest and lowest bile salt concentrations (125 and 17 mEq/liter, respectively). In more recent studies, in the dog, a linear relationship between the concentration of sodium plus potassium and the bile salt concentration was noted, with the regression equation: $[BS^-] = 2.03 [Na^+ + K^-] - 302$, and a correlation coefficient of 0.97 (141).

In Figure 3 the only cation considered was sodium, because this is always the dominant cation in bile. The concentrations of other cations appear, in fact, to vary in the same direction as the sodium concen-

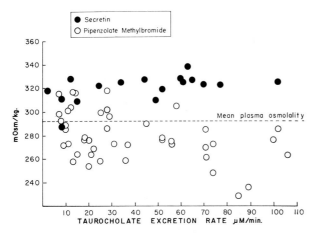

FIG. 2. Osmolality of canine hepatic bile. Multiple samples from four dogs obtained at different rates of bile salt secretion (produced by varying rates of intravenous sodium taurocholate infusion). Highest bile flows correspond to highest rates of taurocholate secretion. During cholinergic blockade (pipenzolate methylbromide) bile is frequently hypotonic with respect to plasma at the higher flows, whereas it tends to be hypertonic during secretin choleresis. Measurements made by freezing-point depression. [From Preissig et al. (95).]

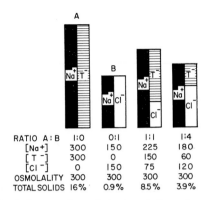

RATIO A:B	1:0	0:1	1:1	1:4
[Na+]	300	150	225	180
[T−]	300	0	150	60
[Cl−]	0	150	75	120
OSMOLALITY	300	300	300	300
TOTAL SOLIDS	16%	0.9%	8.5%	3.9%

FIG. 3. Effect of admixture of an isotonic solution of a micellar bile salt (e.g., Na taurocholate, mol wt 540) with an isotonic solution of simple electrolyte (e.g., NaCl, mol wt 58) on ionic composition, osmolality, and percentage of total solids. It is assumed that Na^+ and $Cl^−$ exhibit ideal osmotic behavior, whereas taurocholate ions are osmotically inactive owing to aggregation. Note that sodium concentration varies linearly with taurocholate concentration, and the percentage of total solids is roughly proportional to taurocholate concentration and inversely related to chloride concentration. Numbers are intended for illustration only and would correspond only roughly to values in actual nonideal solutions.

trations. Thus, in the second, sixth, and eighth entries in Table 1, the highest potassium concentrations were observed in the same specimens of hepatic bile that had the highest sodium concentrations. The peculiarly high concentrations of calcium observed in some specimens of gallbladder bile might at first be thought to reflect concentration of this species due to active transport, reabsorption of water, or possibly chelation by biliary constituents. However, it should be remembered that calcium is a divalent cation and that the electronegativity of the gallbladder lumen (40) would lead to a much higher concentration of divalent than monovalent cations in a state of purely passive electrochemical equilibrium. Pending a more quantitative appraisal of the relation between cation activity gradients and electrical potential differences, it appears reasonable to say that the cation distribution and the unusually high total cation concentrations sometimes seen in bile are not necessarily inconsistent with a state of passive equilibrium between bile and extracellular fluid. Dietschy & Moore's investigation (40) leading to the conclusion that potassium is passively distributed across the gallbladder wall should point the way to similar investigations of other cations and other parts of the biliary tract.

It is reasonable to question the accuracy of the assumption (implicit in Fig. 3) that bile acids are totally inactive osmotically, and other ions totally dissociated. One would expect that cations would be inactivated to some extent by attraction, as "gegen ions" (62, 82), to the large polyanionic micelles and that bile acids, on the other hand, would not be completely inactivated by aggregation. Diamond's measurements (37), using a sodium-sensitive glass electrode in solutions of sodium deoxycholate, showed that the sodium ion activity coefficient was only 0.35–0.4 in solutions of 150–300 mM concentration, identical with the osmotic coefficient for the whole bile salt. To the extent that this observation applies to solutions of sodium taurocholate, the theoretical osmotic activity of sodium assumed in the legend of Figure 3 would indeed be much too high (though the end result would be the same since the osmotic coefficient of whole bile salt, also approximately 0.4, suggests an osmotic activity of bile salt anions higher than that assumed in the legend). More recent measurements by Moore & Dietschy (83) have indicated that the sodium ion activity coefficient in concentrated whole gallbladder bile from three species (man, dog, rabbit) ranges from 0.62 to 0.70, and similar values were obtained in pure sodium bile salt solutions including sodium deoxycholate. These values were appreciably higher than the osmotic coefficients and were significantly but not greatly lower than sodium ion activity coefficients in inorganic salt solutions of comparable concentration. This would come closer to the view, implied in the legend of Figure 3, that the bile salt anions per se have very little osmotic activity. The reason for the discrepancy between these two sets of data regarding sodium activity is not clear. Even though the osmotic phenomena can be rationalized either way, the problem is worthy of further study since the interpretation of biliary transport phenomena must ultimately depend on accurate information about the electrochemical activity of the inorganic ions in bile. An interesting further finding by Moore & Dietschy (83) was that the potassium ion activity coefficients in concentrated potassium bile salt solutions were much lower than the comparable values for sodium, which suggests that potassium is more closely bound to bile salt micelles. This phenomenon contributes to their explanation for the relatively high concentrations of potassium in gallbladder bile (40) mentioned earlier.

Total Solids

In the theoretical situation depicted in Figure 3, in which it was assumed that dissolved solutes have a negligible effect on total volume of solution, it was calculated that the total solid content of an isotonic solution of sodium taurocholate would be approximately 16 g per 100 ml, whereas that of an isotonic solution of sodium chloride would be only 0.9 g per 100 ml. Mixtures of the two solutions would have total solid concentrations between these extremes, but in any case the concentration of bile salt would be the major determinant. In actual bile specimens in which total solid content and bile acid concentration are both measured, this relationship is substantiated. In the sixth entry in Table 1, for example, the bile with the highest cholate concentration, 125 mEq per liter, had a total solid content of 12.2 g per 100 ml and the bile with the lowest cholate concentration, 17 mEq per liter, had a total solid content of only 2.6 per 100 ml. Bile specimens with cholate concentrations in the range of 70 to 90 mEq per liter had total solids ranging from 6 to 8 g per 100 ml. In the study of Thureborn (132), there was a very close correlation between the concentration of bile salts and the percentage of total solids. In most published reports it is not possible to make a direct comparison between total solids and bile salt concentration. Other constituents of bile will, of course, contribute to the measurement of total solids. The phospholipids are the most abundant "heavy" constituents other than bile salts; and the dominant phospholipid, lecithin, accounts for about 20% of the total solids of gallbladder bile (64, 84). In any case, the concentration and excretion rate of phospholipids appear to parallel the concentration of the bile salts in specimens of human hepatic bile (132), in rat bile at various rates of taurocholate administration (I. Sperber, personal communication), and in the bile of isolated perfused rat livers (72). Since measurements of biliary total solid concentration and excretion rate are traditional experimental procedures, it is worth reemphasizing that these measurements are quite well correlated with bile salt concentration and bile salt excretion rate. (For a detailed breakdown of the distribution of total solids in human bile see reference 132.)

At this point, for the sake of completeness, it is appropriate to mention the use of the term "hydrocholeresis." By tradition, this term is usually meant to imply an increase in biliary water output without an increase in output of total solids. Strictly speaking, if bile is isotonic, it can be deduced from Figure 3 that such a state could arise only if there were an increase in the output of water and inorganic electrolytes together with a slight diminution in the output of bile salts (or other large molecules) suffi-

cient to offset the solid content of the inorganic electrolyte (e.g., a major increment in the amount of solution B and a minor decrement in the amount of solution A). As a practical matter, however, a relatively large increment in the output of an isotonic electrolyte solution would have an effect on total solid output often too small to be detected and therefore would be designated a "hydrocholeresis." Unfortunately, the term has often been used more loosely to designate a state in which an increase in bile flow is accompanied by a reduction in total solid concentration, or even a reduction in viscosity. Consequently, compounds such as sodium dehydrocholate (Decholin) and numerous other organic acids (1, 54) could be considered "hydrocholeretic" even though their mechanism of action is probably basically similar to that of the natural bile salts (which are not hydrocholeretics but are sometimes called "eucholeretics") and dissimilar from the action of agents such as secretin (whose effect is as close as possible to that implied by the term hydrocholeresis). These matters have been discussed by Sperber in more detail (120). To avoid confusion the terms "hydrocholeresis," "hydrocholeretic," "eucholeretic," and others are therefore avoided in the remainder of this chapter.

Protein Content

Protein concentrations in normal bile are so low that their possible importance as nondiffusible charged particles can probably be assumed to be negligible. Typical concentrations of protein range from 6 to 40 mg per 100 ml in canine bile and 30 to 300 mg per 100 ml in human bile (57, 102, 107), of which serum albumin is usually the major component. Appreciable concentrations of nonserum ("biliary") proteins may also be detectable by electrophoresis (57, 71), although the existence of a separate class of proteins has been doubted by other investigators (106). Thus bile is comparable to cerebrospinal fluid and urine in total protein content, and it can be assumed that the biliary tract is comparatively impermeable throughout its length to substances of high molecular weight.

As in the case of lipid constituents one cannot dismiss the biliary proteins without mentioning that, however low their absolute concentration, they may (138, 139) or may not (85) have an important role in the structure of macromolecular micellar aggregates found in highly concentrated bile. Thus proteins might possibly be a significant determinant of the physical chemical state of the polyanionic aggregates of mixed bile salt and lipids and their associated cations.

In summary, bile is a highly colored fluid which is, in most species, quite viscous and has a high concentration of total solids. It contains lipid constituents at concentrations clearly much greater than their natural solubility in water. It is, nevertheless, a true solution, the major osmotic constituents of which are inorganic electrolytes. It is not a suspension or emulsion. The stability of this solution results from the incorporation of the lipids into mixed micelles which, owing to their bile acid content, are polyanions. The solution is roughly isotonic with respect to plasma. Its anionic composition is quite variable, but the distribution of cations is similar to that in plasma.

PHYSIOLOGY OF BILE FORMATION

Canalicular Secretion

At present very little can be said with certainty about the intimate mechanisms responsible for bile formation. Nevertheless, it is probably reasonable to begin with tentative and fairly general working hypotheses as a framework for discussion of actual experimental data. The available data are consistent with the theoretical picture presented here, but may be subject to alternative explanations at some future time.

There are no structures in the liver and biliary tract that would suggest an efficient arrangement for hydrostatic filtration of water and solute directly from blood to bile (analogous to renal glomerular filtration). Moreover, the demonstration by Brauer and colleagues (19) that the perfused rat liver can secrete bile against hydrostatic pressures greater than the pressure of the perfusing blood makes it evident that simple hydrostatic filtration cannot be implicated as a major mechanism. In other words, bile formation must depend on intrahepatic chemical energy sources rather than mechanical energy supplied by the heart. That a substantial amount of mechanical energy is (or at least can be) generated in the process is indicated by the fact that bile can be secreted against pressures of the order of 20 cm H_2O (the so-called bile secretion pressure or limiting bile pressure) (8–10, 18, 19, 101), and indeed the data of Brauer et al. (19) and of Barber-Riley (8, 10) suggest that much greater pressures might be possible were

it not for back-leakage of bile out of the system at the level of the maximum secretory pressure.

Three general mechanisms might be considered accountable for these phenomena. First, it is possible that active transport of water occurs per se from the liver cells into the lumen of the biliary tract and that the movement of various solutes follows by passive diffusion, solvent drag, or independent active transport (or a combination of these). Second, the solute and solvent constituents of the bile may be "assembled" in secretory vacuoles or comparable intracellular structures whose contents are then physically extruded into the canalicular lumen. Third, active transport of certain solutes from liver cell to canalicular lumen may create osmotic gradients leading to passive movement of water and other solutes into the lumen. It is not possible to distinguish among these possibilities on the basis of available data, nor are the three postulated mechanisms necessarily mutually exclusive.

The first mechanism, active water transport, seems the least likely, since the existence of this type of transport has never been conclusively demonstrated in any biological system. The uniformity of the chemical potential of water in all mammalian tissues except the renal medulla (80) indicates that cell membranes are highly permeable to water (in contrast to most solute species), so that an active water pump would probably have to keep pace with a high rate of osmotic back-leakage of water to maintain modest net forward movement of solute and water. Moreover, as has been noted in previous discussions of the water pump hypothesis (12), the ratio of water molecules to solute particles in an isotonic solution (ca. 300 milliosmols/kg) is approximately 180:1 so that the capacity of an active water transport carrier would have to be at least 180 times as great as that of an active solute carrier in order to move the same quantity of solution.

The second mechanism, involving a "prepackaging" of bile in vacuoles or other structures within the cell, must be regarded as a reasonable possibility that invites careful morphological investigation of the pericanalicular region of liver cells in various states of secretory function. The Golgi complex, which is situated near the bile canaliculi, has been suggested as a potential site of secretory activity (104). Steiner & Carruthers (122), although less impressed with the intimacy of the association between the Golgi apparatus and the canaliculi, described numerous vacuolar structures in the liver cell cytoplasm around the canaliculi in which the initial stages of bile formation might occur. If such a mechanism could be demonstrated this would move the site of the primary events in bile formation one step proximal to the bile canaliculi, but would still require a chemical mechanism for the generation of a fluid whose composition is very different from that of intracellular fluid.

The third mechanism, which presumes that active solute transport is the primary event in bile formation, was first proposed and discussed by Sperber (119–121). The hypothesis is particularly attractive because it is easy to imagine that the very large surface area of the bile canaliculi (see preceding section) would facilitate passive osmosis and diffusion in response to active transfer of solute into the canalicular lumen. Theoretical predictions of the behavior of such a system should be possible and might be based, for example, on an analysis similar to that employed by Patlak and co-workers (91) for the description of a membrane array driven by active transport of a single solute. Such an analysis would not be particularly useful at present because of lack of knowledge of solute and solvent permeability of the bile canaliculi and of the deviations in behavior of individual solutes from simple passive transport. However, it is worth considering, in qualitative terms, the very simple model illustrated in Figure 4. It is assumed that only two solutes, a and b, are present, that solute a is actively transported from left to right across the membrane, that solute b moves passively, and that the solution on the right is composed entirely of material that has crossed the membrane previously. Thus, the concentrations on the right are determined by the relative net fluxes of solute and solvent from left to right, as shown in the figure. Two cases can be considered, one in which the membrane is completely impermeable to solute b, and the other in which it is partially permeable to solute b. The following definitions apply to both cases:

J_a, J_b, J_w = net fluxes left to right of solute a, solute b, and water, respectively;

C_{al}, C_{bl} = concentrations, on left side, of solutes a and b, respectively;

C_{ar}, C_{br} = concentrations, on right side, of solutes a and b, respectively;

F_{osm} = osmotic force across membrane;

σ_a, σ_b = reflection coefficients for solute a and b, respectively.

Case 1, membrane impermeable to solute b:

$$J_b = 0,\ C_{br} = 0,\ \sigma_b = 1$$
$$F_{osm} = RT\ (\sigma_a C_{ar} - \sigma_a C_{al} - C_{bl})$$
$$= RT\ (\sigma_a J_a/J_w - \sigma_a C_{al} - C_{bl})$$

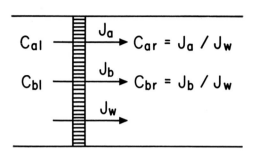

FIG. 4. Model for an osmotic ultrafiltration system driven by active transport of a single solute, a, in the presence of a second solute, b. Since all material on the right is assumed to have arrived through the barrier, the concentration of a given solute on the right must be equal to the ratio of the net solute flux to net flux. If the barrier is permeable to second solute, b, not only will b appear in the effluent but also a greater osmotic force will develop so that output of water should increase. See text for details.

Case 2, membrane partially permeable to solute b:

$$J_b > 0,\ C_{br} > 0,\ 0 > \sigma_b > 1$$
$$F_{osm} = RT\ (\sigma_a C_{ar} - \sigma_a C_{al} + \sigma_b C_{br} - \sigma_b C_{bl})$$
$$= RT\ (\sigma_a J_a/J_w - \sigma_a C_{al} - C_{bl})$$
$$+ RT\ [\sigma_b J_b/J_w + (1 - \sigma_b)\ C_{bl}]$$

In the first case the osmotic force, which is responsible for movement of water across the membrane, is generated entirely by accumulation of actively transported solute (solute a) on the right side in a concentration high enough to oppose both solutes on the left side. In the second case, in which passive movement of a second solute is permitted, the same flux rates of solute a and water would be associated with a greater osmotic force (represented by the second term in the last equation); hence a new steady state should develop in which the water flux, J_w, is increased.

This simple analysis is intended to illustrate how active solute transport can give rise to a steady osmotic force, and also to show that the flow produced by such a system may be greatly influenced by the presence and behavior of solutes other than the one actively transported. If the membrane in this system had a very large area, and hence a very great hydraulic conductivity, the osmotic force required for a given flow might be very small. Consequently, active transport of a single solute species could give rise to excretion of a virtually isotonic solution containing not only the actively transported solute but also appreciable concentrations of other solutes to which the system is permeable. The generation of high "secretion pressures" is also a predictable consequence of the operation of this model.

The application of this model to the biliary system obviously must represent a gross oversimplification in the following respects: *1)* Whereas the model is based on a single secretory compartment, the canalicular network may be functionally heterogeneous. The canaliculi associated with the centrilobular parenchymal cells, for example, may behave differently from those associated with peripheral cells. *2)* The assumption of a simple, more or less fixed membrane bounding the secretory compartment ignores the rather elaborate and possibly labile structural arrangements that are seen in the immediate vicinity of the bile canaliculi on electron microscopy. *3)* It is clearly questionable to apply the assumption that only a single solute is subject to active transport. It should be noted, moreover, that the treatment of the model was based on the behavior of uncharged solutes, whereas all the major osmotically active solute constituents of bile are electrolytes. With this admittedly oversimplified model as a background, we now consider some of the relevant data.

The probable importance of active organic acid secretion in relation to bile formation was first proposed by Sperber (119). It has been known for more than a century (118) that the bile salts themselves are among the most potent choleretic agents, whether administered orally or parenterally. Sperber pointed out that these compounds, together with a large number of other organic acids (some chemically quite dissimilar from bile acids), are excreted in the bile in osmotically significant concentrations. He suggested that active transport of organic acids may provide the primary osmotic force for biliary excretion. In addition to the large variety of actively secreted organic acids known to be choleretic, Sperber also showed that the neutral compound polyethyleneglycol-1500 is actively secreted and is an effective choleretic agent in chickens and turkeys, but not in mammals (120, 121). The organic base procaine amide ethobromide (PAEB), though actively secreted in bile (113, 114), has not as yet been administered in quantities that might be expected, on osmotic grounds, to produce an increment in bile flow, nor has any choleresis been observed with this agent.

In the dog, as illustrated in Figure 5, a direct quantitative relationship exists between bile flow and bile salt secretion rate. In most species the interruption of enterohepatic circulation of bile salts by acute diversion of bile to the exterior results in a significant reduction in bile flow. This phenomenon is very striking in the dog (30, 49, 68, 141, 142) and the cat

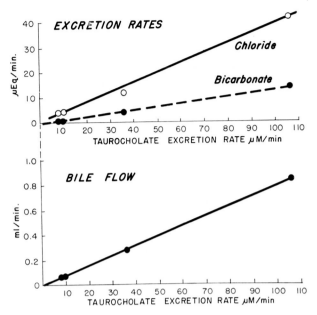

FIG. 5. Relationship between excretion rate of bile salt and the output of chloride, bicarbonate, and water. Illustrative experiment on a dog during cholinergic blockade (pipenzolate methylbromide). Sodium taurocholate was infused intravenously at rates of 8, 40, 118, and 8 μmoles/min (in that order) to obtain the four points. Output of water (bile flow) appeared to be directly proportional to taurocholate excretion rate, as did the output of chloride and bicarbonate ions.

(116), and has also been described in the rat (30, 79), sheep (58), and man (132). Interruption of enterohepatic circulation appears to have no obvious effect in rabbits (116), whose bile flow is characteristically very high. Owing to endogenous hepatic bile salt synthesis, it is obviously impossible to reduce bile salt secretion to zero by diversion of bile. If it were possible to stop bile salt synthesis the data shown in Figure 5 would lead one to predict that bile flow would be very close to zero in dogs. Though the primacy of bile salt secretion is far less tenable in species such as the rabbit, the choleretic effect of increased bile salt secretion is nevertheless readily demonstrable in all species including the rabbit (116).

The second type of evidence which is consistent with the view that active solute secretion stimulates bile flow by exerting an osmotic force is supplied by a comparison of choleretic potency of compounds of varying osmotic activity. Sperber (120, 121) has pointed out that secreted compounds with a minimal tendency to form micelles, and hence with the greatest osmotic activity per mole, are accompanied by the largest amounts of water per mole of solute, and he has described this relationship in a variety of different species (chicken, turkey, goat, rat, and rabbit). Thus, in the chicken, for example, taurocholate is a moderately potent choleretic but is excreted in a relatively high concentration of 116 mM, whereas taurodehydrocholate (a semisynthetic bile salt with little or no tendency to form micelles and hence a much higher osmotic coefficient) is a far more potent choleretic and its excretion is accompanied by enough water so that its biliary concentration is only 52 mM. Taurodehydrocholate, in other words, appears to carry out more than twice as much water per mole of solute. The same phenomenon is probably responsible for the observations of O'Máille et al. (87) reproduced in Figure 6, in which a relationship between bile salt secretion and bile flow similar to that in Figure 5 is shown, but in which it is also evident that much more water is excreted per mole of cholate than per mole of taurocholate. Since an appreciable fraction of cholate is excreted in the unconjugated state, and since the micellar tendency of unconjugated cholate is far less than that of taurocholate, it seems probable that these observations can be accounted for by the greater osmotic effectiveness of the unconjugated bile acid.

The foregoing relationships appear to be reasonable if not inevitable on thermodynamic grounds. Indeed, considering the "osmotic load" that is represented by canalicular bile salt secretion, it would perhaps be more surprising if increments in the rate of bile salt secretion were not accompanied by corresponding increments in water movement into the canaliculi. Whether bile salt transport (or organic anion transport in general) is the primary or dominant mechanism responsible for initiation of canalicular bile secretion in all species remains to be determined. The active transport of other solutes, particularly of inorganic ions, could also lead to enhanced water output, and the relatively high output of bile in rodents and rabbits, even after deprivation of enterohepatic bile salt circulation (16, 30, 116), could be accounted for on this basis.

Even in species such as the dog, where bile flow appears to be almost entirely dependent on bile salt secretion (Figs. 5 and 6), it is well to remember that bile output from the common duct is probably not equal to the rate of canalicular bile production. If absorption of water occurred in the duct system, the relationships illustrated in Figures 5 and 6 might result, in part, from osmotic inhibition of ductal water reabsorption by the bile salts. This would be analogous to the familiar phenomenon of osmotic diuresis in the kidney.

Canalicular Permeability and Canalicular Filtration Rate

By analogy with the kidney, it is probable that some of these questions may be resolved by the use of inert test substances similar to those employed for the measurement of glomerular filtration rate, and that this approach may also provide information about the permeability of the canalicular membrane. The biliary clearance of inulin, for example, was about 50% of the bile flow in Haywood's studies of the toadfish (59) and much lower than this in rats, according to Schanker & Hogben (114). In the latter studies even the clearance of sucrose was appreciably lower than the bile flow. However, the biliary clearance of mannitol in the nephrectomized rat is equal to or greater than that of water (114). Mannitol bile-to-plasma concentration ratios as high as 1.2 were found by these investigators, whereas the ratios for inulin and sucrose were 0.1 and 0.2, respectively, during prolonged steady-state observations. It has been shown that 5- and 6-carbon sugars and polyalcohols achieve rapid equilibrium between plasma

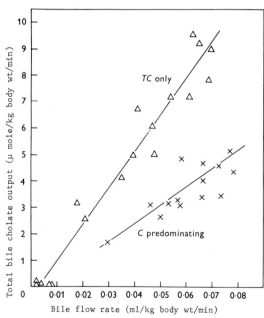

FIG. 6. Effect of bile salts with different osmotic properties on canine bile flow. During sodium taurocholate infusion (*triangles*) bile flow was lower per unit of bile salt excreted than during infusion of sodium cholate (*crosses*). In the latter case at least 50% of the bile salt was excreted as free cholate. Since this anion has a much smaller micellar size than does taurocholate, it is probable that the higher flow can be attributed to the greater osmotic activity of sodium cholate. [From O'Máille et al. (87).]

and liver water (24, 110, 114) even in the absence of insulin, so that it is evident that the sinusoidal liver cell membranes must be highly permeable to such compounds, and that the concentration of these solutes in plasma during a steady state should be approximately equal to their concentration in liver cell water provided they are not rapidly metabolized in the liver. Since the canalicular bile is derived directly from liver cell water, it is possible that the osmotic "ultrafiltration rate" of the canaliculi may be measurable by the same techniques as those employed for measurement of hydrostatic filtration rate of the renal glomeruli, with the use of mannitol or other compounds of comparable molecular size. That Schanker and Hogben's bile-to-plasma mannitol concentration ratios in the rat were greater than 1.0 might thus suggest some reabsorptive activity in a distal portion of the duct system relatively impermeable to mannitol.

Biliary mannitol clearance values in the dog (H. O. Wheeler and S. E. Bradley, unpublished observations) have shown a direct relationship to bile salt secretion rate consistent with the hypothesis that bile salt secretion is a major determinant of canalicular bile production. It is also noteworthy that steady-state bile-to-plasma mannitol concentration ratios in the cholecystectomized dog are often much higher than those reported for the rat by Schanker & Hogben (114). At lower rates of bile salt secretion and bile flow this ratio may achieve values greater than three; this suggests that an appreciable amount of water reabsorption may indeed occur in the canine bile duct system.

Bile Duct Activity

The bile duct walls appear to be quite permeable to sodium and potassium ions, judging by the rapidity of equilibration of ^{24}Na and ^{42}K between blood and bile (29, 78). Their passive permeability to inorganic anions may be more limited (26, 78). Though the usual isotonicity of bile would be consistent with a high degree of passive permeability to water, the occasional observation of measureable hypertonicity and hypotonicity (95) would suggest that there is enough restriction of water movement to be of functional significance at higher bile flows.

The evidence cited in the preceding section for reabsorption of fluid from the bile in structures distal to the canaliculi (i.e., ductules or ducts, or both) tends to support an earlier suspicion based on the composition of bile obtained from the bile ducts of

fasting cholecystectomized dogs (49, 141). The duct system of such dogs is regularly found, on initial catheterization, to contain several milliliters of highly concentrated bile whose composition resembles that of gallbladder bile. It has much lower concentrations of chloride and bicarbonate and a much higher concentration of bile salt than any specimens of flowing hepatic bile obtainable from the same animal. Owing to the efficacy of the sphincter of Oddi and the inherent capacity of the duct system—which can hold a volume equivalent to two or three hours' worth of hepatic bile flow—this could be interpreted as a physiological "stop-flow" experiment demonstrating that the duct system of the cholecystectomized dog, given sufficient time, may be capable of reabsorbing sufficient inorganic solute and water from the bile to achieve a final product similar to normal gallbladder bile. To what extent this presumed reabsorptive activity may represent a chronic adaptive change secondary to cholecystectomy could only be answered by comparable studies in which the gallbladder is removed or excluded acutely, and apparently such experiments have not been reported.

That the duct system may also be the site of secretory activity is suggested by studies of secretin choleresis. Using a constant submaximal biliary excretion rate of the dye sulfobromophthalein sodium (BSP) as an indicator, the volume of previously formed bile which is "washed out" during transition from basal flow to steady-state choleresis may be calculated (140). Taurocholate choleresis is consistently associated with a larger apparent "washout" volume than is secretin choleresis, which suggests that the addition of fluid to the bile in response to secretin occurs at a site distal to the canaliculi. Recently O'Máille et al. (88) have presented other evidence supporting the same conclusion. They found that the apparent excretory transport maximum (Tm) for BSP in anesthetized dogs was augmented up to threefold by taurocholate choleresis, but that it was unaffected by secretin choleresis of comparable magnitude. In a typical study, for example, the basal biliary BSP excretion rate (during a supramaximal intravenous BSP infusion of 0.48 μmole/kg per min) was 0.08 μmole/kg per min at a bile flow of 10 μl/kg per min. When secretin was infused at 0.2 U/kg per min the bile flow increased to 19 μl/kg per min without any effect on steady-state BSP output, but when taurocholate was infused at 0.7 μmole/kg per min the BSP output increased to 0.16 μmole/kg per min at a bile flow of slightly less than 17 μl/kg per min. The authors suggest that maximal BSP secretion rate is a function of canalicular BSP concentration and may therefore be augmented when BSP in the canaliculi is diluted by the water accompanying taurocholate secretion, and that failure of secretin to augment BSP secretion must mean that the secretin choleresis "... originates downstream from the canaliculi, i.e., in the bile ductules or ducts (88). A more detailed description of the effects of secretin appears below.

That the bile ductules and ducts probably play a major role in the modification of bile flow and composition is an idea that has appealed for some time to anatomists and physiologists (3, 4, 52, 130). The evidence cited above provides support for this viewpoint and should serve as a stimulus for the development of more quantitative techniques for the appraisal of ductal and ductular function.

Secretin

The choleretic effect of secretin was first described by its discoverers, Bayliss and Starling, and has been amply documented in numerous species, including man (41, 53, 68–70, 88, 99, 116, 118, 141). It appears that the rabbit may be an exception (2, 116). Scratcherd (116) has shown that preparations of secretin that were highly potent stimulants of rabbit pancreatic flow had no effect on the bile flow of the same animal, and that a preparation of secretin from rabbit duodenum, although ineffective in producing choleresis in the rabbit, proved to be a potent choleretic agent in the cat. In commenting on these results, Scratcherd pointed out that basal bile flow in the rabbit is already very high, and biliary bicarbonate concentration, in the absence of any external stimulus, is of the same order as that obtained by secretin stimulus in other species. He also noted, however, that secretin produced a marked choleretic response in guinea pigs despite their characteristically high basal bile flow and bicarbonate concentration.

Although it has been suggested that the biliary effects of some of the earlier secretin preparations might have been attributable to peptides other than secretin itself (35, 48), recent studies using the highly purified hormone prepared by the method of Jorpes and Mutt are consistent with the view that the response of the biliary system and the pancreas can be attributed to the effect of the same peptide (41, 68–70, 95, 116).

In the dog, cat, and man, the response to secretin consists of increased bile flow without any increase in the output of bile salts or pigments. When it has been

measured, the bicarbonate concentration has been found to increase markedly during secretin choleresis. Although the excretion rate of chloride also increases, there may actually be a diminution in the chloride concentration. The magnitude and direction of these concentration changes depend on the basal state on which the secretin choleresis is superimposed, and it may therefore be more meaningful to consider the calculated volume and composition of the "extra" solution that appears during secretin choleresis than to focus on the composition of the bile as a whole. This approach is based on the tacit assumption that secretin choleresis involves a more or less independent secretory process wherein a solution of characteristic composition is simply added to whatever bile is already being formed by other mechanisms. The assumption finds support from the observation that the increment in bile flow caused by secretin infusion is approximately the same over a wide range of basal bile flows (obtained by intravenous infusion of sodium taurocholate at different rates in dogs receiving an anticholinergic drug) (95). In unanesthetized dogs weighing 20–25 kg the infusion of secretin appeared to result in the addition of 0.26–0.34 ml per min of an aqueous solution containing, on the average, 70 mEq per liter of bicarbonate and 140 mEq per liter of chloride (95). It should be noted that the theoretical solution added in response to secretin is hypertonic (i.e., $[Cl^-] + [HCO_3^-] > 150$ mEq per liter), which is consistent with the higher osmolality noted during secretin administration (Fig. 2) and might possibly suggest that solute is actively transported into the lumen with secondary passive (and incomplete) equilibration of water. At roughly comparable rates of secretin infusion, Jonson and co-workers (68) measured increments in canine fistula bile flow of approximately 0.08–0.1 ml per min above an initial control state in which neither bile salts nor anticholinergic agents were administered. Zaterka & Grossman (142) reported a mean increment of approximately 0.15 ml per min above control flow when Vitrum (Jorpes) secretin was infused at 20 U/kg per hour (approximately 5 U/min) in gastrectomized dogs weighing 13–17 kg. Bicarbonate concentrations rose to 60–70 mEq per liter. Since most other studies have involved single injections rather than infusions of secretin, the data cannot be compared, but, for example, Grossman et al. (53) reported increments in bile flow ranging from 0.15 to 0.8 ml per min within 10 min after an injection of 15 mg of Lilly secretin in five human subjects, and Scratcherd (116) noted an increase of approximately ι g per 15 min in the anesthetized cat after an injection of 0.5 μg (probably about 9 clinical units) of Jorpes secretin. The magnitude of the secretin response must depend not only on the species but also on the experimental preparation and the potency and purity of the hormone administered. The foregoing experiments are therefore cited only as examples. Suffice it to say, however, that the order of magnitude of the maximal biliary response to secretin is, perhaps, only one-fifth to one-tenth as great as the flow of pancreatic juice elicited by comparable doses of this hormone. Pancreatic flows as high as 1–2 ml per min have been observed after secretin administration in dogs weighing 15–20 kg (11), and of course the bicarbonate concentration of pancreatic juice is considerably higher than the highest values reported in bile. Nevertheless the qualitative similarity between the biliary and the pancreatic response to secretin, especially with respect to bicarbonate output, naturally leads one to suspect that the underlying mechanisms are similar.

The dose-response relationships for secretin have not been studied in great detail. Jonson et al. (68) noted an apparently linear relationship between canine bile flow and the logarithm of secretin infusion rate, up to rates of approximately 40 U/kg per hour (roughly 14 U/min in a 20-kg dog). Similarly, in other studies canine biliary response appeared to approach a maximal value when approximately 10 U per min were infused (140). Though these dosage figures are only approximate, interestingly they are quite similar to those reported by Baron and colleagues (11) for maximal canine pancreatic response, which was achieved with secretin infusions of approximately 12 U per min in dogs of comparable size.

The site of secretin administration is important. At submaximal doses the response to hepatic arterial infusion is about 1.5 times as great as the response to either peripheral or portal administration (140). This finding is consistent with the hypothesis—discussed in the preceding section—that the site of action of secretin resides in the ducts or ductules (whose blood supply is derived mainly from the hepatic artery) rather than in the hepatic parenchymal cells.

Endogenous secretin is apparently also an effective choleretic stimulant, as demonstrated by the response to introduction of hydrochloric acid into the duodenum (95, 141). Harrison (58) observed an increase in bile flow of nearly 1 ml per min in the sheep when gastric juice (pH 1.5) was infused into the duodenum. This was accompanied by a diminution in the concentration of total solids and of chloride ion and a

rise in pH from approximately 7.0 to 8.5, consistent with a very marked increase in bicarbonate output (the arrangement of his preparation precluded any possible contamination with pancreatic juice). He concluded that this effect was presumably due to release of endogenous secretin.

The mechanism responsible for secretin choleresis remains obscure. In view of the evidence already presented that the site of action is distal to the canaliculi, it is possible either that secretin stimulates the output of an alkaline aqueous solution or that it acts by selective inhibition of ductal or ductular reabsorption of electrolytes and water. The latter has already been suggested as a mechanism for the effect of secretin on the pancreas (92), but there is little evidence to support either hypothesis for the biliary tract.

Cholecystokinin

Pure cholecystokinin is not available, but it appears that the choleresis elicited in the cholecystectomized dog by available preparations of porcine cholecystokinin is significantly greater than can be accounted for by the secretin contained in these preparations (41, 70, 97). This observation raises, once again, the probability that a separate duodenal hormone, as proposed in 1945 by Friedman & Snape (48) and sometimes referred to as "hepatocrinin" (35), also acts on the biliary system. The fall in biliary concentration of total solids during cholecystokinin choleresis is similar to that observed with secretin, and there also appears to be a rise in pH (97) suggestive of augmented bicarbonate excretion.

Gastrin

The effects of crude gastrin and of pure porcine gastrin II have been studied in unanesthetized gastrectomized dogs by Zaterka & Grossman (142) and are quite similar to the effects of secretin, though the maximal increment in bile flow was considerably less than that obtainable with secretin. The peak response in three dogs averaged about 1.3 ml per 30 min (0.04 ml/min) above interpolated basal flow during an infusion of gastrin II at 4 μg/kg per hour, a dose that appeared to elicit a maximal effect. Biliary bicarbonate concentration rose from approximately 45 mEq per liter during control periods to 60 mEq per liter so that bicarbonate output was markedly increased. (It is of some interest that the basal bicarbonate concentration was quite high in these gastrectomized animals, since they must have had no source of endogenous gastrin, no acid stimulus for endogenous secretin, and no hepatic or biliary vagal innervation.) Biliary chloride concentration was unaffected by gastrin, but chloride output increased with the increase in flow. Finally, as with secretin, bile salt concentration fell sharply during gastrin choleresis so that the output of bile salts (which declined steadily after interruption of enterohepatic circulation) was unaffected by the hormone. The role of endogenous gastrin will be discussed further in relation to the confusing subject of neurogenic effects on bile flow.

Histamine

Earlier observations of histamine-induced choleresis (25) may have been explainable at least in part on the basis of endogenous secretin stimulation mediated through gastric hypersecretion. Recently, however, Zaterka & Grossman (142) have shown that infusion of histamine results in choleresis in gastrectomized dogs, a finding that indicates an effect of this agent not mediated through gastric secretion. Infusion of histamine dihydrochloride at a rate of 4 mg per hour resulted in bile flows approximately 0.07 ml per min above the interpolated basal flow, almost twice as great as that elicited by maximal gastrin stimulus, but less than half of that obtainable with secretin. Larger doses of histamine had no greater effect. The pattern of electrolyte excretion was notably different from that observed during secretin, gastrin, or spontaneous choleresis. Although there was an increase in bicarbonate excretion, the biliary bicarbonate concentration actually decreased. Chloride concentration, on the other hand, rose significantly so that the output of this anion increased much more than that of bicarbonate. This pattern of choleresis, in which chloride is the dominant anion, has been seen after acetazolamide administration (see below) but in no other experimental situation reported thus far.

Carbonic Anhydrase Inhibitors and Hyperventilation

Administration of the carbonic anhydrase inhibitor acetazolamide in large doses (65 mg/kg, iv) to unanesthetized dogs has been shown to cause a choleresis accompanied by a rise in biliary chloride and a fall in bicarbonate concentration (89, 141), a pattern similar to that elicited by histamine. Doses of 200 mg per kg in the rat, however, had no discernible effect on bile production (17). In a single human subject the effects of acetazolamide (500 mg followed by 250 mg po every 6 hours) were equivocal, though a minor rise in the chloride and fall in the bicarbonate concentration of fistula bile was noted (46), which the author equated to a corresponding change in the serum electrolytes.

Recently Maren et al. (81) explored the effects of carbonic anhydrase inhibitors in detail. They did not observe a consistent choleresis in anesthetized dogs, but demonstrated a significant rise in biliary chloride concentration (7–23 mEq/liter) and fall in bicarbonate concentration (2–9 mEq/liter) after administration of acetazolamide and methazolamide in doses ranging from 5 to 65 mg per kg and of CL 11,366 (Lederle) in doses ranging from 3 to 6 mg per kg. All these drugs were excreted in bile and the concentrations of acetazolamide and CL 11,366 (mEq/liter) were several times higher in bile than in plasma so that the drugs had access to the biliary tract epithelium by way of the luminal as well as the nutrient surface. Canine liver was shown to contain carbonic anhydrase in concentrations similar to those found in canine pancreas.

In the same report Maren and colleagues also demonstrated a rise in biliary chloride and fall in bicarbonate concentration during respiratory alkalosis, and these changes were very similar in magnitude to those elicited by carbonic anhydrase inhibition. The authors suggested that the important factor in both situations may have been a rise in the intracellular pH of secretory cells brought about, in one case, by the acute reduction of P_{CO_2} and, in the other case, by retardation of the buffering of hydroxyl ions by CO_2 (a process dependent on carbonic anhydrase). The latter mechanism for alkalosis presupposes a continuing source of excess hydroxyl ions, attributable to transport of hydrogen ions away from the region in which the alkalosis is presumed to develop.

It might also be reasoned that the common denominator between carbonic anhydrase inhibition and hyperventilation could be a reduction in intracellular bicarbonate ion concentration. In the case of the biliary tract it is possible to suppose, for example, that chloride and bicarbonate may move between the lumen and the interior of the epithelial cells by exchange diffusion, a supposition gaining plausibility from the demonstration of anion exchange diffusion in at least one part of the biliary tract—the gallbladder (38). It would then be expected that any maneuver leading to relative reduction in intracellular bicarbonate concentration would result in a fall in luminal bicarbonate and reciprocal rise in luminal chloride concentration without necessarily affecting the total ionic concentration or volume of the luminal contents.

Obviously these observations invite further study; the clues derived from study of carbonic anhydrase inhibition should prove as important in the elucidation of biliary tract physiology as they have in the investigation of other organs.

Maren's studies supplied the additional unexpected information that rat liver carbonic anhydrase is unaffected by any of the inhibitors tested. It may be for this reason that Bizard et al. (17) did not observe any effect of acetazolamide on rat bile production.

Neurogenic Factors

The role of direct neurogenic stimuli on bile secretion has defied precise definition, but the rich autonomic innervation of the liver suggests the probable importance of nervous regulation.

Studies by Tanturi & Ivy (127) on the effects of vagus nerve stimulation on bile production showed marked enhancement of bile flow in the dog (but not in cats or rabbits), even after removal of most of the gastrointestinal tract. Since the stomach could not be removed, its blood supply was ligated, but the studies did not appear to have entirely ruled out an intermediate gastric humoral mechanism. The more recent studies of Fritz & Brooks (49), in which the likelihood of endogenous secretin release was reduced by diversion of gastric secretion, showed that both feeding and hypoglycemia (induced by insulin or tolbutamide) caused a choleresis in dogs that could be prevented by prior vagectomy or by administration of the anticholinergic drug pipenzolate methylbromide. The average magnitude of the choleresis elicited by these maneuvers was approximately 4–7 ml per hour (0.07–0.12 ml/min) above the flows observed during comparable control periods. Electrolyte concentrations were not reported for the periods of choleresis, but there was an apparent increase in the rate of excretion of total solids, a phenomenon requiring further investigation. Similar results were obtained by Baldwin et al. (7) in nine human subjects who had an average increase in bile flow of 0.4 ml per min (above a base line of only 0.25 ml/min) during insulin hypoglycemia. The choleresis could be prevented by prior atropine administration.

Subsequent reports from Brooks' laboratory indicate that the choleretic effect of insulin hypoglycemia is dependent on the presence of the gastric antrum (66) and also that chemical stimulation of the gastric antrum causes a choleresis (67); the authors therefore postulated that the choleresis is caused by a humoral

intermediate released by the gastric antrum in response to vagal stimulation. From the report of Zaterka & Grossman (142), discussed in a preceding section, it would appear very likely that gastrin is the intermediate hormone responsible, at least in part, for the biliary response to vagal stimulation. In view of this evidence one would have to conclude that direct vagal stimulation of bile production has yet to be demonstrated.

Section of the vagus nerves has been reported by Saburov to cause an increase in bile flow and an enhanced response to intraduodenal hydrochloric acid infusion (108). The same author has found that chronic vagal denervation causes an enhanced response to small doses of secretin in dogs but not in cats (109). Thus it may be that the vagus nerve can also carry inhibitory stimuli acting directly or indirectly on the biliary tract.

Stimulation of splanchnic nerves was reported by Tanturi & Ivy (126) to cause a reduction in bile flow in anesthetized dogs. The authors did not feel this necessarily represented a direct effect on secretory tissue but that it might well be attributable to altered vascular perfusion secondary to marked vasoconstriction. Section of splanchnic nerves caused an increase in bile flow.

Posterior hypothalamic stimulation has been reported to increase bile flow in the cat, but the mediation and mechanism have not been explained (13).

Although the probable importance of direct neurogenic regulation of bile secretion should not be minimized, it appears that conclusive data are not presently available and, indeed, the investigation of these phenomena will pose unusually difficult problems in experimental design. It should also be recalled that vagal tone is important to the contractility of bile duct and gallbladder (90, 105), so that the effects of altered motility must be seriously considered in any experiment in which the nerve supply is manipulated.

Effects of Altered Vascular Perfusion

As noted earlier, the secretion of bile does not depend on hydrostatic filtration, and the maximal secretion pressure of bile shows but slight diminution when the portal perfusion pressure of the isolated rat liver is greatly reduced (18, 19). Moreover, complete occlusion of the hepatic arterial supply has been found to have virtually no effect on bile secretion pressure in rats (18). Wide variations in blood pressure induced by adrenaline, noradrenaline, or hexamethonium were found by Kjellgren (74) to have little effect on bile production in rabbits. Chronic occlusion of the canine hepatic artery or portal vein or both (blood supply derived entirely from phrenic collateral branches) has been reported to have no apparent effect on bile production (93); nor does end-to-side portacaval shunt or arterialization of the portal circulation appear to change bile flow in any obvious way (47). In acute studies, Tanturi & Ivy (126) reported an increase in canine bile flow following hepatic arterial occlusion, but this was not confirmed by Engstrand (45).

Though changes in blood flow over a fairly wide range appear to have little effect in any of the species studied thus far, severe reduction in blood flow causes an abrupt reduction or cessation of bile flow (45, 74, 126). That hypoxia may be the major factor responsible for this secretory failure has been suggested by Brauer's studies (18, 19) showing that bile flow is well maintained in isolated rat livers perfused at very low rates with erythrocyte-free fluid, provided the perfusate has been equilibrated with high partial pressures of oxygen (2.5–4 atm). Thus it appears that hepatic ischemia is well tolerated until the point of severe anoxia is reached. On the other hand, elevation of hepatic venous pressure, insufficient to cause a major reduction in hepatic blood flow, leads to marked inhibition of bile formation in dogs (96, 126) for reasons presently unknown.

The whole question of hepatic vascular perfusion must ultimately be dealt with in terms of distribution as well as total hepatic blood flow. It is evident, for example, that a uniform reduction in hepatic blood flow would probably have far less effect on bile production than would a process in which the same reduction in total flow was associated with virtually complete ischemia of some regions of the liver. An example of the latter is the marked regional ischemia, the "restricted circulation," sometimes observed by Daniel & Prichard (32, 33) in rats, rabbits, cats, and monkeys during hepatic nerve stimulation. The hepatic sinusoidal labyrinth is a low-pressure system with many anastomoses, and it is not inconceivable that profound disturbance of uniform sinusoidal perfusion may result from minor local changes in hepatic arteriolar or portal venular resistance or that sinusoidal perfusion might be peculiarly sensitive to minor alterations in hepatic venous pressure. Measurement of changes in the transport maxima of dyes, such as sulfobromophthalein, may provide a useful tool for evaluation of the possibility of local hepatic ischemia.

Inhibitors of Metabolic and Transport Processes

The effects of acetazolamide and other carbonic anhydrase inhibitors have already been discussed.

Bizard, Vanlerenberghe, and their associates (14, 133) have also studied the effect of various inhibitory agents on bile formation in the isolated perfused rat liver. Potassium cyanide was shown to cause marked reduction or cessation in bile flow. The effect of sodium fluoride was inconsistent and may have been due, in those cases where anticholeresis did occur, to an effect on blood flow through the preparation. Monoiodoacetic acid caused a choleresis followed by total cessation of bile flow. Consistent with the action of more specific metabolic inhibitors, a general depression of metabolic activity caused by hypothermia was associated with marked diminution in bile production (134, 135). Phlorizin, which inhibited the output of bilirubin and BSP, caused a marked increase in bile flow. In view of the observations of Jenner & Smyth (65), who noted that phlorizin also causes a choleresis in dogs, it is clear that both the choleresis and the inhibition of secretion of other substances could be attributed to active secretion of osmotically significant quantities of phlorizin itself in bile. Although 2,4-dinitrophenol appears to inhibit bile flow in the isolated rat liver (14), it produces a marked choleresis in dogs (20, 124). This agent causes pyrexia, but it is clear that pyrexia alone is not responsible for its effect on canine bile secretion (124).

In appraising the effects of various metabolic inhibitors on the intact organ or organism, it is necessary to consider at least four problems. *1*) The action of these agents may not be entirely restricted to the particular biochemical processes they are presumed to inhibit. *2*) The observed changes in bile flow may be attributable to circulatory, nervous, thermal, or other effects rather than a direct action on the biliary system itself. *3*) Certain agents (e.g., phlorizin) may themselves be transported into the bile and thereby affect bile flow. *4*) Inhibition of processes associated with reabsorption of fluid may lead to the observation that an agent stimulates bile flow.

Other Factors Influencing Bile Production

The intravascular infusion of hypertonic solutions of mannitol or xylose causes a significant diminution of bile flow in guinea pigs and in perfused rat livers (27, 28, 137). Introduction of hypertonic glucose (150 ml of 50% dextrose) or of 8% sodium chloride solutions into the duodenum causes a significant (45–70%) depression of bile flow in dogs (75). These phenomena might have been predicted from the osmotic relationship between bile and plasma. The magnitude of the anticholeresis suggests, however, that other factors may also contribute to this effect.

Parenteral or oral administration of galactose in rats in doses of 1 mg or more per gram body weight causes an anticholeresis lasting more than 2 hours (60). The mechanism is unexplained but is apparently specific for this monosaccharide.

Sporidesmin, a compound derived from the fungus *Pithomyces chartarum*, produces a profound and prolonged but reversible reduction in bile flow (117) which has been attributed to a direct toxic effect on the biliary tract epithelium, resulting in inflammation and edema.

Icterogenin, rehmannic acid, and related compounds derived from certain plants of the family Verbenaceae cause a profound diminution in bile flow in rabbits and sheep, as well as a reduction in pigment excretion (22, 23, 61). Since these agents produce no histological changes, and because of their marked effect on dye and pigment excretion, it is presumed that they interfere directly with mechanisms of active solute transport into the canaliculi.

Adrenalectomy in rats was followed by a diminution in bile flow to about half the control value (129), which was restored to normal by administration of cortisol (76). Since all these animals were maintained on food and water ad libitum, it is not clear whether the observed effect indicates that there is a direct action of adrenal hormones on the biliary system or whether the phenomena were related to the general alterations in fluid and electrolyte balance associated with adrenal insufficiency. Chronic administration of prednisolone in dogs appears to cause increased bile flow, possibly as a result of an increase in the size of the bile acid pool (50).

Because many experiments are conducted on anesthetized animals it would obviously be important to know the effects of anesthetic agents on bile production. No studies to date provide precise information, and of course the problem is complicated by the need to distinguish more or less direct effects from the effects of circulatory, acid-base, and thermal alterations that may accompany general anesthesia. High bile flows have been reported in dogs under chloralose anesthesia (36). In the same species barbiturate anesthesia has been reported to cause a transient reduction in bile flow (15, 36). In rabbits (15, 36) and rats (34)

barbiturate anesthesia is associated with lower bile flow than is urethan anesthesia. Barbiturates appear to have no effect on the output of bile by perfused rat livers (136).

Antidiuretic hormone has been reported to have no effect in dogs (6), and its transient effect (brief anticholeresis) in rats has been attributed to smooth muscle contraction of the duct system (63). Since bile is usually isotonic, and therefore presumably already in osmotic equilibrium with plasma, it is perhaps not surprising that antidiuretic hormone causes no detectable change. Nevertheless, in view of the data shown in Figure 2 it would be of interest to administer antidiuretic hormone under circumstances where the bile is not isotonic (e.g., secretin or bile salt choleresis).

It will be evident that any experiment designed to detect altered biliary excretion should be designed to minimize alteration in factors other than the one under investigation. The most important alteration in most experimental situations, and the one most likely to confuse interpretation, is the change in enterohepatic circulation of bile salts that is caused by the actual collection of bile itself. This problem can be circumvented by chronic diversion of all bile to the exterior, and many important experiments have been conducted this way. Alternatively, to achieve a more nearly physiological state, bile salts can be returned continuously to the subject by the enteric or intravenous route. In comparatively short-term experiments the intravenous route may be preferable, since it avoids the delay and variability involved in propulsion of the bile salts to the site of intestinal absorption.

Spontaneous Variations in Bile Flow

If bile flow is observed over a protracted period in an unanesthetized dog whose bile acid secretion rate is constant (maintained by intravenous infusion), spontaneous variations of considerable magnitude may be noted. These are associated with consistent changes in composition similar to those seen during secretin or gastrin choleresis in that the higher flows are always associated with higher concentrations of bicarbonate and with higher pH (141). This pattern of response suggests that one possible cause of these variations may be impulses arriving by way of the vagus nerve which lead to release of gastrin or to gastric hydrochloric acid secretion (or both) with subsequent stimulation of endogenous secretin production. This hypothesis is supported by the observation that bouts of spontaneous choleresis sometimes coincide with sudden reductions in duodenal pH, and also by the partial effectiveness of anticholinergic drugs in reducing the frequency and magnitude of spontaneous increments in bile flow (95). On the other hand, it should be recalled that relatively high flows of alkaline bile were noted during control periods on Zaterka & Grossman's gastrectomized dogs (142), which must be explained on another basis, possibly as an effect of vagal denervation (108, 109).

Although spontaneous variations in bile production must obviously be regarded as physiological, they pose a special challenge in the interpretation of experiments in unanesthetized subjects. The studies of Fritz & Brooks (49) and of Zaterka & Grossman (142) would suggest that vagectomized animals might be suitable subjects for the study of effects of humoral agents on bile production, especially since anticholinergic drugs may be only partially effective in stabilizing bile production when given in moderate doses or may have undesirable effects in high doses.

SUMMARY

In Figure 7 are summarized a few of the known or possible phenomena that may be important determinants of the output of water and electrolytes in bile. Without evidence to the contrary it appears reasonable to assume that transport of water itself is not an active process, but occurs in response to solute transport. It is uncertain whether this occurs by simple osmotic equilibration across canalicular or bile duct epithelium or whether there are structural arrangements permitting an even more efficient coupling between solute and water movement, such as those responsible for the "local osmosis" phenomena observable in the gallbladder wall.

Active transport of organic anions is the most clearly defined example of solute transport directly responsible for bile formation, and of course the conjugated bile acids are the most important compounds in this category. These compounds are synthesized in the liver, and additional amounts may be administered, but in the intact animal the major source is the intestinal absorption of previously excreted bile salts. Active transport of other solutes including, quite possibly, inorganic electrolytes could also play an important role in canalicular bile production, but the existence or relative importance of such a transport mechanism has not been established. Regardless of which constituents are introduced by active transport, it is inevitable that many permeant solutes may gain access to the lumen by simple passive diffusion or by osmotic ultrafiltration along with water.

There is good reason to believe that the initial canalicular bile may be substantially modified by processes occurring in the bile ductules or even in the major ducts. Reabsorption of solute and water appears to occur in the dog, and, in addition, the duct system seems to elaborate, in response to secretin stimulation,

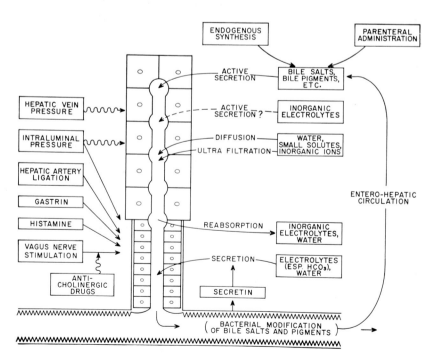

FIG. 7. Diagrammatic summary of some of the factors known to affect bile flow and electrolyte composition. Mechanisms shown on the right are believed to act at canalicular or duct level as shown. Locus and mode of action of factors shown on the left is speculative. See SUMMARY in text.

an alkaline secretion whose volume is added to the bile arriving from more proximal sources.

Also shown in Figure 7 are a number of stimuli known to modify bile production, but whose mechanism and site of action are uncertain. Hepatic venous congestion exerts a profound anticholeretic effect. Marked elevation of intraluminal pressure reduces bile flow, though bile secretion can occur at an unaltered rate against a moderate opposing hydrostatic pressure. Hepatic arterial ligation may cause increased bile flow in dogs, and if so this might possibly be due to alteration of ductular or ductal absorptive mechanisms. Histamine, gastrin, and cholecystokinin cause increased bile production, the last two associated with electrolyte changes similar to those elicited by secretin and possibly therefore attributable to the same mechanism.

It is probable that a much clearer understanding of biliary tract physiology could be obtained by exploitation of the two types of experimental approach that have proved very useful in understanding renal physiology: *1*) the systematic evaluation of biliary "clearance" of a variety of test substances, and *2*) the examination of electric potentials and the chemical composition of fluid obtained directly from identifiable portions of the biliary tract by micropuncture techniques.

ADDENDUM

Since this chapter was prepared Forker et al. (47a, 47b) have studied biliary clearances of labeled erythritol and mannitol in guinea pigs and rats. The clearances of these compounds in both species increase markedly after administration of sodium dehydrocholate but are unaffected (in the guinea pig) by secretin choleresis. Erythritol clearances are appreciably higher than mannitol clearances in the guinea pig and slightly higher in the rat. The data have been interpreted as evidence for osmotic filtration of solution into bile canaliculi in response to dehydrocholate secretion.

Nahrwold & Grossman (83a) have shown that feeding in dogs is associated with a secretin-like choleresis in which biliary bicarbonate concentration is increased and that restoration of enterohepatic circulation (by infusion of bile into the duodenum after 4 hours of biliary drainage) causes an increase in bile salt concentration and output but not an increase in bile flow such as that seen at higher rates of bile salt administration (e.g., Fig. 5). Administration of food plus bile causes a higher bicarbonate output than that observed with food alone and a higher bile salt output than that seen with bile alone.

REFERENCES

1. ACHESON, E. D., G. McHARDY, H. C. DESSAUER, C. FORD, AND D. DUNN. Effect of florantyrone on rate of secretion of hepatic bile and on its chemical and physical properties. *Gastroenterology* 37: 735–740, 1959.

2. AFFOLTER, H., M. PILLER, AND A. GUBLER. Tierexperimentelle untersuchungen über die wirkung von gereinigtem sekretin und cholecystokinin-pankreozymin, sowie von decholin auf die gallensekretion. *Gastroenterologia* 101: 247–258, 1964.

3. ANDREWS, W. H. H. Excretory function of the liver. A re-assessment. *Lancet* II: 166–169, 1955.

4. ANDREWS, W. H. H., B. G. MAEGRAITH, AND C. E. M. WENYON. Studies on the liver circulation II. The microanatomy of the hepatic circulation. *Ann. Trop. Med. Parasitol.* 43: 229–237, 1949.

5. ASHWORTH, C. T., AND E. SANDERS. Anatomic pathway of bile formation. *Am. J. Pathol.* 37: 343–355, 1960.

6. BAISSET, A., P. MONTASTRUC, AND J. PRAT. Recherches sur les actions extra-rénales de l'hormone antidiurétique. Absence d'effet sur la sécrétion intestinale, la sécrétion biliaire et la réabsorption vésiculaire. *Semaine Hop. Pathol. Biol.* 12: 439–446, 1964.

7. BALDWIN, J., F. W. HEER, R. ALBO, O. PELOSO, L. RUBY, AND W. SILEN. Effect of vagus nerve stimulation on hepatic secretion of bile in human subjects. *Am. J. Surg.* 111: 66–69, 1966.

8. BARBER-RILEY, G. Rat biliary tree during short periods of obstruction of common duct. *Am. J. Physiol.* 205: 1127–1131, 1963.

9. BARBER-RILEY, G. The rate of biliary secretion during flow up vertical cannulas of different bore. *Experientia* 20: 639–640, 1964.

10. BARBER-RILEY, G. Measurement of the capacity of the biliary tree. In: *The Biliary System*, edited by W. Taylor. Oxford: Blackwell, 1965, p. 89–97.

11. BARON, J. H., C. V. PERRIER, H. D. JANOWITZ, AND D. A. DREILING. Maximum alkaline (bicarbonate) output of the dog pancreas. *Am. J. Physiol.* 204: 251–256, 1963.

12. BERLINER, R. W., N. G. LEVINSKY, D. G. DAVIDSON, AND M. EDEN. Dilution and concentration of the urine and the action of antidiuretic hormone. *Am. J. Med.* 24: 730–744, 1958.

13. BIRNBAUM, D., AND S. FELDMAN. Effects of hypothalamic stimulation on bile secretion. An experimental study in cats. *J. Lab. Clin. Med.* 60: 914–922, 1962.

14. BIZARD, G. Enzyme inhibitors and biliary secretion. In: *The Biliary System*, edited by W. Taylor. Oxford: Blackwell, 1965, p. 315–324.

15. BIZARD, G., A. ROBELET, AND N. BIZARD-GREGOIRE. Action des barbituriqes sur la sécrétion biliare. *Rev. Intern. Hepatol.* 12: 587–600, 1962.

16. BIZARD, G., AND J. VANLERENBERGHE. Cholérèse et cholérétiques. *J. Physiol., Paris* 48: 207–364, 1956.

17. BIZARD, G., J. VANLERENBERGHE, F. GUERRIN, AND R. GODCHAUX. Rôle de l'anhydrase carbonique dans la formation de la bile. *J. Physiol., Paris* 50: 155–156, 1958.

18. BRAUER, R. W. Hepatic blood supply and the secretion

of bile. In: *The Biliary System*, edited by W. Taylor. Oxford: Blackwell, 1965, p. 41–67.

19. BRAUER, R. W., G. F. LEONG, AND R. J. HOLLOWAY. The effect of perfusion pressure and temperature on bile flow and bile secretion pressure. *Am. J. Physiol.* 177: 103–119, 1954.

20. BRINDLEY, P. M., AND S. L. STONE. The effect of 2,4-dinitrophenol and related compounds on biliary excretion. *J. Physiol., London* 172: 64–65P, 1964.

21. BRISCOE, A. M., AND C. RAGAN. Bile and endogenous fecal calcium in man. *Am. J. Clin. Nutr.* 16: 281–286, 1965.

22. BROWN, J. M. M., AND C. RIMINGTON. Studies on biliary excretion in the rabbit. II. The relationship between the chemical structure of certain natural or synthetic pentacyclic triterpenes and their icterogenic activity. Part 2. The substances on carbon atoms 17, 19, 20 and 22. *Proc. Roy. Soc., London, Ser. B* 160: 246–257, 1964.

23. BROWN, J. M. M., C. RIMINGTON, AND B. C. SAWYER. Studies on biliary excretion in the rabbit. II. Relationship between the chemical structure of certain natural or synthetic pentacyclic triterpenes and their icterogenic activity. *Proc. Roy. Soc., London, Ser. B* 157: 473–491, 1963.

24. CAHILL, G. F., JR., J. ASHMORE, A. S. EARLE, AND S. ZOTTU. Glucose penetration into liver. *Am. J. Physiol.* 192: 491–496, 1958.

25. CARNOT, P., AND Z. GRUZEWSKA. Variations de concentration ionique de la bile et du suc pancréatique pendant la sécrétion acide du suc gastrique. *Compt. Rend. Soc. Biol.* 93: 240–242, 1925.

26. CHENDEROVITCH, J. Les conceptions actuelles des méchanismes de la sécrétion biliaire. *Presse Med.* 71: 2645–2648, 1963.

27. CHENDEROVITCH, J., AND E. PHOCAS. The influence of intravenous hypertonic solutions on bile formation. In: *The Biliary System*, edited by W. Taylor. Oxford: Blackwell, 1965, p. 531–539.

28. CHENDEROVITCH, J., E. PHOCAS, AND M. RAUTUREAU. Effects of hypertonic solutions on bile formation. *Am. J. Physiol.* 205: 863–867, 1963.

29. CHENDEROVITCH, J., S. TROUPEL, H. RENAULT, AND J. CAROLI. Le transfert du Na^{24} et du K^{52} du sang dans la bile chez le cobaye au cours de la cholérèse a débit bloqué ("stop-flow analysis"). *Rev. Franc. Etude Clin. Biol.* 6: 584–589, 1961.

30. COOK, D. L., D. A. BEACH, R. G. BIANCHI, W. E. HAMBOURGER, AND D. M. GREEN. Factors influencing bile flow in the dog and rat. *Am. J. Physiol.* 163: 688–694, 1950.

31. COOK, D. L., C. A. LAWLER, L. D. CALVIN, AND D. M. GREEN. Mechanisms of bile formation. *Am. J. Physiol.* 171: 62–74, 1952.

32. DANIEL, P. M., AND M. M. L. PRICHARD. Variations in the circulation of the portal venous blood within the liver. *J. Physiol., London* 114: 521–537, 1951.

33. DANIEL, P. M., AND M. M. L. PRICHARD. Effects of stimulation of the hepatic nerves and of adrenaline upon the circulation of the portal venous blood within the liver. *J. Physiol., London* 114: 538–548, 1951.

34. DEBRARY, C., J. DE LA TOUR, C. VAILLE, C. ROZÉ, AND M. SOUCHARD. Contribution à l'étude de la sécrétion biliaire et pancréatique externe chez le rat. *J. Physiol., Paris* 54: 459–499, 1962.

35. DEBRARY, C., C. VAILLE, J. DE LA TOUR, AND C. ROZÉ.

Action sur la sécrétion biliaire de diverses sécrétines du commerce. Le problem de l'hépatocrinine. *Semaine Hop. Pathol. Biol.* 11: 1373–1377, 1963.

36. DELAS, R., G. ROUX, AND R. ECOLLE. Influence de l'anesthésie sur la cholérèse expérimentale. *Compt. Rend. Soc. Biol.* 151: 1429–1431, 1957.

37. DIAMOND, J. M. The reabsorptive function of the gallbladder. *J. Physiol., London* 161: 442–473, 1962.

38. DIAMOND, J. M. The mechanism of solute transport by the gall-bladder. *J. Physiol., London* 161: 474–502, 1962.

39. DIAMOND, J. M., AND J. McD. TORMEY. Role of long extracellular channels in fluid transport across epithelia. *Nature* 210: 817–820, 1966.

40. DIETSCHY, J. M., AND E. W. MOORE. Diffusion potentials and potassium distribution across the gallbladder wall. *J. Clin. Invest.* 43: 1551–1560, 1964.

41. EDHOLM, P., G. JONSON, AND L. THULIN. Le débit biliaire du foie: stimulation par la cholécystokinine, la sécrétine et l'alimentation per-orale. *Semaine Hop. Pathol. Biol.* 10: 447–450, 1962.

42. EKWALL, P., K. FONTELL, AND A. STEM. Micelle formation in bile salt solutions. In: *Proceedings 2nd International Congress of Surface Activity*. London: Butterworths, 1957, vol. 1, p. 357–373.

43. ELIAS, H. A re-examination of the structure of the mammalian liver. II. The hepatic lobule and its relation to the vascular and biliary systems. *Am. J. Anat.* 85: 379–456, 1949.

44. ELIAS, H. The geometry of the cell shape and the adaptive evolution of the liver. *J. Morphol.* 91: 365–387, 1952.

45. ENGSTRAND, L. Bile secretion and hepatic nitrogen metabolism in relation to variations of blood and oxygen supply to the liver. *Acta Chir. Scand. Suppl.* 146: 1–190, 1949.

46. FINK, S. Studies on hepatic bile obtained from a patient with an external biliary fistula; its composition and changes after diamox administration. *New Engl. J. Med.* 254: 258–262, 1956.

47. FISHER, B., S. H. LEE, AND E. J. FEDOR. Effect on permanent alteration of hepatic blood flow upon biliary secretion. *A.M.A. Arch. Surg.* 76: 41–45, 1958.

47a. FORKER, E. L. Two sites of bile formation as determined by mannitol and erythritol clearance in the guinea pig. *J. Clin. Invest.* 46: 1189–1195, 1967.

47b. FORKER, E. L., T. HICKLIN, AND H. SORNSON. The clearance of mannitol and erythritol in rat bile. *Proc. Soc. Exptl. Biol. Med.* 126: 115–119, 1967.

48. FRIEDMAN, M. H. F., AND W. J. SNAPE. Comparative effectiveness of extracts of intestinal mucosa in stimulating the external secretions of the pancreas and the liver. *Federation Proc.* 4: 21–22, 1945.

49. FRITZ, M. E., AND F. P. BROOKS. Control of bile flow in the cholecystectomized dog. *Am. J. Physiol.* 204: 825–828, 1963.

50. GANS, J. H., AND K. McENTEE. Comparative effects of prednisolone and thyroid hormone on bile secretion in the dog. *Am. J. Physiol.* 201: 577–581, 1961.

51. GILMAN, A., AND G. R. COWGILL. Osmotic relations between blood and body fluids. IV. Pancreatic juice, bile and lymph. *Am. J. Physiol.* 104: 476–479, 1933.

52. GOLDFARB, S. E., E. J. SINGER, AND H. POPPER. Biliary

ductules and bile secretion. *J. Lab. Clin. Med.* 62: 608–615, 1963.

53. GROSSMAN, M. I., H. D. JANOWITZ, H. RALSTON, AND K. S. KIM. The effect of secretin on bile formation in man. *Gastroenterology* 12: 133–138, 1949.

54. GUNTER, M. J., K. S. KIM, D. F. MAGEE, H. RALSTON, AND A. C. IVY. The choleretic potencies of some synthetic compounds. *J. Pharmacol. Exptl. Therap.* 99: 465–478, 1950.

55. HALE, A. J. The minute structure of the liver: a review. *Glasgow Med. J.* 32: 283–301, 1951.

56. HAMPTON, J. C. An electron microscope study of the hepatic uptake and excretion of submicroscopic particles injected into the blood stream and into the bile duct. *Acta Anat.* 32: 262–291, 1958.

57. HARDWICKE, J., J. G. RANKIN, K. J. BAKER, AND R. PREISIG. The loss of protein in human and canine hepatic bile. *Clin. Sci.* 26: 509–517, 1964.

58. HARRISON, F. A. Bile secretion in the sheep. *J. Physiol., London* 162: 212–224, 1962.

59. HAYWOOD, C. The passage of inulin through the liver of the toadfish with and without choleretics. *J. Cellular Comp. Physiol.* 28: 381–396, 1946.

60. HEGGENESS, F. W. Galactose and bile flow. *Proc. Soc. Exptl. Biol. Med.* 101: 143–144, 1959.

61. HEIKEL, T., B. C. KNIGHT, AND C. RIMINGTON. Studies on biliary excretion in the rabbit. I. The effect of icterogenin and rehmannic acid on bile flow and the excretion of bilirubin, phyloerythyrin, coproporphyrin, alkaline phosphatase and bromsulphalein. *Proc. Roy. Soc., London, Ser. B* 153: 47–79, 1960.

62. HOFMANN, A. Clinical implications of physiochemical studies on bile salts. *Gastroenterology* 48: 484–494, 1965.

63. HOMSHER, E., AND G. C. COTZIAS. Antidiuretic hormone and bile flow. *Nature* 208: 687–688, 1965.

64. ISAKSSON, B. On the lipid constituents of normal bile. *Acta Soc. Med. Upsalien.* 56: 171–195, 1951.

65. JENNER, F. A., AND D. H. SMYTH. The excretion of phlorrhizin. *J. Physiol., London* 146: 563–571, 1959

66. JONES, R. S., AND F. P. BROOKS. The pyloric antrum as a mediator of insulin induced choleresis. *Physiologist* 8: 202–202, 1965.

67. JONES, R. S., K. C. POWELL, AND F. P. BROOKS. The role of the gastric antrum in the control of bile flow. *Surg. Forum* 16: 386–387, 1965.

68. JONSON, G., L. SUNDMAN, AND L. THULIN. The influence of chemically pure secretin on hepatic bile output. *Acta Physiol. Scand.* 62: 287–290, 1964.

69. JORPES, E., V. MUTT, G. JONSON, L. THULIN, AND L. SUNDMAN. The effect of secretin on bile flow. *Gastroenterology* 45: 786–788, 1963.

70. JORPES, E., V. MUTT, G. JONSON, L. THULIN, AND L. SUNDMAN. The influence of secretin and cholecystokinin on bile flow. In: *The Biliary System*, edited by W. Taylor. Oxford: Blackwell, 1965, p. 293–301.

71. KATSUKI, T., H. SHIMURA, C. G. JOHNSTON, AND H. MIYAKE. Constitution of bile proteins. *Proc. Soc. Exptl. Biol. Med.* 103: 272–274, 1960.

72. KAY, R. E., AND C. ENTENMAN. Stimulation of taurocholic acid synthesis and biliary excretion of lipids. *Am. J. Physiol.* 200: 855–859, 1961.

73. KAYE, G. I., H. O. WHEELER, R. T. WHITLOCK, AND N. LANE. Fluid transport in the rabbit gallbladder. A combined physiological and electron microscopic study. *J. Cell Biol.* 30: 237–268, 1966.

74. KJELLGREN, K. Biliary secretion in relation to the liver temperature and the blood pressure. *Acta Soc. Med. Upsalien.* 60: 172–185, 1955.

75. KNIGHTLY, J. J., P. VANAMEE, AND W. LAWRENCE, JR. The effect of intraduodenal hypertonic glucose on biliary and pancreatic secretion. *Surg. Forum* 11: 371–373, 1960.

76. KUUSISTO, A. N., AND A. TELKKÄ. Effect of adrenal hormones on bile flow in adrenalectomized rats. *Acta Endocrinol.* 43: 458–461, 1963.

77. LARGE, A. M., C. G. JOHNSTON, T. KATSUKI, AND H. L. FACHNIE. Gallstones and pregnancy. The composition of gallbladder bile in pregnant women at term. *Am. J. Med. Sci.* 239: 713–720, 1960.

78. LEONG, G. F., R. J. HOLLOWAY, AND R. W. BRAUER. Mechanics of bile formation. Transfer of potassium, sodium, chloride, phosphate and sulfate ions from perfusion medium to bile. *Federation Proc.* 14: 363–364, 1955.

79. LIGHT, H. G., C. WITMER, AND H. M. VARS. Interruption of the enterohepatic circulation and its effect on rat bile. *Am. J. Physiol.* 197: 1330–1332, 1959.

80. MAFFLY, R. H., AND A. LEAF. The potential of water in mammalian tissues. *J. Gen. Physiol.* 42: 1257–1275, 1959.

81. MAREN, T. H., A. C. ELLISON, S. K. FELLNER, AND W. B. GRAHAM. A study of hepatic carbonic anhydrase. *Mol. Pharmacol.* 2: 144–157, 1966.

82. MCBAIN, E. L., AND E. HUTCHINSON. *Solubilization and Related Phenomena.* New York: Acad. Press, 1955, p. 147.

83. MOORE, E. W., AND J. M. DIETSCHY. Na and K activity coefficients in bile and bile salts determined by glass electrodes. *Am. J. Physiol.* 206: 1111–1117, 1964.

83a. NAHRWOLD, D. L., AND M. I. GROSSMAN. Secretion of bile in response to food with and without bile in the intestine. *Gastroenterology* 53: 11–17, 1967.

84. NAKAYAMA, F., AND C. G. JOHNSTON. Fractionation of bile lipids with silicic acid column chromatography. *J. Lab. Clin. Med.* 59: 364–370, 1962.

85. NORMAN, A. Physico-chemical properties of bile constituents. In: *The Biliary System*, edited by W. Taylor. Oxford: Blackwell, 1965, p. 165–174.

86. NOVIKOFF, A. B., AND E. ESSNER. The liver cell. *Am. J. Med.* 29: 102–131, 1960.

87. O'MÁILLE, E. R. L., T. G. RICHARDS, AND A. H. SHORT. Acute taurine depletion and maximal rates of hepatic conjugation and secretion of cholic acid in the dog. *J. Physiol., London* 180: 67–79, 1965.

88. O'MÁILLE, E. R. L., T. G. RICHARDS, AND A. H. SHORT. Factors determining the maximal rate of organic anion secretion by the liver and further evidence on the hepatic site of action of the hormone secretin. *J. Physiol., London* 186: 424–438, 1966.

89. PAK, B. H., S. S. HONG, H. K. PAK, AND S. K. HONG. Effects of acetazolamide and acid-base changes on biliary and pancreatic secretion. *Am. J. Physiol.* 210: 624–628, 1966.

90. PALLIN, B., AND S. SKOGLUND. On the nervous regulation of the biliary system in the cat. *Acta Physiol. Scand.* 51: 187–192, 1961.

91. PATLAK, C. S., D. A. GOLDSTEIN, AND J. F. HOFFMAN.

The flow of solute and solvent across a two-membrane system. *J. Theoret. Biol.* 5: 426–442, 1963.

92. PERRIER, C. V., D. A. DREILING, AND H. D. JANOWITZ. A stop-flow analysis of pancreatic secretion. *Gastroenterology* 46: 700–705, 1964.

93. POPPER, H. L., N. C. JEFFERSON, E. WULKAN, AND H. NECHELES. Bile secretion and blood supply of the liver. *Am. J. Physiol.* 181: 435–438, 1955.

94. POPPER, H., AND F. SCHAFFNER. *Liver: Structure and Function.* New York: McGraw-Hill, 1957, p. 14.

95. PREISIG, R., H. L. COOPER, AND H. O. WHEELER. The relationship between taurocholate secretion rate and bile production in the unanesthetized dog during cholinergic blockade and during secretin administration. *J. Clin. Invest.* 41: 1152–1162, 1962.

96. PREISIG, R., J. G. RANKIN, J. G. SWEETING, R. WILLIAMS, AND S. E. BRADLEY. Bile formation during hepatic ischemia. *J. Clin. Invest.* 42: 966, 1963.

97. RAMORINO, M. L., L. LUZIETTI, AND N. CAMPIONI. Effeti della colecistocinina su l'attivita' biligenitica del fegato. *Folia Endocrinol.* 14: 266–271, 1961.

98. RAVDIN, I. S., C. G. JOHNSTON, C. RIEGEL, AND S. L. WRIGHT, JR. Studies on gall-bladder function. VII. The anion-cation content of hepatic and gall-bladder bile. *Am. J. Physiol.* 100: 317–327, 1932.

99. RAZIN, E., M. G. FELDMAN, AND D. A. DREILING. Studies on biliary flow and composition in man and dog. *J. Mt. Sinai Hosp.* 32: 42–50, 1965.

100. RHEINHOLD, J. G., AND D. W. WILSON. The acid-base composition of hepatic bile: I. *Am. J. Physiol.* 107: 378–387, 1934.

101. RICHARDS, T. G., AND J. Y. THOMSON. The secretion of bile against pressure. *Gastroenterology* 40: 705–707, 1961.

102. ROSENTHAL, W. S., K. KUBO, M. DOLINSKI, J. MARINO, W. L. MERSHEIMER, AND G. B. JERZY GLASS. The passage of serum albumin into bile in man. *Am. J. Digest. Diseases* 10: 271–283, 1965.

103. ROUILLER, C. Les canalicules biliaires. Étude au microscope électronique. *Acta Anat.* 26: 94–109, 1956.

104. ROUILLER, C., AND A.-M. JÉZÉQUEL. Electron microscopy of the liver. In: *The Liver: Morphology, Biochemistry, Physiology,* edited by C. Rouiller. New York: Acad. Press, 1963, vol. 1, p. 195–264.

105. RUDICK, J., AND J. F. S. HUTCHISON. Evaluation of vagotomy and biliary function by combined oral cholecystography and intravenous cholangiography. *Ann. Surg.* 162: 234–240, 1965.

106. RUSSELL, I. S., AND W. BURNETT. The proteins of human bile. *Gastroenterology* 45: 730–739, 1963.

107. RUSSELL, I. S., A. FLECK, AND W. BURNETT. The protein content of human bile. *Clin. Chim. Acta* 10: 210–213, 1964.

108. SABUROV, G. E. Effect of vagotomy on bile secretion of the liver. *Sechenov Physiol. J. USSR* 47: 70–74, 1961.

109. SABUROV, G. E. Effect of secretin on bile secretion under conditions of partial denervation of the liver. *Bull. Exptl. Biol. Med., USSR (English Transl.)* 59: 45–47, 1965.

110. SACKS, J., AND S. BAKSHY. Insulin and tissue distribution of pentose in nephrectomized cats. *Am. J. Physiol.* 189: 339–342, 1957.

111. SCHAFFNER, F., AND H. POPPER. Electron microscopic study of human cholestasis. *Proc. Soc. Exptl. Biol. Med.* 101: 777–779, 1959.

112. SCHAFFNER, F., AND H. POPPER. Morphologic studies of cholestasis. *Gastroenterology* 37: 565–573, 1959.

113. SCHANKER, L. S. Hepatic transport of organic cations. In: *The Biliary System,* edited by W. Taylor. Oxford: Blackwell, 1965, p. 469–480.

114. SCHANKER, L. S., AND C. A. M. HOGBEN. Biliary excretion of inulin, sucrose, and mannitol: analysis of bile formation. *Am. J. Physiol.* 200: 1087–1090, 1961.

115. SCHANKER, L. S., AND H. M. SOLOMON. Active transport of quaternary ammonium compounds into bile. *Am. J. Physiol.* 204: 829–832, 1963.

116. SCRATCHERD, T. Electrolyte composition and control of biliary secretion in the cat and rabbit. In: *The Biliary System,* edited by W. Taylor. Oxford: Blackwell, 1965, p. 515–529.

117. SLATER, T. F., AND D. B. GRIFFITHS. Effects of sporidesmin on bile flow rate and composition in the rat. *Biochem. J.* 88: 60–61P, 1963.

118. SOBOTKA, H. *Physiological Chemistry of the Bile.* Baltimore: Williams & Wilkins, 1937.

119. SPERBER, I. Secretion of organic anions in the formation of urine and bile. *Pharmacol. Rev.* 11: 109–134, 1959.

120. SPERBER, I. Biliary excretion and choleresis. In: *Proceedings International Pharmacology Meeting, 1st, Stockholm, 1961.* Oxford: Pergamon, 1963, vol. 4, p. 137–143.

121. SPERBER, I. Biliary secretion of organic anions and its influence on bile flow. In: *The Biliary System,* edited by W. Taylor. Oxford: Blackwell, 1965, p. 457–467.

122. STEINER, J. W., AND J. S. CARRUTHERS. Studies on the fine structure of the terminal branches of the biliary tree. I. The morphology of normal bile canaliculi, bile pre-ductules (Ducts of Hering) and bile ductules. *Am. J. Pathol.* 38: 639–661, 1961.

123. STERNLIEB, I. Electron microscopic study of intrahepatic biliary ductules. *J. Microscop.* 4: 71–80, 1965.

124. STONE, S. L. Energy requirements for bile secretion. In: *The Biliary System,* edited by W. Taylor. Oxford: Blackwell, 1965, p. 277–292.

125. STRANSKY, E. Untersuchungen über die pharmakologie der gallensekretion. IV. Mitteilung. Ausscheidung von stoffen durch die Galle. *Z. ges. Exptl. Med.* 77: 807–841, 1931.

126. TANTURI, C. A., AND A. C. IVY. A study of the effect of vascular changes in the liver and the excitation of its nerve supply on the formation of bile. *Am. J. Physiol.* 121: 61–74, 1938.

127. TANTURI, C. A., AND A. C. IVY. On the existence of secretory nerves in the vagi for and the reflex excitation and inhibition of bile secretion. *Am. J. Physiol.* 121: 270–283, 1938.

128. TAYLOR, W. (Editor). *The Biliary System.* (A symposium of the NATO Advanced Study Institute.) Oxford: Blackwell, 1965.

129. TELKKÄ, A., AND A. N. KUUSISTO. Bile flow in adrenalectomized rats. *Acta Endocrinol.* 41: 57–60, 1962.

130. THEILER, K. Do bile ducts act solely as biliary channels? *German Med. Monthly* 8: 202–204, 1963.

131. THOMAS, J. E. An improved cannula for gastric and intestinal fistulas. *Proc. Soc. Exptl. Biol. Med.* 46: 260–265, 1941.

132. THUREBORN, E. Human hepatic bile. Composition changes

due to altered enterohepatic circulation *Acta Chir. Scand. Suppl.* 303: 1-63, 1962.

133. VANLERENBERGHE, J. Étude de l'intervention de quelques facteurs enzymatiques dans la cholérèse. II. Action de quelques inhibiteurs enzymatiques sur la cholérèse du foie perfusé. *Rev. Intern. Hepatol.* 9: 497-540, 1959.

134. VANLERENBERGHE, J. The effects of hypothermia on biliary function. In: *The Biliary System*, edited by W. Taylor. Oxford: Blackwell, 1965, p. 263-276.

135. VANLERENBERGHE, J., AND N. BAR. Action de l'hypothermie sur la cholérèse du foie de rat perfusé. *J. Physiol., Paris* 55: 352-353, 1963.

136. VANLERENBERGHE, J., N. BIZARD-GREGOIRE, A. ROBELET, AND F. GUERRIN. Action de quelques barbituriques sur la sécrétion de bile par le foie de rat perfusé. *Anesthesie, Analgesie, Reanimation* 15: 901-907, 1958.

137. VANLERENBERGHE, J., N. TRUPIN, C. BEL, AND L. ADENIS. Action du xylose sur la cholérèse de foie de rat perfusé. *J. Physiol., Paris* 56: 456-457, 1964.

138. VERSCHURE, J. C. M. Electro-chromograms of human bile. *Clin. Chim. Acta* 1: 38-48, 1956.

139. VERSCHURE, J. C. M., AND P. F. MIJNIEFF. The dominating macromolecular complex of human gallbladder bile. *Clin. Chim. Acta* 1: 154-166, 1956.

140. WHEELER, H. O., AND P. L. MANCUSI-UNGARO. Role of bile ducts during secretin choleresis in dogs. *Am. J. Physiol.* 210: 1153-1159, 1966.

141. WHEELER, H. O., AND O. L. RAMOS. Determinants of the flow and composition of bile in the unanesthetized dog during constant infusions of sodium taurocholate. *J. Clin. Invest.* 39: 161-170, 1960.

142. ZATERKA, S., AND M. I. GROSSMAN. The effect of gastrin and histamine on secretion of bile. *Gastroenterology* 50: 500-505, 1966.

CHAPTER 114

Secretion of organic compounds in bile

LEWIS S. SCHANKER[1] | *Laboratory of Chemical Pharmacology, National Heart Institute,*
National Institutes of Health, Bethesda, Maryland

CHAPTER CONTENTS

CONSIDERING THE NUMBER of studies dealing with biliary excretion of organic compounds,[2] one might wonder why so few details of the process have been learned. The current level of our understanding of hepatic excretion is largely comparable to that extant for renal excretion 30 years ago. We know that substances can enter the bile by diffusion or secretion (active transport), and entrance may occur by filtration; but no methods are available to estimate the relative contribution of each of these processes in the biliary excretion of a given compound. Little is known of the sites at which diffusion, filtration, and secretion occur, and nothing is known concerning reabsorption of substances from the biliary tract.

A main difficulty may be that the mechanisms by which many substances enter the bile are closely associated with the mechanism of bile formation (127, 140, 143), and our understanding of the latter process is poor. Also, development of a reasonable hypothesis about bile formation and hepatic excretion has been hampered by a lack of understanding of hepatic structure and of the circulation of hepatic blood and lymph (17, 25, 112).

In addition, few studies of biliary excretion have been directed toward uncovering the fundamentals of the process. Many papers describe only the amount or concentration of a substance in bile, and many of the older studies of this type are of questionable value, because the analytical methods used were not sufficiently specific. Many recent studies deal with the identification of substances and their metabolites in bile and with the enterohepatic circulation of organic compounds (124); but few provide the data needed to explain the mechanisms of hepatic excretion.

Understanding of hepatic excretion is far behind that of renal excretion because too little effort has been made to develop suitable, metabolically stable reference standards or model compounds (such as inulin and *p*-aminohippurate in the kidney) with which to compare biliary excretion of other substances. Too much effort has been expended on the details of excretion of substances such as sulfobromophthalein, the hepatic disposition of which is so complicated by metabolic reactions and tissue binding that there is little likelihood of uncovering basic principles of the excretion process.

This review concerns what is known and generally thought about the passage of organic compounds from the blood into the bile. Changes in composition of bile caused by the gallbladder are not considered. No detailed examination of the excretion of

---

[1] Present address: University of Missouri at Kansas City, Kansas City, Missouri.
[2] See review articles (15, 17, 22, 24, 25, 37, 94, 116, 124, 127) and collections of review reports (23, 134).

endogenous substances such as the bile pigments and bile acids are undertaken, since these topics are covered elsewhere.

METHODOLOGY

Methods In Vivo

To study the mechanism of biliary excretion of a substance, the experimental design should permit, at the minimum, measurements of the substance in both plasma and bile by a highly specific analytical method. Bile volume should be measured, and it may also be helpful to estimate the concentration of compound in hepatic tissue.

If the plasma concentration of injected compound is kept reasonably constant throughout an experiment by a constant intravenous infusion or by simply ligating the renal pedicles, the data readily lend themselves to kinetic analysis, and little error is made in estimating the distribution ratio of compound between bile and plasma at the steady state. If, on the other hand, the level of compound in plasma is allowed to decline rapidly as a result of metabolism or urinary excretion, analysis of the data will be complicated as a true steady-state distribution may not be attained (115).

In an experiment, results are generally expressed in two ways: as a rate of excretion (amount excreted/unit time; percentage of dose excreted/unit time; clearance), and as a bile-to-plasma concentration ratio of compound at the steady state. Collection of these data over a wide range of plasma concentrations often gives a good indication of the nature of the excretion process.

If only the rate of excretion is measured, the results of an experiment can be misleading. When a large proportion of an administered compound is rapidly eliminated in the bile, there is probably no explanation other than excretion by active transport. When the proportion excreted is small, no conclusions can be drawn; for example, studies of guanethidine excretion in the rat (119) have shown that the 2-hour biliary elimination of the drug amounts to only about 0.2% of the administered dose. Yet the concentration of drug in bile is 16–25 times that in plasma over the time period of the experiment. With this compound the slow rate of excretion is a result of the exceedingly low concentration in plasma, most of the compound being tightly held in skeletal muscle by binding.

Data on the rate of excretion can also be misleading when a compound, administered by single injection, is rapidly eliminated by the kidneys. Thus, in dogs with normal renal function, the 3-hour biliary excretion of phenol red amounts to less than 3% of the injected dose, with 75% appearing in the urine; but when the experiment is carried out in nephrectomized animals, the 3-hour biliary excretion of dye amounts to almost 30% of the dose (80). Since many compounds secreted by the liver are eliminated even more rapidly by the kidney (116, 127), the active transport of many substances from plasma to bile probably has gone unnoticed.

A different approach to the study of biliary excretion is provided by intravital fluorescence microscopy of the liver (52, 56, 108). Ideally, the compound studied should be immune to metabolic alteration, since the method of observation will hardly distinguish between a fluorescent substance and its fluorescent metabolites. Though the method does not allow quantitative measurements, it has the obvious advantage of direct observation of the anatomical sites of transfer.

Methods In Vitro

The isolated, perfused liver has been used to a limited extent in studies of biliary excretion (4, 29, 66, 67, 69, 70). This preparation can secrete certain compounds and offers a number of advantages over methods in vivo. The plasma level of a compound can be more easily regulated, the excretion of toxic substances can be investigated more readily, studies of the effect of metabolic poisons and anaerobic conditions on the excretion process are facilitated, and the complications of extrahepatic metabolism and excretion are eliminated.

The liver slice preparation has been investigated to see if uptake by the slice is comparable to transport from plasma to bile. With sulfobromophthalein, the slice preparation seems of no value. Rat liver slices apparently take up the dye by a process of diffusion, and it becomes highly concentrated in the tissue by binding to cell components (5, 9, 10, 26). The uptake is not depressed by anoxia or various metabolic poisons and good uptake occurs with heat-denatured slices.

In contrast, success has been obtained in studying the liver slice uptake of a quaternary ammonium compound, procaine amide ethobromide (125). The cation is taken up by a mechanism that closely resembles the secretory process in vivo. Moreover, anoxia and various metabolic inhibitors interfere with the energy-requiring uptake process.

NATURE OF THE TRANSFER PROCESS

Biliary excretion divides organic compounds into two groups: one appears in bile in a concentration greatly exceeding that of plasma, the other appears in bile in a concentration similar to or less than that in plasma.

Compounds Excreted in a Concentration Higher Than That in Plasma

Compounds of this group include a variety of organic anions, cations, zwitterions, and uncharged molecules. They have no obvious properties in common except that they are relatively polar and exhibit low lipid-to-water partition coefficients at pH values of 7–8. These substances are excreted by active transport, since the uncharged molecules move from plasma to bile against sizable concentration gradients, and many ions attain such high bile-to-plasma concentration ratios that their transfer must certainly take place against an electrochemical potential gradient. Morever, with a number of the compounds, a maximal rate of excretion (transport maximum— TM) has been observed, and certain compounds have been shown to compete with one another for excretion.

It would be oversimplifying to say that biliary excretion of a substance occurs by a process of active transport. This would not account for the fact that there are at least two membranes interposed between plasma (or rather, the extracellular fluid of liver) and the bile; that is, a substance must penetrate a liver cell before it can be secreted into bile. In the concentrative transfer of a compound from plasma to bile, two membrane-transfer processes are involved, one of which must be the type referred to as "active transport."

A number of combinations of transfer processes seem consistent with active biliary secretion. A compound could penetrate one surface of the liver cell by diffusion and then be transported from cell to bile across another surface. Or cell uptake could occur by active transport, with the compound then diffusing into bile. Or instead of diffusion, one of the transfer processes could be an equilibrating carrier mechanism such as facilitated diffusion (145); or cell uptake could occur by pinocytosis (8, 34, 49, 71).

Finally, both processes could be of the active transport type.

Because of the paucity of evidence concerning this question, it is difficult to eliminate completely any of the above combinations. Still, from a few key observations on the liver and from information gained from studies of other cellular systems, it is possible to construct a picture of the more reasonable possibilities.

A combination of uptake by diffusion and output by active transport seems highly unlikely, since a cell freely permeable to large organic anions and cations over a considerable fraction of its surface could hardly maintain the gradients of inorganic ions and other substances necessary for survival and function. Moreover, uptake by diffusion would not be consistent with the microscopic observation in the rat in vivo that the uptake of fluorescein by parenchymal cells is highly sensitive to changes in temperature. The rate of uptake slows considerably as temperature is lowered and appears to cease at temperatures of about 20 C (56).

Uptake by active transport and output by diffusion is another unlikely combination. The microscopic observation in vivo that fluorescein can be present in bile canaliculi in a concentration greatly exceeding that in liver cells (56) is strong evidence that cell-to-bile transfer takes place by a process of active transport. Moreover, "uphill" transport from liver cells to bile is suggested from studies with p-acetylaminohippurate in the rat (83). The concentration of this anion in bile is 20–30 times that in total liver water.

If we accept the thesis that the cellular uptake of secreted substances cannot be explained by diffusion and that transfer from cell to bile must take place by active transport, the question remains whether cell uptake occurs by active transport, facilitated diffusion, or pinocytosis. Although there is little doubt that the hepatic parenchymal cell takes up substances by pinocytosis (8), it is unlikely that this process could operate fast enough to account for a major portion of the uptake of many of the secreted substances. The intracellular concentration of compounds such as sulfobromophthalein and fluorescein is so much greater than that in plasma that the cell would have to engulf many times its own volume of extracellular fluid in a short time to account for the observed uptake.

Whatever the precise nature of the specialized process by which the cell takes up secretable substances, we are still left with the question whether the uptake proceeds against a concentration gradient (e.g., active transport) or down the concentration gradient (e.g., facilitated diffusion). Since at present there is no clear-cut way of distinguishing between cellular accumulation resulting from binding to cell components and that resulting from active transport, it is impossible to rule out one or the other of the specialized uptake processes. A number of secreted substances (or their metabolites) have been shown to attain a concentration in hepatic tissue greatly exceeding that in plasma (5, 26–28, 56, 97); and, in the cases of fluorescein and rose bengal (tetrachlorotetraiodofluorescein), accumulation has been shown to occur in hepatic parenchymal cells (56, 97). Since the cellular accumulation of fluorescein appears to be more highly dependent on temperature variations than would be expected for a protein-binding process (56), this characteristic might be accepted as evidence that accumulation results mainly from active transport rather than from intracellular binding. However, another explanation is possible; that is, assuming that cell uptake occurs only by facilitated diffusion and accumulation results only from binding, an apparent lowering of accumulation at lowered temperatures could result simply from a slowing down of the rate of facilitated diffusion.

More direct evidence bearing on the nature of cellular accumulation has been obtained from studies of the binding of substances in liver slices (5, 10, 12, 26), heat-denatured slices (9), and liver homogenates (11, 77, 104, 119, 125). These investigations show that secreted compounds, such as sulfobromophthalein and related dyes, some sulfonated azo dyes, procaine amide ethobromide, guanethidine, and certain steroids, are moderately to highly bound to components of liver tissue. Thus, it seems clear that the cellular accumulation of certain secreted substances is due, at least in part, to binding; but this does not rule out the possible participation of active transport in the overall accumulation in vivo.

An additional piece of information concerning the topic of cellular accumulation has been obtained from a study of the uptake of procaine amide ethobromide by rat liver slices (117, 125). Although this compound is bound to some extent by tissue components, it appears to become concentrated in the slice mainly by a process of active transport, since accumulation can be blocked by substances that do not interfere with the binding. However, this does not prove that the compound is accumulated within the cells, for the observed accumulation might simply reflect secretion into bile canaliculi within the slice.

In summary, secreted substances seem to be taken up by liver cells by a specialized transport process and transferred from cells to bile by a specialized transport process. Cell-to-bile transfer appears to occur by active transport. Extracellular fluid-to-cell transfer may consist of active transport, facilitated diffusion, pinocytosis, or some combination of these processes. Accumulation within the cell often results from binding to cell components, and it is possible that active transport contributes to the accumulation. Finally, the rate of passive diffusion of secreted substances from extracellular fluid into the cell or from the cell into bile must be much slower than the rates of transfer by the specialized transport processes.

Compounds Excreted in a Concentration Similar to or Less Than That in Plasma

The organic compounds in this group include a number of lipid-insoluble uncharged molecules, a wide variety of highly lipid-soluble weak electrolytes, and a miscellaneous group of organic ions. So little work has been done with these compounds that we know even less about the nature of their hepatic transfer than we do about that of the secreted substances.

Perhaps the excretion of the lipid-soluble weak electrolytes is more readily understood than that of the other substances in this category. Although a survey of the literature on the physiological distribution of drugs and other highly lipid-soluble substances reveals few careful measurements of biliary concentrations, one gets the impression that the substances appear in bile in a concentration similar to that of the unbound fraction of drug in plasma. This is understandable considering that the substances diffuse with ease across most body membranes and become distributed according to their degree of ionization in the fluids bathing either side of the membrane (after correction for the degree of protein binding in the fluids) (115). If the compound is essentially non-ionized, the distribution ratio across the membrane will be unity. However, if the compound is appreciably ionized in the body fluids, the distribution ratio will deviate from unity, either because of a Donnan type of ionic distribution or because of a difference in hydrogen-ion concentration on the two sides of the membrane (31, 72, 116). This unequal distribution of weak electrolytes follows from the fact that most membranes are highly permeable to the lipid-soluble, non-ionized form of a compound and relatively impermeable to the ionized form.

Although the pH differential between bile and

plasma has not been studied in detail, it does not appear to be of great magnitude, at least in the dog (102) and rat (L. S. Schanker, unpublished observations). For example, in a few measurements with rat bile (collected under oil), the pH has been found to be about 7.6. Thus, assuming a pH differential of about 0.2 unit between rat bile and plasma, it can be calculated that the highest bile-to-plasma distribution ratio for a weak electrolyte would be approximately 1.6, and the lowest ratio 0.6 (115). Weak organic acids would have ratios greater than unity, and weak bases, ratios less than unity.

An interesting problem arises when one considers that the ionized form of a weak electrolyte could be actively secreted into bile. As the secreted drug moves along the bile ducts, there might be time, depending on the location of the secretory site, for reequilibration with plasma. Then the collected bile would have a concentration of the compound, which would give no indication that secretion had taken place. This situation probably exists, but it has not been verified. Certainly some of the compounds secreted into bile are weak electrolytes, for example, p-aminohippurate (38, 39) and p-acetylaminohippurate (42, 83); however, very little reabsorption of these two substances would be expected, since their non-ionized forms have a very low lipid solubility and would accordingly diffuse across the bile duct epithelium with difficulty. To approach the problem experimentally, studies would have to be made with compounds having a non-ionized form of high lipid solubility. Renal physiologists, faced with a similar problem, have been able to describe the renal excretion of certain lipid-soluble compounds in terms of active tubular secretion of the ionized form and passive reabsorption of the non-ionized form. In the experiments the degree of ionization of a compound (and thus its rate of passive reabsorption) is varied by altering the pH value of urine. Under these conditions, inhibitors of the secretory process are administered to assess their action on the secretion of the compound (138, 139).

Studies of the hepatic uptake and biliary excretion of lipid-soluble drugs are complicated by the fact that most of these substances are metabolized by the liver (124, 146). In one study, however, this difficulty has been largely overcome by working at low temperatures (84). Thus, in the isolated, perfused rabbit liver, maintained at a temperature near 0 C, compounds of widely different lipid solubilities were shown to penetrate the tissue at rates roughly related to their lipid-to-water partition coefficients as measured at pH 7.4. The relative rates of penetra-

tion were similar to those reported for a number of other body membranes.

Turning next to a different group of compounds, a number of lipid-insoluble saccharides have been shown to be excreted in the bile of various species in a concentration similar to or less than that in plasma (35, 38, 65, 67, 118). In the rat, under the conditions of a steady state, the bile-to-plasma concentration ratios of inulin, sucrose, and mannitol are about 0.1, 0.2, and 1.1, respectively; this suggests a relation between biliary excretion and the size of molecules (118). For a given compound, different bile-to-plasma ratios are obtained in different species; moreover, it appears that the ratio, at least for inulin and sucrose, is dependent on the rate of bile flow, the ratio declining when flow is increased (35, 65, 127). Although the available data are insufficient to allow meaningful interpretations, they do indicate a significant porosity at some locus in the hepatobiliary system and suggest that large, lipid-insoluble molecules enter the bile by processes of restricted diffusion or filtration.

Hepatic parenchymal cells show an unusual degree of permeability to the above-mentioned saccharides—substances generally confined to the extracellular space of tissues. For example, mannitol (118) and sorbitol (32) penetrate into the intracellular water of liver and rapidly equilibrate with all the liver water. Moreover, sucrose appears to penetrate hepatic cells to some extent, since it becomes distributed in a space of 36% of the wet tissue weight. In comparison, the inulin and sodium ion spaces of liver are about 23% of the wet weight (25, 118).

Large, lipid-insoluble molecules could enter liver cells either by diffusing through pores in the cell membrane or by being taken up by some nonspecific transport process such as pinocytosis. Although pores large enough to allow the passage of mannitol, sorbitol, or sucrose would appear to be incompatible with the biochemical integrity of the cell, as long as the pore walls were lined with fixed positive and negative charges that restricted the flow of ions, the cell could conceivably survive. Uptake by a pinocytotic mechanism would also appear to be a plausible explanation, but it is difficult to see how this would account for the different degrees of uptake of sucrose and mannitol.

Though it seems clear that these saccharides can pass from extracellular fluid into hepatic cells, it is by no means certain that they pass from the cells directly into bile. No information is available on this point. An alternative pathway for the passage of these substances from extracellular fluid to bile would be through intercellular spaces. The molecules could move through these narrow channels (8, 111) by restricted diffusion or filtration, or both (39, 127).

Small amounts of very large molecules, such as serum albumin and γ-globulin (57, 106, 110), and particles of methyl methacrylate as large as 0.06–0.11 μ in diameter (76) have been detected in the bile of various species. Since γ-globulin does not appear to be synthesized in liver cells, the protein probably enters the bile directly from the extracellular fluid of liver, presumably by moving through the intercellular channels mentioned above (106). Moreover, the same pathway is suggested by isotope-dilution studies with labeled serum albumin in which it has been shown that most, if not all, bile albumin is derived from the plasma albumin pool (110).

A number of quaternary ammonium ions, such as decamethonium, hexamethonium, and tetraethylammonium, appear in bile in a concentration similar to or less than that in plasma (36, 90, 114, 117). Although it would appear that these substances enter the bile by a passive process of diffusion or filtration, it is difficult to rule out a low degree of affinity for the process which secretes certain other quaternary amines into bile (117). Hexamethonium has been shown to penetrate the rat liver and to attain a concentration in the tissue similar to that in whole blood (90).

SITES OF TRANSFER AND MECHANISM
OF BILE FORMATION

Some of the pathways by which solutes would be expected to pass from plasma to bile are indicated in Figure 1 (8). The drawing is highly diagrammatic and is not intended to show with accuracy the relative dimensions of structures or spaces. For details of structure, see other articles (45, 48, 111, 112).

The wide spaces between cells of the sinusoidal endothelium suggest that most components of blood, other than the formed elements, can pass with ease into the perisinusoidal space of Disse. Direct evidence of a high degree of permeability is provided by the observation of a rapid movement of fluorescein across the endothelium (56), the rapidity with which inulin, dextran, raffinose, and albumin equilibrate between plasma and the extracellular compartment of liver [(25, 32, 51); unpublished observation], and the presence in the Disse space of chylomicrons and fine granular material of plasma (8).

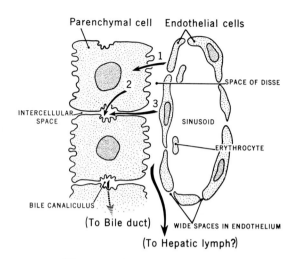

FIG. 1. Diagrammatic representation of some of the pathways (arrows 1, 2, and 3) by which substances might enter the bile. See text for explanation. [Based on diagram by Ashworth & Sanders (8).]

From the space of Disse, solutes can pass into bile by penetrating two surfaces of the parenchymal cell (arrows 1 and 2 in Fig. 1) or by passing along the narrow space between parenchymal cells (arrow 3 in Fig. 1). As suggested above in this article, the former route is the one taken by at least some of the secreted substances (e.g., fluorescein), whereas the latter route may be open to all substances but to a degree dependent on the size of the molecules.

Another pathway through which exchange between plasma and bile can take place (not shown in Fig. 1) is across the bile duct epithelium. Although active secretion of organic compounds at this site is possible (56, 97), the bile duct epithelium does not, according to present views of bile formation, appear to be a major site of secretion, at least not for organic anions such as the bile acids. It has been proposed (127, 140, 143) that the primary event in the formation of bile is the active transport of bile acid anions (and possibly other, though quantitatively less important, compounds) from parenchymal cells into the bile canaliculi. The osmotic effect of these substances results in a flow (diffusion or osmotic filtration, or both) of water and solutes into the bile canaliculi. Since the sodium and potassium concentrations of bile are similar to those of plasma (88, 107), and the ions become equilibrated between the two fluids rapidly despite a relatively slow equilibration between plasma and hepatic tissue (21, 88), it is reasonable to suggest that the movement of the water and its solutes into the canaliculi occurs largely through the spaces between parenchymal cells rather than through the cell cytoplasm. Of course, it is just as reasonable to suggest that equilibration of inorganic ions occurs across the bile duct epithelium (24, 141). Though there is no direct evidence of a bulk flow of fluid through the spaces between parenchymal cells into the bile canaliculi—actually, one would expect flow in the opposite direction, considering the hydrostatic and oncotic pressure differences between bile and sinusoidal plasma (24)—such a continual flow toward the canaliculi would explain why bile components do not ordinarily pass in the reverse direction through the same spaces into the Disse space.

Although it is clear that much work is needed to elucidate the mechanism of bile formation, support for at least one portion of the above view is provided by the observation that many of the acidic substances that are actively secreted into bile increase the rate of bile formation (61, 127–129, 140, 143). When administered in quantities sufficient to increase the flow of bile to a similar large degree, these substances appear in the bile in roughly similar concentrations (128, 129).

Not taken into account in the above discussion is the effect of the hormone secretin on the composition and flow of bile in certain species (122, 141). For example, administration of this substance to dogs leads to the addition to bile of a large volume of bicarbonate-rich fluid (102, 141, 143). It has been suggested that normal fluctuations in the blood levels of endogenous secretin may account for the spontaneous variations in the rate of bile flow observed in animals in which the bile acid-induced fraction of bile has been stabilized by constant infusions of taurocholate (141, 143). Some evidence suggests that the secretin-induced fraction of bile arises from the bile duct epithelium rather than from the region of the parenchymal cells (141).

Even though the bile duct epithelium may be quantitatively unimportant in the biliary secretion of organic acids, there is no evidence to suggest an unimportant role in the secretion of other classes of compounds such as the monoquaternary amines and cardiac glycosides. The fact that choleretic activity has not been reported for these latter substances might suggest that they are secreted at a site different from that of the acids. However, the absence of reports of choleresis could just as well be explained by the limited quantities of these compounds that can be administered to animals because of high toxicity. Perhaps the question could be settled by experiments with the isolated perfused liver.

SECRETION OF ORGANIC COMPOUNDS INTO BILE

It is difficult to deduce from the literature which substances are actively transported into bile. Often no information is given concerning either the concentration of the compounds in plasma or that in bile; instead, excretion is described only in terms of the amount of substance or the percentage of the injected dose that appears in bile in a given time. Thus, in most cases, one cannot say whether transfer from plasma to bile has occurred against a concentration gradient.

Another difficulty is the failure of many reports to provide identification of the substance being measured in bile. For example, results may be presented only as the concentration of radioactivity, antibacterial activity, color, fluorescence, or ultraviolet absorption. In this regard it is worth remembering that many experiments with sulfobromophthalein were carried out under the assumption that all the blue color in bile represented the unaltered dye; when the bile was finally subjected to chromatographic procedures, it was learned that most of the color was due to conjugates of the compound.

Even when bile is assayed by quantitative methods of supposedly high specificity or the substance in bile identified by chromatography, countercurrent distribution, and other techniques, there is a slight possibility of error, since the analytical method may alter the chemical nature of the excreted substance. For instance, if a compound is excreted as one of the more readily hydrolyzable types of glucuronides, the use of acid or alkali in the analytical procedure may convert the conjugate to the parent compound and lead the investigator to an erroneous conclusion (146).

A further difficulty in deciding whether a compound is secreted into bile arises when the compound is an ion and appears in bile in a concentration similar to that in plasma. Since the exact value for the passive distribution of an ion between bile and plasma is not known, it is impossible to distinguish between active and passive transfer in these cases.

In view of the above uncertainties, it is desirable to survey the literature by using a system that provides some indication of how firmly the available evidence establishes the biliary secretion of a given compound. Accordingly, in Tables 1–3 compounds are divided into groups based on the type of data that has been published concerning their biliary excretion. For example, compounds that have been measured in both bile and plasma by a specific analytical method are placed in a group apart from compounds measured only in the bile. The precise criteria used for the various categories are described in the footnotes of Table 1. Since it is sometimes impossible to arrive at definite conclusions about the specificity of the analytical method used in a particular study, judgment of this factor must be based partly on what is generally known about various types of methods and partly on the reviewer's own experience with analytical methods. In some cases the problem is simplified because, although biliary excretion has been assessed by a nonspecific method, it is known from other work that the compound is metabolically stable or that it is excreted to a significant extent as the unchanged compound.

From the foregoing discussion it should be clear that future work may disclose that some compounds in Tables 1–3 are in fact not secreted, as such, into bile. With this in mind the listings can be viewed as a summary of present knowledge and a guide for future investigations.

Finally, some of the compounds in Tables 1–3 have been the subject of so many studies that all the references cannot be given. In these instances, reference will be made to a few of the more important papers or to review articles.

Anions

The organic anions that appear to be secreted into bile are listed in Table 1. The group includes many substances of widely different chemical structure, some endogenous and many foreign to the organism. Most of the compounds contain either carboxylic or sulfonic acid groups, but a few (e.g., chlorothiazide and hydrochlorothiazide) contain neither of these groupings. Thus, the compounds have only one obvious property in common: at the pH of bile and plasma, they exist primarily as anions.

A maximal rate of secretion (TM) has been demonstrated for several of the compounds, including *p*-acetylaminohippurate (83), bromcresol green (126), bromphenol blue (126), sulfobromophthalein sodium (38, 121), chlorothiazide (61), eriocyanin (66), and phenol red (126). In addition, many, if not all, of the organic anions seem to be excreted by the same transport process, since they appear to compete for excretion into bile. For example, the excretion of endogenous cholate is inhibited by dehydrocholate (19, 107) and cinchophen (18, 19). The secretion of sulfobromophthalein (or its metabolites) is inhibited by dehydrocholate (33, 148) and cholate (148), that of fluorescein by bilirubin and cholate (56), that

of phenol red by taurocholate and glycocholate (127), that of taurocholate by bromcresol green (126), and that of indocyanine green by methicillin (58). In addition, the secretion of bilirubin glucuronide is inhibited by indocyaninine green and methicillin (58) and that of *p*-acetylaminohippurate by chlorothiazide (61) and sulfobromophthalein (83). In some of these examples a conjugated form of the injected substance may well be responsible for the inhibitory action, but the list includes also a number of examples of inhibition by nonmetabolized compounds. The kinetics of competitive inhibition in bile excretion studies and the interpretation of data involving competition between endogenous and exogenous substances have been thoroughly discussed in an earlier review (127).

It might appear from the above summary that the anion-secreting process of the liver has little or no specificity and that any organic acid will appear in bile in high concentrations as long as it has a low enough lipid solubility to prevent rapid reabsorption after secretion. However, there are a few examples in which small changes in chemical structure have been reported to result in significant changes in the rate of biliary excretion. For example, with the disulfonate azo dye, lissamine fast yellow 2 G, when both chlorine atoms and the one methyl group are replaced by two hydrogen atoms and a carboxyl group, respectively, resulting in the dye tartrazine, the 6-hour biliary excretion in the rat declines from 96% to 1% of the dose (113). Moreover, a single hydroxyl group seems to be of importance in the biliary excretion of some hydroxybiphenyl glucuronides. For instance, when 4-hydroxybiphenyl glucuronide is injected in rats, 58% of the dose is excreted in 24 hours; and when 4,4′-dihydroxybiphenyl glucuronide is injected, 92% is excreted (147). However, the significance of both of these examples is weakened by the absence of information concerning the rates of urinary excretion of the compounds during the bile-collection periods and by the absence of information about the plasma levels of the substances. If the plasma level of a compound is kept relatively low by tissue binding or urinary excretion, a low rate of biliary excretion would be expected. Thus, at present, there is little evidence of structural specificity in the anion-transport process of the liver.

It is of interest to note that a similar low degree of specificity is found in the secretion of acids by the kidney (127). Moreover, it has been recognized for a number of years that the kidney and liver secrete many of the same anionic compounds. However,

TABLE I. *Organic Anions Actively Secreted Into Bile*

*Strong evidence for secretion**

Miscellaneous anions:
  p-Acetylaminohippuric acid (42, 83)
  p-Aminohippuric acid (38, 39)
  D(−)-6-(α-amino-α-phenylacetamido)penicillanic acid (131)
  Bilirubin (unconjugated) (89)
  Bilirubin glucuronide (7)
  Chlorothiazide (61)
  Fluorescein (56, 137)
  Indocyanine green (79, 142)
  Phenol-3,6-dibromophthalein disulfonate (73)
  Phenol red (62, 70, 80, 126)
  Sulfobromophthalein (25, 37, 38, 81, 109, 124, 144)
  Taurocholic acid, glycocholic acid, and probably many other endogenous acids (13, 63, 64, 126, 127)

Probable secretion†

Miscellaneous anions:
  4-Amino-3-iodohippuric acid (147)
  Dichloromethotrexate (98)
  Methotrexate (68)
  Retinoic acid (149, 150)
  Succinylsulfathiazole (1)
Fluorescein derivatives:
  Dibromofluorescein (137)
  Dibromodiiodofluorescein (137)
  Diiodofluorescein (137)
  Tetrabromofluorescein (eosine) (70, 137)
  Tetrabromotetrachlorofluorescein (137)
  Tetrachlorotetraiodofluorescein (rose bengal) (75, 109)
  Tetraiodofluorescein (137)
Sulfonated azo dyes:
  Amaranth (104, 105, 113)
  Brilliant scarlet (113)
  Carmoisine (113)
  Geranine 2 GS (104, 113)
  Lissamine fast yellow 2 G (104, 113)
  Methyl orange (70, 113)
  Naphthalene fast orange 2 GS (113)
  Orange GCN (113)
  Ponceau SX (105, 113)
  3′-Sulfo-4-dimethylaminoazobenzene (113)
  Sunset yellow (105, 113)
Glucuronides:
  4,4′-Dihydroxybiphenyl monoglucuronide (147)
  4-Hydroxybiphenyl glucuronide (147)
  Phenolphthalein glucuronide (1)
  Sulfadimethoxine-N¹-glucuronide (1, 147)

Some evidence suggesting secretion‡

Miscellaneous anions:
  Acetazolamide (95)
  Alizarin yellow (70)
  Cinchophen (6, 14, 19)
  Hydrochlorothiazide (101)
  Methyl red (66)
  Phenoltetrabromophthalein (109)

TABLE I.—*Concluded*

  Phenoltetrachlorophthalein (109)
  Phloxin J (66)
  Rosolic acid (70)
Fluorescein derivatives:
  Dibromohydroxymercurifluorescein (109)
  Hydroxymercurifluorescein (109)
Sulfonated azo dyes:
  Congo red (66, 70)
  Dechlorolissamine (104)
  Fast yellow (113)
  Orange I (70)
  Orange II (70)
  Ponceau RS (113)
  Red 10 BS (113)
Sulfonphthaleins:
  Bromcresol green (80, 126)
  Bromcresol purple (70)
  Bromphenol blue (66, 70, 80, 126)
  Chlorphenol red (43)
  Cresol red (70)
  Thymol blue (70)
Other sulfonic acid dyes:
  Chlorsulphthalein (109)
  o-Cresoltetrachlorophthalein sulfonate (109)
  Cyanol (70)
  Diamine red B (70)
  Echtrot A (70)
  Eriocyanin (66)
  Erioglaucin (66, 70)
  Indigo carmine (70)
  Iodosulphthalein (109)
  Orange GT (70)
  Patent blue V (70)
Penicillins:
  p-Aminobenzylpenicillin (59)
  L(+)-6-(α-amino-α-phenylacetamido)penicillanic acid (59)
  Ancillin (82)
  Benzylpenicillin (2, 59, 82)
  Methicillin (2, 59, 60)
  Penicillin V (82)
Porphyrins:
  Coproporphyrin (108)
  Deuteroporphyrin (108)
  Hematoporphyrin (108)

* The concentration of compound in hepatic bile greatly exceeds that in plasma.

† The amount of compound or fraction of the injected dose excreted in a given time is so large that the concentration in hepatic bile very probably exceeds that in plasma.

‡ The amount of compound or fraction of the injected dose excreted in hepatic bile is large enough to suggest the possibility of secretion. Or the concentration or amount in hepatic bile is very large, but the analytical method is not specific enough to establish the identity of the material in bile.

there are wide quantitative differences in the relative rates of secretion by the two organs. Thus, acids of comparatively low molecular weight, 200–400, such as p-aminohippurate, tend to be secreted much more efficiently by the kidney than by the liver; the converse seems to be true for acids of high molecular weight, such as the halogenated phthalein sulfonates (127).

The generalization that a high molecular weight favors rapid biliary secretion is supported by the observation that increasing the degree of halogenation of the fluorescein molecule results in a progressive increase in the rate of biliary excretion with a concomitant decrease in urinary excretion (137). However, in the absence of data on the plasma concentrations of the compounds, it is not clear whether the increased biliary excretion results from an increased affinity for the secretion process or simply from higher plasma levels owing to a decreased rate of dye removal by the kidney. Experiments with constant plasma levels of the compounds would help to clarify the problem. But even if the same relationship between the degree of halogenation and biliary excretion could be obtained under these conditions, the question could be raised whether increased hepatic excretion resulted from an increased rate of active transport or from a decreased rate of reabsorption from the biliary tract.

Cations

Table 2 and Figure 2 show the organic cations that appear to be secreted into bile. These compounds are quaternary amines and are completely ionized in solution.

TABLE 2.   *Organic Cations Actively Secreted into Bile**

Strong evidence for secretion
    Procaine amide ethobromide (114, 117, 120)
Probable secretion
    Aprobit (55)
    Cetiprin (54)
    Prothidium (132)

Some evidence suggesting secretion
    Antrenyl (oxyphenonium) (92)
    Benzomethamine (91)
    Carbidium (50)
    Darstine (mepiperphenidol) (114, 120)
    Glycopyrrolate (120)
    BA-3762 (92)
    BA-3854 (92)
    MC-2806 (91)
    MC-2963 (91)

    * For chemical structures, see Fig. 2.

Only one of the compounds, procaine amide ethobromide, has been studied in considerable detail (117). In brief, after intravenous administration in rats with ligated renal pedicles, the compound readily appears in the bile in high concentrations, both as the free compound and as conjugated compound. The biliary concentrations of the free as well as the conjugated compound are about 80 times greater than the plasma concentrations of the two forms. The compound shows a maximal rate of transport into bile, and its excretion is inhibited by benzomethamine, Antrenyl, glycopyrrolate, and Darstine, quaternary amines known to be excreted in bile in large quantities. The two conjugated forms of the compound behave as quaternary amines in that their biliary secretion is inhibited by benzomethamine (120). Both conjugates are readily converted to the parent substance on acid hydrolysis, and there is evidence to suggest that conjugation involves the aromatic amino group of the compound (114).

Inasmuch as high doses of acids, such as sulfobromophthalein and glycocholate, do not inhibit the biliary excretion of procaine amide ethobromide or its conjugates, the quaternary amines appear to be secreted by a process different from that which secretes the organic anions (120). Thus in the liver, as in the kidney (99, 115, 127), there are separate mechanisms for the secretion of organic anions and cations.

The chemical structures of the quaternary ammonium compounds that are apparently secreted into bile (Fig. 2) seem to have only one characteristic in common: a quaternary amine group at one end of the molecule and one or more nonpolar ring structures at the opposite end. The other features of the molecules vary considerably. For example, although in most of the compounds the substituents on the quaternary nitrogen consist of methyl and ethyl groups, in one instance (X) there is an alcoholic group and in three of the compounds (II, XI, XII) the nitrogen is part of a ring structure. Furthermore, the chain connecting the quaternary group to the nonpolar ring structures may be short or long and may consist only of carbons or carbons together with an oxygen or a nitrogen. In addition, the ring structures may vary widely.

Quaternary amines that do not appear to be secreted into bile—those excreted in relatively small proportions of the administered dose—differ from the compounds shown in Figure 2 mainly in lacking a nonpolar ring structure at one end of the molecule. Examples of these include the methonium com-

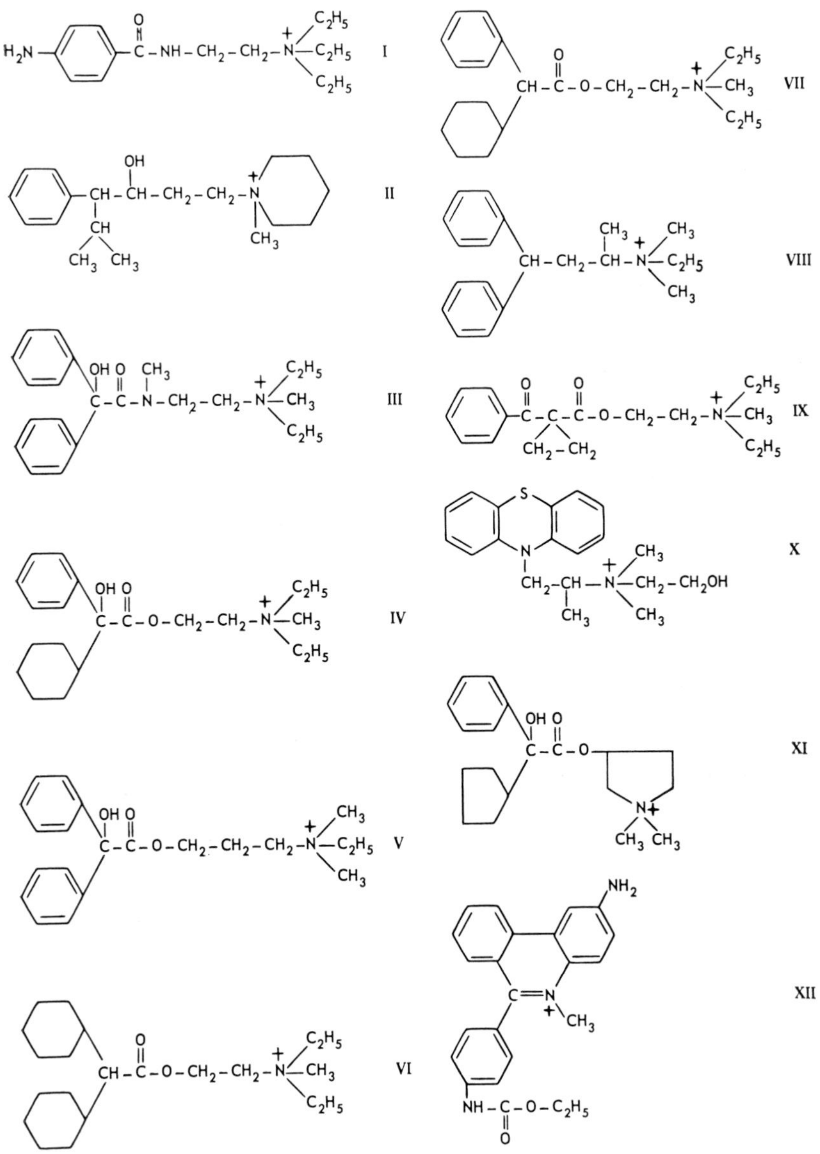

FIG. 2. Chemical structures of some quaternary ammonium compounds that appear to be secreted into bile (see Table 2): I, procaine amide ethobromide; II, Darstine; III, benzomethamine; IV, Antrenyl; V, MC-2963; VI, BA-3762; VII, BA-3854; VIII, Cetiprin; IX, MC-2806; X, Aprobit; XI, glycopyrrolate; XII, carbidium.

pounds, such as hexamethonium and decamethonium, which have quaternary amine groups at both ends of the molecule, and tetraethylammonium, which has a simple symmetrical structure (117). A detailed study of the biliary excretion of decamethonium in nephrectomized rabbits has shown that only about 2% of an injected dose is excreted in 3–4 hours, and that during this period the concentration of the drug in bile is 20–35% lower than that in plasma (36).

Procaine amide ethobromide is taken up by rat liver slices by a process showing all the characteristics of active transport (125). For example, accumulation in the slice against an apparent concentration gradient occurs by a saturable transport process that can be blocked by anoxia and by metabolic inhibitors such as iodoacetate and 2,4-dinitrophenol. Uptake occurs by a process similar to that which secretes the compound into bile in vivo, since accumulation in the slice is inhibited by only those quaternary amines that appear to be secreted into bile. Moreover, the slice uptake is not inhibited by high concentrations of the acidic compound sulfobromophthalein. It is

TABLE 3. *Miscellaneous Compounds Actively Secreted into Bile*

Probable secretion
  Demethylchlortetracycline (30, 93)
  Erythromycin (30, 53, 85–87)
  Glycosides:
    Lanatoside A (41)
    Lanatoside C (41)
    Ouabain (g-strophanthin) (40, 44, 47, 96)
    Scillaren A (123)

Some evidence suggesting secretion
  Tetracycline antibiotics (zwitterions):
    Chlortetracycline (30, 38)
    Oxytetracycline (30, 38)
    Tetracycline (30)
  Glycosides and other uncharged molecules:
    Digitoxin (41)
    Digoxin (41)
    Esculin (52)
    Phorizin (74)
    Polyethylene glycol-1500 (129)
    Thevetin (46)
  Macrolid antibiotics (weak bases):
    Carbomycin (20)
    Oleandomycin (78, 103)
    Spiramycin (30)
  Miscellaneous basic compounds:
    Guanethidine (119)
    Irisamin G (70)
    Neutral red (66, 70, 135, 136)
    Rhodamin 3 B (70)

TABLE 4. *Partial Listing of Conjugated Compounds Appearing in Bile in Large Quantities After Administration of the Unconjugated Compound**

Glucuronides
  Bilirubin diglucuronide
  Chloramphenicol glucuronide
  Diethylstilbestrol monoglucuronide
  Iodopanoic acid ester glucuronide
  Morphine-3-glucuronide
  Phenolphthalein monoglucuronide
  Phenol red glucuronide
  Sulfadimethoxine-N'-glucuronide
  Thyroxin glucuronide
  Triiodothyronine glucuronide
  Vanillic acid ester glucuronide
  Various glucuronides of:
    corticosterone, diphenyl derivatives, estradiol, estrone, fluorescein derivatives, progesterone, testosterone, and many drug metabolites

Ethereal sulfates
  Triiodothyroacetic acid sulfate
  Indoxyl sulfate

Miscellaneous conjugates
  Glutathione conjugates of:
    sulfobromophthalein, naphthalene, and phenanthrene
  Glycine conjugates of:
    4-amino-3-iodobenzoic acid, cholic acid, and deoxycholic acid
  Taurine conjugates of:
    cholic acid

  * For references, see reviews and other general articles (3, 16, 62, 100, 124, 127, 133, 147).

not known whether accumulation in the slice occurs within liver cells, within bile canaliculi, or within both of these compartments.

Miscellaneous Compounds

In Table 3 are listed a number of organic compounds that appear to be secreted into bile and that are neither anions nor quaternary ammonium compounds.

The tetracycline antibiotics, which exist as zwitterions in solutions of neutral pH value (130), appear to be excreted in bile in a concentration higher than that in plasma, but it is not clear whether the substances in bile are the unchanged compounds, metabolites, or both (30, 38). Demethylchlortetracycline, which has been studied more thoroughly than the others of this group (30, 93), appears to have a concentration in rat bile that is two to four times higher than the concentration in plasma (93). Since administration of the acidic compound probenecid results in a lowering of the bile-to-plasma concentration ratio of demethylchlortetracycline (93), it is pos-

sible that the antibiotic is excreted, at least in part, by the anion-secreting process of the liver. However, since probenecid produces a considerable choleresis in rats (61), the lowered bile-to-plasma ratio of the antibiotic might have resulted simply from a dilution of the bile.

The macrolid antibiotics, which include erythromycin, carbomycin, oleandomycin, and spiramycin, are weak bases. They are excreted in the bile of various animals in concentrations 10–90 times that in blood (30), but the chemical form of the antibiotics in bile has not been established except in the case of erythromycin. The latter compound appears in the bile of dogs and rats mainly as unchanged erythromycin together with a small proportion of a metabolite also possessing antibiotic activity (85). Inasmuch as these compounds are partly ionized as cations at physiological pH values, the question arises whether they are excreted by the same process that secretes the quaternary ammonium cations. Moreover, the same question applies to the other basic compounds listed in Table 3—guanethidine, irisamin G, neutral red, and rhodamin 3 B. These substances have not been studied in detail. Guanethidine, as measured by a fairly specific quantitative method, appears in the bile of rats in a concentration 16–25 times that in plasma (119). The compound is a fairly strong base and is almost completely ionized at the pH of bile and plasma.

The cardioactive glycosides are neither acidic nor basic. A number of these, for example, scillaren A, ouabain, and lanatosides A and C, are excreted in the bile of rats in very large proportions of the administered dose as the unchanged molecules (40, 41, 123). Moreover, the concentration of ouabain in rat bile is as much as 300–500 times that in plasma (H. J. Kupferberg and L. S. Schanker, unpublished observations). The biliary excretion of digoxin and digitoxin is considerably lower than that of the above-named glycosides, and metabolites as well as the unchanged compounds are found in rat bile (41). Ouabain is excreted in the bile of man and sheep as well as in that of the rat (44, 96). Since it is highly unlikely that these uncharged molecules could be secreted by the anion-transporting or cation-transporting processes mentioned above, it is possible that the liver possesses a third general secretory mechanism for the cardiac glycosides. Whether the other, less thoroughly studied glycosides and neutral molecules listed in Table 3 are excreted by the same process remains an interesting question.

Conjugates of Administered Compounds

Some of the conjugated forms of organic compounds that appear in bile in large proportions after ad-

ministration of the parent compound are listed in Table 4. The list is highly abbreviated, and a better idea of the immensity of the category can be obtained from the references listed in the footnote to the table.

There is no question that many, if not all, of these conjugates are actively secreted into bile. As mentioned previously (Table 1), a few of them, either isolated from bile or synthesized in vitro, have been administered to animals and shown to be secreted from blood to bile. Inasmuch as a number of the conjugates compete with other acidic substances for excretion into bile (127), it may well be that all of them are secreted by the rather nonspecific anion-transporting process.

If the conjugates are formed within hepatic cells, the question arises whether they are transported directly from cell to bile or are first returned to the extracellular fluid and plasma before secretion. Although many conjugates have been detected in plasma, nothing is known concerning their mode of arrival there. The conjugates might leak slowly from the cells, they might be slowly reabsorbed from bile in the bile ducts, or, in experiments in which bile has entered the intestine, they might be reabsorbed across the intestinal epithelium.

It has been demonstrated for a large number of substances that, after excretion in the bile in conjugated form, the conjugate is split in the intestine, the free compound reabsorbed, and the compound conjugated again and reexcreted in the bile. Many examples of the enterohepatic circulation of substances may be found in the references cited in the footnote to Table 4.

REFERENCES

1. ABOU-EL-MAKAREM, M. M., P. MILLBURN, R. L. SMITH, AND R. T. WILLIAMS. The biliary excretion of foreign compounds in different species. *Biochem. J.* 99: 3P, 1966.
2. ACRED, P., D. M. BROWN, D. H. TURNER, AND D. WRIGHT. Pharmacology of methicillin. *Brit. J. Pharmacol.* 17: 70–81, 1961.
3. ADLERCREUTZ, H. Oestrogens in human bile. In: *The Biliary System*, edited by W. Taylor. Oxford: Blackwell, 1965, p. 369–384.
4. ANDREWS, W. H. H. A technique for perfusion of the canine liver. *Ann. Trop. Med. Parasitol.* 47: 146–155, 1953.
5. ANDREWS, W. H. H., AND I. DEL RIO LOZANO. Some factors affecting the passage of sulphobromophthalein into and out of hepatic parenchymal cells. *Quart. J. Exptl. Physiol.* 46: 238–256, 1961.
6. ANNEGERS, J. H., F. E. SNAPP, A. C. IVY, A. J. ATKINSON, AND A. L. BERMAN. A study of the excretion of cinchophen in bile and urine and the posology of the drug. *Gastroenterology* 1: 597–614, 1943.
7. ARIAS, I. M., L. JOHNSON, AND S. WOLFSON. Biliary excretion of injected conjugated and unconjugated bilirubin by normal and Gunn rats. *Am. J. Physiol.* 200: 1091–1094, 1961.
8. ASHWORTH, C. T., AND E. SANDERS. Anatomic pathway of bile formation. *Am. J. Pathol.* 37: 343–350, 1960.
9. BARBER-RILEY, G. Uptake of bromsulphthalein by incubated rat liver slices. *S. African J. Med. Sci.* 26: 91–97, 1961.
10. BARBER-RILEY, G. The removal of bromsulphthalein from solutions by tissue slices. *S. African J. Med. Sci.* 27: 25–34, 1962.

11. BELLAMY, D. The adsorption of corticosteroids to particulate preparations of rat liver. *Biochem. J.* 87: 334–340, 1963.

12. BELLAMY, D., J. G. PHILLIPS, I. C. JONES, AND R. A. LEONARD. The uptake of cortisol by rat tissues. *Biochem. J.* 85: 537–545, 1962.

13. BERGSTRÖM, S. Bile acid formation and secretion. In: *Liver Function*, edited by R. W. Brauer. Washington, D. C.: Am. Inst. Biol. Sci., 1958, p. 310–324.

14. BERMAN, A. L., AND J. H. IVY. Choleretic action and excretion of cinchophen in rabbit bile. *Proc. Soc. Exptl. Biol. Med.* 45: 853–856, 1940.

15. BOLLMAN, J. L. Liver. *Ann. Rev. Physiol.* 23: 183–206, 1961.

16. BOLLMAN, J. L., AND E. V. FLOCK. The role of the liver in the metabolism of I^{131}-thyroid hormones and analogues. In: *The Biliary System*, edited by W. Taylor. Oxford: Blackwell, 1965, p. 345–367.

17. BRADLEY, S. E. The hepatic circulation. In: *Handbook of Physiology. Circulation*, edited by W. F. Hamilton and P. Dow. Washington, D. C.: Am. Physiol. Soc., 1963, sect. 2, vol. II, p. 1387–1438.

18. BRADLEY, W. B. The effect of cinchophen and dehydrocholic acid on bile secretion. *Am. J. Physiol.* 123: 20–21, 1938.

19. BRADLEY, W. B., AND A. C. IVY. Excretion and determination of cinchophen in bile. *Proc. Soc. Exptl. Biol. Med.* 45: 143–148, 1940.

20. BRAINERD, H. D., N. KAWATA, AND M. SCAPARONE. Studies on the clinical pharmacology of carbomycin. *Antibiot. Chemotherap.* 3: 925–929, 1953.

21. BRAUER, R. W. Observations concerning fluid compartments, blood flow patterns and bile-formation in the isolated rat liver. *J. Natl. Cancer Inst.* 15: 1469–1473, 1955.

22. BRAUER, R. W. Liver. *Ann. Rev. Physiol.* 18: 253–278, 1956.

23. BRAUER, R. W. (Editor). *Liver Function*. Washington, D. C.: Am. Inst. Biol. Sci., 1958.

24. BRAUER, R. W. Mechanisms of bile secretion. *J. Am. Med. Assoc.* 169: 1462–1466, 1959.

25. BRAUER, R. W. Liver circulation and function. *Physiol. Rev.* 43: 115–213, 1963.

26. BRAUER, R. W., AND R. L. PESSOTTI. The removal of bromsulphthalein from blood plasma by the liver of the rat. *J. Pharmacol. Exptl. Therap.* 97: 358–370, 1949.

27. BRAUER, R. W., AND R. L. PESSOTTI. Hepatic uptake and biliary excretion of bromsulphthalein in the dog. *Am. J. Physiol.* 162: 565–574, 1950.

28. BRAUER, R. W., R. L. PESSOTTI, AND J. S. KREBS. The distribution and excretion of S^{35}-labeled sulfobromophthalein-sodium administered to dogs by continuous infusion. *J. Clin. Invest.* 34: 35–43, 1955.

29. BRAUER, R. W., R. L. PESSOTTI, AND P. PIZZOLATO. Isolated rat liver preparation. Bile production and other basic properties. *Proc. Soc. Exptl. Biol. Med.* 78: 174–181, 1951.

30. BRETTE, R., R. LAMBERT, AND R. TRUCHOT. Biliary excretion of antibiotics. In: *The Biliary System*, edited by W. Taylor. Oxford: Blackwell, 1965, p. 419–430.

31. BRODIE, B. B., AND C. A. M. HOGBEN. Some physico-chemical factors in drug action. *J. Pharm. Pharmacol.* 9: 345–380, 1957.

32. CAHILL, G. F., JR., J. ASHMORE, A. S. EARLE, AND S. ZOTTU. Glucose penetration into liver. *Am. J. Physiol.* 192: 491–496, 1958.

33. CANTAROW, A., AND C. W. WIRTS, JR. The effect of dog's bile, certain bile acids and India ink on bilirubinemia and the excretion of bromsulfalein. *Am. J. Digest. Diseases* 10: 261–266, 1943.

34. CHAPMAN-ANDRESEN, C. Measurement of material uptake by cells: pinocytosis. In: *Methods in Cell Physiology*, edited by D. M. Prescott. New York: Acad. Press, 1964, vol. 1, p. 277–304.

35. CHENDEROVITCH, J., E. PHOCAS, AND M. RAUTUREAU. Effect of hypertonic solutions on bile formation. *Am. J. Physiol.* 205: 863–867, 1963.

36. CHRISTENSEN, C. B. Distribution and biliary excretion of decamethonium in doubly nephrectomized rabbits. *Acta Pharmacol. Toxicol.* 23: 275–286, 1965.

37. COMBES, B. Excretory function of the liver. In: *The Liver*, edited by C. Rouiller. New York: Acad. Press, 1964, vol. II, pp. 1–35.

38. COOK, D. L., C. A. LAWLER, L. D. CALVIN, AND D. M. GREEN. Mechanisms of bile formation. *Am. J. Physiol.* 171: 62–74, 1952.

39. COOK, D. L., C. A. LAWLER, AND D. M. GREEN. Studies on the effect of hydrocholeretic agents on hepatic excretory mechanisms. *J. Pharmacol. Exptl. Therap.* 110: 293–299, 1954.

40. COX, E., G. ROXBURGH, AND S. E. WRIGHT. The metabolism of ouabain in the rat. *J. Pharm. Pharmacol.* 11: 535–539, 1959.

41. COX, E., AND S. E. WRIGHT. The hepatic excretion of digitalis glycosides and their genins in the rat. *J. Pharmacol. Exptl. Therap.* 126: 117–122, 1959.

42. DESPOPOULOS, A. Congruence of excretory functions in liver and kidney: hippurates. *Am. J. Physiol.* 210: 760–764, 1966.

43. DESPOPOULOS, A., AND C. W. GROSS. Hepatic conjugation and excretion of phenolsulphonphthaleins. *Federation Proc.* 19: 184, 1960.

44. DUTTA, S., B. H. MARKS, AND C. R. SMITH. Distribution and excretion of ouabain-H^3 and dihydro-ouabain-H^3 in rats and sheep. *J. Pharmacol. Exptl. Therap.* 142: 223–230, 1963.

45. ELIAS, H. Anatomy of the liver. In: *The Liver*, edited by C. Rouiller. New York: Acad. Press, 1963, vol. 1, p. 41–59.

46. ENGLER, R., P. HOLTZ, AND H. W. RAUDONAT. Über die Spaltung herzwirksamer Glykoside im Tierkörper. *Arch. Exptl. Pathol. Pharmakol.* 233: 393–408, 1958.

47. FARAH, A. On the elimination of g-strophanthin by the rat. *J. Pharmacol. Exptl. Therap.* 86: 248–257, 1946.

48. FAWCETT, D. W. Observations on the cytology and electron microscopy of hepatic cells. *J. Natl. Cancer Inst.* 15, Suppl.: 1475–1502, 1955.

49. FAWCETT, D. W. Surface specializations of absorbing cells. *J. Histochem. Cytochem.* 13: 75–91, 1965.

50. GOODWIN, L. G., M. D. GOSS, AND J. A. LOCK. The chemotherapeutic action of phenanthridine compounds: Part III. Carbidium ethanesulphonate. *Brit. J. Pharmacol.* 5: 287–305, 1950.

51. GORESKY, C. A. The nature of transcapillary exchange in the liver. *Can. Med. Assoc. J.* 92: 517–522, 1965.

52. GRAFFLIN, A. L., AND E. H. BAGLEY. Studies of hepatic

structure and function by fluorescence microscopy. *Bull. Johns Hopkins Hosp.* 90: 395-438, 1952.

53. HAMMOND, J. B., AND R. S. GRIFFITH. Factors affecting the absorption and biliary excretion of erythromycin and two of its derivatives in humans. *Clin. Pharmacol. Therap.* 2: 308-312, 1961.

54. HANSSON, E., AND C. G. SCHMITERLÖW. Biological fate of C14-labelled ethyl (3,3-diphenyl-1-methyl-propyl) dimethylammoniumbromide cetiprin, a monoquaternary ammonium compound. *Acta Pharmacol. Toxicol.* 18: 183-190, 1961.

55. HANSSON, E., AND C. G. SCHMITERLÖW. A comparison of the distribution, excretion and metabolism of a tertiary (promethazine) and a quaternary (aprobit) phenothiazine compound labelled with S35. *Arch. Intern. Pharmacodyn.* 131: 309-324, 1961.

56. HANZON, V. Liver cell secretion under normal and pathologic conditions studied by fluorescence microscopy on living rats. *Acta Physiol. Scand.* 28, Suppl. 101: 1-268, 1952.

57. HARDWICKE, J., J. G. RANKIN, K. J. BAKER, AND R. PREISIG. The loss of protein in human and canine hepatic bile. *Clin. Sci.* 26: 509-517, 1964.

58. HARGREAVES, T., AND G. H. LATHE. Inhibitory aspects of bile secretion. *Nature* 200: 1172-1176, 1963.

59. HARRISON, P. M., AND G. T. STEWART. Excretion of antibiotics in bile. *Brit. J. Pharmacol.* 17: 420-423, 1961.

60. HARRISON, P. M., J. A. WHITE, AND G. T. STEWART. The excretion of sodium 6-(2,6-dimethoxybenzamido-penicillanate) monohydrate in rats. *Brit. J. Pharmacol.* 15: 571-573, 1960.

61. HART, L. G., AND L. S. SCHANKER. Active transport of chlorothiazide into bile. *Am. J. Physiol.* 211: 643-646, 1966.

62. HART, L. G., AND L. S. SCHANKER. The chemical forms in which phenol red is secreted into the bile of rats. *Proc. Soc. Exptl. Biol. Med.* 123: 433-435 1966.

63. HASLEWOOD, G. A. D. Recent developments in our knowledge of bile salts. *Physiol. Rev.* 35: 178-196, 1955.

64. HASLEWOOD, G. A. D. Comparative biochemistry of bile salts. In: *The Biliary System*, edited by W. Taylor. Oxford: Blackwell, 1965, p. 107-116.

65. HAYWOOD, C. The passage of inulin through the liver of the toadfish, with and without choleretics. *J. Cellular Comp. Physiol.* 28: 381-396, 1946.

66. HAYWOOD, C., V. C. DICKERSON, AND M. C. COLLINS. The secretion of dye by the fish liver. *J. Cellular Comp. Physiol.* 25: 145-153, 1945.

67. HAYWOOD, C., AND R. HÖBER. The permeability of the frog liver to certain lipoid-insoluble substances. *J. Cellular Comp. Physiol.* 10: 305-319, 1937.

68. HENDERSON, E. S., R. H. ADAMSON, C. DENHAM, AND V. T. OLIVERIO. The metabolic fate of tritiated methotrexate. I. Absorption, excretion, and distribution in mice, rats, dogs and monkeys. *Cancer Res.* 25: 1008-1017, 1965.

69. HÖBER, R. Correlation between the molecular configuration of organic compounds and their active transfer in living cells. *Cold Spring Harbor Symp. Quant. Biol.* 8: 40-50, 1940.

70. HÖBER, R., AND A. TITAJEW. Über die Sekretionsarbeit der Leber vom Frosch. *Arch. Ges. Physiol.* 223: 180-194, 1929.

71. HOLTER, H. Pinocytosis. *Intern. Rev. Cytol.* 8: 481-504, 1959.

72. JACOBS, M. H. Some aspects of cell permeability to weak electrolytes. *Cold Spring Harbor Symp. Quant. Biol.* 8: 30-39, 1940.

73. JAVITT, N. B. Phenol 3,6 dibromphthalein disulfonate, a new compound for the study of liver disease. *Proc. Soc. Exptl. Biol. Med.* 117: 254-257, 1964.

74. JENNER, F. A., AND D. H. SMYTH. The excretion of phlorrhizin. *J. Physiol., London* 146: 563-571, 1959.

75. JIRSA, M., AND P. RABAN. Metabolism of rose bengal. *Nature* 195: 1100-1101, 1962.

76. JUHLIN, L. Excretion of intravenously injected solid particles in bile. *Acta Physiol. Scand.* 49: 224-230, 1960.

77. KALLEE, E. Dye-binding ability of mitochondrial protein fractions. *Arch. Biochem. Biophys.* 60: 265-267, 1956.

78. KAZENKO, A., O. J. SORENSON, JR., L. M. WOLF, W. A. DILL, M. GALBRAITH, AND A. J. GLAZKO. Physiologic disposition of oleandomycin in animals. *Antibiot. Chemotherap.* 7: 410-418, 1957.

79. KETTERER, S. G., B. D. WIEGAND, AND E. RAPAPORT. Hepatic uptake and biliary excretion of indocyanine green and its use in estimation of hepatic blood flow in dogs. *Am. J. Physiol.* 199: 481-484, 1960.

80. KIM, J. H., AND S. K. HONG. Urinary and biliary excretions of various phenol red derivatives in the anesthetized dog. *Am. J. Physiol.* 202: 174-178, 1962.

81. KREBS, J. S. The metabolism of BSP and its effect on the plasma clearance of BSP. In: *Liver Function*. Washington, D. C.: Am. Inst. Biol. Sci., 1958, p. 302-309.

82. KUNIN, C. M. Effect of serum binding on the distribution of penicillins in the rabbit. *J. Lab. Clin. Med.* 65: 406-415, 1965.

83. KUPFERBERG, H. J., H. M. SOLOMON, AND L. S. SCHANKER. Biliary excretion of para-acetylaminohippuric acid (PAAH) in the rat. *Pharmacologist* 6: 177, 1964.

84. KURZ, H. Die Permeation von Giften in die Leber. *Arch. Exptl. Pathol. Pharmakol.* 247: 164-179, 1964.

85. LEE, C. C., R. C. ANDERSON, H. L. BIRD, JR., AND K. K. CHEN. Reabsorption of erythromycin and a microbiologically active metabolite in the bile of dogs and rats. In: *Antibiotics Annual 1953-1954*, edited by H. Welch and F. Marti-Ibanez. New York: Med. Encycloped., 1953, p. 493-495.

86. LEE, C. C., R. C. ANDERSON, AND K. K. CHEN. The biliary and urinary excretion of erythromycin in dogs. In: *Antibiotics Annual 1953-1954*, edited by H. Welch and F. Marti-Ibanez. New York: Med. Encycloped., 1953, p. 485-492.

87. LEE, C. C., R. C. ANDERSON, F. G. HENDERSON, H. M. WORTH, AND P. N. HARRIS. Pharmacology and toxicology of erythromycin propionate. In: *Antibiotics Annual 1958-1959*, edited by H. Welch and F. Marti-Ibanez. New York: Med. Encycloped., 1959, p. 354-363.

88. LEONG, G. F., R. J. HOLLOWAY, AND R. W. BRAUER. Mechanics of bile formation. Transfer of potassium, sodium, chloride, phosphate and sulfate ions from perfusion medium to bile. *Federation Proc.* 14: 363, 1955.

89. LESTER, R., AND R. SCHMID. Bile pigment excretion in amphibia. *Nature* 190: 452, 1961.

90. LEVINE, R. R. The physiological disposition of hexamethonium and related compounds. *J. Pharmacol. Exptl. Therap.* 129: 296-304, 1960.

91. LEVINE, R. M., AND B. B. CLARK. The biotransformation, excretion, and distribution of the anticholinergic quaternary ammonium compound benzomethamine [N-diethyl-aminoethyl-N'-methyl-benzilamide methobromide (MC 3199)] and its tertiary amine analogue (MC 3137) and related compounds in animals. *J. Pharmacol. Exptl. Therap.* 114: 63–77, 1955.

92. LEVINE, R. M., AND B. B. CLARK. The physiological disposition of oxyphenonium bromide (antrenyl) and related compounds. *J. Pharmacol. Exptl. Therap.* 121: 63–70, 1957.

93. LOSERT, W., AND G. SENFT. Die Verteilung von Demethyl-chlortetracyclin zwischen dem extra- und intracellulären Raum der Leber. *Arch. Exptl. Pathol. Pharmakol.* 250: 307–317, 1965.

94. MANN, F. C., AND F. D. MANN. Liver. *Ann. Rev. Physiol.* 15: 473–492, 1953.

95. MAREN, T. H., A. C. ELLISON, S. K. FELLNER, AND W. B. GRAHAM. A study of hepatic carbonic anhydrase. *Mol. Pharmacol.* 2: 144–157, 1966.

96. MARKS, B. H., S. DUTTA, J. GAUTHIER, AND D. ELLIOTT. Distribution in plasma, uptake by the heart and excretion of ouabain-H^3 in human subjects. *J. Pharmacol. Exptl. Therap.* 145: 351–356, 1964.

97. MENDELOFF, A. I. Fluorescence of intravenously administered rose bengal appears only in hepatic polygonal cells. *Proc. Soc. Exptl. Biol. Med.* 70: 556–558, 1949.

98. OLIVERIO, V. T., AND J. D. DAVIDSON. The physiological disposition of dichloromethotrexate-Cl^{36} in animals. *J. Pharmacol. Exptl. Therap.* 137: 76–83, 1962.

99. PETERS, L. Renal tubular excretion of organic bases. *Pharmacol. Rev.* 12: 1–35, 1960.

100. PETERSON, R. E. Biliary excretion of neutral steroids in man. In: *The Biliary System*, edited by W. Taylor. Oxford: Blackwell, 1965, p. 385–397.

101. PRATT, E. B., AND J. K. AIKAWA. Secretion and effect of hydrochlorothiazide in bile and pancreatic juice. *Am. J. Physiol.* 202: 1083–1086, 1962.

102. PREISIG, R., H. L. COOPER, AND H. O. WHEELER. The relationship between taurocholate secretion rate and bile production in the unanesthetized dog during cholinergic blockade and during secretin administration. *J. Clin. Invest.* 41: 1152–1162, 1962.

103. PRESTON, F. W., M. SILVERMAN, G. C. HENEGAR, AND J. C. KUKRAL. Excretion of oleandomycin in human bile. *Am. J. Digest. Diseases* 7: 557–563, 1962.

104. PRIESTLY, B. G., AND W. J. O'REILLY. Protein binding and the excretion of some azo dyes in rat bile. *J. Pharm. Pharmacol.* 18: 41–45, 1966.

105. RADOMSKI, J. L., AND T. J. MELLINGER. The absorption, fate and excretion in rats of the water-soluble azo dyes, FD & C Red No. 2, FD & C Red No. 4, and FD & C Yellow No. 6. *J. Pharmacol. Exptl. Therap.* 136: 259–266, 1962.

106. RAWSON, A. J. Human bile proteins. I. Proteins identified by antibody to human serum. *Clin. Chem.* 8: 310–317, 1962.

107. REINHOLD, J. G., AND D. W. WILSON. The acid-base composition of hepatic bile: I. *Am. J. Physiol.* 107: 378–387, 1934.

108. RIMINGTON, C. Biliary secretion of porphyrins, and hepatogenous photosensitization. In: *The Biliary System*, edited by W. Taylor. Oxford: Blackwell, 1965, p. 325–333.

109. ROSENTHAL, S. M., AND E. C. WHITE. Studies in hepatic function. VI. A. The pharmacological behavior of certain phthalein dyes. B. The value of selected phthalein compounds in the estimation of hepatic function. *J. Pharmacol. Exptl. Therap.* 24: 265–288, 1925.

110. ROSENTHAL, W. S., K. KUBO, M. DOLINSKI, J. MARINO, W. L. MERSHEIMER, AND G. B. J. GLASS. The passage of serum albumin into bile in man. *Am. J. Digest. Diseases* 10: 271–283, 1965.

111. ROUILLER, C. Les canalicules biliaires; étude au microscope électronique. *Acta Anat.* 26: 94–109, 1956.

112. ROUILLER, C., AND A.-M. JÉZÉQUEL. Electron microscopy of the liver. In: *The Liver*, edited by C. Rouiller. New York: Acad. Press, 1963, vol. I, p. 195–264.

113. RYAN, A. J., AND S. E. WRIGHT. The excretion of some azo dyes in rat bile. *J. Pharm. Pharmacol.* 13: 492–495, 1961.

114. SCHANKER, L. S. Concentrative transfer of an organic cation from blood into bile. *Biochem. Pharmacol.* 11: 253–254, 1962.

115. SCHANKER, L. S. Passage of drugs across body membranes. *Pharmacol. Rev.* 14: 501–530, 1962.

116. SCHANKER, L. S. Physiological transport of drugs. In: *Advances in Drug Research*, edited by N. J. Harper and A. B. Simmonds. London: Acad. Press, 1964, p. 71–106.

117. SCHANKER, L. S. Hepatic transport of organic cations. In: *The Biliary System*, edited by W. Taylor. Oxford: Blackwell, 1965, p. 469–480.

118. SCHANKER, L. S., AND C. A. M. HOGBEN. Biliary excretion of inulin, sucrose, and mannitol: analysis of bile formation. *Am. J. Physiol.* 200: 1087–1090, 1961.

119. SCHANKER, L. S., AND A. S. MORRISON. Physiological disposition of guanethidine in the rat and its uptake by heart slices. *Intern. J. Neuropharmacol.* 4: 27–39, 1965.

120. SCHANKER, L. S., AND H. M. SOLOMON. Active transport of quaternary ammonium compounds into bile. *Am. J. Physiol.* 204: 829–832, 1963.

121. SCHOENFIELD, L. J., D. B. McGILL, AND W. T. FOULK. Studies of sulfobromophthalein sodium (BSP) metabolism in man. III. Demonstration of a transport maximum (Tm) for biliary excretion of BSP. *J. Clin. Invest.* 43: 1424–1432, 1964.

122. SCRATCHERD, T. Electrolyte composition and control of biliary secretion in the cat and rabbit. In: *The Biliary System*, edited by W. Taylor. Oxford: Blackwell, 1965, p. 515–529.

123. SIMON, M., AND S. E. WRIGHT. The excretion of scillaren A by rats. *J. Pharm. Pharmacol.* 12: 767–768, 1960.

124. SMITH, R. L. The biliary excretion and enterohepatic circulation of drugs and other organic compounds. In: *Progress in Drug Research*, edited by E. Jucker. Basel: Birkhäuser, 1966, p. 299–360.

125. SOLOMON, H. M., AND L. S. SCHANKER. Hepatic transport of organic cations: active uptake of a quaternary ammonium compound procaine amide ethobromide by rat liver slices. *Biochem. Pharmacol.* 12: 621–626, 1963.

126. SPERBER, I. The biliary excretion and choleretic effect of some phenolsulphonephthaleins. *Acta Physiol. Scand.* 42, Suppl. 145: 129–130, 1957.

127. SPERBER, I. Secretion of organic anions in the formation of urine and bile. *Pharmacol. Rev.* 11: 109–134, 1959.

128. SPERBER, I. Biliary excretion and choleresis. In: *Proceedings of the First International Pharmacological Meeting*, edited by C. A. M. Hogben. New York: Macmillan, 1963, vol. 4, p. 137–143.

129. SPERBER, I. Biliary secretion of organic anions and its influence on bile flow. In: *The Biliary System*, edited by W. Taylor. Oxford: Blackwell, 1965, p. 457–467.

130. STEPHENS, C. R., K. MURAI, K. J. BRUNINGS, AND R. B. WOODWARD. Acidity constants of the tetracycline antibiotics. *J. Am. Chem. Soc.* 78: 4155–4158, 1956.

131. STEWART, G. T., AND P. M. HARRISON. Excretion and re-excretion of a broad-spectrum penicillin in bile. *Brit. J. Pharmacol.* 17: 414–419, 1961.

132. TAYLOR, A. E. R. The absorption, distribution and excretion of prothidium in rats, rabbits and cattle. *Brit. J. Pharmacol.* 15: 235–242, 1960.

133. TAYLOR, W. Biliary excretion of neutral steroid hormone metabolites in animals. In: *The Biliary System*, edited by W. Taylor. Oxford: Blackwell, 1965, p. 399–418.

134. TAYLOR, W. (Editor). *The Biliary System.* Oxford: Blackwell, 1965.

135. VANLERENBERGHE, J. The effects of hypothermia on biliary function. In: *The Biliary System*, edited by W. Taylor. Oxford: Blackwell, 1965, p. 263–276.

136. VANLERENBERGHE, J., G. MILBLED, F. GUERRIN, N. BAR, AND C. VALTILLE. Action de quelques inhibiteurs enzymatiques sur l'excrétion biliaire du rouge neutre par le foie de rat perfusé. *J. Physiol., Paris* 54: 423–424, 1962.

137. WEBB, J. M., M. FONDA, AND E. A. BROUWER. Metabolism and excretion patterns of fluorescein and certain halogenated fluorescein dyes in rats. *J. Pharmacol. Exptl. Therap.* 137: 141–147, 1962.

138. WEINER, I. M., K. C. BLANCHARD, AND G. H. MUDGE. Factors influencing renal excretion of foreign organic acids. *Am. J. Physiol.* 207: 953–963, 1964.

139. WEINER, I. M., AND G. H. MUDGE. Renal tubular mechanisms for excretion of organic acids and bases. *Am. J. Med.* 36: 743–762, 1964.

140. WHEELER, H. O. Determinants of the flow and composition of bile. *Gastroenterology* 40: 584–586, 1961.

141. WHEELER, H. O. Inorganic ions in bile. In: *The Biliary System*, edited by W. Taylor. Oxford: Blackwell, 1965, p. 481–493.

142. WHEELER, H. O., W. I. CRANSTON, AND J. I. MELTZER. Hepatic uptake and biliary excretion of indocyanine green in the dog. *Proc. Soc. Exptl. Biol. Med.* 99: 11–14, 1958.

143. WHEELER, H. O., AND O. L. RAMOS. Determinants of the flow and composition of bile in the unanesthetized dog during constant infusions of sodium taurocholate. *J. Clin. Invest.* 39: 161–170, 1960.

144. WHELAN, F. J., AND G. L. PLAA. The application of thin layer chromatography to sulfobromophthalein metabolism studies. *Toxicol. Appl. Pharmacol.* 5: 457–463, 1963.

145. WILBRANDT, W., AND T. ROSENBERG. The concept of carrier transport and its corollaries in pharmacology. *Pharmacol. Rev.* 13: 109–183, 1961.

146. WILLIAMS, R. T. *Detoxication Mechanisms.* New York: Wiley, 1959.

147. WILLIAMS, R. T., P. MILLBURN, AND R. L. SMITH. The influence of enterohepatic circulation on toxicity of drugs. *Ann. N. Y. Acad. Sci.* 123: 110–124, 1965.

148. WIRTS, C. W., JR., A. CANTAROW, W. J. SNAPE, AND B. DELSERONE. Bile volume and excretion of pigment and bromsulfalein in dogs receiving carbon tetrachloride. *Am. J. Physiol.* 165: 680–687, 1951.

149. ZACHMAN, R. D., P. E. DUNAGIN, JR., AND J. A. OLSON. Formation and enterohepatic circulation of metabolites of retinol and retinoic acid in bile duct-cannulated rats. *J. Lipid Res.* 7: 3–9, 1966.

150. ZACHMAN, R. D., M. B. SINGER, AND J. A. OLSON. Biliary secretion of metabolites of retinol and of retinoic acid in the guinea pig and chick. *J. Nutr.* 88: 137–142, 1966.

CHAPTER 115

Transport mechanisms in the gallbladder

JARED M. DIAMOND | *Department of Physiology, University of California Medical Center at Los Angeles, Los Angeles, California*

CHAPTER CONTENTS

PRESENT INTEREST in the gallbladder stems not only from its specific physiological role but also from the unique opportunity it provides for attacking general problems of transport and permeability. Close parallels between details of solute and water transport in the gallbladder and in the more important epithelia, such as those of the intestine and kidney, make it probable that many of the underlying transport mechanisms are the same in these organs. The physiological and anatomical simplicity of the gallbladder compared with other epithelia offers advantages in analyzing these mechanisms. For example, only one solute transport mechanism is known to exist in the gallbladder, in contrast to the large number of mechanisms operating simultaneously in the intestine or the kidney. The anatomy of the gallbladder is also simple, consisting essentially of a single-layered sac of epithelial cells supported on the outside by connective tissue. The gallbladder maintains one of the highest reported rates of water transport and offers a particularly durable in vitro preparation. It tolerates a pH range of 2.5–11, osmolarities from one-tenth to triple that of plasma, and alcohol concentrations of up to at least 8%. In addition, it has some specific physiological properties that have simplified the analysis of its transport mechanisms, such as the symmetrical permeability characteristics of the epithelial cells and the absence of electrical potential differences associated with ion transport.

This chapter covers only the transport mechanisms of the gallbladder; the means by which the organ expels bile and regulates pressure in the biliary tree is discussed by G. A. Hallenbeck in Chapter 57, Volume II, of this *Handbook*. The material is divided into three sections: *1*) processes involved in the selective reabsorption of bile, *2*) the mechanism of solute transport, and *3*) the mechanism and structural basis of water transport. Since earlier work is well covered in a review by Ivy (43) and there was virtually no published work on transport functions of the gallbladder from 1937 to 1957, the emphasis is on work since 1957. The principal experimental papers since 1957 are references 12–14 (fish gallbladder); 15, 16, 19–22, 24, 26, 61, 76, 78 (rabbit gallbladder); 33, 34, 47 (dog gallbladder); and 15 and 37 (guinea pig gallbladder). Short reviews of transport, particularly water transport, in the gallbladder are in references 17, 18, 23, and 25.

CONCENTRATING ACTIVITY OF THE GALLBLADDER

It is appropriate to begin by asking why the gallbladder exists at all. The reason for its existence arises from the dual function of bile as an excretion and as a digestive fluid, which makes it essential that the secretion of bile by the liver be continuous but its arrival at the intestine periodic. Bile is the principal excretory route for the pigments bilirubin and biliverdin, breakdown products of hemoglobin that give bile its characteristic yellow or green color. Since these pigments are systemically toxic and produce jaundice if they accumulate in the bloodstream, the secretion of bile must proceed constantly so that these compounds may be removed. Many inactivated hormones and steroids are also continually excreted from the bloodstream into bile by the liver (72). However, the other physiologically significant constituents of bile—the bile-acid anions—are necessary for the intestinal absorption of fats and hence are required in the alimentary canal only after meals, i.e., periodically. In most vertebrates these conflicting needs of continuous secretion and periodic delivery are reconciled by storing bile between meals in a saclike outpocketing of the bile ducts, the gallbladder, from which bile is discharged into the intestine during digestion (Fig. 1). Although the volume of the gallbladder is only a small fraction of the volume of bile secreted daily by the liver, the gallbladder concentrates bile to between 10 and 20% of its original volume by selective reabsorption and can therefore accommodate up to half the daily output of hepatic bile. In a few birds and mammals in which digestion goes on virtually continuously, the gallbladder is either absent (e.g. deer and rat) or has a weak concentrating activity (e.g. sheep), but the organ is present in all cold-blooded vertebrates. Since cholesterol and the bile pigments may already be at concentrations near the saturation point in the hepatic bile of some individuals, the concentrating

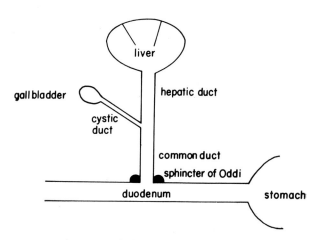

FIG. 1. Anatomy of the human biliary system. Between meals the sphincter of Oddi is closed, and bile secreted by the liver is backed up into the gallbladder, where it is concentrated by selective reabsorption. During meals release of the hormone cholecystokinin causes relaxation of the sphincter and contraction of the gallbladder, which expels bile into the intestine. Some vertebrates have a direct duct from liver to gallbladder, whereas in others part of the secreted bile passes directly from liver to intestine via a separate duct.

activity of the gallbladder may be considered the proximate cause of gallstone formation.

Even before the era of chemical analysis and physiological experimentation, it was realized that there were differences between hepatic bile (the immediate secretion product of the liver) and gallbladder bile that pointed to the reabsorption of fluid by the gallbladder. These differences were summarized as follows in an eighteenth-century textbook by a professor of physiology at Edinburgh: "Therefore a portion of the hepatic bile being received into the gallbladder, there stagnates, only a little shaken by respiration; and there, by degrees, exhales its thinner parts, which, as we see, filtrate through and largely permeate the adjacent membranes. The remainder, as being a fluid of oily subalkaline nature, digesting in a warm place, grows sharp, rancid, more thick, bitter, and of a higher colour: for this is all the difference between the cystic and hepatic bile; which last we find weaker, less bitter, lighter coloured, and of a thinner consistence, while it remains within its proper hepatic ducts" (58).

A more precise and modern picture of these differences may be obtained from Table 1, which compares the composition of hepatic and gallbladder bile in the dog. The concentrations of bile pigment and of bile acid are up to ten times higher in gallbladder bile, accounting respectively for the change in color and the bitterness cited in the eighteenth-century

TABLE I. *Composition of Canine Bile*

	Hepatic Bile, mM	Gallbladder Bile, mM
Na$^+$	174	220–340
K$^+$	6.6	6–10
Cl$^-$	55–107	1–10
HCO$_3^-$	34–65	0–17
Bile acids	28–42	290–340
Ca^{++}	6	25–32
Mg^{++}	3.6	

From the analyses of Ravdin et al. (67), Reinhold & Wilson (68), and Wheeler & Ramos (77).

textbook. Sodium, calcium, and potassium are at higher, and chloride and bicarbonate at lower, concentrations in gallbladder than in hepatic bile. Numerous measurements of freezing-point depression have shown that both hepatic bile and gallbladder bile at all stages of its reabsorption are isotonic with plasma (e.g. 6, 31). This implies that some of the constituents of bile must be osmotically inactive, since the sum of their concentrations increases during reabsorption and may reach in concentrated gallbladder bile a value double the sum of concentrations in plasma. The pH of gallbladder bile is somewhat lower than that of hepatic bile. The principal chemical characteristics of gallbladder bile as an isotonic fluid high in Na, K, bile pigment, and bile salts and low in Cl apply not only to mammals but also to the other vertebrate classes—to representative sharks, fish, amphibians, reptiles (12), and birds (29).

In 1902 Brand (6) pointed out that many of the differences between hepatic and gallbladder bile would become explicable if the gallbladder formed a reabsorbate of isotonic NaCl and NaHCO$_3$, leaving behind the bile pigments and the sodium salts of the bile acids. The first experimental support for the postulate that the gallbladder reabsorbs fluid was provided by Rous & McMaster (69), who prepared dogs surgically so that only half of the hepatic bile entered the gallbladder, while the other half was diverted to bypass the gallbladder and entered a rubber balloon. They found that bile recovered from the gallbladder had on the average a bile pigment concentration 7.1 times higher, and a volume correspondingly lower, than the control hepatic bile from the balloon. That these changes were effected rapidly could be concluded from their observation that the bile that entered the top of the bladder via the cystic duct and was collected as it dripped out a cannula in the bottom of the bladder already had a pigment concentration 3.6 times that of control bile, as a result of fluid absorption during this brief passage through the bladder.

The most unequivocal information about the transformation of hepatic bile into gallbladder bile comes from the classic experiments of Ravdin and his co-workers, who introduced samples of canine hepatic bile of known composition and volume into the gallbladders of unanesthetized dogs and periodically withdrew samples for analysis (66, 67). They observed that the normal gallbladder reabsorbed about 16% of its volume of bile per hour, with a concomitant increase in Ca and bile acid and decrease in Cl and HCO$_3$ concentrations. The concentration of Na initially dropped, then rose to well above its value in hepatic bile. The amounts of bile acid, bile pigment, and cholesterol recovered were the same as those introduced, so that the physiologically significant constituents of bile were neither absorbed nor secreted by the gallbladder but increased in concentration as a result simply of the decrease in volume. When the gallbladder was damaged or infected, absorption ceased. These experiments prove that the normal differences between hepatic and gallbladder bile are due to the selective reabsorption of biliary constituents by the gallbladder. The important additional observation was made that inorganic salt solutions, including isotonic NaCl and NaCl-NaHCO$_3$ mixtures, could also be reabsorbed. More recently Grim (33) found that the gallbladder of a dog could reabsorb the dog's own plasma. Thus, just as in the intestine, fluid absorption by the gallbladder cannot be attributed to passive diffusion and osmosis resulting from bile-to-blood concentration differences and must be actively brought about by the tissue.

Methods for Studying Transport by the Gallbladder

A complete explanation of the transformation of hepatic bile into gallbladder bile requires knowledge of the primary active transport processes and of the passive diffusional fluxes that secondarily modify the concentration gradients established by active transport. Several gallbladder preparations have been developed for analyzing active transport and passive permeability. The most "physiological" of these preparations is that of Ravdin's group (46, 66, 67), who surgically prepared dogs with cannulas in the cystic duct and thereby made it possible to study gallbladder function in a conscious animal. This preparation deserves to be further exploited, particularly since Ravdin's group was able to make some unique discoveries (e.g., of diurnal variation in concentrating activity) that are of potential physiological and clinical importance and remain unexplained. Studies in vivo on acute preparations under anesthesia have been carried out in dogs by Grim & Smith (34) and by Kang & Hong (47), in rabbits by Dietschy & Moore (26) and by Whitlock & Wheeler (78), and in guinea pigs by Herman et al. (37) and by Ostrow (personal communication). A cannula may be introduced into the lumen of the gallbladder via the cystic duct, care being taken that the ligature does not interfere with blood vessels, lymphatics, or nerves supplying the gallbladder. The volume of fluid in the gallbladder at any time may be determined by complete aspiration, or, better, by including ^{131}I-labeled albumin in the luminal fluid (78).

For in vitro measurements, five gallbladder preparations have been developed, each offering advantages for particular kinds of studies:

1. Diamond (12, 15) ligated a cannula into the cystic duct or neck of the isolated gallbladder from a fish, guinea pig, or rabbit. After the organ had been filled with a Ringer solution and placed in a beaker of Ringer solution, the cannula was stoppered with a glass plug to which a hook was attached (Fig. 2). At 5-min intervals the organ was suspended by this hook from the weighing hook of an analytical balance and weighed to the nearest 0.1 mg. Since the cannula, plug, and bladder wall were very light, most of the weight was the luminal fluid, and loss (or gain) of weight represented transfer of fluid from the luminal[1] to the serosal[1] bathing solution (or vice versa). (Figures 6 and 17 illustrate determinations of absorption rates by this method.) It offers the simplest and most accurate technique for measuring fluid transport.

2. Dietschy and Moore (24, 26) introduced an everted gallbladder preparation in which the organ was turned inside out with a fine glass rod before cannulation. This has proved to be the most convenient preparation for measuring electrical potential differences (PDs), since the layer of epithelial cells is directly exposed to the external bathing solution, which can be changed in less than a second by lifting

___

[1] The bathing solutions on opposite sides of the gallbladder may be referred to as the "serosal" solution and the "mucosal" solution, respectively. The serosal solution is in contact with the connective tissue layer of the bladder (on the outside when the organ is in its in vivo orientation), and the mucosal solution is in contact with the mucosal cell layer (facing the lumen or inside in the in vivo orientation). Alternatively, one may speak of the luminal and the outer solutions, but these terms depend on the orientation of the gallbladder. The luminal solution is the mucosal solution under in vivo conditions but is the serosal solution if the gallbladder has been everted.

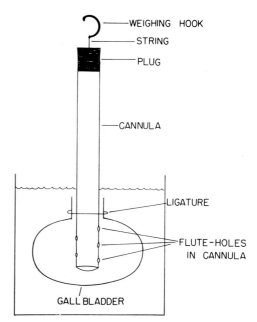

FIG. 2. An in vitro gallbladder preparation in which water transport is followed by weighing. A cannula, with lateral flute holes to facilitate complete aspiration of luminal fluid, is ligated into the neck or cystic duct of a gallbladder. The organ is filled with Ringer solution, and the cannula is closed by means of a glass plug to which a hook is attached. Absorption of fluid from the lumen results in a loss of weight of the whole preparation, monitored by weighing it at 5-min intervals (see, e.g., Figs. 6 and 17). [After Diamond (18).]

the gallbladder from one beaker to another. By this technique one can readily measure the PDs resulting from over a hundred different concentration gradients in an experiment on a single gallbladder (19, 21). Fluid transport can be measured by periodically weighing an everted gallbladder. In weighing experiments the fluid transport rate apparently falls off sooner with time in an everted than a noneverted gallbladder, possibly because of deleterious effects of hydrostatic pressure in the everted orientation during weighing.

3. Wheeler (76) mounted the cannulated gallbladder of a rabbit in the chamber illustrated in Figure 3, which circulated the mucosal and serosal bathing solutions by separate gas lifts. For measurements of fluid transport the serosal bathing solution was periodically sucked into a compartment connected to a vertical capillary in which the height of fluid was read to ± 10 μl. The apparatus is well suited for determining unidirectional tracer fluxes under conditions in which both bathing solutions are stirred and for correlating tracer fluxes with PDs measured simultaneously. Measurements of fluid transport rates are less accurate than by the weighing method

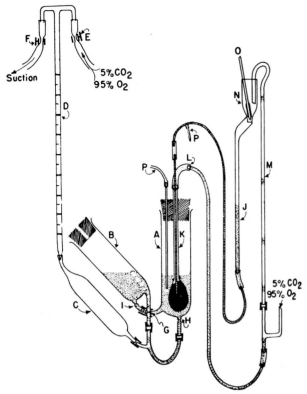

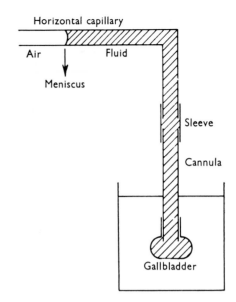

FIG. 4. Horizontal capillary method of measuring water transport by the gallbladder. A continuous column of fluid extends from the lumen of the bladder via a cannula and sleeve to a meniscus in a horizontal capillary lying beside a ruler. As the gallbladder absorbs fluid from its lumen, the meniscus retreats toward the lumen, and readings of its position at 1-min intervals thus give the rate of fluid absorption. Hydrostatic pressure can be varied by raising or lowering the horizontal capillary. [From Diamond (14).]

FIG. 3. A chamber method for measuring water transport in the gallbladder. The volume of the external bathing solution is periodically measured by aspirating it into the glass bulb C and measuring its height in the 2-ml burette D. A, main chamber. B, serosal mixing and sampling chamber. E, serosal gas inflow clamp. F, suction clamp. G, line for adjustment of meniscus during volume measurement. H, I, constrictions in outflow and return tubes to fix fluid levels during volume measurement. J, inflow reservoir for mucosal circuit. K, cannula with gallbladder attached. L, mucosal return tubing with soft rubber connection through which glass inflow tubing is inserted. M, glass tubing through which mucosal fluid is pumped back to inflow reservoir by gas mixture. N, bubble trap and sampling chamber. O, rubber-sheathed glass rod with which outflow from N can be stopped for sampling. P, agar bridges. [From Wheeler (76).]

($\pm$10 μl vs. $\pm$0.3 μl), and net solute fluxes must be calculated from relatively small changes in large bathing solutions. Care is necessary to prevent evaporation of fluid from introducing a systematic error into determinations of transport rates.

4. Diamond (14) connected the cannula of a gallbladder to a horizontal capillary (i.d. = 0.59 mm) lying beside a ruler, so that a continuous column of fluid extended from the meniscus in the capillary to the lumen of the gallbladder (Fig. 4). The position of the meniscus along the ruler was read to the nearest 0.1 mm every minute. In the steady state the recession

of the meniscus 1 cm toward the gallbladder thus implied the absorption of 2.74 μl of fluid from the lumen. Since the height of the horizontal capillary can be raised or lowered, the apparatus is suitable for determining the effect of hydrostatic pressure on fluid transport, but it has not been used for other purposes.

5. Diamond (16) suspended a gallbladder filled with Ringer solution in a closed Goetz tube (Fig. 5) filled with moist oxygen. Thus, there was no outside bathing solution. As in Smyth & Taylor's (70) similar "unilateral" preparation of the small intestine, droplets representing the pure reabsorbate formed by the gallbladder dripped off and were collected in the graduated stem of the Goetz tube. This preparation offers an accurate method for obtaining the composition of the reabsorbate by direct analysis, rather than by having to compute it indirectly from the ratio of the change in amounts of solutes and water in the mucosal bathing solution. Peters & Walser (61) have described a related preparation in which an empty everted gallbladder immersed in a bathing solution is allowed to fill itself up with transported fluid.

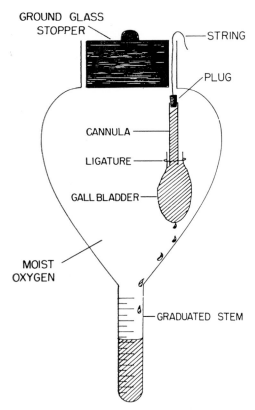

FIG. 5. "Unilateral" gallbladder preparation. A cannulated gallbladder is suspended in a Goetz tube filled with moist oxygen, so that there is no outer bathing solution. Droplets of the pure absorbate transported out of the lumen appear on the outer surface of the gallbladder and drip off into the graduated stem. The absorbate composition may thus be determined by direct chemical analysis rather than by indirect calculations. [After Diamond (16).]

Absorption of Ringer Solutions by In Vitro Preparations

Our understanding of the primary transport processes by which the gallbladder reabsorbs bile has come largely from in vitro studies. The evidence that these transport processes are virtually the same under in vivo conditions is discussed on page 2463.

A convenient starting point is to consider the situation in which a cannulated, isolated gallbladder is filled with a physiological Ringer solution (principal solute NaCl), bathed on the outside with the same Ringer solution, and the cannula is plugged. Under these circumstances there are no differences of solute concentration or of hydrostatic pressure between the luminal and serosal bathing solutions, and there would be no net movements of water or solutes across the gallbladder wall if it behaved as an inert, passive membrane. In fact a net transfer of both water and

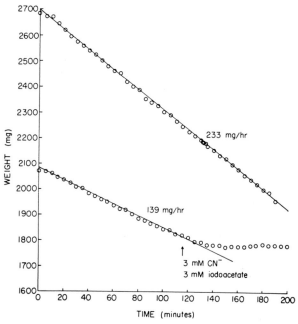

FIG. 6. Effect of cyanide-iodoacetate on fluid absorption by two guinea pig gallbladders in vitro as measured by weighing method (Fig. 2). *Upper curve* represents the weight at 5-min intervals of a preparation initially weighing 2,687 mg, of which 2,326 mg was the luminal fluid and 361 mg the cannula, plug, and gallbladder wall. The linear loss of 233 mg per hour means that each hour 233 μl of luminal fluid is being transported across the gallbladder wall into the external bathing solution. The gallbladder preparation of the *lower curve* initially weighed 2,072 mg, of which 1,748 mg was luminal fluid and 324 mg was the cannula, plug, and gallbladder wall. The preparation lost weight (reabsorbed luminal fluid) steadily for 2 hours at 139 mg per hour, but weight loss ceased after addition of 3 mM CN^- and 3 mM iodoacetate to the external bathing solution. [From Diamond (15).]

NaCl from the luminal to the serosal side is observed. This is illustrated by Figure 6, which depicts the change in weight of two isolated guinea pig gallbladders with identical Ringer solutions on both sides (15). One gallbladder (upper curve) lost weight steadily at 233 mg per hour. Of its initial weight of 2,687 mg, 2,326 mg was the fluid inside the lumen, 181 mg was the gallbladder wall, and 180 mg represented the cannula and plug. Thus, each hour this preparation was absorbing (transferring from the luminal to the serosal solution) 230/2,326 = 9.9% of its initial luminal volume. The second gallbladder (lower curve) lost weight steadily at 139 mg per hour until cyanide and iodoacetate were added to the serosal solution to stop metabolism, with the result that weight loss (absorption of fluid) ceased. Thus, the process responsible for maintaining fluid transport between identical bathing solutions is powered by the metabolism of the gallbladder wall. If the gallbladder is everted so that the mucosal solution is on the outside, the transport of fluid from the mucosal to the serosal solution now results in a gain of weight (24), and this is also brought to a halt by metabolic poisons (see Fig. 10). Control experiments, in which changes in luminal volume were measured directly or by changes in concentration of impermeant dyes, proved that these changes in weight were due quantitatively to changes in the volume of luminal fluid (12, 15, 24).

Analysis of the residual luminal fluid in a non-everted gallbladder, or of the accumulated luminal fluid in an everted gallbladder, shows that in NaCl-Ringer solution the transported fluid consists of NaCl and water in virtually isotonic proportions. Figure 7 depicts the osmolarity of the fluid transported by a noneverted fish gallbladder, as calculated from the decrease in the amounts of salt and water in the mucosal bathing solution. It is apparent that the transported fluid remains isotonic over the entire course of absorption, whether as little as 5% or as much as 81% of the mucosal fluid has been absorbed.

Thus when both sides of the gallbladder are bathed in vitro by identical NaCl-Ringer solutions, the organ transports fluid from the mucosal to the serosal surface at a rate usually between 10% and 30% of the luminal volume per hour, depending on the species of animal used. This finding has been demonstrated for gallbladders from the guinea pig and three species of fish by Diamond (12, 15) and from the rabbit by

Wheeler (76), Dietschy (24), and Diamond (15). If the mucosal surface area is calculated from the luminal volume, by using the formula for a sphere and disregarding folding of the epithelium, then the transport rate related to area is 15 $\mu l/cm^2$ per hour at 17–23 C in a fish, the roach (12), 23 $\mu l/cm^2$ per hour at 37 C in the guinea pig (15), and 43–90 $\mu l/cm^2$ per hour at 37 C in the rabbit (15, 24, 76). Fluid absorption from an isotonic NaCl solution in vivo has been observed in the dog by Ravdin et al. (66), Grim & Smith (34), and by Kang & Hong (47), and in the rabbit by Dietschy (24) and by Whitlock & Wheeler (78). The transported fluid was found to be isotonic within experimental error in three species of fish by Diamond (12), in the rabbit by Dietschy (24), Diamond (15, 16), and Whitlock & Wheeler (78), and in the guinea pig by Diamond (15). Initially Wheeler (76) had calculated the absorbate to be slightly hypertonic in the rabbit, but this finding probably resulted from the experimental difficulties involved in determining absorbate osmolarity by the chamber method, and it was corrected subsequently by Whitlock & Wheeler (78). The most accurate method of determining the composition of the absorbate is provided by the unilateral preparation (Fig. 5), which yields pure samples of the transported fluid for direct chemical analysis. By this means Diamond (16) showed that the absorbate formed by rabbit gallbladder is isotonic to the Ringer solution used within an experimental standard deviation of ±1.6%.

These in vitro experiments thus confirm the correctness of the postulate advanced in 1902 by Brand to explain the differences between hepatic and gallbladder bile, namely that the gallbladder can form a reabsorbate of isotonic saline. Analogous findings apply to the intestine (10) and renal proximal tubule (82), in which transport of isotonic NaCl is responsible for the reabsorption of the digesta and of the glomerular filtrate, respectively.

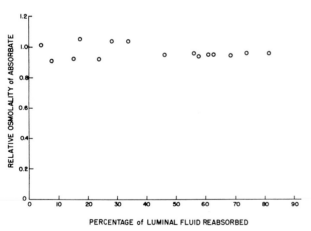

FIG. 7. Osmolality of the absorbate formed by fish gallbladder divided by the bathing solution osmolality (*ordinate*). A value of 1.0 for this ratio means that the absorbate is isotonic. Isolated fish gallbladders, generally with identical NaCl-Ringer solutions on both sides, were allowed to absorb from 5 to 81% of the luminal fluid (*abscissa*), and the absorbate osmolality was computed from the amounts of water and ions absorbed. [After Diamond (12).]

Specificity of Absorption

The replacement of NaCl in the mucosal solution by any other salt except NaBr greatly reduces or abolishes the rate of fluid absorption.

Figure 8 depicts the cation specificity of fluid transport across rabbit gallbladder as measured by the chamber method (76). With both sides of the gallbladder bathed by a choline chloride-Ringer solution containing no sodium, there was no fluid transport. Upon addition of a small concentration of Na (18 mM) to the mucosal solution, fluid transport from

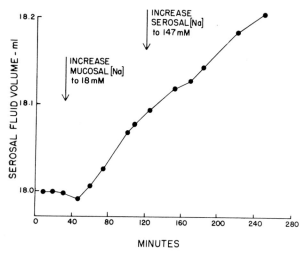

FIG. 8. Cation specificity of fluid transport by isolated rabbit gallbladder as measured by the chamber method (Fig. 3). An increase in the *ordinate* (volume of serosal fluid compartment) means transport of fluid from the mucosal to the serosal compartment. Initially both sides of the gallbladder were bathed by choline Cl-Ringer solution containing no Na. The volume of the serosal compartment began to expand upon addition of Na to the mucosal solution at 18 mM and continued to expand at about the same rate when serosal [Na] was raised to 147 mM. [After Wheeler (76).]

mucosa to serosa commenced and proceeded at approximately the same rate when all the choline in the serosal solution was changed to Na. Evidently fluid absorption requires the presence of Na in the mucosal solution. Replacement of Na in the bathing solutions by the tetraethylammonium cation also reduces fluid transport greatly, though not to zero, in both fish (12) and rabbit (J. M. Diamond and J. M. Tormey, unpublished observation) gallbladders.

Substitution of Br for Cl in the bathing solutions has no effect on fluid absorption in fish gallbladder (12). Replacement of Cl by other anions tested reduces fluid transport to about 20% of its value in NaCl-Ringer solution, but generally not to zero. Specifically, substitution of NaCl by $NaCH_3SO_4$ or by Na_2SO_4 has been shown to decrease fluid transport in the fish (12), and replacement of NaCl by Na_2SO_4 (24, 57), by Na phosphate (J. M. Diamond and J. M. Tormey, unpublished observation), or by Na isethionate (76) decreases fluid transport in the rabbit. The effect appears to depend solely on the mucosal anion, since in fish gallbladder (12) replacement of Cl by SO_4 in the serosal solution did not reduce absorption of mucosal NaCl-Ringer solution, while replacement of serosal SO_4 by Cl did not accelerate absorption of mucosal Na_2SO_4-Ringer solution.

Conversely, if the mucosal solution contains NaCl

together with another salt or with a nonelectrolyte, NaCl is absorbed solely or preferentially in a manner reminiscent of the preferential absorption of NaCl from intestine described by Ingraham & Visscher (41, 42). When a fish gallbladder was filled with a solution containing Na and K at nearly equal concentrations ([Na] = 76.6 mM, [K] = 72.7 mM), mucosal [Na] decreased to 55.2 mM and [K] increased to 94.9 mM by the time 45% of the mucosal fluid had been absorbed; this indicated absorption of 2.5 times as much Na as K. Even this small absorption of K was not due to the primary transport of K but to diffusion of K down its concentration gradient as the decrease in mucosal volume caused mucosal [K] to rise (12). Similarly, rabbit gallbladder preferentially absorbs chloride from chloride-bicarbonate mixtures (15, 16, 76). Lipid-insoluble nonelectrolytes are not absorbed. For example, during the absorption of NaCl and water there is no absorption of sucrose, Evans blue (T-1824), or methemoglobin from fish gallbladder (12), or of sucrose, raffinose, inulin, phenol red, or Evans blue from rabbit gallbladder (15, 16, 76). Striking proof of the specificity of solute absorption comes from the unilateral preparation. When a rabbit gallbladder was filled with 2.418 ml of Ringer solution containing Evans blue at an optical density of 5.20 and was mounted in a Goetz tube without an outer bathing solution, 2.157 ml of colorless (OD = 0.006) transported fluid was collected from the bottom of the tube after 5.5 hours, while the residual fluid in the gallbladder contained the dye of OD = 45.1. Hence 89.2% of the salt and water but only 0.1% of the Evans blue initially in the lumen was absorbed (16).

Thus, water absorption depends specifically on the presence of Na and Cl in the mucosal solution, and NaCl is preferentially or solely absorbed from a mixture of mucosal solutes.

Transport Against Concentration Gradients

Most of the experiments so far described have involved salt and water transport between identical bathing solutions. However, measurements of fluid transport when the salt concentration of the mucosal solution is reduced below that in the serosal solution show that the gallbladder can also transport salt against concentration gradients, just as can the intestine, kidney, frog skin, urinary bladder, and other epithelia.

This is illustrated by Figure 9A, which is based on an experiment by Dietschy (24) using an everted rabbit gallbladder. When all the NaCl (137 mM) and

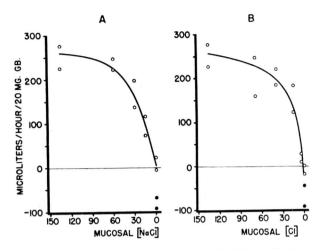

FIG. 9. Rate of fluid absorption by everted rabbit gallbladder as a function of mucosal NaCl or Cl concentration (*abscissa*, in mM). Mucosa-to-serosa fluid movement (i.e., in the physiological direction of absorption) is indicated by positive values of the *ordinate*, serosa-to-mucosa movement by negative values. The serosal solution was Tyrode solution ([NaHCO$_3$] = 12 mM, [NaCl] = 137 mM) throughout. The mucosal solution was similar, except that in *A, open circles*, mucosal [NaCl] was progressively lowered by isosmotic replacement with mannitol; in *B, open circles*, mucosal [Cl] was progressively lowered by replacement with sulfate and addition of sufficient mannitol to maintain isotonicity; in *A* and *B, solid circles*, mucosal NaHCO$_3$, as well as NaCl (*A*) or Cl (*B*), was replaced isosmotically with mannitol. [From Dietschy (24).]

NaHCO$_3$ (12 mM) in the mucosal solution was replaced isosmotically with mannitol, leaving salt concentration in the serosal solution unaltered, a net fluid movement from serosa to mucosa was observed, due to salt diffusing down its concentration gradient from serosa to mucosa accompanied by water. Addition of 12 mM NaHCO$_3$ to the mucosal solution brought the rate of fluid movement to zero; this implied that the mucosa-to-serosa active transport of salt up this steep (12:1) concentration gradient was just balanced by serosa-to-mucosa passive diffusion of salt down its concentration gradient. As the mucosal concentration of NaCl was raised from 0 back to 137 mM, mucosa-to-serosa fluid transport increased rapidly toward the full rate observed between identical bathing solutions in the absence of a salt concentration gradient. Fluid transport had already reached 50% of the maximal rate by the time 20% of the mucosal NaCl concentration had been restored, and the transport rate gradually became saturated at higher levels of mucosal [NaCl]. Figure 9*B* shows that the rate of fluid absorption shows a similar dependence on the mucosal Cl concentration alone, if mucosal [Na] is held constant while mucosal [Cl] is progressively re-

placed with sulfate, so that only Cl is being transported against a concentration gradient. Fish gallbladder can also transport NaCl against concentration gradients of up to 14:1, and the rate shows a similar nonlinear dependence on the mucosal salt concentration (12). These nonlinear, saturable kinetics may be taken to mean that transported salt crosses cell membranes of the gallbladder in combination with a carrier, which is present in limited supply and most of whose binding sites are already occupied at higher salt concentrations. Similar kinetics apply to many other transport mechanisms in a wide variety of tissues.

The ability of the gallbladder in vivo to transport salt against a certain maximal concentrating gradient is well illustrated by the experiments of Kang & Hong (47), who introduced isosmotic NaCl-sucrose mixtures into the gallbladder of an anesthetized dog. When isotonic sucrose was introduced, the salt concentration and volume of the gallbladder initially increased and leveled off to constant values when the luminal [Cl] had risen to an average of 10.7 mM (plasma [Cl] was 113 mM). When solutions with a chloride concentration higher than this were introduced, the same equilibrium value was achieved from the opposite direction by a decrease in luminal volume and [Cl]. Evidently the uphill transport of salt (out of the lumen) and downhill diffusion (into the lumen) were just balanced at this concentration gradient. At lower values of luminal [Cl] the rate of inward diffusion of Cl exceeded the rate of outward transport, whereas the reverse was true for higher values of luminal [Cl]. Once such a stable plateau had been reached, addition of the metabolic inhibitor iodoacetic acid caused the volume of the gallbladder suddenly to begin increasing and the luminal salt concentration to rise toward plasma levels, because of inhibition of salt transport. Analogous plateaus were demonstrated by Dietschy (24) in the gallbladder of the anesthetized rabbit at luminal salt concentrations of 5–20 mM and by Diamond (12) in fish gallbladder in vitro at a luminal salt concentration of 10 mM, the serosal salt concentration being near 150 mM in both cases.

Even when the mucosal salt concentration is lowered to $\frac{1}{10}$–$\frac{1}{2}$ of the serosal value and net transport is proceeding up a salt concentration gradient, the absorbate remains isotonic NaCl (an NaCl solution of plasma osmolarity) in rabbit, fish, and dog gallbladder. This fact is of physiological significance in maintaining gallbladder bile isotonic at all stages of its reabsorption as its chloride content is progressively lowered.

Effects of Inhibitors, Hormones, and Other Agents on Transport

Figure 10 illustrates how several inhibitors block fluid transport in the everted, isolated rabbit gallbladder.

Iodoacetate (5×10^{-5} M) or *iodoacetamide* (5×10^{-5} M) completely inhibits fluid transport by rabbit gallbladder (Fig. 10). Iodoacetate at 10^{-2} M inhibits transport by dog gallbladder in vivo (47). Iodoacetamide abolishes transport by guinea pig gallbladder at 1.5×10^{-3} M but is without effect at 5×10^{-4} M (J. D. Ostrow, personal communication).

Cyanide (2–4 mM) partially inhibits transport by fish gallbladder (12).

Cyanide (3 mM) and *iodoacetate* (3 mM), when present simultaneously, completely inhibit transport by fish, guinea pig, and rabbit gallbladder (12, 15).

Dinitrophenol (5×10^{-5} M) completely inhibits transport by rabbit gallbladder (Fig. 10).

Substitution of *nitrogen* for oxygen completely inhibits transport by rabbit gallbladder (Fig. 10).

Glucose is without effect on transport by isolated rabbit gallbladder (15), which functions well in the absence of exogenous substrate. Evidently, as in rat ileum (3), energy is supplied by metabolism of endogenous substrates, but it is unknown whether these are stored lipid or glycogen.

Diamox (acetazolamide), a carbonic anhydrase inhibitor, is without effect on transport by fish gallbladder, even at concentrations of 10 mM (12).

Bicarbonate (25 mM) doubles the rate of NaCl transport in rabbit gallbladder, as compared with the rate in bicarbonate-free solutions (15, 16). This effect is in addition to the fact that bicarbonate itself is transported.

Acetylcholine apparently causes a small stimulation, and *adrenaline* a small inhibition, of transport by fish gallbladder (12). Similar effects were reported earlier under in vivo conditions in dogs (75) and deserve to be confirmed.

Aldosterone produced a large stimulation of transport by fish gallbladder in a few cases but was more often without effect (17). Even in known target organs, in vitro effects of adrenal steroids on salt transport are notoriously difficult to elicit unless the endogenous tissue steroid is first exhausted. If the effect of aldosterone on the gallbladder is real, the methods developed by Porter & Edelman (64) for eliciting

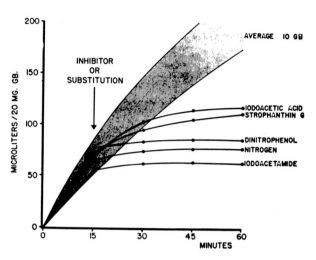

FIG. 10. Effect of metabolic inhibition on fluid transport by everted rabbit gallbladder. *Ordinate* is the cumulative fluid transport since $t = 0$, which in uninhibited bladders (shaded area is mean transport $\pm$ 1 SD for 10 normal bladders) increases linearly with time. The concentrations of inhibitors added at $t = 15$ min were 5×10^{-5} M iodoacetamide, dinitrophenol, or iodoacetic acid; 5×10^{-4} M G-strophanthin (ouabain); complete replacement of O_2 with N_2. [From Dietschy (24).]

aldosterone effects reproducibly in isolated urinary bladder might be profitably applied to the gallbladder.

Antidiuretic hormone had no effect on transport by fish gallbladder, but *oxytocin* produced complete inhibition (12). This effect is surprising, as all known effects of neurohypophyseal hormones in other tissues are stimulatory, but there are reasons for believing that the effect might be real and occur physiologically (p. 2464). The effect of oxytocin in vivo or on a mammalian gallbladder has yet to be tested.

Increasing *temperature* increases the transport rate in fish and rabbit gallbladder.

Removal of *potassium* from the serosal bathing solution reversibly depresses transport by fish gallbladder by 52% after a delay of 25–40 min, but is without effect in the rabbit (12, 15).

The cardiac glycoside *ouabain* inhibits transport by fish gallbladder partially at 10^{-5} M and completely at 10^{-4} M (12) and in the rabbit inhibits partially at 5×10^{-4} M and completely at 10^{-3} M (24, 57).

Transport in many other epithelia [e.g., frog skin (73) and urinary bladder (5)] is blocked by ouabain at far lower concentrations (10^{-6} M) and is completely inhibited by removal of K in much shorter times. Both agents, it has been postulated (49), act on a linked potassium-sodium pump that is responsible in these tissues both for transcellular sodium transport and for maintaining a high intracellular concentration of potassium. In the gallbladder the very high concentrations of ouabain required for inhibition of NaCl transport, and the slowness and incompleteness or absence of the K-free effect, suggest that the effect of these two agents on NaCl transport is secondary. For example, the epithelial cells of the gallbladder resemble most other cells in possessing a high intracellular [K], which may be maintained by the familiar ouabain-sensitive, Na-linked K uptake mechanism present in other cells. If this normal intracellular ionic balance is indirectly necessary for transcellular NaCl transport, disruption of this intracellular balance by ouabain or by removal of external K might lead secondarily to inhibition of fluid transport.

Passive Permeability

The experiments described in the preceding sections demonstrate that the primary transport process in the gallbladder is the transfer, powered by metabolic energy, of NaCl-NaHCO$_3$ and water in isotonic proportions from the mucosal to the serosal bathing solution (i.e., in the direction bile to blood). As the volume of the gallbladder decreases, the concentrations of bile constituents other than NaCl and NaHCO$_3$ increase. The primary absorption of NaCl-NaHCO$_3$ and water thus leads secondarily to the establishment of bile-to-blood concentration gradients for other substances. The rates at which substances diffuse into the bloodstream down these concentration gradients may be predicted from knowledge of the passive permeability properties of the gallbladder, which are briefly summarized.

As regards nonelectrolytes, the permeability of the gallbladder varies approximately as the oil-to-water partition coefficient—i.e., lipid-soluble molecules permeate readily (E. M. Wright and J. M. Diamond, unpublished observation). Relatively water-soluble, lipid-insoluble nonelectrolytes (such as sugars) and electrolytes (such as amino acids and inorganic ions) are virtually impermeant unless their molecular diameter is sufficiently small (less than ca. 6–8 A in fish and rabbit gallbladder). Among the small inorganic ions whose size falls below this limit, cations are considerably more permeant than anions. Both the bile-acid anions and native (i.e., conjugated) bile pigments are virtually impermeant in the undamaged gallbladder [(67); and J. D. Ostrow, unpublished observation].

Selective Reabsorption of Bile

We may now apply this knowledge of transport processes and passive permeability to consideration of how the gallbladder transforms hepatic bile into gallbladder bile. As summarized in Table 1, hepatic bile consists essentially of an isotonic mixture of NaCl, NaHCO$_3$, and the sodium salts of the bile-acid anions, with Cl and HCO$_3$ present in higher concentrations than the bile-acid anions. Gallbladder bile is effectively a concentrated solution of sodium bile salts, with Cl and HCO$_3$ in only low concentrations. The classic experiments of Rous & McMaster (69) and of Ravdin's group (67) had demonstrated that the gallbladder effects this transformation while reducing the volume of bile by 80–90%.

The primary step is the bile-to-blood transport of NaCl-NaHCO$_3$ and water in isotonic proportions. This causes a progressive decrease in bile Cl and HCO$_3$ concentrations and in the volume of bile in the gallbladder (Fig. 11). Since the bile pigments and bile-acid anions are impermeant, their concentrations rise in proportion to the decrease in volume. By the time bile volume has decreased by 80–90%, the concentrations of the bile pigments and bile acids have risen five- to tenfold. The selective reabsorption of bile finally ceases when the bile concentrations of Cl and HCO$_3$ have dropped to that level at which their rate of blood-to-bile diffusion down their concentration gradients is just equal to their rate of bile-to-blood active transport up their gradients. For example, Diamond (12) found that [Cl] in six specimens of gallbladder bile from a fresh-water fish, the roach, fell in the range 7.5–24.7 mM. This is in agreement with the value of 15.6 mM to which luminal [Cl] had to be reduced in order to bring the rate of fluid absorption to zero in an in vitro preparation of roach gallbladder. Similarly, Dietschy showed that the chloride concentrations of 5–12 mM reached in concentrated gallbladder bile from the rabbit agree well with the plateau value (p. 2459) of mucosal [Cl] at which net transport ceases in vitro. Finally, the [Cl] plateau value of 11 mM observed by Kang & Hong (47) in anesthetized dogs is close to the value of [Cl] in concentrated canine gallbladder bile. Thus nothing more than the observed concentration dependence of salt reabsorption need be postulated to explain the final limit of bile reabsorption.

If there were no complicating factors, one might have expected that the conversion of hepatic bile into gallbladder bile by reabsorption of isotonic NaCl-NaHCO$_3$ would cause a decrease in the Na concen-

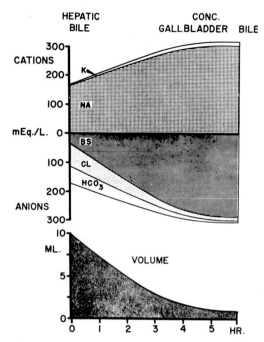

FIG. 11. The changes in bile volume and in concentrations of the major anions and cations in the gallbladder as hepatic bile (*left*) is progressively converted into concentrated gallbladder bile (*right*). *BS* means the bile acid anions. [From Dietschy (24).]

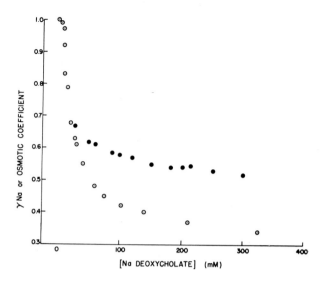

FIG. 12. *Open circles*, the osmotic coefficient *g* of Na deoxycholate, as measured by Johnston & McBain (45); *solid circles*, the sodium activity coefficient γ_{Na} in solutions of Na deoxycholate, as measured by Moore & Dietschy (24). For comparison, *g* is 0.93–0.89 and γ_{Na} is 0.78–0.71 for NaCl in the range 100–300 mM.

tration of bile. In fact [Na] is invariably higher, sometimes twice as high, in gallbladder bile as in hepatic bile. The explanation lies in the osmotic properties of bile salts. With increasing concentration bile salts aggregate more and more into micelles, so that a 300-mM solution of sodium deoxycholate has only 30 % of the osmotic pressure one would have expected if all the sodium and deoxycholate were free and osmotically active. Figure 12 illustrates the precipitous drop of the osmotic coefficient *g* (defined as the observed freezing-point depression divided by that expected if all solute particles were osmotically active) of sodium deoxycholate with increasing concentration. Moore & Dietschy [(59); see also (12)] measured Na and K activity coefficients in bile and in bile salt solutions with cation-sensitive glass electrodes and found that the activity coefficients also dropped with increasing concentration and were lower than they would have been in NaCl or KCl solutions at the same concentration (Fig. 12). Hence during the selective reabsorption of bile by the gallbladder, micelle formation progresses, and the average osmotic coefficient of the bile solutes decreases. Hepatic bile consists largely of an isotonic NaCl-NaHCO₃ solution with the bile salts present in only low concentrations, whereas in the gallbladder the NaCl-NaHCO₃ is reabsorbed to

leave an isotonic solution of bile salts. Since the osmotic coefficient of many bile salts in the concentration range of gallbladder bile (*g* = 0.30–0.48) is half of that in isotonic NaCl (*g* = 0.92), [Na] in an isotonic bile salt solution must be approximately double that in isotonic NaCl or in hepatic bile. Thus, the concentration-dependent micelle formation of bile salts and the requirements of osmotic equilibrium provide a purely physical explanation for the high [Na] of gallbladder bile.

The concentration of potassium in gallbladder bile is higher than in either hepatic bile (Table 1) or in plasma. As fluid is reabsorbed from the gallbladder, [K] in bile will rise, and the ion will diffuse down its concentration gradient to plasma, since it is quite permeant. The reason why the final value of [K] in gallbladder bile is considerably above plasma level was worked out for the rabbit by Dietschy & Moore (26). These authors showed that over a wide variety of conditions K in the gallbladder is at equilibrium according to the Nernst equation, if one takes into account the electrical potential difference and activity coefficients. In rabbit plasma the concentration of K ([K]ₚ) is 3.9 mM, and its activity coefficient (γ_K^p) is about 0.75. In rabbit gallbladder bile the activity coefficient of K (γ_K^{gb}) is considerably lower, about 0.52, because of the effect of the bile-acid anions. When filled with concentrated bile, the bladder lumen is about 18 mv negative to plasma, due to the diffusion potential resulting mainly from Na and Cl activity gradients. The Nernst equation may then be solved for the equilibrium value of $[K]$ in gallbladder bile ($[K]_{gb}$) as follows:

$$E = -18 \text{ mv} = \frac{RT}{F} \log \frac{[K]_p \gamma_K^p}{[K]_{gb} \gamma_K^{gb}}$$

Substituting the values for $[K]_p$, γ_K^p, and γ_K^{gb} and setting $RT/F = 61.5$ mv at 37 C, one obtains $[K]_{gb} = 11$ mM as the predicted equilibrium value of $[K]$ in gallbladder bile, in good agreement with observed values of 10–14 mM. Thus, the low activity coefficient of K in bile and the lumen-negative electrical PD suffice to account for the raised potassium concentration in gallbladder bile passively, without any need to postulate active secretion. It is possible that the high concentrations of calcium in gallbladder bile, which are considerably above those in hepatic bile or in plasma, also represent an equilibrium value according to the Nernst equation. An alternative explanation would be that calcium might be relatively impermeant and that it might therefore be unable to diffuse out sufficiently rapidly as reabsorption of fluid raised its concentration. Since neither the activity of calcium in bile nor its permeability across the gallbladder has been measured, we cannot decide between these two hypotheses at present. The hypothesis that $[Ca]$ in bile represents an equilibrium value is tentatively supported by the observation that $[Ca]$ in the fluid elaborated by a unilateral preparation rises[2] as the fluid goes electrically more negative (61). The reason why gallbladder bile has a lower pH than hepatic bile is also unclear and might be due either

[2] Peters & Walser (61) observed that when K, Li, Rb, Cs, Ca, Mg, or Sr were present on the mucosal surface of a unilateral preparation, all appeared in the transported fluid. They suggested as an interpretation that all seven cations were actively transported from mucosa to serosa by a common mechanism. For K the thorough and careful study of Dietschy & Moore (26), demonstrating passive transepithelial distribution, permits this suggestion to be rejected. Purely passive transepithelial movement of K is also indicated by measurements of K fluxes with radioactive tracers (12, 76) and by an analysis of K distribution in the unilateral preparation (16). Inspection of Peters and Walser's results and consideration of electric PDs suggest that the other six cations also permeate passively into the transported fluid and that there is no need to invoke active processes. For example, the relative concentrations of these cations were found to increase as the fluid went electrically more negative, and the effect was more marked for the divalent calcium than for the monovalent cations. Active Ca absorption seems particularly unlikely because the concentration of Ca in gallbladder bile is always much higher, not lower, than that in hepatic bile or in blood.

to the electrical potential difference, to H^+ secretion, to HCO_3 absorption, or to a combination of these factors.

Thus, the reabsorption of isotonic $NaCl$-$NaHCO_3$, in conjunction with known permeability properties of the gallbladder and osmotic properties of bile salt solutions, will explain the following features of the selective reabsorption of bile by the gallbladder: the decrease in volume by up to 90%, virtual disappearance of Cl and HCO_3, five- to tenfold increase in bile pigment and bile-acid concentrations, twofold increase in $[Na]$, and increase in $[K]$. A quantitative explanation for the rise in $[Ca]$ and drop in pH is still wanting.

Finally, one may inquire whether this account of the concentrating activity of the gallbladder, deduced largely on the basis of in vitro experiments with a small number of species, is also valid in vivo and applies to other vertebrates. The answer to both questions seems to be affirmative. The following properties of the gallbladder have been demonstrated both in vivo and in vitro: absorption of isotonic NaCl; transport of NaCl against concentration gradients, leading to a plateau value of $[Cl]$ that is the same in vivo as in vitro; cessation of transport after treatment with metabolic inhibitors; passive distribution of K according to the Nernst equation; impermeability of bile pigment and bile acid; ability to transport water against an osmotic gradient (p. 2472), which has the same limiting value in vivo as in vitro; sodium diffusion potentials (29), which have the same value in vivo as in vitro; and coupled transport of Na and Cl (p. 2469). Thus, transport mechanisms and permeability characteristics of the gallbladder are little altered under in vitro conditions. As for species differences, the species whose gallbladders have been studied in greatest detail (the fish *Rutilus rutilus* and the rabbit) belong to different classes of vertebrates, yet only minor quantitative differences and no significant qualitative differences were uncovered. Less complete studies on transport in three other species of fish (pike, bream, and carp) and in two other mammals (guinea pig and dog) have given similar results. The properties of gallbladder bile (isotonic to plasma, high $[Na]$ and $[K]$, low $[Cl]$) are much the same in all classes of vertebrates. It will probably be found that species differences affect mainly the rate of transport and the chloride permeability, hence the degree to which bile is concentrated. For example, the gallbladder concentrates bile eight- to tenfold in the fish *Rutilus rutilus*, the rabbit, and the dog, fivefold in man, twofold in the guinea pig (Ostrow, personal communication), and very little in sheep.

Regulation of Bile Reabsorption

The most important and perhaps the only determinant of the extent of reabsorption is the dependence of absorption on luminal chloride concentration already discussed. Good agreement has been obtained in three species of animals between the chloride concentration actually found in gallbladder bile and the mucosal chloride concentration at which the rate of outward salt transport and the rate of inward diffusion become equal. This concentration dependence of salt transport suffices to explain why the volume of hepatic bile drops in the gallbladder to 10–20% of its initial value and no further.

Two findings suggest the possibility that the rate at which this limiting concentration is reached may be under physiological control. First, Johnston et al. (46), working with their surgically prepared unanesthetized dogs, made the interesting observation that absorption proceeds three times more slowly at night than during the day. Second, the concentrating activity of the gallbladder may disappear during parturition, since it has been reported (65) that the gallbladder is distended in pregnant women undergoing cesarean section and contains a dilute bile with much the same concentrations as unmodified hepatic bile.

There appear to be three factors that might explain these physiological variations in absorption rates: *1*) nerves, *2*) aldosterone, and *3*) oxytocin. *1*) Adrenaline has been reported to inhibit, and acetylcholine to stimulate, fluid absorption in vitro (12). These effects might be mediated by branches of the splanchnic and vagus nerves to the gallbladder, respectively, and stimulation of the divided vagus nerve has in fact been claimed to stimulate fluid absorption in vivo (75). *2*) Aldosterone may produce a large increase in fluid transport by the in vitro gallbladder in a manner reminiscent of its effect on urinary bladder. *3*) Oxytocin may inhibit transport by the in vitro gallbladder. The oxytocin effect is particularly intriguing because if it occurred physiologically the pattern of variation of oxytocin levels in the body would be in the right direction to explain the observed inhibition of fluid transport by the gallbladder at night and during parturition. Further speculation is unwarranted until the effects of nerves, aldosterone, and oxytocin have been tested in vivo under physiological conditions with a preparation similar to Ravdin's conscious dogs.

Summary

Since the absorption of salt and water in isotonic proportions is the biological driving force by which the gallbladder concentrates bile, the remainder of this section is devoted to the mechanism of salt and water absorption. Before turning our attention to this subject, let us summarize our present understanding of the concentrating activity of the gallbladder.

Hepatic bile (the primary secretion product of the liver) and gallbladder bile show characteristic differences in composition: gallbladder bile approximates a concentrated isotonic solution of the sodium salts of bile-acid anions, whereas hepatic bile is an isotonic solution in which NaCl and $NaHCO_3$ predominate over bile salts. These differences in composition result from the selective reabsorption of bile by the gallbladder, leading to an 80–90% decrease in the volume of bile. The gallbladder utilizes metabolic energy to transport $NaCl$-$NaHCO_3$ and water in isotonic proportions from bile to blood. Salt transport can go on against concentration gradients and is specific both for Na and for Cl or HCO_3. In conjunction with passive permeability characteristics of the gallbladder and with the low osmotic coefficient of bile salts in micelles, the absorption of isotonic $NaCl$-$NaHCO_3$ will account for most observed differences between hepatic and gallbladder bile. Observations not yet clarified quantitatively are the increase in bile [Ca] and reduction in pH during reabsorption. Reabsorption of bile ceases when bile chloride reaches the concentration at which outward transport of chloride is just balanced by inward diffusion. The most important unresolved problems concern possible physiological variations in the rate of reabsorption and the speculative role of nerves and the hormones aldosterone and oxytocin in these variations.

MECHANISM OF SALT TRANSPORT

There are three possible kinds of explanations for the metabolically driven transport of salt and water by the gallbladder. Either salt transport is active (directly coupled to the expenditure of metabolic energy) with water transport passive and secondary to salt transport, or else water transport is active and salt transport secondary, or else both salt and water transport are active. The following four lines of evidence, each discussed in detail elsewhere in this chapter, show that the correct interpretation is that salt transport is active and water transport secondary: *1*) A primary role for salt is implied by the observation that water transport specifically requires the presence of NaCl or NaHCO$_3$ in the lumen, and no nonelectrolyte and few other salts will suffice. 2) When the lumen contains a mixture of solutes, NaCl is absorbed preferentially or solely, and most other salts and all nonelectrolytes tested remain behind. 3) Both Na and Cl can be transported simultaneously against their electrochemical gradients and against the direction of water flow. Therefore, the transport of both Na and Cl must be active and cannot be secondary to water flow. 4) In the absence of an activity gradient for water between the external bathing solutions, the rate of water transport is directly proportional to the rate of salt transport, and there is no water transport in the absence of salt transport. Therefore, all water flow is a secondary result of salt transport, and there can be no independent mechanism for water transport.

The (Nonexistent) Electrical Potential Difference Associated with Salt Transport

A simple clue to the mechanism of salt transport across a membrane may be obtained by measuring the electric PD when the membrane separates identical bathing solutions. For example, in frog skin (74), urinary bladder (53), kidney proximal tubule (81), and placenta (8) the bathing solution toward which salt is being transported is found to be electrically positive by 20–150 mv. These PDs can be attributed quantitatively to the active transport of positively charged sodium ions across the tissue, with anions passively following the resulting PD. The observation of net sodium fluxes, unaccompanied by anions, in the short-circuited state demonstrates that the transport mechanism itself acts only on Na and that the normal coupling between Na and anion fluxes is electrical in these tissues. In some other epithelia [e.g., salivary gland duct (55), resting stomach (38)] the side toward which the electrolyte is moving is found to be electrically negative by up to 70 mv, due to the active transport of Cl. The PD in these epithelia disappears when transport has been inhibited or when the preparation is moribund.

Although the first published report of the PD across the gallbladder appeared in 1962 (13), a prior unpublished measurement had already been made. The following account of this pioneer work, which has been transmitted to the reviewer at second hand but under circumstances ensuring its authenticity, may be of interest in illustrating the experimental problems initially posed by the peculiar electrical characteristics of the gallbladder. During the early 1950s measurements of PDs and short-circuit currents were rapidly clarifying transport mechanisms in a variety of epithelia. There had been virtually no attention devoted to transport phenomena in the gallbladder since the 1930s, and a visiting American investigator at a European laboratory distinguished for studies of epithelial transport therefore set out to identify the source of the expected short-circuit current across the gallbladder. The first gallbladder tested showed no PD between identical bathing solutions and hence offered nothing to short-circuit. Apparatus and dissecting technique were refined, but a few subsequent experiments gave the same discouraging results. The investigator therefore concluded that these in vitro gallbladders were moribund, chucked them into the wastebucket, and went on to short-circuit more promising epithelia, leaving the transport mechanisms of the gallbladder to relapse into physiological obscurity for several more years.

It is now established that, in contrast to the finding in most other epithelia, there is no PD or short-circuit current between identical bathing solutions across gallbladders known to be transporting salt and water. For example, when roach gallbladder was bathed on both surfaces by NaCl-Ringer solution (13), fluid was transported from the mucosal to the serosal surface at 15 μl/cm^2 per hour, but the PD was only 0.8 $\pm$ 0.6 mv, mucosal surface negative (avg. and SD of measurements in 25 gallbladders). Of these 25 gallbladders, 1 gave -2.5 mv, 1 gave -2.3 mv, 3 more -1.5 to -1.0 mv, and the other 20 between -1.0 and 0.0 mv. After fluid transport had been depressed 61% by cyanide, the PD was -0.3 mv, and after complete inhibition of transport with cyanide and iodoacetate, -0.4 mv. Thus changes in transport rate are not associated with changes in PD. The absence of a PD or short-circuit current related to salt transport has been confirmed for gallbladders from all 12 species of vertebrates tested: the roach, bream, pike, plaice, frog, bullfrog, toad, turtle, guinea pig, rabbit, cat, and dog. Most of these measurements have been made in vitro, but the absence of a PD associated with salt transport in vivo has been confirmed for the rabbit and dog. This absence of a transport PD in the gallbladder is the most distinctive feature of its transport mechanisms.

A possible explanation for the absence of a PD would be that the gallbladder actively transports both Na and Cl in the same direction, independently, and fortuitously at the same rate, so that the PDs of the Na and Cl pumps are equal and opposite and cancel each other. In this case replacing Na with a nonabsorbed cation should leave only the Cl pump and unmask its PD (serosa negative, mucosa positive). However, replacing Na in roach gallbladder with the nonabsorbed cations K or tetraethylammonium (13), and replacing Na in rabbit gallbladder with the nonabsorbed cations tetraethylammonium, K, or choline (24, 76), still leaves the PD within a millivolt of zero. Similarly, if there were independent Na and Cl pumps normally canceling each other's PD, replacing Cl with a poorly absorbed anion should leave only the Na pump and unmask its PD (serosa positive, mucosa negative). However, replacing Cl by the poorly absorbed anions SO_4 or CH_3SO_4 in roach gallbladder (13) and by SO_4, isethionate, and cholate (21, 24, 62, 76) in rabbit gallbladder still leaves the PD under 2 mv. These findings contrast with results of analogous experiments in the stomach, which also transports a cation (H^+) and an anion (Cl^-) actively and in the same direction but more or less independently. Replacement of Cl by SO_4 gives the expected positive PD for an H^+ pump, whereas elimination of H^+ secretion leaves a large negative PD due to independent Cl^- transport (36).

Thus, one fails to observe the PDs one would expect if the gallbladder had independent mechanisms for transporting Na and Cl. The absence of PDs would be understandable if the transport of Na and Cl were tightly and directly coupled, that is, if there were an electrically neutral mechanism transporting one Na for every Cl and thus transferring no net charge. However, the argument against independent Na and Cl pumps is not quantitative until one can state how many millivolts such pumps would produce if they existed. For example, if the passive permeability of the gallbladder were sufficiently high, independent Na and Cl pumps might generate PDs that were too low to detect with confidence, but the pumps could still transport ions at the observed rates. The expected PDs can be calculated from measurements of ion permeability by means of diffusion potentials and tracer fluxes. We shall therefore postpone a decision on the question of independent Na and Cl pumps versus a neutral NaCl pump until after consideration of these measurements.

Passive Permeability to Ions

The failure to observe PDs caused by ion transport in the gallbladder contrasts strongly with the ease and reproducibility with which one can measure the large PDs associated with passive movements of ions: diffusion potentials of up to 63 mv and streaming po-

tentials of up to 20 mv. The absence of a transport PD has greatly facilitated the analysis of diffusion potentials and streaming potentials in the gallbladder as compared with other epithelia.

DIFFUSION POTENTIALS. When the bathing solutions on both sides of the gallbladder are identical, the PD across the gallbladder is zero, regardless of bathing solution composition (21). When part of the salt on one side is removed, adding an impermeant nonelectrolyte such as sucrose or mannitol to maintain constant osmolarity, the low-salt side goes electrically positive by up to 63 mv, indicating greater permeability to cations than to anions. Figure 13 illustrates diffusion potentials caused by different concentration gradients of NaCl in fish gallbladder. If the mucosal and serosal solutions are reversed, one obtains a PD of the opposite orientation but the same magnitude, indicating that the gallbladder is symmetrical— i.e., that the mucosal and serosal cell membranes have the same relative permeability coefficients. In contrast, some other epithelia are notably asymmetrical:[3] for example, the inner face of frog skin is preferentially permeable to K, while the outer face is more permeable to Na (49).

Although both fish and rabbit gallbladders are more permeable to cations than to anions, there are species differences in the absolute magnitudes of the diffusion potentials and relative permeabilities. In roach gallbladder Na_2SO_4 concentration gradients give the theoretical Nernst potentials for a cation electrode (58 mv for a tenfold activity ratio of Na), indicating complete impermeability to sulfate. A tenfold NaCl gradient gives 50 mv, implying a small but nonzero permeability to chloride, which reduces the PD below the value for a Na electrode. If one uses the constant-field equations to calculate (see references 13, 21, and 24) relative permeability coefficients (P's) from diffusion potentials, then for roach gallbladder the relative P's are $P_{Na} = 1.0$, $P_K = 1.0$, $P_{Br} = 0.07$, $P_{CH_3SO_4} = 0.05$, $P_{Cl} = 0.04$, $P_{TEA} = 0.02$, $P_{SO_4} = 0.00$. In rabbit gallbladder the permeability to anions is not so

---

[3] For this reason a model of epithelial Na transport proposed by Koefoed-Johnsen & Ussing (49) cannot explain transport by the gallbladder. The model proposes that one membrane of an epithelial cell behaves as a potassium electrode and carries out a forced K-Na exchange, while the opposite membrane behaves as a sodium electrode. In the gallbladder both membranes have the same ratio of K permeability to Na permeability, and in fish gallbladder the K and Na permeabilities are in fact identical at both membranes, so that the model would result in one-for-one transepithelial cation exchange without net cation transport.

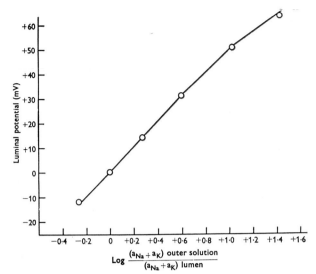

FIG. 13. Diffusion potentials arising from NaCl concentration gradients across fish gallbladder in vitro. While [NaCl] in one bathing solution was maintained at 144 mM, [NaCl] in the other bathing solution was lowered by isosmotic partial replacement with mannitol, always maintaining [K] at 4.5 mM. *Abscissa:* the activity ratio for the sum of [Na] + [K] (a positive value of the logarithm means that [Na] and [Cl] are higher in the outer = serosal solution than in the luminal = mucosal solution). *Ordinate:* potential of lumen with respect to serosa. *Circles* are experimental points, while the *curve* gives theoretical diffusion potentials calculated from the constant-field equation, assuming $P_K : P_{Na} : P_{Cl} = 1.00 : 1.00 : 0.04$. [From Diamond (13).]

low, so that a tenfold NaCl gradient gives 22 mv rather than the Nernst value of 58 mv. The relative permeability coefficients for rabbit gallbladder come out $P_K = 2.3$, $P_{Na} = 1.0$, $P_{Cl} = 0.33$, $P_{cholate} = 0.00$.

The most plausible explanation for anion permeabilities being consistently below cation permeabilities is that the channels by which ions traverse the gallbladder contain negative fixed charges. In free solution K and Cl have the same mobility, and Cl has a smaller hydrated diameter and higher mobility than Na, so that without charge effects Cl should be as permeant as K and more so than Na. The presence of negative fixed charges in the membrane would greatly decrease permeability to monovalent anions and could reduce permeability of the divalent anion sulfate to zero. The effect of pH on anion-cation discrimination by the gallbladder shows that these fixed charges are acidic groups with a pK in the vicinity of pH 3 (Wright and Diamond, unpublished observation). The low permeability of the intestine to anions is also due to acidic groups with a pK in this range (71). The following experiments on streaming potentials confirm the existence of these negative fixed charges.

STREAMING POTENTIALS. In the nineteenth century physical chemists observed that the flow of water across a charged membrane set up a PD, in which the side of the membrane toward which water was flowing acquired a potential opposite in sign to the charge of the membrane. The origin of these so-called streaming potentials is that if a membrane bears, say, negative fixed charges, aqueous channels through the membrane must contain an excess of positive over negative mobile ions from the bathing solutions to balance the membrane fixed charge. Water flow through these channels will then sweep out a fluid initially containing an excess of positive mobile ions and make the side of the membrane toward which water is flowing electrically positive. The magnitude of the streaming potential is directly proportional to the rate of water flow.

Streaming potentials have been demonstrated in roach gallbladder (14) and in rabbit gallbladder (14, 24) in which they are up to 20 mv and have been subjected to detailed study (19–21). The observation is that if one adds an impermeant nonelectrolyte to one side of the gallbladder to make it hypertonic and set up osmotic water flow, that side goes electrically positive by an amount directly proportional to the rate of water flow (Fig. 14). The PD is due to osmotic flow rather than anisotonicity per se, because *1*) the same PD is obtained if the mucosal solution is made hypertonic by a small amount or the serosal solution hypotonic by the same amount; and *2*) if a PD is set up by the mucosal solution being made hypertonic, making the serosal solution equally hypertonic to eliminate osmotic water flow brings the PD back to zero. These PDs arising across a charged membrane in response to and in proportion to water flow therefore fulfill the classic definition of streaming potentials. The sign of the streaming potentials (side toward which water is flowing goes electrically positive) confirms the conclusion drawn from diffusion potentials, that cell membranes of the gallbladder must contain negative fixed charges. Effects of pH and divalent cations on diffusion potentials and streaming potentials show that both kinds of PD must be due to the same negative fixed charges. As in artificial membranes, measured streaming potentials in the gallbladder consist not only of the electrokinetic flow potential itself, but also contain a large boundary-diffusion-potential component due to salt concentration changes caused by water flow in the unstirred layers immediately adjacent to the epithelium.

The significance of streaming potentials as a physiological tool arises from the fact that they offer a

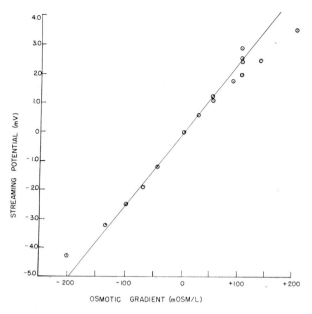

FIG. 14. Streaming potentials in rabbit gallbladder bathed in Na_2SO_4-Ringer solution. Both mucosal and serosal solutions had the same electrolyte composition, but osmotic gradients were created by adding sucrose to one of the solutions. A positive osmotic gradient means mucosal solution is hypertonic; a positive PD means mucosal solution is positive. The fall-off below linearity at high gradients is due to a decrease in water permeability in hypertonic solutions. [From Diamond & Harrison (21).]

virtually instantaneous method of measuring water flow across a membrane. For example, an experiment on the relation between the osmotic gradient and the rate of water flow across the gallbladder took 7 hours when water flow was measured gravimetrically but 2–30 min when water flow was measured by means of streaming potentials (20, 21). Smyth & Wright (71) observed PDs that they suggested were streaming potentials in the intestine.

The physiological significance of the fixed charges responsible for diffusion potentials and streaming potentials in the gallbladder is that they reduce chloride permeability and thereby enable the gallbladder to concentrate bile to a greater extent. As already discussed, the limit to the reabsorption of bile occurs when bile chloride is reduced to that level at which the rate of transport outward equals the rate of diffusion inward. Fixed negative charges reduce the rate of chloride diffusion and thereby increase the maximum gradient against which chloride can be transported.

ELECTRICAL RESISTANCE. Roach gallbladder behaves as a linear ohmic resistor with a value of 113 ohm-cm²

(13). The resistance of rabbit gallbladder is about half as large.

TRACER FLUXES. Tracer measurements have been carried out in roach, rabbit, and dog gallbladder.

The fluxes across roach gallbladder are summarized in Figure 15. As measured by Na^{24}, the Na influx (serosa-to-mucosa) and Na efflux (mucosa-to-serosa) are 8.4 and 10.8 μmoles/cm² per hour, respectively. The difference of 2.4 μmoles/cm² per hour represents the net efflux generated by active transport and is abolished by cyanide-iodoacetate. Although measurements of diffusion potentials showed that bromide is much less permeable than Na, its one-way tracer fluxes are somewhat higher than those for Na, and are in fact 22 times higher than those calculated from its relative permeability and the membrane resistance on the assumption that the Br back-flux is due to simple diffusion. As with chloride fluxes in the stomach (38), the assumed explanation is that most of the Br flux is due to exchange diffusion (an electrically nonconducting flux due to the shuttling back and forth of Br on a carrier). The influxes of K and Na, however, are in good agreement with predictions based on diffusion potentials and membrane resistance and may be attributed to simple diffusion (13). The potassium flux is unaffected by cyanide-iodoacetate, in agreement with the evidence of Dietschy & Moore (26) that the transepithelial distribution of K is entirely passive.

In rabbit gallbladder Wheeler (76) found that the chloride tracer fluxes were much larger than predicted from electrical measurements and concluded that most of these chloride fluxes were due to exchange diffusion, as with Br (and presumably Cl) in roach gallbladder. The back-fluxes of K and Na implied that K was twice as permeant as Na, in agreement

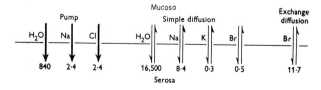

FIG. 15. One-way fluxes (μmoles/cm² per hour) across fish gallbladder when both sides are bathed by NaCl- (or NaBr-) Ringer solution, as measured by radioactive tracers. "Pump" refers to net mucosa-to-serosa fluxes resulting from active NaCl transport. Simple diffusion and exchange diffusion produce equal and opposite fluxes in both directions. The pump fluxes of Br and Cl are nearly the same, and this is also presumed true for the simple-diffusion and exchange-diffusion fluxes. [From Diamond (13).]

with the conclusion drawn by other investigators (21, 24) from measurements of diffusion potentials in rabbit gallbladder. Hence, in rabbit and in fish gallbladder the back-fluxes of K and Na may be attributed to simple diffusion. The back-flux of water, measured with D_2O or THO and related to gallbladder surface area (neglecting mucosal folding), is 16,500 μmoles/cm² per hour in the roach (13), 37,500 μmoles/cm² per hour in the rabbit (24), and 28,700 μmoles/cm² per hour in the dog (34).

Mechanism of Na and Cl Transport

EVIDENCE FOR ACTIVE TRANSPORT. The following arguments show that the transport of both Na and Cl is active in both roach and rabbit gallbladders.

We have seen that roach and rabbit gallbladders can transport NaCl from the mucosal to the serosal bathing solution against concentration gradients of up to approximately 14:1. Under these circumstances the mucosal solution goes electrically positive and the serosa negative by an amount somewhat less than the Nernst equilibrium potential for Na, because P_{Na} is greater than P_{Cl} but P_{Cl} is not zero. Therefore Cl transport occurs simultaneously against a concentration gradient of up to 14:1 and against a PD of up to 47 mv and must be active. Na is moving with the PD but against its concentration gradient. Since the PD is less than the Nernst equilibrium value, the favorable PD is insufficient to balance the adverse concentration gradient, and the transport of Na must be against its electrochemical gradient ($RT \ln a_m/a_s + zF \Delta V$, where a is Na activity and subscripts m and s refer to the mucosal and serosal solutions, respectively) and therefore active. Alternatively, when 50% of mucosal Na is replaced with K in roach gallbladder, Na transport goes on against a 2:1 concentration gradient; when up to 92% of mucosal Cl is replaced with sulfate in rabbit gallbladder, Cl transport goes on against a concentration gradient of up to 12:1. But in both cases the PD is near zero, so that transport is against the electrochemical gradient and therefore active. Bicarbonate can also move simultaneously against a concentration gradient and PD in rabbit gallbladder (76). Finally, Wheeler (76) made the mucosal solution hypertonic with mannitol to reverse the direction of water flow and found that Na, Cl, and HCO_3 could all move simultaneously against their electrochemical gradients and against the water stream; this eliminates explanations involving solvent drag. Whitlock & Wheeler (78) subsequently demonstrated in vivo that

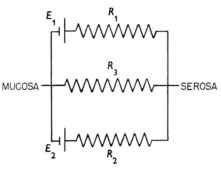

FIG. 16. Equivalent electric circuit that would describe the gallbladder if it had independent cation and anion pumps, and it does not. E_1 would be the electromotive force of the Na or cation pump, in series with a Na resistance R_1; E_2 and R_2 would be the same quantities for Cl or other transported anions; and R_3 would be the leak resistance due to all passively moving ions, of which K is the most important. [From Diamond (13).]

reversing the direction of water flow has little effect quantitatively on the rate of active solute transport.

COUPLED VERSUS INDEPENDENT TRANSPORT OF NA AND CL. We may now return to the question of why active transport of Na and Cl in the gallbladder does not lead to the development of PDs. Before one can accept as the explanation that Na and Cl transport are tightly coupled and nonindependent, one must first calculate whether the PDs that independent pumps would set up would be large enough to detect. These PDs may be calculated from the electrical and tracer measurements presented on pages 2466–2469.

If there were independent cation and anion pumps, the equivalent electrical circuit would be given by Figure 16. A cation battery would drive cations (mainly Na) through a cation resistance, with a similar anion battery and resistance (mainly for Cl) in parallel, and with a third parallel resistor representing conductance to all anions moving passively (mainly a potassium conductance). Two methods are available for calculating the voltage E of the active transport batteries: 1) from the ratio of the tracer fluxes at electrochemical equilibrium, by the expression $E = RT/F \ln M_{ms}/M_{sm}$, in which M_{ms} is the unidirectional tracer flux from mucosa to serosa and M_{sm} the reverse flux from serosa to mucosa; 2) from the electrical measurements of diffusion potentials and membrane resistance, using Ohm's law, $E = MzF/G$, in which G is the partial conductivity of the transported ion and M its net flux at electrochemical equilibrium due to active transport. The resistance associated with each ion may likewise be obtained either from tracer fluxes (neglecting the contribution of exchange diffusion to anion fluxes) or from electrical measurements. Solution of the electrical circuit of Figure 16 then gives the PD one would observe if there were independent Na and Cl pumps.

The detailed calculations for roach gallbladder are given in reference 13. It turns out that the voltages of the Na and Cl pumps (with respect to the mucosal solution) are -7 and $+189$ mv, respectively. If the Na and Cl pumps could function in each other's absence, one would then expect to observe the following PDs: -5.5 mv in Na_2SO_4 or in $NaCH_3SO_4$ (due to an Na pump), and $+7.5$ mv with KCl in the lumen or $+79.3$ mv in TEACl (due to the Cl pump). These PDs would be easily detectable, but the observed PDs are ± 0.3 to 1.7 mv in all cases. Hence in roach gallbladder there cannot be independent Na and Cl pumps that function in each other's absence.

Similar calculations may be carried out for rabbit gallbladder from the tracer measurements of Wheeler (76) and the electrical measurements of Dietschy (24) and of Diamond & Harrison (21). One finds that the voltages of the Na and Cl pumps are -20 and $+58$ mv, respectively. If the Na and Cl pumps could function independently, one would observe -18 mv in Na_2SO_4 (due to the Na pump) and $+45$ mv in choline chloride (due to the Cl pump). As the observed PDs are again close to zero, the Na and Cl pumps also cannot function independently in rabbit gallbladder.

These calculations, then, quantitatively rule out the possibility that transepithelial transport in the gallbladder can involve independent cation or anion pumps like those found in most other epithelia. Under all circumstances there must be a direct, obligate, one-to-one coupling between Na and Cl transport. This is shown by the fact that there is no PD in NaCl-Ringer solution in the absence of ion concentration gradients and that the PDs observed when mucosal Na and Cl or both are partially replaced do not deviate from simple diffusion potentials. Thus, the transport mechanism conveys no net charge and is an electrically neutral NaCl pump.

A hypothesis for the operation of such a neutral pump would be that an Na binding site and a Cl binding site are located on the same carrier molecule and that the carrier can cross the membrane only when both sites are occupied (13). Such a carrier would result in the linked transport of one Na and one Cl. Since neither site could move in the absence of the counter-ion, no PD could be set up even in solutions such as Na_2SO_4 or choline chloride, in which either Cl or Na is absent.

At the time it was discovered (13), the neutral pump

in the gallbladder appeared to be biologically unique. However, there is now suggestive evidence for coupled active transport of cations and anions in four other tissues: 1) rat duodenum, in which the PD in the absence of actively transported sugars is small and in which Smyth & Wright (71) have proposed a neutral NaCl pump similar to that in the gallbladder to account for salt absorption; 2) fish intestine, which transports Na and Cl and resembles the gallbladder in developing no PD in NaCl, Na_2SO_4, or choline chloride (40); 3) dogfish stomach, in which Hogben & Clifton (39) found secretion of H^+ and Cl^- without a PD, suggesting a neutral HCl pump; and 4) beet root, in which Poole (63) proposed a neutral KCl pump to account for salt uptake into the cells.

METABOLIC EVIDENCE FOR A NEUTRAL PUMP. Further information regarding the coupling of cation and anion transport in the gallbladder has come from measurements of the rate of oxygen consumption.

In tissues in which salt transport involves active sodium transport but passive movement of chloride, it has been found that there is a fraction of the total oxygen consumption that specifically requires the presence of Na in the bathing solution. The rate of extra oxygen consumption in the presence of Na is linearly related to the rate of Na transport (84). Whittam (80) suggested as the probable mechanism by which transport controls oxygen consumption that transport involves the breakdown of ATP to ADP, which has been shown by Chance & Williams (7) to control the rate of mitochondrial respiration. If one assumes that all the energy for Na transport comes from the extra O_2 consumed, then one may calculate ratios of Na ions transported to O_2 molecules consumed, and these ratios are much the same in several tissues with independent Na pumps: $Na:O_2 = 18$ for frog skin (84), 19 for toad urinary bladder (54), 25 for rabbit kidney (52), and 28 for dog kidney (51). If one assumes P:O ratios of 3, one may calculate that 3–4 sodium ions are transported per high-energy phosphate bond split, in agreement with Na:P ratios obtained by more direct methods in nerve (2) and red cell (32).

In rabbit gallbladder Martin & Diamond (57) found a fraction of the total oxygen consumption that required the simultaneous presence of Na and Cl in the mucosal solution was not stimulated by Na or Cl alone, was independent of the ionic composition of the serosal solution, and was abolished by ouabain. The characteristics of this transport-linked oxygen uptake therefore correspond closely with the properties of the coupled Na-and-Cl pump as deduced from electrical experiments. From the stoichiometry one can calculate that the gallbladder transports twice as many ions actively (25 Na + 25 Cl = 50 ions) per O_2 consumed as do epithelia that transport only Na actively. The net work of salt transport is still the same, since electrical coupling in other epithelia ensures the passive transport of one Cl for every Na actively pumped. Evidently it costs no more ATP to drive a carrier with both an Na and a Cl binding site than to drive one that conveys Na alone.

Localization of Solute Pumps Within Epithelial Cells

In the experiments discussed so far we have analyzed measurements of fluxes and PDs across the whole gallbladder wall and considered it as a black box. Since 95% of the tissue resistance to ions lies in the epithelial cell layer and since the connective tissue is equally permeable to different solutes, one is safe in assuming that the pumps must reside in the epithelial cells and not in the connective tissue. Like most other animal cells, the epithelial cells of the gallbladder contain lower Na and Cl concentrations and a higher K concentration than the bathing medium (12). As measured by microelectrode techniques, the interior of epithelial cells from rabbit gallbladder is negative to the bathing solutions by 40–80 mv. Calculation of electrochemical gradients shows that active transport is almost surely necessary to pump salt from the cells to the serosal solution, and this conclusion is supported by the observation that extrusion of salt and water from the cells to the serosal solution continues for some time after all salt has been removed from the mucosal solution (12). Whether another neutral pump is required to transport NaCl from the mucosal solution into the cells is uncertain. Most of our information about localization of pumps has in fact come from studies of water transport, which is considered in the remainder of this chapter.

Summary

At this point we may conveniently summarize present knowledge of salt transport in the gallbladder before introducing the problem of water transport.

Unlike most other epithelia, the gallbladder transports NaCl without developing a PD or short-circuit current between identical bathing solutions. Nevertheless both Na and Cl are actively transported. The explanation is that the cation and anion pumps are not independent but tightly coupled, so that there is a one-to-one transport of Na and Cl by an electrically neutral NaCl pump. Measurements of oxygen consumption confirm this picture of direct coupling between Na and Cl transport. Diffusion potentials and streaming potentials indicate that the gallbladder is considerably more permeable to most cations than to most anions, presumably due to the presence of negative fixed charges in the cell membranes. Although there is as yet little direct evidence about the localization of solute pumps within the epithelial cells, there is a large measure of agreement between different investigators, using different apparatus and species, on the transmural fluxes and PDs; and eventual models of transport at the subcellular level must account for these "black-box" findings.

MECHANISM OF WATER TRANSPORT

In the absence of external driving forces (e.g., when the mucosal and serosal solutions are identical) the gallbladder generates a net mucosa-to-serosa flux not only of NaCl but also of water. The proportions are such that the absorbed fluid is isotonic to plasma. As previously discussed, the water transport must somehow result secondarily from active salt transport, because there is no water transport in the absence of salt transport and because the amount of water transported is directly proportional to the amount of salt transported. Identical findings apply to the intestine (10) and kidney proximal tubule (82). We must therefore rephrase the problem of isotonic water transport in the following terms: how does the transport of 1 molecule of NaCl lead to the transport of about 400 molecules of water?

This question is posed by all epithelia secreting or absorbing fluids, and it has fascinated physiologists for a century. Several physiological and anatomical parallels suggest that epithelia share a single mechanism whereby isotonic water transport results secondarily from active solute transport, whether the actively transported solute is sodium chloride, as in the gallbladder and proximal tubule; hydrochloric acid, as in the stomach; bile salts, as in the liver; or salt and numerous metabolites, as in the intestine. Because of its physiological and anatomical simplicity the gallbladder is well suited for investigating this coupling mechanism and has provided much of the direct experimental information on the subject.

Physical theories of the coupling mechanism are considered first and the ultrastructural basis is discussed in the final part of this chapter.

Physical Theories of the Coupling Mechanism

EXTERNAL OSMOTIC FORCES. A common erroneous impression is that water transport by epithelia is due to osmotic gradients established by active solute transport between plasma and the secreted fluid or the fluid being absorbed. As applied to the gallbladder, for example, one might assume that active NaCl transport reduced the osmolarity of bile and increased the osmolarity of the blood in the capillaries of the gallbladder and that water moved out down the resulting osmotic gradient. In fact, such external osmotic gradients do not exist; bile, like the glomerular filtrate in the renal proximal tubules, is isotonic to plasma at all stages of its reabsorption. In vitro the gallbladder maintains a flux of water between identical Ringer solutions, and Grim (33) showed that in vivo the organ can reabsorb fluid when filled with plasma. Since water transport normally proceeds in the absence of an external osmotic gradient, one might suspect that water can also be transported up an external osmotic gradient, and this suspicion has been confirmed.

Figure 17 illustrates the results of a weighing experiment on a noneverted fish gallbladder, demonstrating its ability to transport water against osmotic gradients. With identical Ringer solutions inside and outside, the organ lost weight (absorbed fluid) at 40.4 mg per hour. The impermeant nonelectrolyte sucrose was then added to the luminal (mucosal) solution at 20 mM to make it hypertonic by 0.5 atm. Nevertheless, net absorption of fluid continued against this osmotic gradient at the reduced rate of 19.8 mg per hour. Finally, metabolism and active solute transport were stopped with cyanide and iodoacetate, and the same osmotic gradient (lumen hypertonic by 20 mM sucrose) was applied. The sac now gained weight, and this indicated that water was flowing down its osmotic gradient into the hypertonic solution at 15.8 mg per hour. Thus, passive water flow in response to external osmotic gradients certainly occurs across the gallbladder, but with metabolism intact an additional force is exerted on water by active solute transport, and this suffices to carry water against a finite osmotic gradient.

Water transport against various osmotic gradients by rabbit gallbladder in vivo is illustrated by the experiment of Figure 18. As the contents of the gallbladder were made progressively more hypertonic by addition of sucrose, the net efflux of fluid decreased and finally came to zero at an adverse gradient of just under 100 milliosmols in this rabbit. On the average, an osmotic gradient of about 80 milliosmols (2 atm) is required to bring net fluid absorption to zero in rabbit gallbladder, as shown by four different methods [chamber method (76); gravimetric method in the everted gallbladder (24); gravimetric method in the noneverted gallbladder (15); and in vivo (78)]. Fish gallbladder (14) transports water against gradients of up to 40 milliosmols (1 atm). Other epithelia that can transport water against external osmotic gradients are the intestine, the renal proximal tubule, and the choroid plexus.

The observation of water movement against external osmotic gradients does not require postulating active water transport, but simply means that active solute transport exerts a force on water and is capable of carrying water against a certain opposing force. Irreversible thermodynamics in fact predicts the possibility of water movement coupled to active solute transport and permits one to estimate the maximum osmotic gradient against which such water movement will take place (11).

HYDROSTATIC PRESSURE. That hydrostatic pressure within the lumen cannot be responsible for water transport follows from the demonstration, using the apparatus illustrated in Figure 4, that variations of hydrostatic pressure within the physiological range

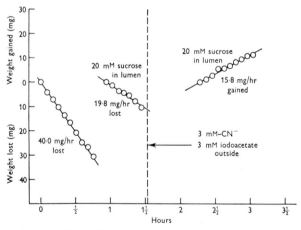

FIG. 17. Effect of osmotic gradients on water transport by a fish gallbladder. *Ordinate,* change in weight of the gallbladder preparation after the first weighing in each series. Weight loss means fluid movement out of the lumen; weight gain means fluid movement into the lumen. In the *first curve* identical Ringer solutions were in the lumen and on the outside. In the *second* and *third curves* the luminal bathing solution contained 20 mM sucrose in addition to the usual components of Ringer and was thus hypertonic. After *t* = 1.5 hours the metabolism of the gallbladder was stopped by addition of cyanide and iodoacetate as a neutral isotonic solution to the outer bathing fluid, to yield final concentrations of 3 mM. *Third curve* was thus obtained from a poisoned gallbladder. [From Diamond (14).]

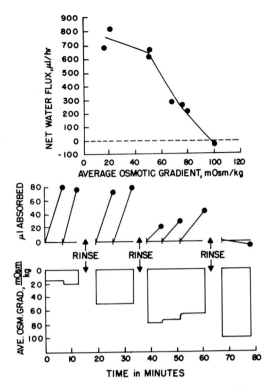

FIG. 18. Water transport against various osmotic gradients by rabbit gallbladder in vivo. The luminal solution was a NaCl-Ringer solution made hypertonic to plasma by addition of increasing concentrations of sucrose in four experimental periods, each involving one to three measurements with the same solution followed by a rinse before the next sucrose concentration was tested. *Lower graph* gives the average osmotic gradient across the gallbladder (lumen always hypertonic) and the *middle graph* the cumulative fluid absorption for each filling. These results are replotted in the *upper graph,* which displays the net rate of water absorption (from the slope of the *middle graph*) against the average osmotic gradient. Net absorption is seen to proceed against gradients of up to 98 milliosmols per kg in this rabbit. [From Whitlock & Wheeler (78).]

(6–20 cm H₂O) do not affect the rate of water absorption (14). Furthermore, Dietschy (24) found that the everted gallbladder can transport fluid into its lumen against hydrostatic pressure heads. The reason hydrostatic pressure is of negligible importance became apparent when the filtration coefficient of the gallbladder was measured by an osmotic method: this coefficient is low enough that luminal pressures in excess of those required to burst the gallbladder would be necessary to produce even a few percent of the normal water flow by filtration. Filtration can similarly be discounted as a mechanism of water transport by the intestine, liver, stomach, and choroid plexus.

ELECTROOSMOSIS. This is the flow of water observed across a charged membrane to which an electric PD is applied. The phenomenon arises from the frictional drag exerted on water by ions carrying the current through the membrane and is the converse of streaming potentials (the PD set up across a charged membrane through which water is forced). Since biological membranes are generally charged and support PDs, electroosmosis is sometimes invoked as a mechanism for solute-linked water transport.

Although electroosmosis has yet to be detected in any animal membrane, its expected magnitude may be calculated from measurements of streaming potentials by the formula $H/P = v/i$, in which P is the applied pressure and H the resulting PD in a streaming potential experiment, and i is the applied current and v the resulting flow rate in an electroosmosis experiment. Insertion of experimental values of H/P for rabbit gallbladder into this formula yields the conclusion that the PD would have to be 77 mv, lumen positive, to account for the observed rate of water transport by electroosmosis (62). The actual PD is less than 1 mv, lumen negative. In fish gallbladder (14), and rat small intestine (71) as well, measurement of streaming potentials enables one to calculate that electroosmosis would be far too small and in the wrong direction to account for water transport.

PINOCYTOSIS. Pinocytosis, the transport of luminal solution in vacuoles from lumen to blood, has been suggested as the mechanism of salt and water transport by Grim on the basis of experiments in which the only luminal solute was NaCl (33). This suggestion seems incompatible with the observation that if the lumen contains NaCl plus one or several of 22 other compounds, NaCl is absorbed and the other 22 compounds remain behind (16, 25, 78). Pinocytosis or other kinds of solution pumps would also be incompatible with the evidence (discussed on p. 2464 and p. 2469) that Na and Cl can be actively transported in the direction opposite to that of water flow, and that water flow is entirely dependent on active NaCl transport. Finally, the relative lack of vacuoles in epithelial cells of rabbit gallbladder and the failure to observe ferritin uptake into the cells (J. M. Tormey, personal communication) make pinocytosis unlikely on morphological grounds as well.

LOCAL OSMOTIC FORCES. It would be possible to reconcile an osmotic mechanism for water absorption with the observation of water transport in the absence of or against external osmotic gradients, if the osmotic gradient set up by active solute transport were a local one within the tissue itself. That is, the active transport mechanism might continually dump NaCl into some confined region in the vicinity of the epithelial cells, and water would cross the cell membranes in response to this local osmotic gradient. Water transport could then go on against an osmotic gradient in the external bathing solutions until it was equal and opposite to the gradient generated within the tissue by active solute transport.

An experimental means of testing for local osmosis is to vary the osmolarity of the bathing solution and observe whether the osmolarity of the transported fluid varies in parallel. It is well established that when the bathing solution is 300 milliosmols (rabbit plasma osmolarity), the transported fluid is also 300 milliosmols. However, if the bathing solution osmolarity were, say, 600 milliosmols, local osmotic equilibration should now take place until the absorbate was 600 milliosmols rather than 300 milliosmols. Similarly, a 50-milliosmol bathing solution would yield a 50-milliosmol absorbate by local osmosis. In general, one would expect the absorbate osmolarity always to be identical to the bathing solution osmolarity, whatever the latter's absolute value, if and only if the mechanism of water transport involved the complete osmotic equilibration of actively transported solute locally.

The "unilateral" gallbladder preparation appears to be the method of choice for this experiment, since it yields directly the primary transported fluid without contamination by an outer bathing solution and unmodified by secondary diffusion. The need for calculating absorbate composition indirectly is obviated, and analysis of experimental errors indicates that the accuracy of determining NaCl concentrations in the transported fluid is about ±2 %. Using the unilateral preparation, Diamond (16) varied the osmolarity of the luminal bathing solution from 68 to 578 milliosmols by varying its NaCl concentration or by adding varying amounts of the impermeant nonelectrolytes sucrose and raffinose. As seen in Figure 19, when the principal luminal solute was NaCl and its concentration was varied, the cation concentration of the transported fluid was virtually the same as that of the bathing solution for the range [Na] = 26.6–294.5 mM. As seen in Figure 20, when the lumen contained NaCl plus an impermeant sugar whose concentration was varied, the transported fluid contained virtually no sugar but had a higher cation concentration than the luminal solution. The proportions were such that for

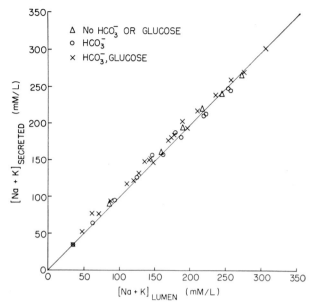

FIG. 19. [Na] + [K] in the fluid secreted by rabbit gallbladders without an outer bathing solution (*ordinate*) when the luminal [NaCl] is varied. Three slightly different Ringer solutions were used, containing bicarbonate (○), bicarbonate and glucose (×), or neither (△), but in all solutions NaCl accounted for most of the osmolarity. [Na] was always considerably larger than [K] in both the luminal and secreted fluids. *Straight line* is the line of 45-deg slope. [From Diamond (16).]

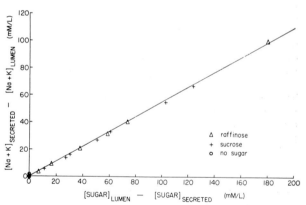

FIG. 20. Effect of addition of sucrose (+) or raffinose (△) to the luminal bathing solution on the fluid secreted by a rabbit gallbladder without an outer bathing solution. *Ordinate* is the difference between secreted and luminal cation concentrations, which were nearly equal to each other (see Fig. 19) in the absence of added sugar. [Na] is much greater than [K] in both the secreted and luminal fluids. Sugar concentration in the secreted fluid ([sugar]$_{secreted}$) is insignificant, so that the *abscissa* is practically the same as just [sugar]$_{lumen}$. [From Diamond (16).]

each 2 mM sugar in the lumen, the transported fluid contained an extra ca. 1 mM NaCl—i.e., 2 mM osmotically active particles. When these results are translated into osmolarities (Fig. 21), one finds that

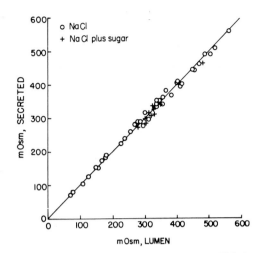

FIG. 21. Osmolarity of the fluid secreted by rabbit gallbladders without an outer bathing solution as a function of the osmolarity of the luminal bathing solution. *Straight line* is the line of 45-deg slope. The luminal solution was either mainly NaCl or NaCl plus the impermeant sugars sucrose or raffinose. [After Diamond (16).]

the osmolarity of the transported fluid is identical to that of the bathing solution within a standard deviation of ±2.5%, regardless of the nature of the luminal solute, and over an eightfold range of osmolarities. D. J. Marsh (personal communication) also observed identity of the transported and luminal osmolarity both in the presence and in the absence of impermeant sugars in the lumen. These results are thus fully in accord with the view that water transport involves the complete local equilibration of actively transported solute.

Whitlock & Wheeler (78) performed similar experiments of studying absorbate osmolarity at various bathing solution osmolarities in gallbladders with outer bathing solutions, using the chamber technique of Figure 3. As in the unilateral preparation, the transported fluid was found to be a NaCl solution isosmolar to the bathing solution if no impermeant sugar was present. In apparent disagreement with results obtained on the unilateral preparation, the transported fluid was hypertonic by 18–34% in the presence of added sucrose, particularly if sucrose was in the serosal solution. To explain these results, Whitlock and Wheeler invoked a model for water transport based on the properties of a system with two dissimilar membranes in series (9, 27, 60). They showed that it was possible to find values for a set of eight membrane parameters [called σ_1, σ_2, σ_1', σ_2', P_2, P_2', L, and (PD)$_1$] considered physiologically reasonable that, when inserted into the mathematical equations describing the double-membrane model, yielded ab-

sorbate osmolarities and PDs consistent with those observed experimentally.

Probably the principal explanation for the partial discrepancy between results from the unilateral preparation and from the chamber method is the opportunity for diffusional artifacts introduced into the latter technique by the presence of a serosal bathing solution. Whenever the primary absorbate produced at the serosal face of the epithelial cells comes into contact with a serosal bathing solution of different composition, the absorbate composition will become secondarily modified by diffusion. For example, if the mucosal and serosal solutions were 100 mM NaCl +200 mM sucrose, the epithelial cells would produce an isotonic primary absorbate of 200 mM NaCl at their serosal surface. NaCl would then diffuse away down its concentration gradient into the serosal solution; the resulting hypotonicity of the fluid near the serosal membrane would cause some back movement of water by osmosis into the mucosal solution; and this secondary modification would leave the transported fluid hypertonic, as found by Whitlock and Wheeler under these conditions. Only in the absence of added nonelectrolyte can and did (78) a preparation with outer bathing solution yield an isotonic transported fluid unmodified by secondary diffusion, since only under these conditions will the primary transported fluid and the bathing solutions have the same NaCl concentration. In the unilateral preparation, modification of the absorbate by secondary diffusion cannot occur, since there is no outer bathing solution. Additional unresolved technical problems in computing absorbate osmolarities by the chamber method are indicated by the considerable scatter in results (SD's of ±7% to ±19% as opposed to ±1.6% to ±2.5% in unilateral preparations), due possibly to the experimental difficulties mentioned earlier (page 2454); by the observation of hypertonic transport after partial isosmotic replacement of mucosal NaCl, in conflict with other results and with the known isotonic course of bile reabsorption; and by the unexplained earlier observation (76) of hypertonic transport even in the absence of added nonelectrolyte by the chamber method, in disagreement with the subsequent results by this method (78) and by all other methods. Finally, closer scrutiny of the calculations by which Whitlock and Wheeler fitted their results to the double-membrane model indicates that the apparent agreement between experiment and model predictions cannot be construed as supporting the validity of the model. The value of one of the eight model parameters ($\sigma_1 = 0.9$) is stated by the authors to have been selected completely arbitrarily (78, p. 2258) and is then used to calculate two further parameters (called P_2 and P_2'). Specific arbitrary assumptions are made about values of four other parameters ($\sigma_2 = 0 = \sigma_2'$, $\sigma_1 = 1$, L very large), because these assumptions are shown to be necessary for obtaining agreement with experimental findings. The value selected for the eighth, electrical parameter is now known to be 2.6 times the correct value, since it was assumed that a tenfold NaCl concentration gradient yields the Nernst PD of 58 mv in rabbit gallbladder, whereas it actually yields 22 mv. Although selection of different values for other model parameters might have permitted one to use the correct value of the electrical parameter and still obtain agreement between double-membrane predictions and experiment, the number of arbitrary assumptions required for the computation renders its significance doubtful.

Relation of Fluid Transport to Cell Ultrastructure

The evidence discussed in the previous section indicates that the coupling mechanism by which active NaCl transport leads to isotonic water transport across the gallbladder is local osmosis. That is, active salt transport must create a local region of hypertonicity near the epithelial cell membranes, and water follows in response to this local osmotic gradient until the transported fluid has equilibrated to isotonicity. Isotonic fluids are secreted or absorbed by numerous other epithelia (e.g., small intestine, renal proximal tubule, liver, pancreas, stomach, etc.). In every vertebrate epithelium that has been analyzed to date, secretion or absorption has been shown to involve the active transport of some solute, with water transport a secondary consequence of active solute transport. Since water transport in these other epithelia proceeds in the absence of an osmotic gradient between the external bathing solutions, it is quite possible that local osmotic phenomena within the tissue will prove generally to be the mechanism of solute-linked water transport in epithelia. The observation that the transported osmolarity in intestine, pancreas, and insect Malpighian tubule varies in parallel with the bathing solution osmolarity, as in the gallbladder, lends experimental support to this view.

Several findings point to the importance of epithelial ultrastructure in making local osmosis possible. It seems at first surprising that actively transported solute does not simply diffuse away before

osmotic equilibration is complete, yielding a hypertonic absorbate. This argument suggests the necessity for considering what structural devices exist within an epithelium that could retard solute diffusion until water had followed in isotonic proportions. Alternatively, physiologists working on several different epithelia have wondered whether the final absorbate or secretion really is sufficiently hypertonic to explain the observed rates of water flow osmotically, given measured values for the osmotic water permeability of the tissue. For rabbit gallbladder it has been calculated (16) from experimental measurements of water permeability that the absorbate would have to be hypertonic by 161 milliosmols if the osmotic gradient between the absorbate and the luminal solution were to be responsible for the observed rate of water flow. Yet the absorbate is known to be isotonic within an experimental error of less than ±10 milliosmols. Application of similar reasoning to the ciliary body (1), small intestine, renal proximal tubule, stomach, and choroid plexus (16) shows that the fluids produced by these epithelia are also much too close to isotonic to explain observed rates of water flow osmotically. In most of these tissues the transported fluids are in fact isotonic within experimental error. One must therefore look for structural features within the gallbladder and other epithelia that would 1) prevent actively transported solute from diffusing away before osmotic equilibration was complete and 2) enable osmotic equilibration to take place progressively, so that the initial osmotic gradient set up by active solute transport was much greater than the slight or nonexistent hypertonicity of the final absorbate.

Figure 22 is an electron micrograph of epithelial cells from rabbit gallbladder. At the mucosal surface the cells bear an array of microvilli similar in structure to those in the brush border of the small intestine. Prominent intracellular organelles are mitochondria, present throughout the cell but in somewhat greater concentration near the mucosal end, and the nucleus. Adjacent cells are separated laterally by long, narrow, and tortuous intercellular spaces, which are open at the serosal end but are sealed at the mucosal end by terminal bars (tight junctions) similar to those encountered in most epithelia. Under physiological conditions in which these spaces are closed, fine cytoplasmic projections into them from adjacent cells interdigitate tightly. The whole epithelium rests on a basement membrane, beyond which lies connective tissue, smooth muscle bundles, and blood

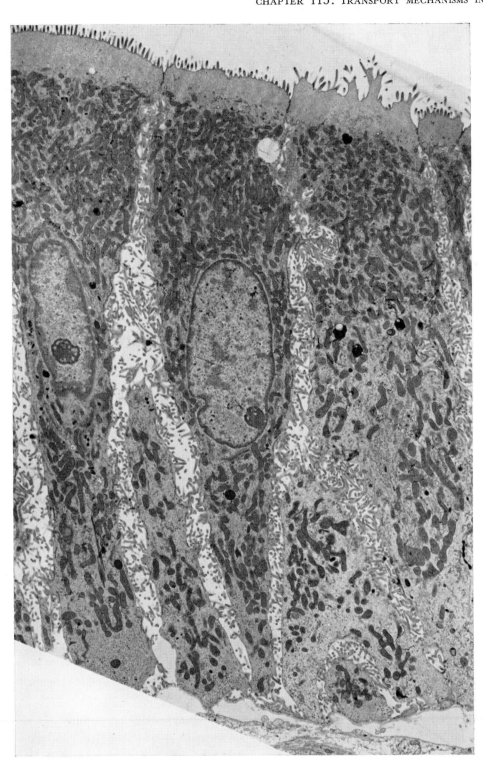

FIG. 22. Electron micrograph (4050 ×) of rabbit gallbladder epithelium, kindly provided by Dr. John M. Tormey. The lumen of the gallbladder is at the *top* of the picture, and the connective tissue layer begins to appear at the *bottom*, so that the direction of fluid transport is from *top* to *bottom*. At the luminal border (*top*) is an array of microvilli, followed by a short mitochondria-free zone and then by a mitochondria-rich region. The nucleus is visible in the middle of the left cell and the central cell. Adjacent cells are separated by clear, narrow channels, the lateral intercellular spaces, into which numerous villus-like, fine, cytoplasmic projections extend from the adjacent cells. These spaces communicate with the connective tissue layer (*below*), but are sealed off from the lumen (*top*) by a terminal bar.

capillaries. The fine structure of human (28), mouse (35, 83), and dog (44) gallbladders is rather similar.

Insight into the route of water transport across the cell layer has been gained by studying changes in the ultrastructure of the epithelium under different physiological conditions. Diamond & Tormey (22, 23) manipulated the rate of water transport by varying temperature or bathing solution composition, then fixed the gallbladder simultaneously from both sides with glutaraldehyde or osmium and examined sections by phase-contrast or electron microscopy. The most striking changes in epithelial ultrastructure involved the lateral intercellular spaces. Under physiological conditions in which fluid transport was maximal (NaCl-NaHCO₃-Ringer solutions at 37 C), the spaces were observed to be distended, so that adjacent cells were separated by an average distance of 1 μ except where firmly joined at the terminal bar. Under a wide variety of conditions in which fluid transport was inhibited (e.g., treatment with ouabain or cyanide-iodoacetate, low temperatures, replacement of mucosal NaCl with sucrose or poorly transported salts), the lateral spaces were found to be collapsed, so that their width was frequently below the resolving power of the light microscope. Whitlock et al. (79) have also reported changes in the lateral spaces associated with changes in transport rates.[4]

The simplest interpretation of these findings would be that the route of solute-linked water transport is via the lateral intercellular spaces, which become distended. However, two alternative explanations must be considered. First, if changes in fluid transport had caused consistent changes in cell volume (e.g., cell swelling), the observed alterations in the lateral spaces might have been secondary to the changes in cell geometry. This explanation is eliminated by the observation that inhibition of transport causes cell swelling, shrinkage, or no change in volume, depending on the agent used, although all agents that inhibit fluid transport cause collapse of the lateral spaces (22). Second, the observed distention of the spaces during transport might have been due to back hydrostatic pressures set up in the connective tissue by fluid transport. However, it was found experimentally that back hydrostatic pressures applied from the connective tissue side failed to cause distention of the spaces until grossly unphysiological pressures were used, which destroyed the fluid transport mechanism irreversibly (22).

Thus, one may safely conclude that the distention of the lateral intercellular spaces observed during fluid transport does in fact implicate the spaces as the route of transport (Fig. 23). Evidently NaCl is pumped from the cells into the lateral spaces, and this makes them hypertonic; it is within the spaces that the local osmotic gradient responsible for water transport is set up. Water then enters the spaces osmotically along their entire length, sweeping NaCl down them, until the fluid emerging at the serosal end is an isotonic NaCl solution. Kaye & Lane (48) have obtained evidence that lateral intercellular spaces in the intestine similarly distend during fluid transport; thus they too are implicated as routes of transport.

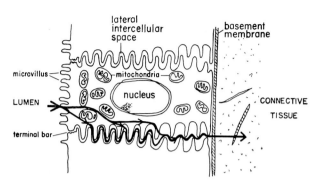

FIG. 23. Route of water transport across rabbit gallbladder, as deduced from combined physiological-anatomical experiments. Salt is pumped from the cells into the lateral intercellular spaces and makes them hypertonic. Water enters osmotically along the length of the spaces and distends them; an isotonic NaCl solution emerges from the ends of the spaces facing the connective tissue. [From Diamond & Tormey (22).]

Standing-Gradient Osmotic Flow: A Model for Solute-Linked Water Transport

As a working hypothesis to account for isotonic water-to-solute coupling in the gallbladder and also to explain the striking geometry of the lateral intercellular spaces through which fluid transport takes place, Diamond & Tormey (23) proposed the model for water transport illustrated in Figure 24. It consists of a long and narrow channel, open at one end and closed at the other, whose walls consist of a semipermeable membrane. A solute pump continually dumps solute into the closed end of the channel,

---

[4] Since this manuscript was prepared, detailed reports of these ultrastructural changes associated with transport in the gallbladder have been published by Kaye et al. (*J. Cell Biol.* 30: 237–268, 1966) and by Tormey & Diamond (*J. Gen. Physiol.* 50: 2031–2060, 1967). Diamond & Bossert (*J. Gen. Physiol.* 50: 2061–2083, 1967; *J. Cell Biol.* in press, 1968) have presented a mathematical analysis of the standing-gradient model and its implications for fluid-transporting epithelia.

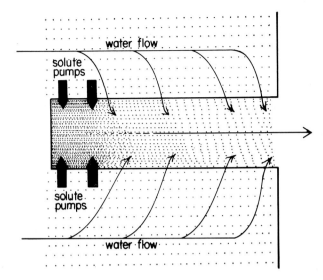

FIG. 24. Standing-gradient osmotic flow: a model for fluid transport across epithelia. Solute pumped into the closed end of a long and narrow channel makes it hypertonic and pulls in water osmotically. The solute moves toward the open end of the channel as a result of the water flow and of diffusion down its concentration gradient. Osmotic equilibrium is progressively approached as water enters along the length of the channel until the emergent solution is isotonic. The standing gradient in this flow system is continually maintained by active solute transport. For diagrammatic purposes the solute pump is indicated only at the base of the channel, but it may operate over a greater fraction of the channel length. Given appropriate values for the channel length and water permeability, the model can also yield a hypertonic solution of fixed osmolarity. Epithelial structures to which the model may find application in understanding solute-linked water transport are lateral intercellular spaces (intestine and gallbladder), basal membrane infoldings (kidney, salt gland, ciliary body, etc.), and intracellular canaliculi (stomach). [From Diamond & Tormey (23).]

making it hypertonic, and water follows by osmosis. Solute moves down the channel as a result of diffusion down its concentration gradient and by being swept along with the water stream. Water continues to come in osmotically along the length of the channel; its contents therefore become progressively less hypertonic, until finally an isotonic solution emerges from the open end. The standing gradient in this flow system would be continually maintained by active solute transport. While the solute pump has been pictured for clarity in Figure 24 as operating only in the bottom fifth of the channel, solute could actually be dumped in over a much greater fraction of the channel length and still equilibrate to isotonicity by the time it was swept out the open end, given an appropriate value for the water permeability of the channel walls.

As applied to the lateral intercellular spaces of the

gallbladder, the standing-gradient flow model adequately accounts for the distinctive features of solute-linked water transport demonstrated to date. First, the length of the channels readily explains why NaCl does not simply diffuse away before water can follow in isotonic proportions. Second, the model offers an explanation for the striking morphology of the long and narrow lateral spaces by suggesting a geometrical significance for these structures. Finally, the progressive attainment of osmotic equilibrium indicates why sufficient water flow can be maintained osmotically, although no difference in osmolarity between the bathing solution and the final absorbate can be detected. It is not the slight or nonexistent hypertonicity of the final absorbate or secretion that causes osmotic flow, but the much higher osmolarities present in the lower part of the channel.

Several morphological observations suggest that this reconstruction of events in the lateral intercellular spaces of the gallbladder during fluid transport may have relevance to other epithelia. The presence of long, narrow channels open at one end is a characteristic ultrastructural feature of epithelia carrying out isotonic fluid transport. Examples are the lateral intercellular spaces of the intestine (which are quite similar to those of the gallbladder); basal membrane infoldings in the renal proximal tubule, the ciliary body, and the choroid plexus; and intracellular canaliculi in the stomach. All these epithelia face the same physiological problem as the gallbladder—to prevent actively transported solute from diffusing away before achievement of complete osmotic equilibrium. In the case of the lateral spaces in the intestine the channels have been shown to enlarge during fluid transport. It is therefore possible that standing osmotic gradients are set up in these channels of other tissues, and this serves to explain the observed isotonic water-to-solute coupling, as in the gallbladder.

Long, narrow extracellular channels are also prominent features of epithelia performing hypertonic transport. Examples are the lateral intercellular spaces of frog skin and the basal labyrinths of the renal distal tubule, avian salt gland, and parotid gland striated duct. The distinctive physiological property of these organs is their ability to maintain hypertonic absorbates and secretions over a range of transport rates, even at very low rates. If one numerically evaluates the standing-gradient model, choosing a sufficiently low value for the water permeability, the standing-gradient system yields a hypertonic secretion of constant osmolarity relatively little affected by the transport rate. Thus, given physiologically appropriate permeability characteristics of the bounding membranes, the model may also clarify an otherwise puzzling property of epithelia performing hypertonic transport. The suggestion that standing osmotic gradients may be set up in the channels of such epithelia is supported by the findings that the lateral intercellular spaces of frog skin (H. H. Ussing, personal communication) and the basal labyrinth of avian salt gland (50) distend during fluid transport.

More experimental evidence concerning changes in ultrastructure with function in other epithelia is necessary before the range of applicability of the standing-gradient flow model can be assessed. The present value of the model is that it suggests how the long, narrow channels that are characteristic of epithelial ultrastructure and have already been demonstrated to be the route of fluid transport in four epithelia may generate the distinctive solute-to-water coupling ratios characteristic of epithelial physiology. The fact that long, narrow channels arising in such varied ways (as basal membrane infoldings, lateral intercellular spaces, or intracellular canaliculi) appear to serve generally as pathways for water transport in epithelia reinforces the suggestion, implicit in the model, that they possess some purely geometrical significance in addition to providing increased surface area. As Fawcett pointed out, "There is physiological meaning in the geometry of the cell surface as well as in its biochemistry" (30).

SUMMARY

A summary of present understanding of water transport in the gallbladder begins with the statement that water transport is a secondary consequence of active solute transport, as in other epithelia. It is the coupling between solute transport and water transport that makes it possible for water movement to go on between identical bathing solutions or against an external osmotic gradient. The roles of filtration, electroosmosis, pinocytosis, and osmotic gradients between the external bathing solution can be shown to be negligible. Instead, water transport results from local osmotic forces built up within the tissue by active transport of solute into restricted regions near the epithelial cell membranes. The demonstration that the primary transported fluid is always isotonic to the bathing solution, regardless of the latter's absolute value, indicates that osmotic equilibrium of actively transported solute proceeds to completion. Correlated physiological-anatomical experiments, in which changes in the rate of fluid transport have been found to cause consistent changes in epithelial ultrastructure, indicate that the route of fluid transport is via long and narrow lateral spaces between adjacent epithelial cells. The model of standing-gradient osmotic flow suggests how these spaces may possess a geometrical significance in maintaining isotonic water-to-solute coupling, and similar considerations may underlie tissue ultrastructure and water-to-solute coupling in other epithelia.

REFERENCES

1. AURICCHIO, G., AND E. H. BARANY. On the role of osmotic water transport in the secretion of the aqueous humour. *Acta Physiol. Scand.* 45: 190–210, 1959.
2. BAKER, P. F. Phosphorus metabolism of intact crab nerve and its relation to the active transport of ions. *J. Physiol., London* 180: 383–423, 1965.
3. BARRY, B. A., J. MATTHEWS, AND D. H. SMYTH. Transfer of glucose and fluid by different parts of the small intestine of the rat. *J. Physiol., London* 157: 279–288, 1961.
4. BARRY, R. J. C., D. H. SMYTH, AND E. M. WRIGHT. Short-circuit current and solute transfer by rat jejunum. *J. Physiol., London* 181: 414–431, 1965.
5. BENTLEY, P. J. The effects of ionic changes on water transfer across the isolated urinary bladder of the toad *Bufo marinus. J. Endocrinol.* 18: 327–333, 1959.
6. BRAND, J. Beitrag zur Kenntnis der menschlichen Galle. *Arch. Ges. Physiol.* 90: 491–522, 1902.
7. CHANCE, B., AND G. R. WILLIAMS. The respiratory chain and oxidative phosphorylation. *Advan. Enzymol.* 17: 65–134, 1956.
8. CRAWFORD, J. D., AND R. A. MCCANCE. Sodium transport by the choriollantoic membrane of the pig. *J. Physiol., London* 151: 458–471, 1960.
9. CURRAN, P. F., AND J. R. MCINTOSH. A model system for biological water transport. *Nature* 193: 347–348, 1962.
10. CURRAN, P. F., AND A. K. SOLOMON. Ion and water fluxes in the ileum of rats. *J. Gen. Physiol.* 41: 143–168, 1957.
11. DIAMOND, J. M. Thermodynamics of water transport. *J. Physiol., London* 158: 21–22P, 1961.
12. DIAMOND, J. M. The reabsorptive function of the gall-bladder. *J. Physiol., London* 161: 442–473, 1962.
13. DIAMOND, J. M. The mechanism of solute transport by the gall-bladder. *J. Physiol., London* 161: 474–502, 1962.
14. DIAMOND, J. M. The mechanism of water transport by the gall-bladder. *J. Physiol., London* 161: 503–527, 1962.
15. DIAMOND, J. M. Transport of salt and water in rabbit and guinea pig gall-bladder. *J. Gen. Physiol.* 48: 1–14, 1964.
16. DIAMOND, J. M. The mechanism of isotonic water transport. *J. Gen. Physiol.* 48: 15–42, 1964.
17. DIAMOND, J. M. The concentrating activity of the gall-

bladder. In: *The Biliary System*, edited by W. Taylor. Oxford: Blackwell, 1965, p. 495-514.

18. DIAMOND, J. M. The mechanism of isotonic water absorption and secretion. In: *The State and Movement of Water in Living Organisms, XIXth Symp. Soc. Exptl. Biol.* Cambridge: Cambridge Univ. Press, 1965, p. 329-347.

19. DIAMOND, J. M. Non-linear osmosis. *J. Physiol., London* 183: 58-82, 1966.

20. DIAMOND, J. M. A rapid method for determining voltage-concentration relations across membranes. *J. Physiol., London* 183: 83-100, 1966.

21. DIAMOND, J. M., AND S. C. HARRISON. The effect of membrane fixed charges on diffusion potentials and streaming potentials. *J. Physiol., London* 183: 37-57, 1966.

22. DIAMOND, J. M., AND J. M. TORMEY. Role of long extracellular channels in fluid transport across epithelia. *Nature* 210: 817-820, 1966.

23. DIAMOND, J. M., AND J. M. TORMEY. Studies on the structural basis of water transport across epithelial membranes. *Federation Proc.* 25: 1458-1463, 1966.

24. DIETSCHY, J. M. Water and solute movement across the wall of the everted rabbit gall bladder. *Gastroenterology* 47: 395-408, 1964.

25. DIETSCHY, J. M. Recent developments in solute and water transport across the gall-bladder epithelium. *Gastroenterology* 50: 692-707, 1966.

26. DIETSCHY, J. M., AND E. W. MOORE. Diffusion potentials and potassium distribution across the gallbladder wall. *J. Clin. Invest.* 43: 1551-1560, 1964

27. DURBIN, R. P. Osmotic flow of water across permeable cellulose membranes. *J. Gen. Physiol.* 44: 315-326, 1960.

28. EVETT, R. D., J. A. HIGGINS, AND A. L. BROWN. The fine structure of normal mucosa in human gall bladder. *Gastroenterology* 47: 49-60, 1964.

29. FARNER, D. S. Digestion and the digestive system. In: *Biology and Comparative Physiology of Birds*, edited by A. J. Marshall. New York: Acad. Press, 1960, vol. 1, p. 411-467.

30. FAWCETT, D. W. Physiologically significant specializations of the cell surface. *Circulation* 26: 1105-1125, 1962.

31. GILMAN, A., AND G. R. COWGILL. Osmotic relations between blood and body fluids. IV. Pancreatic juice, bile, and lymph. *Am. J. Physiol.* 104: 476-479, 1933.

32. GLYNN, I. M. Activation of adenosinetriphosphatase activity in a cell membrane by external potassium and internal sodium. *J. Physiol., London* 160: 18P, 1962.

33. GRIM, E. A mechanism for absorption of sodium chloride solutions from the canine gall bladder. *Am. J. Physiol.* 205: 247-254, 1963.

34. GRIM, E., AND G. A. SMITH. Water flux rates across dog gallbladder wall. *Am. J. Physiol.* 191: 555-560, 1957.

35. HAYWARD, A. F. Aspects of the fine structure of the gall bladder epithelium of the mouse. *J. Anat.* 96: 227-236, 1962.

36. HEINZ, E., AND R. DURBIN. Evidence for an independent hydrogen-ion pump in the stomach. *Biochim. Biophys. Acta* 31: 246-247, 1959.

37. HERMAN, R. H., T. H. WILSON, AND L. KAZYAK. Electrolyte migrations across the wall of the guinea pig gall bladder. *J. Cellular Comp. Physiol.* 51: 133-144, 1958.

38. HOGBEN, C. A. M. Active transport of chloride by isolated frog gastric epithelium. *Am. J. Physiol.* 180: 641-649, 1955.

39. HOGBEN, C. A. M., AND J. A. CLIFTON. Anion substitution: coupling of H and Cl ion active transport by dogfish gastric mucosa. *Federation Proc.* 24: 407, 1965.

40. HOUSE, C. R., AND K. GREEN. Ion and water transport in isolated intestine of the marine teleost *Cottus scorpius*. *J. Exptl. Biol.* 42: 177-189, 1965.

41. INGRAHAM, R. C., AND M. B. VISSCHER. The production of chloride-free solutions by the action of the intestinal epithelium. *Am. J. Physiol.* 114: 676-680, 1936.

42. INGRAHAM, R. C., AND M. B. VISSCHER. Further studies on intestinal absorption with the performance of osmotic work. *Am. J. Physiol.* 121: 771-785, 1938.

43. IVY, A. C. The physiology of the gall bladder. *Physiol. Rev.* 14: 1-102, 1934.

44. JOHNSON, F. R., R. M. McMINN, AND R. F. BIRCHENOUGH. The ultrastructure of the gall-bladder epithelium of the dog. *J. Anat.* 96: 477-487, 1962.

45. JOHNSTON, S. A., AND J. W. McBAIN. Freezing-points of solutions of typical colloidal electrolytes; soaps, sulphonates, sulphates and bile salt. *Proc. Roy. Soc., London, Ser. A* 181: 119-133, 1942.

46. JOHNSTON, C. G., I. S. RAVDIN, J. H. AUSTIN, AND J. L. MORRISON. Studies of gall-bladder function. V. The absorption of calcium from the bile-free gall bladder. *Am. J. Physiol.* 99: 648-655, 1932.

47. KANG, D. H., AND S. K. HONG. Water and chloride exchange across the gall bladder of the anesthetized dog. *Am. J. Physiol.* 203: 1015-1018, 1962.

48. KAYE, G. I., AND N. LANE. The epithelial basal complex: a morphophysiological unit in transport and absorption. *J. Cell Biol.* 27: 50A, 1965.

49. KOEFOED-JOHNSEN, V., AND H. H. USSING. The nature of the frog skin potential. *Acta Physiol. Scand.* 42: 298-308, 1958.

50. KOMNICK, H. Funktionelle Morphologie von Salzdrusenzellen. In: *Sekretion und Exkretion.* Berlin: Springer, 1965, p. 289-314.

51. LASSEN, N. A., O. MUNCK, AND J. HESS THAYSEN. Oxygen consumption and sodium reabsorption in the kidney. *Acta Physiol. Scand.* 51: 371-384, 1961.

52. LASSEN, U. V., AND J. HESS THAYSEN. Correlation between sodium transport and oxygen consumption in isolated renal tissue. *Biochim. Biophys. Acta* 47: 616-618, 1961.

53. LEAF, A., J. ANDERSON, AND L. B. PAGE. Active sodium transport by the isolated toad bladder. *J. Gen. Physiol.* 41: 657-668, 1958.

54. LEAF, A., AND E. DEMPSEY. Some effects of mammalian neurohypophyseal hormones on metabolism and active transport of sodium by the isolated toad bladder. *J. Biol. Chem.* 235: 2160-2163, 1960.

55. LUNDBERG, A. Anionic dependence of secretion and secretory potentials in the perfused sublingual gland. *Acta Physiol. Scand.* 40: 101-112, 1957.

56. MARSH, D. J., AND S. SOLOMON. Analysis of electrolyte movement in thin Henle's loops of hamster papilla. *Am. J. Physiol.* 208: 1119-1128, 1965.

57. MARTIN, D. W., AND J. M. DIAMOND. Energetics of coupled active transport of sodium and chloride. *J. Gen. Physiol.* 50: 295-315, 1966.

58. MONRO, A. *System of Anatomy and Physiology* (2nd ed.). Edinburgh: Elliot, 1787, vol. 2, p. 404.

59. MOORE, E. W., AND J. M. DIETSCHY. Na and K activity coefficients in bile and bile salts determined by glass electrodes. *Am. J. Physiol.* 206: 1111-1117, 1964.

60. PATLAK, C. S., D. A. GOLDSTEIN, AND J. F. HOFFMANN. The flow of solute and solvent across a two-membrane system. *J. Theoret. Biol.* 5: 426–442, 1963.

61. PETERS, C. J., AND M. WALSER. Transport of cations by rabbit gall-bladder: evidence suggesting a common cation pump. *Am. J. Physiol.* 210: 677–683, 1966.

62. PIDOT, A. L., AND J. M. DIAMOND. Streaming potentials in a biological membrane. *Nature* 201: 701–702, 1964.

63. POOLE, R. J. The influence of the intracellular potential on potassium uptake by beetroot tissue. *J. Gen. Physiol.* 49: 551–563, 1966.

64. PORTER, G. A., AND I. S. EDELMAN. The action of aldosterone and related corticosteroids on sodium transport across the toad bladder. *J. Clin. Invest.* 43: 611–620, 1964.

65. POTTER, M. G. Observations of the gallbladder and bile during pregnancy at term. *J. Am. Med. Soc.* 106: 1070–1074.

66. RAVDIN, I. S., C. G. JOHNSTON, J. H. AUSTIN, AND C. RIEGEL. Studies of gall-bladder function. IV. The absorption of chloride from the bile-free gall-bladder. *Am. J. Physiol.* 99: 638–647, 1932.

67. RAVDIN, I. S., C. G. JOHNSTON, C. RIEGEL, AND S. L. WRIGHT, JR. Studies of gall-bladder function. VII. The anion-cation content of hepatic and gall-bladder bile. *Am. J. Physiol.* 100: 317–327, 1932.

68. REINHOLD, J. G., AND D. W. WILSON. The acid-base composition of hepatic bile. I. *Am. J. Physiol.* 107: 378–387, 1934.

69. ROUS, P., AND P. D. McMASTER. The concentrating activity of the gall bladder. *J. Exptl. Med.* 34: 47–73, 1921.

70. SMYTH, D. H., AND C. B. TAYLOR. Transfer of water and solutes by an *in vitro* intestinal preparation. *J. Physiol., London* 136: 632–648, 1957.

71. SMYTH, D. H., AND E. M. WRIGHT. Streaming potentials in the rat small intestine. *J. Physiol., London* 182: 591–602, 1966.

72. TAYLOR, W. (Editor). *The Biliary System.* Oxford: Blackwell, 1965.

73. USSING, H. H., P. KRUHOFFER, J. HESS THAYSEN, AND N. A. THORN. *The Alkali Metals in Biology.* Berlin: Springer, 1960.

74. USSING, H. H., AND K. ZERAHN. Active transport of sodium as the source of electric current in the short-circuited isolated frog skin. *Acta Physiol. Scand.* 23: 110–127, 1951.

75. WESTPHAL, K., F. GLEICHMANN, AND G. SOIKA. Tierexperimentelle Beobachtungen über nervös bedingte Resorptionsschwankungen der Gallenblase mit teilweiser Berücksichtigung des Lebergallenflusses. *Arch. Ges. Physiol.* 227: 204–219, 1931.

76. WHEELER, H. O. Transport of electrolytes and water across wall of rabbit gall-bladder. *Am. J. Physiol.* 205: 427–438, 1963.

77. WHEELER, H. O., AND O. L. RAMOS. Determinants of the flow and composition of bile in the unanesthetized dog during constant infusions of sodium taurocholate. *J. Clin. Invest.* 39: 161–170, 1960.

78. WHITLOCK, R. T., AND H. O. WHEELER. Coupled transport of solute and water across rabbit gallbladder epithelium. *J. Clin. Invest.* 43: 2249–2265, 1964.

79. WHITLOCK, R. T., H. O. WHEELER, G. I. KAYE, AND N. LANE. Structural-functional aspects of water transport across gall-bladder epithelium. *Federation Proc.* 24: 589, 1965.

80. WHITTAM, R. Active cation transport as a pace-maker of respiration. *Nature* 191: 603–604, 1961.

81. WHITTEMBURY, G., AND E. E. WINDHAGER. Electrical potential difference measurements in perfused single proximal tubules of *Necturus* kidney. *J. Gen. Physiol.* 44: 679–687, 1961.

82. WINDHAGER, E. E., G. WHITTEMBURY, D. E. OKEN, H. J. SCHATZMANN, AND A. K. SOLOMON. Single proximal tubules of the Necturus kidney. III. Dependence of H_2O movement on NaCl concentration. *Am. J. Physiol.* 197: 313–318, 1959.

83. YAMADA, E. The fine structure of the gall bladder epithelium of the mouse. *J. Biophys. Biochem. Cytol.* 1: 445–458, 1955.

84. ZERAHN, K. Oxygen consumption and active sodium transport in the isolated and short-circuited frog skin. *Acta Physiol. Scand.* 36: 300–318, 1956

CHAPTER 116

Fate of bile in the bowel

C. H. GRAY

D. C. NICHOLSON

R. V. QUINCEY

Department of Chemical Pathology, King's College Hospital Medical School, London, England

CHAPTER CONTENTS

THIS CHAPTER is concerned mainly with the fate in the gut of the specific constituents unique to bile—that is, the bile pigments and bile acids. Only brief reference is made to the other constituents such as mucins, phospholipids, cholesterol, and electrolytes. The last is considered elsewhere in this volume; the further metabolism in the gut of the other substances has not been as fully studied as that of the bile pigments and bile acids. As far as possible the topics are considered in relation to man, but findings in labora-tory animals and other species are described where these appear relevant. No account has been included of the pathological changes caused by deficiency or abnormal metabolism of the constituents of the bile except insofar as they have thrown light on the normal physiological changes occurring in the gut.

BILE PIGMENTS

Bile pigments are the tetrapyrrolic end products of the catabolism of hemoglobin and probably of other heme proteins. They are excreted in the bile into the duodenum in a conjugated form, and the changes occurring during passage down the gut include hy-drolysis, hydrogenation, oxidation (dehydrogenation), and degradation of the tetrapyrrolic structure; only some of the resulting substances are absorbed from the gut. An understanding of these changes requires knowledge of the structures of the compounds involved (37, 45, 174) and of their mode of conjugation.

Although the precise mechanism of catabolism of hemoglobin to bile pigment is still a subject of investi-gation (46, p. 19–28; 88; 104; 127; 162; 164), the heme moiety of hemoglobin undoubtedly undergoes oxidative fission at the α-methane bridge and removal of iron to form the bis-oxy open-chain tetrapyrrolic pigment biliverdin (Fig. 1). The conversion of hemo-globin (perhaps as a haptoglobin complex) of red cells at the end of their life span is catalyzed specifically by the enzyme α-methenyl oxygenase (113, 114); therefore, all pigments derived from it bear the "IXα" order of pyrrole beta side chains (51) The bile pigments are also formed in association with erythropoiesis (52) and probably from some nonhe-

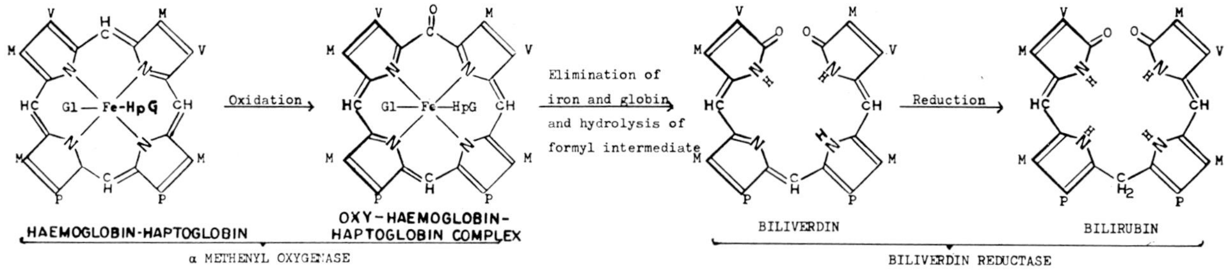

FIG. 1. Formation of bilirubin from hemoglobin. M = methyl; V = vinyl; P = carboxyethyl.

moglobin hemes (80, 81, 138, 176), and these sources normally contribute 15–20% of the daily production (49); in certain pathological conditions this contribution is considerably increased (47). This fraction is called the "early labeled" bile pigment since it is rapidly labeled after administration of ^{14}C-glycine (80).

Biliverdin has two pyrrolenone rings joined via methene-bridge carbon atoms to the alpha positions of a central dipyrrylmethene group. The whole molecule then has four constituent rings, the terminal oxygen atoms, and all three linking methene bridges included in one extensive chromophore. In the reticuloendothelial system, hydrogenation occurs specifically at the central methene carbon atom and adjacent ring under the influence of a reductase (151). The resulting pigment, bilirubin, has two chromophores, each consisting of a terminal dipyrrylmethene unit and joined to each other by a central methane group. This bilirubin passes to the liver, where it is converted from the free lipid-soluble compound to a water-soluble conjugate (11, 12) that constitutes the major part of the bile pigment in hepatic or fistula bile, where it is present to the extent of 20–200 mg per 100 ml (172, 173). Concentration takes place in the gallbladder, and bile entering the duodenum contains as much as 1% (w/v) (172, 173) of conjugated bilirubin complexed with phospholipid, lipoprotein, bile salts, and cholesterol (115). The bilirubin molecule contains 12 double bonds, 6 of which are reduced in the molecule of stercobilinogen, the product of greatest hydrogenation in the gut. The reduction normally occurs mainly in the large intestine with production of a number of intermediates (163) (Fig. 2). These, differing in the degree and position of their residual double bond, include dihydrobilirubin, mesobilirubin, dihydromesobilirubin, d-urobilinogen, mesobilirubinogen, and stercobilinogen. Some of these compounds are colorless but are readily dehydrogenated to form colored compounds, e.g. mesobiliviolin

and mesobilirhodin. d-Urobilin, i-urobilin, and stercobilin are readily formed when the feces are extracted and treated in vitro. The properties of these dehydrogenation products are summarized in Table 1, but whether they are present in intestinal contents as intermediaries during hydrogenation of the bile pigment is unknown. With (175) has drawn attention to the misconception that the color of normal feces is due to these pigments. Some other pigment must be responsible, for freshly passed feces contain the colorless chromogens except when the excretion of bile pigment is very high, as in hemolytic jaundice or anemia. The polymeric dipyrryl compounds—the mesobilifuscins (147–149)—are formed in vitro by decomposition of tetrapyrroles; they were long supposed to be produced by a similar process in the gut. However, they may be formed, at any rate in part, in association with the early labeled bile pigment fraction (40).

Bile Pigments in Bile

Biliverdin is rarely found in human bile, and the small quantity of free bilirubin invariably found is probably formed by hydrolysis during manipulation. Almost all the pigment is present in conjugated form, of which part is alkali labile and part alkali stable. The major component of the former consists of bilirubin glucuronide (11–13, 142); the remainder of the alkali-labile fraction has been believed to consist of bilirubin monoglucuronide, but some workers consider this to be a molecular complex of free bilirubin with the diglucuronide (53, 124, 169). The alkali-stable conjugates in rat bile incorporate ^{35}S-sulfate and have been assumed to be sulfates (54, 82). Analytical methods for the accurate determination of the proportions of the various bilirubin conjugates (11, 168) in bile are not yet satisfactory (79).

Commercial bilirubin obtained from cattle gallstones has been shown to contain small quantities of

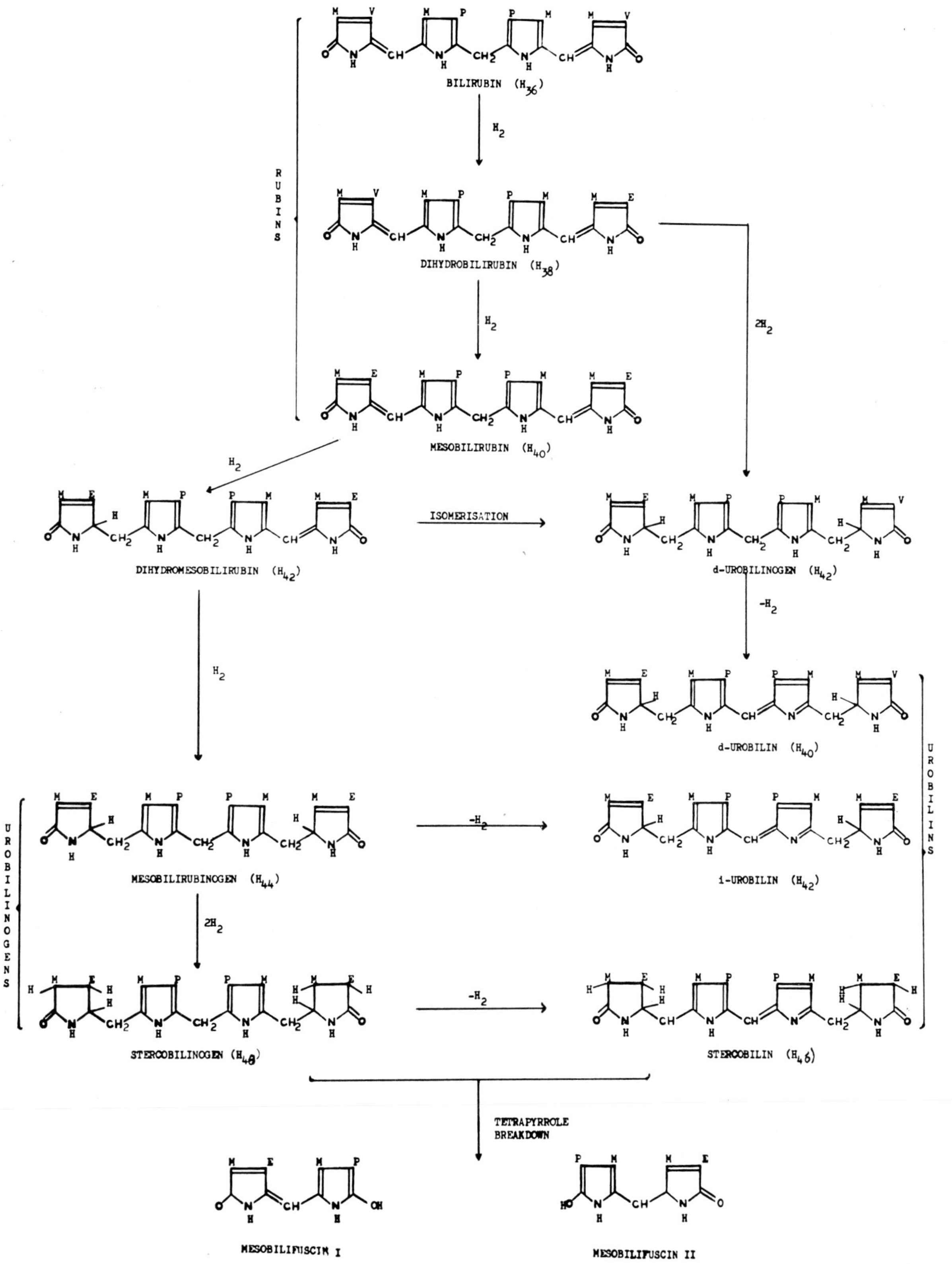

FIG. 2. Bilirubin and its reduction and degradation products. M = methyl; V = vinyl; E = ethyl; P = carboxyethyl.

TABLE 1. *Chemical and Physical Properties of Bile Pigments*

Pigment and Molecular Formula	Spectral Absorption Maximum (mμ) in Chloroform	Molecular Optical Rotation in Chloroform	Stability or Source
d-Urobilin $C_{33}H_{40}O_6N_4$	499 [8.5]	$+29 \times 10^3$	Unstable: is both isomerized and oxidized
i-Urobilin $C_{33}H_{42}O_6N_4$	496–497	Optically inactive	Unstable: is oxidized
Stercobilin $C_{33}H_{46}O_6N_4$	496–498 [8.75]	-24×10^3	Stable
Mesobiliviolin $C_{33}H_{40}O_6N_4$	565	Optically inactive	Produced by oxidation of i-urobilin
Mesobilirhodin $C_{33}H_{40}O_6N_4$	505, 570–575	Optically inactive	Produced by isomerization of d-urobilin

dihydrobilirubin and mesobilirubin (K. Abdulla and D. Nicholson, unpublished observation), although the last may be absent from human bile (128); small quantities of urobilinogen may also be present (161, 172). These hydrogenated pigments are presumed to have been reabsorbed from the intestine. Biliviolin, although said to be absorbed from the gut (107), has not yet been found in the bile. If mesobilifuscins are formed, not by the degradation of the tetrapyrrolic bile pigments in the gut but in association with the early labeled fraction, they should be present in bile. There is no evidence of this, although they may be present in the monomeric leuko forms—the mesobilileukans (31, 149). Alternatively, it is possible that the mesobilifuscins are excreted through the gut wall as is bilirubin in the Gunn rat (56) or in the Crigler-Najjar syndrome (20) (see below).

HYDROLYSIS OF BILE-PIGMENT CONJUGATES IN THE GUT. The fate of bile pigments in the gut and other changes they undergo must depend on the extent of hydrolysis of the conjugated bilirubin (41) and on the site of that hydrolysis, since the chemical, physical, and biological properties of free and conjugated bilirubin are very different. Thus bilirubin glucuronide is not absorbed, but free bilirubin is readily absorbed from the intestine in the rat and in man (39, 91–94). The urobilinogens are absorbed (96, 97), whereas under

physiological conditions the urobilins are probably not.

The ease with which bilirubin glucuronide is hydrolyzed (13, 142) and the known presence within the gut of bacterial and intestinal β-glucuronidases suggest that the free pigments might be liberated from glucuronides in the intestinal tract. It is not yet known whether the conjugates are hydrolyzed before or after reduction, although a quantitative conversion of bilirubin glucuronide to urobilinogen but not of bilirubin was brought about in vitro by normal fecal flora in broth cultures (165). Watson et al. (165) have shown that a relatively crude preparation of conjugated bilirubin, when administered by intraduodenal intubation to normal subjects, was almost quantitatively converted to "fecal urobilinogen," whereas this was not the case when bilirubin was given. On the other hand, poor recoveries of fecal urobilinogen were obtained even from the conjugated bilirubin preparations when administered intraduodenally to a subject suffering from a refractory anemia or to patients with acholic feces (41). However, the recoveries of fecal urobilinogen are very variable and depend on many factors; the results of such experiments need to be interpreted with considerable care. Urobilinogen and urobilin glucuronides have not been isolated from human feces or from the contents at various levels of the intestine (163).

Noro (123) found that a part of the urinary urobilinoids could only be extracted with chloroform after hydrolysis with alkali, and Kahan (83) produced electrophoretic evidence of the existence in urine of urobilinoid glucuronide as well as of another sugar-linked form. Clearly this is a field in which further research would be very profitable. Since bilirubin may be conjugated with glucuronic acid in tissues other than the liver (55), the presence of conjugated urobilin in the urine does not prove that urobilins are absorbed from the gut. Relatively little bilirubin normally remains unreduced in the intestine and is excreted in the feces; it is not known if this is conjugated or not. However, since urobilins and urobilinogens are the main fecal tetrapyrrolic pigments excreted, considerable quantities of bilirubin glucuronide may well reach the colon.

REDUCTION OF BILE PIGMENTS IN THE GUT. The conversion of bilirubin in the gut to the final products—the urobilinogens—is generally accepted as a stepwise reduction effected by dehydrogenases of the intestinal bacteria (89). This view supersedes an earlier theory of Baumgärtel that i-urobilin and its precursor,

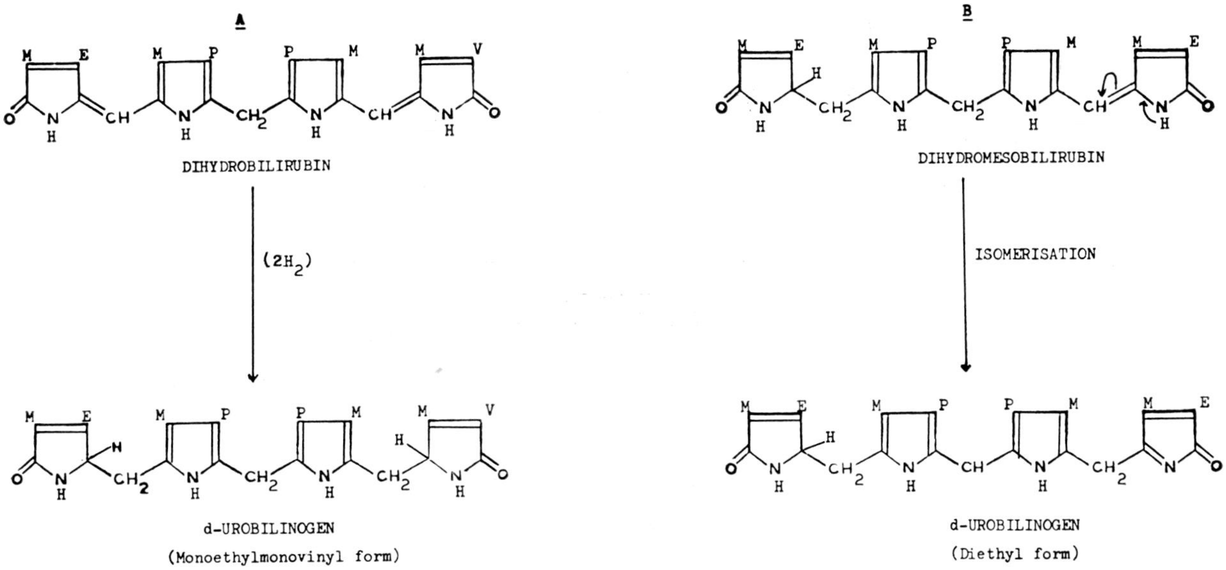

FIG. 3. Formation of d-urobilinogen. A, by reduction of dihydrobilirubin (50) and B, by isomerization of dihydromesobilirubin (167).

mesobilirubinogen, have their origin in liver or hepatobiliary cells (3), especially in bile stasis, whereas stercobilin is formed only in the intestine. The extensive evidence for the enterogenous nature of the urobilins has been repeatedly reviewed (46, p. 31–37; 163; 173). That all are produced by the activities of intestinal bacteria is evident from the fact that they are absent from the feces of infants lacking the necessary flora and from adults given oral antibiotics, and that they are normally absent from the sterile upper part of the small intestine (163). Most significantly, Gustafsson has shown complete absence of fecal urobilinogen in germ-free rats (58) and its appearance when these animals are exposed to infection by organisms from the colon of normal rats. Little is known of the nature of the organisms responsible for hydrogenation of the bile pigments except that Gustafsson found one such organism to be an anaerobic *Clostridium* whose action was synergized by *Escherichia coli*. This could not be observed in vitro by Watson, who found the *Clostridium* differed from mixed human fecal flora in rarely producing *d*-urobilin from conjugated bilirubin (163). In vitro *d*-urobilin was reduced slowly to mesobilirubinogen and stercobilinogen and *i*-urobilinogen to stercobilinogen. Watson, moreover, has converted mesobilirubin to mesobilirubinogen and to stercobilinogen (166) and ^{15}N-mesobilirubinogen to ^{15}N-stercobilinogen by incubation with fecal cultures (106). Possibly, mixed flora contain an isomerase necessary for the production of *d*-urobilin, an enzyme for the conversion of dihydro-

bilirubin or dihydromesobilirubin to *d*-urobilinogen, or even an inhibitor of the enzyme responsible for reduction of the remaining vinyl group in dihydrobilirubin (see below).

Astonishingly little is known of the detailed course of intestinal reduction of bilirubin. Pertinent problems concern the role of the glucuronyl radical, the role of cofactors in the bile, and the order with which and the sites at which the various pigments arise and whether reduction alone explains their formation. The proportions of *i*-urobilin, *d*-urobilin, and stercobilin that can be obtained from the feces are unpredictable and are independent of diet or disease (167).

Bilirubin, although largely reduced to urobilinogen in the course of its passage through the intestine, is nevertheless excreted in quantities ranging from 5 to 20 mg a day in the feces. Dihydrobilirubin (44), mesobilirubin, dihydromesobilirubin (105), and mesobilirubinogen (167) have all been isolated from feces and are thought to be intermediates between bilirubin and stercobilinogen.

i-Urobilin and stercobilin (163, 167) also appear in feces, but they cannot be formed by direct hydrogenation of bilirubin (which bears a central CH$_2$ group); there must be dehydrogenation of the corresponding chromogens, mesobilirubinogen and stercobilinogen. Isomerization involving conversion of the —CH$_2$— group of bilirubin to a —CH= group has been demonstrated in vitro (50); a similar change might occur in vivo and provide a mechanism whereby

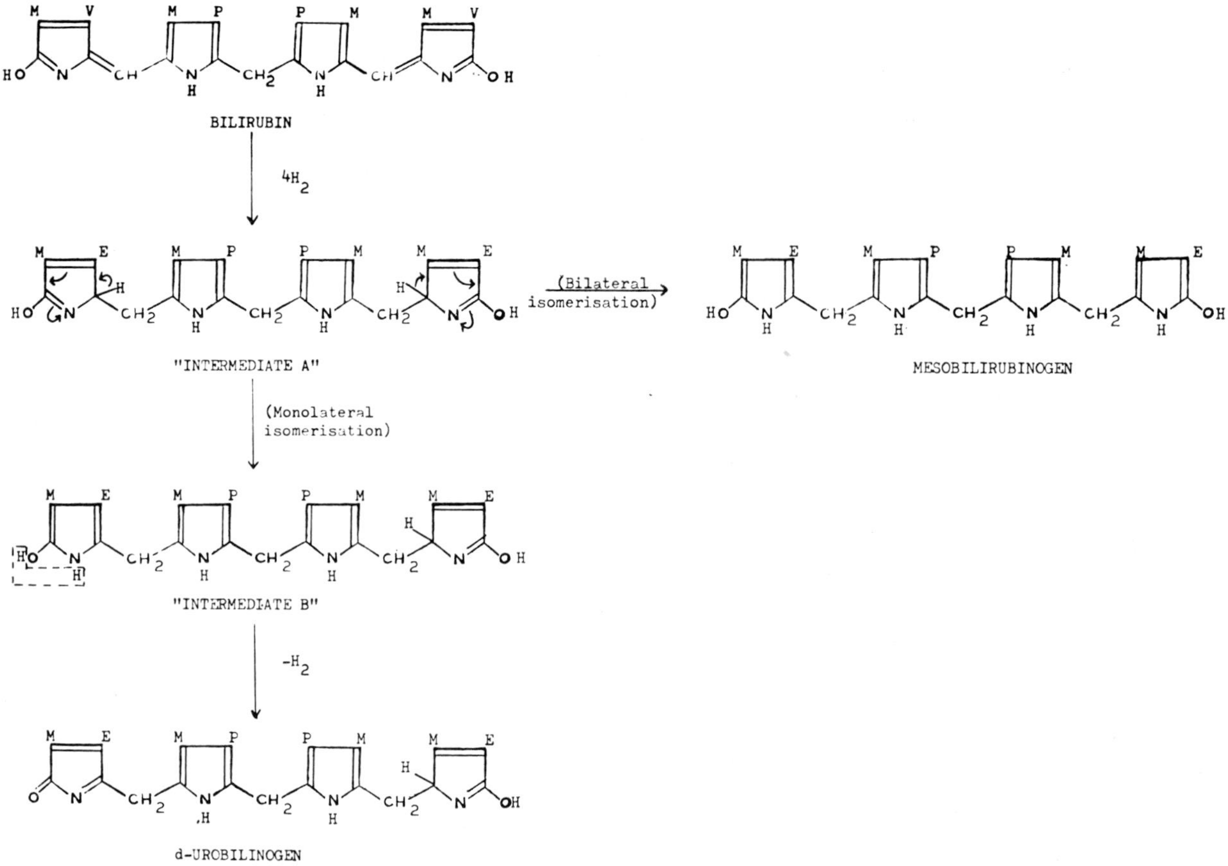

FIG. 4. Formation of *d*-urobilinogen according to Siedel (147).

urobilins might occur as primary products undergoing subsequent reduction to urobilinogens.

Mesobiliviolins (160), *d*-urobilinogen, and *d*-urobilin (163, 167) appear in feces but are also difficult to accommodate in a stepwise reduction from bilirubin to stercobilinogen. There is little doubt that violins arise by dehydrogenation of urobilins.

d-Urobilinogen may formally be derived from dihydrobilirubin by reduction at the chromophores with retention of one unreduced vinyl group (50) (Fig. 3).

However, an alternative structure has been proposed for *d*-urobilin in which the unsaturation of the vinyl group has moved by tautomerization into the end ring (146). On this basis, Watson & Weimer (167) have suggested *d*-urobilinogen is produced by the simple isomerization of dihydromesobilirubin, a pigment sometimes accompanying it in the gut (Fig. 3).

Siedel (146) has suggested the formation in the gut of an intermediate (A) isomeric with mesobilirubinogen to which it is converted by the migration of a proton at each end of the molecule; a single migration at one end of the molecule affords a second intermediate (B) that gives *d*-urobilinogen on dehydrogenation (Fig. 4). This theory would postulate an oxidative step unlikely to occur in the reducing environment of the gut. Moreover these changes demand a structural formula for bile pigments with end hydroxy groups instead of one with the oxo groups now generally accepted.

It is unlikely that particular pigments will be associated with particular gut levels. Since the stomach and proximal parts of the small intestine are normally free from microorganisms, except for some concerned with lactic fermentation, reduction of bilirubin would not be expected to occur there. Bacterial growth may occur in the terminal ileum and other parts of the small intestine, however, and Lester et al. (97) consider that urobilinogen is commonly formed there. Mesobilirubinogen has long been assumed to be formed in the small intestine.

Watson's work on the persistence of conjugated bilirubin down the small intestine and on the preferential reduction of this compound rather than free bilirubin is consistent with the main reduction to urobilinogens occurring in the colon (163). Watson & Weimer (167) have studied the relative amounts of the three urobilinogens occurring at different levels of the intestine in patients who died suddenly and to whom no antibiotics had been given. Sometimes the cecum and the sigmoid colon were found to contain d-urobilin alone or accompanied by i-urobilin. One patient who had d-urobilin in the cecum had i-urobilin (75%) and stercobilin (25%) only in the sigmoid colon. Another showed progressive changes of predominantly d-urobilin in the cecum through i-urobilin to stercobilin in the sigmoid colon. In a living subject the urine contained only d-urobilin absorbed from the ascending colon at a time when the fecal urobilin consisted of about 80% of i-urobilin and 20% of stercobilin, presumably formed lower in the colon. Watson considered these observations to indicate progressive hydrogenation along the colon, d-urobilin being a normal precursor of i-urobilin and stercobilin.

Many of the possible alterations in the tetrapyrrole molecule caused by bacteria remain to be studied in detail. In particular, the bacterial enzymes directing reduction of bile pigments to form levorotatory, dextrorotatory, or optically inactive urobilins and their precursors would be especially worthy of study. It would be interesting to know if the bacterial production of d-urobilinogen and l-stercobilinogen proceeded via racemic intermediates in which one or another of the enantiomorphs has a transient existence prior to bacterial metabolism. This might account for much of the discrepancy between expected and found bile pigment in daily excretion (see below).

FURTHER DEGRADATION OF UROBILINOGENS. The quantities of urobilinogen excreted daily in the feces are consistently lower than the quantities calculated from circulating hemoglobin and the life span of red cells. Gray (46, p. 24–27) has recalculated Eppinger's values (34) for the excretion of bilirubin in bile, and the figure obtained of 300–350 mg daily is approximately equal to that which should derive from red cell destruction. This agreement is probably fortuitous, however, since 15–20% of excreted bilirubin does not represent catabolized hemoglobin. The normal excretion of urobilinogen in the feces usually ranges from 100 to 200 mg a day, but even allowing for the small amount of bilirubin in the feces, much pigment is unaccounted for. Stich considered that at least 40–50% of the bile pigment in the gut was degraded to mesobilifuscins (154) and found that the sum of daily fecal urobilinogen and mesobilifuscin approximately equaled the

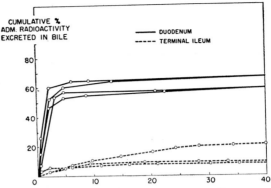

FIG. 5. Radioactivity in bile after administration of ¹⁴C-mesobilirubinogen into the intestine. [From Lester & Schmid (96).]

calculated value. However, since the mesobilifuscins may be anabolic in origin (40), the agreement found by Stich must be fortuitous.

The discrepancies between the theoretical daily production of bile pigments and the excretion of measurable pigments in the feces might be due to the formation of polar degradation products (see below), to the bacterial degradation of enantiomorphs (see above), or to intestinal absorption of bile pigments followed by urinary excretion.

Absorption of Pigments from the Intestine

The absorption of urobilinogen in the colon with its normal return to the liver and reexcretion in the bile constitutes the enterohepatic circulation first postulated by Müller (111) and repeatedly reviewed since (46, p. 31–37; 98; 99; 165). However, in the early and in the recovery stages of hepatogenous jaundice, urobilinogen absorbed from the intestine is excreted in the urine in large amounts. Early demonstrations of this circulation depended on such experiments as the appearance of urobilinoid substances in the bile after enemas containing mesobilirubinogen had been administered to patients with biliary fistulas.

Recent methods for the production of isotopically labeled bilirubin (126) and mesobilirubinogen (96) have permitted unequivocal demonstration of the intestinal absorption not only of mesobilirubinogen but also of bilirubin.

ABSORPTION OF UROBILINOGENS Absorption and an enterohepatic circulation of ¹⁴C-mesobilirubinogen have been demonstrated after introduction of the labeled pigment into either the terminal ileum or the duodenum of rats (96). The relative rates of absorption from these two parts of the intestine are shown in Figure 5. In human subjects with cholelithiasis, duodenal instillation of ^{14}C-mesobilirubinogen was followed by the appearance of about 50% of the administered dose in the bile; one of the subjects with hepatobiliary insufficiency excreted 14% in the urine (97). Similar administration in the terminal ileum revealed slower absorption, the total biliary excretion being about 20%. The slower removal from the ileum was believed to result from the reduced surface area available for absorption and to adsorption of the urobilinogen on fecal solids. The radioactivity of the bile and the urine was associated only with the urobilinogen; since the bilirubin in the bile was unlabeled, no conversion of mesobilinogen to bilirubin occurred.

The absorption of stercobilin from washed, isolated loops of the small intestine of dogs has been studied in situ by Kahan et al. (84). About 30% passed through the gut wall; some appeared as stercobilinogen in the urine, but some persisted as the unreduced pigment bound to albumin and globulin in the blood. The 40% of pigment recovered from the loop remained unabsorbed when placed in a fresh washed loop and was shown by electrophoresis to be bound to mucoprotein.

Urobilinogenuria has long been regarded as resulting from impaired reexcretion into the bile due to liver disease, biliary trauma, and infection. It is quite possible, however, that the presence of liver disease may permit invasion of the ileum by microorganisms and that urobilinogen formation may occur higher in the intestine than normal. Absorption is more rapid and complete in this part of the gut, so that urobilinogenuria may reflect enhanced intestinal chromogen absorption as well as impaired hepatic excretion (97). Infection of the biliary tract by certain microorganisms capable of forming d-urobilin from bilirubin glucuronide is associated with d-urobilinogenuria, and this too may be due to spread of those organisms to the gut. d-Urobilinogen in the urine may thus be due to absorption of this chromogen from the gallbladder itself or from the upper part of the small intestine.

ABSORPTION OF BILIRUBIN. Lester & Schmid (93) demonstrated the appearance of isotopic bilirubin in the bile of normal rats after intraduodenal administration of both conjugated and unconjugated ^{14}C-bilirubin. The appearance of isotope in the bile was more rapid with the unconjugated pigment and suggests preferential absorption. This was confirmed with Gunn rats; these animals are unable to conjugate bilirubin,

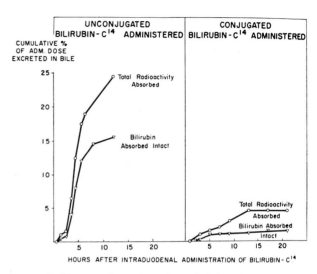

FIG. 6. Pigment absorption after administration of unconjugated ^{14}C-labeled bilirubin and conjugated ^{14}C-labeled bilirubin to two human subjects. [From Lester & Schmid (94).]

which therefore is not excreted in bile. Free ^{14}C-bilirubin was absorbed and could be detected in the blood but not in bile. No radioactivity appeared in the bile after administration of conjugated ^{14}C-bilirubin, and because these animals are able to excrete intravenously administered conjugate in bile, conjugated bilirubin cannot have been absorbed. Some radioactive bilirubin appeared in the blood as a result of absorption of free bilirubin produced by hydrolysis of the conjugates. Subsequent experiments showed that absorption occurred throughout the entire length of the small intestine and in the colon.

Lester & Schmid (94) studied also absorption of ^{14}C-bilirubin from the intestine in humans with biliary fistulas (Fig. 6). In a subject given the free pigment, 24.5% of the radioactivity was excreted mostly as unchanged bilirubin in the bile in 12 hours. A second subject given the conjugate excreted less than 5% of the radioactivity in the bile, only one-third of which was associated with intact bilirubin. Last, when ^{14}C-bilirubin was fed to a boy with congenital hyperbilirubinemia, 80% of the radioactivity administered was demonstrated to be present in plasma; after administration of the conjugate the plasma radioactivity was unmeasurable. Gilbertsen et al. (37) have similarly demonstrated absorption of ^{15}N-labeled free bilirubin with rapid appearance in in the bile. Thus, in humans there seems less intestinal hydrolysis of conjugated bilirubin than in rats, and in normal man little enterohepatic circulation of bilirubin occurs (97).

In a patient with a congenital defect of hepatic

bilirubin conjugation and inability to excrete bilirubin in the bile, injected ¹⁴C-bilirubin was degraded to water-soluble monopyrroles or perhaps even smaller molecules, which appeared principally in the feces. Similar observations were reported for the Gunn rat, which has a similar genetic defect. However, in the Gunn rat, crystalline-labeled bilirubin was isolated in considerable quantity from the stools; this indicated that bilirubin can pass also from blood through intestinal mucosa to lumen. This is an excretory route of obvious value when hepatic excretion is limited and possibly occurs normally to a minor extent. An attempt has been made, unsuccessfully, to increase excretion in subjects with defective conjugation of bilirubin by this route by the oral administration of cholestyramine, which can adsorb bilirubin (90).

BILE ACIDS

Discussion of the metabolism of bile acids is limited to that of the C_{24} acids found in the bile of mammals. C_{24} bile acids are formed from cholesterol in the liver (14) and are excreted in bile as peptide conjugates of glycine and taurine. Acids thus formed are termed "primary bile acids," and in most species these consist only of cholic and chenodeoxycholic acids (21, 63). However, in a few species, chenodeoxycholic acid, as distinct from cholic acid, is not an end product of cholesterol metabolism in the liver and is converted into trihydroxycholanic acids. These must be regarded as primary bile acids but they are abundant only in the domestic pig. Other bile acids in bile arise by metabolism of the primary bile acids during enterohepatic circulation and are termed "secondary bile acids." Secondary bile acids generally predominate in feces and there are unconjugated. The chemical structures of the main bile acids discussed here are shown in Figure 7.

Hepatic bile of human subjects contains 1–2 % by weight of bile acids. Concentration of the bile occurs in the gallbladder, and the bile acid content rises to 2–8 % by weight.

Absorption of Bile Acids in the Intestine

At least 95 % of the bile acids excreted in the bile are reabsorbed in the gut, and absorption in vivo at various sites has been investigated in man by Borgström et al. (16). Subjects were given test meals containing ³⁵S-taurocholic acid and polyethylene glycol, a nonabsorbable reference compound. Samples of intestinal contents were obtained through a tube, and the absorption of the bile acid was determined by measuring its concentration relative to that of the reference compound. In that way changes of concentration due to dilution were eliminated, but difficulties of interpretation arose through recirculation of the labeled bile acid. Other workers have measured the absorption of bile acids from isolated segments of intestine left in situ. The advantage of this method is that experimental conditions are approximately physiological. Absorption may be determined from the amount of bile acid remaining in the segment (2, 38) or from the amount appearing in the bile (42, 170). When measurements are made by the latter method, radioactive bile acid should be used to avoid confusion with excretion of endogenous bile acid. Measurement of the radioactivity of bile after administration of ³⁵S-taurocholic acid to animals with partial resection of the intestine has also been used (132).

The results of these investigations clearly show that in all mammals investigated, absorption of bile acids occurs primarily in the ileum and only to a limited extent in the proximal part of the small intestine. Little hydrolysis of the peptide bond of conjugated acids occurs in vivo in the small intestine, and absorption is mainly of the conjugated acid (133), although unconjugated bile acids are also absorbed.

In vitro preparations of segments of intestine are required for investigations of the mechanism of absorption, and information on the site of absorption is obtained by taking segments from various parts. Good oxygenation, particularly of the mucosa, is important and presents difficulties. The most commonly used preparation is the everted gut sac of Wilson & Wiseman (171), in which the metabolically active mucosal surface is everted and easily oxygenated. Another advantage of the method is that the volume of the serosal compartment is small so that any transport from the mucosal surface causes a rapid rise in the concentration within the serosal compartment. Disadvantages are that oxygenation of the serosal surface may be insufficient and that the eversion may injure the tissue. Also passage of bile acid across the whole of the intestinal wall does not normally occur in vivo, and in vitro the rate of passage may be limited by the rate of diffusion of the absorbed material across the serosa and not by the rate of absorption by the mucosa. There is some evidence that diffusion across the serosa limits the rate at which bile acids accumulate in the serosal compartment (75, 86); the everted gut sac therefore is not ideal for studies of the kinetics of bile acid absorption. How-

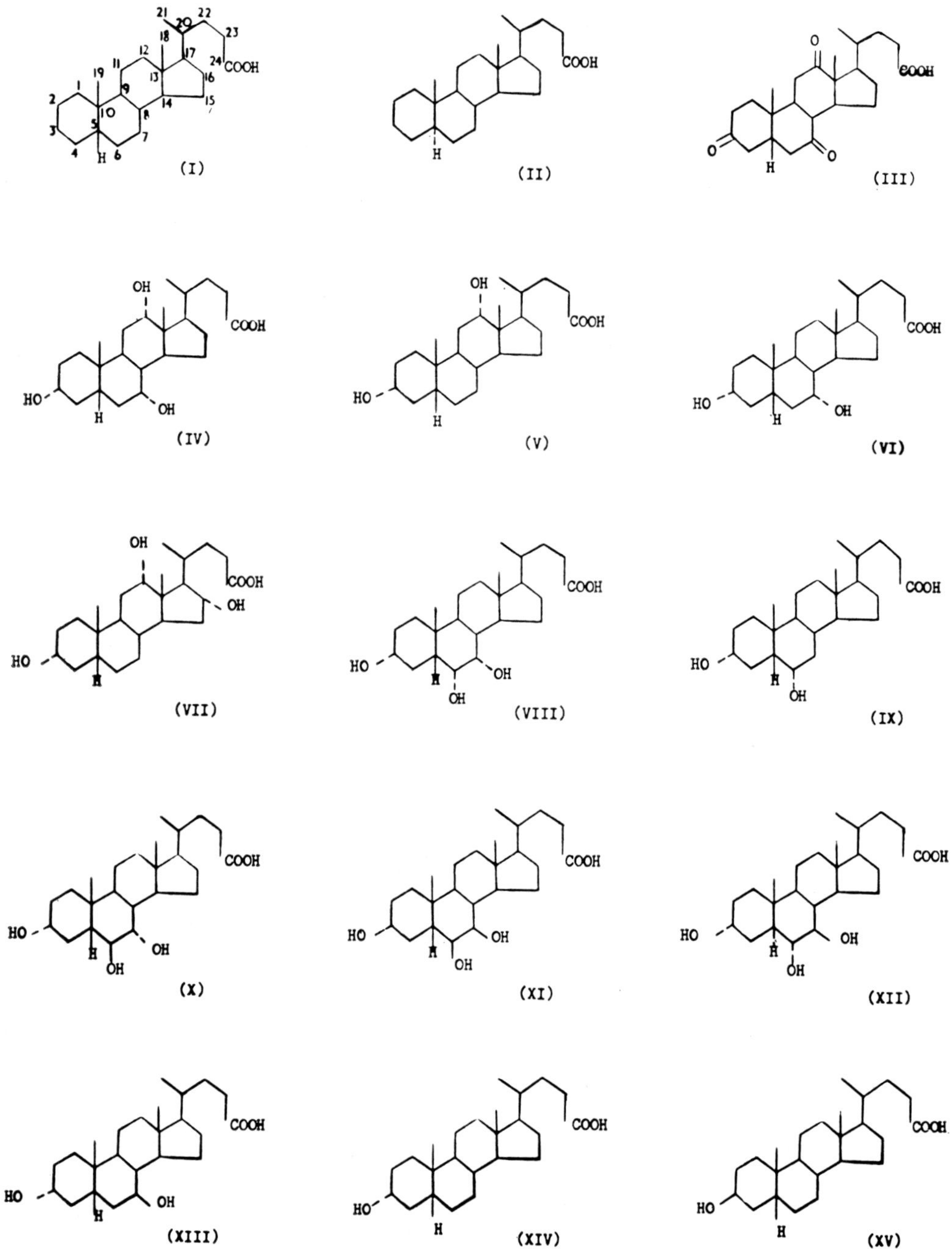

FIG. 7. Chemical structures of bile acids. I: cholanic or 5β-cholanoic acid with carbon atoms numbered. II: *allo*cholanic or 5α-cholanoic acid. III: 3,7,12-triketocholanic acid (dehydrocholic acid). IV: 3α,7α,12α-trihydroxycholanic acid (cholic acid). V: 3α,12α-dihydroxycholanic acid (deoxycholic acid). VI: 3α,7α-dihydroxycholanic acid (chenodeoxycholic acid). VII: 3α,12α,16α-trihydroxycholanic acid (pythocholic acid). VIII: 3α,6α,7α-trihydroxycholanic acid (hyocholic acid). IX: 3α,6α-dihydroxycholanic acid (hyodeoxycholic acid). X: 3α,6β,7α-trihydroxycholanic acid (α-muricholic acid). XI: 3α,6β,7β-trihydroxycholanic acid (β-muricholic acid). XII: 3α,6α,7β-trihydroxycholanic acid (ω-muricholic acid). XIII: 3α,7β-dihydroxycholanic) acid (ursodeoxycholic acid). XIV: 3α-hydroxycholanic acid (lithocholic acid). XV: 3β-hydroxycholanic acid (isolithocholic acid).

ever, transport against a concentration gradient is easily demonstrated with the preparation, and the method has also been used in a number of kinetic studies. Active transport of bile acids may also be studied by measurement of the *initial* rate of accumulation of bile acid by small slices of intestine; since the method does not depend on passage across the intestinal wall, the possibility of diffusion being rate limiting can be excluded. The method is suitable for kinetic studies and has been used by Holt (75).

In all mammals investigated, transport of conjugated bile acids against a concentration gradient is observed in everted sacs of ileal tissue (75, 86, 87, 131). Active transport of unconjugated bile acids proceeds at a rate similar to that of the conjugated bile acids (29). No transport is observed with sacs prepared from other parts of the intestine. Transport in ileal sacs obeys Michaelis-Menten saturation kinetics and is inhibited by anoxia, dinitrophenol, azide, and the absence of sodium ions in the medium; it is therefore active. Transport of taurocholic acid is competitively inhibited by glycocholic acid and by cholic acid; this suggests that the unconjugated and conjugated bile acid share the same transport mechanism. This may affect the composition of bile acids in bile (87).

Using everted sacs of ileum from albino rats Playoust & Isselbacher (131) showed that conjugated bile acids are not hydrolyzed during transport. ^{35}S-taurocholic acid and unlabeled taurine were added to the medium bathing the mucosa, and the specific activity of the taurocholate appearing in the serosal compartment was measured. Similar experiments with ^{14}C-glycocholate and unlabeled glycine were performed, and in no case was the specific activity of the conjugated bile acid altered.

Absorption of bile acids in parts of the intestine other than the ileum takes place by passive diffusion, and both conjugated and unconjugated acids are absorbed. Bile acids in the large intestine are absorbed only slowly, and the absorption is less complete than in the small intestine (120). This is due partly to the formation of insoluble metabolites or metabolites bound to bacteria (59, 119) and presumably also to the absence of an active transport system. However, only 10–15% of the conjugated bile acid excreted in bile is unabsorbed in the small intestine and passes into the cecum, where hydrolysis of the peptide bond and metabolism of the steroid moiety occur. Of this amount, at least two-thirds is absorbed and returns to the liver, where conjugation always occurs and further metabolism of the steroid moiety sometimes occurs (102, 125). The remainder is eliminated in feces.

Quantitative Aspects of Bile Acid Metabolism

Early attempts to quantitate bile acid metabolism (pool size and elimination in feces) were hindered by the absence of reliable chemical methods for the estimation of the various bile acids. The introduction of isotopic methods for use in intact animals greatly facilitated study of these aspects of bile acid metabolism and of the factors affecting it (98, 100).

Excretion of bile acids in the urine is negligible in man and rats and occurs only to a limited extent in rabbits. In normal animals, therefore, synthesis of bile acids equals elimination in feces if there is no destruction during enterohepatic circulation, and the bile acid is assumed to enter and leave a single pool, the size of which remains constant as a result of a homeostatic regulation of bile acid synthesis (5). The rate of replenishment of the pool (fractional turnover, T) and the half-life ($t_{1/2}$) of a bile acid and its metabolites may be determined by measurement of the rate of excretion in feces of radioactivity derived from a trace amount of radioactive bile acid administered to an animal (100). These parameters, which are related by the expression $T = (\ln 2)/t_{1/2}$, do not fully describe the system, however, and the values are required for two of the variables in the equation: production rate = $(\ln 2 \times \text{pool size})/t_{1/2}$. Simultaneous determination of two of the variables is achieved by measuring the decline in specific activity of a bile acid in bile after administration of a trace amount of the radioactive bile acid (98). The half-life is obtained from the slope of the graph of the logarithm of specific activity against time, and the pool size is obtained from the value for specific activity at zero time, obtained by extrapolation. Interconversions of bile acids do not affect these measurements of turnover and production, and in the rat, mouse, and possibly also the guinea pig, these are important (26, 27, 102, 125). The bile acids undergoing interconversion would, however, be included in estimates of the pool size measured by the kinetic method.

Bile acid turnover has been studied most in man, rats, and rabbits. Rat bile contains mainly cholic acid (80% by weight) and chenodeoxycholic acid, both conjugated principally with taurine. Estimates of the size of the pool of cholic acid in rats weighing about 200 g and fed a normal laboratory diet range from 14 mg (34) to 20 mg (134). Cholic acid production in such rats is estimated to be 4–5 mg per day (36, 60). The fractional turnover of chenodeoxycholic acid in rats is similar to that of cholic acid (100).

In rabbits, bile acids in bile consist almost entirely

of deoxycholic acid conjugated with glycine, and on a normal laboratory diet about 80 mg of bile acids are formed daily (21). The turnover of deoxycholic acid in rabbits has been studied by Hellström & Sjövall (73), and a pool size of about 800 mg is indicated.

In healthy human subjects cholic acid, chenodeoxycholic acid, and deoxycholic acid are the most abundant bile acids in bile and are present in the ratio of 1.1:1.0:0.6 (152). Conjugation is with glycine and taurine. Production of cholic and chenodeoxycholic acids amounts to 0.5–0.7 g daily; although estimates vary slightly, it is probable that the two acids are produced in approximately equal amounts (22, 98). Pool sizes of 1.4 g, 1.45 g, and 0.77 g for cholic acid, chenodeoxycholic acid, and deoxycholic acid were found by Lindstedt (98); but in experiments in which the pools of cholic and chenodeoxycholic acids were measured simultaneously, values of 0.9 g and 2.5 g for those two acids were found (22).

These and other estimates of bile acid production and pool size are considered in detail by Danielsson (21). Further discussion of the quantitative aspects of bile acid metabolism is confined here to consideration of the magnitude and efficiency of the enterohepatic circulation and the influence of diet and microorganisms on bile acid metabolism. Effects of hormones on bile acid turnover have been observed, but these appear to be due mainly to effects on synthesis.

ENTEROHEPATIC CIRCULATION. After oral administration of radioactive conjugated bile acid to rats, 80–90% of the radioactivity appears in bile within 2 hours (133, 153). This suggests that there is a vigorous and fairly efficient enterohepatic circulation of bile acids in the rat. A proper measure of the enterohepatic circulation is obtained by relating pool size to excretion in bile and elimination in feces. Excretion in bile is difficult to measure since collection of bile interrupts the enterohepatic circulation and causes bile acid synthesis to increase (35, 157, 158). Bergström & Danielsson (5), however, made use of this effect and determined the amount of taurochenodeoxycholic acid (5–10 mg per hour) that had to be administered parenterally to reduce synthesis of cholic acid in rats with bile fistulas to 5 mg per day, the level observed in intact rats. The results provided further evidence of the homeostatic control mechanism and suggested also that in intact animals excretion of bile acid in bile might average 5–10 mg per hour. Using the entirely different technique of measuring the radioactivity of ^{3}H-cholic acid in the portal blood of rats after administration of a trace amount of the labeled acid,

Olivecrona & Sjövall (125) concluded that 144 mg of cholic acid passed from the intestine to the liver each day. Deoxycholic acid and other metabolites were also found in portal blood but constituted only 15 % of the total, the remainder being cholic acid. Thus, although the cholic acid pool of 15 mg in rats circulates at least ten times each day, less than one-third of the pool is eliminated by excretion in feces. In man too 20–30 g of bile acids are excreted daily in bile (4), yet only 0.5–0.7 g appears in feces. Thus absorption of bile acids in the intestine is efficient and rapid.

EFFECTS OF DIET. Effects of diet have been studied mainly in rats and man. Portman & Murphy (134) observed marked changes in pool size and production of cholic acid in rats fed various diets. In animals fed synthetic diets containing little indigestible material and with cornstarch, sucrose, or cellulose flour as carbohydrate, the pool of cholic acid and metabolites was half that of animals fed Purina chow, and the production rate was also markedly decreased. Fractional turnover, however, was less varied because the changes in pool size and production rate were compensatory. The changes have been attributed to diet-induced modification of the microbial flora and indeed are less marked in animals treated orally with antibiotics (136). An effect of indigestible material on the rate of passage of bile acid into the large intestine has also been suggested. However, the large changes in pool size that occur without large changes in fractional turnover suggest that other factors may also be involved.

The influence of dietary fat on bile acid metabolism has been studied since the serum cholesterol concentration is generally elevated by the feeding of saturated fats and lowered by unsaturated fats. It has been suggested that the type of dietary fat may alter the rate of cholesterol degradation to bile acids; although this has not been proved, supporting evidence has been obtained from experiments in man in which bile acids in feces were estimated by chemical means (43, 70). However, other recent experiments, also on human subjects, have shown no correlation between changes in serum cholesterol concentration and changes in the production of bile acids (99). No consistent changes either of pool size or of turnover as determined by the method of Lindstedt (98) were observed in subjects fed liquid or solid diets or with variation in dietary fat content.

EFFECTS OF MICROORGANISMS. The effects of microorganisms on bile acid metabolism in the rat have

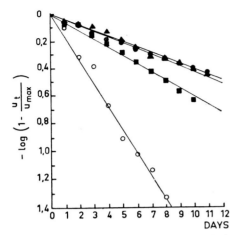

FIG. 8. Semilogarithmic plot of elimination of cholic acid in the rat. ●———● germ-free, ■———■ infected with *Aspergillus niger*, ▲———▲ infected with *Aspergillus niger* and *Clostridium perfringens*, ○———○ totally infected. [From Gustafsson et al. (57).]

been well defined. Oral treatment of rats with antibiotics increased the half-life of cholic acid from 2–3 to more than 10 days (101). Similar results were obtained in germ-free animals [Fig. 8; (57)]. Infection of the gut of germ-free animals with *Aspergillus niger* or with *Clostridium perfringens* did not affect the half-life, although infection with *Clostridium perfringens* caused hydrolysis of the bile acid conjugates. No hydrolysis of conjugated bile acids was observed in the germ-free animals, and the only bile acid detected in their feces was taurocholic acid. The method of Lindstedt & Norman (100) was used by both groups; pool size was measured only in the germ-free rats and was 30 mg, or about twice normal. Thus, in the absence of microorganisms, fractional turnover is greatly reduced as a result of the lower rate of synthesis and lower elimination of bile acid and the much increased pool size. These conclusions were confirmed by Gustafsson et al. (60), who measured cholic acid production rate and pool size in normal and germ-free rats and in germ-free rats infected with *Escherichia coli*. In the last two groups production of cholic acid was less than half normal (2 mg per day), and the pool size (18–20 mg) was slightly raised. Therefore microorganisms accelerate removal of bile acids from the pool either by complete degradation or by the formation of metabolites that are not readily absorbed.

Qualitative Aspects of Bile Acid Metabolism

METABOLISM OF BILE ACIDS BY MICROORGANISMS IN VITRO. Several species of bacteria when incubated

TABLE 2. *Transformations of Bile Acids by Microorganisms In Vitro*

Substrate	Microorganism	Products	Ref.
Cholic acid	*Alcaligenes faecalis*	dehydrocholic acid	143
	Escherichia coli	3α,12α-dihydroxy-7-oxo-cholanic acid	66
	Streptomyces gelatinus	7α-hydroxy-3,12-dioxo-Δ⁴-bisnor-cholenic acid	65
		7α,12α-dihydroxy-3-oxo-cholanic acid	
		7α-hydroxy-3,12-dioxo-cholanic acid	
		7α-hydroxy-3,12-dioxo-Δ⁴-cholenic acid	
	Streptomyces rubescans	7α,12α-dihydroxy-3-oxo-Δ⁴-cholenic acid	67
		7α-hydroxy-3,12-dioxo-Δ⁴-cholenic acid	
		12α-hydroxy-3-oxo-Δ⁴,⁶-choladienic acid	
		3,12-dioxo-Δ⁴,⁶-choladienic acid	
	Mixed fecal organisms	deoxycholic acid	116
		7-oxo-deoxycholic acid	
		12-oxo-lithocholic acid	
		3,12-dioxo-cholanic acid	
3,7-Dioxo-cholanic acid	*E. coli communis*	chenodeoxycholic acid	150
Cholic acid	Mixed fecal organisms and a single but unidentified organism	deoxycholic acid	135
	E. coli	7-oxo-deoxycholic acid	135
	*Corynebacterium simplex**	7α,12α-dihydroxy-3-oxo-cholanic acid	68
		7α,12α-dihydroxy-3-oxo-Δ⁴-cholenic acid	
		12α-hydroxy-3-oxo-Δ⁴,⁶-choladienic acid	

TABLE 2.—*Concluded*

Substrate	Microorganism	Products	Ref.
		12α-hydroxy-3-oxo-Δ⁴-cholenic acid	
		12α-hydroxy-3-oxo-Δ¹,⁴-choladienic acid	
	Mixed fecal organisms	deoxycholic acid	119
Chenodeoxy-cholic acid	Mixed fecal organisms	lithocholic acid	119
Dehydrocho-lic acid	*E. coli commu-nis, Proteus vulgaris*	7α-hydroxy-3,12-dioxo-cholanic acid	110
	Proactinomyces erythropolis	3,7,12-trioxo-Δ⁴-aetienic acid	159
3-Oxo-Δ⁴-cholenic acid	*Proactinomyces erythropolis*	3-oxo-Δ⁴-aetienic acid	159

* Grows slowly in otherwise germ-free rats.

with conjugated bile acids effect hydrolysis of the peptide bond. Hydrolysis of ^{14}C-labeled taurocholic and glycocholic acids by strains of *Clostridia* and *Enterococci* (117) and of the glycine and taurine conjugates of cholic and deoxycholic acid by strains of *Bacteroides* and *Lactobacillus bifidus* (30) has been observed. Enzymes that effect the hydrolysis have been found in cell-free extracts of *Clostridium perfringens* (112) and as extracellular enzymes in cecal contents (122). Both types may contribute to the hydrolysis of conjugated bile acids in the intestine.

The metabolism of unconjugated bile acids by microorganisms in vitro has been studied mainly under aerobic conditions. Reactions that occur are the oxidation and reduction of oxygen substitutents at C-3, C-7, and C-12, elimination of oxygen at C-7, and the introduction of double bonds into the steroid nucleus. Metabolites are formed in which one or more of these processes may have occurred (Table 2).

The mechanism of removal of the 7α-hydroxyl group has been elucidated by Samuelsson (141) after administration of [6α,6β,8β-³H] cholic acid to rats and rabbits and involves a diaxial transelimination of water and reduction of the Δ⁶ intermediate. This occurs by transaddition of two equatorial hydrogen atoms (Fig. 9). The Δ⁶ compounds isolated after incubation of cholic acid with *Streptomyces rubescans* (67) and after incubation with *Corynebacterium simplex* (68) may thus be intermediates formed during elimination of the 7α-hydroxyl group.

Some microorganisms also are able to utilize bile acids as the sole source of carbon, and metabolites

with shortened side chains (bisnor and etio acids) have been isolated (Table 2). These acids, however, may not be end products of the metabolism.

METABOLISM OF BILE ACIDS IN VIVO. The metabolism of the two major primary bile acids of mammals—cholic acid and chenodeoxycholic acid—has been studied in a number of species, and common features of metabolism are observed. Since these two acids are not metabolically interconvertible (4, 21) their metabolism is considered separately. A separate section is devoted to the metabolism of hyocholic acid, the major primary bile acid of the domestic pig. For ease of discussion, no reference is made to the conjugation of those unconjugated bile acids that enter the liver; such conjugation is assumed to be essentially complete.

Cholic acid. Cholic acid is not metabolized by the liver of any mammal so far investigated. Metabolism of the conjugated cholic acid excreted in bile does not occur in the small intestine (16, 59, 121), and it is only on entering the cecum that hydrolysis of the peptide bond of the conjugated acid and metabolism of the free bile acid commences.

Metabolism of cholic acid in rats and mice is very similar and is characterized by facile interconversion of cholic and deoxycholic acids during enterohepatic circulation (9, 27, 108). In rats transformation of ^{14}C-cholic acid (I) has been studied by injection of the acid into the cecum of animals with bile fistulas (120). Metabolites arising solely from the action of microorganisms were isolated from feces, and metabolites arising from metabolism in the liver and intestine were isolated from bile. In feces, deoxycholic acid (II), 12-ketolithocholic acid (III), 7-ketodeoxycholic acid (IV), and 3α,7β,12α-trihydroxycholanic acid (V) were isolated. The metabolic pathways envisaged are outlined in Figure 10. Although conversion of administered 7-ketodeoxycholic acid to deoxycholic acid and 12-ketolithocholic acid was observed, 7-ketodeoxycholic acid is not an important precursor of deoxycholic acid, which is formed mainly by direct elimination of the 7α-hydroxyl group of cholic acid (141). 12-Ketolithocholic acid also is probably formed from deoxycholic acid rather than directly from cholic acid. Reabsorption of all the metabolites except 12-ketolithocholic acid occurred to some extent, and these, together with cholic acid, appeared in bile.

In rats and mice the formation from deoxycholic acid of trihydroxycholanic acids other than cholic acid has been observed only in surgically jaundiced animals, in which small amounts of 3α,6β,12α-trihydroxycholanic acid are found (137).

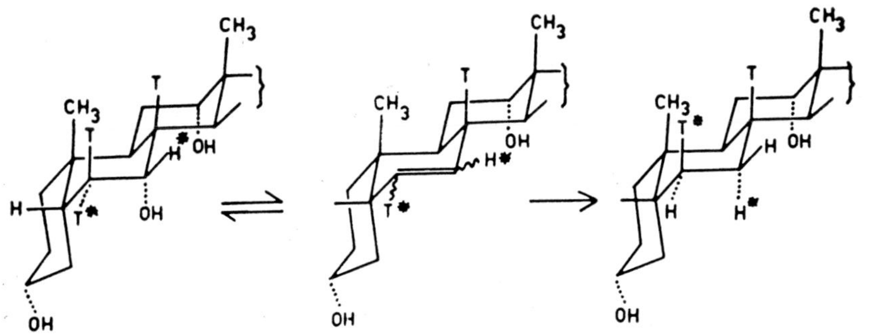

FIG. 9. Mechanism of elimination of the 7α-hydroxyl group of cholic acid. [From Samuelsson (141).]

The extent of the interconversion of cholic acid and deoxycholic acid during enterohepatic circulation has been determined in rats by measurement of the concentration of deoxycholic acid in portal blood (125) and by kinetic methods using $[7\beta\text{-}^3\text{H},24\text{-}^{14}\text{C}]$ cholic acid (102) and amounts to 50–80% of the cholate pool each day.

Hydroxylation in the liver of deoxycholic acid formed in the large intestine also occurs in pythons, and results in the formation of $3\alpha,12\alpha,16\alpha$-trihydroxycholanic acid (pythocholic acid), which predominates in the bile (7). In the feces, 12-ketolithocholic acid and $3\alpha,12\alpha$-dihydroxy-16-ketocholanic acid are found and are derived from deoxycholic acid and pythocholic acid, respectively, probably by the action of microorganisms.

Because of the rapid conversion of deoxycholic acid to cholic acid in the livers of rats and mice, deoxycholic acid is virtually absent from their bile. In humans and rabbits, however, deoxycholic acid is abundant in bile and is not metabolized by the liver. It is absent from the bile of both rabbits and humans with long-standing bile fistulas and as in other species is formed by the action of microorganisms on cholic acid (32, 33, 103). Conversion of cholic acid to deoxycholic acid proceeds more efficiently in rabbits than in humans, and in the rabbit 7-ketodeoxycholic acid also acts as a precursor of deoxycholic acid. As in the rat, however, this pathway contributes little to the formation of deoxycholic acid (8).

Deoxycholic acid in rabbits is metabolized to $3\beta,12\alpha$-dihydroxycholanic acid and is presumably formed by microorganisms in the large intestine since it appears in feces but not in bile (23). In an extension to that study Danielsson et al. (25) reported the isolation from rabbit feces of ^{14}C-labeled 3β-hydroxy-12-ketocholanic acid, 3α-hydroxy-12-ketocholanic acid, $3\beta,12\alpha$-dihydroxycholanic acid, and $3\alpha,12\alpha$-dihydroxyallocholanic acid as metabolites of ^{14}C-deoxycholic acid. No distinction between metabolism in the

liver and intestine was made. Determination of the specific activity of the *allo* acid showed that formation had been from deoxycholic acid rather than from *allo*cholic acid.

In man ^{3}H-labeled 3β-hydroxy-12-ketocholanic acid, 12-ketocholanic acid, and $3\beta,12\alpha$-dihydroxycholanic acid have been isolated from feces as metabolites of ^{3}H-cholic acid and were probably formed from deoxycholic acid, which was also found in feces (22). Additional metabolites of deoxycholic acid in man may include $3\alpha,12\beta$-dihydroxycholanic acid and 12α-hydroxy-3-ketocholanic acid (1).

Metabolism of deoxycholic acid is thus similar in man and rabbits. Inversion of the hydroxyl groups at C-3 and C-12 occurs, probably by formation of intermediary keto compounds.

The metabolism of cholic acid in guinea pigs has not been studied in any detail, and cholic acid until recently was thought to be absent in guinea pigs (26, 129).

Hyocholic acid. Hyocholic acid has been found only in the domestic pig. The bile contains hyodeoxycholic acid, hyocholic acid, chenodeoxycholic acid, and small amounts of $3\beta,6\alpha$-dihydroxycholanic acid, 3α-hydroxy-6-keto*allo*cholanic acid, and possibly also lithocholic acid (62). The metabolic relationship of these acids was studied by Bergström et al. (6). In animals with bile fistulas, ^{14}C-hyocholic acid was isolated from bile after intraperitoneal administration of ^{14}C-chenodeoxycholic acid; no metabolism was observed of ^{14}C-hyodeoxycholic acid similarly administered. Since hyocholic acid was converted to hyodeoxycholic acid in intact animals, it was concluded that hyodeoxycholic acid was formed from hyocholic acid by the action of microorganisms in the intestine and that hyocholic acid itself was formed in the liver from chenodeoxycholic acid.

The other components of pig bile—$3\beta,6\alpha$-dihydroxycholanic acid and $3\beta,6\alpha$-dihydroxy*allo*cholanic acid—are probably formed from hyodeoxycholic acid

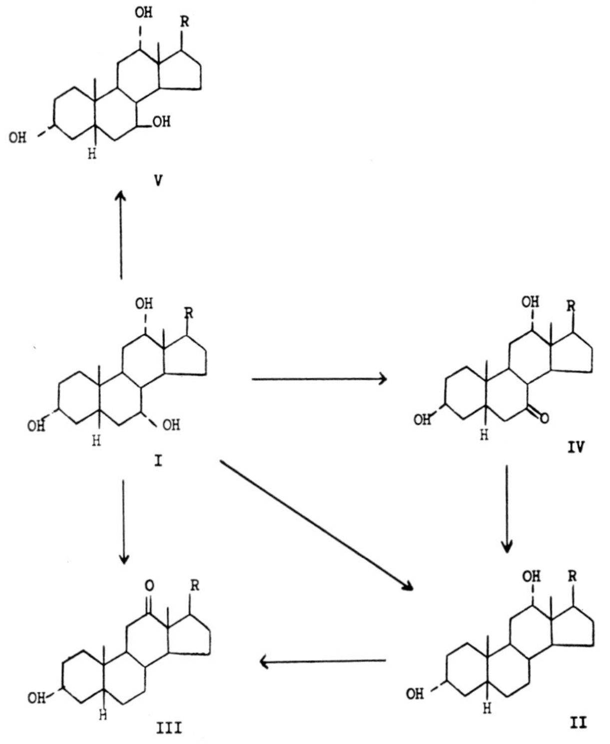

FIG. 10. Microbial transformations of cholic acid in rats. R = CH(CH₃)CH₂CH₂COOH. [From Norman & Sjövall (121).]

by microorganisms, and lithocholic acid is certainly formed from chenodeoxycholic acid by microorganisms.

Chenodeoxycholic acid. In the domestic pig chenodeoxycholic acid is almost completely metabolized in the liver to hyocholic acid and is itself present in pig bile only in small amounts. Metabolism of chenodeoxycholic acid to trihydroxycholanic acids also occurs in the livers of rats and mice.

The formation in rats of two trihydroxycholanic acids from chenodeoxycholic acid was first observed by Bergström & Sjövall (10), and these have since been studied intensively by Doisy and co-workers. Their experimental technique has been to administer labeled chenodeoxycholic acid intraperitoneally or intragastrically to animals with ligated bile ducts or biliary fistulas. In the animals with ligated bile ducts, bile acids are retained for a longer period, are more completely metabolized, and are excreted in urine. In a series of papers the isolation and identification of the two acids as 3α,6β,7β-trihydroxycholanic acid (β-muricholic acid) and 3α,6β,7α-trihydroxycholanic acid (α-muricholic acid) were described (76–78, 109). Also α- and β-muricholic acids were isolated in equal amounts from bile of fistulated animals and were

shown to be normal but minor constituents of rat bile. α-Muricholic acid is probably formed directly from chenodeoxycholic acid, whereas β-muricholic acid is formed by irreversible inversion of the 7α-hydroxyl group of α-muricholic acid, probably by formation of an intermediate 7-keto acid (140). This may explain the dominance of β-muricholic acid in the urine of rats with ligated bile ducts (108, 109).

Formation in the livers of humans of muricholic acids from chenodeoxycholic acid has not been observed.

In mice α- and β-muricholic acids are formed as in the rat (27, 178) and formation of 3α,6α,7β-trihydroxycholanic acid (ω-muricholic acid) also occurs (177). Rats do not form ω-muricholic acid from chenodeoxycholic acid but are able to form ω-muricholic acid from hyodeoxycholic acid (76), an acid that occurs naturally only in the domestic pig.

Ursodeoxycholic acid and 7-ketolithocholic acid are normal but minor constituents of rat and mouse bile and are also found as metabolites of chenodeoxycholic acid in the fistula bile or urine of surgically jaundiced animals (27, 140, 178). Samuelsson (140) observed conversion of 7-ketolithocholic acid to ursodeoxycholic by livers of rats with bile fistulas; it therefore seems likely that ursodeoxycholic acid is formed from chenodeoxycholic acid in the liver by intermediate formation of 7-ketolithocholic acid.

In guinea pigs, however, 7-ketolithocholic acid is not formed in the liver but is produced by the action of microorganisms on chenodeoxycholic acid in the large intestine (26). 7-Ketolithocholic acid thus formed is metabolized to chenodeoxycholic acid in the liver (cf. rats).

Ursodeoxycholic acid in humans is formed by the action of microorganisms on chenodeoxycholic acid (72), and in rabbits too, ursodeoxycholic acid and 7-ketolithocholic acid, which are readily formed from chenodeoxycholic acid in intact animals (71), are probably also formed by microbial action.

Probably the major reaction undergone by chenodeoxycholic acid in the intestine, however, is elimination of the 7α-hydroxyl group leading to production of the lithocholic acid (121). In humans lithocholic acid is converted in the intestine to 3-ketocholanic acid and to isolithocholic acid, and all three acids appear in feces (22, 118). Lithocholic acid in intestinal contents is in an insoluble or bound form (59, 118, 119) and hence is not reabsorbed to any great extent. However, if lithocholic acid is administered to rats with bile fistulas, formation in the liver of chenodeoxycholic acid, α- and β-muricholic acids, and 3α,6βdihydroxycholanic acid is observed (156). Lithocholic acid is not metabolized by the livers of humans to any great extent (18).

OTHER CONSTITUENTS

Cholesterol

Cholesterol in bile is unesterified and is solubilized by lecithin and bile acids, with which it forms mixed micelles. In the intestine, cholesterol from bile mixes with cholesterol from dietary sources and is probably dissolved partly in emulsified fat and partly in mixed micelles of bile acid, free fatty acid, and monoglyceride (74). The proportion in each phase would be determined by the partition coefficient. Since absorption takes place from the micellar phase, the partition coefficient might well influence the rate of cholesterol absorption. Absorption of cholesterol, as of fat, occurs mainly in the proximal part of the small intestine (15) but is markedly less complete than that of fat. In man less than 50% of cholesterol in the small intestine is absorbed (15, 69).

Formation of coprostanol (5β-cholestan-3β-ol) from cholesterol in vivo has been demonstrated by isolation of deuterated coprostanol after administration of deuterium-labeled cholesterol (144). In feces of normal animals, coprostanol is the most abundant neutral sterol, but in feces of germ-free animals or animals treated orally with antibiotics, cholesterol is most abundant and coprostanol is absent (19, 24). A major part of the unabsorbed cholesterol in intestinal contents is thus transformed into coprostanol by microorganisms in the large intestine. This process occurs by direct saturation of the Δ^5 double bond of cholesterol (72).

Neutral sterols other than cholesterol and coprostanol are found in feces and are of diverse origin (21). However, it is probable that some of these may arise partly from cholesterol by metabolism in the intestine. Such sterols include cholestanol (5α-cholestan-3β-ol), coprostanone (5β-cholestan-3-one), cholestanone (5α-cholestan-3-one), and epicoprostanol (5β-cholestan-3α-ol).

Lecithin

Lecithin is amphipathic and in bile forms mixed micelles with bile acids and cholesterol (28, 115). Lecithin in the small intestine is hydrolyzed by phosphatidases from pancreatic juice. The actions of phosphatidases on lecithin have been reviewed in detail by Kates (85) and are briefly summarized here; classification is according to Kates (85).

Lysolecithin is formed by removal of one fatty acid residue from lecithin. The reaction is performed by phosphatidase A and appears to involve specific hydrolysis of the ester linkage in the beta position (155). Lysolecithin is hydrolyzed to fatty acid and L-α-glycerylphosphorylcholine by lysophosphatidase, an enzyme that has been isolated from pancreas, *Serratia plymuthicum*, and some molds (64, 145). L-α-Glycerylphosphorylcholine may also be formed directly from lecithin by the action of phosphatidase B, which removes both fatty acid residues. Further metabolism of L-α-glycerylphosphorylcholine presumably occurs in the large intestine, where the initial reaction might well be formation of L-α-glycerophosphate and choline by phosphodiesterases of bacteria.

Mucin

Although the concentration of mucin in vesicular bile is 1–4% by weight and mucin is secreted in large amounts by the epithelia of the gastrointestinal tract, little is known of its fate. Mucins from different sources have similar structures and have high molecular weights. All have a protein core to which oligosaccharides composed of sialic acid or L-fucose and hexoseamines (or both) are attached. The protein core contains large amounts of serine, threonine, glycine, alanine, and proline and only small amounts of aromatic or sulfur-containing amino acids (130).

Treatment of solutions of mucins with the proteolytic enzymes of digestion such as pepsin, trypsin, and chymotrypsin causes a rapid decrease in viscosity but is accompanied by only a small increase in the titer of free amino groups. Treatment of mucins with proteases from *Streptomyces griseus* and from *B. subtilis*, however, results in a large increase in the titer of free amino groups. Large amounts of dialyzable components are produced during proteolysis with the enzyme from *S. griseus* (61). Thus mucin in bile is little affected by the proteolytic enzymes of the small intestine but may be quite extensively degraded by bacteria in the large intestine.

Alkaline Phosphatase, Protoporphyrin, Coproporphyrin, and Chlorophyll Degradation Products

Many other substances, either endogenous or exogenous in origin, are excreted in the bile. Examples of endogenous substances are alkaline phosphatase, protoporphyrin, and coproporphyrin. Little is known of the fate of alkaline phosphatase excreted into the gut. Protoporphyrin and coproporphyrin are excreted in small quantities in the bile of normal individuals and in greater quantities in subjects with certain forms of porphyria. There is evidence of an enterohepatic circulation of protoporphyrin, especially in patients with erythropoietic protoporphyria. Of exogenous substances, the chlorophyll degradation product phylloerytherin is reabsorbed from the gut and reexcreted in the bile in ruminants; some chlorophyll degradation products may be reabsorbed from the gut and reexcreted in the bile of some human subjects (C. H. Gray, unpublished observation).

CONCLUSIONS

This chapter has considered the chemical and physiological changes undergone by the bile pigments and bile acids in considerable detail and the other constituents of the bile in less detail. In each case the secretion of these constituents, their chemistry, the changes they undergo in the gut, and the extent of their absorption and of their degradation products have been discussed.

With the exception of lecithin, substances in bile are unaffected by the enzymes of digestion but are extensively attacked by the enzymes of microorganisms present in the intestine. Absorption in the near-sterile small intestine, however, reduces the amount of material entering the large intestine and is therefore an important factor in determining the fate of each constituent of bile. Material that is absorbed may take part in an enterohepatic circulation or be excreted in urine. Only qualitative investigation of these aspects has been possible with the bile pigments because of the instability of conjugated bilirubin and of many of the intermediate and final reduction and degradation products.

Schmid regards the permeability of the gut to tetrapyrroles to be dependent on polarity rather than molecular size. The relative behavior of bilirubin and its glucuronide indicates that molecules of low polarity are most readily absorbed by the intestine. Extrapolating this and emphasizing the high polarity of the free compounds, Schmid (97) concludes that absorption of urobilinogen glucuronides is improbable.

Conjugated bile pigments are not absorbed, and their hydrolysis normally is significant only in the large intestine, but here absorption of these pigments and of the reduction products is less rapid. It therefore seems probable that the enterohepatic circulation of bile pigments is of smaller quantitative significance than that of the bile acids, the quantitative assessment of the degradation, absorption, and reexcretion of which has been possible because of their stability and the ease with which they may be labeled with isotopes. The bile acids, unlike the bile pigments which are essentially waste products to be excreted, play an important role in digestion; their conservation by an enterohepatic circulation is important to the economy of the body.

There is need for further work on the degradation of the bile pigments in the gut, especially to determine the site at which the chemical changes occur and also to assess the significance of the discrepancy between pigment excretion in the bile and measurable bile pigment conversion products in the feces.

REFERENCES

1. ALI, S. S., A. KUKSIS, AND J. M. R. BEVERIDGE. Excretion of bile acids by three men on a fat-free diet. *Can. J. Biochem. Physiol.* 44: 957–970, 1966.
2. BAKER, R. D., AND G. W. SEARLE. Bile salt absorption at various levels of rat small intestine. *Proc. Soc. Exptl. Biol. Med.* 105: 521–523, 1960.
3. BAUMGÄRTEL, T. *Physiologie und Pathologie des Bilirubinstoffwechsels als Grundlagen der Ikterusforschung.* Stuttgart: Thieme, 1950, p. 65–144.
4. BERGSTRÖM, S. Bile acids: formation and metabolism. In: *Ciba Found. Symp., Biosyn. Terpenes Sterols.* London: Churchill, 1959, p. 202.
5. BERGSTRÖM, S., AND H. DANIELSSON. On the regulation of bile acid formation in the rat liver. *Acta Physiol. Scand.* 43: 1–7, 1958.
6. BERGSTRÖM, S., H. DANIELSSON, AND A. GÖRANSSON. On the bile acid metabolism in the pig. Bile acids and steroids 81. *Acta Chem. Scand.* 13: 776–783, 1959.
7. BERGSTRÖM, S., H. DANIELSSON, AND T. KAZUNO. Bile acids and steroids 98. The metabolism of bile acids in python and constrictor snakes. *J. Biol. Chem.* 235: 983–988, 1960.
8. BERGSTRÖM, S., S. LINDSTEDT, AND B. SAMUELSSON. Bile acids and steroids. 82. On the mechanism of deoxycholic acid formation in the rabbit. *J. Biol. Chem.* 234: 2022–2025, 1959.
9. BERGSTRÖM, S., M. ROTTENBERG, AND J. SJÖVALL. Über den Stoffwechsel der Cholsäure und desoxycholsäure in der Ratte. x. Mitteilung über Steroide und Gallensäuren. *Z. Physiol. Chem.* 295: 278–285, 1953.
10. BERGSTRÖM, S., AND J. SJÖVALL. Occurrence and metab-

olism of chenodesoxycholic acid in the rat. Bile acids and steroids 13. *Acta Chem. Scand.* 8: 611–616, 1954.

11. BILLING, B. H. Bile pigments in jaundice. *Advan. Clin. Chem.* 2: 267–299, 1959.

12. BILLING, B. H. Bilirubin metabolism. *Postgrad. Med. J.* 39: 176–187, 1963.

13. BILLING, B. H., P. G. COLE, AND G. H. LATHE. The excretion of bilirubin as a diglucuronide giving the direct van den Bergh reaction. *Biochem. J.* 65: 774–784, 1957.

14. BLOCH, K., B. N. BERG, AND D. RITTENBERG. The biological conversion of cholesterol to cholic acid. *J. Biol. Chem.* 149: 511–517, 1943.

15. BORGSTRÖM, B. Studies on intestinal cholesterol absorption in the human. *J. Clin. Invest.* 39: 809–815, 1960.

16. BORGSTRÖM, B., G. LUNDH, AND A. HOFMANN. The site of absorption of conjugated bile salts in man. *Gastroenterology* 45: 229–238, 1963.

17. CAREY, J. B., AND G. WILLIAMS. Pathways of secondary bile acid formation as excretion of metabolites of cholesterol: conversion of primary to secondary bile acids in man. *J. Lab. Clin. Med.* 60: 865, 1962.

18. CAREY, J. B., AND G. WILLIAMS. Metabolism of lithocholic acid in bile fistula patients. *J. Clin. Invest.* 42: 450–455, 1963.

19. COLEMAN, D. L., AND C. A. BAUMAN. Intestinal sterols. III. Effects of age, sex and diet. *Arch. Biochem. Biophys.* 66: 226–233, 1957.

20. CRIGLER, J. R., AND V. A. NAJJAR. Congenital familial non-hemolytic jaundice with kernicterus. *Pediatrics* 10: 169–179, 1952.

21. DANIELSSON, H. Present status of research on catabolism and excretion of cholesterol. *Lipid Res.* 1: 335–385, 1963.

22. DANIELSSON, H., P. ENEROTH, K. HELLSTRÖM, S. LINDSTEDT, AND J. SJÖVALL. On the turnover and excretory products of cholic and chenodeoxycholic acid in man. Bile acids and steroids 134. *J. Biol. Chem.* 238: 2299–2304, 1963.

23. DANIELSSON, H., P. ENEROTH, K. HELLSTRÖM, AND J. SJÖVALL. Synthesis of some 3β-hydroxylated bile acids and the isolation of 3β,12α-dihydroxy-5β-cholanic acid from faeces. Bile acids and steroids 123. *J. Biol. Chem.* 237: 3657–3659, 1962.

24. DANIELSSON, H., AND B. GUSTAFSSON. On serum-cholesterol levels and neutral fecal sterols in germ-free rats. Bile acids and steroids 59. *Arch. Biochem. Biophys.* 83: 482–485, 1959.

25. DANIELSSON, H., A. KALLNER, AND J. SJÖVALL. On the composition of the bile acid fraction of rabbit faeces and the isolation of a new bile acid: 3α,12α-dihydroxy-5α-cholanic acid. Bile acids and steroids 136. *J. Biol. Chem.* 238: 3846–3852, 1963.

26. DANIELSSON, H., AND T. KAZUNO. On the metabolism of bile acids in the guinea pig. Bile acids and steroids 86. *Acta Chem. Scand.* 13: 1137–1140, 1959.

27. DANIELSSON, H., AND T. KAZUNO. On the metabolism of bile acids in the mouse. Bile acids and steroids 87. *Acta Chem. Scand.* 13: 1141–1144, 1959.

28. DESAI, J. G., J. GLOVER, AND C. N. JOO. The form of dispersion of sterols in bile and plasma. In: *The Biliary System*, edited by W. Taylor. Oxford: Blackwell, 1965, p. 145–164.

29. DIETSCHY, J. M., H. S. SALOMON, AND M. D. SIPERSTEIN.

Bile acid metabolism. I. Studies on the mechanisms of intestinal transport. *J. Clin. Invest.* 45: 832–846, 1966.

30. DRASER, B. S., M. J. HILL, AND M. SHINER. The deconjugation of bile salts by human intestinal bacteria. *Lancet* 1: 1237–1238, 1966.

31. DUESBERG, R. Physiologie und Klinik des Urobilinstoffwechsels. In: *Viertes Freiburger Symposium über Pathologie Diagnostik und Therapie der Leberkrankheiten*. Berlin: Springer, 1956, p. 171–179.

32. EKDAHL, P. M., AND J. SJÖVALL. Metabolism of desoxycholic acid in the rabbit. Bile acids and steroids 28. *Acta Physiol. Scand.* 34: 287–294, 1955.

33. EKDAHL, P. M., AND J. SJÖVALL. On the conjugation and formation of bile acids in the human liver. I. On the excretion of bile acids by patients with postoperative choledochostomy drainage. Bile acids and steroids 61. *Acta Chir. Scand.* 114: 439–452, 1957.

34. EPPINGER, H., AND E. RANZI. *Die Hepatolienalen Erkrankimigen*. Berlin: Springer, 1920.

35. ERIKSSON, S. Biliary excretion of bile acids and cholesterol in bile fistula rats. Bile acids and steroids. *Proc. Soc. Exptl. Biol. Med.* 94: 578–582, 1957.

36. ERIKSSON, S. Bile acid pool in the rat. Bile acids and steroids 78. *Acta Physiol. Scand.* 48: 439–442, 1960.

37. FISCHER, H., AND H. ORTH. *Die Chemie des Pyrrols*. Leipzig: Akad. Verlagsges., 1937.

38. FRÖHLICHER, E. Die resorption von gallensäuren aus verschiedenen dünndarmabschnitten. *Biochem. Z.* 283: 273–279, 1936.

39. GILBERTSEN, A. S., I. BOSSENMAIER, AND R. CARDINAL. Enterohepatic circulation of unconjugated bilirubin in man. *Nature* 196: 141–142, 1962.

40. GILBERTSEN, A. S., P. T. LOWRY, V. HAWKINSON, AND C. J. WATSON. Studies of the dipyrrylmethene ("fuscin") pigments. I. The anabolic significance of the fecal mesobilifuscin. *J. Clin. Invest.* 38: 1166–1174, 1959.

41. GILBERTSEN, A. S., AND C. J. WATSON. Studies of the dipyrrylmethene ("fuscin") pigments. III. The variable fate of bilirubin depending upon conjugation and other factors. *J. Clin. Invest.* 41: 1041–1049, 1962.

42. GLASSER, J. E., I. M. WEINER, AND L. LACK. Comparative physiology of intestinal taurocholate transport. *Am. J. Physiol.* 208: 359–362, 1965.

43. GORDON, H., B. LEWIS, L. EALES, AND J. F. BROCH. Effect of different dietary fats on the faecal end-products of cholesterol metabolism. *Nature* 180: 923–924, 1957.

44. GÖRGES, T., AND H. GOHR. Untersuchungen über das Vorkommen von Dihydromesobilirubin in den Faeces beim Menschen. *Deut. Z. Verdauungs. Stoffwechselkrankh.* 14: 187–190, 1954.

45. GRAY, C. H. *The Bile Pigments*. London: Methuen, 1960.

46. GRAY, C. H. Haemoglobin breakdown and bile pigment formation. In: *Bile Pigments in Health and Disease*. Springfield, Ill.: Thomas, 1961.

47. GRAY, C. H. Bile pigments. In: *Comprehensive Biochemistry*, edited by M. Florkin and E. H. Stotz. Amsterdam: Elsevier, 1963, vol. 9, p. 98–111.

48. GRAY, C. H., A. KULCZYCKA, AND D. C. NICHOLSON. The chemistry of the bile pigments. III. Prototropy of bilirubin to a verdinoid pigment. *J. Chem. Soc.* 2268–2275, 1961.

49. GRAY, C. H., A. NEUBERGER, AND P. H. A. SNEATH.

Studies in congenital porphyria. 2. Incorporation of ¹⁵N in the stercobilin in the normal and in the porphyric. *Biochem. J.* 47: 87–92, 1950.

50. GRAY, C. H., AND D. C. NICHOLSON. The chemistry of the urobilins. Structures of stercobilins and d-urobilin. *J. Chem. Soc.* 627: 3085–3099, 1958.

51. GRAY, C. H., D. C. NICHOLSON, AND R. A. NICOLAUS. The IXα structure of the common bile pigments. *Nature* 181: 183–185, 1958.

52. GRAY, C. H., AND J. J. SCOTT. The effect of haemorrhage on the incorporation of [α-¹⁴C] glycine into stercobilin. *Biochem. J.* 71: 38–42, 1959.

53. GREGORY, C. H. Studies of conjugated bilirubin. III. Pigment I, complex of conjugated and free bilirubin. *J. Lab. Clin. Med.* 61: 917–925, 1963.

54. GREGORY, C. H., AND C. J. WATSON. Studies of conjugated bilirubin. II. Problems of sulfates of bilirubin *in vivo* and *in vitro*. *J. Lab. Clin. Med.* 60: 17–30, 1962.

55. GRODSKY, G. M., AND J. V. CARBONE. The synthesis of bilirubin glucuronide by tissue homogenates. *J. Biol. Chem.* 226: 449–458, 1957.

56. GUNN, C. H. Hereditary acholuric jaundice in a new mutant strain of rats. *J. Heredity* 29: 137–139, 1938.

57. GUSTAFSSON, B. E., S. BERGSTRÖM, S. LINDSTEDT, AND A. NORMAN. Turnover and nature of fecal bile acids in germ-free and infected rats fed cholic acid-24-¹⁴C. Bile acids and steroids 41. *Proc. Soc. Exptl. Biol. Med.* 94: 467–471, 1957.

58. GUSTAFSSON, B. E., AND L. S. LANKE. Bilirubin and urobilins in germ-free, ex-germfree and conventional rats. *J. Exptl. Med.* 112: 975–982, 1960.

59. GUSTAFSSON, B. E., AND A. NORMAN. Comparison of bile acids in intestinal contents of germ-free and conventional rats. *Proc. Soc. Exptl. Biol. Med.* 110: 387–389, 1962.

60. GUSTAFSSON, B. E., A. NORMAN, AND J. SJÖVALL. Influence of *E. coli* infection on turnover and metabolism of cholic acid in germ-free rats. *Arch. Biochem. Biophys.* 91: 93–100, 1960.

61. HASHIMOTO, Y., S. TSUIKI, K. NISIZAWA, AND W. PIGMAN. Action of proteolytic enzymes on purified bovine submaxillary mucin. *Ann. N.Y. Acad. Sci.* 106: 233–246, 1963.

62. HASLEWOOD, G. A. D. Comparative studies of bile salts. 9. The isolation and chemistry of hyocholic acid. *Biochem. J.* 62: 637–645, 1956.

63. HASLEWOOD, G. A. D. The biological significance of chemical differences in bile salts. *Biol. Rev.* 39: 537–574, 1964.

64. HAYAISHI, O., AND A. KORNBERG. Metabolism of phospholipids by bacterial enzymes. *J. Biol. Chem.* 206: 647–663, 1954.

65. HAYAKAWA, S., T. FUJII, Y. SABURI, AND T. EGUCHI. Microbiological degradation of cholic acid. *Nature* 179: 537–538, 1957.

66. HAYAKAWA, S., AND S. MORIMOTO. Collected papers of Hiroshima Medical School, vol. 2, p. 9, quoted by S. Bergström, H. Danielsson, and B. Samuelsson in *Lipide Metabolism*, edited by K. Bloch. New York: Wiley, 1960, p. 304.

67. HAYAKAWA, S., Y. SABURI, K. TAMAKI, AND H. HOSHIJIMA. An alternative pathway for the degradation of cholic acid by microorganisms. *Nature* 181: 906, 1958.

68. HAYAKAWA, S., AND B. SAMUELSSON. Transformation of cholic acid *in vitro* by *Corynebacterium simplex*. Bile acids and steroids 132. *J. Biol. Chem.* 239: 94–97, 1964.

69. HELLMAN, L., E. L. FRANZELL, AND R. S. ROSENFELD. Direct measurement of cholesterol absorption via the thoracic duct in man. *J. Clin. Invest.* 39: 1288–1294, 1960.

70. HELLMAN, L., R. S. ROSENFELD, W. INSULL, JR., AND E. H. AHREN, JR. Intestinal excretion of cholesterol: a mechanism for regulation of plasma levels. *J. Clin. Invest.* 36: 898, 1957.

71. HELLSTRÖM, K., AND J. SJÖVALL. Metabolism of chenodeoxycholic acid in the rabbit. Bile acids and steroids 104. *Acta Chem. Scand.* 14: 1763–1769, 1960.

72. HELLSTRÖM, K., AND J. SJÖVALL. On the origin of lithocholic and ursodeoxycholic acids in man. *Acta Physiol. Scand.* 51: 218–223, 1961.

73. HELLSTRÖM, K., AND J. SJÖVALL. Turnover of deoxycholic acid in the rabbit. *J. Lipid Res.* 3: 397–404, 1962.

74. HOFMANN, A. F., AND B. BORGSTRÖM. Physicochemical state of lipids in intestinal content during their digestion and absorption. *Federation Proc.* 21: 43–50, 1962.

75. HOLT, P. R. Intestinal absorption of bile salts in the rat. *Am. J. Physiol.* 207: 1–7, 1964.

76. HSIA, S. L., W. H. ELLIOTT, J. T. MATSCHINER, E. A. DOISY, JR., S. A. THAYER, AND E. A. DOISY. Bile acids XIII. Further contribution to the constitution of muricholic acids. *J. Biol. Chem.* 235: 1963–1967, 1960.

77. HSIA, S. L., W. H. ELLIOTT, J. T. MATSCHINER, T. A. MAHOWALD, E. A. DOISY, JR., S. A. THAYER, AND E. A. DOISY. Bile acids XI. Structures of the isomeric 3α-6,7-trihydroxycholanic acids. *J. Biol. Chem.* 233: 1337–1339, 1958.

78. HSIA, S. L., J. T. MATSCHINER, T. A. MAHOWALD, W. H. ELLIOTT, E. A. DOISY, JR., S. A. THAYER, AND E. A. DOISY. Bile acids VI. The structure and synthesis of acid II. *J. Biol. Chem.* 226: 667–671, 1957.

79. IBBOTT, F. A., AND D. O'BRIEN. A re-appraisal of extraction methods for bilirubin assay and of the role of bilirubin monoglucuronide in neonatal hyperbilirubinemia. *Pediatrics* 34: 418–419, 1964.

80. ISRAELS, L. G., J. SKANDERBEG, H. GUYDA, W. ZINGG, AND A. ZIPURSKY. A study of the early-labeled fraction of bile pigment: the effect of altering erythropoiesis on the incorporation of 2-¹⁴C glycine into haem and bilirubin. *Brit. J. Haematol.* 9: 50–62, 1963.

81. ISRAELS, L. G., T. YAMAMOTO, J. SKANDERBEG, AND A. ZIPURSKY. Shunt bilirubin: Evidence for two components. *Science* 139: 1054–1055, 1963.

82. ISSELBACHER, K. J., AND E. A. McCARTHY. Studies on bilirubin sulphate and other nonglucuronide conjugates of bilirubin. *J. Clin. Invest.* 38: 645–651, 1959.

83. KAHAN, I. L. Studies on urobilinoids. *Stud. Med. Szegedinensia* 1: 5–74, 1961.

84. KAHAN, I. L., L. CSERNAY, AND V. VARRO. Some experimental data on the intestinal absorption of urobilinoids. *Clin. Chim. Acta* 7: 392–397, 1962.

85. KATES, M. Lipolytic enzymes. In: *Lipide Metabolism*, edited by K. Bloch. New York: Wiley, 1960, p. 165–237.

86. LACK, L., AND I. M. WEINER. *In vitro* absorption of bile salts by small intestine of rats and guinea pigs. *Am. J. Physiol.* 200: 313–317, 1961.

87. LACK, L., AND I. M. WEINER. Intestinal absorption of bile

salts and some biological implications. *Federation Proc.* 22: 1334–1338, 1963.

88. LEMBERG, R. Chemical mechanism of bile pigment formation. *Rev. Pure Appl. Chem.* 6: 1–23, 1956.

89. LEMBERG, R., AND J. W. LEGGE. *Haematin Compounds and the Bile Pigments.* New York: Interscience, 1949.

90. LESTER, R., L. HAMMAKER, AND R. SCHMID. A new therapeutic approach to unconjugated hyperbilirubinaemia. *Lancet* 2: 1257, 1962.

91. LESTER, R., J. D. OSTROW, AND R. SCHMID. Enterohepatic circulation of bilirubin. *Nature* 192: 372, 1961.

92. LESTER, R., AND R. SCHMID. Mechanism of intestinal absorption of bilirubin. *J. Clin. Invest.* 41: 1379, 1962.

93. LESTER, R., AND R. SCHMID. Intestinal absorption of bile pigments. I. The enterohepatic circulation of bilirubin in the rat. *J. Clin. Invest.* 42: 736–746, 1963.

94. LESTER, R., AND R. SCHMID. Intestinal absorption of bile pigments. II. Bilirubin absorption in man. *New Engl. J. Med.* 269: 178–182, 1963.

95. LESTER, R., AND R. SCHMID. Bilirubin metabolism. *New Engl. J. Med.* 270: 779–786, 1964.

96. LESTER, R., AND R. SCHMID. Intestinal absorption of bile pigments. III. The enterohepatic circulation of urobilinogen in the rat. *J. Clin. Invest.* 44: 722–730, 1965.

97. LESTER, R., W. SCHUMER, AND R. SCHMID. Intestinal absorption of bile pigments. IV. Urobilinogen absorption in man. *New Engl. J. Med.* 272: 939–943, 1965.

98. LINDSTEDT, S. The turnover of cholic acid in man. Bile acids and steroids 51. *Acta Physiol. Scand.* 40: 1–9, 1957.

99. LINDSTEDT, S., J. AVIGAN, D. S. GOODMAN, J. SJÖVALL, AND D. STEINBERG. The effect of dietary fat on the turnover of cholic acid and on the composition of the biliary acids in man. *J. Clin. Invest.* 44: 1754–1765, 1965.

100. LINDSTEDT, S., AND A. NORMAN. The turnover of bile acids in the rat. Bile acids and steroids 39. *Acta Physiol. Scand.* 38: 121–128, 1956.

101. LINDSTEDT, S., AND A. NORMAN. The excretion of bile acids in rats treated with chemotherapeutics. Bile acids and steroids 40. *Acta Physiol. Scand.* 38: 129–134, 1956.

102. LINDSTEDT, S., AND B. SAMUELSSON. Bile acids and steroids LXXXIII. On the interconversion of cholic and deoxycholic acid in the rat. *J. Biol. Chem.* 234: 2026–2030, 1959.

103. LINDSTEDT, S., AND J. SJÖVALL. On the formation of deoxycholic acid from cholic acid in the rabbit. Bile acids and steroids 48. *Acta Chem. Scand.* 11: 421–426, 1957.

104. LONDON, I. M. The conversion of haematin to bile pigment. *J. Biol. Chem.* 184: 373–376, 1960.

105. LOWRY, P. T., AND C. J. WATSON. The isolation of crystalline d-urobilinogen. *J. Biol. Chem.* 218: 633–639, 1956.

106. LOWRY, P. T., N. R. ZIEGLER, R. CARDINAL, AND C. J. WATSON. Conversion of ^{15}N mesobilirubinogen to stercobilinogen by fecal bacteria. *J. Biol. Chem.* 208: 543–548, 1954.

107. LOZZIO, B., E. RODRIGUEZ-GARAY, AND M. ROYER. Metabolism of mesobiliviolinoids (MBV) in the rat. I. Their transformation into bilirubin. *Gastroenterologia* 101: 150–162, 1964.

108. MAHOWALD, T. A., J. F. MATSCHINER, S. L. HSIA, R. RICHTER, E. A. DOISY, JR., W. H. ELLIOTT, AND E. A. DOISY. Bile acids II. Metabolism of deoxycholic acid-24-

C^{14} and chenodeoxycholic acid-24-C^{14} in the rat. *J. Biol. Chem.* 225: 783–793, 1957.

109. MATSCHINER, J. F., T. A. MAHOWALD, W. H. ELLIOTT, E. A. DOISY, JR., S. L. HSIA, AND E. A. DOISY. Bile acids I. Two new acids from rat bile. *J. Biol. Chem.* 225: 771–779, 1957.

110. MORI, T. Bildung der 7-oxy-3.12-diketocholan säure aus dehydrocholsäure durch Protens bazillen. *J. Biochem., Tokyo* 29: 87–90, 1939.

111. MÜLLER, F. VON. Untersuchungen über Ikterus. *Z. Klin. Med.* 12: 45–113, 1887.

112. NAIR, P. P., M. GORDON, S. GORDON, J. REBACK, AND A. I. MENDELOFF. The cleavage of bile acid conjugates by cell-free extracts from *Clostridium perfringens. Life Sci.* 4: 1887–1892, 1965.

113. NAKAJIMA, H. Studies on heme α-methenyl oxygenase. II. Isolation and characterization of final reaction product, possible precursor of bilirubin. *J. Biol. Chem.* 238: 3797–3801, 1963.

114. NAKAJIMA, H., T. TAKEMURA, O. NAKAJIMA, AND K. YAMAOKA. Studies on heme α-methenyl oxygenase. I. Enzymatic conversion of pyridine hemichromogen and hemoglobin-haptoglobin into possible precursor of biliverdin. *J. Biol. Chem.* 238: 3784–3796, 1963.

115. NORMAN, A. Physico-chemical properties of bile constituents. In: *The Biliary System,* edited by W. Taylor. Oxford: Blackwell, 1965, p. 165–174.

116. NORMAN, A., AND S. BERGMAN. The action of intestinal microorganisms on bile acids. Bile acids and steroids 101. *Acta Chem. Scand.* 14: 1781–1789, 1960.

117. NORMAN, A., AND R. GRUBB. Hydrolysis of conjugated bile acids by Clostridia and Enterococci. *Acta Pathol. Microbiol. Scand.* 36: 537–547, 1955.

118. NORMAN, A., AND R. H. PALMER. Metabolites of lithocholic acid-24-^{14}C in human bile and faeces. *J. Lab. Clin. Med.* 63: 986–1001, 1964.

119. NORMAN, A., AND M. SHORB. *In vitro* formation of deoxycholic and lithocholic acids by human intestinal microorganisms. *Proc. Soc. Exptl. Biol. Med.* 110: 552–555, 1962.

120. NORMAN, A., AND J. SJÖVALL. On the transformation and enterohepatic circulation of cholic acid in the rat. *J. Biol. Chem.* 233: 872–885, 1958.

121. NORMAN, A., AND J. SJÖVALL. Formation of lithocholic acid from chenodeoxycholic acid in the rat. Bile acids and steroids 103. *Acta Chem. Scand.* 14: 1815–1818, 1960.

122. NORMAN, A., AND O. A. WIDSTRÖM. Hydrolysis of conjugated bile acids by extracellular enzymes present in rat intestinal contents. *Proc. Soc. Exptl. Biol. Med.* 117: 442–444, 1964.

123. NORO, T. *Igaku Kenkyu* 21: 862, 1951. Quoted in ref. 163.

124. NOSSLIN, B. Direct diazo reaction of bile pigments in serum: experimental and clinical studies. *Scand. J. Clin. Lab. Invest.* 12, Suppl. 49: 1–176, 1960.

125. OLIVECRONA, T., AND J. SJÖVALL. Bile acids in rat portal blood. Bile acids and steroids 77. *Acta Physiol. Scand.* 46: 284–290, 1959.

126. OSTROW, J. D., L. HAMMAKER, AND R. SCHMID. The preparation of crystalline ^{14}C bilirubin. *J. Clin. Invest.* 40: 1442–1452, 1961.

127. OSTROW, J. D., J. H. JANDL, AND R. SCHMID. The formation of bilirubin from hemoglobin *in vivo. J. Clin. Invest.* 41: 1628–1637, 1962.

128. Pearson, L. B., and C. J. Watson. A study of the reported occurrence of mesobilirubin in human bile. *Proc. Soc. Exptl. Biol. Med.* 112: 756–758, 1963.

129. Peric-Golia, L., and R. S. Jones. Cholic acid in guinea pig bile. *Proc. Soc. Exptl. Biol. Med.* 105: 337–339, 1960.

130. Pigman, W. Mucous secretions. Concluding remarks. *Ann. N.Y. Acad. Sci.* 106: 808–809, 1963.

131. Playoust, M. R., and K. J. Isselbacher. Studies on the transport and metabolism of conjugated bile salts by intestinal mucosa. *J. Clin. Invest.* 43: 467–476, 1964.

132. Playoust, M. R., L. Lack, and I. M. Weiner. Effect of intestinal resection on bile salt absorption in dogs. *Am. J. Physiol.* 208: 363–369, 1965.

133. Portman, O. W., and G. V. Mann. The disposition of ^{35}S-taurine and ^{35}S-taurocholate in the rat. Dietary influences. *J. Biol. Chem.* 213: 733–743, 1955.

134. Portman, O. W., and P. Murphy. Excretion of bile acids and β-hydroxysterols in rats. *Arch. Biochem. Biophys.* 76: 367–376, 1958.

135. Portman, O. W., S. Shah, A. Antonis, and B. Jorgensen. Alteration of bile salts by bacteria. *Proc. Soc. Exptl. Biol. Med.* 109: 959–965, 1962.

136. Portman, O. W., and F. J. Stare. Dietary regulation of serum cholesterol levels. *Physiol. Rev.* 39: 407–442, 1959.

137. Ratliff, R. L., J. T. Matschiner, E. A. Doisy, Jr., S. L. Hsia, S. A. Thayer, W. H. Elliott, and E. A. Doisy. Bile acids. xii. A new metabolite of deoxycholic acid. *J. Biol. Chem.* 234: 3133–3136, 1959.

138. Robinson, S. H., C. A. Owen, Jr., E. V. Flock, and R. Schmid. Bilirubin formation in the liver from non-haemoglobin sources. *Blood* 26: 823–829, 1965.

139. Rosenfeld, R. S., D. K. Fukushima, L. Hellman, and T. F. Gallagher. The transformation of cholesterol to coprostanol. *J. Biol. Chem.* 211: 301–311, 1954.

140. Samuelsson, B. On the metabolism of chenodeoxycholic acid in the rat. Bile acids and steroids 85. *Acta Chem. Scand.* 13: 976–983, 1959.

141. Samuelsson, B. Bile acids and steroids 96. On the mechanism of the biological formation of deoxycholic acid from cholic acid. *J. Biol. Chem.* 235: 361–366, 1960.

142. Schmid, R. Identification of direct-reacting bilirubin as bilirubin glucuronide. *J. Biol. Chem.* 229: 881–888, 1957.

143. Schmidt, L. H., H. B. Hughes, M. H. Green, and E. Cooper. Studies on bile acid metabolism. ii. The action of *Alcaligenes faecalis* on cholic acid. *J. Biol. Chem.* 145: 229–236, 1942.

144. Schoenheimer, R., D. Rittenberg, and M. Graff. Deuterium as an indicator in the study of intermediary metabolism. iv. The mechanism of coprosterol formation. *J. Biol. Chem.* 111: 183–192, 1935.

145. Shapiro, B. Purification and properties of a lysolecithinase from pancreas. *Biochem. J.* 53: 663–666, 1953.

146. Siedel, W. Über die Konstitution des d-Urobilins und des Stercobilins. In: *Viertes Freiburger Symposium über Pathologie Diagnostik und Therapy der Leberkrankheiten.* Berlin: Springer, 1956, p. 209–211.

147. Siedel, W., and H. Möller. Über Mesobilifuscin ein neues physiologisches Abbauprodukt des Häms bzw. Hämatins. *Z. Physiol. Chem.* 259: 113–136, 1939.

148. Siedel, W., W. von Pölnitz, and F. Eisenreich. Bilifuscin und Mesobilifuscin als natürliche Abbauprodukte des Blutfarbstoffes; über Vorkommen und Bildung. *Naturwissenschaften* 34: 314–315, 1947.

149. Siedel, W., W. Stich, and F. Eisenreich. Promesobilifuscin (Meso-bilileukan) ein neues physiologisches Abbauprodukt des Blutfarbstoffes. *Naturwissenschaften* 35: 316–317, 1948.

150. Sihn, T. S. Synthese der chenodesoxycholsäure aus Dehydrochenodesoxycholsäure durch Bacillus coli communis. *J. Biochem., Tokyo* 28: 165–168, 1938.

151. Singleton, J. W., and L. Laster. Biliverdin reductase of guinea pig liver. *J. Biol. Chem.* 240: 4780–4789, 1965.

152. Sjövall, J. Bile acids in man under normal and pathological conditions. Bile acids and steroids 73. *Clin. Chim. Acta* 5: 33–41, 1960.

153. Sjövall, J., and I. Åkeson. Intestinal absorption of taurocholic acid in the rat. Bile acids and steroids 26. *Acta Physiol. Scand.* 34: 273–278, 1955.

154. Stich, W. *Viertes Freiburger Symposium über Pathologie Diagnostik und Therapy der Leberkrankheiten.* Berlin: Springer, 1956, p. 184–188.

155. Tattrie, N. H. The positional distribution of saturated and unsaturated fatty acids on egg lecithin. *J. Lipid Res.* 1: 60–65, 1959.

156. Thomas, P. J., S. L. Hsia, J. T. Matschiner, E. A. Doisy, Jr., W. H. Elliott, S. A. Thayer, and E. A. Doisy. Bile acids. xix. Metabolism of lithocholic acid-24-^{14}C in the rat. *J. Biol. Chem.* 239: 102–105, 1964.

157. Thompson, J. C., and H. M. Vars. Biliary excretion of cholic acid and cholesterol in hyper-, hypo- and euthyroid rats. *Proc. Soc. Exptl. Biol. Med.* 83: 246–248, 1953.

158. Thompson, J. C., and H. M. Vars. Influence of thyroid activity on the hepatic excretion of cholic acid and cholesterol. *Am. J. Physiol.* 179: 405–409, 1954.

159. Turfitt, G. E. The microbiological degradation of steroids. 4. Fission of the steroid molecule. *Biochem. J.* 42: 376–383, 1948.

160. Watson, C. J. Isolation of mesobiliviolin from human feces. Its origin and nature. *Proc. Soc. Exptl. Biol. Med.* 30: 1207–1209, 1933.

161. Watson, C. J. Discussion. *Gastroenterology* 3: 296, 1944.

162. Watson, C. J. Pyrrole pigments and haemoglobin metabolism. *Minn. Med.* 39: 294–300, 403–412, 467–474, 1956.

163. Watson, C. J. Recent studies of the urobilin problem. *J. Clin. Pathol.* 16: 1–11, 1963.

164. Watson, C. J. The continuing challenge of hemoglobin and bile pigment metabolism. *Ann. Internal Med.* 63: 931–944, 1965.

165. Watson, C. J., M. Campbell, and P. T. Lowry. Preferential reduction of conjugated bilirubin to urobilinogen by normal fecal flora. *Proc. Soc. Exptl. Biol. Med.* 98: 707–711, 1958.

166. Watson, C. J., V. Sborov, and S. Schwartz. Formation of (laevorotatory) stercobilin from mesobilirubinogen in human feces. *Proc. Soc. Exptl. Biol. Med.* 49: 647–649, 1942.

167. Watson, C. J., and M. Weimer. Composition of the urobilin group in urine, bile and feces and the significance of variations in health and disease. *J. Lab. Clin. Med.* 54: 1–25, 1959.

168. Weber, A. P., and L. Schalm. Quantitative separation and determination of bilirubin and conjugated bilirubin in human serum. *Clin. Chim. Acta* 7: 805–810, 1962.

169. Weber, A. P., L. Schalm, and J. Witmans. Bilirubin monoglucuronide (pigment 1) complex. *Acta Med. Scand.* 173: 19–24, 1963.

170. WEINER, I. M., AND L. LACK. Absorption of bile salts from the small intestine *in vivo*. *Am. J. Physiol.* 202: 155–157, 1962.

171. WILSON, T. H., AND G. WISEMAN. The use of sacs of everted small intestine for the study of the transference of substances from the mucosal to the serosal surface. *J. Physiol., London* 123: 116–125, 1954.

172. WITH, T. K. Bilirubin and urobilinoid contents of human bile. *Acta Med. Scand.* 122: 513–528, 1945.

173. WITH, T. K. *Die Gallenfarbstoff der Galle in Biologie der Gallenfarbstoffe*. Stuttgart: Thieme, 1960, p. 264–276.

174. WITH, T. K. Die Gallenfarbstoffe—Chemie und Analytik. *Z. Klin. Chem.* 2: 1–6, 44–52, 80–86, 1964.

175. WITH, T. K. Stercobilin and colour of faeces: a perpetual textbook error. In: *Bilirubin Metabolism*, edited by I. A. Bouchier and B. Billing. Oxford: Blackwell, 1967.

176. YAMAMOTO, T., J. SKANDERBEG, A. ZIPURSKY, AND L. G. ISRAELS. The early appearing bilirubin: evidence for two components. *J. Clin. Invest.* 44: 31–41, 1965.

177. ZIBOH, V. A., S. L. HSIA, J. T. MATSCHINER, E. A. DOISY, JR., W. H. ELLIOTT, S. A. THAYER, AND E. A. DOISY. Bile acids. XVIII. Further studies on the metabolism of chenodeoxycholic acid-24-^{14}C in surgically jaundiced mice. *J. Biol. Chem.* 238: 3588–3590, 1963.

178. ZIBOH, V. A., J. T. MATSCHINER, E. A. DOISY, JR., S. L. HSIA, W. H. ELLIOTT, S. A. THAYER, AND E. A. DOISY. Bile acids. XIV. Metabolism of chenodeoxycholic acid-24-^{14}C in surgically jaundiced mice. *J. Biol. Chem.* 236: 387–390, 1961.

CHAPTER 117

Functions of bile in the alimentary canal[1]

ALAN F. HOFMANN | *Gastrointestinal Research Unit, Mayo Clinic and*
Mayo Foundation, Rochester, Minnesota

CHAPTER CONTENTS

---

[1] Preparation of this chapter was supported in part by Research Grant AM-6908, National Institutes of Health, Bethesda, Md.

BILE is a concentrated micellar solution composed chiefly of bile salts and lecithin (80, 86, 140, 144). It is these two groups of compounds that are responsible for the distinctive dispersing and solvent properties of bile for other lipids. Bile pigments and cholesterol are present in bile in lower concentrations (140, 144), but these compounds are probably excretory products and have no significant function in the assimilation of nutrients. When bile enters the small-intestinal lumen, the lecithin is hydrolyzed and absorbed. Thus the functions of bile in the alimentary canal appear to be mediated chiefly by the bile salts of bile.

Bile salts transport lipids. Cholesterol and more polar lipids such as bilirubin conjugates are transported from the interior of the hepatic cell to the environment—that is, the intestinal lumen—via the micelles in bile (96); water-insoluble nutrients are transported from the intestinal lumen to the interior of the intestinal mucosal cell via the micelles in intestinal content (74, 76, 78). Here we discuss the interactions of bile salts with materials normally present in the mammalian small- and large- intestinal lumen and within the mucosal cells of the alimentary tract. When such events appear beneficial to the organism, they may be defined as functions of bile salts or bile.

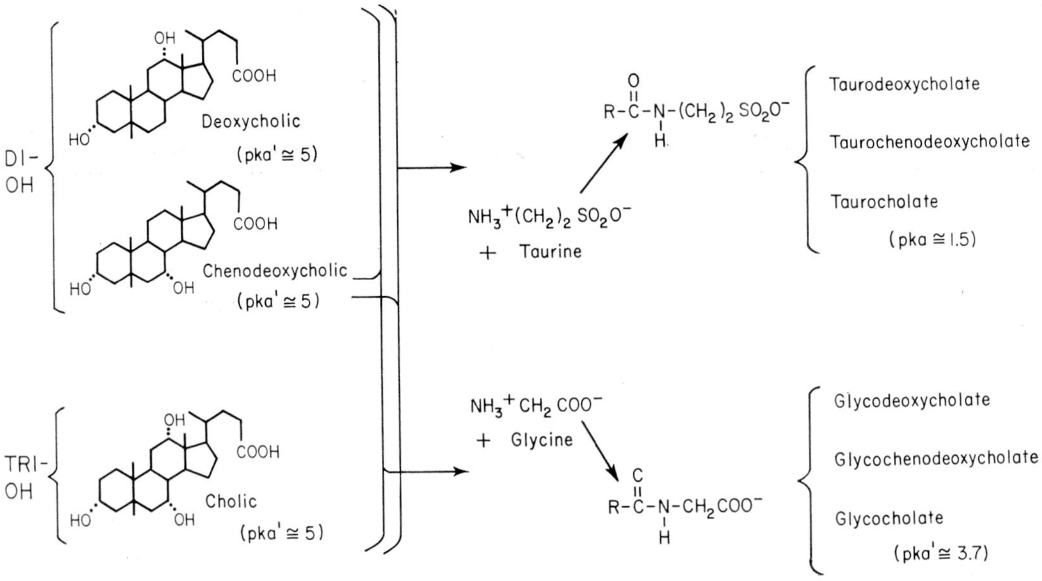

FIG. 1. Predominant bile salts of human bile. The two primary bile acids—cholic and chenodeoxy-cholic—and the secondary bile acid—deoxycholic—are conjugated with glycine or taurine in a pep-tide bond resistant to all digestive enzymes. Conjugation alters the solubility properties: taurine con-jugates are soluble at all pH values, glycine conjugates precipitate from solution below pH 4–5, and the unconjugated bile salts precipitate from solution below pH 7 (39, 71, 80). The pK_a values given are those of the bile salts below their critical micellar concentration. When the bile salts are in micel-lar form the pK_a values will be about 1 unit higher (39). The mean bile salt composition of bile in healthy man has been reported to be (moles %): glycocholate, 30%; glycochenodeoxycholate, 30%; glycodeoxycholate, 15%; taurocholate, 10%; taurochenodeoxycholate, 10%; taurodeoxycholate, 5% (138). [Modified from Hofmann (73).]

DIGESTION AND ABSORPTION:
GENERAL CONSIDERATIONS

Intestinal absorption is remarkably efficient, if efficiency is defined as intake minus output divided by intake (27). Such efficiency requires many rapid physicochemical transformations in the intestinal lumen: large aggregates are transformed or dispersed into smaller aggregates; polymers are transformed to monomers or dimers. A second requirement for efficiency is that the absorptive surface be large and clean. A third requirement, at least for substances absorbed by diffusion, is that the molecules that enter the mucosal cell be rapidly transferred to blood or lymph so that the concentration of nutrient in the mucosal cell does not progressively increase.

Another aspect of efficiency involves the recovery of endogenous metabolites that participate in di-gestion and absorption. Bile salts are efficiently re-absorbed from the ileum after their participation in digestion; the remarkable efficiency of absorption means that a pool of 3,000 mg may be maintained and circulated twice with each meal despite a daily synthesis of only 300 mg (12, 24, 74, 146) (see Weiner and Lack, Volume III of this *Handbook*). Water and

electrolytes enter the intestinal lumen during the digestive process and are reabsorbed at its completion. Other metabolites are digested during their residence in the intestinal lumen and are absorbed in the form of their products—pancreatic enzymes are cleaved to peptides and amino acids, biliary lecithin is trans-formed to lysolecithin and fatty acid, and so on. Bile salts appear to contribute to both of these aspects of efficiency in intestinal absorption; possible mecha-nisms are discussed.

CHEMISTRY OF BILE SALTS

Bile acids are C-24 carboxylic acids with a steroid nucleus containing hydroxyl groups (64, 65). They are formed in the liver from cholesterol by a number of enzymatic steps that result in the stereospecific saturation of the Δ^{5-6} double bond of cholesterol to give a 5β A/B *cis* steroid (24); the flat, weakly polar, water-insoluble cholesterol molecule is transformed into a kinked, polar molecule with high aqueous solubility (73). Bile acids are secreted from the liver as glycine or taurine conjugates (65). These bile acid conjugates, which are termed bile salts, have lower pK_a values than those of their precursors, the unconjugated bile acids, and accordingly are soluble in acidic conditions under which unconjugated bile acids are not (38, 39, 71, 80) (Fig. 1).

Bile is a mosaic of primary and secondary bile acids. Primary bile acids are formed from cholesterol; secondary bile acids result from bacterial alteration, usually in the large intestine, of the hydroxyl groups of primary bile acids (12, 24, 65). Secondary bile acids are absorbed from the intestinal lumen, reconjugated by the liver, and secreted in bile as the glycine or taurine conjugates. In some instances the secondary bile acids are still further modified (for example, by further hydroxylation) during their passage through the liver. The composition of bile thus reflects the combined effects of hepatic and bacterial biochemical transformations.

In man, as in most mammals, the primary bile acids dominate. Human bile is composed of about 40 % cholate and 40 % chenodeoxycholate; the remainder is largely the secondary bile acid deoxycholate, which is formed from cholate in the intestine (138). Although many mammalian species have exclusively glycine or taurine conjugates, man has both glycine and taurine conjugates. The glycine-to-taurine ratio is generally about 3, but will decrease to 1 if taurine supplements are fed (136). Conversely, the omission of sulfur from the diet of the rat, which normally has exclusively taurine conjugates, results in the formation of glycine conjugates (122).

The bile salt composition of jejunal content should be identical with that of bile since it appears that bile salts are not chemically altered in the lumen of the upper small intestine. Since individual bile salt conjugates do not differ significantly in their dispersing and solubilizing properties (71), changes in the bile salt composition of bile should not influence fat digestion and absorption. However, it has been claimed that only bile acids having a 7α-hydroxyl group (cholic and chenodeoxycholic acids) activate cholesterol esterase and protect it from chymotryptic digestion (see Treadwell & Vahouny, Volume III of this *Handbook*). A similar structural requirement has been observed for vitamin D absorption (129) (see below).

PHYSICAL CHEMISTRY OF BILE SALT SOLUTIONS

Typical Detergents and Properties of Their Aqueous Solutions

Bile salts have been used as soaps since antiquity. Their remarkable ability to dissolve fatty acids and the importance of this property for fat digestion and absorption were clearly described 67 years ago (111). The physical properties of bile salt solutions, reviewed elsewhere (80), determine their functions in digestion and absorption. These physical properties are intelligible only when compared with the behavior of ionic detergents at interfaces and in bulk. Ionic detergents are amphipathic molecules—that is, they possess appropriately arranged hydrophilic and hydrophobic regions that impart to such molecules a characteristic behavior in aqueous environments (4, 61, 62, 87, 121, 133).

CONCENTRATION EFFECTS. The molecular arrangement of amphipathic molecules in an aqueous environment is determined by their concentration (Fig. 2). At extremely low concentrations, detergents form molecular solutions. A fraction of the molecules concentrates at the air/water interface in a monomolecular layer; this lowers the interfacial tension. When the concentration in the bulk phase reaches a critical level, which is approximately the molecular solubility of the detergent, hydrated polymolecular aggregates, called micelles, form. The concentration at which molecular aggregation occurs is called the critical micellar concentration. The hydrophobic regions of the molecule, usually paraffin chains, are responsible for the low molecular solubility of most detergents; hydrophilic regions, usually one or more charged groups, prevent the formation of a true separate phase. The micelle, which is believed to be spherical in most instances, has an interior of liquid hydrocarbon chains. The micellar molecules are believed to be in rapid exchange with the molecularly dispersed detergent molecules around them. The critical micellar concentration is characteristic of a given soap, but is influenced by experimental parameters such as the concentration of ions of opposite charge (counter-ions) and other additives. Micelles of many anionic detergents have an anhydrous particle weight of 20,000–100,000—too small to disperse light—and therefore micellar solutions are clear on inspection.

At still higher concentrations of detergent, more ordered aggregates of detergent occur (4, 80, 95, 103, 139). The formation of such aggregates is generally signaled by a marked increase in viscosity and turbidity. The aggregates have the form of long cylinders, whose cross section is identical to that of the micelle—that is, they have a radius approximately equal to the length of the hydrocarbon chain. At still higher concentrations, bimolecular lamellae occur. All these changes in molecular arrangement with concentration are best described by binary phase diagrams. The

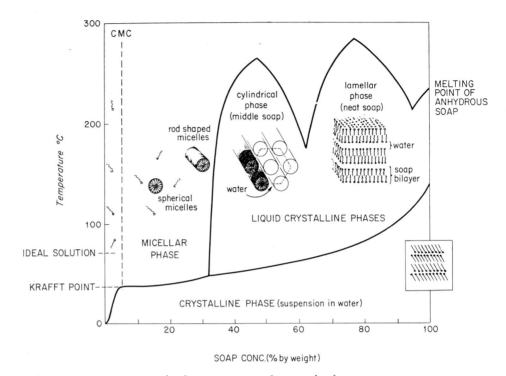

SOAP CONC.(% by weight)

FIG. 2. Influence of concentration and temperature on molecular arrangement of soap molecules in water. The soap-water phase diagram of McBain (108) has been modified to show the molecular arrangement of the ideal solution, the micellar phase, and the liquid crystalline phases, which are of two types, middle soap (cylindrical) and neat soap (lamellar). The temperature at which the transition from crystals to micelles occurs (critical micellar temperature or Krafft point) is relatively independent of concentration. The diagram applies to many paraffin chain salts and shows the three requirements for micelle formation: *1*) concentration above the critical micellar concentration, *2*) temperature above the critical micellar temperature (Krafft point), and *3*) concentration below that at which the transition to a liquid crystalline phase occurs. [From Hofmann & Small (80).]

ordered phases, which have some liquidity when examined by the microscope (127, 139, 140), still have molecular order by X-ray diffraction techniques (21, 31, 139, 140). They are therefore termed "liquid crystalline."

TEMPERATURE EFFECTS. Micelle formation occurs only if the paraffin chains of the detergent are liquid. At this critical temperature for micelle formation or critical micellar temperature (73), the solubility of the detergent increases enormously (61, 133); there is a phase change from crystalline to micellar. Experimentally, if a micellar solution of detergent is cooled, it becomes an opaque gel or curd at the critical micellar temperature. With rewarming it returns to its micellar state at the critical micellar temperature. The critical micellar temperature may be well below the melting point of the anhydrous compound (95); it is often called the "Krafft point" (Fig. 3).

INTERACTION WITH ADDITIVES. The micelle possesses a liquid hydrocarbon interior, and water-insoluble compounds are partitioned between it and the aqueous phase. This phenomenon is characteristic of soap solutions and is termed micellar solubilization (95, 107, 133). Two types of micellar solutes are distinguished: *1*) nonpolar lipids in which the solute molecule is believed to be present in the center of the micelle (examples are heptane, benzene, and azobenzene) and *2*) polar but water-insoluble lipids in which the solute molecule is interdigitated between the detergent ions with its polar group toward the aqueous phase (examples are long-chain alcohols and monoglycerides). The two types of micellar solutes may be solubilized independently, but in general the alteration of micellar structure by solubilization of a polar lipid increases the solubility of a nonpolar lipid since a greater volume of hydrocarbon is available to the nonpolar solute.

The phase equilibria in systems composed of a

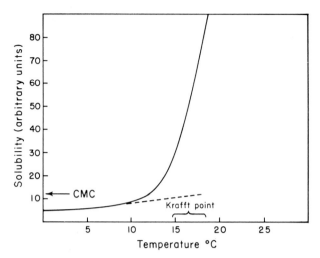

FIG. 3. Effect of temperature on solubility of a typical ionic detergent (for example, lauryl sulfate) in water. The striking increase in solubility over a narrow temperature range is a unique characteristic of amphipathic molecules and is indicated by the horizontal line separating the crystalline phase and the micellar phase areas in the binary phase diagram (Fig. 2). The critical micellar temperature, or Krafft point, is that temperature at which the concentration of the detergent reaches its critical micellar concentration (CMC) in water and may also be considered as the melting point of the hydrated amphipathic ion (61, 133). Certain bile salts (for example, lithocholate) also manifest a similar striking increase in solubility over a narrow temperature range despite the difference in their molecular configuration from that of typical ionic detergents (72, 80). [From Hofmann (73).]

detergent, a water-insoluble additive, and water are described by ternary composition phase diagrams that are plotted with triangular coordinates (80, 95, 139, 140) (Fig. 4). The construction of such diagrams enables the comparison of bile salts with detergents or the interaction of a given bile salt with a series of homologous additives.

Properties of Bile Salt Solutions

The bile salt molecule has a rigid, disk-shaped body fixed to a small side chain. All of the polar hydroxy groups are on one side of the molecule, spatially separated from the charged group, which is at the end of the isopentyl side chain. The bile salt molecule is thus completely dissimilar in its arrangement of polar and nonpolar groups to typical ionic detergents, which generally have a flexible hydrophobic paraffin chain ending in one or more charged groups; accordingly the bulk and surface properties of bile salts differ markedly from those of typical detergents.

CONCENTRATION EFFECTS. Bile salts form micelles, but the transition from a molecular to a micellar solution is more gradual, and the aggregates are considerably smaller and more hydrated than those of typical ionic detergents (38, 80, 94). At high concentrations bile salt solutions do not form a viscous, birefringent liquid crystalline phase as was described for ionic detergents, but remain transparent; this indicates that the hydrated bile salt molecule does not readily pack into a lamellar array (71, 80, 140) (Fig. 5).

TEMPERATURE EFFECTS. The critical micellar temperature of all the prevalent bile salt conjugates is below 0 C. However, the critical micellar temperature of lithocholate, one of the two major secondary bile acids formed in man, is considerably above body temperature (80); the insolubility of this bile salt at body temperature probably has an important effect on its metabolism (85).

INTERACTION WITH ADDITIVES. The distinctive properties of bile salt solutions are most apparent in their interaction with certain water-insoluble, yet amphipathic lipids, such as lecithin (21, 31, 80, 140) and monoglyceride (70, 102), which display a characteristic behavior in water (4, 21, 31, 80, 103, 114, 139, 140). Such compounds disperse spontaneously in water into hydrated lamellar or cylindrical aggregates that are in a liquid crystalline phase (Fig. 6); molecules displaying this unusual behavior in water have been termed "swelling amphipaths" (80). Bile salts rapidly disperse such aggregates to far smaller particles; the result is a marked reduction in the turbidity and viscosity of the original dispersion and indeed a phase change (71, 80, 140).

Such dispersion, which may also be termed solubilization or hydrotropy, occurs only above the critical micellar concentration of a bile salt. The critical micellar concentration of such a bile salt-swelling amphipath-water system is considerably below that of the bile salt-water system without such an additive (71) (Table 1). For the bile salt-lecithin-water system or bile salt-monoglyceride-fatty acid-water system, the critical micellar concentration is about 2 mM (2, 71). Probably the contents of bile and upper small intestine are both well above their critical micellar concentrations.

Ionic detergents also disperse monoglycerides or lecithin to smaller aggregates, but no detergent has been found that disperses these lipids as effectively as bile salts, if effectiveness is defined as the molar ratio

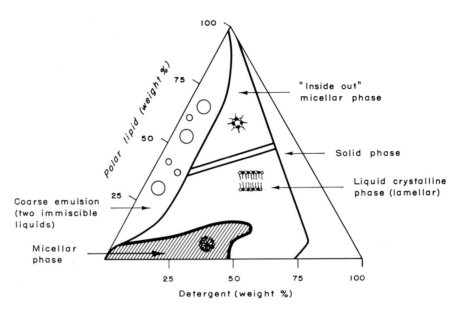

FIG. 4. A ternary phase diagram (46) of the system water-soap-polar lipid. The polar lipid here is hexanoic acid, which has a low solubility in water; the soap is cetyltrimethylammonium bromide. Any point depicts a concentration of the three substances and the molecular arrangement at that concentration. The term "weight %" refers to the weight of the component divided by the weight of all three components (soap + polar lipids + water). The increase in the area of the micellar phase (*lower left*) indicates the increase in solubility of the polar lipid with increasing soap concentration. At high soap, low water concentrations, one or more liquid crystalline phases occur (although only one phase is indicated in the figure). Such diagrams are essential for concise presentation of the heterogeneous equilibria present in intestinal content and bile, both of which consist of water, ionic detergents (bile salts), and polar lipids (lecithin for bile, and monoglyceride and fatty acid for intestinal content) (80).

of polar lipid to bile salt that can be achieved without turbidity. This property of bile salts is most properly represented in a ternary phase diagram of the system of bile salts, polar lipid, and water (Fig. 7). The micellar area of such a system is much larger than that observed in a system of typical detergent, polar lipid, and water.

Present evidence is that the bile salt molecule resembles a wetting agent more than a typical ionic detergent. If a monolayer of monoglyceride is spread on a Langmuir trough, the bile salt molecules do not penetrate the film, but adsorb to it (37). In a monolayer (at an air/water interface) composed of bile salts alone, the bile salt molecule is considered to lie flat with its hydrophobic side upward and its hydroxy groups and ionic moiety in contact with the water. This orientation of the bile salt molecule at interfaces and its inability to penetrate monoglyceride or lecithin monolayers—as well as other evidence—have led to several proposals for the molecular arrangement of the bile salt-polar lipid micelle (Fig. 8). At present it appears that the only long-chain polar lipids that manifest extremely high micellar solubilities in micel-

lar solutions are lipids that form myelin figures spontaneously in water.

Bile salt solutions in the absence of swelling amphipaths are poor solvents for nonpolar additives such as cholesterol or heptane (71). When polar additives such as lecithin or monoglyceride are added (Fig. 9), the solubility of nonpolar lipid rises markedly and in proportion to the amount of added polar lipid (71, 80, 141). This striking change in the solvent properties of bile salts when polar lipid is added reflects the distinctive molecular arrangement of the bile salt micelle—that is, the liquid hydrocarbon region of the micelle derives almost exclusively from the polar lipid (37).

JEJUNUM

Intraluminal Effects on Digestion and Absorption of Nutrients

In 1957 Borgström and his colleagues (19) reported a series of experiments in which a test meal containing

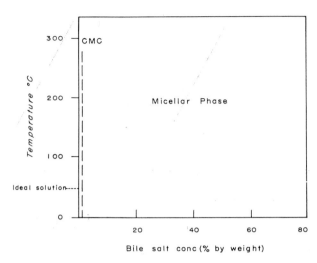

FIG. 5. Influence of concentration and temperature on the molecular arrangement of conjugated bile salt molecules in water. The critical micellar temperature, or Krafft point, of conjugated bile salts is below the freezing point of water, and therefore a Krafft point does not appear in the phase diagram. Bile salts differ from typical anionic detergents in their failure to form a liquid crystalline phase at high aqueous concentrations (71, 140). At very high concentrations (50–70% by weight) the bile salt will crystallize from solution (at 37 C). The molecular arrangement of the bile salt micelle has not been established; the molecules probably pack into a lamellar arrangement, which, according to partial specific volume measurements (94), is extensively hydrated. This diagram is based largely on the work of Small et al. (140).

all of the major classes of nutrients plus a nonabsorbable reference material was fed to human subjects; the site of absorption of each of the major components of the meal was determined by comparing its concentration with that of the marker at various intestinal levels. These experiments confirmed and united the work of many previous investigators that had indicated the jejunum was the major site of fat, carbohydrate, and protein digestion and absorption in man (146). Thus the jejunal lumen may be considered to be a reaction vessel into which detergents, enzymes, and fluids are continuously added to partially digested foodstuffs entering from the stomach; homogeneous and heterogeneous catalysis proceeds rapidly, and the products formed are rapidly absorbed. The concentration of a given component in jejunal contents during digestion represents the momentary resultant of addition, digestion, and absorption.

PROTEINS AND ENZYMES. *Action of enzymes on bile salts.* Beznák (13), working in Verzaár's laboratory, incubated conjugated bile salts with trypsin and observed

that the peptide bond of the bile salts was not cleaved. The observation (58) that the fecal bile acids of the germ-free rat are entirely conjugated confirms these early experiments and suggests further that the peptide bond of conjugated bile salts is resistant to all digestive enzymes.

Actions of bile salts on enzymes. It is clear that the digestive enzymes of the pancreas are active in the presence of bile salts in vivo. Recent studies in vitro (100) have shown that pure conjugated bile salts in concentrations similar to those present during digestion (19, 47, 137) do not significantly influence trypsin, chymotrypsin, and amylase activity. It would be of interest to compare typical anionic detergents with bile salts in this respect.

There is no reason to postulate any interaction be-

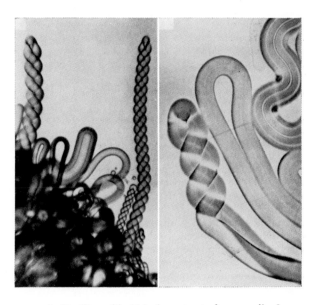

FIG. 6. Swelling of lecithin in water to form myelin figures (× 180, *left*; × 360, *right*) (114). The myelinics are composed of sheets of bimolecular lamellae with water between the charged surfaces of the bilayer (4, 31, 139, 140). Hydrocarbon chains are closely packed, yet liquid (21). The liquid crystalline phase is termed "paracrystalline"; the phenomenon is termed "lyotropic mesomorphism" (86); the compounds exhibiting such behavior have been termed "swelling amphipaths" (80). This characteristic behavior in water is manifested by lecithin, a zwitterionic amphipath, and monoglyceride, a nonionic amphipath, at extremely low concentrations; typical ionic detergents form such phases in water only at extremely high concentrations. Bile salts adsorb to myelinics and disperse them into much smaller aggregates; in the ternary phase diagram one moves from a liquid crystalline phase to a micellar phase. Although monoglyceride forms such a mesomorphic phase in water, this may not occur in intestinal content because an oil phase composed chiefly of higher glycerides is also present, and the monoglycerides of fatty acids formed by pancreatic lipolysis are partitioned between the oil and the micellar phase.

TABLE I. *Solvent Properties of Pure Bile Salt Conjugates, a Mixture Simulating That Present in Human Intestinal Content (Simulated Intestinal Content), and Three Typical Anionic Detergents**

	Critical Micellar Concentration, mM		Saturation Ratio $\left(\dfrac{\text{Moles of Micellar Solute}}{\text{Moles of Micellar Bile Salt or Detergent}}\right)$	
	Azobenzene	Monoolein	Azobenzene	Monoolein
Sodium glycodeoxycholate	1.9	0.6	0.056	1.7
Sodium taurodeoxycholate	1.9	0.6	0.044	1.7
Sodium glycochenodeoxycholate	2.4	0.8	0.036	1.7
Sodium taurochenodeoxycholate	2.5	0.8	0.036	1.6
Sodium glycocholate	8.0	4.2	0.034	1.4
Sodium taurocholate	10.0	4.2	0.024	1.4
Simulated intestinal content	3.5	1.4	0.035	1.4
Sodium *n*-octylbenzene-*p*-sulfonate	2.3	ND	0.085	0.9
Sodium oleyl taurate	0.1	ND	0.100	0.3
Sodium lauryl sulfate	0.4	ND	0.109	0.4

* The critical micellar concentration of bile salts is considerably lower in the presence of the swelling amphipath monoolein. Bile salts are much better solvents for monoolein than are the anionic detergents, although they are poorer solvents for the nonpolar solute azobenzene. The bile salt-monoolein micelle has a saturation ratio for azobenzene quite similar to that of the typical ionic detergents; this indicates that the combination of bile salt and polar lipid forms a micelle with solvent properties similar to those of the micelle of typical ionic detergents. ND = not determined. [Modified from Hofmann (71).]

tween bile salts and liberated polypeptides and amino acids, and there is no experimental evidence to suggest that bile salts influence the rate of amino acid absorption directly.

CARBOHYDRATES. Bile salts probably do not influence the digestion and absorption of dietary carbohydrate. An interaction between bile salts and intestinal mucus may occur, however, and may influence intestinal absorption. Bile salts should disperse intestinal mucus and thus reduce the thickness of the barrier between the interior of the mucosal cell and the intestinal lumen. Whether a part of the malabsorption observed with biliary diversion is related to this hypothetical loss of mucus removal by bile salts is unknown.

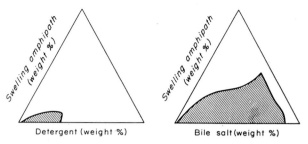

FIG. 7. Schematic representation depicting the micellar area of the ternary phase diagram of a typical ionic detergent-monoglyceride-water system (*left*) and the bile salt-monoglyceride-water system (*right*). The bile salt phase diagram has a much larger micellar area and a much smaller liquid crystalline area than the figure on the *left*, where bile salt has been replaced by typical ionic detergent. The large micellar area at *right* reflects the absence of liquid crystal formation by bile salts even at extremely high concentration (Fig. 5). Bile salts are thus superior to typical ionic detergents for the dispersion of lipids such as monoglyceride or lecithin into a micellar phase. Absorption should occur more rapidly from a micellar solution than a dispersion of liquid crystalline aggregates, since diffusion rates should be much greater in the former.

LIPIDS. *Triglycerides*. Bile salts and lipase act in concerted fashion to transform the coarse emulsion of dietary triglycerides entering the small intestine into a micellar solution of bile salts, fatty acid, and monoglyceride, from which absorption of the fatty acid and monoglyceride rapidly occurs (10, 22, 32, 74, 76, 78, 132, 146). The transformation involves interdependent physical and chemical changes.

1) Emulsification. Pure bile salts lower the interfacial tension of an oil-water interface only moderately and are poor emulsifying agents (26, 37). The addition of polar lipid such as lecithin or monoglyceride and fatty acid results in a much greater lowering of the interfacial tension, and the resultant mixture has much greater emulsifying power (49). It is probable that the triglyceride entering the small-intestinal lumen is emulsified by the mixture of lecithin and bile salts in bile. Pancreatic lipase has been demonstrated to adsorb readily to a triglyceride-water interface when bile salts are present (8), and such should occur in vivo.

2) Pancreatic lipolysis. Pancreatic lipase cleaves the 1-ester bond of lecithin to form a β-lysolecithin and fatty acid (30). It is probable that both of these products rapidly leave the interface and are incorporated into the bile salt micelles that surround the emulsified oil droplets. The dominant action of pancreatic lipase is to split the 1-ester bonds of triglyceride; thus the hydrolytic activity of lipase at the

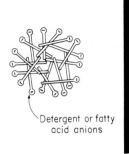

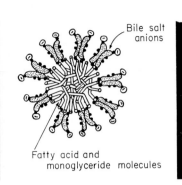

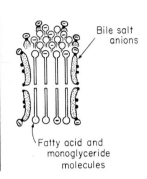

Bile salt anions

Detergent or fatty acid anions

Fatty acid and monoglyceride molecules

Bile salt anions

Fatty acid and monoglyceride molecules

FIG. 8. The probable molecular arrangement of a typical soap or anionic detergent micelle (*left*) is contrasted to two proposed models for the bile salt-polar lipid micelle (*center* and *right*). A cross section of each micelle is shown: the aggregate on the *left* and in the *center* is spherical; that on the *right*, disk shaped. Bound counter-ions, although present, are not shown, nor is the rapid exchange of molecules presumed to occur between those of the micelle and the much smaller fraction in true solution. The center of the micelle is composed of liquid paraffin chains of the polar lipid, and these hydrocarbon chains are chiefly responsible for the solvent capacity of the bile salt-polar lipid micelle. The model on the *right* was proposed by Small (personal communication) for the bile salt-lecithin micelle and is compatible with both monolayer and nuclear magnetic resonance studies on bile salt-lecithin systems. The model in the *center* was proposed by Dreher et al. (37) on the basis of monolayer data, but such data cannot exclude the model shown on the *right*. In both models, the bile salts serve as adsorbed, dispersing agents for lipids capable of spontaneously forming large hydrated bimolecular leaflets in water. Bile salts transform these large, lamellar, weakly charged aggregates into small, charged disks or spheres. With higher ratios of polar lipid to bile salt, the aggregate will elongate to a cylinder with a bimolecular diameter (*center*) or a larger disk of bimolecular thickness (*right*). (From A. F. Hofmann, *Medium Chain Triglycerides*, edited by J. R. Senior. Univ. of Pennsylvania Press, 1968, p. 9–19.)

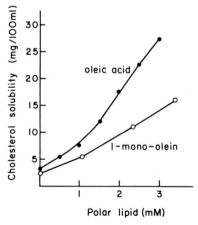

FIG. 9. Effect of monoglyceride or fatty acid on cholesterol solubility in bile salt solution (76). The liquid hydrocarbon chain of the fatty acid or monoglyceride in the micelle acts as a solvent for cholesterol. The behavior of cholesterol in a bile salt-monoglyceride or fatty acid-water system may be represented by a tetrahedron whose base has the coordinates of Figure 7, and whose apex is cholesterol (46, 141). Figure 9 thus represents a section of this phase diagram, and the plotted solubility is a line separating the micellar zone of excess crystalline cholesterol. The influence of mixtures of fatty acid and monoglyceride is intermediate between that of either pure additive (134).

oil-water interface results in the continuous generation of 2-monoglycerides and fatty acids (18). The 2-ester linkage of triglycerides is resistant to pancreatic lipase (18, 77, 104, 131), and continued lipolysis requires the exposure of new ester linkages at the interface—that is, monoglyceride and fatty acid that are formed must either move into the interior of the oil droplet or pass to the aqueous phase.

3) Micellar solubilization. If a monolayer of monoglyceride and fatty acid is made and bile salt is injected beneath it, the bile salt adsorbs to the polar groups of the surface molecules (37). If the bile salt concentration is raised above the critical micellar concentration, the monoglyceride and fatty acids move from the interface into the bulk phase. Such a mechanism could transfer the products of pancreatic lipolysis from the oil-water interface to the bulk phase. Although Benzonana & Desnuelle (8) have shown that the rate of pancreatic lipolysis is proportional to the interfacial area, the rapidity with which bile salts transfer the products of lipolysis to the bulk phase suggests that lipolysis could occur rapidly in vivo even with a relatively coarse emulsion of ingested triglyceride. It is not known whether the combination of bile salt, fatty acid, monoglyceride, and water forms a transient liquid crystalline phase at the interface or whether the products of pancreatic lipolysis are transferred to the micellar phase as rapidly as they are formed.

In order to clarify the physical chemistry of in-

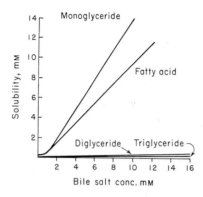

FIG. 10. Solubility in bile salt solution of the four classes of lipids present in the small-intestinal lumen during the digestion and absorption of fat. The values were obtained with triolein, diolein, monoolein, and oleic acid under conditions similar to those present in the jejunal lumen during digestion (pH 6.3; 37 C; Na+, 0.15 M). When present in excess, the diglyceride and triglyceride form a separate oil phase, which appears as a crude emulsion. The monoglyceride and fatty acid (if partially ionized) form a liquid crystalline state together with the bile salts (71, 72). The solubility curves for monoglyceride and fatty acid are the edges of the micellar region if a phase diagram is used to depict the phase equilibria.

testinal content during fat digestion, the behavior of glycerides and their lipolytic products in water has been examined and contrasted to their behavior in bile salt solution (71, 72). These studies have shown that monoglycerides and fatty acid (in mixture) interact with water; they form lamellar liquid crystalline aggregates.[2] Diglycerides and triglycerides do not interact with water and remain as oil droplets. When bile salts are added, the striking differences in the behavior of these classes persist. The liquid crystalline aggregates of monoglycerides and fatty acids are dispersed to a micellar solution; the diglycerides and triglycerides, on the other hand, remain as oil droplets (Fig. 10).

These in vitro findings enable a prediction to be made of the phase equilibria in intestinal content in vivo. A micellar phase of bile salt, fatty acid, and monoglyceride should be in equilibrium with an oil phase of diglyceride and triglyceride. Figure 11 shows the concentration of glycerides and fatty acids in the oil and micellar phases of human intestinal content obtained during fat digestion (78). Although the lipids of the micellar phase are largely fatty acid and monoglyceride, and those of the oil phase contain

[2] Fatty acids in water do not form a liquid crystalline phase unless they are partially ionized or monoglyceride is also present (or both). The temperature of the system must be above the transition temperature of the mixture—that is, the paraffin chains must be liquid.

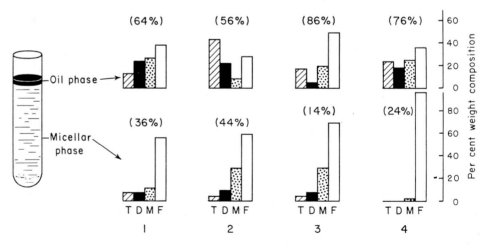

FIG. 11. Composition of the micellar and oil phases of four samples of human intestinal content as percentage by weight of determined triglyceride (T), diglyceride (D), monoglyceride (M), and fatty acid (F) (78). The percentage of total lipid present in each phase is indicated in parentheses; the concentration of micellar lipid was from 2 to 6 mg per 100 ml aqueous phase. The lipids of the micellar phase are chiefly monoglyceride and fatty acid in agreement with the in vitro solubilities shown in Figure 10. The higher glycerides are largely in the oil phase, which also contains a considerable concentration of fatty acid. [From Hofmann & Borgström (78).]

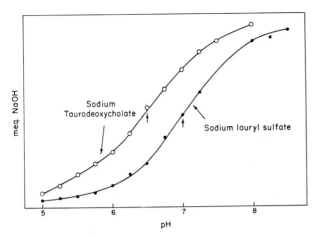

FIG. 12. Titration of oleic acid (5 mM) as a micellar solute in micelles of sodium taurodeoxycholate (16 mM) or sodium lauryl sulfate (16 mM). The bile salt micelle has a higher surface pH than the lauryl sulfate micelle, which enhances fatty acid ionization for a given bulk pH. Pancreatic lipolysis is driven in the direction of greater hydrolysis since fatty acid, when ionized, cannot be reesterified to higher glycerides. The pK_a of long-chain fatty acid in a bile salt micelle is about 6.5; this indicates that a significant fraction of the fatty acid present in the micellar phase in intestinal content during fat digestion and absorption is ionized—that is, present as a soap. *Vertical arrows* indicate the pH corresponding to the pK_a under these conditions. [Modified from Hofmann (75).]

virtually all the diglyceride and triglyceride in the sample, the influence of ionization on fatty acid behavior complicates the scheme. Considerable un-ionized fatty acid is present in the oil phase, and its concentration suggests that fatty acid may well be present in the interior of the oil droplet, possibly in dimer form.

Bile salts do not disperse appreciable concentrations of long-chain fatty acids unless the fatty acid is partially ionized. The degree of ionization of fatty acids in the micellar phase has been clarified recently by potentiometric determination of the pK_a of fatty acid present as a micellar solute (75). A typical titration curve of fatty acid in a bile salt micelle compared with its titration curve when present in a typical anionic detergent micelle is shown in Figure 12. The lower pK_a of the fatty acid when it is present as a micellar solute in the bile salt micelle indicates that the microenvironment of the bile salt micelle, that is, its higher surface pH, enhances fatty acid ionization. Fatty acid, when ionized (A^-), cannot be transesterified with partial glycerides by pancreatic lipase to form higher glycerides. Accordingly the enhancement of fatty acid ionization in the bile salt micelle drives lipolysis in the direction of greater hydrolysis.

Therefore bile salts, just as serum albumin, transport a mixture of soaps and fatty acids. When the soap moves to a membrane where the surface pH is lower, protonation occurs, and the carboxyl group may be readily esterified.

Small-intestinal content then contains two phases—an oil phase and a micellar phase in equilibrium with each other (Fig. 13). Nonpolar lipids such as cholesterol and the fat-soluble vitamins are partitioned between the two phases (44, 78), but little information is available on the distribution coefficients or factors influencing them. The components of the micelle are absorbed into the jejunal mucosal cell, but whether bile salts are absorbed depends on their ionic group [unpublished observations from this laboratory; (20, 99, 134); and see Weiner and Lack, Volume III of this *Handbook*]. If a micellar solution of taurine-conjugated bile salts and polar lipid is perfused through

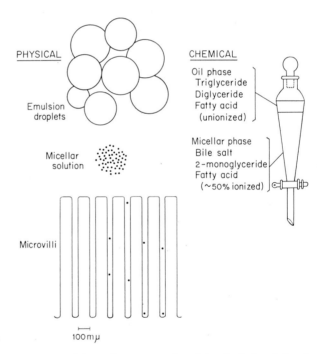

FIG. 13. Schematic representation of the physical and chemical states of lipids in intestinal content during fat digestion and absorption. An oil phase composed of higher glyceride and some un-ionized fatty acid is in equilibrium with aqueous micellar phase of bile salt, monoglycerides, un-ionized fatty acids, and fatty acid soaps. Nonpolar lipids—for example, fat-soluble vitamins, cholesterol, and hydrocarbons—are partitioned between the two phases. The emulsion droplets, micelles, and microvillae are drawn approximately to scale. Each *black dot* represents a single micelle. In addition to the oil phase and the micellar phase, an insoluble sediment is also present (134). Its lipids have not been characterized. [From Hofmann & Small (80).]

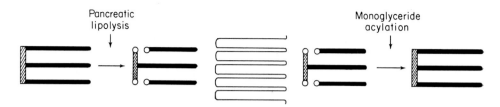

FIG. 14. Dominant chemical events during fat digestion and absorption in man. The bile salts enhance pancreatic lipolysis by emulsifying the substrate, promoting the adsorption of the enzyme, desorbing the products from the interface, and solubilizing them in micellar form.

the human jejunum, no net disappearance of bile salts occurs; this indicates that bile salts need not enter the mucosal cell or, if they enter, rapidly return to the lumen (134). Present experiments are compatible with the absorption of micellar solutes in molecular form, for it is probable that there is a finite concentration of molecularly dispersed species of all components of the micelle (81). However, the necessity of collision between the micelle and the mucosal cell for the absorption of nonpolar lipids such as cholesterol is another possibility.

4) Resynthesis of triglyceride in the mucosal cell. Data based on studies in animals (89, 106, 128) and human beings (88) agree that most of the chylomicron triglyceride molecules occurring after a fat meal are of dietary origin and are absorbed in the chemical form of 2-monoglyceride and fatty acid; resynthesis to triglyceride by acylation occurs in the mucosal cell without cleavage of the 2-ester linkage (Fig. 14). Although, in buffer, 2-monoglycerides rapidly and spontaneously isomerize to the 1-isomer (105), the rate of isomerization appears to be decreased when the 2-monoglyceride is incorporated into the bile salt micelle (70). Nevertheless most analyses of intestinal content have shown that a significant fraction of the monoglyceride is present as the 1-isomer (78), and it appears that a smaller fraction of triglyceride molecules is absorbed in the form of the 1-isomer (88, 106) and acylated to triglyceride without cleavage of the 1-ester linkage (88, 89, 106). A thorough discussion of triglyceride synthesis in the intestinal mucosal cell has been presented earlier in this series (see Johnston, Volume I of this *Handbook*). Whether bile salts directly influence triglyceride synthesis in the mucosal cell is considered below.

Cholesterol. Bile contains cholesterol in micellar form (80). This micellar cholesterol mixes with dietary cholesterol that enters the small-intestinal lumen dissolved in the emulsified fat droplets of gastric contents. Biliary cholesterol, like dietary cholesterol, is

unesterified; and there are no significant chemical changes in cholesterol during its digestion and absorption. In the absence of bile, cholesterol is not absorbed (32, 53, 54, 135), and therefore an interaction occurs between cholesterol and bile salts in the intestinal lumen that is essential for cholesterol absorption. This interaction is presumably the micellar solubilization of cholesterol, for the micellar phase of intestinal content contains significant cholesterol (17, 78), and when the intestine is perfused by cholesterol in micellar solution such cholesterol is readily absorbed (134). Cholesterol esters, if present in intestinal content, would be partitioned virtually entirely into the oil phase; this should in part explain their poor absorption (32, 53) (see Treadwell and Vahouny, Volume III of this *Handbook*). It seems unlikely that any individual bile salt conjugate should be necessary for cholesterol absorption, but few studies have been performed in which the influence of individual bile salt conjugates on cholesterol absorption has been examined.

Pancreatic juice contains an enzyme, cholesterol ester hydrolase, that catalyzes the hydrolysis of cholesterol esters or their formation from cholesterol and fatty acid. The activity of this enzyme, just as that of pancreatic lipase and presumably the phospholipase also present in pancreatic juice, is markedly influenced by the presence of bile salts (see Treadwell and Vahouny, Volume III of this *Handbook*). It seems probable that bile salts promote the adsorption of enzyme to the oil-water interface and remove the end products from the interface by transferring them to the aqueous micellar phase. The enhanced ionization of the fatty acid in the bile salt micelle (Fig. 12) should drive the reaction in the direction of hydrolysis.

Bile salt conjugates protect cholesterol ester hydrolase from chymotryptic inactivation, and some bile salt conjugates are more protective than others (see Treadwell and Vahouny, Volume III of this *Handbook*). Whether this effect is related to bile salts promoting the adsorption of cholesterol esterase to the oil-water interface or to some type of interaction with the enzyme, the enzyme-interface combination, or chymotrypsin has not been established.

It does not appear that cholesterol esterase should play a significant role in cholesterol absorption unless an abnormal diet containing large quantities of esterified cholesterol is consumed. Ingested cholesterol esters are readily hydrolyzed in the intestinal lumen and ingested free cholesterol is esterified to a limited extent (18, 53, 54) (see Treadwell and Vahouny, Volume III of this *Handbook*); this indicates that equilibrium lies on the side of almost total hydrolysis in vivo.

The solubility of cholesterol in bile salt solution is extremely low, but rises in direct proportion to added monoglyceride or fatty acid or both (76, 134). Therefore the ability of dietary fat to enhance cholesterol absorption may reflect its content of polar lipid, which is essential for the micellar solubilization of cholesterol in appreciable concentration. When a micellar solution of bile salt, cholesterol, and monoglyceride is infused into the human jejunum, the monoglyceride disappears far more rapidly than the cholesterol (134) (Fig. 15). As the polar lipid, which is essential for cholesterol solubilization, is absorbed, the cholesterol precipitates from solution (134). Such data suggest that the presence of polar lipid in the micellar phase may critically influence the extent of cholesterol absorption.

The feeding of plant sterols such as sitosterol reduces cholesterol absorption (54). A mechanism by which this effect might be mediated is the competition of plant sterols with cholesterol for the micellar phase.

Lecithin. Biliary and dietary lecithin are cleaved by pancreatic lipase to 2-lysolecithin and fatty acid (30), and pancreatic extracts also contain a lecithinase that cleaves the 1-ester linkage of lecithin (145). Since the fatty acids of ingested lecithin appear in triglyceride (14) and since the fatty acid pattern of chylomicron lecithin is virtually independent of ingested lecithin (150), extensive hydrolysis of lecithin must occur between lumen and lymph. It has not been clarified to what extent the 2-lysolecithin isomerizes to its 1-isomer, to what extent either isomer becomes incorporated into the bile salt micelle, to what extent hydrolysis of these isomers occurs in the lumen, or, conversely, what fraction of the lysolecithin is absorbed unhydrolyzed to be split in the mucosal cell. Some lysolecithin molecules may be absorbed intact and acylated to form lecithin, which composes the major chylomicron phospholipid.

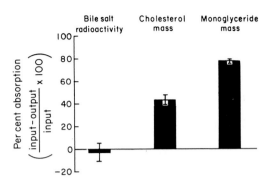

FIG. 15. Extent of absorption of bile salt, cholesterol, and glyceryl monooleate—all micellar components—from a perfused jejunal segment in man. No net bile salt absorption occurred despite nearly complete monoglyceride absorption. Cholesterol absorption was significantly slower than monoglyceride absorption (134).

Fat-soluble vitamins. Bile salts are essential for the absorption of β-carotene and vitamins D, E, and K. The older experimental evidence summarized by Deuel (32) indicates that no demonstrable absorption of these compounds occurs in bile-fistula animals and that absorption is restored when bile salts are fed. Two additional features of absorption appear to be common to these vitamins: their absorption is increased by the ingestion of triglyceride and reduced by the ingestion of mineral oil. These absorption characteristics are also manifested by cholesterol, and it is probable that all these compounds, despite their dissimilar metabolic functions, follow a common pathway during absorption—that is, solubilization in the bile salt-fatty acid-monoglyceride micelle. A significant fraction of these relatively nonpolar compounds should be present in the oil phase, and the reduction in absorption induced by mineral oil may be explained by an alteration of the micellar phase-oil phase partition in favor of the oil phase. Studies are needed in vivo and in vitro to define the influence of bile salts on the physical state of the fat-soluble vitamins in small-intestinal content. Further, since the components of the mixed bile salt micelle are not absorbed at equal rates, kinetic studies of the absorption of these vitamins from micelles are desirable.

Whether bile salts alone produce the required type of aggregate is unclear since few studies have been carried out with surfactants whose interaction with lipids is similar to that of bile salts. β-Carotene, when dissolved in bile salt micelles, is absorbed and cleaved by intestinal slices; if presented in a Tween micelle, the carotene is adsorbed but not cleaved (120). Vitamin D absorption by the everted gut sac is enhanced by taurocholate but not by taurochenodeoxycholate and taurodeoxycholate (129). Whether this observation indicates a true specificity of taurocholate for vitamin D absorption is unclear.

Recently it has been shown that vitamin A (151) and vitamin D (2), but not vitamin E (109), are metabolized to more polar sulfates, glucuronides, and glutathione conjugates that are excreted in bile. The extent of reabsorption of these vitamin conjugates and the influence of bile on this have not been elucidated.

In contrast to β-carotene, retinol, which is derived from β-carotene by enzymatic cleavage, may be absorbed in the absence of bile (120), although whether the rate of retinol absorption is influenced by bile salts is unclear. Retinol is considerably more polar than β-carotene and may be dispersed in water in an unknown physical state.

HYDROGEN ION AND BICARBONATE. Bile is alkaline and this indicates that its glycine and taurine conjugates are fully neutralized and present as anions. In theory the glycine conjugates (pK_a = 3.6) and even the taurine conjugates (pK_a = 1.5) could act as buffers when mixed with strongly acidic gastric juice. In the jejunum, lipolysis and micellar solubilization of the resultant fatty acid result in proton release from about half of the liberated fatty acid that should be neutralized by pancreatic bicarbonate. In the absence of bile salts, pancreatic lipolysis is unimpaired (92, 124), and the fatty acid may be present either as droplets of un-ionized fatty acid, as insoluble calcium soaps, or as liquid crystalline aggregates of acid soap (HA A$^-$)n; these physical states should be associated with no ionization, complete ionization, or half ionization, respectively. To what extent acid-base balance is influenced by the fatty acid-soap buffer system is unknown.

CALCIUM. It would be remarkable, in view of the vast efforts of the detergent industry to develop detergents resistant to hard water, if the detergent selected during biochemical evolution were not also resistant to calcium precipitation. Simple in vitro experiments demonstrate that the bile salts, especially the taurine conjugates, are far more resistant to precipitation from solution by the addition of calcium ions than are typical anionic detergents (71). The resistance of bile salts to precipitation by added calcium ions is influenced by *1*) the type of A/B ring juncture—that is, whether it is A/B *cis* or A/B *trans* (79), *2*) the type of conjugation—that is, whether with glycine or taurine (80), and *3*) the number (and probably position and orientation) of substituents (80). When bile contains appreciable concentrations of bile acids that are susceptible to precipitation by calcium ions, precipitation may occur—that is, cholelithiasis or choledocholithiasis. Thus, rabbits fed cholestanol form glycoallodeoxycholic acid (the A/B *trans* stereoisomer of glycodeoxycholic acid), which precipitates in the gallbladder as an insoluble calcium salt (79). Rats fed lithocholic acid and a taurine-deficient diet form glycolithocholic acid, which precipitates in the biliary system as an insoluble calcium salt (122). The concentration of bile salts in intestinal content is far below that of bile, and insoluble precipitates of calcium salts of conjugated bile salts have not been reported to occur in the intestinal lumen.

The profound osteomalacia observed in the bile-fistula animal (67) and in patients with biliary cirrhosis probably reflects the additive effects of vitamin D deficiency and reduced calcium absorption. As noted, bile salts are essential for vitamin D absorption. Recently a series of papers by Webling & Holdsworth (147, 148) has confirmed and extended older experiments that claimed bile salts had a direct effect on calcium absorption apart from their effect on vitamin D uptake. Webling and Holdsworth demonstrated that bile salts enhanced the absorption of calcium phosphate and suggested that the mechanism was related to the ability of bile salts to increase the aqueous solubility of this normally sparingly soluble salt. Presumably the binding of calcium ions to the bile salt micelle, with release of sodium counter-ions (112), thus reduces the activity of calcium ion and therefore increases the total amount of calcium ion present in dissolved form. These experiments also complement recent work of Schedl et al. (130), who observed that when calcium chloride was added to washed intestinal loops of dogs, it promptly precipitated from solution as an insoluble phosphate. Together these experiments suggest that bile salts may enhance calcium absorption directly by reducing the extent to which it forms insoluble precipitates in the jejunal lumen. Whether, in the ileum, calcium ions are absorbed as the counter-ion to bile salts has not been examined. Further information is desirable on the physical state of calcium in the intestinal lumen in normal and bile-deprived subjects.

DRUGS. Bile salts should not influence the absorption or metabolism of water-soluble drugs. According to present concepts, any drug ingested as a solid must be suspended and then brought into either a molecular or a micellar state for efficient absorption. Recent

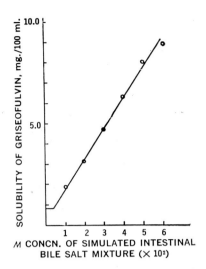

FIG. 16. Solubility of griseofulvin, a water-insoluble anti-fungal antibiotic, in a mixture of conjugated bile salts simulating human intestinal content at 37 C. The slope of the *curve* represents the saturation ratio (71)—that is, the ratio of micellar griseofulvin to micellar bile salt when the micelle is saturated with griseofulvin. [From Bates et al. (5).]

studies (5) have shown that bile salts are effective in dispersing and solubilizing a number of insoluble drugs (Fig. 16). The molecular interactions described above have generally been ignored in the design of drug preparations. If micellar solubilization is a prerequisite for the absorption of drugs with limited aqueous solubilities, it may be possible in some cases to predict the extent of absorption in vivo by appropriate in vitro studies.

Intracellular Effects in the Jejunum

FAILURE OF CONJUGATED BILE SALTS TO INFLUENCE INTRACELLULAR METABOLISM. If conjugated bile salts do not enter the mucosal cells of the jejunum, they cannot directly influence the metabolic events occurring there.[3] By enhancing the entrance of materials into the cell, either through micelle formation or by the maintenance of a clean cell surface, bile salts must influence the metabolic activity of the jejunal mucosal cell. But this influence cannot be considered a direct, intracellular effect of bile salts.

Early studies using impure bile salts had shown that

[3] Recent experiments in this laboratory (I. G. Hislop, A. F. Hofmann, and L. J. Schoenfield, unpublished observations) using intestinal perfusion have shown that glycine dihydroxy and unconjugated dihydroxy and trihydroxy bile acids are readily absorbed from the human jejunum. However, the importance of jejunal absorption in the enterohepatic circulation of glycine dihydroxy bile acids remains unknown.

bile salts markedly inhibit enzyme activities (100), and these studies, together with the view that bile salts entered the cell with digested fat, led to the belief that the enterohepatic circulation of bile salts through the jejunal cell should influence the rate of synthetic activities occurring there—for example, triglyceride resynthesis. The report that conjugated bile salts enhance the incorporation of glucose into triglyceride glycerol (29) prompted investigators to examine the effect of bile salts on many of the activities of the jejunal mucosal cell such as amino acid transport, sodium transport, glucose transport, and so on. The results of these experiments varied, curiously, and the lack of agreement between laboratories has been clarified only recently by Pope et al.(125), who have reexamined the effect of conjugated bile salts of unimpeachable purity on the metabolism of the jejunal mucosal cell. These workers observed the rates of translocation mechanisms (urea transport, amino acid transport, sodium transport) as well as synthetic mechanisms (acetate incorporation into fatty acid, acetate incorporation into cholesterol, amino acid incorporation into protein, and fatty acid incorporation into triglyceride). No effect of conjugated bile salts could be detected. Morgan (113) has reported, in agreement, that triglyceride synthesis returns to normal in the bile-fistula rat when the animal recovers from the effect of the operation.

Pure conjugated bile salts do inhibit a variety of biochemical pathways in subcellular fractions, but all data available are consistent with bile salts having no effect on the events in the jejunal mucosal cell, provided the integrity of the cell is maintained. If further dissection of the jejunal mucosal cell reveals the existence of multienzyme complexes in the cell membrane of the microvillus, or between the microvilli, bile salts may well prove to have a direct effect at what may be considered to be the cell-lumen interface. Such, however, cannot be considered an intracellular locus of action.

CYTOTOXICITY OF FREE BILE SALTS. In their study of triglyceride synthesis by the everted gut sac, Dawson & Isselbacher (29) made the significant observation that replacement of taurodeoxycholate by deoxycholate resulted in a complete destruction of the mucosal cells of their preparation. The striking cytotoxicity of deoxycholate seemed astonishing in view of many older studies in which free bile acids had been fed to animals without apparent deleterious effect; and although this particular mucosal pathology may well never occur in vivo, the observation has stimulated much experimentation of the cytotoxicity of free bile salts. The mucosal cell destruction strongly suggests that deoxycholate must have entered the mucosal cell. No studies on the absorption of deoxycholate by the jejunum have been reported, but it has been clearly shown that cholate is readily absorbed from the rat jejunum by nonionic diffusion (33).

Dawson & Isselbacher (29) observed that deoxycholate was cytotoxic at 5 mM, but that cholate was not cytotoxic until used at a concentration three times higher. They further observed that 0.5 mM deoxycholate inhibited triglyceride synthesis, but that cholate was not inhibitory until a much higher concentration was used. The marked inhibition of triglyceride synthesis by deoxycholate, but not by cholate, has been confirmed by Donaldson (36); similar results have been obtained for glucose transport (125). Free bile salts also inhibit water transport, and dihydroxy bile salts (chenodeoxycholate, deoxycholate, ursodeoxycholate, and hyodeoxycholate) are inhibitory at concentrations well below that for cholate (48). The reason for the much greater influence of dihydroxy bile salts on the intracellular metabolism of the jejunal cell is unknown. The dihydroxy bile salts are more surface active (37) and, generally, less soluble. They may be absorbed more rapidly, and in the cell they may adsorb to organelles, precipitate from solution, or be esterified with fatty acids, whereas trihydroxy bile salts might remain in solution and pass into the portal blood. Deoxycholate and chenodeoxycholate may form viscous gels between pH 6 and 7; cholate does not (80).

If fed to experimental animals, ingested free bile salts probably precipitate from solution as the un-ionized acid in the stomach. In the duodenum the free bile salts are solubilized by conjugated bile salt micelles, although a fraction remains in molecular solution. The presence of conjugated bile salts may well reduce the cytotoxicity of free bile salts and could explain the ability of the rat to tolerate 2 % deoxycholate in its diet (50), as well as the normal histology frequently observed in animals with a surgically produced blind loop containing free bile salts (36, 91, 123). The cyotoxicity of free bile salts has been studied in very few species, and there may be considerable species variation in the resistance of the mucosal cell. Further, cytotoxicity has only been demonstrated with in vitro preparations of small intestine.

ILEUM

Intraluminal Effects on Digestion and Absorption of Nutrients

The awareness that digestive enzymes are localized to particular regions of the small intestine is of rather recent origin with respect to carbohydrate absorption (23) and fat absorption (28). The ileum has generally been considered to be a reserve absorptive site; substances that passed the jejunum without being absorbed were absorbed in the ileum. This view is being progressively modified as more refined techniques are brought to bear on the site of absorption of various nutrients.

The enormous fluxes of water and electrolyte that occur in the jejunum during digestion probably occur to a lesser extent in the ileum, where the direction of water movement is toward net absorption (27). It appears unlikely that conjugated bile salts influence this reabsorptive process other than by their osmotic effect, which is small.

Vitamin B_{12} and intrinsic factor are absorbed in the ileum (27), but bile salts are unnecessary for this absorption; megaloblastic anemia does not develop in the bile-fistula patient.

If the products of pancreatic lipolysis are completely absorbed in the jejunum, only the bile salt of the bile salt-fatty acid-monoglyceride micelle should pass into the ileum. Aspirates of ileal content obtained late in the digestion of a meal are clear and contain bile salt, fatty acid, and cholesterol (78). This observation, together with the results of perfusion experiments that indicate a progressive decrease in specific activity of perfused radioactive cholesterol and fatty acid (134), suggests that there is a continuous movement of fatty acid and cholesterol into the intestinal lumen. The source of these lipids is presumably the mucosal cells that are continuously sloughing into the intestinal lumen (27). The fatty acid serves as a polar lipid that enhances the micellar solubility of cholesterol. It is probable that these micellar lipids—fatty acid and cholesterol—are continuously absorbed as new fatty acid and cholesterol molecules enter the lumen; or, expressed differently, there is a continuous exchange of cholesterol and fatty acid between the bile salt micelle and the mucosal cell of the ileum. There is thus a continuous return to the organism of the lipids that make up the mucosal cell.

The bile salt micelle binds counter-ions (112), especially polyvalent cations such as calcium. This binding may prevent the precipitation of insoluble phosphates in the ileum (147, 148).

Intracellular Effects: Bile Salt Absorption from the Ileum

The convincing experiments of Borgström and his colleagues (19), which showed that fat was absorbed chiefly in the jejunum, were considered to indicate that bile salts were absorbed at the same locus. The significance of older experiments, summarized by Verzár (146), which indicated that bile salts were absorbed much more rapidly from the ileum than the jejunum in the rat, was unclear. In 1960 Baker & Searle (3) showed that conjugated bile salts were absorbed much more rapidly from cannulated ileal loops than from cannulated jejunal loops in the rat. The following year Lack & Weiner (93), using the everted gut sac technique, demonstrated that active transport of taurocholate occurred with ileal preparations but not with jejunal preparations. These two papers have stimulated a needed reinvestigation of the site of bile salt absorption; the available information has been well summarized in Volume III of this *Handbook* by Weiner and Lack, who have made extensive contributions.

It is now well established that bile salts are transported by the ileum and that this transport mechanism fulfills the requirements for active transport, namely absorption in the absence of an electrochemical gradient (33). The transport system is located in the ileum and is absent in the jejunum in all mammals examined to date (52), although passive ionic diffusion in the jejunum may be appreciable in some species (33). The transport system does not distinguish the type of A/B ring juncture or the number, position, or orientation of hydroxylic substituents, although relatively few bile salts have been examined (see Weiner and Lack, Volume III of this *Handbook*). Kinetics are consistent with a carrier-mediated diffusion process; mutual inhibition has been observed (83), and T_m values have been calculated (33, 82, 83) (see Weiner and Lack, Volume III of this *Handbook*). In man absorption of taurine conjugates does not occur in the jejunum or proximal region of the ileum (99, 134), but does occur in the distal part of the ileum, as shown by feeding experiments with labeled bile salts as well as the results of ileal bypass or resection (1, 20).

The virtual absence of bile salts in peripheral blood indicates that bile salts are efficiently cleared from the portal blood by the liver. Indeed, were the ileal trans-

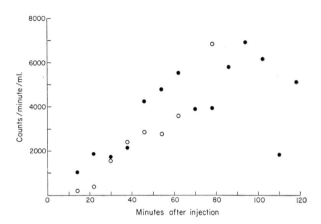

FIG. 17. Recycling of bile salts during the digestion of a fat meal by a human subject. Labeled taurine-conjugated bile salts were injected from an indwelling intestinal tube located in the proximal jejunum, ●, or the proximal ileum, ○. The radioactivity sampled represents bile salt that had undergone one complete enterohepatic cycle. The short time required for reappearance—about 1 hour—is in agreement with estimates (19) that the bile salt pool circulates at least twice during the digestion of a fat meal in man. [From Borgström et al. (20).]

port rate to exceed the hepatic clearance rate, bile salts should spill over into the systemic circulation. Dietschy et al. (33) made the significant observation that the T_m of the hepatic clearance of bile salts was about five times that of the ileal transport T_m (in the rat). The ileal and hepatic transport systems may be considered to be coupled, and their relationship may be analogous to that of the renal glomerulus and tubule. Information is needed on the comparative chemical specificities of these two transport systems. For many compounds—for example, bilirubin—conjugation by the liver appears to block transport by the ileum (96) and thus prevents enterohepatic cycling.

The physiological importance of the ileal transport system for bile salts is that it retains bile salts and results in a large pool of bile salts despite a small daily synthesis (74). Micellar solubilization may well be rate limiting for the absorption of cholesterol and fat-soluble vitamins. Efficient ileal reabsorption maintains a large bile salt pool and thus allows a high intraluminal concentration of bile salts. The bile salt pool has been estimated to cycle at least twice during the digestion of a meal (19), and the enterohepatic circulation of bile salt has been directly demonstrated (20) (Fig. 17).

The influence of free or conjugated bile salts on the metabolism of the ileal cell has not been clarified. Bile salts inhibit cholesterol synthesis in the rat ileum (34), but whether this inhibition occurs in other species or is of physiological significance is unknown.

There is little information available on the synthetic activity of the mucosal cells of the ileum.

LARGE INTESTINE

Intraluminal Effects

The colon is considered to be a desiccator, an ion exchanger, a pelleter of excreta, and a container with semipermeable walls for an enormous mass of only partially characterized bacteria whose metabolic activities are not fully understood (27, 35). Its reservoir and motor functions permit voluntary infrequent defecation. Bile salts are altered chemically by the colonic bacteria; the resulting products are less water soluble and adsorb to bacteria. It is unlikely that bile salts are present in micellar concentrations in the content of the large intestine, and it is therefore unlikely that bile salts normally have a significant transport role there.

LAXATIVE PROPERTIES OF BILE SALTS. Considerable experimental evidence may be interpreted to show that bile salts influence the motility of the large intestine and are important determinants of fecal frequency. It appears that a laxative action is a major function of bile salts in the colon (9).

Bile salts have been demonstrated to stimulate colonic motility in a variety of isolated tissue preparations (110). In intact dogs the addition of bile salts to an enema invariably caused defecation, whereas the same enema without bile salts did not (51). In rats there is a linear correlation between fecal weight and bile salt output (15), and free bile salts strikingly inhibit water absorption from ligated colonic loops (48). In man the continuous administration of cholate, deoxycholate, and taurocholate causes a mild to severe diarrhea; that several days are required for the effect to take place suggests that a loading dose is necessary to expand the bile salt pool to a level where the T_m of the ileal transport system is reached (S. M. Grundy and E. H. Ahrens, Jr., personal communication). Patients with surgical bypass of the ileum may show an increased fecal bile salt excretion and a marked increase in fecal frequency and diarrhea that seems of greater magnitude than the observed steatorrhea. Patients with biliary-colic fistula usually have severe diarrhea (16). Perfusion of the small intestine with a solution of conjugated bile salts may cause a severe diarrhea of sudden onset (I. G. Hislop and A. F. Hofmann, unpublished observations).

These observations agree in suggesting that bile salts may influence the frequency, amount, and content of stools by inhibiting sodium and water absorption from the colon and possibly by influencing colonic motility. Several experimenters have found that free bile salts are much more potent than conjugated bile salts (48, 110), and it is not clear whether bacterial hydrolysis of the peptide bond is required for bile salts to manifest a cathartic action.[4]

EFFECTS OF BILE SALTS ON BACTERIAL FLORA OF LARGE INTESTINE. It is not known whether the quantity or composition of the bacterial flora of the colon is influenced by the quantity or composition of bile salts delivered from the ileum.

EFFECTS OF BACTERIAL FLORA OF LARGE INTESTINE ON BILE SALTS. The peptide linkage of the conjugated bile salt molecule is hydrolyzed by bacterial enzymatic activity. Hydrolysis occurs in the cecum and is extensive, since fecal bile acids are largely in the unconjugated form (12). The enzyme (or enzymes), which may or may not be proteolytic, is produced by *Clostridia perfringens*, *Aerobacter aerogenes*, and several species of the enterococci, and has recently been isolated in soluble form from *C. perfringens* (115). The isolated enzyme splits all the common conjugated bile salts, although glycine conjugates appear to be cleaved more rapidly than taurine conjugates.

The hydroxyl substituents of the resulting free bile acids are extensively altered by bacterial enzymes with the formation of a great variety of secondary bile acids (12, 24, 25). Available data suggest, for man (and probably most other mammals), that 7-dehydroxylation occurs, but that 3- and 12-dehydroxylation do not occur. Thus chenodeoxycholic acid gives rise to lithocholic acid and cholic acid gives rise to deoxycholic acid (25). These metabolites exist in equilibrium with their precursors, and all hydroxylic substituents appear to be susceptible to oxidation (to a keto substituent), which may be followed by reduction to a mixture of alpha and beta epimers. To exemplify, there may be three fecal bile acids with substituents on the 3 position—that is, the 3α-hydroxy, the 3-keto, and the 3β-hydroxy acid. There are 9 possibilities for bile acids with substituents on the 3 and 7 positions as well

---

[4] Recent experiments in this laboratory (H. S. Mekhjian, S. F. Phillips, and A. F. Hofmann, unpublished observations) have shown that perfusion of the human colon with conjugated bile salts completely blocks the net transport of sodium and water by the colon. In these experiments, hydrolysis of the peptide bond did not occur.

as 9 additional possibilities for bile acids with substituents on the 3 and 12 positions. There are 27 possible trisubstituted acids. The challenge of the overwhelming complexity of the composition of the fecal bile acids has been met by the development of powerful analytical techniques, especially coupled gas-liquid chromatography and mass spectrometry. A series of papers from Sjövall's laboratory by Eneroth and colleagues (40, 41) has identified many of the predicted metabolites of the primary bile acids. Recently the organism responsible for this important 7-dehydroxylation step has been isolated (59).

Changes in physical properties accompany these changes in chemical structure. Lithocholate, the major metabolite of chenodeoxycholate, has a critical micellar temperature above 60 C and is thus insoluble at body temperature (72, 80). Deoxycholate, the major metabolite of cholate, is insoluble at neutral pH (80). Norman (116) prepared an aqueous homogenate of human feces and showed that after ultracentrifugation, a large fraction of the fecal bile acids was to be found in the sediment. In a subsequent paper (117), he and Palmer demonstrated that bile acids that were acylated with fatty acid in the 3 position were present in the human feces. Such compounds should be far less soluble than their nonacylated precursors.

The alteration in the physical properties of bile salts in the large-intestinal lumen may be contrasted with the events occurring during triglyceride lipolysis. In the large intestine the formation of less polar derivatives results in their adsorption to bacteria and a probable reduction in their absorption. In the jejunum lipolysis converts triglyceride to the more polar derivatives—fatty acid and monoglyceride; these compounds are readily dispersed in water by bile salts and are efficiently absorbed.

If ^{14}C-ring-labeled bile acids are administered to animals, radioactivity is not detected in the expired carbon dioxide (24); complete recovery of 24-^{14}C-labeled cholic and chenodeoxycholic acids administered orally to two human subjects has been reported (56). The evidence showing compounds that normally pass through the alimentary tract without chemical alteration may be extensively degraded in individuals with sluggish fecal flow has been summarized (27), and in agreement Grundy & Ahrens (55) have recently claimed that administered 24-^{14}C-labeled bile acids may be degraded in some individuals on liquid formula diets. Nevertheless, bile acid synthesis rates estimated by isotope dilution (98) agree closely with those estimated by balance techniques (55); this sug-

gests that most individuals do not degrade the side chain or steroid nucleus of bile acids to a significant extent during their passage through the large intestine.

Intracellular Effects: Bile Salt Absorption

The presence of deoxycholate, a bacterial metabolite, in bile probably indicates that some absorption of bile salts occurs from the large intestine. The absence of other metabolites suggests that only deoxycholate is absorbed in appreciable amounts; it seems unlikely that other metabolites are absorbed from the large intestine and converted by the liver to primary bile acids or deoxycholate. The absorption of cholate and chenodeoxycholate from the cecum in rats has been demonstrated (118), but few data exist on the absorption of conjugated bile salts from the colon, either in intact animals or in perfused or everted gut segments in experiments in which the physical state of bile salts was well controlled. Although little bile salt absorption is considered to occur in the large intestine (see Weiner and Lack, Volume III of this *Handbook*), it should be noted that the efficient ileal reabsorption means that normally probably less than 1 g daily of bile salts reaches the cecum from the ileum. Absorption of 0.5 g a day from the large intestine would reduce fecal excretion and the synthesis requirement by half.

The passage of deoxycholate through the mucosal cell appears to inhibit water and ion transport (48) as noted. Whether other metabolic activities of the mucosal cells of the large intestine are affected by deoxycholate absorption is unknown.

HOMEOSTASIS

Bile Salt Pool as a Determinant of Intraluminal Bile Salt Concentration

The major function of bile salts in the jejunal lumen is to facilitate the diffusion of lipids to the mucosal surface by increasing their concentration in the aqueous phase. Such lipid transport can occur only if bile salts are above their critical micellar concentration—about 2 mM—and below this concentration bile salts should be much less effective in vivo. Since bile salts do not appear to be absorbed in the jejunum, their concentration depends on the amount of bile reaching the intestinal lumen and its dilution by intestinal content.

Lindstedt (98) injected ^{14}C-cholic acid into normal subjects and followed the specific activity of biliary

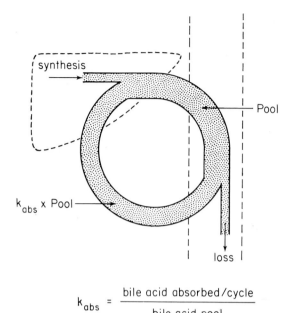

$$k_{abs} = \frac{\text{bile acid absorbed/cycle}}{\text{bile acid pool}}$$

FIG. 18. Schematic representation of the enterohepatic circulation of bile salts. It is customary, in the manner of Lindstedt (98), to estimate the size of the bile salt pool by extrapolating the specific activity decay curve for biliary bile acids to zero time. The bile salt pool thus represents the sum of the fraction of the bile salt pool absorbed during the previous cycle (K pool) plus that bile acid synthesized by the liver during that particular enterohepatic cycle. If the pool remains constant in size, daily loss is equal to $(1 - K) PC$, where C is the number of enterohepatic cycles per day (74). Most of the bile salt reabsorption is considered to occur in the ileum where there is an active transport mechanism for bile salts (see Weiner and Lack, Volume III of this *Handbook*).

cholic acid over several weeks. The injected bile acid was dilated by a large "pool" of nonradioactive bile acid (about 3,000–4,000 mg) and the decay in bile acid specific activity followed first-order kinetics. The half-time of the pool was calculated to be about 3 days and the daily synthesis of bile acids about 350 mg. This figure, together with other observations (19, 20), indicated that each bile salt molecule participates in 15–20 enterohepatic cycles before excretion. The bile salt pool size, which is thus roughly six to ten times the amount synthesized daily (98), is probably a major determinant of the concentration of bile salts in the intestinal lumen.

The ratio of the pool size to the synthesis rate is determined by the efficiency of ileal reabsorption (74). If a fractional coefficient of absorption, K, is defined as the fraction of the pool that is absorbed during one enterohepatic cycle, it is probable that K is greater than 0.9 for normal individuals (74, 98). In the steady state, synthesis is equal to fecal loss. If a pool, P, circu-

lates C times daily, KP is absorbed during each cycle, and KCP is the amount of bile salt absorbed from the ileum each day if the liver continuously restores the pool to constant size (Fig. 18). Daily fecal loss is $C(1 - K)P$, which is equal to daily synthesis. Daily synthesis is also equal to P times e, in which e is the rate constant of the specific activity decay curve. Therefore, $e = C(1 - K)$ and the decay curve is a measure of the product of the number of cycles and the efficiency of ileal reabsorption. A more detailed mathematical model of the enterohepatic circulation of bile salts is desirable.

Hepatic synthesis of bile acids is regulated homeostatically. Thus, the feeding of cholic acid depresses both cholic and chenodeoxycholic acid synthesis in rat (6) and man (57), and bile salt infusion into the portal vein of a bile-fistula rat decreases its rate of bile acid synthesis (11). The interruption of the enterohepatic circulation, by cholestyramine administration (7), ileectomy (1, 57), or bile fistula (12, 24), causes a marked increase in bile acid synthesis. Since synthesis can probably increase only to about four to six times the normal rate, the bile salt pool may decrease, despite increased synthesis, if no bile salts recirculate.[5]

The opposite situation occurs when bile salts are fed by mouth (57). The bile salt pool expands until the ileal T_m is reached, at which point the administered bile salt appears in the stool and diarrhea occurs. The expanded bile salt pool inhibits bile acid synthesis, and when equilibrium is reached, the fecal output is equal to the oral intake; the bile salt pool is expanded, however, despite the virtual absence of synthesis.

Alteration of Bile Salts in Small-Intestinal Lumen by Bacteria

The concentration of bile salts in solution in the jejunal lumen is dependent not only on the pool size but also on the absence of destruction or absorption of bile salt. In mammals other than the rabbit, evidence suggests that the scanty bacterial flora of the jejunal lumen do not chemically alter the biliary bile

[5] Bile acid kinetics probably cannot be described by first-order kinetics in ileectomized patients, especially those with steatorrhea. In such patients the effective bile salt pool is derived largely from synthesis, and the longer the interval since the last meal, the greater will be the bile salt pool. Such patients may have normal jejunal bile acid concentrations at breakfast, but decreased jejunal bile acid concentration during subsequent meals (J. S. Fordtran, personal communication).

acids. However, bacterial overgrowth in various clinical situations results in deconjugation and dehydroxylation (36, 91, 143) with the following possible sequelae: *1)* the resultant free bile acids may precipitate from solution, *2)* the resultant free bile acids may be absorbed, or *3)* the resultant free bile acids may alter the metabolism of or destroy the cells of the jejunal mucosa. Thus the consequences of bacterial alteration of bile salts are to be interpreted in terms of bile salt deficiency or the cytotoxicity of the products (or both)—that is, an intracellular effect.

In a dog with a surgically induced blind loop, the concentration of micellar lipid below the loop is reduced (91). In such animals the mucosal architecture generally appears normal by light microscopy (36, 124). The lack of mucosal destruction and the marked reduction in the steatorrhea when conjugated bile salts are administered are consistent with the hypothesis that the major mechanism for steatorrhea is a deficiency of bile salts with decreased micelle formation. This deficiency is caused by absorption or precipitation (or both) of the free bile acids formed. However, since deoxycholate is formed and has been demonstrated to inhibit fatty acid esterification in a variety of in vitro preparations of the small intestine (28, 36, 125), a toxic effect of the free bile acids on the metabolic activity of the mucosal cell may also contribute.

Sequestration of Bile Salts in Small-Intestinal Lumen

Bile salts must be in solution to be effective. Cholestyramine, an anion-exchange resin, binds bile salts in vitro and causes increased bile salt excretion and steatorrhea in vivo (7, 63). Neomycin, a dibasic tetrasaccharide, precipitates bile salts from solution in vitro (43) and causes increased bile salt excretion with steatorrhea in vivo (84). However, its effects are complicated by its inhibition of pancreatic lipase as well as its antibiotic effects, which decrease the rate of conversion of cholic acid to deoxycholic acid (60).

DIGESTION AND ABSORPTION OF NUTRIENTS IN ABSENCE OF BILE SALTS

In the experimental animal, exclusion of bile from the intestinal lumen is usually produced by biliary fistula, a manipulation that causes an enormous increase in bile acid excretion as well as a continuous loss of sterol, lecithin, glycine or taurine (or both), and other compounds, such as steroids and the fat-soluble vitamins, which customarily undergo enterohepatic circulation. Therefore some of the metabolic alterations in the bile-fistula animal may not be related solely to the absence of bile salts from the intestinal lumen. In biliary obstruction the substances normally excreted in bile are retained, and again the metabolic abnormality cannot be assumed to result solely from the absence of bile salts in the intestinal lumen. Although Whipple (149) summarized his long experience with bile-fistula dogs by stating that "secretion of bile into the intestine is necessary... for... continuation of life beyond a few months period," this observation contrasts with the clinical impression that patients with complete biliary obstruction remain in relatively good health for a much longer period; and it seems probable that in Whipple's dogs the loss of all biliary components plus the deficient absorption of lipids resulting from biliary diversion together proved a fatal combination. Today, with advances in our knowledge of bile salt function, efficacious replacement therapy should permit a relatively normal life expectancy were such dogs to be prepared now, assuming there were no complications from the operative manipulation per se. The following abnormalities should develop in the animal with biliary diversion according to the functions of bile salts discussed previously: *1)* decreased fat absorption, *2)* decreased absorption of fat-soluble vitamins, *3)* decreased absorption of calcium and possible decreased absorption of other polyvalent cations, and *4)* decreased absorption of cholesterol.

Fat Absorption

The studies of Knoebel & Ryan (92), as well as earlier studies of Heersma & Annegers (69), showed that the extent of lipolysis of fat present in the intestinal lumen, as determined by analysis of fatty acids and partial glycerides, is not significantly influenced by biliary diversion. Such determinations measure the composition of intestinal content at a fixed point, and since the rate of absorption of fat in such animals is decreased, the initial rate of ester bond cleavage may actually be decreased. The comparable analytical values may merely indicate that dietary fat was exposed to pancreatic lipase for a longer period of time in the bile-fistula animal. Pancreatic lipase is considered to be present in extremely high concentrations during the digestive period (27), and extensive lipolysis can be obtained in vitro in the absence of bile salts (68).

If the function of bile salts is to disperse lipids into an aqueous, micellar phase, the absence of bile salts should be associated with the absence of the micellar phase. The aqueous solubility of monoglycerides is extremely low, but fatty acid has a definite aqueous solubility that increases with pH (101, 126). Since the pH of the intestinal content of the bile-deprived animal is reported to be identical to that of the normal animal (92) (that is, 5–7) fatty acid should be present in low concentration in the aqueous phase in a molecularly dispersed, ionized form. Bile-fistula dogs during fat digestion have a higher intraluminal concentration of monoglyceride than normal dogs (92); this may represent a decreased absorption rate or decreased isomerization rate or both.

The aqueous phase of normal subjects after the ingestion of a fat meal contains 2–6 mg per ml, chiefly monoglyceride and fatty acid (78). The aqueous phase of patients with biliary obstruction contains generally less than 1 mg per ml of lipid, and this lipid is almost solely fatty acid (A. F. Hofmann, unpublished observations). If the monoglyceride present in the intestinal content of bile-deprived subjects is present solely in the oil phase, it is to be predicted that little or no chylomicron glycerol would be derived from dietary fat; studies are needed.

If bile salts have no intracellular effect in the jejunum, triglyceride resynthesis in the mucosal cell should proceed normally in the bile-fistula animal, although resynthesis might not involve the usual monoglyceride acylation pathway. Release of chylomicron triglyceride from the cell would be less, since less fat enters the cell. Morgan (113) has shown convincingly that the bile-fistula rat, if allowed to recover from the effects of the operation, can resynthesize chylomicron triglyceride at a normal rate, provided fatty acid absorption is enhanced by emulsification with the appropriate nonionic detergent. The observation of Kern & Borgström (90), as well as of Knoebel & Ryan (92), that the mucosal cell of the bile-fistula animal contains relatively more fatty acid and less higher glycerides than the mucosal cell of the normal animal may merely indicate that the monoglyceride is not absorbed and that the resynthesis of triglyceride via the α-glycerophosphate pathway (see Johnston, Volume I of this *Handbook*) is slower than the rate at which fatty acid is absorbed.

It is probable that dietary phospholipid as well as that deriving from sloughed mucosal cells can be cleaved by the phospholipases present in pancreatic juice in the absence of bile. Although lysolecithin in concentrations above its critical micellar concentration forms micelles that could conceivably fulfill a transport function similar to that of the bile salt micelle, it seems unlikely that lysolecithin is present in micellar concentration. Detailed studies on the composition and physical state of lipids in the intestinal content of bile-deprived subjects are needed.

Absorption of Fat-Soluble Vitamins

The cholecystopyelostomy dogs of Hawkins and Whipple rapidly developed bleeding (67), and pursuit of this clotting abnormality contributed to the discovery of vitamin K (66). Vitamin E is not considered to be excreted in bile although bile is essential for its absorption (32, 109). Bile is also essential for the absorption of vitamins A and D, and an additional loss of these vitamins will occur in bile-fistula animals if their polar metabolites in bile (2, 151) undergo an enterohepatic circulation.

Cholesterol Absorption

The bile-fistula animal does not absorb dietary cholesterol and continuously loses its biliary cholesterol. The intestinal wall synthesizes cholesterol, and considerable evidence has been adduced for the intestine being a major site of extrahepatic cholesterol synthesis (97); such cholesterol enters the intestinal lymphatics and mixes with dietary cholesterol. It is probable that much of the cholesterol synthesized by the intestinal mucosa is structural and that when the cell is sloughed this cholesterol is reabsorbed. For such reabsorption bile is almost certainly necessary. Therefore in the bile-fistula animal on a sterol-free diet there should be a continuous excretion of cholesterol in the stool as was demonstrated many years ago by Sperry (142). Interpretation of stool excretion data under these conditions is difficult since cell turnover, bacterial flora, and other processes may be altered in the bile-fistula animal.

Calcium Absorption

The bile-fistula animal develops osteomalacia; the mechanism by which bile salts might influence calcium absorption (147, 148) has been discussed previously. Whether the bile-fistula animal develops deficiencies in other cations has not been considered.

To summarize, the absorption of nonpolar lipids such as cholesterol and the fat-soluble vitamins is negligible in the absence of bile. The absorption of more polar lipids such as fatty acids is appreciable although still considerably reduced. Whether the apparent requirement of bile salts for absorption of nonpolar lipids is to be explained solely by the effect of bile salts on the physical state of these compounds in the intestinal lumen, or whether a more specific interaction between the bile salt micelle and the mucosal cell is required, is unclear. Finally, in the absence of surfactant from the small-intestinal lumen, it is possible that particulate material may adsorb to the cell and that fluxes in and out of the cell of all solutes and water may be decreased.

Many of the ideas expressed here resulted from discussions with D. M. Small, B. Borgström, W. J. Simmonds, A. S. C. Lawrence, and J. H. Schulman. Bengt Borgström and E. H. Ahrens, Jr., have generously supported the author's work in the past. Mrs. Gayle Dunlap and Mrs. Mary Olness gave efficient secretarial assistance.

REFERENCES

1. AUSTAD, W. I., L. LACK, AND M. P. TYOR. Importance of bile acids and of an intact distal small intestine for fat absorption. *Gastroenterology* 52: 638–646, 1967.
2. AVIOLI, L., S. W. LEE, J. McDONALD, AND H. DeLUCA. Hepatic metabolism and biliary excretion of ^{3}H-vitamin D_3 in man (abstr.). *Clin. Res.* 14: 432, 1966.
3. BAKER, R. D., AND G. W. SEARLE. Bile salt absorption at various levels of rat small intestine. *Proc. Soc. Exptl. Biol. Med.* 105: 521–523, 1960.
4. BANGHAM, A. D. Physical structure and behavior of lipids and lipid enzymes. In: *Advances in Lipid Research*, edited by R. Paoletti and D. Kritchevsky. New York: Acad. Press, 1963, vol. 1, p. 65–104.
5. BATES, T. R., M. GIBALDI, AND J. L. KANIG. Solubilizing properties of bile salt solutions. II. Effect of inorganic electrolyte, lipids, and a mixed bile salt system on solubilization of glutethimide, griseofulvin, and hexestrol. *J. Pharm. Sci.* 55: 901–906, 1966.
6. BEHER, W. T., G. D. BAKER, W. L. ANTHONY, AND M. E. BEHER. The feedback control of cholesterol biosynthesis. *Henry Ford Hosp. Med. Bull.* 9: 201–213, 1961.
7. BEHER, W. T., M. E. BEHER, AND B. RAO. Bile acid and cholesterol metabolism in the mouse as affected by cholestyramine. *Proc. Soc. Exptl. Biol. Med.* 122: 881–884, 1966.
8. BENZONANA, G., AND P. DESNUELLE. Etude cinétique de l'action de la lipase pancréatique sur des triglycérides en émulsion: essai d'une enzymologie en milieu hétérogène. *Biochim. Biophys. Acta* 105: 121–136, 1965.
9. BERGMANN, M. Ueber die peristaltische Wirksamkeit der Gallensäuren und ihre klinische Anwendung. *Wien. Klin. Wochschr.* 64: 704–707, 1952.
10. BERGSTRÖM, S., AND B. BORGSTRÖM. The intestinal absorption of fats. In: *Progress in the Chemistry of Fats and Other Lipids*, edited by R. T. Holman, W. O. Lundberg, and T. Malkin. New York: Pergamon, 1955, vol. 3, p. 351–393.
11. BERGSTRÖM, S., AND H. DANIELSSON. On the regulation of bile acid formation in the rat liver. *Acta Physiol. Scand.* 43: 1–7, 1958.
12. BERGSTRÖM, S., H. DANIELSSON, AND B. SAMUELSSON. Formation and metabolism of bile acids. In: *Lipide Metabolism*, edited by K. Bloch. New York: Wiley, 1960, p. 291–336.
13. BEZNÁK, A. VON. Die Wirkung von Trypsin auf die geparten Gallensäuren. *Biochem. Z.* 210: 261–264, 1929.
14. BLOMSTRAND, R., N. A. THORN, AND E. H. AHRENS, JR. The absorption of fats, studied in a patient with chyluria. I. Clinical investigation. *Am. J. Med.* 24: 958–966, 1958.
15. BLOOMFIELD, D. K. Dynamics of cholesterol metabolism. I. Factors regulating total sterol biosynthesis and accumulation in the rat. *Proc. Natl. Acad. Sci. U.S.* 50: 117–124, 1963.
16. BOCKUS, H. L. *Gastroenterology* (2nd ed.). Philadelphia: Saunders, 1965, vol. 3, p. 854.
17. BORGSTRÖM, B. Studies on intestinal cholesterol absorption in the human. *J. Clin. Invest.* 39: 809–815, 1960.
18. BORGSTRÖM, B. Influence of bile salt, pH, and time on the action of pancreatic lipase: physiological implications. *J. Lipid Res.* 5: 522–531, 1964.
19. BORGSTRÖM, B., A. DAHLQVIST, G. LUNDH, AND J. SJÖVALL. Studies of intestinal digestion and absorption in the human. *J. Clin. Invest.* 36: 1521–1536, 1957.
20. BORGSTRÖM, B., G. LUNDH, AND A. HOFMANN. The site of absorption of conjugated bile salts in man. *Gastroenterology* 45: 229–238, 1963.
21. CHAPMAN, D., P. BYRNE, AND G. G. SHIPLEY. The physical properties of phospholipids. I. Solid state and mesomorphic properties of some 2, 3-diacyl-DL-phosphatidyl-ethanol-amines. *Proc. Roy. Soc., London, Ser. A* 290: 115–142, 1966.
22. CLÉMENT, G. La digestion et l'absorption des graisses. *J. Physiol., Paris* 56: 111–192, 1964.
23. DAHLQVIST, A., AND B. BORGSTRÖM. Digestion and absorption of disaccharides in man. *Biochem. J.* 81: 411–418, 1961.
24. DANIELSSON, H. Present status of research on catabolism and excretion of cholesterol. In: *Advances in Lipid Research*, edited by R. Paoletti and D. Kritchevsky. New York: Acad. Press, 1963, vol. 1, p. 335–385.
25. DANIELSSON, H., P. ENEROTH, K. HELLSTRÖM, S. LINDSTEDT, AND J. SJÖVALL. On the turnover and excretory products of cholic and chenodeoxycholic acid in man: bile acids and steroids 134. *J. Biol. Chem.* 238: 2299–2304, 1963.
26. DASHER, G. F. Surface activity of naturally occurring emulsifiers. *Science* 116: 660–663, 1952.
27. DAVENPORT, H. W. *Physiology of the Digestive Tract: An Introductory Text* (2nd ed.). Chicago: Year Book, 1966, 230 p.
28. DAWSON, A. M., AND K. J. ISSELBACHER. The esterification of palmitate-1-C^{14} by homogenates of intestinal mucosa. *J. Clin. Invest.* 39: 150–160, 1960.
29. DAWSON, A. M., AND K. J. ISSELBACHER. Studies on lipid

metabolism in the small intestine with observations on the role of bile salts. *J. Clin. Invest.* 39: 730–740, 1960.

30. DE HAAS, G. H., L. SARDA, AND J. ROGER. Positional specific hydrolysis of phospholipids by pancreatic lipase. *Biochim. Biophys. Acta* 106: 638–640, 1965.

31. DERVICHIAN, D. G. The physical chemistry of phospholipids. In: *Progress in Biophysics and Molecular Biology*, edited by J. A. V. Butler and H. E. Huxley. New York: Macmillan, 1964, vol. 14, p. 263–342.

32. DEUEL, H. J., JR. *The Lipids: Their Chemistry and Biochemistry. Biochemistry: Digestion, Absorption, Transport and Storage.* New York: Interscience Publishers, 1955, vol. II, p. 282–332.

33. DIETSCHY, J. M., H. S. SALOMON, AND M. D. SIPERSTEIN. Bile acid metabolism. I. Studies on the mechanisms of intestinal transport. *J. Clin. Invest.* 45: 832–846, 1966.

34. DIETSCHY, J. M., AND M. D. SIPERSTEIN. Cholesterol synthesis by the gastrointestinal tract: localization and mechanisms of control. *J. Clin. Invest.* 44: 1311–1327, 1965.

35. DONALDSON, R. M., JR. Normal bacterial populations of the intestine and their relation to intestinal function. *New Engl. J. Med.* 270: 938–945, 994–1001, 1050–1056, 1964.

36. DONALDSON, R. M., JR. Studies on the pathogenesis of steatorrhea in the blind loop syndrome. *J. Clin. Invest.* 44: 1815–1825, 1965.

37. DREHER, K. D., J. H. SCHULMAN, AND A. F. HOFMANN. Surface chemistry of the monoglyceride-bile salt system: its relationship to the function of bile salts in fat absorption. *J. Colloid Interface Sci.* 25: 71–83, 1967.

38. EKWALL, P., K. FONTELL, AND A. STEN. Micelle formation in bile salt solutions. In: *Gas/Liquid and Liquid/Liquid Interface: Proc. 2nd Intern. Congr. Surface Activity.* London: Butterworth, 1957, vol. I, p. 357–373.

39. EKWALL, P., T. ROSENDAHL, AND N. LÖFMAN. Studies on bile acid salt solutions. I. The dissociation constants of cholic and desoxycholic acids. *Acta Chem. Scand.* 11: 590–598, 1957.

40. ENEROTH, P., B. GORDON, R. RYHAGE, AND J. SJÖVALL. Identification of mono- and dihydroxy bile acids in human feces by gas-liquid chromatography and mass spectrometry. *J. Lipid Res.* 7: 511–523, 1966.

41. ENEROTH, P., B. GORDON, AND J. SJÖVALL. Characterization of trisubstituted cholanoic acids in human feces. *J. Lipid Res.* 7: 524–530, 1966.

42. ENTRESSANGLES, B., H. SARI, AND P. DESNUELLE. On the positional specificity of pancreatic lipase. *Biochim. Biophys. Acta* 125: 597–600, 1966.

43. FALOON, W. W., D. WOOLFOLK, H. NANKIN, K. WALLACE, AND E. N. HARO. The role of bile salts in neomycin-induced malabsorption (abstr.). *J. Clin. Invest.* 43: 1254, 1964.

44. FELDMAN, E. B., AND B. BORGSTRÖM. Phase distribution of sterols: studies by gel filtration. *Biochim. Biophys. Acta* 125: 136–147, 1966.

45. FELDMAN, E. B., AND B. BORGSTRÖM. The behavior of glyceride-fatty acid mixtures in bile salt solution: studies by gel filtration. *Lipids* 1: 430–438, 1966.

46. FINDLAY, A. *Phase Rule and Its Applications* (9th ed.), revised and edited by A. N. Campbell and N. O. Smith. New York: Dover, 1951, 494 p.

47. FORDTRAN, J. S., AND T. W. LOCKLEAR. Ionic constituents and osmolality of gastric and small-intestinal fluids after eating. *Am. J. Digest. Diseases* 11: 503–521, 1966.

48. FORTH, W., W. RUMMEL, AND H. GLASNER. Zur resorptions-hemmenden Wirkung von Gallensäuren. *Arch. Pharmakol. Exptl. Pathol.* 254: 364–380, 1966.

49. FRAZER, A. C., J. H. SCHULMAN, AND H. C. STEWART. Emulsification of fat in the intestine of the rat and its relationship to absorption. *J. Physiol., London* 103: 306–316, 1944.

50. FRY, R. J. M., AND E. STAFFELDT. Effect of a diet containing sodium deoxycholate on the intestinal mucosa of the mouse. (Letter to the Editor.) *Nature* 203: 1396–1398, 1964.

51. GALAPEAUX, E. A., R. D. TEMPLETON, AND E. L. BORKON. The influence of bile on the motility of the dog's colon. *Am. J. Physiol.* 121: 130–136, 1938.

52. GLASSER, J. E., I. M. WEINER, AND L. LACK. Comparative physiology of intestinal taurocholate transport. *Am. J. Physiol.* 208: 359–362, 1965.

53. GOODMAN, DEW. S. Cholesterol ester metabolism. *Physiol. Rev.* 45: 747–839, 1965.

54. GOULD, R. G., AND R. P. COOK. The metabolism of cholesterol and other sterols in the animal organism. In: *Cholesterol: Chemistry, Biochemistry, and Pathology*, edited by R. P. Cook. New York: Acad. Press, 1958, p. 237–307.

55. GRUNDY, S. M., AND E. H. AHRENS, JR. An evaluation of the relative merits of two methods for measuring the balance of sterols in man: isotopic balance versus chromatographic analysis. *J. Clin. Invest.* 45: 1503–1515, 1966.

56. GRUNDY, S. M., E. H. AHRENS, JR., AND T. A. MIETTINEN. Quantitative isolation and gas-liquid chromatographic analysis of total fecal bile acids. *J. Lipid Res.* 6: 397–410, 1965.

57. GRUNDY, S. M., A. F. HOFMANN, J. DAVIGNON, AND E. H. AHRENS, JR. Human cholesterol synthesis is regulated by bile acids (abstr.). *J. Clin. Invest.* 45: 1018–1019, 1966.

58. GUSTAFSSON, B. E., S. BERGSTRÖM, S. LINDSTEDT, AND A. NORMAN. Turnover and nature of fecal bile acids in germ-free and infected rats fed cholic acid-24-^{14}C: bile acids and steroids 41. *Proc. Soc. Exptl. Biol. Med.* 94: 467–471, 1957.

59. GUSTAFSSON, B. E., T. MIDTVEDT, AND A. NORMAN. Isolated fecal microorganisms capable of 7 α-dehydroxylating bile acids. *J. Exptl. Med.* 123: 413–432, 1966.

60. HAMILTON, J. G., J. E. MULDREY, B. H. McCRACKEN, G. A. GOLDSMITH, AND O. N. MILLER. The effect of neomycin on cholesterol metabolism. *J. Am. Oil Chem. Soc.* 41: 760–762, 1964.

61. HARTLEY, G. S. Aqueous solutions of paraffin-chain salts: a study in micelle formation. In: *Actualités Scientifiques.* Paris: Hermann, 1936, 72 p.

62. HARTLEY, G. S. Solutions of soap-like substances. In: *Progress in the Chemistry of Fats and Other Lipids*, edited by R. T. Holman, W. O. Lundberg, and T. Malkin. New York: Pergamon, 1955, vol. 3, p. 20–55.

63. HASHIM, S. A., AND T. B. VAN ITALLIE. Cholestyramine resin therapy for hypercholesteremia. *J. Am. Med. Asosc.* 192: 289–293, 1965.

64. HASLEWOOD, G. A. D. Bile salts. In: *Comprehensive Biochemistry: Sterols, Bile Acids and Steroids*, edited by M. Florkin and E. H. Stotz. New York: Elsevier, 1963, vol. 10, p. 23–31.

65. HASLEWOOD, G. A. D. The biological significance of

chemical differences in bile salts. *Biol. Rev.* 39: 537–574, 1964.

66. HAWKINS, W. B., AND K. M. BRINKHOUS. Prothrombin deficiency the cause of bleeding in bile fistula dogs. *J. Exptl. Med.* 63: 795–801, 1936.

67. HAWKINS, W. B., AND G. H. WHIPPLE. Bile fistulas and related abnormalities: bleeding, osteoporosis, cholelithiasis and duodenal ulcers. *J. Exptl. Med.* 62: 599–620, 1935.

68. HEATH, T. J., AND B. MORRIS. The role of bile and pancreatic juice in the absorption of fat in ewes and lambs. *Brit. J. Nutr.* 17: 465–474, 1963.

69. HEERSMA, J. R., AND J. H. ANNEGERS. Effect of bile preparations on fat absorption in bile fistula dogs. *Proc. Soc. Exptl. Biol. Med.* 67: 339–341, 1948.

70. HOFMANN, A. F. The behavior and solubility of monoglycerides in dilute, micellar bile-salt solution. *Biochim. Biophys. Acta* 70: 306–316, 1963.

71. HOFMANN, A. F. The function of bile salts in fat absorption: the solvent properties of dilute micellar solutions of conjugated bile salts. *Biochem. J.* 89: 57–68, 1963.

72. HOFMANN, A. F. *The Function of Bile Salts in Fat Absorption* (M.D. Thesis). Lund, Sweden: Univ. of Lund, 1964.

73. HOFMANN, A. F. Clinical implications of physicochemical studies on bile salts. *Gastroenterology* 48: 484–494, 1965.

74. HOFMANN, A. F. A physicochemical approach to the intraluminal phase of fat absorption. *Gastroenterology* 50: 56–64, 1966.

75. HOFMANN, A. F. Molecular association in fat digestion: the interaction in bulk of monoolein, oleic acid, and sodium oleate with dilute micellar bile salt solutions. In: *Molecular Association in Biological Systems. Advances in Chemistry.* Washington, D.C.: Am. Chem. Soc. In press.

76. HOFMANN, A. F., AND B. BORGSTRÖM. Physico-chemical state of lipids in intestinal content during their digestion and absorption. *Federation Proc.* 21: 43–50, 1962.

77. HOFMANN, A. F., AND B. BORGSTRÖM. Hydrolysis of longchain monoglycerides in micellar solution by pancreatic lipase. *Biochim. Biophys. Acta* 70: 317–331, 1963.

78. HOFMANN, A. F., AND B. BORGSTRÖM. The intraluminal phase of fat digesion in man: the lipid content of the micellar and oil phases of intestinal content obtained during fat digestion and absorption. *J. Clin. Invest.* 43: 247–257, 1964.

79. HOFMANN, A. F., AND E. H. MOSBACH. Identification of allodeoxycholic acid as the major component of gallstones induced in the rabbit by 5α-cholestan-3β-ol. *J. Biol. Chem.* 239: 2813–2821, 1964.

80. HOFMANN, A. F., AND D. M. SMALL. Detergent properties of bile salts: correlation with physiological function. *Ann. Rev. Med.* 18: 333–376, 1967.

81. HOGBEN, C. A. M. Fat absorption: a transport problem. *Gastroenterology* 50: 51–55, 1966.

82. HOLT, P. R. Intestinal absorption of bile salts in the rat. *Am. J. Physiol.* 207: 1–7, 1964.

83. HOLT, P. R. Competitive inhibition of intestinal bile salt absorption in the rat. *Am. J. Physiol.* 210: 635–639, 1966.

84. JACOBSON, E. D., R. B. CHODOS, AND W. W. FALOON. An experimental malabsorption syndrome induced by neomycin. *Am. J. Med.* 28: 524–533, 1960.

85. JAVITT, N. B. Cholestasis in rats induced by taurolithocholate. (Letter to the Editor.) *Nature* 210: 1262–1263, 1966.

86. JUNIPER, K., JR. Physicochemical characteristics of bile and their relation to gallstone formation. *Am. J. Med.* 39: 98–107, 1965.

87. KAVANAU, J. L. *Structure and Function in Biological Membranes.* San Francisco: Holden-Day, 1965, vol. 1, 336 p.

88. KAYDEN, H. J., J. R. SENIOR, AND F. H. MATTSON. Demonstration that 2-monoglycerides are incorporated intact into human lymph triglycerides (abstr.). *J. Clin. Invest.* 45: 1031–1032, 1966.

89. KERN, F., JR., AND B. BORGSTRÖM. Quantitative study of the pathways of triglyceride synthesis by hamster intestinal mucosa. *Biochim. Biophys. Acta* 98: 520–531, 1965.

90. KERN, F., JR., AND B. BORGSTRÖM. The effect of a conjugated bile salt on oleic acid absorption in the rat. *Gastroenterology* 49: 623–631, 1965.

91. KIM, Y. S., N. SPRITZ, M. BLUM, J. TERZ, AND P. SHERLOCK. The role of altered bile acid metabolism in the steatorrhea of experimental blind loop. *J. Clin. Invest.* 45: 956–962, 1966.

92. KNOEBEL, L. K., AND J. M. RYAN. Digestion and mucosal absorption of fat in normal and bile-deficient dogs. *Am. J. Physiol.* 204: 509–514, 1963.

93. LACK, L., AND I. M. WEINER. In vitro absorption of bile salts by small intestine of rats and guinea pigs. *Am. J. Physiol.* 200: 313–317, 1961.

94. LAURENT, T. C., AND H. PERSSON. A study of micelles of sodium taurodeoxycholate in the ultracentrifuge. *Biochim. Biophys. Acta* 106: 616–624, 1965.

95. LAWRENCE, A. S. C. Polar interaction in detergency. In: *Surface Activity and Detergency*, edited by K. Durham. London: Macmillan, 1961, p. 158–192.

96. LESTER, R., AND R. SCHMID. Bilirubin metabolism. *New Engl. J. Med.* 270: 779–786, 1964.

97. LINDSEY, C. A., JR., AND J. D. WILSON. Evidence for a contribution by the intestinal wall to the serum cholesterol of the rat. *J. Lipid Res.* 6: 173–181, 1965.

98. LINDSTEDT, S. The turnover of cholic acid in man: bile acids and steroids 51. *Acta Physiol. Scand.* 40: 1–9, 1957.

99. LINSCHEER, W. G., J. F. PATTERSON, E. W. MOORE, R. J. CLERMONT, S. J. ROBINS, AND T. C. CHALMERS. Medium and long chain fat absorption in patients with cirrhosis. *J. Clin. Invest.* 45: 1317–1325, 1966.

100. LIPPEL, K., AND J. A. OLSON. The activity of non-lipolytic digestive enzymes of the pancreas in the presence of conjugated bile salts. *Biochim. Biophys. Acta* 127: 243–245, 1966.

101. LUCASSEN, J. Hydrolysis and precipitates in carboxylate soap solutions. *J. Phys. Chem.* 70: 1824–1830, 1966.

102. LUTTON, E. S. Phase behavior of aqueous systems of monoglycerides. *J. Am. Oil Chem. Soc.* 42: 1068–1070, 1965.

103. LUZZATI, V., AND F. HUSSON. The structure of the liquidcrystalline phases of lipid-water systems. *J. Cell Biol.* 12: 207–219, 1962.

104. MATTSON, F. H., AND L. W. BECK. The specificity of pancreatic lipase for the primary hydroxyl groups of glycerides. *J. Biol. Chem.* 219: 735–740, 1956.

105. MATTSON, F. H., AND R. A. VOLPENHEIN. Synthesis and properties of glycerides. *J. Lipid Res.* 3: 281–296, 1962.

106. MATTSON, F. H., AND R. A. VOLPENHEIN. The digestion and absorption of triglycerides. *J. Biol. Chem.* 239: 2772–2777, 1964.

107. MCBAIN, E. L., AND E. HUTCHINSON. *Solubilization and*

Related Phenomena: Physical Chemistry. New York: Acad. Press, 1955, vol. 4, p. 84–109.

108. McBain, J. W. The states of matter exemplified by a typical colloid: soap and the soap boiling processes. In: *Colloid Chemistry: Theoretical and Applied. Theory and Methods,* edited by J. Alexander. New York: Chemical Catalog Co., 1926, vol. 1, p. 137–164.

109. Mellors, A., and M. McC. Barnes. The distribution and metabolism of α-tocopherol in the rat. *Brit. J. Nutr.* 20: 69–77, 1966.

110. Meyer, A. E., and J. P. McEwen. Bile acids and their choline salts applied to the inner surface of the isolated colon and ileum of the guinea pig. *Am. J. Physiol.* 153: 386–392, 1948.

111. Moore, B., and W. H. Parker. On the functions of the bile as a solvent. *Proc. Roy. Soc., London* 68: 64–76, 1901.

112. Moore, E. W., and J. M. Dietschy. Na and K activity coefficients in bile and bile salts determined by glass electrodes. *Am. J. Physiol.* 206: 1111–1117, 1964.

113. Morgan, R. G. H. The effect of bile salts on the lymphatic absorption by the unanaesthetized rat of intraduodenally infused lipids. *Quart. J. Exptl. Physiol.* 49: 457–465, 1964.

114. Nageotte, J. *Morphologie des Gels Lipoïdes.* Paris: Hermann, 1936, 176 p.

115. Nair, P. P., M. Gordon, S. Gordon, J. Reback, and A. I. Mendeloff. The cleavage of bile acid conjugates by cell-free extracts from *Clostridium perfringens. Life Sci.* 4: 1887–1892, 1965.

116. Norman, A. Faecal excretion products of cholic acid in man. *Brit. J. Nutr.* 18: 173–186, 1964.

117. Norman, A., and R. H. Palmer. Metabolites of lithocholic acid-24-C14 in human bile and feces. *J. Lab. Clin. Med.* 63: 986–1001, 1964.

118. Norman, A., and J. Sjövall. On the transformation and enterohepatic circulation of cholic acid in the rat: bile acids and steroids 68. *J. Biol. Chem.* 233: 872–885, 1958.

119. Norman, A., and O. A. Widström. Hydrolysis of conjugated bile acids by extracellular enzymes present in rat intestinal contents. *Proc. Soc. Exptl. Biol. Med.* 117: 442–444, 1964.

120. Olson, J. A. The effect of bile and bile salts on the uptake and cleavage of β-carotene into retinol ester (vitamin A ester) by intestinal slices. *J. Lipid Res.* 5: 402–408, 1964.

121. Osipow, L. I. *Surface Chemistry: Theory and Industrial Applications.* New York: Reinhold, 1962, 473 p.

122. Palmer, R. H., and Z. Hruban. Production of bile duct hyperplasia and gallstones by lithocholic acid. *J. Clin. Invest* 45: 1255–1267, 1966.

123. Panish, J. F. Experimental blind loop steatorrhea. *Gastroenterology* 45: 394–399, 1963.

124. Playoust, M. R., L. Lack, and I. M. Weiner. Effect of intestinal resection on bile salt absorption in dogs. *Am. J. Physiol.* 208: 363–369, 1965.

125. Pope, J. L., T. M. Parkinson, and J. A. Olson. Action of bile salts on the metabolism and transport of water-soluble nutrients by perfused rat jejunum *in vitro. Biochim. Biophys. Acta* 130: 218–232, 1966.

126. Rosano, H. L., K. Breindel, J. H. Schulman, and A. J. Eydt. Mechanisms of ionic exchange with carrier molecules through non-aqueous liquid membranes. *J. Colloid Interface Sci.* 22: 58–67, 1966.

127. Rosevear, F. B. The microscopy of the liquid crystalline neat and middle phases of soaps and synthetic detergents. *J. Am. Oil Chem. Soc.* 31: 628–639, 1954.

128. Savary, P., M. J. Constantin, and P. Desnuelle. Sur la structure des triglycérides des chylomicrons lymphatiques du rat. *Biochim. Biophys. Acta* 48: 562–571, 1961.

129. Schacter, D., J. D. Finkelstein, and S. Kowarski. Metabolism of vitamin D. I. Preparation of radioactive vitamin D and its intestinal absorption in the rat. *J. Clin. Invest.* 43: 787–796, 1964.

130. Schedl, H. P., G. W. Osbaldiston, and I. H. Mills. Small intestinal secretion and absorption of calcium in the dog: role of intraluminal calcium compartments (abstr.). *J. Lab. Clin. Med.* 68: 1013–1014, 1966.

131. Schønheyder, F., and K. Volqvartz. Studies on the lipolytic enzyme action. III. Hydrolysis of tripropionyl glycerol. *Biochim. Biophys. Acta* 8: 407–415, 1952.

132. Senior, J. R. Intestinal absorption of fats. *J. Lipid Res.* 5: 495–521, 1964.

133. Shinoda, K., T. Nakagawa, B. Tamamushi, and T. Isemura. *Colloidal Surfactants: Some Physicochemical Properties.* New York: Acad. Press, 1963, 310 p.

134. Simmonds, W. J., A. F. Hofmann, and E. Theodor. Absorption of cholesterol from a micellar solution: intestinal perfusion studies in man. *J. Clin. Invest.* 46: 874–890, 1967.

135. Siperstein, M. D., I. L. Chaikoff, and W. O. Reinhardt. C14-cholesterol. V. Obligatory function of bile in intestinal absorption of cholesterol. *J. Biol. Chem.* 198: 111–114, 1952.

136. Sjövall, J. Dietary glycine and taurine on bile acid conjugation in man: bile acids and steroids 75. *Proc. Soc. Exptl. Biol. Med.* 100: 676–678, 1959.

137. Sjövall, J. On the concentration of bile acids in the human intestine during absorption: bile acids and steroids 74. *Acta Physiol. Scand.* 46: 339–345, 1959.

138. Sjövall, J. Bile acids in man under normal and pathological conditions: bile acids and steroids 73. *Clin. Chim. Acta* 5: 33–41, 1960.

139. Small, D. M., and M. Bourgès. Lyotropic paracrystalline phases obtained with ternary and quaternary systems of amphiphilic substances in water. *Mol. Crystals* 1: 173–193, 1966.

140. Small, D. M., M. C. Bourgès, and D. G. Dervichian. The biophysics of lipidic associations. I. The ternary systems lecithin-bile salt-water. *Biochim. Biophys. Acta* 125: 563–580, 1966.

141. Small, D. M., M. Bourgès, and D. G. Dervichian. Ternary and quaternary aqueous systems containing bile salt, lecithin, and cholesterol. *Nature* 211: 816–818, 1966.

142. Sperry, W. M. Lipid excretion. IV. A study of the relationship of the bile to the fecal lipids with special reference to certain problems of sterol metabolism. *J. Biol. Chem.* 71: 351–378, 1927.

143. Tabaqchali, S., and C. C. Booth. Jejunal bacteriology and bile-salt metabolism in patients with intestinal malabsorption. *Lancet* 2: 12–15, 1966.

144. Tera, H. Stratification of human gallbladder bile *in vivo. Acta Chir. Scand. Suppl.* 256: 1–85, 1960.

145. van den Bosch, H., N. M. Postema, G. H. de Haas, and L. L. M. van Deenen. On the positional specificity of phospholipase A from pancreas. *Biochim. Biophys. Acta* 98: 657–659, 1965.

146. VERZÁR, F. *Absorption from the Intestine*. New York: Longmans, Green, 1936, 294 p.

147. WEBLING, D. D'A., AND E. S. HOLDSWORTH. The effect of bile, bile acids and detergents on calcium absorption in the chick. *Biochem. J.* 97: 408–421, 1965.

148. WEBLING, D. D'A., AND E. S. HOLDSWORTH. Bile salts and calcium absorption. *Biochem. J.* 100: 652–660, 1966.

149. WHIPPLE, G. H. The origin and significance of the constituents of the bile. *Physiol. Rev.* 2: 440–459, 1922.

150. WHYTE, M., A. KARMEN, AND D. S. GOODMAN. Fatty acid esterification and chylomicron formation during fat absorption. 2. Phospholipids. *J. Lipid Res.* 4: 322–329, 1963.

151. ZACHMAN, R. D., P. E. DUNAGIN, JR., AND J. A. OLSON. Formation and enterohepatic circulation of metabolites of retinol and retinoic acid in bile duct-cannulated rats. *J. Lipid Res.* 7: 3–9, 1966.

CHAPTER 118

A concept of the digestive-absorptive surface of the small intestine

ROBERT K. CRANE | *Department of Physiology, Rutgers Medical School,*
New Brunswick, New Jersey

CHAPTER CONTENTS

IT HAS BEEN CLEAR for some years that the digestive and absorptive functions of the small intestine are not adequately expressed in the simple concept that enzymatic cleavage and membrane transport are sequential but otherwise separate processes. On the contrary, these processes are closely integrated. Their efficient cooperation to achieve lumen-blood transfer is enhanced by spatial organization of some of their functional components, as is particularly well revealed at the brush-border membrane covering the luminal surface of the mucosal cells. It was to accent this organization that Miller & Crane (68) introduced the concept of a digestive-absorptive surface. This concept developed from *1*) the discovery that the brush border is a structurally integrated, isolable subcellular organelle (68), *2*) the identification of the brush border as the site of membrane transport absorptive function for sugars (63), and *3*) the localization of disaccharidase activity to a site within the brush border close but external to the sugar transport process (16, 20, 67, 68).

ENZYMATIC ACTIVITIES INTRINSIC TO THE BRUSH BORDER

The brush border is the junctional barrier through which absorbed materials must pass between the lumen of the gut and the body. The first indication that it possessed enzymatic activity came in 1941 when Gomori (42) noted a positive histochemical reaction for alkaline phosphatase on the surface of human intestinal epithelial cells. Bourne (10), and later Deane & Dempsey (26), confirmed this finding and further localized the reaction to the structure that was then called the striated border. Description of this structure in terms of the microvilli projections came in 1950 with application of the electron microscope (43). In 1960 Nachlas et al. (70) demonstrated, also by histochemical means, the presence of a peptidase able to catalyze hydrolysis of leucyl naphthylamide. In 1961 Miller and Crane succeeded in isolating brush borders from hamster epithelial cells. They found that the isolated brush borders contained the digestive disaccharidases of the cell (68), and with this finding came understanding of the brush border as the locale of intense and varied digestive hydrolytic activity as well as of absorption function.

All the digestive disaccharidases, namely maltase, isomaltase, sucrase, and lactase, as well as alkaline phosphatase, leucine aminopeptidase, and trehalase, have been demonstrated in isolated brush borders (35, 36, 45, 68).

The inappropriate application of histochemical techniques to the question of localization introduced an early controversy (21, 23) that has lately been resolved. Dahlqvist & Brun (23) reported finding the digestive disaccharidases associated with small granules rather than with the brush border. However, Doell et al. (33) supported the brush-border localization for sucrase and lactase on the basis of results with fluorescent-antibody techniques. This work did not represent complete confirmation inasmuch as the enzyme preparations used as antigen were not highly purified. There was a reasonable possibility that the active antigen was a nonenzymatic component of the brush border. More recently Lojda (59) has proved that the disaccharidase granules of Dahlqvist and Brun are artifacts introduced by the method employed. Jos et al. (52) have greatly improved the procedure of Dahlqvist and Brun and completely confirmed the brush-border localization of digestive disaccharidases. Dahlqvist (22) has recently withdrawn his earlier contention.

Lactase is present in the brush border. However, brush-border lactase is not the only β-galactosidase of the cell, and from this fact some confusion arose that is only now close to being dispelled. Doell & Kretchmer (32), and earlier Heilskov (44), reported the presence of two β-galactosidase activities in homogenates of whole intestine; one was soluble and the other particulate. This finding appears to be much the same from species to species. However, what is not the same is the relative rate of utilization by these individual β-galactosidases of the two substrates ordinarily used, lactose and o-nitrophenyl-β-galactoside—hence, the confusion. The presence of two enzymes has been confirmed (56). They have been separated on Sephadex columns (85) and designated lactase-1 and lactase-2. Lactase-1 is the β-galactosidase of the brush border; in man, this enzyme hydrolyzes only lactose. Lactase-2 hydrolyzes both substrates and is thought to have a lysosomal origin (46). Studies of the residual mucosal enzyme in individuals with specific lactose malabsorption show that only lactase-1 is reduced in activity (98). Thus, prospectively, only the brush-border enzyme, lactase-1, is functional in the digestion of lactose (55, 98).

Isolated brush borders possess potent Na+- and K+-dependent ATPase activity (6, 89). These ATPases are generally regarded as the in vitro expression of an in vivo membrane function known as the Na+ pump (87). There is no reason to take a different view for brush-border ATPase, though its stability and kinetic characteristics differ from those of the membrane ATPase of red cells (7). The brush-border enzyme has been said to be under continuous endogenous repres-

sion (7). It is possible that there are two ATPases (7, 37), differing in their location within the brush border (35). The possible function of the ATPase activity of the brush border as a Na+ pump seems out of keeping with its location. However, the existence of such a pump has been invoked as a part of the brush-border role in Na+-dependent active transport (20, 79).

Alkaline phosphatase is thought to be, ubiquitously, a component of mammalian cell plasma membranes (14). This is possibly not the only location of alkaline phosphatase within the gut epithelial cell (12, 47). However, the tremendous mass of membrane at the brush border makes this the predominant location. The microvillar projections at the brush border increase the area covered by the plasma membrane 30- to 40-fold (11) beyond the nominal flat surface area of the luminal face of the cell.

The question of function for alkaline phosphatase will not be easily settled. It was earlier thought to serve in sugar absorption (94) as a part of a mechanism that has been clearly denied (15). Recently, it has been suggested that it plays a role in cell adhesion (69). However, the possibility that it is a digestive enzyme (68) should not be discarded. First, the other enzymes found in substantial amounts in the brush border all have digestive function. Second, intestinal alkaline phosphatase catalyzes hydrolysis of a wide variety of phosphorylated compounds, which are ubiquitous and plentiful in nature. Third, phosphate esters do not readily penetrate cell membranes, whereas their nonmineral moiety usually does and frequently by means of a specific transport process. On this basis, it seems creditable that the function of alkaline phosphatase is largely that of a digestive enzyme wherever it is to be found—digestive, that is, in the sense of cleaving a nonpenetrating molecule into transportable components.

Aminopeptidase of the brush border has recently received extensive attention (83). With some substrates, it is an unimpressive proportion of the peptidase activity of the whole cell. However, with the tripeptide Leu-Leu-Leu as substrate, the specific activity of the enzyme approaches that of the digestive enzyme sucrase. A basis is thus provided for believing that brush-border aminopeptidase is, like sucrase, a digestive enzyme. Intracellular peptidases are reputed also to have a digestive function; at least, some small peptides can enter the cell and be hydrolyzed within it (72). The experiments of Ugolev & Kooschuck (93), which suggest to them that all digestive peptidase activity is confined to the brush-border membrane, unfortunately do not take into account the intense bidirectional flux of amino acids across the mucosa of the small intestine (13) that would be expected to contribute the amino acid product of cellular peptidase activity to the lumen. Only two peptidases have yet been found in isolated brush borders—leucine aminopeptidase (83) and an activity against leucyl-glycine that can be separated from leucine aminopeptidase by papain treatment (A. Eichholz, unpublished observations).

Recent work indicates that some hydrolytic activity against cholesteryl and retinyl esters resides in the brush-border membrane (25, 61), although this is contrary to earlier suggestions (41). Inasmuch as similar and potent enzymes are present in the secretions of the pancreas, it is reassuring to note that these presumed brush-border enzymes do not share the property of adsorbed pancreatic enzymes (see below) in being easily removed from association with the membrane.

Some glyceride synthesis—that is, ^{14}C-palmitate incorporation—has been reported to occur in isolated brush borders (39). It is accounted for by the presence of palmitate thiokinase and monoglyceride and diglyceride acylase activities. As the activity in the brush border is no more than a few percent of the total cellular activity, clear confirmation of this observation would be desirable. Should the implication be confirmed that these enzymes are an integral part of the brush border, they would represent the only known synthetic activity of this structure.

Salivarectomized-pancreatectomized animals were found by McGeachin & Ford (64) to possess a mucosal amylase activity that was functional in the digestion of starch. This finding, difficult to understand before knowledge of the brush-border localization of digestive enzymes, has been confirmed. Two amylases are present in homogenates of mucosa from normal rats (24). One of these is an α-amylase (i.e., maltose liberating) presumably of pancreatic origin and present, as would fit this identity, in the soluble supernatant fraction of the homogenates. The other, however, is a γ-amylase (i.e., glucose liberating) and is present in the particulate fraction. The γ-amylase possesses equal activity as a maltase and is very probably one of the brush-border maltases (see Semenza, Chapter 119 in this *Handbook*). The occurrence of a mucosal γ-amylase has been further confirmed by Auricchio et al. (3), who documented its presence in the intestine of the 3-month-old fetus, before the development of significant pancreatic function.

Evidence has recently been obtained for the presence in the brush-border membrane of a β-glucosidase that has a specificity appropriate for it to be called "phlorizin hydrolase" (62). The role of this enzyme in the digestive-absorptive process has yet to be evaluated.

TRANSPORT ACTIVITIES OF BRUSH BORDER
AND THEIR LOCALIZATION

Current concepts of membrane transport in animal cells (97) as well as bacteria (53) hold that the first interaction of the entering substrate is with a specific protein component of the membrane. Recent success in isolation of substrate-binding components of appropriate properties from the human erythrocyte membrane (9) and several species of bacteria (40, 78, 81) would seem to bear this out. As is well known, the substrate specificity and kinetic characteristics of the "mobile carriers" of animal membrane transport and the "permeases" of bacterial transport are substantially the same as the characteristics of enzymes. Transport proteins, however, "catalyze" translocation of the interacting molecular species rather than covalent bond formation or rupture. The specific interactions required for translocation were localized to the brush border first by McDougal et al. (63) for sugars and later by Kinter & Wilson (54) for amino acids.

Identification of the process with the plasma membrane of the brush border depended, in early studies (16, 17), on analogy with membrane transport in other cells. However, precise localization has now been achieved. On the one hand, studies of the rare disease glucose-galactose malabsorption (57, 58) have shown (34, 66, 84) that the lesion is in the failure of these monosaccharides to enter the epithelial cell—that is, to pass the barrier of the brush-border membrane, although lactase is still active. On the other hand, extension of the impressive techniques of Kinter to the level of the electron microscope has shown (88) that the concentration gradient accompanying sugar absorption is established precisely at the membrane.

The initial interaction for sugar absorption is thus at the plasma membrane. There is no adequate justification for believing otherwise for other substances, such as amino acids and bile salts, which like glucose are linked with Na$^+$ in their transport (17), or for that matter with substances like fructose (67), which are not. This is not to say that lumen-blood transfer of all substances that can be absorbed depends on substrate-protein interaction at the brush-border membrane. However, it is likely true of most.

LOCATION AND FUNCTIONAL RELATIONS OF ENZYMES
INTRINSIC TO BRUSH BORDER

Each of the brush-border enzymes mentioned above
has been identified as a firmly bound component of
membranes isolated after tris-disruption of the brush
borders (35, 36). Moreover, studies of the distribution
within intact tissue of the products of hydrolysis by
sucrase, maltase, and alkaline phosphatase, when transport is inhibited as compared with controls, have
demonstrated that these enzymes are external to the
transport process (16, 67, 71) and thus must be in the
outer surface.

Histochemical findings of the localization of alkaline phosphatase by the electron microscope are in
agreement. Ito (48) found alkaline phosphatase "to
be localized in or on the trilaminar plasma membrane
and in the immediately adjacent region of the surface
coat." Ito (48) also reported a similar location for
ATPase activity that Ashworth et al. (1) found associated with the membrane of the microvilli. However,
others (73, 75) have found ATPase to be associated
with the internal side of the membrane, not only in the
intestine but also in the microvilli of the kidney tubular cell (95). It is not certain from the reports available
which enzyme has been viewed—whether the Na^+-
and K^+-dependent ATPase or another. Alkaline phosphatase, for example, will hydrolyze ATP. An internal
localization agrees with studies of the erythrocyte (96)
and fits better with current ideas of membrane ATPase
function (87). However, more work will be needed to
provide a reliable answer to ATPase localization.
ATPase activity is found in two fractions of disrupted
brush borders; one of these is the membrane fraction,
the other has not been identified with a component of
the brush border of intact cells (35, 36).

A surface specialization of the brush-border membrane has been described by Overton et al. (76, 77)
and by Oda et al. (73, 74). Negative staining reveals
membrane surface particles of approximately 50 A in
diameter. A later publication on this subject (51)
confirmed the initial observations and described the
particles as 60-A knobs attached by stalks to the
luminal surface of the plasma membrane. Their morphology thus strongly resembles the enzymatically
active particles of inner mitochondrial membranes
(38).

These knobs have been strongly implicated as the
site of disaccharidase activity. They are removed by
papain treatment (51, 73), as are the disaccharidases
(2), and may be recovered from Sephadex columns in
the same fraction as the disaccharidases (51).

By controlling the conditions of papain digestion

it has been possible to remove membrane enzymes in a
stepwise fashion (18, 37). The digestive disaccharidases are removed most rapidly and completely.
Alkaline phosphatase, leucine aminopeptidase, and
trehalase are removed later. The precise meaning of
this difference is not yet clear; that is, it has not been
firmly decided whether these enzymes are removed at
different rates because they are in different structures
of the membrane or because different portions of the
same structure are removed at different rates. The
presently available information favors the former alternative.

There is evidence of a functional spatial order of the
membrane components that confers a "kinetic advantage" for absorption (18). The glucose product of
sucrase activity possesses this kinetic advantage when
compared with the glucose product of alkaline phosphatase activity (18, 67). Two possibilities to account
for this kinetic advantage are immediately apparent
and not easily distinguishable. The first possibility
derives from the fact that microvilli are very long and
the spaces between them very narrow (90). If the
transport activities of the membrane were restricted to
the lower portion of the microvilli and sucrase activity
was similarly located, but alkaline phosphatase was
predominantly closer to the tips of the microvilli, a
kinetic advantage could be expected without invoking
the second possibility—namely a close relationship
between sucrase and the transport system within the
structure of the membrane. On the other hand, the
observations of Semenza et al. (86) of an activation of
disaccharidases by Na^+ with species-specific kinetic
constants closely similar to those of Na^+ activation of
glucose transport (19, 60) have suggested a very close
structural relationship indeed.

ENZYMES ADSORBED TO MUCOSAL SURFACE

In recent years the characteristics of the exposed
surface of living cells have come to be understood in
terms of a mucopolysaccharide layer in addition to the
better-known lipoidal membrane. This layer appears
to be present in all cells (80, 82) and may be an essential
functional element of the surface. It is currently called
the "glycocalyx" (5). The adsorption of environmental proteins to this charged surface appears to be a
well-accepted phenomenon (4).

The unusually strong PAS-staining properties of
the brush border (8) result from the presence of this
coat. Studies with the electron microscope reveal, in
the cat, bat, and man, a conspicuous layer of fine
filaments radiating from the outer dense portion of

the plasma membrane of the microvilli (48). In other species this coat is less well developed but nonetheless present. This coat is not derived from goblet cell mucus (49). Ito believes it to be the glycocalyx of the epithelial cells.

Johnson (51) has concluded from his studies of the specialized surface knobs discussed above that they are in fact the glycocalyx. Evidence to support this belief has not been produced. It is not known what conformation either the knobs or the polysaccharide filaments may have in the living, unfixed cell, as it is possible that both conformations seen in the electron microscope are artifactual. However, understanding the surface as charged mucopolysaccharide interspersed with or layered over functional protein does not take great liberty with present knowledge, whatever may be the actual conformation of these elements on the living surface.

Enzymes of pancreatic origin are reputed to bind to the surface of the brush border and to function in that location (28, 91). Inasmuch as the enzymes studied bind to mucin (29), it seems very likely that binding to the brush-border membrane, if it indeed occurs, is to the glycocalyx, which is chemically similar to mucin. The possibility of hydrophobic bonding into the lipoidal structure of the membrane, as has been suggested (92), would seem more remote. Binding is dependent on the total surface area available (27, 30) and is readily reversible by washing (50). As earlier shown by McLaren for enzymes adsorbed to surfaces (65), the kinetic parameters of pancreatic amylase are altered by adsorption to the mucosal surface (31).

The whole of these findings on adsorbed enzymes has been incorporated into a generalized concept

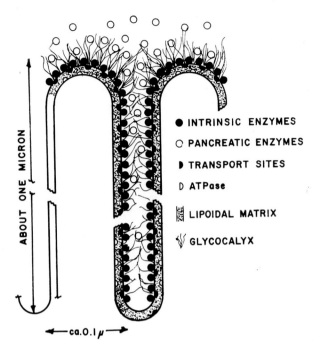

FIG. 2. Some elements responsible for digestive-absorptive function as experiment and the electron microscope have revealed them. The use of a single symbol for intrinsic enzymes of the membrane or for various transport proteins has no particular significance. Regularity of arrangement of the symbols, however, follows from the experiments suggesting "kinetic advantage."

called "membrane (contact) digestion" (91, 92). The possible usefulness of this concept is marred by its author's failure to distinguish clearly between *1*) intrinsic enzymes such as alkaline phosphatase and the disaccharidases that are integral components of the structure of the brush-border membrane elaborated by the epithelial cell and *2*) adsorbed enzymes of pancreatic origin.

DIGESTIVE-ABSORPTIVE SURFACE

The concept of the digestive-absorptive surface has been extensively delineated above. Figures 1 and 2 make the concept clear with respect to the molecular and functional organization of the brush-border membrane. Figure 1 is an adaptation of the original proposal of functional organization made in 1960 (18, 20). As redrawn here, it includes the concept that pancreatic hydrolases may be adsorbed to the mucosal surface. Figure 2 has been prepared with regard to what has been seen in the electron microscope, including the length and width of microvilli and the spaces between them (90). Figure 2 may be compared with Figure 1 of Ugolev (91) if a better understanding of the conceptual difference in viewpoints is desired.

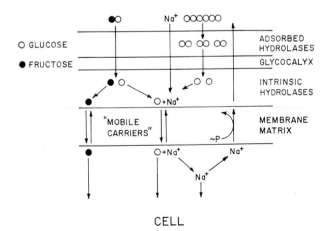

FIG. 1. Some functional relationships within the digestive-absorptive surface of the small intestine.

REFERENCES

1. ASHWORTH, C. T., F. J. LINBEL, AND S. C. STEWART. ATPase in membrane of microvilli. *J. Cell Biol.* 17: 1–18, 1963.

2. AURICCHIO, S., A. DAHLQVIST, AND G. SEMENZA. Solubilization of the human intestinal disaccharidases. *Biochim. Biophys. Acta* 73: 582–587, 1963.

3. AURICCHIO, S., A. RUBINO, AND G. MURSET. Intestinal glycosidase activities in the human embryo, fetus, and newborn. *Pediatrics* 35: 944–954, 1965.

4. BELL, L. G. E. Polysaccharide and cell membranes. *J. Theoret. Biol.* 3: 132–133, 1962.

5. BENNETT, H. S. Morphological aspects of extracellular polysaccharidases. *J. Histochem. Cytochem.* 11: 14–23, 1963.

6. BERG, G. G., AND B. CHAPMAN. The sodium and potassium activated ATPase of intestinal epithelium. I. Location of enzymatic activity in the cell. *J. Cellular Comp. Physiol.* 65: 361–372, 1965.

7. BERG, G. G., AND J. SZEKERCZES. The sodium and potassium activated ATPase II. Comparative study of intestinal epithelium and red cells. *J. Cell Physiol.* 67: 487–500, 1966.

8. BLOOM, W., AND D. W. FAWCETT. *A Textbook of Histology.* Philadelphia: Saunders, 1962, p. 16.

9. BOBINSKI, H., AND W. D. STEIN. Isolation of a glucose-binding component from human erythrocyte membranes. *Nature* 211: 1366–1368, 1966.

10. BOURNE, G. Distribution of alkaline phosphatase in various tissues. *Quart. J. Exptl. Physiol.* 32: 1, 1943.

11. BROWN, A. L., JR. Microvilli of the human jejunal epithelial cell. *J. Cell Biol.* 12: 623–627, 1962.

12. CHASE, W. H. The demonstration of alkaline phosphatase activity in frozen dried mouse gut in the electron microscope. *J. Histochem. Cytochem.* 11: 96–101, 1963.

13. CHRISTENSEN, H. N., B. H. FELDMAN, AND A. B. HASTINGS. Concentrative and reversible character of intestinal amino acid transport. *Am. J. Physiol.* 205: 255–260, 1963.

14. CLARK, S. L., JR. The localization of alkaline phosphatase in tissues of mice, using the electron microscope. *Am. J. Anat.* 109: 57–84, 1961.

15. CRANE, R. K. Intestinal absorption of sugars. *Physiol. Rev.* 40: 789–825, 1960.

16. CRANE, R. K. Hypothesis for mechanism of intestinal active transport of sugars. *Federation Proc.* 21: 891–895, 1962.

17. CRANE, R. K. Na⁺-dependent transport in the intestine and other animal tissues. *Federation Proc.* 24: 1000–1006, 1965.

18. CRANE, R. K. Structural and functional organization of an epithelial cell brush border. In: *Intracellular Transport,* edited by K. B. Warren. (Symp. Intern. Soc. Cell Biol.) New York: Acad. Press, 1967, vol. v, p. 71–103.

19. CRANE, R. K. Absorption of sugars. In: *Handbook of Physiology. Alimentary Canal,* edited by C. F. Code. Washington, D.C.: Am. Physiol. Soc., 1968, sect. 6, vol. III, Chapt. 69, 1323–1351.

20. CRANE, R. K., D. MILLER, AND I. BIHLER. The restrictions of possible mechanisms of intestinal active transport of sugars. In: *Membrane Transport and Metabolism,* edited by A. Kleinzeller and A. Kotyk. New York: Acad. Press, 1961, p. 439–450.

21. DAHLQVIST, A. Intestinal hydrolysis absorption of glycogen-derived oligosaccharides. In: *Ciba Found. Symp., Control of Glycogen Metabolism,* edited by W. J. Whelan and M.-P. Cameron. London: Churchill, 1964, p. 53.

22. DAHLQVIST, A. The localization of the disaccharide hydrolysis of small intestine. *Biochem. J.* 100: 17–18P, 1966.

23. DAHLQVIST, A., AND A. BRUN. A method for the histochemical demonstration of disaccharidase activities: application to invertase and trehalase in some animal tissues. *J. Histochem. Cytochem.* 10: 294–302, 1962.

24. DAHLQVIST, A., AND D. L. THOMSON. Separation and characterization of two rat-intestinal amylases. *Biochem. J.* 89: 272–277, 1963.

25. DAVID, J. S. K., P. MALATHI, AND J. GANGULY. Role of the intestinal brush border in the absorption of cholesterol in rats. *Biochem. J.* 98: 662–668, 1966.

26. DEANE, H. W., AND E. W. DEMPSEY. The localization of phosphatase in the Golgi region of intestinal and other epithelial cells. *Anat. Record* 93: 401–417, 1945.

27. DE LAEY, P. Development of the intestinal digestion mechanism of starch as a function of age in rats. *Nature* 212: 78–79, 1966.

28. DE LAEY, P. Die Membranverdauung der Starke. I. Mitt der einfluss von seiten der perfusionsgeschwindigkeit und der amylolytischen aktivität des pankreassaftes auf die, *in vivo,* verdauung der starke. *Die Nahrung* 10: 641–648, 1966.

29. DE LAEY, P. Die Membranverdauung der Starke. 2 Mitt der einfluss von mucinen auf die membranverdauung. *Die Nahrung* 10: 649–653, 1966.

30. DE LAEY, P. Die Membranverdauung der Starke. 4. Mitt der einfluss der grosse der intestinalen schleimhaut auf die membranverdauung. *Die Nahrung* 11: 1–8, 1967.

31. DE LAEY, P. Die Membranverdauung der Starke. 5. Mitt. Zur zweigestaltigkeit der membranverdauung der starke. *Die Nahrung* 11: 9–15, 1967.

32. DOELL, R. G., AND N. KRETCHMER. Studies of small intestine during development. I. Distribution and activity of β-galactosidase. *Biochim. Biophys. Acta* 62: 353–362, 1962.

33. DOELL, R. G., G. ROSEN, AND N. KRETCHMER. Immunochemical studies of intestinal disaccharidase during normal and precocious development. *Proc. Natl. Acad. Sci. U.S.* 54: 1268–1273, 1965.

34. EGGERMONT, E., AND H. LOEB. Glucose-galactose intolerance. *Lancet* 2: 343, 1966.

35. EICHHOLZ, A. Structural and functional organization of the brush border intestinal epithelial cells. III. Enzymic activities and chemical composition of various fraction of tris-disrupted brush borders. *Biochim. Biophys. Acta* 135: 475–482, 1967.

36. EICHHOLZ, A., AND R. K. CRANE. Studies of the organization of the brush border in intestinal epithelial cells. I. Tris-disruption of isolated hamster brush borders and density gradient separation of fractions. *J. Cell Biol.* 26: 687–691, 1965.

37. EICHHOLZ, A., AND R. K. CRANE. Sub-fractions of brush border membranes isolated from intestinal epithelial cells. *Federation Proc.* 25: 656, 1966.

38. FERNANDEZ-MORAN, H., T. ODA, P. V. BLAIR, AND D. E. GREEN. A macromolecular repeating unit of mitochondrial structure and function. Correlated electron microscopic and biochemical studies of isolated mitochondria and submitochondrial particles of beef heart muscle. *J. Cell Biol.* 22: 63–100, 1964.

39. FORSTNER, G. G., E. M. RILEY, S. J. DANIELS, AND K. J. ISSELBACHER. Demonstration of glyceride synthesis by brush

border of intestinal epithelial cells. *Biochem. Biophys. Res. Commun.* 21:83–88, 1965.

40. Fox, C. F., and E. P. Kennedy. Specific labelling of partial purification of the M protein, a component of the β-galactoside transport system of *Escherichia coli. Proc. Natl. Acad. Sci. U.S.* 54:891–899, 1965.

41. Gallo, L. L., and C. R. Treadwell. Localization of cholesterol esterase and cholesterol in mucosal fractions of rat small intestine. *Proc. Soc. Exptl. Biol. Med.* 114: 69–72, 1963.

42. Gomori, G. Distribution of phosphatase in normal organs and tissues *J. Cellular Comp. Physiol.* 17:71–84, 1941.

43. Granger, B., and R. F. Baker. Electron microscope investigation of the striated border of intestinal epithelium. *Anat. Record* 107:423–436, 1950.

44. Heilskov, N. S. C. *Studier Over Animalsk Lactase.* Copenhagen: Munksgaard, 1956, p. 137–159.

45. Holt, J. H., and D. Miller. The localization of phosphomonoesterase and aminopeptidase in brush borders isolated from intestinal epithelial cells. *Biochim. Biophys. Acta* 58:239–243, 1962.

46. Hsia, D. Y. Y., M. Makler, G. Semenza, and A. Prader. β-Galactosidase activity in human intestinal lactases. *Biochim. Biophys. Acta* 113:390–393, 1966.

47. Hugon, J., and M. Borgers. Ultrastructural localization of alkaline phosphatase activity in the absorbing cells of the duodenum of mouse. *J. Histochem. Cytochem.* 14: 629–640, 1966.

48. Ito, S. The enteric surface coat on cat intestinal microvilli. *J. Cell Biol.* 27:475–491, 1965.

49. Ito, S., and J. P. Revel. Autoradiography of intestinal epithelial cells. In: *Proc. Intern. Congr. Electron Microscope, 6th, Kyoto.* 1966, p. 585.

50. Jesuitova, N. N., P. De Laey, and A. M. Ugolev. Digestion of starch *in vivo* and *in vitro* in a rat intestine. *Biochim. Biophys. Acta* 86: 205–210, 1964.

51. Johnson, C. F. Disaccharidase localization in hamster intestine brush borders. *Science* 155:1670–1672, 1967.

52. Jos, J., J. Frezal, J. Rey, M. Lamy, and R. Wegmann. La localization histochimique des disaccharidases intestinales par un nouveau procédé. *Ann. Histochim.* 12 : 53–61, 1967.

53. Kepes, A. The place of permeases in cellular organization. In: *The Cellular Functions of Membrane Transport,* edited by J. F. Hoffman. Englewood Cliffs, N. J.: Prentice Hall, 1964, p. 155.

54. Kinter, W. B., and T. H. Wilson. Autoradiographic study of sugar and amino acid absorption by everted sacs of hamster intestine. *J. Cell Biol.* 24: 19–39, 1965.

55. Koldovsky, O., A. Heringova, and V. Jirsova. β-Galactosidase activity of the jejunum and ileum of suckling rats. Comparison of activities of β-galactosidase at different concentration of substrates (o-nitrophenyl-β-D-galactoside and lactose) at different pH. *Biol. Neonatorum* 10: 241–253, 1966.

56. Koldovsky, O., R. Noack, G. Schenk, V. Jirsova, A. Heringova, H. Brana, F. Chytil, and M. Fridirch. Activity of β-galactosidase in homogenates and isolated microvilli fraction of jejunal mucosa from suckling rats. *Biochim. J.* 96:492–494, 1965.

57. Laplane, R., C. Polonovski, M. Etienne, P. Debray, J. C. Lods, and B. Pissarro. L'intolerance aux sucres à

transfert intestinal actif. *Arch. Franc. Pediat.* 19: 895–944, 1962.

58. Lindquist, B., G. Meeuwisse, and K. Melin. Glucosegalactose malabsorption. An inborn error of metabolism. *Lancet* 2: 666, 1962.

59. Lojda, Z. Some remarks concerning the histochemical detection of disaccharidase and glucosidases. *Histochemie* 5: 339–360, 1965.

60. Lyon, I., and R. K. Crane. Studies on transmural potentials *in vitro* in relation to intestinal absorption. 1. Apparent Michaelis constants for Na+-dependent sugar transport. *Biochim. Biophys. Acta* 112:278–291, 1966.

61. Malathi, P. Localization of cholesteryl and retinyl ester hydrolases in the microvillus membrane of brush borders isolated from intestinal epithelial cells. (Abstr.) *AGA Mtg. Colorado Springs, May 23–27, 1967.*

62. Malathi, P., and R. K. Crane. β-Glucosidase (phlorizin hydrolase) activity in intestinal brush borders. *Federation Proc.* 27: 385, 1968.

63. McDougal, D. B., K. D. Little, and R. K. Crane. Studies on the mechanism of intestinal absorption of sugars. IV. Localization of galactose concentrations within the intestinal wall during active transport, *in vitro. Biochim. Biophys Acta* 45: 483–489, 1960.

64. McGeachin, R. L., and N. K. Ford. Distribution of amylase in the gastrointestinal tract of the rat. *Am. J. Physiol.* 196: 972–974, 1959.

65. McLaren, A. D. Concerning the pH dependence of enzyme reactions on cells, particulates and in solution. *Science* 125: 697, 1957.

66. Meeuwisse, G., and A. Dahlqvist. Glucose-galactose malabsorption. *Lancet* 2 : 858, 1966.

67. Miller, D., and R. K. Crane. The digestive function of the epithelium of the small intestine. 1. An intracellular locus of disaccharide and sugar phosphate ester hydrolysis. *Biochim. Biophys. Acta* 52: 281–293, 1961.

68. Miller, D., and R. K. Crane. The digestive function of the epithelium of the small intestine. II. Localization of disaccharide hydrolysis in the isolated brush border portion of intestinal epithelial cells. *Biochim. Biophys. Acta* 52: 293–298, 1961.

69. Millington, P. F., and A. C. Brown. Electron microscope studies of the distribution of phosphatases in rat intestinal epithelium from birth to ten days after weaning. *Histochemie* 8: 109–121, 1967.

70. Nachlas, M. M., B. Monis, D. Rosenblatt, and A. M. Seligman. Improvement in the histochemical localization of leucine aminopepidase with a new substrate, L-leucyl-4-methoxy-2-naphthylamide. *J. Biophys. Biochem. Cytol.* 7: 261, 1960.

71. Newey, H., P. A. Sanford, and D. H. Smyth. Location of function in the intestinal epithelial cell in relation to carbohydrate absorption. *J. Physiol., London* 168:423–434, 1963.

72. Newey, H., and D. H. Smyth. Intracellular hydrolysis of dipeptides during intestinal absorption. *J. Physiol., London* 152: 367–380, 1960.

73. Oda, T., and R. Sato. Elementary particles of the microvilli of rabbit intestinal epithelial cells. *Symp. Am. Soc. Cell Biol. 1964, Cleveland, Ohio.*

74. Oda, T., and S. Seki. In: *Proc. Intern Congr. Electron Microscope, 6th, Kyoto.* 1966, p. 387.

75. OVERTON, J. Fine structure of the free cell surface in developing mouse intestinal mucosa. *J. Exptl. Zool.* 159: 195–202, 1965.

76. OVERTON, J., A. EICHHOLZ, AND R. K. CRANE. Fine structure of the microvilli of hamster small intestine. *J. Cell Biol.* 23: 110A, 1964.

77. OVERTON, J., A. EICHHOLZ, AND R. K. CRANE. Studies on the organization of brush border in intestinal epithelial cells. II. Fine structure of fractions of tris-disrupted hamster brush border. *J. Cell Biol.* 26: 693–706, 1965.

78. PARDEE, A. B., L. S. PRESTIDGE, M. B. WHIPPLE, AND J. DREYFUSS. A binding site for sulfate and its relation to sulfate transport into *Salmonella typhimurium*. *J. Biol. Chem.* 241: 3962–3969, 1966.

79. PARSONS, D. S. Salt and water absorption by the intestinal tract. *Brit. Med. Bull.* 23: 252–257, 1967.

80. PEASE, D. C. Polysaccharides associated with the exterior surface of epithelial cells: kidney, intestine, brain. *J. Ultrastruct. Res.* 15: 555–588, 1966.

81. PIPERNO, J. R., AND D. L. OXENDER. Amino acid-binding protein released from *Escherichia coli* by osmotic shock. *J. Biol. Chem.* 241: 5732–5735, 1966.

82. RAMBOURG, A., M. NEUTRA, AND C. B. LEBLOND. Presence of a "cell coat" rich in carbohydrate at the surface of cells in the rat. *Anat. Record* 154: 41–72, 1966.

83. RHODES, J. B., A. EICHHOLZ, AND R. K. CRANE. Studies on the organization of the brush border in intestinal epithelial cells. IV. Amino-peptidase activity in microvillus membranes of hamster intestinal brush borders. *Biochim. Biophys. Acta* 135: 959–965, 1967.

84. SCHNEIDER, A. J., W. B. KINTER, AND C. E. STIRLING. Glucose-galactose malabsorption. *New Engl. J. Med.* 274: 305–312, 1966.

85. SEMENZA, G., S. AURICCHIO, AND A. RUBINO. Multiplicity of human intestinal disaccharidase. I. Chromatographic separation of maltase and of two lactases. *Biochim. Biophys. Acta* 96: 487–497, 1965.

86. SEMENZA, G., R. TOSI, M. C. VALLOTTON-DELACHAUX, AND E. MULHAUPT. Sodium activation of human intestinal sucrase and its possible significance in the enzymic organization of brush border. *Biochim. Biophys. Acta* 89: 109–116, 1964.

87. SKOU, J. C. Enzymatic basis for active transport of Na^+ and K^+ across cell membrane. *Physiol. Rev.* 45: 596–617, 1965.

88. STIRLING, C. E., AND W. B. KINTER. High resolution autoradiography of galactose H^3 accumulation in rings of hamster intestine. *J. Cell Biol.* 35: 585, 1967.

89. TAYLOR, C. G. Cation-stimulation of an ATPase system from the intestinal mucosa of the guinea pig. *Biochim. Biophys. Acta* 60: 437–440, 1962.

90. TRIER, J., AND C. E. RUBIN. Electron microscopy of the small intestine. A review. *Gastroenterology* 49: 574–603, 1965.

91. UGOLEV, A. M. Membrane (contact) digestion. *Physiol. Rev.* 45: 555–595, 1965.

92. UGOLEV, A. M. Die membran-(Kontakt-)verdauung in der physiologie und pathologie des magen-darm traktes. *Die Nahrung* 10: 483–498, 1966.

93. UGOLEV, A. M., AND R. I. KOOSCHUCK. Hydrolysis of dipeptides in cells of the small intestine. *Nature* 212: 859–860, 1965.

94. VERZÁR, F., AND E. J. MCDOUGAL. *Absorption from the Intestine*. London: Longmans, 1936.

95. WACHSTEIN, M., AND M. BESEN. Electron microscopic localization of phosphatase activity in the brush border. *J. Histochem. Cytochem.* 11: 447, 1963.

96. WHITTAM, R. The asymmetrical stimulation of a membrane adenosine triphosphatase in relation to active cation transport. *Biochem. J.* 84: 110–118, 1962.

97. WIDDAS, W. F. Membrane transport of sugars. In: *Carbohydrate Metabolism and Its Disorders*, edited by F. Dickens, P. J. Randle, and W. J. Whelan. London: Acad. Press, 1968, vol. 1, p. 1–23.

98. ZOPPI, G. B., R. HADORN, R. GITZELMANN, H. KISTLER, AND A. PRADER. Intestinal β-galactosidase activities in malabsorption syndromes. *Gastroenterology* 50: 557–561, 1966.

CHAPTER 119

Intestinal oligosaccharidases and disaccharidases

G. SEMENZA | *Biochemisches Institut der Universität Zürich, Zürich, Switzerland*

CHAPTER CONTENTS

A LARGE NUMBER of disaccharides and oligosaccharides are hydrolyzed by enzymes present in the small-intestinal mucosa. They include the two main disaccharides of the diet, sucrose and lactose, as well as maltose, maltotriose, and other oligosaccharides arising from α-amylase degradation of starch and glycogen. Minor disaccharides and oligosaccharides that may occur in the diet or arise during digestion or that may be used in biochemical and clinical investigation are trehalose (α-D-glucopyranosyl-α-D-glucopyranoside) occurring in insects, mushrooms, plants, yeasts, algae, and other microorganisms (19, 39, 154); isomaltose (6-α-D-glucopyranosyl-D-glucopyranose); palatinose (isomaltulose, 6-α-D-glucopyranosyl-D-fructofuranose); cellobiose (4-β-D-glucopyranosyl-D-glucopyranose); and dextran.

DISTRIBUTION OF SMALL-INTESTINAL GLYCOSIDASE ACTIVITIES IN VERTEBRATES

For details on the earlier literature the reader is referred to Prosser's treatise (169).

Since investigations of intestinal disaccharidases have been performed for purposes other than taxonomy, information regarding different species of animals is widespread throughout modern scientific literature. Table 1 presents most of the recent data on the occurrence of maltase, isomaltase, sucrase,[1] tre-

---

[1] The trivial name "invertase" is well established for β-fructofuranosidase (β-D-fructofuranoside fructohydrolase, EC 3.2.1.26). Since the small-intestinal enzyme is a glucohydrolase and glucotransferase (see below), it seems more appropriate to designate it with the other trivial name.

TABLE 1. *Distribution of Small-Intestinal Disaccharidase Activities in Some Classes of Vertebrates*

	Maltase	Sucrase	Isomaltase (Oligo-1,6-α-glucosidase)	Trehalase	Lactase	References
Mammalia						
Primates						
Man, *Homo sapiens*	+	+	+	+	+	13, 50, 52, 78, 80, 83, 119, 149, 192, 206; and others
Rhesus monkey, *Macaca mulatta*	+	+		+	+	192, 193
Rodentia						
Rat, *Rattus rattus*	+	+	+	+	+	51, 53, 67, 73, 75, 88, 132, 143, 173
Guinea pig, *Cavia porcellus*	+	+		+	+	71, 107, 123, 143
Hamster, *Cricetus cricetus*	+	+	+	+	+	82, 150, 180
Squirrel	+	+		+		143
Mouse, *Mus musculus*					+	123, 140
Lagomorpha						
Rabbit, *Oryctolagus cuniculus*	+	+	+	+	+	34, 73, 95, 123, 125, 132, 143, 190
Pinnipedia						
Tasmanian fur seal, *Arctocephalus tasmanicus*	+	−	+	−	Traces	118
New Zealand fur seal, *Arctocephalus forsterii*	+	−	+	−	Traces	118
Californian sea lion, *Zalophus californianus*	+	−	+[1]	−	−	191
Stellar sea lion, *Eumatopius jubatus*	+	−		−	−	127, 191
Walrus, *Odobenus r. divergens*	+		+[2]		Traces	160
Harbor seal, *Phoco vitulina*	+	−		−	+	127
Southern elephant seal, *Mirounga leonina*	+	−	+	−	Traces	118
Carnivora						
Cat, *Felis catus*	+	+	+[3]	−	+	71, 103, 107
African lion, *Felis leo*	+	+	+[3]	−	+	103
Polar bear, *Thalarctus maritimus*	+	+	+[3]	+	+	103
Dog, *Canis familiaris*	+	+	+[3]	+	+	31, 32, 71, 103, 143, 207
Ferret, *Mustela putorius*	+	+	+[3]	+	+	103
Perissodactyla						
Horse, *Equus caballus*		+		+		86
Artiodactyla						
Collared peccary, *Tayassu tajacu*	+	+	+	Traces	+	5
Domestic pig, *Sus scrofa*	+	+	+	+	+	16, 49, 53, 71, 132, 133, 142
Domestic cow, *Bos taurus*	+	+	+	+	+	86, 99, 106, 154, 178
Sheep, *Ovis aries*	+			+	+	195a, 201
Goat, *Capra hircus* (?)	+	+		+	+	142
Proboscidea						
Indian elephant, *Elephans maximus*	+	+		+	−[4]	5
Monotremata						
Echidna, *Tachiglossus aculeatus*	+	−	+	+	+	118
Marsupiala						
Gray kangaroo, *Macropius robustus*	+	−	+	+	+	118
Koala, *Phascolactos cinereus*	+	+	+	−	+	118
Ring-tailed possum, *Pseudocheirus peregrinus*	+	Traces	+		+	118
Brush-tailed possum, *Trichosurus vulpecula*	+	+	+	+	+	118
Short-nosed bandicoot, *Isodoon obesulus*		−		+		118

α-Glucosidase activities refer to the adult animals; lactase activity refers to the preweaned young.

[1] Personal communication of P. Sunshine to K. R. Kerry, 1967.

[2] Palatinase activity.

[3] Personal communication from P. Hore, 1967.

[4] Adult specimen.

[5] G. Zoppi and D. H. Schmerling, "Intestinal disaccharidase," article in preparation.

TABLE I.–*Concluded*

	Maltase	Sucrase	Isomaltase (Oligo-1,6-α-glucosidase)	Trehalase	Lactase	References
Marsupiala						
Long-nosed bandicoot, *Perameles nasuta*	+	+	+	+	+	118
Tiger cat, *Dasyrus maculatus*	+	+	+	+	+	118
Pouched mouse, *Antechinus stuatii*	+	+	+	+	+	118
Aves						
Quail, *Coturnix chinensis*	+	+	+	−	−	5
Domestic fowl		+			−	30, 100, 162
European crane, *Grus grus*	+	+	+	−	−	5
King penguin, *Aptenodytes patagonia*	+	Traces			−	6
Rock Hopper penguin, *Eudyptes crestatus*	+	Traces			−	6
Gentoo penguin, *Pygoscelis papua*	Traces	−			−	6
Skua gull, *Stercorarius skua*	+	+			−	5
Dominican gull, *Larus dominicanus*	+	+			−	6
Reptilia						
Greek turtle, *Testudo hermanii*	+	+	+	+	−	5
Amphibia						
Toads, *Bufo vulgaris, Rana temporaria, R. pipiens*	+	−		+	−	159

[6] Personal communication from K. R. Kerry, 1967.

halase, and lactase in the intestine of vertebrates. These data, however, should be interpreted with caution as the presence of a particular enzymatic activity does not indicate necessarily that the enzyme is located in the brush border. In addition, the reported absence of an enzymatic activity may only be related to the age of the animal examined or to the technique employed.

Keeping these limitations in mind the following may be stated: most mammals have the five disaccharidase activities. Notable exceptions are the lion, domestic cat, and koala that lack trehalase; the echidna, gray kangaroo, and short-nosed bandicoot that lack sucrase; and the pinnipeds that lack both of these enzymes and have only traces, if any, of lactase. Correspondingly, the milk of pinnipeds contains only traces of lactose (118, 160, 161, 191).

Data on other classes are very scanty. Lactase is absent in all nonmammals investigated. The few birds investigated do not possess any trehalase in other organs either (139), and frogs do not possess sucrase.

Among fishes, trehalase has been reported to be present in *Raniceps raninus, Labrus berggylta, Pleuronectes platessa*, and *Cottus scorpius* (208); sucrase is present in *Colotomus, Thalassema*, and *Salarias*, but absent in *Sphaeroides* (108).

Some β-glucosides are split by small-intestinal mucosa (199). A notable β-glucosidase recently found in the brush borders is a phlorizin hydrolase (141). β-Glucosidase activities also show species differences, as exemplified by arbutin (hydroquinone-β-glucoside), which is split in the intestinal mucosa of guinea pig and rabbit but not by that of hamster, chicken, or man [(4); G. Semenza, unpublished results].

α-Galactosides (94), lactulose[2] (62, 175), α-methyl-glucoside, cellulose, pentosanes, and inulin are not hydrolyzed, to any significant extent, by small-intestestinal enzymes. Dextran is split either by a specific enzyme (133) or by isomaltase (51).

Two enzymes attacking sphingoglycolipids, and not identical with any previously known disaccharidases, have been purified from rat intestine. One (28) catalyzes the hydrolysis of both glucosyl ceramide and galactosyl ceramide. The other (27) specifically cleaves the terminal galactosyl residue from trihexoside ceramide. Both enzymes are particle-bound and can be solubilized by cholate treatment. They may have digestive significance, since they occur in the small intestine in much larger amounts than in other organs.

Thioglycosidase activity occurs in a number of mammalian tissues, particularly in the small intestine (96).

[2] 4-β-D-Galactopyranosyl-fructofuranose. It may arise from lactose during the manufacture of artificial baby food from milk (3).

TABLE 2. *Average Oligo- and Disaccharidase Activities of Normal Human Intestinal Mucosa*

	M	S	I	P	MT*	T*	L	C	M/I	S/I	L/I
Duodenum	4.7	0.67	0.71		3.8	1.7	0.13		9.5	0.76	0.46
Jejunum	22.2	6.8	6.8	1.9			2.7	0.61	3.26	0.99	0.44

All activities are expressed as units (μmoles oligosaccharide hydrolyzed per minute at 37 C) per gram wet weight mucosa. Abbreviations: M, maltase; S, sucrase; I, isomaltase; P, palatinase; MT, maltotriase; T, trehalase; L, lactase; C, cellobiase. Unless stated otherwise, the data were obtained by Auricchio et al. (13). Samples were obtained from adults during abdominal surgery.

* From peroral biopsies on children (figures of activities from peroral biopsies are usually higher than in samples from operations, because biopsies are less "diluted" with inactive components). [From Messer & Kerry (149).]

LOCATION OF SMALL-INTESTINAL GLYCOSIDASES

Juice Versus Cells

As early as 1880 Brown & Heron (29) reported that small-intestinal mucosa had much higher sucrase and maltase activities than the intestinal juice. Their observation was confirmed and extended to other disaccharidase activities. Cajori, in particular, published two very important papers in the 1930s (31, 32) in which he reported that much sucrase activity of the juice sedimented upon centrifugation, and that the low level of sucrase and lactase activities in the juice could not possibly account for the rate of sucrose and lactose disappearance from the gut in vivo. It appeared, therefore, that cell-bound disaccharidases, rather than those of the "succus entericus," were responsible for the digestion of dissaccharides. Somehow this notion was soon substituted by the concept that disaccharidases were "secreted" into the lumen (see, e.g., ref. 15), and more recently the older, correct notion had to be rediscovered and substantiated by use of better methods. Miller & Crane (150, 151) provided functional evidence for cellular location (see below); Cajori's data and calculations were confirmed in man by Borgström et al. (25) and Gray & Ingelfinger (97). Fractional centrifugation of homogenated intestinal mucosa showed that all disaccharidases investigated are particulate (8, 23, 130). Thus, what was stated in 1941 by Florey et al. (89) holds true again: "It seems likely that few of the enzymes are actually secreted but that most of them" (including the disaccharidases) "enter the juice, as it were incidentally, from the break-up of the cells" followed by solubilization (see below).

There have been both older and newer claims that nervous or hormonal stimulation of fluid secretion in the gut is accompanied by a "secretion" of disaccharidases as well. The evidence at present appears unconvincing. The present view (113) is that no nervous or hormonal control of disaccharidase "secretion" exists.

Mucosa Versus Intestinal Flora

Bacterial contamination does not contribute significantly to the disaccharidase activities of intestinal extracts. In fact, *a*) levels of intestinal disaccharidases are not lower in germ-free rats as compared with conventional rats. They may be equal (60, 131) or even higher (170). This latter observation may be related to the longer life span of epithelial cells in germ-free rats (2), or to the inactivation of enzymes by intestinal flora, or both (24, 79). *b*) Meconium, which is sterile and consists mainly of desquamated intestinal cells, is rich in disaccharidase activities (79). *c*) Several intestinal disaccharidases begin to develop in intrauterine life (see below). *d*) Administration of antibiotics to hogs does not depress their levels of intestinal disaccharidase activities (131).

Distribution Along the Small Intestine

In man (13, 83, 99, 155, 192) (Table 2), sucrase, isomaltase, maltase, trehalase, and lactase activities are the highest in jejunum, lower in ileum, and even lower in the duodenum. A knowledge of the distribution of disaccharidase activities in the various parts of the duodenum in man is particularly important because this segment of intestine is the most accessible for peroral biopsies in the diagnosis of disaccharidase deficiencies. The beginning of the duodenum is essentially free from sucrase, isomaltase, and lactase[3] activities (Figs. 1 and 2).

From this distribution one should expect the beginning of the jejunum to be the site of the most active absorption of disaccharides in man. This has actually been found to be the case for lactose (58), maltose, and sucrose (97; see, however, 58).

[3] Note that the levels of sucrase and maltase activities do not change very much for 30 cm beyond the Treitz ligament, whereas that of lactase does, and very noticeably. Since this is the area from which peroral biopsies are usually obtained, they present a wide scatter of normal intestinal lactase activity (13, 98).

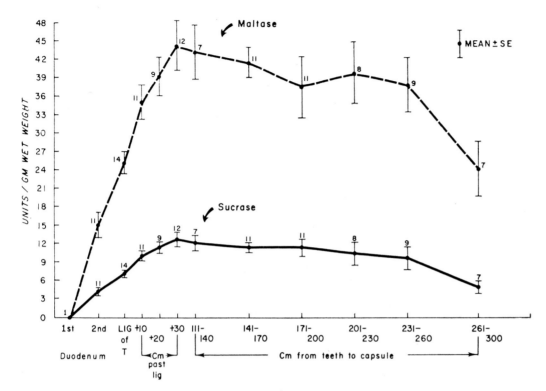

FIG. 1. Distribution of sucrase and maltase activities in the small bowel of 14 subjects. Samples of mucosa were obtained by peroral biopsies. Numbers on the lines designate number of subjects biopsied. [From Newcomer & McGill (155).]

Apart from minor differences, monkey (192), rat (67, 68), hamster (209), chicken [at least for sucrase (100)], and most other mammals show the same pattern of disaccharidase distribution. In pigs, trehalase and lactase are reported to be higher in the proximal part; maltase, sucrase, and isomaltase in the distal part of the small intestine (53).

Villi Versus Crypts

By using an elegant microdissection technique, van Genderen & Engel (92) established in 1938 that intestinal maltase is located in the intestinal villi and not in the crypts (Fig. 3). Their data have recently been confirmed (65) and extended to other disaccharidases. This conclusion agrees with the observation that secondary disaccharidase deficiencies are often related to atrophy of the villi, but not necessarily of the crypts (205, 210).

Intracellular Location

The problem of intracellular location, which is of obvious importance for the assessment of the exact physiological role of disaccharidases, has been a matter of some dispute over the past few years. Four approaches have been used.

BY ENZYME HISTOCHEMISTY. 6-Bromo-2-napthyl-α-glucoside is split in rat intestinal mucosa by two maltases, one of which is identical with sucrase (61). Very careful histochemical work by Lojda (138) shows that 6-bromo-2-napthol-α-glucoside is split in the brush-border region of the enterocytes. It thus follows that sucrase and at least one other maltase are located in these structures. Even with disaccharides as substrates (maltose, sucrose, isomaltose, lactose, trehalose) the corresponding hydrolytic activities can be demonstrated in the brush border, provided that diffusion of the reaction products is reduced and proper reagents are used (114, 114a, 138). A controversy in the field (54, 59) has finally abated (56). It was due, in all likelihood, to the methods employed. For a discussion, the reader is referred to Lojda's very important paper.

The ability of the intestine to hydrolyze 6-bromo-2-napthyl-β-galactoside (138, 210) and 6-bromo-2-

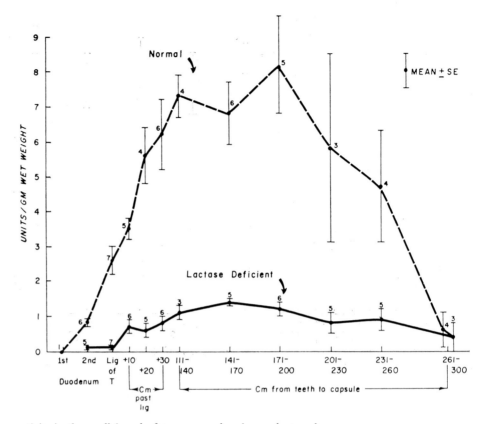

FIG. 2. Distribution of lactase activity in the small bowel of seven normal and seven lactase-deficient subjects. See legend to Fig. 1. [From Newcomer & McGill (155).]

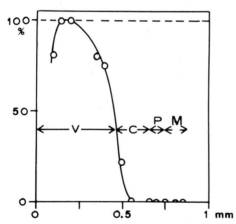

FIG. 3. Maltase activity of thin sections of rat ileum. On the abscissas, distance from the surface of mucosa (in millimeters). On the ordinate, maltase activity (as percent of the maximum). V, villi; C, crypts; P, Paneth cells; M, muscle. [From van Genderen & Engel (92).]

napthyl-β-glucoside (138) is not located in the brush border.

BY IMMUNOCHEMISTRY. Doell et al. (75) have prepared fluorescent antibodies against purified intestinal sucrase and lactase. The only cell structure reacting with these highly specific reagents was shown to be the brush border of intestinal columnar cells.

BY CELL FRACTIONATION TECHNIQUES. Miller & Crane (151) have recovered at least 75% of sucrase and maltase activities of the original homogenate in the brush isolated border. It seems very unlikely that so much of these activities could be due to contamination from other cell structures; similar results were obtained by Porteous & Clark (164, 165), by Hübscher et al. (107), by Ruttloff et al. (176), and by Forstner et al. (90a) with different fractionation techniques.

By the use of an elegant fractionation technique, Eichholz and Crane have further demonstrated that the disaccharidases are located in the membrane of the brush border (82, 158); this fraction was identified by electron microscopy.

Two groups (111, 112, 157) have obtained evidence for the association of intestinal sucrase activity with sessile particles occurring on the outer leaflet of the brush-border membrane. The particles, some 25 or

40–60 A in diameter, can be "solubilized" by papain treatment and purified according to a procedure strikingly similar to the one worked out for the isolation of sucrase-isomaltase (124, 125).

FUNCTIONAL EVIDENCE. If disaccharide hydrolysis takes place in an area external to the monosaccharide transport system, inhibition of monosaccharide transport must result in the diffusion of the products of disaccharide hydrolysis into the medium. This is actually what has been observed by Miller & Crane (150) and by Newey et al. (156), who used either sucrose or maltose. Inasmuch as the locus of transport of monosaccharides is at or near the brush border of epithelial cells (144), maltase and sucrase must also be at or near the brush border.

If sucrase is bound to or is a part of the cell membrane, once the transport of monosaccharides through the membrane is inhibited the reaction products of sucrase must appear first in the immediate vicinity of the membrane and later diffuse into the medium. Ugolev et al. (197) have shown that this is actually the case. Under similar experimental conditions shaking should bring about an apparent stimulation of sucrase by removing the reaction products and renewing the substrate available to the enzyme. Again, this was also shown to be the case (198).

Finally, if, on the contrary, there were a diffusional barrier between gut lumen and intestinal sucrase, one should observe a larger apparent K_m for sucrose in intact rings than in homogenates. (For a theoretical discussion of this kinetic problem see ref. 22.) This, however, is not the case: in intestinal slices and in homogenates the apparent K_m of sucrase for its substrate is the same (180; see, however, ref. 69).

Thus, from all these data, collected by different techniques and along different experimental designs, the conclusion seems inescapable that disaccharidases, in general, are bound to or are building blocks of the brush-border membrane. There is no significant diffusional barrier between gut lumen and membrane-bound sucrase.

It is still conceivable that disaccharidases are first secreted into the lumen and then immediately adsorbed onto the brush border. Although not definitely disproved, this hypothesis has no real experimental basis and is rendered unlikely by the need of proteolysis for solubilizing disaccharidases (see below).

Except for phlorizin hydrolase (141), β-glucosidases and nonspecific β-galactosidase are probably not located in the brush border (138). Finally, other maltases of the type occurring in other organs may

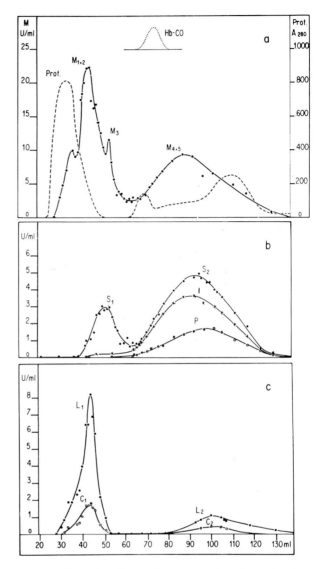

FIG. 4. Sephadex G-200 chromatography of papain-solubilized human intestinal disaccharidases. M, maltase; S, sucrase; I, isomaltase; P, palatinase; L, lactase; C, cellobiase activities. For the abbreviations, see Table 3. [From Semenza et al. (183).]

also occur in intestinal cells outside the brush-border region.

Solubilization Procedures

Solubilization of disaccharidases has been attempted in a number of ways. The procedure that is effective in most species and for most disaccharidases is papain digestion in potassium phosphate buffer (8, 61, 125). Other treatments found effective sometimes include: trypsin digestion (23, 47), autolysis (183), ficin digestion (66), sonication followed by

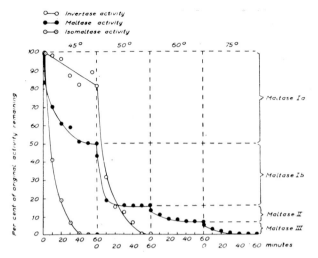

FIG. 5. Heat inactivation of human intestinal α-glucosidases in four steps. [From Dahlqvist (50).]

butanol extraction (95), and Triton X-100 treatment (78). Treatment with deoxycholate (34) or sonication alone (34, 95) brings about a partial and unstable solubilization.

NUMBER AND KINDS OF
INTESTINAL DISACCHARIDASES

The procedures used in the study of multiplicity of intestinal disaccharidases include solubilization followed by chromatographic separation (Fig. 4), inactivation by heat (Fig. 5) or by other means, and mutual competitive inhibition among the various substrates (Fig. 6). Although each of these approaches has its own sources of error, in most cases all three have led to the same conclusions.

Table 3 reports the number and types of disaccharidases demonstrated in normal human intestinal mucosa. There are four or five maltases, two[4] (or one) of which attack sucrose as well as maltose, and one of which splits maltose, isomaltose, and isomaltotriose (14, 50, 182). Maltase 1 or maltase 2 are probably indentical with glucoamylase (see below).

[4] Recently (125) we have obtained evidence that sucrase 1 may arise artificially from the sucrase-2-isomaltase complex by inactivation or separation of the isomaltase hyphezyme.[5] One sucrase hyphezyme only may occur in the intact brush-border membrane. This problem, however, should be regarded as unsettled, because two different sucrases have been solubilized from human small-intestinal mucosa by a variety of treatments [papain digestion (183), autolysis (183), freezing and thawing (36), Triton X-100 treatment (Z. Lojda, personal communication, 1967)].

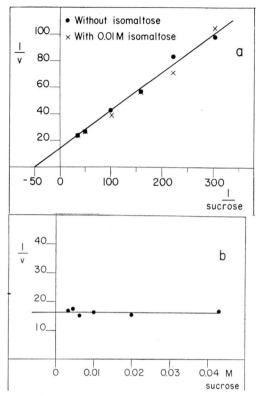

FIG. 6. Lack of effect of isomaltose on the activity of sucrase 2 and lack of effect of sucrose on the activity of isomaltase. Solubilized and partially purified human enzymes. *a*: Sucrase activity with (×) or without (●) isomaltose. *b*: Isomaltase activity in the presence of various concentrations of sucrose. [From Auricchio et al. (14).]

Two enzymes split lactose and cellobiose; one of them, lactase 2, is a soluble, nonspecific β-galactosidase (104, 182, 183). Table 4 reports the percent contributions of each "hyphezyme"[5] to the total disaccharidase activity of the homogenate.

[5] When more enzymes are bound to, or are building blocks of, a membrane, the usual concept of "enzyme" as a well-defined chemical entity appears to be stretched beyond its limits if applied to such complexes. Shall we consider the whole membrane as a single polyfunctional enzyme, or shall we speak rather of several enzymes bound together? The molecular limits artificially assessed to one such enzyme need not be the same in the various procedures used to separate it from its neighborhood. This artificially separated enzyme need not be identical with a chemical species acting as a precursor in the biosynthesis of the membrane. It seems appropriate to use a different word—perhaps "hyphezyme," from *ὑ φ ή*, fabric—to indicate the sum of those structures bound to, or a part of, a membrane, which are responsible for a given catalytic activity (e.g., substrate sites, allosteric sites, etc.). The size of catalytically inert membrane fabric surrounding the hyphezyme is immaterial in this definition; thus, the same hyphezyme solubilized by different procedures may well have different molecular weights.

TABLE 3. *Disaccharidases Present in Human Normal Intestinal Mucosa*

Zurich Classification (14, 182, 183) (By Sephadex G-200 chromatography of papain-solubilized enzymes) (Semenza and Auricchio, 1962; Auricchio, Semenza, and Rubino, 1965)	Lund Classification (50) (By heat inactivation of particle-bound enzymes) (Dahlqvist, 1962)
α-Glucosidases	
Maltases 1 + 2	Maltases III + II
Maltase 3 (= sucrase-1)*	Maltase I b (= invertase)
Maltase 4 (= sucrase-2)	
Maltase 5 (= isomaltase)	Maltase I a (= isomaltase)
Trehalase	Trehalase
β-Galactosidases	
Lactase 1	Lactase
Lactase 2 (= nonspecific β-galactosidase)	

* See footnote 4.

TABLE 4. *Percent Distribution of Human Intestinal Oligo- and Disaccharidase Activities Among Single Maltases (Ileum)*

Hyphezyme*	Maltase Act.	Sucrase Act.†	Isomaltase Act.	Maltotriase Act.‡
Maltases 1 + 2	40	0	Traces	24
Maltase 3	ca. 10	20		
Maltase 4		80		28
Maltase 5	ca. 50		ca. 100	48

* See footnote 5.

† See footnote 4.

‡ Data from Messer & Kerry (149). All other data are from Auricchio et al. (14).

TABLE 5. *Apparent Substrate and Cation Dissociation Constants of Intestinal Sucrases and of Intestinal Sugar Transport Systems*

	Sucrase, pH 5.4	Sugar Transp. Syst., pH 6.3
Rabbit*		
K_{Na}/K'_{Na}	1–1.2	1–1.2
K_K'/K'_{Na}	ca. 0.12	ca. 0.12
K_K'/K'_{Na}, pH 6.7–7.2	ca. 0.45	ca. 0.6†
K'_{Na}, pH 6.8	ca. 0.8 mM	ca. 0.9 mM
Hamster		
K'_{Na}	ca. 1 mM	ca. 1 mM
K'_{Na} (from Hill plots)	ca. 4 mM	
K_{Na}	ca. 11 mM	ca. 19 mM
K_{Na} (from Hill plots)	ca. 19 mM	
K_s	333 mM	
K_s'	16 mM	
Rat		
K_{Na}	ca. 50 mM	
K'_{Na}	ca. 0.58 mM	
K_s	ca. 1560 mM	
K_s'	ca. 18 mM	
	(pH 5.8)	
Man‡		
K_{Na}/K'_{Na}	1–1.2	
K'_{Na}	2.5–6 mM	
K_K'	0.1 mM	
K'_{Rb}	ca. 1.5 mM	
K'_{NH_4}	3.5 mM	
K_s'	20–25 mM	

* From Kolínská & Semenza (125).

† Calculated by Semenza (179) from data on glucose-dependent short-circuit current.

‡ From Semenza et al. (186).

All other constants are from unpublished experiments of G. Semenza, 1966.

The pattern of disaccharidases is not the same in all species. In pig intestinal mucosa six disaccharidases have been reported: one maltase-sucrase, two maltase-isomaltase, one specific isomaltase, one lactase, and one trehalase (53). In the rat seven disaccharidases have been reported: two maltases, one maltase-sucrase, one maltase-isomaltase, one trehalase (53), one lactase, and one nonspecific soluble β-galactosidase (73). The existence of a nonspecific β-galactosidase, besides the lactase, has also been reported in the small intestine of calf (99) and of rabbit (73). In the pinnipeds examined, who lack both sucrase and trehalase (Table 1), maltase and isomaltase are due to a single hyphezyme (118).

Sucrase and Isomaltase

CATALYTIC AND MOLECULAR PROPERTIES. Sucrase has been partially purified from the intestinal mucosa of the hog (48), the rabbit (33), and the rat (75). Iso-

maltase has been partially purified from the ox (178) and the hog (53, 133). The sucrase-isomaltase complex has been partially purified from the rabbit (95), the rat (51), and the human intestinal mucosa (183). Its complete isolation from rabbit (124, 125) and human (46) small intestine has been achieved recently. Since the procedure is based on the specific interaction of papain-solubilized sucrase-isomaltase with Sephadex, it is likely that the same procedure can also be applied to the isolation of the sucrase-isomaltase complex of other species.

The substrate specificity of both sucrase and isomaltase is still scarcely known. Sucrase hydrolyzes, besides sucrose, turanose [3-α-glucopyranosyl-fructofuranose; (48)] as well as maltose (34, 48, 125), maltotriose (149), and maltitol (G. Semenza, unpublished results). Isomaltase splits 1,6-α glucosidic bonds occurring in a number of di- and oligosaccharides, e.g., in isomaltose, palatinose (14, 183), panose (132, 133), isomaltotriose (129), and limits dextrins produced when α-amylase (133, 178) acts on dextran (51, see, however, ref. 133). In addition, isomaltase hydrolyzes the 1,4-α glucosidic bonds of maltose (133), maltotriose (149), and maltitol (unpublished results). The few contradictions present in the literature may be due to species differences.

Table 5 reports the K_s values for sucrose hydrolysis at nearly optimal Na$^+$ concentration and pH for some species.

It has not been possible so far to separate sucrase from isomaltase.[6] However, one can destroy one activity without affecting the other. Sucrase-isomaltase, as isolated from rabbit (124, 125) or purified from human intestinal mucosa (46, 80), has a molecular weight of approximately 200,000. The turnover number for sucrose hydrolysis is estimated to be approximately 3,000. The activation energy of sucrose hydrolysis is 10 kcal/mole, as estimated in crude extracts of rat intestinal mucosa (20).

Tris(hydroxymethyl)aminomethane is a fully competitive inhibitor of both isomaltase [K_i for the hog enzyme: 0.14 mM (130)] and sucrase [K_i for the rabbit enzyme: 0.4 mM (125)]. Sulfhydryl reagents do not inhibit sucrase or isomaltase, whereas some heavy metals (Cu^{++}, Zn^{++}, Hg^{++}) do (125, 130). This observation, and plots of pK_m versus pH and the disappearance of isomaltase activity upon photo-oxidation in the presence of methylene blue indicate a possible role of an imidazol group in the catalysis (130). The pH activity curves of sucrase are also compatible with this (Fig. 7).

We have recently found that, during the hydrolysis of either sucrose or palatinose, α-glucose (and not β-glucose) is formed (185). This observation, along with those preceding ones, is compatible with a double-displacement reaction mechanism of the type suggested for other carbohydrases (126, 203).

Unlike yeast invertase, intestinal sucrase is an α-glucosidase. Besides its substrate specificity (see above), this is shown by its transglucosidase activity and lack of transfructosidase activity (33, 57).

High substrate concentrations and the presence of glucose or other monosaccharides often inhibit disaccharidase activities. This inhibition may be due partially to the transglucosidase activity of the disaccharidases.

---

[6] This was achieved very recently, by first splitting the sucrase-isomaltase complex into subunits (G. Semenza and Mosimann, unpublished data).

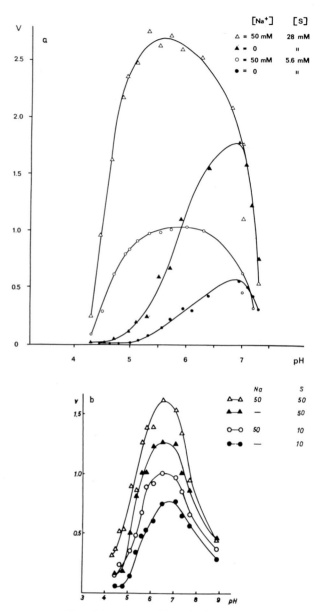

FIG. 7. pH activity curves of intestinal sucrase in the presence and in the absence of Na$^+$, at two substrate concentrations. a: In the hamster; b: in the rabbit. [From G. Semenza, unpublished results; and Semenza & Kolínská (125).]

NA$^+$ ACTIVATION OF SUCRASE AND ITS RELATION TO NA$^+$ ACTIVATION OF SUGAR CARRIER. Na$^+$ activation of intestinal sucrase, briefly mentioned in previous papers (33, 42), has recently been thought to bear a relation to Na$^+$ activation of sugar carrier (180, 186) and has been investigated in some detail. Most data reported in what follows are unpublished results obtained by the reviewer and his group.

The mode of activation of sucrase by Na$^+$ is different in different species. In the hamster the degree of

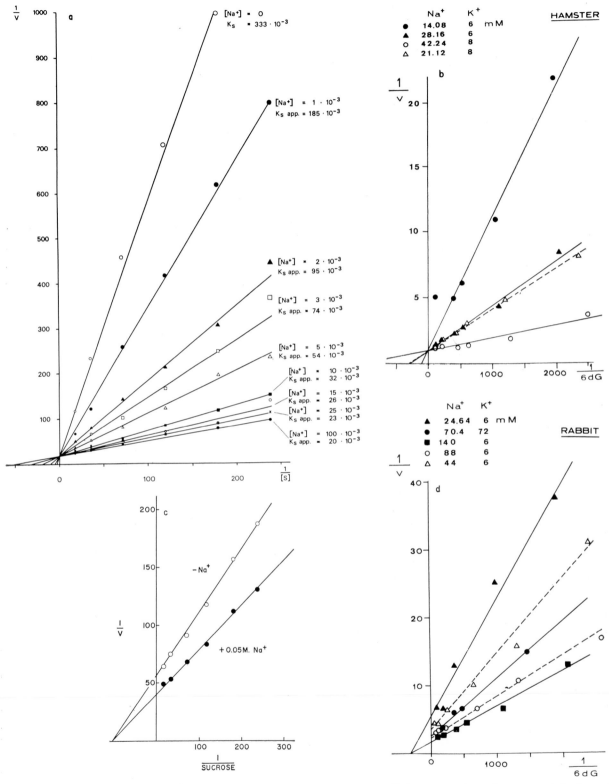

FIG. 8. Double-reciprocal plots (136) at various Na$^+$ concentrations of sucrase activity (*a* and *c*) and of sugar uptake (*b* and *d*) in the hamster (*a* and *b*) and in the rabbit intestine (*c* and *d*). *6dG*, 6-deoxy-D-glucose concentration. (G. Semenza, unpublished results.)

activation by Na⁺ depends on the pH (Fig. 7a). Double reciprocal plots of 1/velocity versus 1/substrate concentration show that Na⁺ affects the apparent affinity of sucrase for sucrose, whereas the maximum velocity is essentially unaffected (Fig. 8a). Using appropriate equations (177, 179), one can estimate the cation dissociation constants at [sucrose] = ∞ (K'_{Na}) and at [sucrose] = 0 (K_{Na}) (Table 5). A plot of Na-dependent velocity as a function of Na⁺ concentrations according to the empirical Hill's equation (101) reveals a slope greater than one, as it is often observed with allosteric effectors (153).

In the rat, Na⁺ activation of sucrase follows a similar pattern. The cation dissociation constants are reported in Table 5.

In man (186) and in the rabbit (125), the pattern is different altogether. The degree of activation by Na⁺ does not depend so strongly on the pH as in the case of the hamster (Fig. 7b). Moreover, double reciprocal plots of 1/velocity versus 1/substrate show that Na⁺ does not significantly affect the apparent affinity of sucrase for sucrose; the major effect is on the maximum velocity instead (Fig. 8c). Thus, $K_{Na} \simeq K'_{Na}$ (Table 5).

Potassium is a poor activator of sucrase. Thus, by competing with sodium, potassium inhibits all intestinal sucrases investigated. The potassium-sucrase dissociation constants have been determined in a number of cases (Table 5), and they are always smaller than the corresponding constants for sodium. The constants for Li⁺, Rb⁺, Cs⁺, and NH₄⁺ have also been determined for human sucrase, and it has been shown that all these cations compete for the same "cation-accepting site" of sucrase (186).

Na⁺ activation and K⁺ inhibition of intestinal sucrase bear a striking resemblance to Na⁺ activation and K⁺ inhibition of intestinal sugar transport (172). In fact, in the hamster, as shown by Crane et al. (44) and confirmed by us (180), Na⁺ and K⁺ affect the apparent Michaelis-Menten constants, without significantly affecting the maximum velocity (Fig. 8b). In the rabbit, on the contrary, these cations affect the maximum transport velocity without significantly affecting the apparent Michaelis-Menten constants [Fig. 8d; (180)].

Furthermore, in spite of large species variations, the Na⁺- and K⁺ dissociation constants, as determined for sugar transport system, agree reasonably well with the corresponding constants determined for sucrase activation (Table 5).

Finally, the other cations of the first group and ammonium are competitive inhibitors of Na⁺ activa-

Sucrase

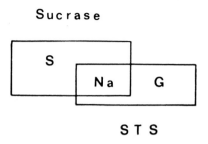

STS

FIG. 9. Possible spatial relation between intestinal sucrase and intestinal sugar transport system (STS). S: sucrose site; Na: sodium site; G: sugar site of the carrier.[7]

tion of sugar transport (26, 179) in much the same way as they are competitive inhibitors of Na⁺ activation of sucrase (186).

In summary, there are both qualitative and quantitative species differences in the Na⁺ activation and cation inhibition of both intestinal sucrase and intestinal sugar transport, but within the same species both sucrase and sugar transport are activated in the same way and all kinetic parameters measured, although different in different species, agree well with each other within the same species.

The possible interpretations of this close parallelism range from the conservative one that the Na⁺ site[7] of sucrase has similar chemical properties as the Na⁺ site of sugar carrier to the extreme one that sucrase and the sugar carrier share a common cation-accepting site. This last hypothesis is illustrated in Figure 9. It agrees with Miller and Crane's observation that sucrase and sugar carrier are spatially closely related to each other in the brush border (150) and with Crane's concept of the brush-border membrane as a mosaic composed of different building blocks, each capable of reacting with a substrate or with an allosteric effector. Hydrolysis or transport may ensue, according to the groups involved. This concept is discussed by Crane, Chapter 118, this Handbook. Elsewhere (181) we have discussed the hypothesis that the similarity in Na⁺ activation of sucrase and sugar carrier may indicate a close quaternary association permitting the allosteric transition to propagate.

To avoid misunderstandings, it may be stated that there is no evidence that sucrase is, itself, the sugar carrier. What evidence exists is, if anything, to the contrary. Competitive inhibitors for the substrate of

[7] Here, in the following, and in Fig. 9 the term "site" is used to indicate the structure or structures reacting with Na⁺ with consequent effect on sucrase activity or on sugar transport. No stoichiometric relation between Na⁺ site and substrate site is necessarily implied.

sucrase [such as tris(hydroxymethyl)aminomethane] (125) do not inhibit sugar transport (26). Conversely, competitive inhibitors for the substrate of the carrier (such as phlorizin) do not inhibit sucrase (180). Furthermore, animals not possessing sucrase can absorb monosaccharides, and genetic disturbances of sugar intestinal absorption do not affect sucrase (1, 81, 148). It is clear that the substrate sites of intestinal sucrase and of sugar carrier are not coincident.

Na+ activation of intestinal sucrase is probably of no great importance in the digestion of sucrose in the gut, with the possible exception of hamster intestine at acidic pH values (Fig. 7a). However, its parallelism with Na+ activation of sugar carrier strongly suggests that a study of this property of sucrase will yield information on Na+ activation of sugar carrier. The reviewer's group is presently pursuing this line of investigation, using solubilized and isolated sucrase. In this state the enzyme is still Na+ activated and K+ inhibited, with the same cation dissociation constants as when it was bound to the membrane (125).

Maltases and Amylases

Pancreatic amylase, albeit quantitatively the most important, is not the only enzyme of the gut that splits starch and glycogen. Early workers (29, 84, 92) detected a strong amylase activity in small-intestinal mucosa. Evidence that at least one-tenth of this activity is not of pancreatic origin was given by McGeachin et al. (145, 146) by surgically removing the pancreas and salivary glands of rats and finding a strong reduction but not a disappearance of the amylase activity of the small-intestinal mucosa. More recently, Dahlqvist & Thompson (66) and Ruttloff et al. (174) have separated two amylases from the small intestine. One is indistinguishable from pancreatic α-amylase, having the following characteristics: Cl⁻ activation, pH optimum between 7 and 8, inhibition by complexing agents, no formation of free glucose from starch, and no maltase activity. It is probably pancreatic α-amylase adsorbed onto the surface of intestinal mucosa, as suggested by Ugolev's group (110).

The other amylase is not activated by Cl⁻, has a slightly acidic pH optimum, and splits both starch and maltose to free glucose. It is, therefore, a glucoamylase (α-1,4-glucan glucohydrolase, EC 3.2.1.3, α-amylase). Very probably it is identical with one of the intestinal maltases not possessing sucrase or isomaltase activity (in man, maltases 1 and 2) (80, 174).

Maltases 1 and 2 are probably located in the brush border of enterocytes and probably play a physiological role in splitting maltose present in the lumen. In fact, in sucrose-isomaltose malabsorption (in which the residual maltase activity is due essentially to maltases 1 or 2, see below), maltase is digested in an almost normal way (9, 167).

Partial purification of these maltases has been achieved in man (80, 183), rat (66), and hog (53, 130, 174).

Since other enzymes with maltase-glucoamylase activity have been reported in other organs, it is possible that they also occur in intestinal mucosa and that they contribute to the total maltase activity of intestinal mucosal homogenates.

Trehalase

Trehalase has been partially purified from hog intestinal mucosa (47) after trypsin digestion and ion-exchange chromatography. Thus far no substrate has been found for this enzyme other than α,α-trehalose (K_m: 3 mM). The α,β- and β,β-isomers are not attacked to any significant extent. Trehalase, unique among intestinal disaccharidases, does not have detectable transglycosidase activity. It is not inhibited by excess of substrate. Phlorizin is a fully competitive inhibitor (K_i at pH 5.4, 2 mM) (G. Semenza and L. Řihová, unpublished results).[8] Sodium does not activate trehalase, either before or after solubilization. The particle-bound enzyme shows an evident homologous cooperative interaction among substrate sites, which is lost upon solubilization with trypsin (G. Semenza and L. Řihová, unpublished results).

Since trehalose occurs mainly in insects, algae, and mushrooms (19, 39, 154), it does not play a significant role in the diet of present-day Europeans and Americans. Correspondingly, intestinal trehalase also plays a minor role in these ethnic groups, and trehalase deficiencies, if they occur at all, are likely to remain asymptomatic. But trehalose-containing foodstuffs are present in larger amounts in the diet of some populations of the Far East, and it is estimated (39) that trehalose was actually more important than sucrose in the diet of ancient man.

Lactase

A number of tissues (37, 138), including small-intestinal mucosa (138), contain at least one soluble, nonspecific β-galactosidase. This enzyme is not

[8] Renal trehalase is inhibited by phlorizin (40).

TABLE 6. *Substrate Specificity of Calf Intestinal Lactase*

Substrate	Velocity of* Hydrolysis at [s] = 10 mM	Maximum* Velocity	K_m, mM
o-Nitrophenol-β-D-galactoside	95.5	139	4.51
p-Nitrophenol-β-D-galactoside	54.2	115	1.14
α-Lactose	120	214	7.63
β-Lactose	89.6	214	1.38
Equilibrium mixture of α- and β-lactoses	107	214	1.0
3-(β-D-Galactosido)-D-glucose	149	214	4.39
6-(β-D-Galactosido)-D-glucose	3.1	3.8	2.0
6-(β-D-Fucosido)-D-glucose	0.98		
Phenol-β-D-galactoside	1.56		
o-Nitrophenol-α-L-arabinoside	5.93	8.05	3.63
3-(α-L-Arabinosido)-D-glucose	3.18		
4-(α-L-Arabinosido)-D-glucose	1.64		
6-(α-L-Arabinosido)-D-glucose	0.07		
3-(β-D-Galactosido)-D-fructose	+++		
α-L-Fucosido-lactose	− −		
Ethyl-β-D-fucopyranoside	+++		
Methyl-β-D-galactopyranoside	++		
Methyl-α-D-galactopyranoside	− −		
Ethyl-β-D-galactofuranoside	− −		
Ethyl-β-D-galactopyranoside	++		
Methyl-β-L-arabinoside	− −		
Phenol-β-L-arabinoside	− −		
3-(β-D-Galactosido)-N-acetyl-glucosamine	++		
4-(β-D-Galactosido)-N-acetyl-glucosamine	++		
6-(β-D-Galactosido)-N-acetyl-glucosamine	+		
Lacto-N-triose	+		
Lactosazone	−		
Allolactosazone	−		
3-(β-D-Galactosido)-glucosazone	−		
5-(β-D-Galactosido)-D-arabinose	+		
2-Methylethyl-β-D-galactoside	−		
3-Deoxyethyl-β-D-galactoside	−		
4-Methylethyl-β-D-galactoside	−		

From Wallenfels & Fischer (202).

* Micromoles hydrolyzed substrate per minute, at 40 C, per milligram protein.

+, Hydrolyzed (lactose, ++++); −, not hydrolyzed.

located in the brush border (73, 210). Since it splits lactose much less rapidly than other β-galactosides (73, 104) and is present at essentially normal levels in human lactose intolerance (210), it probably does not play any significant role in the digestion of dietary lactose.

A different enzyme, which appears to be a true "lactase," occurs in the brush border. A first attempt at a partial purification from dog small intestine was reported by Cajori as early as 1935 (32). Partial purification of small-intestinal lactase has been reported from the calf (99), from man (183), and from the rat (7a, 75). An almost complete isolation

was obtained from the calf by Wallenfels & Fischer (202) and by us (G. Semenza, K. R. Kerry, and P. Hore, unpublished results) from the rat. Most data reported in what follows have been drawn from Wallenfels and Fischer's paper.

The enzyme, although purified some 2,100 times, was not completely pure, as shown by ultracentrifugation (203). The preparation contained rather large amounts of carbohydrates, mainly N-acetylglucosamine and galactose, and attempts to separate this carbohydrate moiety from the protein resulted in complete inactivation. The enzyme is also inactivated irreversibly by urea at unusually low concentrations, and more at 5 C than at 20 C.

The activation energy for the hydrolysis of o-nitrophenyl-β-galactoside is 14.2 kcal/mole, that is larger than for *E. coli* β-galactosidase. The pH activity curve has a maximum at pH 5.5; the heat of dissociation of the group responsible for the acidic shoulder is 0, that of the group for the alkaline shoulder, some 5.65 kcal/mole. Lactase is inhibited by heavy metals (Ag^+, Hg^{++}, Cu^{++}), but not by sulfhydryl reagents. These data indicate that a carboxyl and an imidazol group may be involved in the catalysis. Accordingly, reaction mechanisms have been suggested, implying a single or a double displacement (203).

The substrate specificity has been studied very thoroughly. The pertinent data are collected in Table 6. The only sugar which is a better substrate than α- or β-lactose is its 3-isomer. Tris(hydroxymethyl)aminomethane ($K_i = 1.55$ mM) and o-nitrophenyl-β-D-thiogalactoside ($K_i = 6.9$ mM) are competitive inhibitors. Galactose also and, to a much lesser degree, glucose are inhibitors, probably competitive in nature. The enzyme has significant transgalactosidase activity (202).

Rat intestinal lactase is not activated by Na^+ (G. Semenza, K. R. Kerry, and P. Hore, unpublished data).

DEVELOPMENT AND CONTROL OF
DISACCHARIDASE ACTIVITIES IN MAMMALS[9]

Whereas some information on the genetic control of intestinal disaccharidases can be inferred from genetically determined deficiencies (see below), virtually nothing is known about the biochemical mechanisms of disaccharidase biosynthesis. (As a matter of fact, very little is known about the biosynthesis of cell membrane components.) The following data are available on disaccharidase development and on its alimentary and hormonal control.

[9] This subject is reviewed extensively by J. J. Deren in Chapter 62, Volume III of this *Handbook*.

α-Glucosidases

Probably in most mammals α-glucosidases are absent at birth and develop later in life (Fig. 10). Again, significant species differences warrant quotation of a few individual examples. In the intestine of the newborn pig no sucrase, trehalase, or isomaltase and very little maltase activity is present (16, 49, 200). Administration of sucrose or maltose to piglets is followed by diarrhea, failure to thrive, and eventually death. The same is true for the rat (74, 173), calf (106), lamb (195a, 201), dog, rabbit, and mouse.

In man, α-disaccharidases develop during intrauterine life. Sucrase and isomaltase activities appear during the third month of gestation or shortly before

and trehalase shortly thereafter. Maltases 1 and 2 appear later, after the sixth month (11, 64, 90). By the sixth to eighth month of gestation all α-disaccharidases, with the exception of maltase 1, have reached adult levels. This latter enzyme is not completely developed even at birth. Man may be the only mammal equipped at birth with the hydrolases necessary for the digestion of disaccharides present in artificial baby food.

In the chick (30, 100), sucrase slowly increases from the ninth to the nineteenth day of incubation; it decreases significantly at the twentieth day, and sharply increases soon after hatching (i.e., after approximately the twenty-first day).

Hydrocortisone and ACTH appear to trigger the development of intestinal sucrase, as ascertained both by enzymatic determination (74, 100) and by immunological techniques (75). However, they only stimulate its precocious appearance, not an excess synthesis over normal levels (Fig. 11). Sucrase activity soon decreases when the hormonal medication is discontinued. Hydrocortisone clearly acts within the intestinal cells, because it is effective in in vitro cultures of small-intestinal cells (74, 100). It is possible that the hormone acts by stimulating the synthesis of mRNA, as it has been suggested for other systems (17, 85).

Once the first weeks of life have elapsed, corticosteroids apparently have no effect on sucrase levels, as shown by lack of any effect of either adrenalectomy or cortisone administration. Moreover, the response to sucrose feeding (see below) is the same in adrenalectomized as in normal rats (72).

Oral sucrose does not stimulate precocious synthesis of sucrase (in calves, 106). It does, however, affect sucrase levels in the adult animal. In fact, in adult

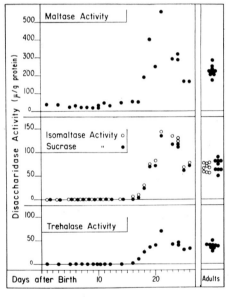

FIG. 10. α-Glucosidase activities in the intestine of suckling and adult rats. [From Rubino et al. (173).]

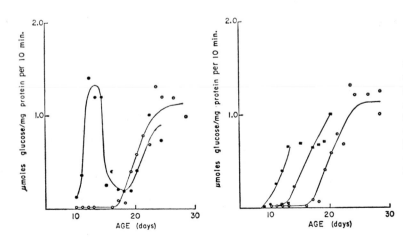

FIG. 11. *Left*: effect of hydrocortisone on the development of intestinal sucrase in rats. ○, Controls; ●, hydrocortisone injected intramuscularly (50 mg/kg) at 9 days of age. *Right*: effect of ACTH on the development of sucrase. ○, Controls; □, ACTH injected twice daily (40 USP units/kg) from 9 days of age; ■, ACTH injected twice daily from 5 days of age. [From Doell & Kretchmer (74). Copyright 1964 by the American Association for the Advancement of Science.]

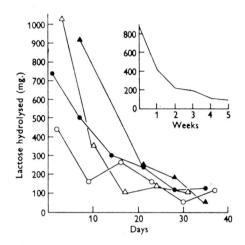

FIG. 12. Decline of intestinal lactase activity in pigs after birth. Lactase activity is expressed as milligrams lactose hydrolyzed per hour per gram small intestine dry matter. [From Walker (200).]

rats, fasting or sugar-free diets reduce the level of sucrase activity to about half the normal within two to four days. Prolonged treatment does not reduce it further. Administration of sucrose, galactose, melizitose, α-methylglucoside, fructose, or maltose brings sucrase back to normal levels (21, 72). Surprisingly, glucose, mannose, and xylose are ineffective. The meaning of these differences among sugars is not apparent.

Lactase

The pattern of development of this enzyme in most animals is almost the mirror image of that of the other disaccharidases. Lactase is present at birth at high levels and tends to decrease thereafter [calves (106); hog (16, 49, 200) and Fig. 12; rabbit (73, 123); rat (5, 73, 121) and Fig. 13; mice (123); dog (71, 207); cat (103)]. For some time the decrease in lactase activity is compensated by the growth of the intestine (200). The guinea pig is born with low lactase levels, which decrease but little thereafter (123). This may be related to the unusually long intrauterine life of this animal.

In man, lactase begins to develop after the fifth month of gestation [(11, 64); Fig. 14] and decreases but little during adult life (13).

It is not known whether adrenal steroids can trigger a precocious development of lactase, as they do for sucrase. At any rate, they do not stimulate lactase synthesis in the rat after birth or in in vitro cultures of intestinal cells (74).

Adrenalectomy, if performed early in extrauterine life, delays the decrease of lactase in adult age (121), and the administration of aldosterone cancels this effect of adrenalectomy (122).

The possible effect of lactose administration on intestinal lactase levels has been a matter of considerable controversy during more than half a century, and many facets still remain unclear. Lactose does not trigger the development of lactase in the embryo, as Doell & Kretchmer (74) have shown conclusively; fetuses from completely mastectomized rabbits have normal intestinal lactase levels. In man also, lactose is probably of no importance in triggering the development of intestinal lactase; galactosemic children, fed on lactose-free diets from early infancy, respond to oral lactose tolerance tests in an essentially normal way (120).

Concerning the effect on lactase levels in adulthood, there have been old claims of "lactose-induced" lactase biosynthesis, even in birds. Some of these claims were disproved as early as 1906 (162). Modern investigations have established that addition of lactose to the diet does not prevent the decline of lactase activity in the intestine of calves (106), rabbits (99), or rats (5, 91, 195). However, it is possible that lactose delays the decline of lactase only when it is the sole source of carbohydrate in the diet [(93, 121); but see refs. 91, 195; and Torralba, personal communication]. At any rate, once the lactase level has decreased it can no longer be increased without

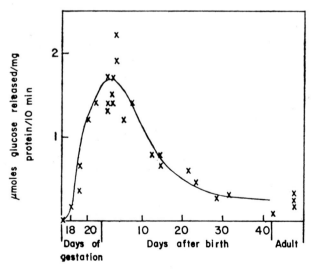

FIG. 13. Lactase activity in homogenates from rat small intestine. [From Doell & Kretchmer (73).]

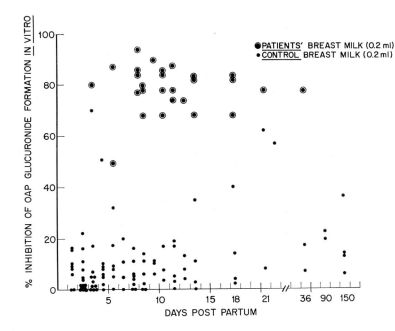

FIG. 6. Inhibition of glucuronyl transferase activity by milk from five mothers of seven jaundiced infants and from control mothers in vitro (OAP = o-aminophenol). [From Arias et al. (18).]

jaundiced infants significantly inhibited the formation of direct-reacting bilirubin and o-aminophenol glucuronide by guinea pig liver preparations as compared with results observed with normal human or cow's milk (Fig. 6). Crystalline pregnane-3(α),20(β)-diol was isolated from inhibitory milk and identified by thin-layer and gas-liquid chromatography and infrared spectroscopy (Fig. 7). This steroid competitively inhibits glucuronyl transferase activity in vitro and accounted for the major inhibitory activity of maternal milk. Administration of pregnane-3(α),20(β)-diol to two full-term infants following subsidence of the physiological jaundice of the newborn resulted in unconjugated hyperbilirubinemia which abated after cessation of steroid administration [(16); Fig. 8]. Older infants and one adult did not demonstrate a similar response to steroid administration. The steroid may act in vivo as a competitive inhibitor, and jaundice probably occurs only in newborns because of the reduction in glucuronyl transferase activity in neonatal liver. The significance of the unusual isomer, its source, and the mechanism of excretion in breast milk are unknown. A maternal abnormality in steroid metabolism is postulated because mothers of the jaundiced breast-fed infants excreted variable amounts of pregnane-3(α),20(β)-diol in their urine, whereas this steroid isomer was not detected in postpartum urine obtained from 50 consecutive normal women (12, 210a)

TRANSFER OF CONJUGATED BILIRUBIN FROM LIVER CELL INTO BILE

In mammals, virtually all the bilirubin in freshly obtained bile is conjugated (20, 224). In elasmobranchs, UCB is also found and is apparently excreted without prior conjugation and hydrolysis (10). Although CB has never been identified or measured in the bile canaliculus, it is assumed that the excretory process is energy dependent and operates against a concentration gradient. Support for this view is found in the work of Hanzon, who studied the effect of UCB on the transfer of uranin, a fluorescent dye, from blood to bile in rabbit liver (119). Hanzon concluded that UCB diffuses passively across the liver cell and is actively concentrated at the canalicular surface before excretion in the bile. Although reabsorption of water and electrolytes may occur in biliary epithelium, available evidence supports the view that hepatic cellular excretory transport is the primary and major event.

The capacity of the liver to excrete bilirubin is limited (20, 270), and in mammals excretion depends on prior conjugation (20, 224). Weinbren & Billing (270) demonstrated that in rats injected with UCB the maximal hepatic excretory rate was 61 ± 8.0 μg of bilirubin excreted per min per 100 g body wt. Others confirmed this (20), observed a progressive increase in the plasma concentration of CB, and obtained the same excretory maximum when CB was injected into mutant Gunn rats (20). In patients with

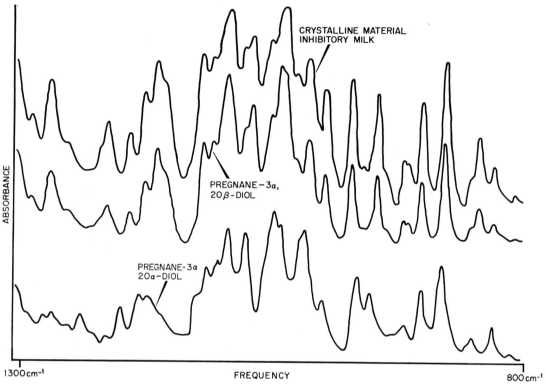

FIG. 7. Infrared spectrum of crystalline material isolated from inhibitory human milk compared with pure pregnane-3(α), 20(β)-diol, and pregnane-3(α), 20(α)-diol (potassium bromide dispersion, sodium chloride prism). [From Arias et al. (18).]

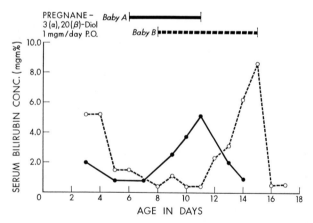

FIG. 8. Effect of ingestion of pregnane-3(α), 20(β)-diol on the serum bilirubin concentration in two full-term newborn infants. Dosage 1 mg/day orally. [From Arias & Gartner (16).]

hemolytic disease, the plasma concentration of CB is increased (58, 216, 256). These observations indicate that the ability of the liver cell to excrete CB is rate limiting in the overall transfer of bilirubin from blood to bile.

Because UCB-^{14}C but not CB-^{14}C can be reabsorbed from the gallbladder (199) and intestinal tract (102,

164), it has been suggested that UCB and CB are excreted by the liver but that only the former is selectively reabsorbed by intrahepatic biliary epithelium (165). An objection to this theory is that the Gunn rat, which has no CB and only a trace of UCB in bile, does not increase biliary excretion of UCB after receiving large intravenous doses of UCB (20, 224).

Under physiological conditions, hepatic storage of CB is not observed, and CB is rapidly excreted from the cell into the bile (32). After injection of UCB-^{3}H in normal rats and subsequent subcellular fractionation, Bernstein and associates (32) were unable to recover CB-^{3}H from cell fractions, although CB-^{3}H was readily recovered after injection of CB-^{3}H in normal rats or its addition in vitro to homogenates of normal liver. The failure to recover CB-^{3}H or its corresponding azo derivative from either the supernatant or microsomal fractions of normal rat liver after injection of UCB-^{3}H suggests several possibilities: *1*) CB may be more strongly bound to cytoplasmic proteins than is UCB and is not extracted during the recovery procedure; *2*) CB is degraded or hydrolyzed during cell fractionation, or *3*) after conjugation, CB rapidly leaves the cell. The first two possibilities are unlikely in view of the ease with which CB was recovered from subcellular fractions after its injection in vivo or addition in vitro.

The participation of cellular organelles, particularly lysosomes, in bilirubin excretion by the liver has been suggested by electron-microscopic observations (5, 104, 215) and studies of the subcellular distribution of UCB-^{3}H (48). Bernstein and associates (32) studied this problem from a functional standpoint in the rat. From 1 to 60 min after the intravenous injection of 50 μg of UCB-^{3}H, only 5% of intrahepatic counts were observed in a subcellular fraction which biochemically and morphologically contains primarily lysosomes and microbodies (Fig. 9). With increasing time the radioactivity in the fraction, when expressed as percentage of total radioactivity in liver, increased from 5% at 1 hour to 26% in 6 hours; however, when expressed as percentage of administered dose, the radioactivity in the fraction remained constant during the 6-hour period. This indicates that rapid turnover of radiobilirubin in lysosomes or microbodies is unlikely and does not play a role in excretory transport of bile pigment.

The mechanism and control of the excretion of CB across the canalicular portion of the plasma membrane are unknown. Dissociated glucuronyl groups may confer on the pigment a polar-nonpolar structure permitting orientation of the molecule across a lipid-water interface, and the rate of secretion may be determined by the relative affinity of the pigment for the two phases (223). Specific membrane-bound protein car-

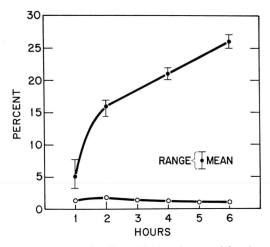

FIG. 9. Incorporation of radioactivity into lysosomal fraction of liver homogenates from normal rats after intravenous administration of UCB-^{3}H. Radioactivity in the lysosomal fraction is expressed as percentage of total radioactivity in liver (●———●) and as percentage of administered dose (○———○). [From Bernstein et al. (32).]

riers may be involved. Present methods and concepts have not resolved these problems.

Specificity of Hepatic Excretory Mechanisms

In addition to CB, several other organic anions such as porphyrins, bile acids, dyes, and drugs are secreted in bile in concentrations greatly exceeding their plasma concentrations. Their mutual competition for biliary excretion suggests a common excretory mechanism for all polar organic anions, as proposed by Sperber (240). Organic cations do not compete with organic anions for biliary excretion, and separate excretory mechanisms are postulated (232). A unique opportunity to investigate the multiplicity of hepatic excretory mechanisms was provided by Cornelius's discovery of mutant Corriedale sheep with an inherited disorder that is functionally and morphologically identical to the Dubin-Johnson syndrome in man (13, 14, 254). The biliary excretion of several organic anions was studied in normal and mutant sheep with complete biliary fistulas (S. Alpert, A. Shanske, and I. M. Arias, unpublished observations). Biliary Tm BSP, endogenous phylloerythrin excretion, and excretion of test doses of iodopanoic acid, metanephrine glucuronide, and CB were greatly reduced in mutant sheep when compared with results in normal sheep; however, the maximal biliary excretion of taurocholate, the major organic anion in sheep bile, was the same in normal and mutant sheep. Intravenous infusion of taurocholate to mutant sheep did not increase the biliary excretion of simultaneously infused BSP or bilirubin. These observations in an inherited disorder demonstrate that the bile salt may be excreted by a different mechanism from that involving CB, dyes, endogenous metabolites, drugs, and phylloerythrin. Mutant sheep with the Dubin-Johnson syndrome have selective bile secretory failure in the latter excretory mechanism but not in the excretion of bile salts. Pathologically there is no cholestasis. Presumably, intrahepatic cholestasis results from generalized bile secretory failure affecting the excretion of bile acids as well as other organic anions.

Reduction in Hepatic Excretion of Bilirubin Produced by Drugs and Hormones

Hypophysectomized rats have normal hepatic uptake and conjugation of UCB; however, biliary excretion of CB is reduced to less than 50% of normal (97, 99). The excretory defect is promptly restored after administration of several growth hormone preparations as well as thyroxin (100). The mechanisms responsible for these effects are unknown.

Various drugs and chemicals selectively interfere with the excretory phase of bilirubin transport through the liver. Billing and associates administered bunamiodol to rats infused with UCB and CB and demonstrated reduced hepatic excretion of CB (42). Hargreaves made similar observations with novobiocin and other compounds (120, 121). Heikel and associates (127) studied the effect of icterogenin, a triterpene acid derived from the plant *Lippia rehmanni*, on bile pigment metabolism in rabbits and observed decreased bile flow and inability of the liver to excrete intravenously administered conjugates of bilirubin and BSP. The liver was normal by light-microscopic examination of sections stained with hematoxylin and eosin. Icterogenin and various C-17 alkylated anabolic steroids selectively interfere with hepatic excretory transport in normal rats infused with UCB and in Gunn rats infused with CB (10, 11). In rats, the hepatic excretory maximum for bilirubin must be reduced by approximately 90% before hyperbilirubinemia occurs (10). This observation may account for the rarity of hyperbilirubinemia in patients treated with C-17 alkylated anabolic steroids despite significant reduction in hepatic Tm BSP (153, 219). Morphological studies of liver after administration of anabolic steroids or icterogenin reveal blunted canalicular microvilli and abnormal histochemical staining reactions of cell membranes in rats (104, 215) and less pronounced changes in man (153, 219). The significance of the morphological changes in regard to the mechanism of hepatic excretion is unknown.

Congenital and Inheritable Defects in Hepatic Excretory Function in Man and Sheep

Occasionally newborn infants with hemolytic disease have very high plasma concentrations of CB (inspissated bile syndrome) (124), and delayed development of hepatic excretory mechanisms has been postulated. The developmental pattern of hepatic excretory function has not been adequately studied in man; however, several investigations have been performed in guinea pigs. After injection of fetal and newborn guinea pigs with UCB-^{14}C or CB-^{14}C, less than 1 and 10%, respectively, of the administered dose was excreted in the cannulated bile duct, whereas adult guinea pigs excreted approximately 90% of either administered radiobilirubin (218).

In 1954, Dubin and Johnson (70, 71) and Sprinz & Nelson (241) described a previously unrecognized syndrome characterized by chronic nonhemolytic jaundice with CB in the serum and an unidentified pigment in liver cells. In 1948, Rotor and associates (212) described similar cases in which abnormal hepatic pigmentation was not observed. The Rotor syndrome appears to be transmitted with the characteristics of an autosomal dominant gene (126, 220). Although the hereditary nature of the Dubin-Johnson syndrome has not been fully established, the syndrome occurs as a familial disorder (29, 70, 229), more than than one generation has been affected, and a high frequency of consanguinity has been noted in affected families (I. M. Arias, unpublished observations). In both syndromes, jaundice is chronic and the concentration of CB is increased in the plasma. Only liver function tests that are primarily associated with hepatic excretory function give abnormal results except for serum bile acid concentrations and alkaline phosphatase activity which are normal (6, 71, 220). Hepatic Tm BSP is virtually zero although the relative hepatic storage of BSP is normal (6, 271). Studies of glucuronide formation are normal in vitro and in vivo (6). Radiological visualization of the gallbladder with iodopanoic acid is usually abnormal in the Dubin-Johnson syndrome (71) and normal in the Rotor syndrome (220). Mandema and associates (177) observed an increase in the plasma BSP concentration of patients with the Dubin-Johnson syndrome 90 min after intravenous administration of 5 mg BSP per kg body wt. Plasma BSP at this time was conjugated (269). For these reasons, jaundice in these syndromes is postulated to result from a defect in the transfer of CB and other organic anions, excluding bile salts, from liver cells to bile.

The amount of pigment found in patients with the Dubin-Johnson syndrome varies considerably and may be indistinguishable from that found in normal liver (150, 274, 277). In a family in which an aunt and two nephews had chronic jaundice of this type, abnormal hepatic pigmentation was observed in the aunt and one nephew; however, repeated morphological study of liver from the other nephew failed to reveal abnormal pigmentation (6). The pigment is usually confined to parenchymal liver cells primarily in the centrolobular area (71, 241). Electron-microscopic and enzyme-cytochemical studies reveal that the pigment is primarily found in pericanalicular dense bodies having staining characteristics of lysosomes (80). The chemical nature and etiology of the hepatic pigment in the Dubin-Johnson syndrome and its relationship to the functional excretory defect remain obscure. The pigment was described as belonging to

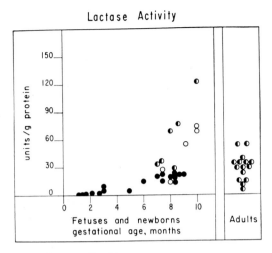

FIG. 14. Lactase activity in human embryo, fetus, newborn, and adults. [From Auricchio et al. (11).]

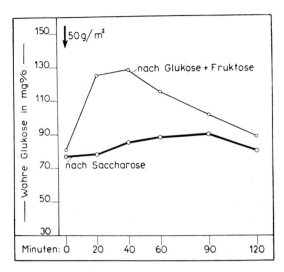

FIG. 15. Oral tolerance test with sucrose or with glucose and fructose in a sucrase-isomaltase-deficient subject. [From Prader et al. (167).]

a concomitant increase in weight of the small intestine.[10]

In 1906, Plimmer stated that "Of the mammals, the carnivora and omnivora have lactase present during the whole of their lives, but herbivora only when they are young, with the exception of the rabbit" (162). It is clear, however, that more and more extensive investigations are still needed as to whether such a correlation between diet and intestinal lactase actually exists and in what sense it works; whether, for example, it is the level of intestinal lactase that influences the feeding habits of the animal.

DISACCHARIDASE DEFICIENCIES

Except for very small quantities, intact disaccharides are not absorbed from the gut lumen (e.g., 188, 194). Thus, in the absence of a particular disaccharidase activity, the oral tolerance test with the corresponding disaccharide is not followed by a rise in blood sugar; instead a watery diarrhea ensues. The symptoms, therefore, are similar to those arising in glucose-galactose malabsorption during a glucose or galactose load (128, 135). It is characteristic of disaccharide malabsorption that the symptoms are evoked by a disaccharide load, whereas a load with the

constituent monosaccharides is tolerated normally (Fig. 15).

Disaccharidase deficiencies in humans have been the object of intense investigation during the last few years. A number of reviews have appeared (6, 43, 55, 77, 98, 109, 115, 137, 166, 168, 171, 196). I shall briefly report some data of more physiological than clinical importance.

Laxative Action of Disaccharides and Intestinal Disaccharidases

Some disaccharides have laxative action. This is related to a deficient intestinal hydrolysis. In fact, administration of sucrose to animals (106) or to humans lacking sucrase, and of lactose to animals or humans lacking lactase, is followed by diarrhea; gluconate, which inhibits lactase (88) but not sucrase, enhances the laxative effect of lactose but not that of sucrose (152); administration of a disaccharide in amounts surpassing the hydrolytic ability of the small intestine is followed by diarrhea (88).

In 1949 Fischer & Sutton (87) reviewed the older literature on the laxative action of lactose. As they pointed out, the diarrhea is most likely of "osmotic" origin.[11] This has been shown experimentally in sucrose and lactose malabsorption by Launiala (134),

---

[10] According to a recent suggestion (97a), the administration of lactose must last long before being effective (5 weeks at least in the rat).

[11] The origin of osmotic diarrheas is discussed by J. S. Fordtran and F. J. Ingelfinger in Chapter 74, Volume III of this *Handbook*.

with intubation studies. The administered disaccharide prevents the absorption of water and salts, and may even provoke movement of water, Na^+, and Cl^- into the lumen. The concentrations of Na^+ and Cl^- in the small-intestinal lumen are each approximately 100 mM. The total concentration of osmotically active solutes is not too far from isosmolarity. Since only a part of the liquid which has moved into the lumen of the small intestine is later absorbed in the colon, diarrhea ensues, apparently because of the water movements in the small intestine and not because of fermentation. In fact, the concentration of lactic acid in the small intestine is not affected by administration of nondigestible disaccharides. Surprisingly, the absorption of glucose, alanine, or palmitate is not noticeably affected by these water movements.

Sucrose-Isomaltose Malabsorption

Sucrose malabsorption was first described by Weijers et al. (204) in 1960 in three children. Five patients were reported by Auricchio and colleagues in 1961 (9). A large number of cases have been reported since. Except for a very few subjects, sucrose malabsorption is accompanied by isomaltose (and palatinose) malabsorption.

Congenital sucrose-isomaltose malabsorption reveals itself at the moment when the child is exposed to dietary sucrose or starch, that is, at the moment of weaning. If the offending sugars are removed from the diet the symptoms disappear and growth resumes normally. The clinical symptoms of sucrose and isomaltose malabsorption often become less severe as the child grows (A. Prader, personal communication). This improvement is poorly understood (intestinal sucrase and isomaltase activities still remain low); it may be simply related to the growth of the small intestine with corresponding increase of total sucrase and isomaltase activities that are available.

The condition is transmitted by a single, autosomal recessive genetic factor and is characterized by a complete or almost complete absence of sucrase and isomaltase activities in intestinal mucosa (7, 12, 119, 171, 184). Maltase activity is reduced to about one-fourth and stems mostly from maltases 1 or 2 or both [Fig. 16; (12, 184)]. All observations, therefore, show that sucrase-maltase and isomaltase-maltase are either absent or inactive in this condition. Inasmuch as the presence of an inhibitor is excluded (12, 184), it must be inferred that sucrase and iso-

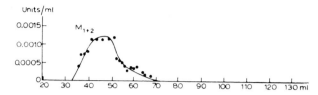

FIG. 16. Sephadex G-200 chromatography of papain-solubilized intestinal disaccharidases from a sucrase-isomaltase-deficient subject. Compare with Fig. 4. [From Semenza et al. (184).]

maltase hyphezymes are under common genetic control. This conclusion agrees well with the observation that the sucrase-isomaltase ratio is essentially the same in a large number of specimens of normal human intestinal mucosa (13, 79).

According to recent observations the sedimentation behavior of maltases 1 and 2 is also changed in this disease (80).

Lactose Malabsorption

Durand (76), Holzel et al. (102), and other authors have reported cases of lactose malabsorption in infants. This syndrome is more severe than sucrase-isomaltase malabsorption because it causes diarrhea, malnutrition, and failure to thrive at a much younger age, that is, when the baby is exposed to milk. Change of the formula to a lactose-free diet results in substantial improvement. Some cases are associated with lactosuria and with renal damage; the prognosis for the latter is more severe.

Another lactose malabsorption syndrome in adults was described in 1963 (10, 63, 116). Apparently, it is a different clinical entity from lactose malabsorption in infants. It appears in adults who tolerated milk normally in their childhood. Genetic factors may be responsible since a particularly high frequency of this type of lactase deficiency is found among American Negroes (18, 45, 105), some African tribes (38), Greek Cypriots (147), Chinese, Indians, Japanese (35a, 70), and Australian aborigines (82a).

Biopsy specimens from these patients reveal an almost complete absence of intestinal lactase activity (10, 63) of the type lactase 1. Lactase 2 is essentially at normal levels (210).

Secondary Disaccharide Malabsorption

A great number of diseases of the intestinal tract are accompanied by a decrease in intestinal disaccharidase levels. Therefore, secondary disaccharide malabsorption syndromes may complicate the clinical picture. A list of diseases associated with or causing decreased disaccharidase levels includes acute and subacute enteritis, celiac disease, cystic fibrosis, ulcerative colitis, giardiasis, kwashiorkor, and others (35, 41, 137, 163, 187, 189).

Often, disaccharidase levels are much reduced before any morphological changes can be detected with the light microscope. In general, lactase activity is the first to disappear and the last to reappear upon recovery. Sucrase and isomaltase can decrease independently from each other (163), an observation agreeing with and supporting the biochemical evidence that sucrose and isomaltose are split by different hyphezymes.

The author expresses his thanks to Dr. K. R. Kerry and Dr. M. Messer for critically revising the manuscript and for supplying unpublished results from their work.

REFERENCES

1. ABRAHAM, J. M., B. LEVIN, V. G. OBERHOLZER, AND A. RUSSEL. Glucose-galactose malabsorption. *Arch. Disease Childhood* 42: 592–597, 1967.

2. ABRAMS, G. D., H. BAUER, AND H. SPRINZ. Influence of the normal flora on mucosal morphology and cellular renewal in the ileum. A comparison of germ-free and conventional mice. *Lab. Invest.* 12: 355–364, 1963.

3. ADACHI, S., AND S. PATTON. Presence and significance of lactulose in milk products: A review. *J. Dairy Sci.* 44: 1375–1393, 1961.

4. ALVARADO, F., AND R. K. CRANE. Studies on the mechanism of intestinal absorption of sugars. VII. Phenylglycoside transport and its possible relationship to phlorizin inhibition of the active transport of sugars by the small intestine. *Biochim. Biophys. Acta* 93: 116–135, 1964.

5. ALVAREZ, A., AND J. SAS. β-Galactosidase changes in the developing intestinal tract of the rat. *Nature* 190: 826–827, 1961.

6. ANDERSON, C. M. Intestinal malabsorption in childhood. *Arch. Disease Childhood* 41: 571–596, 1966.

7. ANDERSON, C. M., M. MESSER, R. R. W. TOWNLEY, AND M. FREEMAN. Intestinal sucrase and isomaltase deficiency in two siblings. *Pediatrics* 31: 1003–1010, 1963.

7a. ASP, N. G., AND A. DAHLQVIST. Rat small-intestinal β-galactosidases. Separation by ion-exchange chromatography and gel filtration. *Biochem. J.* 106: 841–845, 1968.

8. AURICCHIO, S., A. DAHLQVIST, AND G. SEMENZA. Solubilization of the human intestinal disaccharidases. *Biochim. Biophys. Acta* 73: 582–587, 1963.

9. AURICCHIO, S., A. PRADER, G. MÜRSET, AND G. WITT. Saccharoseintoleranz. Durchfall infolge hereditären Mangels an intestinaler Saccharaseaktivität. *Helv. Paediat. Acta* 16: 483–505, 1961.

10. AURICCHIO, S., A. RUBINO, M. LANDOLT, G. SEMENZA, AND A. PRADER. Isolated intestinal lactase deficiency in the adult. *Lancet* 2: 324–326, 1963.

11. AURICCHIO, S., A. RUBINO, AND G. MÜRSET. Intestinal glycosidase activities in the human embryo, fetus and newborn. *Pediatrics* 35: 944–954, 1965.

12. AURICCHIO, S., A. RUBINO, A. PRADER, J. REY, J. JOS, J. FRÉZAL, AND M. DAVIDSON. Intestinal glycosidase activities in congenital malabsorption of disaccharides. *J. Pediat.* 66: 555–564, 1965.

13. AURICCHIO, S., A. RUBINO, R. TOSI, G. SEMENZA, M. LANDOLT, H. KISTLER, AND A. PRADER. Disaccharidase activities in human intestinal mucosa. *Enzymol. Biol. Clin.* 3: 193–208, 1963.

14. AURICCHIO, S., G. SEMENZA, AND A. RUBINO. Multiplicity of human intestinal disaccharidases. II. Characterization of the individual maltases. *Biochim. Biophys. Acta* 96: 498–507, 1965.

15. BABKIN, B. P. *Secretory Mechanism of the Digestive Glands.* New York: Hoeber, 1950.

16. BAILEY, C. B., W. D. KITTS, AND A. J. WOOD. The development of digestive enzyme system of the pig during its pre-weaning phase of growth. B. Intestinal lactase, sucrase and maltase. *Can. J. Agr. Sci.* 36: 51–58, 1956.

17. BARNABEI, O., B. ROMANO, G. DI BITONTO, V. TOMASI, AND F. SERENI. Factors influencing the glucocorticoid-induced increase of ribonucleic acid polymerase activity of rat liver nuclei. *Arch. Biochem. Biophys.* 113: 478–486, 1966.

18. BAYLESS, T. M., AND N. S. ROSENSWEIG. A racial difference in incidence of lactase deficiency. A survey of milk intolerance and lactase deficiency in healthy adult males. *J. Am. Med. Assoc.* 197: 968–972, 1966.

19. BIRCH, G. C. Trehaloses. *Advan. Carbohydrate Chem.* 18: 201–225, 1963.

20. BLAIR, D. G. R., AND J. TUBA. Rat intestinal sucrase. I. Intestinal distribution and reaction kinetics. *Can. J. Biochem. Physiol.* 41: 905–916, 1963.

21. BLAIR, D. G. R., W. YAKIMETS, AND J. TUBA. Rat intestinal sucrase. II. The effects of rat age and sex and of diet on sucrase activity. *Can. J. Biochem. Physiol.* 41: 917–929, 1963.

22. BLUM, J. J., AND D. J. JENDEN. Rate behavior and concentration profiles in geometrically constrained enzyme systems. *Arch. Biochem. Biophys.* 66: 316–332, 1957.

23. BORGSTRÖM, B., AND A. DAHLQVIST. Cellular localization, solubilization and separation of intestinal glycosidases. *Acta Chem. Scand.* 12: 1997–2006, 1958.

24. BORGSTRÖM, B., A. DAHLQVIST, B. E. GUSTAFSSON, G. LUNDH, AND J. MALMQUIST. Trypsin, invertase and amylase content of feces of germfree rats. *Proc. Soc. Exptl. Biol. Med.* 102: 154–155, 1959.

25. BORGSTRÖM, B., A. DAHLQVIST, G. LUNDH, AND J. SJÖVALL. Studies of intestinal digestion and absorption in the human. *J. Clin. Invest.* 36: 1521–1536, 1957.

26. BOSAČKOVÁ, J., AND R. K. CRANE. Studies on the mecha-

nism of intestinal absorption of sugars. VIII. Cation inhibition of active sugar transport and ^{22}Na influx into hamster small intestine, *in vitro. Biochim. Biophys. Acta* 102: 423–435, 1965.

27. BRADY, R. O., A. E. GAL, R. M. BRADLEY, AND E. MÅRTENSSON. The metabolism of ceramide trihexosides. I. Purification and properties of an enzyme that cleaves the terminal galactose molecule of galactosyl-galactosylglucosylceramide. *J. Biol. Chem.* 242: 1021–1026, 1967.

28. BRADY, R. O., A. E. GAL, J. N. KANFER, AND R. M. BRADLEY. The metabolism of glucocerebrosides. III. Purification and properties of a glucosyl- and galactosylceramide-cleaving enzyme from rat intestinal tissue. *J. Biol. Chem.* 240: 3766–3770, 1965.

29. BROWN, H. T., AND J. HERON. Ueber die hydrolytischen Wirkungen des Pankreas und des Dünndarmes. *Ann. Chem. Pharmacol.* 204: 228–251, 1880.

30. BROWN, K. M., AND F. MOOG. Invertase activity in the intestine of the developing chick. *Biochim. Biophys. Acta* 132: 185–187, 1967.

31. CAJORI, F. A. The enzyme activity of dogs' intestinal juice and its relation to intestinal digestion. *Am. J. Physiol.* 104: 659–668, 1933.

32. CAJORI, F. A. The lactase activity of the intestinal mucosa of the dog and some characteristics of intestinal lactase. *J. Biol. Chem.* 109: 159–168, 1935.

33. CARNIE, J. A., AND J. W. PORTEOUS. The invertase activity of rabbit small intestine. *Biochem. J.* 85: 450–456, 1962.

34. CARNIE, J. A., AND J. W. PORTEOUS. The solubilization, thermolability, chromatographic purification and intracellular distribution of some glycosidases of rabbit small intestine. *Biochem. J.* 85: 620–629, 1962.

35. CEVINI, G., M. GIOVANNINI, AND P. CAREDDU. Alterazioni della digestione e dell'assorbimento intestinale dei glucidi nei disturbi acuti e cronici della nutrizione del lattante. *Minerva Pediat.* 14: 831–835, 1962.

35a. CHUNG, M. H., AND D. B. McGILL. Lactase deficiency in Orientals. *Gastroenterology.* 54: 225–226, 1968.

36. CLARKE, J. T., W. QUILLAN, AND H. SHWACHMAN. Chronic diarrhea and failure to thrive due to intestinal disaccharidase insufficiency. *Pediatrics* 34: 807–813, 1964.

37. COHEN, R. B., K.-C. TSOU, S. H. RUTENBURG, AND A. M. SELIGMAN. The colorimetric estimation and histochemical demonstration of β-D-galactosidase. *J. Biol. Chem.* 195: 239–249, 1952.

38. COOK, G. C., AND S. K. KAJUBI. Tribal incidence of lactase deficiency in Uganda. *Lancet* 1: 725–729, 1966.

39. COURTOIS, J. E. Les disaccharidases. In: *Problèmes Actuels de Biochimie Appliquèe* (2 ème série), edited by Mil. Girard. Paris: Masson. In press.

40. COURTOIS, J. E., AND J. F. DEMELIER. Répartition de la tréhalase chez l'homme et quelques mammifères. *Bull. Soc. Chim. Biol.* 48: 277–286, 1966.

41. COZZETTO, F. J. Intestinal lactase deficiency in a patient with cystic fibrosis. Report of a case with enzyme assay. *Pediatrics* 32: 228–233, 1963.

42. CRANE, R. K. Hypothesis for mechanism of intestinal active transport of sugars. *Federation Proc.* 21: 891–895, 1962.

43. CRANE, R. K. Enzymes and malabsorption: a concept of brush border membrane disease. *Gastroenterology* 50: 254–262, 1966.

44. CRANE, R. K., G. FORSTNER, AND A. EICHHOLZ. Studies on the mechanism of the intestinal absorption of sugars. X. An effect of Na$^+$ concentration on the apparent Michaelis constants for intestinal sugar transport, *in vitro. Biochim. Biophys. Acta* 109: 467–477, 1965.

45. CUATRECASAS, P., D. H. LOCKWOOD, AND J. R. CALDWELL. Lactase deficiency in the adult: a common occurrence. *Lancet* 1: 14–18, 1965.

46. CUMMINS, D., R. GITZELMANN, J. LINDENMANN, AND G. SEMENZA. Immunochemical study of isolated human and rabbit intestinal sucrase. *Biochim. Biophys. Acta.* In press.

47. DAHLQVIST, A. Characterization of hog intestinal trehalase. *Acta Chem. Scand.* 14: 9–16, 1960.

48. DAHLQVIST, A. Characterization of hog intestinal invertase as a glucosido-invertase. III. Specificity of purified invertase. *Acta Chem. Scand.* 14: 63–71, 1960.

49. DAHLQVIST, A. Intestinal carbohydrases of a new-born pig. *Nature* 190: 31–32, 1961.

50. DAHLQVIST, A. Specificity of the human intestinal disaccharidases and implications for hereditary disaccharide intolerance. *J. Clin. Invest.* 41: 463–470, 1962.

51. DAHLQVIST, A. Rat-intestinal dextranase. Localization and relation to the other carbohydrases of the digestive tract. *Biochem. J.* 86: 72–76, 1963.

52. DAHLQVIST, A. Method for assay of intestinal disaccharidases. *Analyt. Biochem.* 7: 18–25, 1964.

53. DAHLQVIST, A. In: *Disorders Due to Intestinal Defective Carbohydrate Digestion and Absorption,* edited by P. Durand. Rome, Italy: Il Pensiero Scientifico, 1964, p. 5.

54. DAHLQVIST, A. In: *Control of Glycogen Metabolism* (Ciba Foundation Symposium), edited by W. J. Whelan and M. P. Cameron. London: Churchill, 1964, p. 53.

55. DAHLQVIST, A. Enzyme deficiency in the small intestine. In: *Recent Advances in Gastroenterology,* edited by J. Badenoch and B. N. Brooks. London: Churchill, 1965, p. 116.

56. DAHLQVIST, A. The localisation of the disaccharide hydrolases of small intestine. *Biochem. J.* 100: 17–18P, 1966.

57. DAHLQVIST, A., AND B. BORGSTRÖM. Characterization of intestinal invertase as a glucosido-invertase. II. Studies on transglycosylation by intestinal invertase. *Acta Chem. Scand.* 13: 1659–1667, 1959.

58. DAHLQVIST, A., AND B. BORGSTRÖM. Digestion and absorption of disaccharides in man. *Biochem. J.* 81: 411–418, 1961.

59. DAHLQVIST, A., AND A. BRUN. A method for the histochemical demonstration of disaccharidase activities: application to invertase and trehalase in some animal tissues. *J. Histochem. Cytochem.* 10: 294–302, 1962.

60. DAHLQVIST, A., B. BULL, AND B. E. GUSTAFSSON. Rat intestinal 6-bromo-2-naphthyl-glycosidase and disaccharidase activities. I. Enzymic properties and distribution in the digestive tract of conventional and germ-free animals. *Arch. Biochem. Biophys.* 109: 150–158, 1965.

61. DAHLQVIST, A., B. BULL, AND D. L. THOMSON. Rat intestinal 6-bromo-2-naphthyl glycosidase and disaccharidase activities. II. Solubilization and separation of the small-intestinal enzymes. *Arch. Biochem. Biophys.* 109: 159–167, 1965.

62. DAHLQVIST, A., AND J. D. GRYBOSKI. Inability of the human small-intestinal lactase to hydrolyze lactulose. *Biochim. Biophys. Acta* 110: 635–636, 1965.

63. DAHLQVIST, A., J. B. HAMMOND, R. K. CRANE, J. V. DUNPHY, AND A. LITTMAN. Intestinal lactase deficiency and lactose intolerance in adults: preliminary report. *Gastroenterology* 45: 488–491, 1963.

64. DAHLQVIST, A., AND T. LINDBERG. Development of the intestinal disaccharidase and alkaline phosphatase activities in the human foetus. *Clin. Sci.* 30: 517–528, 1966.

65. DAHLQVIST, A., AND C. NORDSTRÖM. The distribution of disaccharidase activities in the villi and crypts of the small-intestinal mucosa. *Biochim. Biophys. Acta* 113: 624–626, 1966.

66. DAHLQVIST, A., AND D. L. THOMSON. Separation and characterization of two rat-intestinal amylases. *Biochem. J.* 89: 272–277, 1963.

67. DAHLQVIST, A., AND D. L. THOMSON. The digestion and absorption of sucrose by the intact rat. *J. Physiol., London* 167: 193–209, 1963.

68. DAHLQVIST, A., AND D. L. THOMSON. The digestion and absorption of lactose by the intact rat. *Acta Physiol. Scand.* 61: 20–33, 1964.

69. DAHLQVIST, A., AND D. L. THOMSON. The hydrolysis of sucrose by intact and homogenized cells of rat small intestine. Influence of pH and substrate concentration. *Biochim. Biophys. Acta* 92: 99–104, 1964.

70. DAVIS, A. E., AND T. BOLIN. Lactose intolerance in Asians. *Nature* 216: 1244–1245, 1967.

71. DE GROOT, A. P., AND P. HOOGENDOORN. The detrimental effect of lactose. II. Quantitative lactase determinations in various mammals. *Neth. Milk Dairy J.* 11: 290–303, 1957.

72. DEREN, J. J., S. A. BROITMAN, AND N. ZAMCHECK. Effect of diet upon intestinal disaccharidases and disaccharide absorption; its implication in clinical disorders of disaccharide absorption. *J. Clin. Invest.* 46: 186–195, 1967.

73. DOELL, R. G., AND N. KRETCHMER. Studies of small intestine during development. I. Distribution and activity of β-galactosidase. *Biochim. Biophys. Acta* 62: 353–362, 1962.

74. DOELL, R. G., AND N. KRETCHMER. Intestinal invertase: precocious development of activity after injection of hydrocortisone. *Science* 143: 42–44, 1964.

75. DOELL, R. G., G. ROSEN, AND N. KRETCHMER. Immunochemical studies of intestinal disaccharidases during normal and precocious development. *Proc. Natl. Acad. Sci. U.S.* 54: 1268–1273, 1965.

76. DURAND, P. Lattosuria idiopatica in un paziente con diarrea cronica ed acidosi. *Minerva Pediat.* 10: 706–711, 1958.

77. DURAND, P. (Editor). *Disorders Due to Intestinal Defective Carbohydrate Digestion and Absorption.* Rome, Italy: Il Pensiero Scientifico, 1964.

78. EGGERMONT, E. Sedimentation behaviour of human intestinal disaccharidases. *1st Meeting Federation European Biochemical Society, London, 1964* (abst.), A 116.

79. EGGERMONT, E. Enzymic activities in meconium from human foetuses and newborns. *Biol. Neonat.* 10: 266–280, 1966.

80. EGGERMONT, E. *The Biochemical Defects in Sucrose Intolerance and in Glucose-Galactose Malabsorption* (M.D. Thesis). Louvain, Belgium: Univ. of Louvain, 1968.

81. EGGERMONT, E., AND H. LOEB. Glucose-galactose intolerance. *Lancet* 2: 343–344, 1966.

82. EICHHOLZ, A., AND R. K. CRANE. Studies on the organization of the brush border in intestinal epithelial cells.

1. Tris disruption of isolated hamster brush borders and density gradient separation of fractions. *J. Cell Biol.* 26: 687–692, 1965.

82a.ELLIOTT, R. B., G. M. MAXWELL, AND N. VAWSER. Lactose maldigestion in Australian aboriginal children. *Med. J. Australia* 1: 46–49, 1967.

83. EULER, H. VON, AND O. SVANBERG. Ueber Darm-Saccharase. *Z. Physiol. Chem.* 115: 43–67, 1921.

84. FALLOISE, A. Distribution et origine des ferments digestifs de l'intestin grêle. *Arch. Intern. Physiol.* 2: 299–321, 1904.

85. FEIGELSON, M., P. R. GROSS, AND P. FEIGELSON. Early effects of cortisone on nucleic acid and protein metabolism of rat liver. *Biochim. Biophys. Acta* 55: 495–504, 1962.

86. FISCHER, E., AND W. NIEBEL. Ueber das Verhalten der Polysaccharide gegen einige tierische Sekrete und Organe. *Chem. Zentr.* 1: 499–501, 1869.

87. FISCHER, J. E., AND T. S. SUTTON. Effects of lactose on gastrointestinal motility: a review. *J. Dairy Sci.* 32: 139–162, 1949.

88. FISCHER, J. E., AND T. S. SUTTON. The hydrolysis of sucrose, lactose and cellobiose by small intestinal mucosa *in vitro*. Relationship to laxation in the rat produced by these disaccharides *in vivo*. *Ohio J. Sci.* 57: 75–80, 1957.

89. FLOREY, H. W., R. D. WRIGHT, AND M. A. JENNINGS. The secretions of the intestine. *Physiol. Rev.* 21: 36–69, 1941.

90. FOMINA, L. S. The activities of some enzymes in the intestine and other organs of human foetus. *Vopr. Med. Khim.* 6: 176–183, 1960.

90a.FORSTNER, G. G., S. M. SABESIN, AND K. J. ISSELBACHER. Rat intestinal membranes. Purification and biochemical characterisation. *Biochem. J.* 106: 381–390, 1968.

91. GAÓN, D., A. VALLE, AND C. MARINA-FIOL. Aparición y desarrollo de la actividad de alcunas disacaridasas en el intestino delgado de ratas. *Rev. Clin. Espan.* 97: 229–237, 1965.

92. GENDEREN, H. VAN, AND C. ENGEL. On the distribution of some enzymes in the duodenum and the ileum of the rat. *Enzymologia* 5: 71–80, 1938.

93. GIRARDET, P., R. RICHTERICH, AND I. ANTENER. Adaptation de la lactase intestinale à l'administration de lactose chez le rat adulte. *Helv. Physiol. Pharmacol. Acta* 22: 7–14, 1964.

94. GITZELMANN, R., AND S. AURICCHIO. Handling of soya α-galactosides by a normal and a galactosemic child. *Pediatrics* 36: 231–235, 1965.

95. GITZELMANN, R., E. A. DAVIDSON, AND J. OSINCHAK. Disaccharidase of rabbit small intestine: Intracellular distribution, solubilization, purification and specificity. *Biochim. Biophys. Acta* 85: 69–81, 1964.

96. GOODMAN, I., J. R. FOUTS, E. BRESNICK, R. MENEGAS, AND G. H. HITCHINGS. A mammalian thioglycosidase. *Science* 130: 450–451, 1959.

97. GRAY, G. M., AND F. J. INGELFINGER. Intestinal absorption of sucrose in man: the site of hydrolysis and absorption. *J. Clin. Invest.* 44: 390–398, 1965.

97a.GRÜTTE, F-K., J. SCHULZE, AND H. GÄRTNER. Erhöhung der intestinalen β-Galactosidase-Aktivität bei Ratten nach Lactosefütterung. *Die Nahrung* 11: 901–902, 1967.

98. HAEMMERLI, U. P., H. J. KISTLER, R. AMMAN, T. MARTHALER, G. SEMENZA, S. AURICCHIO, AND A. PRADER. Acquired milk intolerance in the adult caused by lactose malabsorption due to a selective deficiency of intestinal lactase activity. *Am. J. Med.* 38: 7–30, 1965.

99. HEILSKOV, N. S. C. *Studier Over Animalsk Lactase.* (M. D. Thesis). Aarhus, Denmark: Aarhus University, 1956.

100. HIJMANS, J. C., AND K. S. McCARTHY. Induction of invertase activity by hydrocortisone in chick embryo duodenum cultures. *Proc. Soc. Exptl. Biol. Med.* 123: 633–637, 1966.

101. HILL, A. V. The possible effects of the aggregation of the molecule of hemoglobin on its dissociation curves. *J. Physiol., London* 40: iv–vii, 1910.

102. HOLZEL, A., V. SCHWARZ, AND K. W. SUTCLIFFE. Defective lactose absorption causing malnutrition in infancy. *Lancet* 1: 1126–1128, 1959.

103. HORE, P., AND M. MESSER. Studies on disaccharidase activities of the small intestine of the domestic cat and other carnivores. *Comp. Biochem. Physiol.* 24: 717–726, 1968.

104. HSIA, D. Y. Y., M. MAKLER, G. SEMENZA, AND A. PRADER. β-Galactosidase activity in human intestinal lactases. *Biochim. Biophys. Acta* 113: 390–393, 1966.

105. HUANG, S.-S., AND T. M. BAYLESS. Lactose intolerance in healthy children. *New Engl. J. Med.* 276: 1283–1287, 1967.

106. HUBER, J. T., N. L. JACOBSON, AND R. S. ALLEN. Digestive enzyme activities in the young calf. *J. Dairy Sci.* 44: 1494–1501, 1961.

107. HÜBSCHER, G., G. R. WEST, AND D. N. BRINDLEY. Studies on the fractionation of mucosal homogenates from the small intestine. *Biochem. J.* 97: 629–642, 1965.

108. ISHIDA, J. Distribution of the digestive enzymes of stomachless fishes. *Annot. Zool. Japan* 15: 263–284, 1936.

109. JARNUM, S. Disakkaridmalabsorption. *Ugeskrift. Laeger* 127: 1395–1402, 1965.

110. JESUITOVA, N. N., P. DE LAEY, AND A. M. UGOLEV. Digestion of starch *in vivo* and *in vitro* in a rat intestine. *Biochim. Biophys. Acta* 86: 205–210, 1964.

111. JOHNSON, C. F. Intestinal invertase activity and a macromolecular repeating unit of hamster brush border plasma membrane. *Intern. Congr. Electron Microscopy, 6th, Kyoto, 1966* (abstr.), p. 389–390.

112. JOHNSON, C. F. Disaccharidase: localization in hamster intestine brush borders. *Science* 155: 1670–1672, 1967.

113. JORPES, E., AND V. MUTT. In: *The Hormones*, edited by G. Pincus, K. V. Thimann, and E. B. Astwood. New York: Acad. Press, 1964, p. 365.

114. JOS, J., J. FRÉZAL, J. REY, AND M. LAMY. Histochemical localization of the intestinal disaccharidases. Application to peroral biopsy specimens. *Nature* 213: 516–518, 1967.

114a. JOS, J., J. FRÉZAL, J. REY, AND M. LAMY. Etude histochimique de la muqueuse duodénojéjunale dans la maladie coeliaque. *Pediat. Res.* 1: 27–38, 1967.

115. KERN, F., JR., AND J. E. STRUTHERS, JR. Intestinal lactase deficiency and lactose intolerance in adults. *J. Am. Med. Assoc.* 195: 927–930, 1966.

116. KERN, F., JR., J. E. STRUTHERS, JR., AND W. L. ATTWOOD. Lactose intolerance as a cause of steatorrhea in an adult. *Gastroenterology* 45: 477–487, 1963.

117. KERRY, K. R. Intestinal disaccharidase activities in a monotreme and eight species of marsupials. *Comp. Biochem. Physiol.* In press.

118. KERRY, K. R., AND M. MESSER. Intestinal glycosidases of three species of seals. *Comp. Biochem. Physiol.* 24: 1968.

119. KERRY, K. R., AND R. R. W. TOWNLEY. Genetic aspects of intestinal sucrase-isomaltase deficiency. *Australian Paediat. J.* 1: 223–235, 1965.

120. KOGUT, M. D., G. N. DONNELL, AND K. N. F. SHAW. Studies of lactose absorption in patients with galactosemia. *J. Pediat.* 71: 75–81, 1967.

121. KOLDOVSKÝ, O., AND F. CHYTIL. Postnatal development of β-galactosidase activity in the small intestine of the rat. Effect of adrenalectomy and diet. *Biochem. J.* 94: 266–270, 1965.

122. KOLDOVSKÝ, O., V. JIRSOVÁ, AND A. HERINGOVÁ. Effect of aldosterone and cortisone on β-galactosidase and invertase activity in the small intestine of rats. *Nature* 206: 300–301, 1965.

123. KOLDOVSKÝ, O., A. HERINGOVÁ, V. JIRSOVÁ, F. CHYTIL, AND J. HOŠKOVÁ. Postnatal changes in β-galactosidase activity in the jejunum and ileum of mice, rabbits, and guinea pigs. *Can. J. Biochem.* 44: 523–527, 1966.

124. KOLÍNSKÁ, J., AND G. SEMENZA. Isolation and properties of sucrase from rabbit intestine. *Helv. Physiol. Pharmacol. Acta* 24: c30–c33, 1966.

125. KOLÍNSKÁ, J., AND G. SEMENZA. Studies on intestinal sucrase and on intestinal sugar transport. V. Isolation and properties of sucrase-isomaltase from rabbit small intestine. *Biochim. Biophys. Acta* 146: 181–195, 1967.

126. KOSHLAND, D. E., JR. Group transfer as an enzymatic substitution mechanism. In: *A Symposium on the Mechanism of Enzyme Action*, edited by W. D. McElroy and B. Glass. Baltimore: The Johns Hopkins Univ. Press, 1954, p. 608–641.

127. KRETCHMER, N., AND P. SUNSHINE. Intestinal disaccharidase deficiency in the sea lion. *Gastroenterology* 53: 123–129, 1967.

128. LAPLANE, R., C. POLONOWSKI, M. ETIENNE, P. DEBRAY, J. C. LODS, AND B. PISARRO. L'intolérance aux sucres à transfert intestinal actif. *Arch. Franc. Pediat.* 19: 895–944, 1962.

129. LARNER, J. Hydrolysis of isomaltotriose by oligo-1,6-glucosidase. *J. Am. Chem. Soc.* 77: 6385–6386, 1955.

130. LARNER, J., AND R. E. GILLESPIE. Gastrointestinal digestion of starch. II. Properties of the intestinal carbohydrases. *J. Biol. Chem.* 223: 709–726, 1956.

131. LARNER, J., AND R. E. GILLESPIE. Gastrointestinal digestion of starch. III. Intestinal carbohydrase activities in germ-free and non-germ-free animals. *J. Biol. Chem.* 225: 279–285, 1957.

132. LARNER, J., AND C. M. McNICKLE. Action of intestinal extracts on "branched" oligosaccharides. *J. Am. Chem. Soc.* 76: 4747–4748, 1954.

133. LARNER, J., AND C. M. McNICKLE. Gastrointestinal digestion of starch. I. The action of oligo-1,6-glucosidase on branched saccharides. *J. Biol. Chem.* 215: 723–736, 1955.

134. LAUNIALA, K. The effect of unabsorbed disaccharides on the intestinal absorption in congenital disaccharide malabsorption. *Ann. Paediat. Fenniae.*

135. LINDQUIST, B., AND G. W. MEEUWISSE. Chronic diarrhea caused by monosaccharide malabsorption. *Acta Paediat.* 51: 674–685, 1962.

136. LINEWEAVER, H., AND D. BURK. The determination of enzyme dissociation constants. *J. Am. Chem. Soc.* 56: 658–666, 1934.

137. LITTMAN, A., AND J. B. HAMMOND. Diarrhea in adults caused by deficiency in intestinal disaccharidases. *Gastroenterology* 48: 237–249, 1965.

138. LOJDA, Z. Some remarks concerning the histochemical

detection of disaccharidases and glucosidases. *Histochemie* 5: 339–360, 1965.

139. LUKOMSKAYA, I. S., AND G. I. TARASOVA. Trehalase of vertebrates and man. *Biokhimiya* 30: 95–99, 1965.

140. MAIO, J. J., AND H. V. RICKENBERG. The β-galactosidase of mouse strain L-cells and mouse organs. *Biochim. Biophys. Acta* 37: 101–106, 1960.

141. MALATHI, P., AND R. K. CRANE. β-Glucosidase (phlorizin hydrolase) activity in intestinal brush borders. *Federation Proc.* 27: 385, 1968.

142. MALHOTRA, O. P., AND G. PHILIP. Hydrolytic enzymes of mammalian intestines. I. Distribution of hydrolytic enzymes in the goat and pig intestine. *Indian J. Med. Res.* 52: 68–74, 1964.

143. MALHOTRA, O. P., AND G. PHILIP. Hydrolytic enzymes of mammalian intestines. II. Distribution of hydrolytic enzymes in the dog, guinea-pig, squirrel, albino rat and rabbit intestines. *Indian J. Med. Res.* 53: 410–416, 1965.

144. McDOUGAL, D. B., JR., K. D. LITTLE, AND R. K. CRANE. Studies on the mechanism of intestinal absorption of sugars. IV. Localization of galactose concentrations within the intestinal wall during active transport, *in vitro. Biochim. Biophys. Acta* 45: 483–489, 1960.

145. McGEACHIN, R. L., AND N. K. FORD, JR. Distribution of amylase in the gastrointestinal tract of the rat. *Am. J. Physiol.* 196: 972–974, 1959.

146. McGEACHIN, R. L., J. R. GLEASON, AND M. R. ADAMS. Amylase distribution in extrapancreatic, extrasalivary tissues. *Arch. Biochem. Biophys.* 75: 403–411, 1958.

147. McMICHAEL, H. B., J. WEBB, AND A. M. DAWSON. Jejunal disaccharidases and some observations on the cause of lactase deficiency. *Brit. Med. J.* 2: 1037–1041, 1966.

148. MEEUWISSE, G., AND A. DAHLQVIST. Glucose-galactose malabsorption. *Lancet* 2: 858, 1966.

149. MESSER, M., AND K. R. KERRY. Intestinal digestion of maltotriose in man. *Biochem. Biophys. Acta* 132: 432–443, 1967.

150. MILLER, D., AND R. K. CRANE. The digestive function of the epithelium of the small intestine. I. An intracellular locus of disaccharide and sugar phosphate ester hydrolysis. *Biochim. Biophys. Acta* 52: 281–293, 1961.

151. MILLER, D., AND R. K. CRANE. The digestive function of the epithelium of the small intestine. II. Localization of disaccharidase hydrolysis in the isolated brush border portion of intestinal epithelial cells. *Biochim. Biophys. Acta* 52: 293–298, 1961.

152. MITCHELL, H. S., G. M. COOK, AND K. L. O'BRIEN. Effect of several calcium salts on the utilization of lactose. *J. Nutr.* 18: 319–327, 1939.

153. MONOD, J., J.-P. CHANGEUX, AND F. JACOB. Allosteric proteins and cellular control systems. *J. Mol. Biol.* 6: 306–329, 1963.

154. MYRBÄCK, K. Trehalose und Trehalase. *Ergeb. Enzymforsch.* 10: 168–190, 1949.

155. NEWCOMER, A. D., AND D. B. McGILL. Distribution of disaccharidase activity in the small bowel of normal and lactase-deficient subjects. *Gastroenterology* 51: 481–488, 1966.

156. NEWEY, H., P. A. SANFORD, AND D. H. SMYTH. Location of function in the intestinal epithelial cell in relation to carbohydrate absorption. *J. Physiol., London* 168: 423–434, 1963.

157. ODA, T., AND S. SEKI. Molecular basis of structure and function of the plasma membrane of the microvilli of intestinal epithelial cells. *Intern. Congr. Electron Microscopy, 6th, Kyoto, 1966* (abstr.), p. 387–388.

158. OVERTON, J., A. EICHHOLZ, AND R. K. CRANE. Studies on the organization of the brush border in intestinal epithelial cells. II. Fine structure of fractions of Tris-disrupted hamster brush borders. *J. Cell Biol.* 26: 693–706, 1965.

159. PARSONS, D. S., AND J. S. PRICHARD. Hydrolysis of disaccharides during absorption by the perfused small intestine of amphibia. *Nature* 208: 1097–1098, 1965.

160. PETERSON, M. L. Data quoted in references 118 and 127.

161. PILSON, M. E. Q., AND A. L. KELLY. Composition of the milk from *Zalophus californianus*, the California sea lion. *Science* 135: 104–105, 1962.

162. PLIMMER, R. H. A. On the presence of lactase in the intestine of animals and on the adaptation of the intestine to lactose. *J. Physiol., London* 35: 20–31, 1906.

163. PLOTKIN, G. R., AND K. J. ISSELBACHER. Secondary disaccharidase deficiency in adult celiac disease (nontropical sprue) and other malabsorption states. *New Engl. J. Med.* 271: 1033–1037, 1964.

164. PORTEOUS, J. W., AND B. CLARK. The isolation and characterisation of subcellular components of the epithelial cells of rabbit small intestine. *Biochem. J.* 96: 159–171, 1965.

165. PORTEOUS, J. W., AND B. CLARK. The isolation and properties of epithelial-cell "ghosts" from rat small intestine. *Biochem. J.* 96: 539–551, 1965.

166. PRADER, A., AND S. AURICCHIO. Defects of intestinal disaccharide absorption. *Ann. Rev. Med.* 16: 345–358, 1965.

167. PRADER, A., S. AURICCHIO, AND G. MÜRSET. Durchfall infolge hereditären Mangels an intestinaler Saccharaseaktivität (Saccharoseintoleranz). *Schweiz. Med. Wochschr.* 91: 465–468, 1961.

168. PRADER, A., G. SEMENZA, AND S. AURICCHIO. Intestinale Absorption und Malabsorption der Disaccharide. *Schweiz. Med. Wochschr.* 93: 1272–1279, 1963.

169. PROSSER, C. L. (Editor). *Comparative Animal Physiology.* Philadelphia: Saunders, 1950, p. 144–186.

170. REDDY, B. S., AND B. S. WOSTMANN. Intestinal disaccharidase activities in the growing germfree and conventional rats. *Arch. Biochem. Biophys.* 113: 609–616, 1966.

171. REY, J., AND J. FRÉZAL. Les anomalies des disaccharidases. *Arch. Franc. Pediat.* 24: 65–101, 1967.

172. RIKLIS, E., AND J. H. QUASTEL. Effects of cations on sugar absorption by isolated surviving guinea pig intestine. *Can. J. Biochem. Physiol.* 36: 347–362, 1958.

173. RUBINO, A., F. ZIMBALATTI, AND S. AURICCHIO. Intestinal disaccharidase activities in adult and suckling rats. *Biochim. Biophys. Acta* 92: 305–311, 1964.

174. RUTTLOFF, H., R. FRIESE, AND K. TÄUFEL. Zur Bestimmung der intestinalen-Amylase. *Nahrung* 11: 206–213, 1967.

175. RUTTLOFF, H., H. HAENEL, A. TÄUFEL, AND K. TÄUFEL. Die intestinal-enzymatische Spaltung von Galakto-Oligo-Sacchariden im Darm von Tier und Mensch mit besonderer Berucksichtigung von Lactobacillus bifidus. *Med. Ernährung* 7: 281–282, 1966.

176. RUTTLOFF, H., R. NOACK, R. FRIESE, AND G. SCHENK. Zur Lokalisation von Carbohydrasen im Bürstensaum der Rattenmucosa. *Biochem. Z.* 341: 15–22, 1964.

177. SEGAL, H. L., J. F. KACHMAR, AND P. D. BOYER. Kinetic analysis of enzyme reactions. *Enzymologia* 15: 187–198, 1952.

178. SEIJI, M. Studies on digestion of starch by α-limit-dextrinase. *J. Biochem., Tokyo* 40: 519–525, 1953.

179. SEMENZA, G. Rate equations of some cases of enzyme inhibition and activation. Their application to sodium-activated membrane transport systems. *J. Theoret. Biol.* 15: 145–176, 1967.

180. SEMENZA, G. Sucrase and sugar transport in the small intestine. In: *Protides Biol. Fluids, Proc. Colloq.* 5: 201–208, 1962.

181. SEMENZA, G. Digestion and absorption of sugars. *Mod. Probl. Pediat.* In press.

182. SEMENZA, G., AND S. AURICCHIO. Chromatographic separation of human intestinal disaccharidases. *Biochim. Biophys. Acta* 65: 173–175, 1962.

183. SEMENZA, G., S. AURICCHIO, AND A. RUBINO. Multiplicity of human intestinal disaccharidases. I. Chromatographic separation of maltases and of two lactases. *Biochim. Biophys. Acta* 96: 487–497, 1965.

184. SEMENZA, G., S. AURICCHIO, A. RUBINO, A. PRADER, AND J. D. WELSH. Lack of some intestinal maltases in a human disease transmitted by a single genetic factor. *Biochim. Biophys. Acta* 105: 386–389, 1965.

185. SEMENZA, G., C.-H. CURTIUS, J. KOLÍNSKÁ, AND M. MÜLLER. Studies on intestinal sucrase and intestinal sugar transport. VI. Liberation of α-glucose by sucrase and isomaltase from the glycone moiety of the substrates. *Biochim. Biophys. Acta* 146: 196–204, 1967.

186. SEMENZA, G., R. TOSI, M. C. VALLOTTON-DELACHAUX, AND E. MÜLHAUPT. Sodium activation of human intestinal sucrase and its possible significance in the enzymic organization of brush borders. *Biochim. Biophys. Acta* 89: 109–116, 1964.

187. SHMERLING, D. H., S. AURICCHIO, A. RUBINO, B. HADORN, AND A. PRADER. Der sekundäre Mangel an intestinaler Disaccharidaseaktivität bei der Cöliakie. *Helv. Paediat. Acta* 19: 507–527, 1964.

188. STERK, V. V., AND N. KRETCHMER. Studies of small intestine during development. IV. Digestion of lactose as related to lactosuria in the rabbit. *Pediatrics* 34: 609–614, 1964.

189. STRUTHERS, J. E., JR., J. W. SINGLETON, AND F. KERN. Intestinal lactase deficiency in ulcerative colitis and regional ileitis. *Ann. Internal Med.* 63: 221–228, 1965.

190. SUNSHINE, P., AND N. KRETCHMER. Studies of small intestine during development. III. Infantile diarrhea associated with intolerance to disaccharides. *Pediatrics* 34: 38–50, 1964.

191. SUNSHINE, P., AND N. KRETCHMER. Intestinal disaccharidases: absence in two species of sea lions. *Science* 144: 850–851, 1964.

192. SWAMINATHAN, N., AND A. N. RADHAKRISHNAN. Distribution of α-glucosidase activities in human and monkey small intestine. *Indian J. Biochem.* 2: 159–163, 1965.

193. SWAMINATHAN, N., AND A. N. RADHAKRISHNAN. Studies on intestinal disaccharidases: Part II. Specificity of monkey intestinal β-galactosidases. *Indian J. Biochem.* 4: 64–68, 1967.

194. TÄUFEL, K., W. KRAUSE, H. RUTTLOFF, AND R. MAUNE. Zur intestinalen Spaltung von Oligosacchariden. *Z. Ges. Exptl. Med.* 144: 54–66, 1967.

195. TORRALBA, A. Glicosidasas y otros enzimas del intestino delgado de rata durante los periodos fetal y postnatal. In: *VIes Journées Biochimiques Latines, Geneva* (abstr.), *1961*, p. 96.

195a. TOURNAIRE, D., P. BASTIDE, AND G. DASTUGUE. Activités enzymatiques dans l'intestin grêle d'agneau. (Phosphatase acide et alcaline, glucose-6-phosphatase, α-D-méthyl-glucosidase, invertase, lactase.) *Compt. Rend. Soc. Biol.* 160: 1597–1600, 1966.

196. TOWNLEY, R. R. W. Disaccharidase deficiency in infancy and childhood. *Pediatrics* 38: 127–141, 1966.

197. UGOLEV, A. M., N. N. JESUITOVA, AND P. DE LAEY. Localization of invertase activity in small intestinal cells. *Nature* 203: 879–880, 1964.

198. UGOLEV, A. M., N. N. JESUITOVA, N. M. TIMOFEEVA, AND I. N. FEDIUSHINA. Location of hydrolysis of certain disaccharides and peptides in the small intestine. *Nature* 202: 807–809, 1964.

199. VEIBEL, S. In: *The Enzymes*, edited by J. Summer and K. Myrbäck. New York: Acad. Press, 1950, vol. 1, p. 583.

199a. VON EULER, H., AND O. SVANBERG. See EULER, H. VON, AND O. SVANBERG (83).

200. WALKER, D. M. The development of the digestive system of the young animal. II. Carbohydrase enzyme development in the young pig. *J. Agr. Sci.* 52: 357–363, 1959.

201. WALKER, D. M. The development of the digestive system of the young animal. III. Carbohydrase enzyme development in the young lamb. *J. Agr. Sci.* 53: 375–380, 1959.

202. WALLENFELS, K., AND J. FISCHER. Untersuchungen über milchzuckerspaltende Enzyme. X. Die Lactase des Kälberdarms. *Z. Physiol. Chem.* 321: 223–245, 1960.

203. WALLENFELS, K., AND O. P. MALHOTRA. Galactosidases. *Advan. Carbohydrate Chem.* 16: 239–298, 1961.

204. WEIJERS, H. A., J. H. VAN DE KAMER, W. K. DICKE, AND J. IJSSELING. Diarrhoea caused by deficiency of sugar splitting enzymes. *Acta Paediat.* 50: 55–71, 1961.

205. WELSH, J. D., G. V. ROHRER, R. DREWRY, J. C. MAY, AND A. WALKER. Human intestinal disaccharidase activity. II. Diseases of the small intestine and deficiency states. *Arch. Internal Med.* 117: 495–503, 1966.

206. WELSH, J. D., G. V. ROHRER, AND A. WALKER. Human intestinal disaccharidase activity. I. Normal individuals. *Arch. Internal Med.* 117: 488–494, 1966.

207. WELSH, J. D., AND A. WALKER. Intestinal disaccharidase and alkaline phosphatase activity in the dog. *Proc. Soc. Exptl. Biol. Med.* 120: 525–527, 1965.

208. WILLSTÄDT, H., AND M. BORGGÅRD. Sur la tréhalase. *Arkiv Kemi, Mineral., Geol., B*, 23 (no. 1): 1–12, 1946.

209. WILSON, T. H., AND T. N. VINCENT. Absorption of sugars *in vitro* by the intestine of the golden hamster. *J. Biol. Chem.* 216: 851–866, 1955.

210. ZOPPI, G., B. HADORN, R. GITZELMANN, H. KISTLER, AND A. PRADER. Intestinal β-galactosidase activities in malabsorption syndromes. *Gastroenterology* 50: 557–561, 1966.

CHAPTER 120

Biochemistry of pepsins

W. H. TAYLOR | *Department of Chemical Pathology,*
The United Liverpool Hospitals, Liverpool, England

CHAPTER CONTENTS

HISTORICAL INTRODUCTION

HISTORICALLY, knowledge of the proteolytic enzymes of the stomach has developed from two sources. Varro (146), writing on farming in 36 B.C., first described the milk-coagulating property of extracts of animal stomachs which was then, and is now, utilized in the making of junkets and cheeses. The substance responsible has been found to be a proteolytic enzyme, rennin.

The second source, the study of what happens to food when it is exposed to gastric juice, has been the more fruitful, although the earliest recorded observations occur surprisingly late. Until the middle of the eighteenth century, opinion was divided between the mechanical and the putrefactive theories of gastric digestion. Borelli (1608–1679) had shown that hollow glass and leaden balls and tough animal shells could be pulverized in the turkey's stomach and had calculated that the ". . . force of the turkey's stomach is not less than the power of 1,350 lbs." (28). In 1752 de Réaumur obtained gastric juice from a pet kite that would swallow, and eventually regurgitate, small metal tubes containing foods or sponges. By squeezing the sponges he obtained gastric juice in a fairly pure state and found that it would, in vitro, partially digest meat without putrefaction, whereas, in a control experiment, meat in water putrefied. Stevens in 1777 and Spallanzani in 1783 made similar observations in man, which clearly distinguished the solvent action of gastric juice from the ". . . three kinds of fermentation: the vinous or sweet, the acetous and the putrid" (28, 32).

Although de Réaumur had found the gastric juice of the kite to be acid, Spallanzani had described human gastric juice as neutral. Not until 1824 was

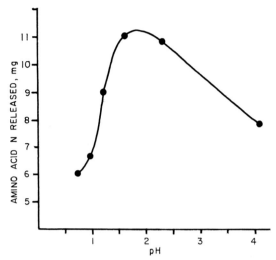

FIG. 1. The pH activity curve for the digestion of egg albumin by pepsin. [Drawn from original data of Sørensen (120).]

the issue clearly settled by Prout's demonstration of the existence of hydrochloric acid in gastric contents. Beaumont (5) in 1833, during his famous studies on Alexis St. Martin, confirmed Prout's finding but demonstrated that hydrochloric acid was not alone responsible for the solution of foodstuffs in the stomach. Eberle observed in 1834 that neutral gastric juice was inactive alone but active when mixed with hydrochloric acid, and suggested the presence in gastric juice and gastric mucosal extracts of a specific ferment, to which in 1836 Schwann (116) gave the name "pepsin." It thus happened that activity in acid solution became an integral part of our historical conception of the action of pepsin.

Pepsin

No sooner was the existence of pepsin postulated than efforts were made to isolate it, notably by Wassman (147) in 1839, Pekelharing (92) in 1896, and Fenger et al. (25) in 1928. In 1930, almost a century after the name pepsin was first used, Northrop (87) achieved one of the major advances of modern biochemistry by isolating the enzyme in crystalline form from pig gastric mucosa.

In 1909 Sørensen (120), having devised a notation for and a means of measuring hydrogen ion concentration, determined the earliest pH activity curves for peptic activity, thus defining more closely the property of acidic digestion. The pH maximum for pepsin was *etwas kleiner als 2*. Northrop's crystalline material subsequently showed a similar maximum. The pH activity curve in Figure 1 is drawn from the original data of Sørensen (120).

Rennin

The different historical origins of pepsin and rennin had led physiologists to think of them as separate substances (28), but because of the close association of the two activities in many species, Pavlov & Parastschuk (91) in 1904 and Pekelharing (93) in 1917 concluded that the two substances were really one. This view attracted opposition (4, 143), particularly from those who thought that "rennins" were widely distributed in nature (23). Hammarsten (37), in a series of papers published between 1908 and 1923, established the separate identity of gastric rennin in the calf by obtaining it free from pepsin and demonstrating that it too was a proteolytic enzyme, but that it differed from pepsin in being able to digest legumin in acid-free solution. Subsequently it was found that most proteinases, including pepsin, could, under suitable conditions, bring about the coagulation of milk. The first stage in this process is indeed the proteolytic conversion of casein to paracasein (78), preceding the precipitation of calcium paracaseinate. Instances of the rennin-like action of nongastric tissue extracts were thus explained. The existence of a rennin or preponderantly milk-clotting enzyme can therefore be accepted, even in gastric juice, only if the effect of pepsin or other proteinases can be excluded. Other groups (77, 131) have since achieved separation of calf rennin from pepsin, and Hankinson (38) in 1943 and Berridge (8) in 1945 have successfully crystallized the enzyme. The latter has shown it to be a proteolytic enzyme which will digest hemoglobin with a pH optimum of 3.7 (8). Rennin is thus a definitive substance, but its presence has been established only in the fourth stomach (abomasum) of young calves, although it is likely to occur also in the anatomically similar stomachs of the lamb and kid.

FORMATION OF PEPSIN FROM PEPSINOGEN

Pepsin is present in gastric mucosa in the form of an inactive precursor, pepsinogen (67). Swine pepsinogen also has been isolated in crystalline form, by Herriott & Northrop (53). It may be distinguished from pepsin by its higher molecular weight and by its stability in neutral or slightly alkaline solutions.

Pepsinogen is converted to pepsin in solutions which are more acidic than pH 5. The pepsin so formed is then extremely labile if exposed to a pH above 6. The conversion of pepsinogen to pepsin is catalyzed also by pepsin, below pH 4, that is, the reaction is autocatalytic.

The molecular weight of crystalline swine pepsin is approximately 35,000 and that of pepsinogen 42,000 so that a fragment of approximately 7,000 mol wt is lost during the conversion. This appears not as a single polypeptide but as six, one of which inhibits peptic action at pH 5.5 (47–49) and is called "pepsin inhibitor."

pepsinogen → pepsin + inhibitor + miscellaneous peptides

Pepsin Inhibitor

Pepsin inhibitor has been isolated in crystalline form by Herriott (48) and has a molecular weight of 3,242. It consists of a straight chain of 29 amino acids, for there is only one *N*-terminal amino acid residue, leucine (Tables 1 and 2, 144). Pepsin inhibitor combines reversibly with pepsin between pH 5 and 6 to form a compound the existence of which has been demonstrated (47). Below pH 5 the inhibitor dissociates from this pepsin-inhibitor compound, and the enzyme, thus liberated, slowly destroys the inhibitor (47–49). The pH maximum for this last reaction is 4.0. Pepsin inhibitor does not inhibit crystalline trypsin, crystalline chymotrypsin, or commercial rennet. Swine pepsin inhibitor also inhibits bovine pepsin but not chicken pepsin.

EVIDENCE FOR EXISTENCE OF
MORE THAN ONE PEPSIN

Running throughout the history of gastric digestion have been suggestions that there are other gastric proteinases than pepsin. During the period when it was doubtful whether all enzymes were proteins, several workers claimed the isolation of a "protein-free" pepsin (14, 115, 125). In 1874 Ebstein & Grützner (21) described a digestive ferment in the deep parts of the pyloric glands of dogs, and in 1902 Glaessner (34) correctly concluded that this pyloric pepsin, which he called "pseudopepsin," was different from (fundic) pepsin. In 1932 Northrop (88) described a proteolytic enzyme from the stomach, gelatinase, which he had obtained free from pepsin. Gelatinase differed from pepsin in possessing a much greater ability to hydrolyze gelatin, a much smaller ability to split hemoglobin and other proteins, and greater activity at pH 4.7 than at pH 2.0. During the 1940s the discovery that, under certain experimental circumstances, gastric juice digested substrates with two maxima near pH 2.0 and pH 3.5, rather than at pH 2.0 alone as did pepsin, caused later workers to conclude that a second proteinase, the so-called gastric cathepsin, was present (15, 30). Despite the similarity between the latter "enzyme" and the properties of calf rennin, it has been shown (132) that the activity at pH 3.5 can also be exhibited by crystalline pepsin and is really part of the activity of pepsin. This finding explains why so many workers had failed to isolate gastric "cathepsin" (15, 30, 82, 105, 133). Only recently, with the descriptions in the same year, 1959, of the pyloric proteinase (134) "gastricsin" (129) and "parapepsins I and II" (110), has the existence of two or more pepsins become definitely established, although, as the following sections make clear, several isolated, earlier observations have pointed to the same conclusion.

Salt Fractionation

Philpot & Small (100) found that pepsin could be fractionated to give an easily soluble crystalline fraction and a less soluble noncrystalline fraction of lower specific activity. Desreux et al. (18, 51) obtained a similar separation. The more active and more soluble component was isolated by repeated extraction with 0.6 saturated magnesium sulfate at pH 5.0, and the less soluble fraction by repeated precipitation with 0.45 saturated magnesium sulfate at pH 5.0. Northrop et al. (89) have emphasized that since in all experiments of this type the pepsins have been prepared in bulk from many individual animals, it cannot be assumed that both are present in any one individual.

Moving Boundary and Paper Electrophoresis

Tiselius and co-workers (140) subjected several different samples of crystalline swine pepsin to moving boundary electrophoresis and observed two components, one with a sharp and the other with a more diffuse boundary. Removal of the latter, which was inactive, increased the specific activity of the former. They confirmed the earlier observation of Ringer (106) that pepsin was not positively charged even at pH as low as 1.08. Hoch (56) found that this single, principal, electrophoretic component of crystalline swine pepsin (Armour), which constituted 96% of the whole, yielded on prolonged electrophoresis in the Tiselius apparatus two major components and two other minor components. Unfortunately the components were not separable, and there is no evidence that more than one was proteolytically active. Merten and his colleagues, working with swine pepsin and swine mucosal extracts (81), and Taylor, working with human gastric juice (133), have identified and separated two proteolytically active protein components from each source. Both of the human components moved to the anode at pH 2.5, thus resembling pepsin. With paper electrophoresis of individual human gastric mucosal extracts at pH 4.0, Taylor and Fisher (unpublished observations) found two proteins moving to the anode. Upon elution of the appropriate zones, both proteins exhibited proteinase activity near pH 2 and near pH 3.5. In pooled human gastric juice, Tang et al. (129) found two proteinases which moved to the anode below pH 5. One was identified as pepsin and and the other isolated as gastricsin.

pH Activity Curves

The two pepsins separated electrophoretically by Taylor (133) were found to have different pH activity curves, as were the two fractions into which crystalline swine pepsin could be fractionated by salt precipitation (133). These are discussed more fully in a later section. They provide further evidence of the existence of two pepsins and have been used to identify one or the other pepsin in gastric juices from patients with various gastric diseases (135–137).

Ion-Exchange Chromatography

Ryle & Porter (110) subjected crude swine pepsin to gradient elution upon diethylaminoethylcellulose columns and isolated from it, as minor components, two proteolytic enzymes, which they have called parapepsin I (renamed "pepsin B" by Ryle), and parapepsin II (renamed "pepsin C"). Both enzymes were obtained in a homogeneous state, as tested by electrophoresis and ultracentrifugation. Unlike crystalline pepsin, neither contains a phosphate group. Parapepsin I splits acetyl-DL-phenylalanyl-L-diiodotyrosine readily with a pH optimum at 1.8, and hydrolyzes gelatin much more easily than hemoglobin or plasma albumin. Parapepsin II readily hydrolyzes hemoglobin and plasma albumin but has little activity on acetyl-DL-phenylalanyl-L-diiodotyrosine. Neither enzyme, unlike pepsin, hydrolyzed cysteyltyrosine or tyrosylcysteine. Pepsin inhibitor inhibited the action of parapepsin II but not

of parapepsin I. Ryle (107) has isolated from pig fundic mucosa the pepsinogens corresponding to the two parapepsins.

Lee & Ryle (68) have subsequently found a fourth minor pepsinogen, pepsinogen D, in pig fundic mucosa. It resembles the other pepsinogens closely but it has no phosphate group and it possesses a different N-terminal group (Table 2). The four zymogens are not always all found in individual pigs (108). The zymogen of pepsin B has been found upon activation to give two enzymes in about equal amounts. The second of these is so far unnamed; it brings the potential number of pig pepsins up to five.

Tang and his colleagues (129) initially separated two proteinases from human gastric juice, using Amberlite IRC-50-XE 64. One behaved like pig pepsin and is therefore considered to be human pepsin. The other, which moved more slowly to the anode on electrophoresis, they have named "gastricsin." Subsequently, Tang & Tang (128) isolated a zymogen from the combined gastric mucosae of patients with duodenal ulcer. The zymogen appeared homogeneous upon electrophoresis and ultracentrifugation. Upon activation at pH 2.5 it yielded not one but two active proteinases which were identical with pepsin and gastricsin. Taylor and Fisher (unpublished observations) repeated the observations of Tang and his colleagues on normal human gastric juice and confirmed that at least two proteinases, and sometimes three, may be obtained.

Seijffers and co-workers (118) have separated two proteinases, with the properties of pepsin, from human gastric juice by chromatography on epichlorohydrin-triethanolaminocellulose. Subsequently, using diethylaminoethyl cellulose and gastric mucosal extracts from patients with peptic ulcer, they obtained three proteins which, upon acid activation, behaved as pepsins. They named these pepsinogens, I, II, and III. When the mucosae were acidified before fractionation (118), the chromatographic elution pattern showed three peaks of proteolytic activity. These were ascribed to the corresponding pepsins I, II, and III. Acidification of the isolated pepsinogens confirmed that pepsinogens I or III gave rise to pepsins I and III, respectively, but pepsinogen II gave rise to two proteolytic fractions which were named pepsins IIA and IIB. These four individual pepsins were not further purified and were not studied by paper or starch electrophoresis.

The advent of ion-exchange chromatography has therefore revealed an increasingly complex pattern of

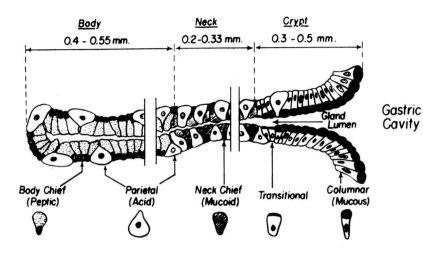

FIG. 2. Diagrammatic representation of a gastric gland tubule (dimensions approximate). (From F. Hollander, *Am. J. Med.* 13: 454, 1952.)

gastric proteolytic enzymes. The potential number of pepsins in the pig is five and in man four. In both man and pig there is evidence too that two enzymes may share a common precursor.

Agar Gel, Starch Gel, and Immunoelectrophoresis

These techniques each enable proteolytic enzymes to be detected in situ on an electrophoretic plate in the presence of other protein impurities. The agar gel method was first described by Uriel (141) and has been applied to human gastric mucosal extracts by Kushner et al. (66), who have demonstrated four pepsinogens which, upon acid inactivation, give rise to five enzymes with pepsin-like activity at or near pH 2.0. The pepsinogens were designated P I to P IV in order of decreasing mobility, and P III gives rise to two proteolytic spots after acidification. Similar studies on human gastric juice from patients with a variety of gastric diseases also reveal the presence of "... at least four constituents with proteolytic activity" (54). Immunoelectrophoretic studies by the same authors (54) indicate that P II, P III, and P IV are antigenic and differ immunochemically from one another. P I was not antigenic, by the methods employed.

Hanley and colleagues (40), using starch gel electrophoresis, found three pepsinogens in porcine crystalline pepsinogen, obtained from a commercial source, and in the fundic mucosal extracts of man, pig, and rabbit, but noted that the bands designated by them PG II and PG III were in fact double bands.

The results of these electrophoretic studies thus confirm that at least three pepsins occur in the pig and four in man.

CELLS OF ORIGIN OF PEPSINS

The gastric mucosa of man and other animals contains glands of three sorts. The cardiac glands, near the entry of the esophagus, are lined only with mucus-secreting cells. The fundic glands of the fundus and body of the stomach are longer and more complex (Fig. 2). They contain cells of three kinds—the mucus-secreting cells; the chief cells, so named because they form the bulk of the cells lining the lumen of the gland; and the parietal cells, which lie outside the chief cells and do not appear to abut at the lumen. The pyloric glands occur in the region of the pylorus and contain mucus-secreting cells and chief cells but no parietal cells. There is direct evidence that the parietal cells secrete the hydrogen ions of the gastric juice and the mucous cells secrete the mucus. The evidence that the chief cells elaborate the pepsinogens is partly by exclusion, for there is direct evidence for the known functions of the other cell types. In addition, protein granules are present in the cytoplasm of the body chief cells of the resting mucosa which disappear during gastric secretion and are therefore called pepsinogen granules. Furthermore, the pyloric glands produce an alkaline secretion (there are no parietal cells) that contains pepsin, which is most likely therefore to be derived from the pyloric chief cells.

At one time it was deduced that the pyloric glands secreted only mucus. This deduction was the result of the failure of the early histologists to find typical (fundic) chief cells, with pepsinogen granules, in the pyloric glands (7, 42). The cardiac glands today are labeled as mucus producers entirely on the basis of histological evidence, and it may be that further investigation will, as in the case of the pyloric glands, establish the fact that peptic enzymes occur in their secretion.

The early work of Ebstein & Grützner (21) and of Glaessner (34) in establishing the existence of a pyloric pepsin has already been discussed. Further evidence for the presence of this enzyme was given in 1935 by Holter & Linderstrøm-Lang (57), who found pepsin in swine pyloric mucosa and most abundantly at a depth of 2 mm from the surface. The cells in this region are known as the pyloric chief cells. Taylor (134) in 1959 extracted the pyloric enzyme from normal human pyloric mucosa and showed that it possessed different pH maxima from the fundic enzyme.

Pyloric juice itself has been collected from pyloric pouches by a number of investigators. All early experiments, except those of Ivy & Oyama (59), agreed in showing that pepsin is present in the secretion even though this is alkaline (1, 17, 43, 126). Jennings & Florey (61), in the cat, and more recently Taylor (134), in the pig, have shown that pyloric juice is alkaline and contains a pepsin. Taylor (134) has shown that the proteolytic pH maxima of the juice are similar to those of pig pyloric mucosal extracts. There can thus be no doubt that at least one of the pepsins secreted into pig gastric juice arises from the pyloric glands.

The fundic glands were found by Linderstrøm-Lang and co-workers (75) in 1935 to show up to three zones of proteolytic activity along their long axes. They identified these zones, from the luminal surface inward, as those containing epithelial cells, neck chief cells, and body chief cells. They observed furthermore that only the pepsin in the deeper layers of the fundus can be extracted by 30% glycerine, whereas the pepsin of all regions could be extracted quantitatively by hydrochloric acid. Their work suggests that at least two pepsins are derived from the fundic glands—one perhaps from the body chief cells, with their conspicuous pepsinogen granules, and the other from the neck chief cells, which do not possess obvious granules. Histologists have long noted (7, 42) that the pyloric glands appear to correspond to the neck region of the fundus glands without the parietal cells. It was also noted (134) that the fundic and pyloric pepsins were present in gastric juice in more nearly equal amounts than the respective mucosal areas occupied by the fundic and pyloric glands. Taylor (134) therefore has suggested that the pyloric enzyme may arise also from the neck chief cells of the fundic glands.

No further evidence is available to determine with greater precision the sites or cell types that are responsible for each of the four or more pepsins, or whether an individual cell can elaborate more than one pepsin.

NOMENCLATURE OF PEPSINS

The Report of the Commission on Enzymes of the International Union of Biochemistry recommends that the highly active enzyme prepared by Herriott and colleagues (51), which is presumed to be the principal pepsin, quantitatively, should retain the name they gave it, "pepsin A"; the other pig pepsins isolated by Ryle & Porter (110) should be named "pepsin B." Since there are three of them, Ryle (108) has subsequently used B for the former parapepsin I, C for parapepsin II, and D for the third. But this alphabetical system is now inadequate, for B has been found to have two components. Fortunately, none of the groups working with human material have used the A, B, C nomenclature, so that for the time being these initials, which are also given to the corresponding pepsinogens, can still be used for the porcine pepsins.

The first subdivision of the human pepsins was into fundic and pyloric enzymes (134). This differentiation continues to have a physiological validity but has proved inadequate now that more than two human pepsins are known. Unfortunately, each of the groups that have worked on human material has adopted its own nomenclature so that, for example, the pepsin I of Seijffers et al. (118) is evidently the pyloric enzyme described earlier by Taylor (134) and is the PG II of Hanley et al. (40) but probably the P III of Kushner et al. (66). This chaotic situation clearly should be resolved. The author has, over the past 16 years, worked with all the separative techniques that have been described earlier in this chapter and has found that agar gel electrophoresis provides the quickest method of scanning a gastric mucosal extract for pepsins. It can be the most easily standardized, it gives the sharpest separation of the individual enzymes, it recognizes more pepsins than any other method, and, being exquisitely sensitive, it can be carried out with only a small amount of enzymatic material. It seems only reasonable, therefore, to base a nomenclature upon this technique. Anyone then working with a gastric fraction can check the behavior of its pepsins, at any stage in a manipulative procedure, by agar gel electrophoresis.

With such a nomenclature in mind, over 200 gastric juice and gastric mucosal extracts, from normal subjects and from patients with diseases affecting the gastric mucosa, have been analyzed by agar gel electrophoresis, described in a recent study by Etherington & Taylor (24a). The variety of patterns displayed reveals that seven proteolytic bands may arise (Fig. 3). Accordingly it is suggested that these be numbered 1 to 7 in order of decreasing mobility. Figure 4 shows that there is more than one pyloric enzyme, and that the pyloric pepsin 5 is not quite identical with the correspondingly placed band in fundic extracts. Consequently the number should be prefixed by the initial of the material used: F = fundic, P = pyloric, D = duodenal, M = whole gastric mucosal, J = gastric juice. Figure 3 shows further that human pepsin 3 and pig pepsin A are

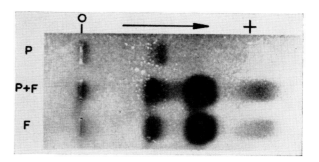

FIG. 4. Pepsins of fundic and pyloric mucosa from a patient with peptic ulcer, displayed on agar gel electrophoresis. P: pyloric mucosal extract, showing pyloric pepsins 5 and 7. F: fundic mucosal extract, showing pepsins 1, 3, 3a, 5, and 7. P + F: a mixture of the two extracts which indicates that the pyloric 5 and fundic 5 enzymes have different mobilities.

not identical, although they appear to be in other respects analogous, so that a further prefix, denoting the animal, could be used: H = human, P = pig, D = dog. Thus HF3 would indicate the principal human fundic pepsin, and PP5 the principal pig pyloric pepsin. Not all these proteolytic bands may indicate an active, pure enzyme, but this is no disadvantage. Thus the 4 band, which we find to be labile, may perhaps be a pepsin-inhibitor complex (117), but it can clearly exist in gastric juice as a definite biochemical compound, and it may well have a physiological significance in this form. The above nomenclature would not only locate it accurately for all laboratories but would describe its transformation into, say, band 3, with economy and precision, if the letter I is used for inhibitor, for example, HJ4I → HJ3 + I.

Until such a nomenclature is widely adopted it is necessary to record those correlations between the various present nomenclatures that have been established. Thus pepsin C (Ryle) is analogous to pyloric pepsin (Taylor), which is the same as pepsin I (Seijffers et al.) and as P III (Kushner et al.). Pepsin B (Ryle) is probably gelatinase (Northrop). Pepsin A (Herriott, Desreux, and Northrop) is analogous to the fundic pepsin (Taylor), pepsin II or III (Seijffers et al.), and P II (Kushner et al.). By the newly suggested nomenclature pepsin A would be 3, and pepsin C, 5. The position of pepsin B is not known. As Figure 5 shows, rennin is 7.

PHYSICAL AND CHEMICAL STRUCTURES AND
PROPERTIES OF PEPSINS AND PEPSINOGENS

Many studies of the physical and chemical structures of the pepsins and pepsinogens preceded the

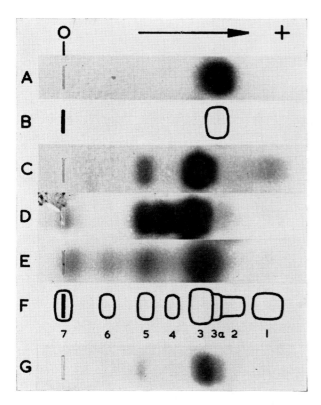

FIG. 3. Agar gel electrophoresis of the pepsins. Strips illustrate the seven bands that may be seen in normal gastric juice. A: crystalline swine pepsin; the pepsin is analogous to, but electrophoretically different from, human pepsin 3. B: is a drawing of A. C: a human gastric juice showing pepsins 1, 3, 3a and 5. D: shows pepsins 2, 3, 3a, 4, 5, and 7. E: shows pe'psins 3, 5, 6, and 7. F: a drawing illustrating the position of the above zones of proteolytic activity. G: a chromatographic fraction that illustrates more clearly than in C and D that pepsin 3 may sometimes contain a more rapidly moving anodal fraction, numbered 3a.

recognition that more than one pepsin exists. Some recent investigations have ignored this discovery. Often, therefore, investigators have not stated precisely the origin and degree of homogeneity of the enzyme they have used. For these reasons there must continue to be uncertainty as to the validity of many of the conclusions about the structure of "pepsin" that are described in this section. Except where mentioned otherwise, it is assumed that the preparations that have been used consist mainly or wholly of pig

pepsin A, or pig pepsinogen A, which, using the agar gel nomenclature, would be PM 3.

Molecular Weights

Pepsinogen has a molecular weight of 41,000 (2) to 43,000 (49), as calculated from its amino acid composition. The molecular weight of pepsinogen B is 39,000, as determined by ultracentrifugal and diffusion studies (108), and of pepsinogen C, 41,400 (109), from its amino acid composition. Pepsinogen B is now thought to contain two zymogens.

Pepsin has a molecular weight of 35,000 from osmotic pressure measurements (87); 35,500 from ultracentrifugation (99); 34,500 (46, 47) and 34,800 (66) from its phosphate content; 35,000 (19) and 37,600 (65) from light-scattering measurements; and 36,400 (9) from its amino acid analysis. The molecular weight of pepsin B is 38,600 (110), close to that of pepsinogen B, and that of pepsin C is 36,000 (109).

The molecular weights of the human pepsinogens and pepsins have not been determined.

Amino Acid Composition (Table 1)

Amino acid composition has been determined only for the porcine pepsins. Pepsinogen and pepsin contain one phosphate group per molecule. Pepsinogens C and D and pepsins B, C, and D do not contain phosphate, but the component of pepsinogen B with

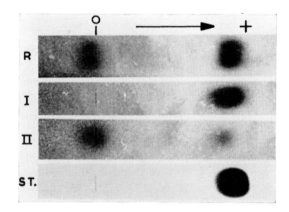

FIG. 5. Proteolytic enzymes of a commercial rennet solution. *R:* commercial rennet, showing enzymes in the positions 3 and 7. *ST:* crystalline swine pepsin, as a standard. *I:* a chromatographic fraction of rennet containing only calf pepsin 3. *II:* a chromatographic fraction containing mainly rennin, which is in position 7.

TABLE 1. *Amino Acid Composition of Pepsinogens, Pepsins, and Pepsin Inhibitor*

	Pepsinogen (A)		Pepsin (A)		Pepsin Inhibitor (144, 145)	Pepsinogen C (109)	Pepsin C (109)
	(144, 145)	(2)	(12)	(9)			
Lysine	12	11	2	1	4	12	4
Histidine	4	3	2	1		2	1
Arginine	3	4	2	2	1	7	4
Aspartic acid	46	46	41	44	4	30	28
Threonine	25	28	28	28	1	25	25
Serine	53	47	40	44	2	35	35
Glutamic acid	32	30	28	27	2	46	41
Proline	20	19	15	15	3	20	18
Glycine	36	36	29	38	1	35	32
Alanine	27	21	21	18	2	23	21
Cystine (half)	6	6	6	4		6	6
Valine	27	25	21	21	2	22	20
Methionine	5	4	4	5		5	4
Isoleucine	64	25	28	27	5	16	14
Leucine		33	27	28		40	34
Tyrosine	16	17	16	18	1	22	18
Phenylalanine	20	15	13	14	1	24	21
Tryptophan	4	6	4	6		6	6

Numbers in parentheses indicate reference numbers.

TABLE 2. *The C- and N-Terminal Groups of Swine Pepsins*

	C-Terminal	N-Terminal
Pepsinogen (A)	alanine-leucine or isoleucine-valine- *or* alanine-valine-	-isoleucine or leucine-leucine
Pepsin (A)	alanine-leucine or isoleucine-valine- *or* alanine-valine-	-glycine-isoleucine
Pepsin inhibitor		-glutamic-leucine
Pepsinogen B (2 components)		-methionine -histidine
Pepsin B		-alanine
Pepsinogen C		-serine
Pepsin C		-serine -leucine or isoleucine
Pepsinogen D		-leucine or isoleucine
Pepsin D		-valine

an *N*-terminal histidine may contain phosphate, which, unlike that of pepsinogen (A), is lost during activation.

The data of Table 1 show that during the conversion of pepsinogens (A) and C to the pepsins (A) and C, there is a loss of many basic amino acids (lysine, histidine, arginine) but relatively less loss of neutral and acidic amino acids. This explains the observation that the pepsins migrate more quickly to the anode than do the pepsinogens. The high content of aspartic and glutamic acids, together with the phosphate residue, explains partly (10) why pepsin (A) has a low isoelectric point (140). The absence of phosphate, the lower content of aspartate, and the higher content of lysine and arginine would explain why pepsin C has a higher isoelectric point than has pepsin (A).

Pepsin inhibitor, as would be expected, is relatively rich in lysine. It inhibits pepsin C as well as pepsin (A) (110).

Table 1 reveals certain incompatibilities, for example, with threonine, which suggest that these compositions must be regarded as only approximate.

Physical Properties

Pepsin has a sedimentation constant of 3.2×10^{-13} sec (99), pepsin C of 3.32×10^{-13} (110). Pepsinogen B has a sedimentation constant of 2.99×10^{-13} sec (108).

The diffusion coefficient of pepsin (A) is 9.0×10^{-7} (99) and that of pepsinogen B, 7.4×10^{-7} cm² per sec (108).

The isoelectric point of pepsin (A) is near pH 1 (104, 140).

N-Terminal Groups (Table 2)

End-group analyses of pepsinogen (A) reveal only a single *N*-terminal amino acid, which is leucine (90, 145). Pepsin (A) has isoleucine as the *N*-terminal residue (44, 123, 145, 148), and pepsin inhibitor has leucine (144). The second amino acid at the *N*-terminal end is isoleucine or leucine in pepsinogen, glycine in pepsin, and glutamic acid in the inhibitor (144, 145). Thus, neither the enzyme nor the inhibitor occupies the *N*-terminal position in pepsinogen.

The *N*-terminal amino acids of the two components of pepsinogen B are methionine and histidine, and those of pepsinogens C and D are serine and leucine or isoleucine, respectively. The *N*-terminal groups of pepsins B, C, and D are, respectively, alanine, leucine or isoleucine and serine, and valine (68, 108, 109). It would seem therefore that in all the pepsins so far sufficiently characterized the enzyme does not occupy the *N*-terminal part of the zymogen.

C-Terminal Groups (Table 2)

The terminal carboxylic amino acid of pepsinogen is alanine (49, 76). The next two amino acids are leucine or isoleucine and valine (49), but this is contested by others (90, 122) who consider valine to be the second amino acid. Both the American and the Soviet workers are, however, agreed that the same *C*-

terminal amino acids are present in pepsin as in pepsinogen. Pepsin, therefore, probably occupies the C-terminal position in pepsinogen.

Secondary and Tertiary Structures

The existence of only one N- and one C-terminal group for each pepsinogen and pepsin that has been adequately characterized suggests that each molecule consists of a single unbranched peptide chain.

Pepsinogen has a low intrinsic viscosity which on reduction of one of its three cystine disulfide bonds is little changed (11, 64). That there is also little loss of activity suggests that this bond is remote from the active site(s). Reduction of a second disulfide bond causes a rise in viscosity with some loss of potential enzyme activity. The third disulfide bridge can only be split with difficulty and with complete loss of activity. After reduction of all three bridges the osmotic pressure is unchanged (64). This last observation confirms that the molecule consists of one chain and not of several identical chains linked by disulfide bridges. The low viscosity indicates that this chain is coiled, and the changes on reduction show that it is held in shape by two disulfide bridges.

Pepsin, similarly, is a single-chain peptide. Rotary dispersion measurements (62, 96) suggest that in the active state there is little helical coiling, but the chain

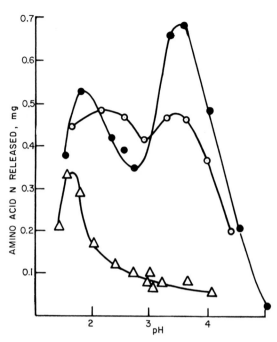

FIG. 7. The pH activity curves for the digestion of different proteins by human gastric juice. Note that 2 maxima occur, except with egg albumin, △. ○, Human plasma protein; ●, human serum albumin.

is folded to give a relatively globular particle with an axial ratio of about 3.0 (22).

Other Chemical Properties

Pepsin is stable in acid solutions below pH 6, provided the temperature is sufficiently low to prevent autodigestion. Pepsin is inactivated and denatured at pH above 6. The denaturation is accompanied by an increase in intrinsic viscosity, which suggests an unfolding of the molecule, and an increase in axial ratio of 3 to 16 (22). Herriott has put together much of the above information to derive a sketch of the pepsinogen and pepsin molecules (Fig. 6).

Pepsinogen is, in contrast, converted to pepsin below pH 5 but is stable in neutral and weakly alkaline solutions, being reversibly denatured between pH 8 and 10. Above pH 11.5, a time-dependent irreversible loss of structure occurs (29).

PHYSIOLOGICAL ACTIONS OF PEPSINS

pH Activity Curves

The earliest pH activity curves showed, as we have seen in Figure 1, a single pH maximum near pH

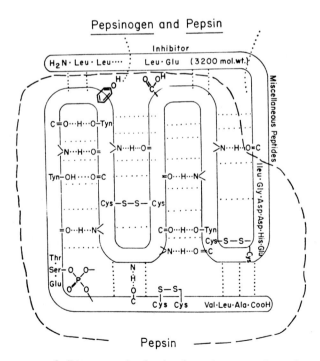

FIG. 6. Diagrammatic sketch of pepsinogen and pepsin. [From Herriott (49).]

2. There have been numerous reports, dating from 1909 [summarized (132)], that gastric juice, gastric mucosal extracts, and pepsin, in various degrees of purity, give curves with two pH maxima (Fig. 7), the second occurring in the region of pH 3.3 to 4.0. Generally speaking, the second maximum is demonstrated most readily when *a)* gastric juice and gastric mucosal extracts are used; *b)* proteolysis is measured by methods, such as formol titration or biuret, which measure all split peptide bonds, rather than by methods relying on the liberation of tyrosine; *c)* the incubating medium has an ionic strength above 0.15 (114); and *d)* protein substrates other than egg albumin are used. This protein substrate, which was used initially by Sørensen, characteristically yields only one pH maximum near pH 1.8 (Figs. 1 and 7).

The obvious interpretation to place on the second maximum was that it was caused by a second enzyme, and the occurrence of this second maximum has indeed proved a potent stimulus to the subsequent discovery of the several pepsins. However, none of the other pepsins exhibits a single pH maximum in the region of pH 3.3–4.0. Furthermore, several workers (81, 114, 132) have shown that both maxima occur with authentic samples of pure pepsin (A), under the conditions defined above. It is concluded therefore that both maxima may result from the activity of a single enzyme. Earlier views that the maximum near pH 4 resulted from the secretion of a separate gastric cathepsin (see 132) are unlikely to be correct. With impure enzyme preparations the shape of the pH activity curve is complicated by two other factors: other pepsins may show two maxima but at differing pH values (134), and second, the pH maximum may shift with the duration of digestion (110, 120), although this has not always been found to be the case (133).

The mechanism by which one enzyme yields a pH activity curve with two maxima is of some theoretical interest. Of nine possible mechanisms that were investigated it was concluded (133), on the basis of the evidence then available, that it was most likely that the two maxima are produced by two different active centers on the pepsin molecule, each attacking two different sorts of peptide bond, as expressed by an equation such as

$$2E_{A+B} + 2S_{x+y} \rightarrow E_A S_x + E_B S_y$$

The double pH maxima of pepsin are not unique, for a similar phenomenon has been reported for liver β-glucuronidase (73), Ehrlich ascites ribonuclease (16), myosin ATPase (33), and bovine seminal 5'-nucleotidase (72). With the last of these, four sites are postulated to be involved in the interaction of the enzyme and the substrate.

Substrate Specificity

Pepsin (A) attacks most native proteins, but not keratins, protamines, ovomucin, mucins, conchiolin, and spongin (130). The sites of action of several pepsins on the B chain of oxidized insulin have been studied, and the results are summarized in Table 3. From this table it is seen that the pepsins split, most readily, bonds involving phenylalanine, tyrosine, and leucine. Bonds involving glutamic acid are split but less readily. The A chain of insulin has also been used as a substrate (111), and again bonds involving these four amino acids proved susceptible to attack by pepsin (A), but additionally a valine-cysteyl bond was split mildly, and a tyrosine-cysteyl bond was not attacked. It may be noted that the valine-cysteyl bond of the B chain was not attacked. With a larger protein, oxidized bovine ribonuclease (102, 119), the major sites of action of pepsin (A) again involved phenylalanine, tyrosine, leucine, glutamic acid, and valine. In addition, an alanine-alanine bond was hydrolyzed mildly, but several tyrosyl bonds escaped, namely, tyrosine-cysteyl, tyrosine-serine, and tyrosine-lysine. With adrenocorticotrophic hormone, alanine-serine and aspartic-aspartic bonds were attacked (74).

The many studies involving synthetic substrates mirror the action of pepsin on B insulin. Fruton & Bergmann (31) showed that pepsin can hydrolyze synthetic peptide derivatives containing tyrosine or phenylalanine, such as carbobenzoxy-L-glutamyl-L-tyrosine. This activity differs from the action on proteins in two important respects: it is slow, appreciable hydrolysis taking 24 hours at 37 C, and the pH optimum is around pH 4 and not pH 2. At the latter pH, Fruton and Bergmann found hydrolysis of synthetic substrates to be virtually absent. Harington & Pitt-Rivers (41) observed that cysteyl-tyrosine, tyrosyl-cysteine, and their carbobenzoxy derivatives are split by crystalline pepsin in like manner. Only in the case of cysteyl-tyrosine and its carbobenzoxy derivative was significant splitting achieved at pH 1.8 after 48 hours. Baker (3) has found, however, using very small concentrations of enzyme and substrate, that crystalline "pepsin" and pepsin A will fairly rapidly split N-acetyl-L-tyrosyl-L-tyrosine, acetyl-L-phenylalanine-L-phenylalanine, and N-carbobenzoxy-L-tyrosyl-L-phenylalanine with pH optima around 2. Of the second of these substances 68 % was hydrolyzed in as little as 3.25 hours. A complete list of the synthetic di- and tripeptides split by pepsin (A) is available (20). The principal discrepancy between the action of pepsin (A) on proteins and on simple peptides lies in the relative failure to attack the tyrosine-cysteyl bond in the former, compared with its ready hydrolysis in the latter.

The fact that some synthetic dipeptides are hydrolyzed maximally by pepsin (A) near pH 2 and some near pH 4 is compatible with the observations,

TABLE 3. *Peptide Bonds of the B-Chain of Oxidized Insulin That Are Split by Various Proteinases from the Stomach, Pancreas, and Spleen*

Amino Acids of B-Chain of Insulin	Crystalline Swine Pepsin (A) (112)	Human Pepsin 3 (Etherington & Taylor, unpubl. observ.)	Swine Pepsin C (109)	Human Pepsin 5 (Etherington & Taylor, unpubl. observ.)	Swine Pepsin B (110)	Rennin (26)	Chymo-trypsin (112)	Elastase (Pancreatic) (85)	Bovine Spleen Cathepsin D (103)	Trypsin (112)
Phenylalanine	+									
Valine										
Aspartic acid										
Glutamic acid	+	++								
Histidine										
Leucine								+|		
Cysteic acid										
Glycine								+		
Serine								++		
Histidine										
Leucine	++	++	++	+	+	+		+		
Valine										
Glutamic acid	+	+		+					+	
Alanine	+	+	+++	+	+			++		
Leucine	+	+	+	++	++	++	+	+++	++	
Tyrosine	++	+++	+++	+++	++	++	++		+	
Leucine										
Valine							++			
Cysteic acid										
Glycine										
Glutamine										
Arginine										++
Glycine	+			+				++		
Phenylalanine	++	+	++	+++	+++	++			+|	
Phenylalanine	++	+++	+	+	+	++	++	+	++	
Tyrosine							++	+		
Threonine										
Proline										
Lysine										++
Alanine										

noted above, of proteolytic pH activity curves with double maxima, and with the hypothesis that pepsin (A) may have two active sites.

Apart from the differences between the pepsins noted in Table 3, pepsin B differs from the other pepsins in having little activity against hemoglobin. On the other hand, it splits gelatin much more readily than does pepsin (A). Like pepsins (A) and D, it hydrolyzes the dipeptide acetyl-L-phenylalanyl-L-diiodotyrosine. Pepsin C does not hydrolyze this dipeptide (108).

Effect of Inhibitors and Activators

The free amino groups of pepsin (A) can be acetylated (52) or deaminated with nitrous acid (101) without loss of enzymic activity. Two tryptophan residues per molecule may be converted to N'-formylkynurenine also without loss of activity (104). N-Bromosuccinamide destroys methionine residues and three tryptophan residues per molecule (76) and inactivates pepsin. Blocking the methionine residues with iodoacetic acid does not affect enzymic activity (76). If these observations on tryptophan can be directly related to each other, it would appear that a third tryptophan residue is so situated as to have a bearing on the activity of the molecule.

Of the acid groups, the phosphate, which is absent from some of the pepsins, is not essential for activity (95). On the other hand, when the carboxyl groups are selectively esterified with sulfur mustard the activity falls progressively (50). Acetylation (52), iodination (45), and nitration (101) of the tyrosine residues also resulted in a progressive loss of activity. Liberation of the phenolic groups of tyrosine restored activity. Pepsin inhibitor is rich in lysine, and polylysine peptides also inhibit the action of pepsin (A) (63). N-Acetyl-D-phenylalanyl-L-diiodotyrosine, an isomer of a dipeptide which is readily hydrolyzed by pepsin, inhibits peptic action upon dipeptides (49), as do phenylacyl derivatives, such as p-chlorophenylacyl bromide (24). Yet the latter only partly inhibited the action on hemoglobin, and the pH inactivation curve is similar in shape to a pH activity curve with two maxima. A differential effect on the proteolytic and dipeptidase activities has also been obtained by acetylation of pepsin (A) with acetylimidazole; the former activity was depressed to 60%, the latter increased 2.5-fold (97). Different investigators have offered differing reasons for such differential effects,

but all would be explained by the existence of more than one active center.

Role of Pepsins in Digestion

Gastric mucosa is the usual starting material for the preparation of the swine pepsins, so some uncertainty must remain as to which pepsins are actually secreted into gastric juice in this species. In man there is ample evidence from agar gel electrophoresis (Fig. 3) that, in normal subjects, pepsins 3 and 5 are secreted into gastric juice together with smaller quantities of pepsins 1 and 2. Pepsin 3 is usually the preponderant enzyme.

The pH of the resting gastric contents just before food is ingested may, in different individuals and in the same individuals at differing times, vary from around pH 2 to pH 7.4. Ingested food and fluids have a pH near 7 and usually a considerable buffering power. It seems inevitable therefore that, whatever the pH of the resting contents, the food bolus should experience an initial pH in the stomach near 7 and should take a finite time to fall to pH 2 as gastric secretion continues. From the evidence of the peptic pH activity curves, proteolytic digestion will begin as the pH nears 4.0. In vitro experiments have shown (132) that proteolytic activity at the pH maximum near pH 3.5 is of the same order as that near pH 2.0. With six different protein substrates in 17 subjects the ratio of maximal activity at pH 2.0 to that at pH 3.5 varied from 0.79 to 2.4, and the activity at the latter maximum was actually the higher in about one-third of the experiments. The proteolytic properties of pepsins at the maximum near pH 3.5 must therefore play an important role in the normal intragastric digestion of proteins.

The time that food remains in the stomach will determine chiefly, so long as there is normal gastric secretion, whether the intragastric contents reach pH 2.0 and whether they are thus subjected to the lower of the two in vitro maxima of pepsin. Reliable data on the intragastric pH after a normal meal are few; the author has found, experimenting on himself, that after a meal of bacon and eggs, though the stomach had emptied, the intragastric pH had fallen only to 3.05, so that the full digestive power of the pepsins was not attained. In the duodenum and small intestine the pH of the acid contents leaving the stomach rises toward neutrality. Again, digestion by pepsins could occur, by virtue of their activity up to pH 4.0.

It would seem, then, that the capacity for proteolvtic digestion by the gastric pepsins may often be greater in man than the normal physiological control of the stomach allows. Certainly the human pepsins are not essential for the normal quantitative digestion and absorption of proteins, for it is well established that after partial or total gastrectomy and in pernicious anemia when there is absence of pepsin secretion, the nitrogen content of the stools is not increased.

ACTIVE CENTER(S) OF PEPSIN

Most of the groups working on this problem assume that there is only one active center per molecule of pepsin. Should this prove to be untrue, many observations will need reevaluating. In Herriott's scheme (Fig. 6), the active site is portrayed, from the evidence presented above, as lying "beneath" the inhibitor portion of the pepsin molecule and consisting of a carboxyl group and a phenolic tyrosyl group. These are on contiguous parts of the folded chain, to account for the loss of activity which occurs when the chain is unfolded during denaturation. The carboxyl group is probably from aspartic acid, for during the reversible inactivation of pepsin by p-bromophenacyl bromide the β-carboxyl group of a residue of aspartic acid is esterified (24, 36). The amino acids at this part of the chain are claimed to be glycine-glycine-aspartic-serine-glutamic (36). Erlanger and his colleagues draw attention to the resemblance of this sequence to that for the active center of "serine esterases" such as chymotrypsin and acetylcholinesterase, although pepsin is not inactivated, as are the others, by diisopropylfluorophosphate and diphenylcarbamyl chloride. Lokshina & Orekhovich (76) feel that the tryptophan residues fulfill a vital structural role, stabilizing the active configuration of pepsin rather than directly participating in the structure of the active center.

The phosphate group in pepsin (A) is known to be attached to serine (27) in the amino acid sequence threonine-serine-glutamic. The known sequence at this point of the molecule has been extended to glutamic - alanine - threonine - serine (- P) - glutamic-glutamic-leucine (124) and clearly cannot be the same as the serine sequence at the active center.

Herriott (49) envisages that in the case of aromatic dipeptides hydrolyzed by pepsin (A) at pH 1.8, the hydroxyl group of tyrosine at the active center forms a hydrogen bond with the carbonyl (C=O) group of the peptide bond of the substrate, and that

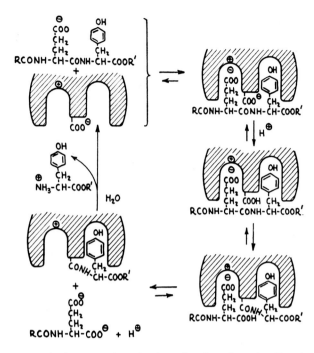

FIG. 8. A proposed mechanism of action of pepsin; N-acyl-L-glutamyl-L-tyrosine ester represented as substrate. [From Bovey et al. (10).]

the active carboxyl group of the center forms one or more hydrogen bonds with the free carboxyl group of the dipeptide. Bovey & Yanari (10), on the other hand, suggest that a complex is formed in which the two (aromatic) side groups of the substrate are each bound to the enzyme. A protonated carboxyl group from the enzyme then reacts with the peptide bond of the substrate, releasing the N-terminal amino acid and binding the C-terminal amino acid, via its amino group, to the carboxyl group of the enzyme, from which it is subsequently hydrolyzed. Jackson et al. (60) conclude from kinetic studies that, as demanded by both hypotheses, the substrate is bound at two points near the active site, but their evidence otherwise favors the second hypothesis (Fig. 8).

PEPSINS OF SPECIES OTHER THAN MAN AND PIG

Bovine pepsin has been crystallized by Northrop from pooled gastric juice (89). Canine gastric juice has been found to digest proteins with two peaks of activity below pH 4.0 (94, 98). Three pepsinogens and their corresponding pepsins have been isolated from the mucosa of the chick forestomach (71). Unlike porcine pepsin A, none of them contained phosphorus and none cleaved acetyl-L-phenylalanyl-L-tyrosine. Two did not attack gelatin, but the third did. Each gave a pH optimum near pH 2.0 for the digestion of hemoglobin. The sites of action of one of them on the B-chain of oxidized insulin have been determined (70). Unlike swine pepsin, the tyrosine 16-leucine 17 bond was not attacked, nor was the alanine 14-leucine 15 bond (see Table 3).

Crystalline and amorphous preparations of salmon pepsin have been prepared (86). The crystalline preparation yielded a pH activity curve with the two typical maxima; and it was noted that, as with swine pepsin (A), the maximum at pH 3.5 to 4.0 was more prominent when digestion was carried out in the presence of 0.1 N NaCl. Shark pepsin has also been found to digest proteins with maxima near pH 2.0 and near pH 3.5 (121).

Thus in those vertebrate species in which the pepsins have been sufficiently characterized, the properties of crystallization, of formation from a pepsinogen, of pH activity curves with two maxima, and of generally similar sites of action on B insulin are manifest. Differences occur between species with regard to the phosphate content, the ability to split synthetic peptides, and the splitting of individual bonds of B insulin. In the calf the enzyme occupying the agar electrophoretic number 7 is produced in relatively large amounts and is known as rennin.

Interestingly the species of pitcher plant *Nepenthes* so far investigated liberate into their pitchers hydrochloric acid and a proteolytic enzyme with maximal activity near pH 2.0 (84).

SERUM AND URINARY PEPSINOGENS

Brücke (13) discovered in 1861 "a digestive substance" in the urine which was active at an acid pH and which was named "uropepsin" by Bendersky in 1890 (6). The absence of uropepsin from the urine of the gastrectomized dog was demonstrated in 1903 (80), and marked diminution was observed in patients with pernicious anemia or extensive gastric neoplasia (127); this pointed to the stomach as the source of the enzyme.

Such a source implied the presence of the enzyme in serum, and this was first demonstrated by Van Calcar (142) and Saxl (113). Knowledge of the existence of the precursor, pepsinogen, led to the realization that the enzyme must be present in this form in serum and urine, otherwise it would be inactivated at the neutral pH of these fluids. Gottlieb (35) showed

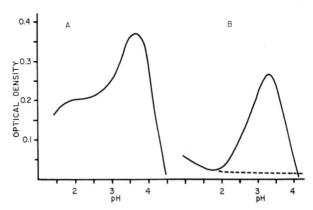

FIG. 9. The pH activity curves for the digestion of hemoglobin by A: a normal serum; B: serum from a patient who has had a total gastrectomy. [Redrawn from Hanley (39).]

that the serum level of pepsinogen remained reasonably constant in any one individual, and Mirsky and his colleagues (83) found that the level could be used as an index of a subject's gastric secretory cell mass. Hirschowitz (55) has calculated that the amount of pepsinogen entering the blood is about 1 % of that entering the gastric lumen during 24 hours.

The actual levels of serum pepsinogen are measured in units and differ with the methods of individual authors. With any one method an important factor in obtaining consistent results is the accurate control of pH. This is illustrated by Figure 9, which shows pH activity curves for the digestion of hemoglobin by the serum pepsinogen of a patient who had had a total gastrectomy, and by that of a normal individual. The former curve indicates that a catheptic enzyme, not derived from the stomach, is active over the pH range 2.5 to 4.5 and that below pH 2.0 the substrate is partly digested by acid hydrolysis. The digestion caused by serum pepsinogen is superimposed upon this latter part of the curve and tends to rise with rising pH.

The mean value for serum pepsinogen is higher in the male than in the female and is approximately doubled in patients with chronic duodenal ulcer. Mean values are altered little in chronic gastric ulcer and in patients with functional dyspepsia, but are reduced or are absent in pernicious anemia, or after total gastrectomy.

PEPSINS IN GASTRIC DISEASE

Gastric proteinase activity has been studied extensively in diseases in which the gastric mucosa is either hypertrophic or degenerate.

Pernicious Anemia

In this disease there is total atrophy of the fundic glands and sometimes of the pyloric glands as well, but occasionally the pyloric mucosa is preserved (79). Proteinase activity at pH 2 in the gastric juice is low or absent (see 135 for refs.), and the same is true of mucosal extracts. Histamine or insulin stimulation causes no appreciable increase in proteolytic activity, nor does washing the stomach with dilute hydrochloric acid during the collection period to prevent the inactivation of pepsins at the neutral pH of gastric secretion which is typical of this disease (58). Occasional patients are described who, despite anacidity, secrete appreciable though still subnormal amounts of pepsin into the gastric juice (139).

The proteolytic pH activity curves yield variable results. Some juices are completely inactive. Those with most activity give pH activity curves typical of those of pepsin 5, the enzyme associated with the pyloric mucosa, thus suggesting that these are the patients in whom the pyloric glands are preserved. Many patients secrete juices with unusual maxima, and the nature of the responsible enzymes is unclear. Some may be derived from zones of intestinal metaplasia that often replace the destroyed fundic glands, and others may be abnormal enzymes or "fragments" of normal pepsins (135). Agar gel electrophoresis

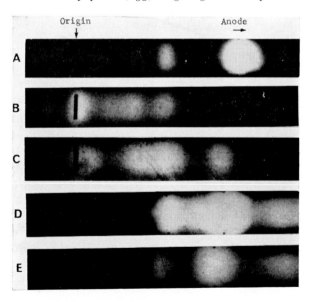

FIG. 10. Agar gel electrophoresis of the pepsins present in the gastric juice of *A:* a normal subject, showing bands 3, 3a, and 5 (see Fig. 3); *B:* a patient with pernicious anemia, showing absence of 3; *C:* a patient with idiopathic hypochromic anemia, showing a more prominent 5 than 3; *D:* a patient with duodenal ulcer, showing a prominent 1; *E:* a patient with gastric ulcer, showing a prominent 1.

confirms that in some of these patients pepsin 5 predominates in the gastric juice (Fig. 10).

Idiopathic Hypochromic Anemia

The proteinase activity of the gastric juice at pH 2 is reduced or, occasionally, absent in this disorder (see 137 for refs.). The pH activity curves vary in different patients. There may be no activity, there may be normal curves with two maxima, but in about half the patients the pyloric type of curve occurs (137). Agar gel electrophoresis confirms that in some patients pepsin 5 predominates but that pepsin 3 also is usually present. When these observations were first made the mechanism causing this changed proportion proved puzzling; it was simply suggested, therefore, that the pyloric type of pH activity curve "... might be merely the activity of a gastric juice in which the normally less abundant (pyloric) secretion has become predominant, through failure of secretion of the normally preponderant fundal-type pepsin" (137). A subsequent study (69) of the histology of the gastric mucosa in idiopathic hypochromic anemia has made possible a more exact interpretation of the pH activity curves; some patients were found to have a gross atrophy of the fundic and body mucosa, but in others there was a tendency for the neck chief cells, which histologically resemble the cells of the pyloric glands, to proliferate at the expense of the "true" chief cells. In 4 of 19 patients there was "marked replacement of normal by pseudo-pyloric glands."

Idiopathic Steatorrhea

About half of the patients with this disease have peptic activity at pH 2 within the normal range; in the others it is reduced or absent (see 137 for refs.). As in idiopathic hypochromic anemia, the pyloric type of pH activity curve is found (137), and agar gel electrophoresis sometimes shows the predominance of pepsin 5. The mechanism of this changed proportion has not yet been ascertained.

Peptic Ulcer

It was thought at first (see 136 for refs.) that peptic activity of the gastric juice near pH 2 was increased in both gastric and duodenal ulcer, but more strikingly so in the latter disease. These studies were carried out mainly on resting juices or on the separated products of an Ewald meal. It was shown subsequently, however, that the values only appeared increased because of the lower pH at which the gastric juice was usually secreted in peptic ulcer patients compared with normal subjects (58). It is now established (see 136 for refs.) that the concentration of pepsin does not differ from that of normal subjects, but that, in duodenal ulcer particularly, the total amount of enzyme secreted is greater because of the increased volume of gastric secretion, both at rest and in response to a given stimulus.

The pH activity curves of many patients with peptic ulcer exhibit three maxima below pH 4 (136); in this they resemble a minority of normal subjects (132). Agar gel electrophoresis reveals that in many patients with peptic ulcer pepsin 1 is more abundant than in normal subjects (Fig. 10). Whether pepsin 1 could account for the unusual pH activity curves has not yet been established. Nor is there yet any established connection between peptic ulcer and the minority of normal subjects exhibiting the same type of pH activity curve; the possibility arises that in the normal population there is a group of subjects who, by an inherited or acquired mechanism (or both), secrete a juice resembling in its pepsins that of peptic ulcer, and that peptic ulceration occurs more frequently in this group than in the remainder of the population.

Conclusion

The variety of proteolytic activity exhibited by the gastric juice of patients with diseased gastric mucosa can to an increasing extent be explained in terms of our newer knowledge of the nature and multiplicity of the pepsins, although important gaps remain to be filled.

COMPARATIVE PROTEINASE ACTIVITY OF GASTROINTESTINAL MUCOSA

Extracts of the mucosa from the first part of the duodenum of man give proteolytic pH activity curves with two maxima resembling those of pepsin 5 (pyloric pepsin) (138), and subsequently it has been shown that the pepsins of pyloric and duodenal mucosa behave similarly chromatographically (117, 118) and upon agar gel electrophoresis (Etherington and Taylor, unpublished observations).

In the remainder of the duodenum and in the jejunum, colon, ileum, and rectum, mucosal extracts give proteolytic pH activity curves with a single

maximum near pH 3.5 (139), and agar gel electrophoresis indicates that the responsible enzyme does not migrate as a pepsin but remains near the origin (Etherington and Taylor, unpublished observations). The enzymes are in fact the "acid" cathepsins. They digest most proteins but not egg albumin; it will be recalled that pepsin enzymes do not digest egg albumin at the second maximum near pH 3.5, at which they digest most other protein substrates.

RELATION OF PEPSINS TO ENZYMES GENERALLY

It is easy to think of pepsins as unique and isolated among enzymes, for they occur only in a limited part of the gastrointestinal tract, they are the only enzymes with so low an optimal pH activity as pH 2.0, and they are the only enzymes—indeed, probably the only proteins—to have isoelectric points below pH 2. Biologically, the problem then arises as to how they have evolved, or differentiated, from the primitive gut endoderm.

Recent advances in our knowledge of the pepsins, as well as proof that two major enzymes and at least one minor enzyme exist in man, provide links between the pepsins and enzymes generally. Thus the upper maximum at pH 3.5 relates pepsin to the acid cathepsins of the rest of the gut, and of tissues generally. The failure of acid cathepsins to attack egg albumin and of pepsins to attack it at their "catheptic" maximum relates the pepsins and cathepsins, from the point of view of specificity. Perhaps even more remarkable in this respect are the data of Table 3, which show that the pepsins of two species, man and pig, the rennin of the calf, chymotrypsin and elastase from the pancreas, and spleen cathepsin D (not derived from endoderm) exert remarkably similar actions on the peptide bonds of the B chain of oxidized insulin, whereas trypsin attacks the chain quite differently.

These links, and other evidence, have caused the author to speculate (138, 139) that there is, or was, a primitive gut proteinase and that pyloric pepsin (pepsin 5) and the pepsin of the upper duodenum may have differentiated from this by the acquisition of a second active center. Fundic pepsin (pepsin 3) would, on this hypothesis, have arisen from a further differential step. Such a simple hypothesis is already outdated by the discovery of further pepsins and by evidence from the author's laboratory (Etherington and Taylor, unpublished observations) that three acid cathepsins exist in human intestinal mucosa, one of which exhibits weak maximal activity near pH 2 as well as near pH 3.5. The evolutionary and developmental links between the gut enzymes are thus not yet clear, but it seems reasonable to seek such links because the data of Table 3 are not sufficiently random to permit the alternative hypothesis that each of these enzymes has arisen de novo and individually.

REFERENCES

1. AKERMAN, J. H. Experimentelle Beiträge zur Kenntniss des Pylorussecretes beim Hunde. *Skand. Arch. Physiol.* 5: 134–149, 1894.

2. ARNON, R., AND G. E. PERLMANN. The amino-acid composition of chromatographically purified pepsin. *J. Biol. Chem.* 238: 653–656, 1963.

3. BAKER, L. E. The kinetics of the action of pepsin on synthetic substrates. *J. Biol. Chem.* 211: 700–716, 1954.

4. BANG, I. Pepsin and chymosin. *Z. Physiol. Chem.* 54: 359–362, 1908.

5. BEAUMONT, W. *Experiments and Observations on the Gastric Juice and Physiology of Digestion.* Plattsburg, N. Y.: Allen, 1833.

6. BENDERSKY, J. Über die Auscheidung der Verdauungsfermente aus dem Organismus bei gesunden und Dranken Menschen. *Arch. Pathol. Anat. Physiol.* 121: 554–597, 1890.

7. BENSLEY, R. R. The structure of the mammalian gastric glands. *Quart. J. Microscop. Sci.* 41: 361–389, 1898.

8. BERRIDGE, N. J. The purification and crystallisation of rennin. *Biochem. J.* 39: 179–186, 1945.

9. BLUMENFELD, O. O., AND G. E. PERLMANN. The amino-acid composition of crystalline pepsin. *J. Gen. Physiol.* 42: 553–561, 1959.

10. BOVEY, F. A., AND S. S. YANARI. Pepsin, In: The Enzymes (2nd. ed.), edited by P. D. Boyer, H, A. Lardy, and K. Myrback. New York: Acad. Press, 1960, vol. 4, p. 63–92.

11. BOVEY, F. A., AND S. S. YANARI. Quoted in ref. 49.

12. BRAND, E. Quoted in ref. 89.

13. BRÜCKE, E. VON. Die Verdauende Substanz im Urin. *Sitzber. Deut. Akad. Wiss. Math. Nat.* 43: 618, 1861.

14. BRÜCKE, E. VON. *Vorlesungen über Physiologie* (2nd ed.).: Braumüller, 1875, vol. 1, p. 299.

15. BUCHS, S. *Die Biologie des Magenkathepsins.* New York: Karger, 1947.

16. COLTER, J. S., J. KUHN, AND K. A. O. ELLEN. The ribonucleases of mouse ascites tumours. *Cancer Res.* 21: 48–51, 1961.

17. CONTEJEAN, C. Sur la sécrétion pylorique du chien. *Compt. Rend. Soc. Biol.* 5: 620–622, 1893.

18. DESREUX, V., AND R. M. HERRIOTT. Existence of several active components in crude pepsin preparations. *Nature* 144: 287–288, 1939.

19. DIEU, H. Quoted in ref. 49.

20. DIXON, M., AND E. C. WEBB. *Enzymes* (2nd. ed.). London: Longmans, Green, 1964.

21. EBSTEIN, W., AND P. GRÜTZNER. Über Pepsinbilding im Magen. *Arch. Ges. Physiol.* 8: 122–151, 1874.

22. EDELHOCH, H. The denaturation of pepsin. Macromolecular changes. *J. Am. Chem. Soc.* 79: 6100–6102, 1957.

23. EFFRONT, J. *Biochemical Catalysts in Life and Industry*, translated by S. C. Prescott. New York: Wiley, 1917.

24. ERLANGER, B. F., S. M. VRATSANOS, N. WASSERMANN, AND A. G. COOPER. A chemical investigation of the active center of pepsin. *Biochem. Biophys. Res. Commun.* 23: 243–245, 1966.

24a. ETHERINGTON, D. J., AND W. H. TAYLOR. Nomenclature of the pepsins. *Nature* 216: 279–280, 1967.

25. FENGER, F., R. H. ANDREW, AND A. W. RALSTON. On the isoelectric precipitation of pepsin. *J. Biol. Chem.* 80: 187–190, 1928.

26. FISH, J. C. Activity and specificity of rennin. *Nature* 180: 345, 1957.

27. FLAVIN, M. The linkage of phosphate to protein in pepsin and ovalbumin. *J. Biol. Chem.* 210: 771–784, 1954.

28. FOSTER, M. *A Textbook of Physiology* (2nd ed.). London: Macmillan, 1877.

29. FRATTALI, V., R. F. STEINER, AND H. EDELHOCH. Native and unfolded states of pepsinogen. *J. Biol. Chem.* 240: 112–127, 1965.

30. FREUDENBERG, E. Über das Kathepsin des Magens. *Enzymologia* 8: 385–391, 1940.

31. FRUTON, J. S., AND M. BERGMANN. The specificity of pepsin. *J. Biol. Chem.* 127: 627–641, 1939.

32. FULTON, J. F. *Selected Readings in the History of Physiology.* Springfield, Ill.: Thomas, 1930.

33. GILMOUR, D. Activity in relation to pH of myosin-5'-nucleotidase. *Nature* 186: 295–298, 1960.

34. GLAESSNER, K. Über die örtliche Verbreitung der Profermente in der Magenschleimhaut. *Beitr. Chem. Physiol. Pathol.* 1: 24–33, 1902.

35. GOTTLIEB, E. Über die Propepsinmengen im Blut und Harn. *Skand. Arch. Physiol.* 46: 1–50, 1925.

36. GROSS, E., AND J. L. MORRELL. Evidence for an active carboxyl group in pepsin. *J. Biol. Chem.* 241: 3638–3639, 1966.

37. HAMMARSTEN, O. Studien über Chymosin und Pepsinwirkung. *Z. Physiol. Chem.* 130: 55–71, 1923.

38. HANKINSON, C. L. The preparation of crystalline rennin. *J. Dairy Sci.* 26: 53–62, 1943.

39. HANLEY, W. B. *Hereditary Aspects of Duodenal Ulcer* (M.D. thesis). Liverpool: Univ. of Liverpool, 1963.

40. HANLEY, W. B., S. H. BOYER, AND M. A. NAUGHTON. Electrophoretic and functional heterogeneity of pepsinogen in several species. *Nature* 209: 996–1002, 1966.

41. HARINGTON, C. R., AND R. V. PITT-RIVERS. The synthesis of cysteine-(cystine-) tyrosine peptides and the action thereon of crystalline pepsin. *Biochem. J.* 38: 417–423, 1944.

42. HARVEY, B. C. H. A study of the structure of the gastric glands of the dog and of the changes which they undergo after gastroenterostomy and occlusion of the pylorus. *Am. J. Anat.* 6: 207–243, 1907.

43. HEIDENHAIN, R. Über die Pepsinbildung in den Pylorusdrüsen. *Arch. Ges. Physiol.* 18: 169–171, 1878.

44. HEIRWEGH, K., AND P. EDMAN. Purification and N-terminal

determination of crystalline pepsin. *Biochim. Biophys. Acta* 24: 219–220, 1957.

45. HERRIOTT, R. M. Inactivation of pepsin by iodine and the isolation of di-iodotyrosine from iodinated pepsin. *J. Gen. Physiol.* 20: 335–352, 1937.

46. HERRIOTT, R. M. Isolation, crystallization and properties of swine pepsinogen. *J. Gen. Physiol.* 21: 501–540, 1938.

47. HERRIOTT, R. M. Kinetics of the formation of pepsin from swine pepsinogen and identification of an intermediate compound. *J. Gen. Physiol.* 22: 65–78, 1938.

48. HERRIOTT, R. M. Isolation, crystallization and properties of pepsin inhibitor. *J. Gen. Physiol.* 24: 325–338, 1941.

49. HERRIOTT, R. M. Pepsinogen and pepsin. *J. Gen. Physiol.* 45: 57–76, 1962.

50. HERRIOTT, R. M., M. L. ANSON, AND J. H. NORTHROP. Reaction of enzymes and proteins with mustard gas. *J. Gen. Physiol.* 30: 185–210, 1946.

51. HERRIOTT, R. M., V. DESREUX, AND J. H. NORTHROP. Fractionation of pepsin. *J. Gen. Physiol.* 24: 213–246, 1940–1941.

52. HERRIOTT, R. M., AND J. H. NORTHROP. Crystalline acetyl derivatives of pepsin. *J. Gen. Physiol.* 18: 35–67, 1934.

53. HERRIOTT, R. M., AND J. H. NORTHROP. Isolation of crystalline pepsinogen from swine gastric mucosae and its autocatalytic conversion to pepsin. *Science* 83: 469–470, 1936.

54. HIRSCH-MARIE, H., P. BURTIN, AND M. CONTE. Etude électrophorétique et immuno-électrophorétique des enzymes protéolytiques du suc gastrique normal et pathologique. *Acta Gastro-Enterol. Belg.* 28: 373–381, 1965.

55. HIRSCHOWITZ, B. I. Pepsinogen in the blood. *J. Lab. Clin. Med.* 46: 568–579, 1955.

56. HOCH, H. Electrophoretic heterogeneity of crystallized pepsin. *Nature* 165: 278–279, 1950.

57. HOLTER, H., AND K. LINDERSTRØM-LANG. The distribution of pepsin in the gastric mucosa. *Compt. Rend. Trav. Lab. Carlsberg* 20: 1–23, 1935.

58. IHRE, B. Human gastric secretion: quantitative study of gastric secretion in normal and pathological conditions. *Acta Med. Scand. Suppl.* 95: 1–226, 1938.

59. IVY, A. C., AND Y. OYAMA. Studies on the secretion of the pars pylorica gastri. *Am. J. Physiol.* 57: 51–60, 1921.

60. JACKSON, W. T., M. SCHLAMOWITZ, AND A. SHAW. Kinetics of the pepsin-catalysed hydrolysis of N-acetyl-L-phenyl-alanyl-L-di-iodotyrosine. *Biochemistry* 4: 1537–1543, 1965.

61. JENNINGS, M. A., AND H. W. FLOREY. The influence of the vagus on the secretion of mucus by the stomach. *Quart. J. Exptl. Physiol.* 30: 329–339, 1940.

62. JIRGENSONS, B. Optical rotation and viscosity of native and denatured proteins. *Arch. Biochem. Biophys.* 74: 70–83, 1958.

63. KATCHALSKI, E., A. BERGER, AND H. NEUMANN. Reversible inhibition of pepsin by polylysine. *Nature* 173: 998–999, 1954.

64. KERN, H. L. Quoted from ref. 49.

65. KRONMAN, M. J., AND M. D. STERN. A light scattering investigation of the molecular weight of pepsin. *J. Phys. Chem.* 59: 969–973, 1955.

66. KUSHNER, I., W. RAPP, AND P. BURTIN. Electrophoretic and immunochemical demonstration of the existence of four human pepsinogens. *J. Clin. Invest.* 43: 1983–1993, 1964.

67. LANGLEY, J. N. On the destruction of ferments in the alimentary canal. *J. Physiol., London* 3: 246–268, 1882.

68. LEE, D., AND A. P. RYLE. Pepsinogen D, a zymogen from pig gastric mucosa. *Biochem. J.* 87: 44P, 1963.

69. LEES, F., AND F. D. ROSENTHAL. Gastric mucosal lesions before and after treatment in iron-deficiency anaemia. *Quart. J. Med.* 27: 19–26, 1958.

70. LEVCHUK, T. P., M. I. LEVYANT, AND V. N. OREKHOVICH. The specific action of chicken pepsin and a new "acid" cathepsin from hog kidney on protein substrates. *Biokhimiya* 30: 986–992, 1965.

71. LEVCHUK, T. P., AND V. N. OREKHOVICH. Production and some properties of chick pepsin. *Biokhimiya* 28: 1004–1010, 1963.

72. LEVIN, S. J., AND O. BODANSKY. The double pH-optimum of 5′-nucleotidase of bull seminal plasma. *J. Biol. Chem.* 241: 51–56, 1966.

73. LEVVY, G. A., AND C A. MARSH. Preparation and properties of β-glucuronidase. *Advan. Carbohydrate Chem.* 14: 381–428, 1959.

74. LI, C. H. Hormones of the anterior pituitary gland. *Advan. Protein Chem.* 11: 101–190, 1956.

75. LINDERSTRØM-LANG, K., H. HOLTER, AND A. S. OHLSEN. Studies on enzymatic histo-chemistry. XIII. The distribution of enzymes in the stomach of pigs as a function of its histological structure. *Compt. Rend. Trav. Lab. Carlsberg* 20: 66–116, 1933–1935.

76. LOKSHINA, L. A., AND V. N. OREKHOVICH. The significance of certain amino-acid residues in the pepsin molecule for its enzymic activity. *Biochemistry* 29: 300–305, 1964.

77. LUERS, H., AND J. BADER. Über die Reinigung des Chymosins. *Biochem. Z.* 190: 122–142, 1927.

78. LUNDSTEEN, E. Über das Reaktionsoptimum des Chymosins. *Biochem. Z.* 271: 259–263, 1934.

79. MAGNUS, H. A., AND C. C. UNGLEY. The gastric lesion in pernicious anaemia. *Lancet* 1: 420–421, 1938.

80. MATTHES, M. Über die Herkunft der Fermente im Urin. *Arch. Exptl. Pathol. Pharmakol.* 49: 107–113, 1903.

81. MERTEN, R., G. SCHRAMM, W. GRASSMANN, AND K. HANNIG. Untersuchungen zur Reindarstellung des Magenkathepsins. *Z. Physiol. Chem.* 289: 173–187, 1952.

82. MILHAUD, D., AND J. EPINEY. Etude physico-chimique et clinique des deux protéases du suc gastrique. *Gastro-enterologia* 77: 193–230, 1951.

83. MIRSKY, A., P. FLUTTERMAN, S. KAPLAN, AND R. H. BROH-KAHN. Plasma pepsinogen, the source, properties and assay. *J. Lab. Clin. Med.* 40: 17–26, 1952.

84. MORRISSEY, S. Chloride ions in the secretion of the pitcher plant. *Nature* 176: 1220–1221, 1955.

85. NAUGHTON, M. A., AND F. SANGER. The action of elastase on the B chain of insulin. *Biochem. J.* 70: 4P, 1958.

86. NORRIS, E., AND E. ELAM. Preparation and properties of crystalline salmon pepsin. *J. Biol. Chem.* 134: 443–453, 1940.

87. NORTHROP, J. H. Crystalline pepsin: isolation and tests of purity. *J. Gen. Physiol.* 13: 739–780, 1929–1930.

88. NORTHROP, J. H. Presence of gelatin liquefying enzyme in crude pepsin preparations. *J. Gen. Physiol.* 15: 29–43, 1932.

89. NORTHROP, J. H., M. KUNITZ, AND R. M. HERRIOTT. *Crystalline Enzymes* (2nd ed.). New York: Columbia Univ., 1948.

90. Orekhovich, V. N., L. A. Lokshina, V. A. Mant'ev, and O. V. Troitskaya. Quoted in ref. 49.

91. Pavlov, I. P., and S. W. Parastschuk. Über die ein und demselben Eiweissfermente zukommende proteolische und Milchkoagulierende Wirkung verschiedener Verdauungssafte. Z. Physiol. Chem. 42: 415–452, 1904.

92. Pekelharing, C. A. Über eine neue Bereitungsweise des Pepsins. Z. Physiol. Chem. 22: 233–244, 1896.

93. Pekelharing, C. A. Über die Frage, ob neben dem Pepsin ein anderes Enzym, Chymosin, anzunehmen ist. Arch. Ges. Physiol. 167: 254–266, 1917.

94. Penitschka, W. Experimentelle Untersuchungen über die zweite Magenproteinase Kathepsin. Arch. Klin. Chir. 273: 904–911, 1953.

95. Perlmann, G. E. The nature of phosphorus linkages in phosphoproteins. Advan. Protein Chem. 10: 1–30, 1955.

96. Perlmann, G. E. Effects of solvents and of temperature on the optical rotary properties of pepsin. Proc. Natl. Acad. Sci. U.S. 45: 915–922, 1959.

97. Perlmann, G. E. Acetylation of pepsin and pepsinogen. J. Biol. Chem. 241: 153–157, 1966.

98. Pfisterer, H. G. Kathepsin und pepsin nach Magenresektion und Gastrektomie. Arch. Klin. Chir. 280: 123–142, 1955.

99. Philpot, J. St. L., and I. B. Ericksson-Quensel. An ultracentrifugal study of crystalline pepsin. Nature 132: 932–933, 1933.

100. Philpot, J. St. L., and P. A. Small. Quoted in ref. 140.

101. Philpot, J. St. L., and P. A. Small. The action of nitrous acid on p-cresol and tyrosine. Biochem. J. 32: 534–541, 1938.

102. Potts, J. T., A. Berger, J. Cooke, and C. B. Anfinsen. A re-investigation of the sequence of residues 11 to 18 in bovine pancreatic ribonuclease. J. Biol. Chem. 237: 1851–1855, 1962.

103. Press, E. M., R. R. Porter, and J. Cebra. The isolation and properties of a proteolytic enzyme, cathepsin D, from bovine spleen. Biochem. J. 74: 501–514, 1960.

104. Previero, A., M. A. Coletti, and L. Galzigna. Modification of tryptophan residues in trypsin, α-chymotrypsin and pepsinogen. Biochem. Biophys. Res. Commun. 16: 195–198, 1964.

105. Ramer, Z. Activation of pepsin and cathepsin by potassium cyanide and hydrogen sulphide. Z. Physiol. Chem. 296: 73–78, 1954.

106. Ringer, W. E. Weitere Studien am Pekelharingschen Pepsin. Z. Physiol. Chem. 95: 195–258, 1915.

107. Ryle, A. P. Parapepsinogen II: the zymogen of parapepsin II. Biochem. J. 75: 145–150, 1960.

108. Ryle A. P. Pepsinogen B: the zymogen of pepsin B. Biochem. J. 96: 6–16, 1965.

109. Ryle, A. P., and M. P. Hamilton. Pepsinogen C and pepsin C. Biochem. J. 101: 176–183, 1966.

110. Ryle, A. P., and R. R. Porter. Parapepsins; two proteolytic enzymes associated with porcine pepsin. Biochem. J. 73: 75–86, 1959.

111. Sanger, F., and E. O. P. Thompson. The amino-acid sequence in the glycyl chain of insulin. II. The investigation of peptides from enzymic hydrolysates. Biochem. J. 53: 366–374, 1953.

112. Sanger, F., and H. Tuppy. The amino-acid sequence in the phenylalanyl chain of insulin. I. The investigation of

113. Saxl, P. Über das Vorkommen und den Nachweis von Pepsin im Blutserum. Wien. Med. Wochschr. 65: 458, 1915.

114. Schlamowitz, M., and L. U. Peterson. The effect of sodium chloride on peptic digestion of bovine serum albumin. Biochim. Biophys. Acta 46: 381–383, 1961.

115. Schrumpf, P. Darstellung des Pepsinfermentes aus Magenpressaft. Hofmeister's Beitr. 6: 396–397, 1905.

116. Schwann, T. Über das Wesen des Verdauung-sporzen. Müller's Arch. Anat. Physiol. p. 90, 1836.

117. Seijffers, M. J., H. L. Segal, and L. L. Miller. Separation of pepsinogen I, pepsinogen II and pepsinogen III from human gastric mucosa. Am. J. Physiol. 205: 1099–1105, 1963.

118. Seijffers, M. J., H. L. Segal, and L. L. Miller. Separation of pepsin I, pepsin II A, pepsin II B, and pepsin III from human gastric mucosa. Am. J. Physiol. 205: 1106–1112, 1963.

119. Smyth, D. G., W. H. Stein, and S. Moore. On the sequence of residues 11 to 18 in bovine pancreatic ribonuclease. J. Biol. Chem. 237: 1845–1850, 1962.

120. Sørensen, S. P. L. Enzymstudien. Biochem. Z. 21: 131–304, 1909.

121. Sprissler, G. P. An Investigation of the Proteinase of the Gastric Mucosa of the Shark. Washington, D.C.: Catholic Univ. of America Press, 1942.

122. Stepanov, V. M., and T. I. Greil. Determination of C-terminal amino-acids of hog pepsin. Biochemistry 28: 437–441, 1963.

123. Stepanov, V. M., T. I. Vaganova, and Y. S. Kuznetsov. Estimation of the N-terminal acids of hog pepsin. Biochemistry 29: 529–533, 1963.

124. Stepanov, V. M., E. A. Vakhitova, C. A. Egorov, and S. M. Avaeva. Sequence of animo-acid residues surrounding the phosphoserine residue in hog pepsin. Biochim. Biophys. Acta 110: 632–634, 1965.

125. Sundberg, C. Ein Beitrag zur Kenntniss der Pepsine. Z. Physiol. Chem. 9: 319–322, 1885.

126. Takata, M. Studies in the gastric juice. IV. The pyloric juice. J. Biochem., Tokyo 2: 33–42, 1923.

127. Takeda, K. Über das Harnpepsin, als differential-diagnostiche Kriterium zwischen carcinoma ventriculi und apepsia gastrica. Deut. Med. Wochschr. 36: 1807–1810, 1910.

128. Tang, J., and K. I. Tang. Purification and properties of a zymogen from human gastric mucosa. J. Biol. Chem. 238: 606–612, 1963.

129. Tang, J., S. Wolf, R. Caputto, and R. E. Trucco. Isolation and crystallization of gastricsin from human gastric juice. J. Biol. Chem. 234: 1174–1178, 1959.

130. Tauber, H. Chemistry & Technology of Enzymes. New York: Wiley, 1949.

131. Tauber, H., and I. S. Kleiner. Studies on rennin. I. The purification of rennin and its separation from pepsin. J. Biol. Chem. 96: 745–753, 1932.

132. Taylor, W. H. Studies on gastric proteolysis. I. The proteolytic activity of human gastric juice and pig and calf gastric mucosal extracts below pH 5. Biochem. J. 71: 73–83, 1959.

133. Taylor, W. H. Studies on gastric proteolysis. II. The nature of the enzyme-substrate interaction responsible

for gastric proteolytic pH-activity curves with two maxima. *Biochem. J.* 71: 373–383, 1959.

134. TAYLOR, W. H. Studies on gastric proteolysis. III. The secretion of different pepsins by fundic and pyloric glands of the stomach. *Biochem. J.* 71: 384–388, 1959.

135. TAYLOR, W. H. Gastric proteolysis in disease. I. The proteolytic activity of gastric juice from patients with pernicious anaemia. *J. Clin. Pathol.* 12: 210–214, 1959.

136. TAYLOR, W. H. Gastric proteolysis in disease. II. The proteolytic activity of gastric juice and gastric mucosal extracts from patients with chronic gastric and duodenal ulcer. *J. Clin. Pathol.* 12: 338–343, 1959.

137. TAYLOR, W. H. Gastric proteolysis in disease. III. The proteolytic activity of gastric juice in chronic hypochromic anaemia and in idiopathic steatorrhoea. *J. Clin. Pathol.* 12: 473–476, 1959.

138. TAYLOR, W. H. Aspects of the mechanism of action of gastrointestinal proteinases. *Bull. Soc. Chim. Biol.* 42: 1313–1318, 1960.

139. TAYLOR, W. H. Proteinases of the stomach in health and disease. *Physiol. Rev.* 42: 519–553, 1962.

140. TISELIUS, A., G. E. HENSCHEN, AND H. SVENSSON. Electrophoresis of pepsin. *Biochem. J.* 32: 1814–1818, 1938.

141. URIEL, J. The direct detection of proteolytic enzymes after electrophoresis in agar gel. *Nature* 188: 853–854, 1960.

142. VAN CALCAR, R. P. Über die physiologisch-pathologische Bedeutung der weissen Blut-Korperchen. *Arch. Ges. Physiol.* 148: 257–263, 1912.

143. VAN HASSELT, J. F. B. Notiz zur Pepsin-Chymosinfrage. *Z. Physiol. Chem.* 70: 171–185, 1911.

144. VAN VUNAKIS, H., AND R. M. HERRIOTT. Structural changes associated with the conversion of pepsinogen to pepsin. I. The N-terminal amino-acid residue and amino-acid composition of pepsin inhibitor. *Biochim. Biophys. Acta* 22: 537–543, 1956.

145. VAN VUNAKIS, H., AND R. M. HERRIOTT. Structural changes associated with the conversion of pepsinogen to pepsin. II. The N-terminal amino-acid residues of pepsin and pepsinogen. *Biochim. Biophys. Acta* 23: 600–608, 1959.

146. VARRO, M. T. *On Farming* (36 B.C.), translated by L. Storr-Best. London: Bell, 1912.

147. WASSMANN. *De digestione nonnulla.* Berolini, 1839, quoted in ref. 34.

148. WILLIAMSON, M. B., AND J. M. PASSMANN. The amino-acid sequence at the N-terminus of pepsin. *J. Biol. Chem.* 222: 151–157, 1956.

CHAPTER 121

Peptidases of the small intestine

JAMES B. RHODES | *Departments of Medicine and Physiology, University of Kansas Medical Center, Kansas City, Kansas*

CHAPTER CONTENTS

PEPTIDASES ARE ENZYMES that hydrolyze peptide bonds
$$(R-\overset{\overset{\text{O}}{\|}}{C}-\overset{\overset{\text{H}}{|}}{N}-R')$$
of proteins and polypeptides where R and R′ are amino acids or peptides. The best known peptidases are those secreted by the pancreas. Many mammalian tissues contain a number of intracellular peptidases, some in high concentration with relatively high activity. Some of these peptidases are labile and consequently difficult to isolate.

Peptidases have been divided into two subgroups (9). Endopeptidases (proteinases) hydrolyze peptide bonds within protein molecules as well as certain model peptides that are commonly used as substrates; an example is the intestinal endopeptidase activity that hydrolyzes hemoglobin (54). Exopeptidases hydrolyze *N*-terminal or carboxy-terminal amino acids from peptides and some proteins; examples are the intestinal amino-, tri-, and dipeptidases. Certain poly-, tri-, and dipeptides are used for their determination (115, 116).

The small-intestine intracellular peptidases appear to be numerous, but none has been obtained in a homogeneous state comparable to the crystalline pancreatic peptidases. Their specific properties remain to be reliably determined. However, considerable information about their properties has been obtained from relatively crude preparations. It is possible that some of the reported activities may be due to the same enzyme. Many other small-intestinal enzymes have been reviewed (125).

FUNCTIONS

The first recognized function of a peptidase was the digestion of dietary protein by secreted pancreatic endopeptidases. Other peptidases are involved in blood clotting and lysis, and some release hypertensive or hypotensive peptides from proteins. A number of intracellular endopeptidases (cathepsins) are associated with other acid hydrolyases in lysosomes. Some peptidases, such as aminopeptidases and dipeptidases, have been substantially purified and characterized but have unknown functions.

The biological functions of small-intestine intracellular peptidases have not been elucidated. Most frequently mentioned functions are: *1*) digestive hydrolysis, *2*) peptide or protein synthesis, and *3*) intracellular catabolism of native or foreign proteins.

1. It is now evident that some peptidases of the intestinal epithelial cell must be involved in terminal endogenous and exogenous protein digestion at the peptide level. Peptides are the primary hydrolytic products of the pancreatic endopeptidases (5, 49, 101) and have been demonstrated in vivo in the intestinal lumen (16, 26, 30). These peptides rapidly disappear from the lumen (20, 26, 91) and are not found in any significant amounts in the portal or mesenteric veins (17, 30, 70) nor in homogenates of intestinal epithelial cells (27). Free amino acids predominate in the portal and mesenteric veins (17, 30, 70) and in intestinal epithelial cells (27). In man ^{15}N-labeled peptides rapidly disappear from the lumen in subjects with pancreatic insufficiency or in whom the pancreas has been surgically removed (27). Therefore peptide hydrolysis is quite rapid and primarily occurs at the level of the epithelial cell. Current evidence, based mainly on the hydrolysis of glycylglycine, suggests that this hydrolytic process occurs within the epithelial cell rather than at the membrane surface of the microvilli (86).

It has been suggested that intestinal endopeptidases (cathepsins) may be involved in the processes of nutritional protein digestion by pinocytosis (54). Although this mechanism is present in some cells, there is little evidence that this process is nutritionally important in the intestine of adult mammals. However, it has been shown that some proteins (such as albumin, for example) are considerably hydrolyzed by isolated loops of small intestine. In addition, patients with pancreatic insufficiency or pancreatectomy can appreciably digest protein, but this digestion is nutritionally insufficient (20, 92). It is probable that intracellular endopeptidases do contribute to protein digestion. Since pinocytotic vesicles are not common in

adults, perhaps endopeptidases are liberated during normal epithelial cell turnover and are active in the lumen.

The overall process of protein digestion has been reviewed (47).

2. Some peptidases might be involved in synthetic reactions that must be very active to account for the rapid turnover of the intestinal epithelium (69, 72, 84). A number of peptidases can form peptide bonds, including the well-characterized digestive endopeptidases secreted by the pancreas. Current concepts of protein synthesis make these synthetic reactions of uncertain biological significance (76).

Certain peptidases might be involved in other steps of protein synthesis where the mechanisms are not well understood. For example, *N*-terminal formyl-methionine is common in protein synthesis in *Escherichia coli*, but is seldom found in the released protein (105). In addition a peptidase is present in *E. coli* ribosomes (75). Hence a peptidase that liberates *N*-terminal formyl-methionine may have a role in protein synthesis in *E. coli*. Peptidases could be involved in the synthesis of peptide bonds or might release the completed polypeptide chain from the ribosome at the carboxy-terminal end. They might also be involved in the formation of complete proteins from the newly synthesized polypeptide chains (63). However, there is no current evidence that peptidases participate in protein synthesis.

3. Perhaps other intestinal peptidases are involved in protein catabolism or hydrolyze foreign proteins that have entered the cell. These intracellular endopeptidases are associated with other acid hydrolyases in isolated lysosomes from the liver (29) and kidney (133) and could degrade plasma proteins to provide endogenous amino acids for essential protein synthesis. De Duve & Wattiaux (29) have recently and extensively reviewed the lysosome concept.

ENDOPEPTIDASES

An endopeptidase that hydrolyzes hemoglobin at pH 3.8 in acetate buffer has been reported in intestinal homogenates. Mucosal scrapings were briefly homogenized in 0.25 M sucrose and fractionated by differential centrifugation with a procedure designed for the liver. The specific activity of the whole intestinal homogenate was 20% greater than that of the liver. The activity was associated to some extent with other acid hydrolyases, suggesting an association with lysosomes. The rather broad distribution of the acid

TABLE 1. *Rat Small-Intestine Enzymes in Mucosal Fractions*

Fraction Precipitate	Recovered Activity, %			
	Cathep-sin	Aryl sulfat-ase*	Acid phos-phatase*	Alkaline phos-phatase†
480 × g for 10 min	24	33	31	16
5,000 × g for 10 min	33	38	39	20
16,000 × g for 20 min	18	12	11	17
30,000 × g for 30 min	11	3	7	13
100,000 × g for 60 min	1	5	10	3
Supernatant	4	24	19	3
Total Recovery	91	115	117	83

* Aryl sulfatase and acid phosphatase are primarily associated with lysosomes.

† Alkaline phosphatase is primarily associated with microvillus membranes.

From Hsu & Tappel (54).

hydrolyases led the authors to postulate considerable variation in the size of lysosomes. The endopeptidase activity was 95% localized to particulate fractions. About 33% of the total activity resided in a "heavy mitochondrial" fraction [(54); Table 1].

This endopeptidase activity was subsequently determined along the length of the gastrointestinal tract in whole homogenates. The highest activity was present in the stomach, which the authors attributed to gastric pepsin. The activity in the small intestine was less than that in the colon. Four other acid hydrolyases were determined in the colon superficial mucosa, deep mucosa, and muscle coat. The deep mucosal layer was most active, whereas the superficial mucosa contained the lesser activity (55). This distribution would be unusual for digestive function (97).

Catheptic Endopeptidases in Other Tissues

Five different endopeptidases have been described in extracts from other tissues. The cathepsins are a general group of endopeptidases and, except for purified cathepsin C, hydrolyze denatured hemoglobin or serum albumin or both. They also hydrolyze certain model peptides that are also split by pancreatic endopeptidases. Cathepsins can be more thoroughly characterized by their hydrolysis of the isolated alpha or beta insulin chains and identification of the resulting peptides (23, 94, 102, 103).

Cathepsin A is a labile enzyme and hydrolyzes benzylcarbonyl-*l*-glutamyl-*l*-tyrosine at the glutamyl-tyrosine bond. The activity is maximal at pH 5.7 and is not enhanced by sulfhydryl compounds (71).

Cathepsin B deamidates benzoyl-*l*-argininamide or hydrolyzes the ester (esterase) at pH 5.0 and is enhanced by sulfhydryl compounds. The activity is inhibited by phenylhydrazine (39). Cathepsin B has been purified 150-fold from beef spleen (43).

Cathepsin C deamidates glycyl-*l*-tyrosinamide at pH 5, is enhanced by sulfhydryl compounds, and contains esterase activity. In contrast to other cathepsins, this is relatively a heat-stable enzyme, and more highly purified preparations do not hydrolyze denatured hemoglobin. The hydrolytic reactions with dipeptide amides occur most rapidly with substrates containing a relatively small *N*-terminal amino acid such as glycine, *l*-alanine, or *l*-serine in peptide linkage with aromatic amino acids such as *l*-phenylalanine, *l*-tyrosine, or *l*-tryptophan. At pH 7.5 this enzyme can catalyze the formation of polypeptides from dipeptide amides, such as glycyl-*l*-phenylalaninamide, into a 6- or 8-amino acid-containing polypeptide in which *N*-terminal glycine is attached to the carboxy-terminal phenylalanine with loss of the terminal amide. Metrione et al. (79) have recently proposed that this activity is the biological function for cathepsin C in spleen, which is therefore a dipeptidyl transferase.

Cathepsin D was highly purified from extracts of hog spleen and accounted for two-thirds of the total catheptic activity. This preparation hydrolyzed denatured hemoglobin maximally at pH 3.5 and was not enhanced by cysteine. This enzyme did not hydrolyze the substrates commonly used for the determination of cathepsins A, B, or C. Denatured hemoglobin was hydrolyzed 40 times as rapidly as denatured serum albumin, which was maximally split at pH 4.2. Partially purified preparations could be chromatographically separated into ten different fractions. Some characteristics of all active fractions were similar, and evidence was presented that this activity was not an artifact of preparation (94).

In 1962 apparently another acid cathepsin was separated from cathepsins A, B, C, and D from bovine spleen preparations. Cathepsin E in the spleen had a relatively low activity. This enzyme hydrolyzed denatured hemoglobin maximally at pH 2.5 and was not enhanced by cysteine, but was enhanced by cysteine at pH 3.5–4.5. Bone marrow and polymorphonuclear leukocytes contained high activity whereas lymphocytes contained relatively low activity (67). Table 2 summarizes some of these characteristics of the five known cathepsins.

In the liver, cathepsins B and C are reported to be associated with the lysosomal fraction (13).

TABLE 2. *Some Properties of Intracellular Cathepsins*

Cathepsin	Usual Substrate	pH Optimum	Effect of Heat	Sulfhydryl Effect	Ref.
A	Carbobenzoxy-*l*-glutamyl-*l*-tyrosine	5.7	Labile	No enhancement	71
B	Benzoyl-*l*-argininamide	5.0	Labile	Activated	39
D	Denatured hemoglobin and serum albumin*	3.5	Labile	No enhancement	94
E	Denatured serum albumin*	2.5	Labile	No enhancement	67
C	Glycyl-*l*-tyrosinamide	5.0	Stable	Activated	79
	Dipeptidyl transferase	7.5		Activated	79

* Cathepsins D and E do not hydrolyze A, B, and C substrates.

If intestinal endopeptidase(s) are only associated with lysosomes, these endopeptidase(s) are likely to be associated with particles if the disruption methods are mild and likely to yield intact lysosomes. If the methods include steps that disrupt lysosomes (134), then the activity is more likely to be in the supernatant. The presence of an endopeptidase could result in destruction of itself or other enzymes and might result in a "labile" enzyme. A more acid pH would be expected to favor the activity. The further characterization of intestinal endopeptidases remains to be explored.

Enterokinase

Enterokinase is the intraluminal duodenal enzyme that can convert trypsinogen to tryspin. Kunitz purified this activity 4,000-fold on a dry-weight basis from hog duodenal contents (66, 68). The autocatalytic conversion of trypsinogen to active trypsin is due to liberation of the N-terminal hexapeptide Val-(Asp$_4$)-Lys, which leaves an N-terminal isoleucine (31). Trypsinogen activation by enterokinase also leaves an N-terminal isoleucine with the activated trypsin (141). Trypsinogen can also be converted to active trypsin by other enzymes such as a mold endopeptidase (31) and a cathepsin B preparation (43). The earlier literature has been reviewed (34).

Enterokinase was further purified 65-fold over Kunitz's preparation and appeared to be 80% pure. The activity was not destroyed by prolonged incubation with duodenal juice nor by an erepsin extract. The purified preparation contained some carbohydrate (142).

POLY-, TRI-, AND AMINOPEPTIDASES

Most reports on small-intestine peptidases encompass this group of enzymes.

In 1901 Cohnheim (18) reported peptidase activity in extracts of intestinal mucosa that he called erepsin. This report stimulated considerable interest that resulted in numerous investigations (132). By about 1930 it was evident that erepsin contained more than one peptidase (47). By 1942 it was clear that at least three peptidases were present in erepsin extracts (58), and by 1951 the number had increased to four or six (114). Subsequent attempts to further purify an aminopeptidase from erepsin extracts encountered problems of stability after a 30- to 90-fold purification was obtained (119). The purification of the intestinal aminopeptidase was abandoned when a 1,600-fold purification was obtained from hog kidney extracts (124). This enzyme, with some additional purification, has been extensively used in determining the amino acid content and sequence of peptides and proteins (50, 51). This success may partially account for the relatively few reports on intestinal peptidases since 1955. Interest in other peptidases such as the cathepsins, tripeptidase, and various dipeptidases continued but was primarily focused on tissues other than the intestine (115).

Intestinal amino-, tri-, and dipeptidases are generally most active at pH 7.0–10.0, are usually affected by certain divalent cations, and are frequently inhibited by metal-chelating agents.

Aminopolypeptidase

An aminopolypeptidase that hydrolyzes several tripeptides was characterized from extracts of hog small intestine in the late 1930s. This activity was extracted from fresh intestine and was absent in freeze-dried intestinal extracts. *dl*-Alanylglycylglycine was actively hydrolyzed whereas dipeptide hydrolysis was quite low. This preparation also hydrolyzed prolylglycylglycine and glycylglycylglycine at appreciable rates. N-methylalanylglycylglycine and sarcosylglycylglycine were also hydrolyzed but at lower rates. This preparation hydrolyzed some dipeptides such as *dl*-

alanylglycine, prolylglycine, and glycylglycine but at much slower rates. The hydrolysis of *dl*-leucylglycine was very low (57). Magnesium and zinc had no effect on the enzymatic activity (6, 39). The aminopolypeptidase was only slightly inhibited by 0.0025 M hydrogen sulfide and the ratios of peptide hydrolysis remained constant when the preparation was partially inactivated by five different methods (57). It was differentiated from the glycylglycinase as well as a leucylpeptidase (6, 40). This activity was shown to be present in small-intestine extracts of man, rat, hog, and chicken by Berger & Johnson (7, 58), who in 1942 reviewed the general area of peptidases.

Agren reported 100-fold purification of a similar activity from hog antral-duodenal mucosa. This activity hydrolyzed alanylglycylglycine 140 times as rapidly as alanylglycine. Activity was lost on dialysis and partially restored by incubating the inactivated enzyme in the dialysate. Manganese did not restore the activity. Activity was partially inhibited by copper acetate, cysteine, and pyrophosphate but not affected by 0.01 N cyanide (2, 3).

Tripeptidase

A somewhat similar enzyme, later designated a tripeptidase, was studied by another group. This preparation hydrolyzed alanylglycylglycine, leucylglycylglycine, glycylglycylglycine, and glycylglycylproline at the *N*-terminal amino acid. Leucylglycylglycine and glycylglycylglycine were hydrolyzed at about equal rates (118). Other di- and tripeptides were hydrolyzed at lower rates as were some di- and tripeptide amides. The activity did not require metal activation and was inhibited over 90% by 0.083 M cyanide (10). The activity was only slightly inhibited by 0.03 M phenylhydrazine, which markedly reduced the hydrolysis of leucylglycine. The activity appeared to be different from an aminopeptidase, for the hydrolyses of leucinamide, leucylglycine, and leucylglycylglycine were not parallel during the purification procedures (10). The results of this group of workers with this particular activity has been reviewed (114).

A somewhat similar enzyme has been purified about 1,000-fold from human erythrocytes. This enzyme hydrolyzed alanylglycylglycine, leucylglycylglycine, and glycylglycylglycine but not glycylglycine. Hydrolysis was maximal at pH 7.0. However, cobalt, magnesium, and zinc enhanced the activity whereas EDTA and cysteine were inhibitors (128).

Aminopeptidase

This activity hydrolyzes a wide variety of amino acid amides, some dipeptides and their diastereoisomers, and several dipeptide amides (120, 121, 123). It is present in extracts from fresh and dried intestine and withstands acetone and alcohol precipitation. One aminopeptidase (aminoexopeptidase) was purified 20- to 45-fold from the original erepsin extract and hydrolyzed leucinamide (45-fold), leucylglycine (35-fold), and leucylglycylglycine (20-fold) (119). The hydrolysis of glycylleucine, alanylglycine, and prolylglycine decreased during the purification procedures, but they were hydrolyzed at low rates. *d*-Leucylglycine and *N*-CBZ-leucylglycine were not hydrolyzed (118), nor were some cathepsin substrates (121). The activity was enhanced by manganese and magnesium and partially inactivated by cysteine after 3 hours of incubation (118) and probably inhibited by cyanide (10). Essentially no esterase activity was present at pH 8.5 (120).

An enzyme with similar characteristics has been purified 1,600- to 2,000-fold and more extensively characterized from hog kidney. It was estimated to be about 97.5% pure on electrophoresis and ultracentrifugation. Manganese activation resulted in first-order kinetics whereas magnesium activation resulted in zero-order kinetics. The activity was reduced by chelating agents and no transamidation was noted at pH 8.5 (51, 119, 122, 124).

Glycyldehydroalanine Hydrolysis

The hydrolysis of glycyldehydroalanine has been described in intestinal homogenates. This activity is widely distributed with comparable rates in many tissues (45). A similar enzyme preparation has been purified 2,000-fold from a hog kidney particulate fraction that hydrolyzes a large number of peptides and appears to be an aminopeptidase (96).

From these studies, one could conclude that there are at least two to four enzymes in intestinal mucosa that hydrolyze certain tripeptides. One enzyme does not require metal activation, is most active at pH 7.0–8.0, and hydrolyzes tripeptides with little or no activity on similar di- and tetrapeptides. Glycylglycylglycine is rapidly hydrolyzed. Another enzyme, probably the classic aminopeptidase, requires manganese or magnesium for maximal activity, is most active at pH 8.0–10.0, and hydrolyzes leucinamide, other aliphatic amino acid amides, and dipeptides, whereas glycylglycylglycine hydrolysis is absent or very low.

d-Leucylglycine and *N*-CBZ-leucylglycine are not hydrolyzed.

Cellular Localization

Rat brush borders isolated by density-gradient centrifugation contained 22 % of the total "aminotripeptidase" and 35 % of the total "aminopeptidase." The particulate-associated proteolytic activity was apparently not a brush-border enzyme (38).

DIPEPTIDASES

Another group of enzymes hydrolyzing certain dipeptides has been described in erepsin extracts. These activities include the primary hydrolysis of glycylglycine, prolylglycine (prolinase), glycylproline (prolidase), and β-alanylhistidine (carnosinase).

Glycylglycine Hydrolysis

A glycylglycine dipeptidase was most active in hydrolyzing glycylglycine, whereas sarcosylglycine was hydrolyzed at a slower rate and *N*-CBZ-glycylglycine was not hydrolyzed. Since this intestinal dipeptidase was unstable, it has not been further purified. This activity was enhanced by cobalt and to a lesser degree by manganese. Magnesium had no effect, and the activity was inhibited by cysteine. The activity was stabilized by 50–85 % glycerol (6, 40, 113).

TABLE 3. *Rat Intestinal Enzymes in Mucosal Fractions*

Fraction*	Total Activity, %				
	Protein	Leu-Gly	Gly-Gly	Alkaline phos-phatase†	Cyto-chrome ox-idase‡
Mucus	20	1	0	15	44
Mitochondrial	5	2	6	22	47
Microsomal	10	7	9	63	9
Supernatant	65	90	85	0	0
Total recovery	99	94	94	80	70

* Fractions examined by electron microscopy showed a predominance of the particular organelle with some contamination in all fractions.

† Alkaline phosphatase is primarily associated with brush borders.

‡ Cytochrome oxidase is associated with mitochondria in rat liver.

From Robinson (98).

TABLE 4. *Rat Small-Intestine Dipeptide Hydrolysis in Mucosal Fractions*

Fraction	Specific Activity, μmoles/min per mg		
	Leu-Gly pH 8.3	Gly-Gly pH 7.5*	Gly-Gly, pH 8.0*
Mucus	0.06	0	0
Mitochondrial	0.28	0.52	0.56
Microsomal	0.39	0.42	0.48
Supernatant	1.17	0.56	0.69

* In the presence of 1 mM cobalt.

From Robinson (98).

An enzyme from human uterus was more stable and had similar characteristics. Benzoylglycylglycine, glycylglycineamide, and benzoylglycylglycineamide were not hydrolzyed, and 0.01 M citrate had no effect (113).

Glycylglycine is hydrolyzed by supernatant fractions of intestinal homogenates from rat, pig, and sheep, and the activity is generally higher in the midportion of the small intestine (60, 98, 127). The activity of the small intestine is 5–8 times that of the colon (99), and mucosal cells hydrolyze glycylglycine 100 times more rapidly than the luminal contents (127).

Although there may be a single enzyme in small intestine that hydrolyzes glycylglycine only or maximally, it appears that other peptidases also hydrolyze this dipeptide, some at appreciable rates. The hydrolysis of glycylglycine by a crude intestinal erepsin extract is enhanced threefold by manganese in the presence of cysteine, which strongly inhibits glycylglycine dipeptidase (8). On the basis of tissue fractionation and pH curves, glycylglycine is hydrolyzed by at least two intestinal enzymes (97, 99). Of the total activity, 80–90 % is associated with the high-speed supernatant (Table 3), but the specific activities of the mitochondrial and microsomal fractions are comparable to that of the supernatant [(98); Table 4].

In the kidney, glycylglycine is hydrolyzed by three different highly purified peptidases. An aminopeptidase from hog kidney hydrolyzed glycylglycine slowly (119), whereas a particulate aminopeptidase and dipeptidase hydrolyzed it quite rapidly (15, 96). The dipeptidase, which was homogeneous on acrylamide-gel electrophoresis and ultracentrifugation, hydrolyzed 22 dipeptides at variable rates. Glycylglycine was the dipeptide most rapidly split and was hydrolyzed twice as fast as the next dipeptide, alanylglycine. Peptides not hydrolyzed included leucinamide, some common tripeptides, *d*-leucylglycine, and CBZ-glycyl-*l*-phenylalanine. Casein and hemoglobin likewise were not hydrolyzed. The enzyme contained 1 mole of zinc per mole of enzyme, but the activity on some substrates was enhanced by cobalt and magnesium and inhibited by cadmium and nickel. The authors concluded that this dipeptidase was not a specific glycylglycine dipeptidase since their more purified enzyme had different characteristics from those previously described with a cruder preparation (15).

It is clear that at least three kidney peptidases hydrolyze glycylglycine. At least two hydrolyze this dipeptide at appreciable rates. It appears that glycylglycine hydrolysis by crude homogenates would not identify a specific dipeptidase.

Prolidase (Glycylproline) Imidopeptidase

This activity hydrolyzes glycylproline, which does not have a free hydrogen at the peptide bond. The activity is low in most tissues, and a 30-fold purification has been obtained from intestinal extracts. The activity was stable to acetone and remained in the supernatant. Glycylhydroxyproline was hydrolyzed at about one-eighth the rate of glycylproline. Slight hydrolysis occurred with glycylalanine, leucylglycine, leucylglycylglycine, and prolinamide. No hydrolysis was noted with prolylglycine, glycylglycine, glycylleucine, or the N-CBZ derivatives of glycylproline and glycylhydroxyproline. Manganese enhanced the activity but magnesium had no effect, and cobalt, cadmium, and zinc were inhibitors (118). The activity was only slightly reduced by 0.083 M cyanide, which markedly reduced the hydrolysis of tripeptides and dl-leucylglycine (10).

A similar hog kidney enzyme has been purified 12,000-fold and estimated to be about 90 % pure. This activity was quite low in the whole kidney homogenate. The enzyme was more extensively characterized and had similar characteristics. Glutathione, 1 mM, stabilized the enzyme but higher concentrations inhibited it (25).

Prolylglycine (Prolinase) Iminopeptidase

Hydrolysis of prolylglycine was produced by intestinal extracts prepared from fresh specimens and not by extracts from freeze-dried intestine. A crude extract, free from glycylglycine, alanylglycine, and leucylglycine activity, hydrolyzed prolylglycine, d-leucylglycine, and dl-N-methylleucylglycine. The hydrolysis of the last three compounds was enhanced by manganese and cysteine, whereas cobalt inhibited it (8, 40).

A 30-fold purification of a similar activity was

obtained from hog kidney. The activity was labile but was stabilized by manganese. Hydroxyprolylalanine, -leucine, -phenylalanine, and -tyrosine were also hydrolyzed. Tripeptidase and aminopeptidase activities were not present. Glycylglycine was rapidly hydrolyzed but prolylglutamic and prolylaspartic were not hydrolyzed. Manganese and cadmium enhanced the activity, and metal-chelating agents, such as pyrophosphate and citrate, inhibited the activity (24).

Carnosinase

Crude water extracts from the small intestine do not hydrolyze carnosine (β-alanylhistidine) (48). However, a subsequent study of extracts from fresh intestine identified the hydrolysis of carnosine (138). This activity may be absent in freeze-dried intestine. A carnosinase has been purified from hog kidney (100).

It has been assumed that a number of specific dipeptidases are present in the small intestine and other tissues (60, 112, 115). This assumption is based on earlier reports with relatively crude preparations using divalent cations and a 12,000-fold purified prolidase from hog kidney (25) that is present in low concentration. These dipeptidase preparations did not hydrolyze tripeptides, acyldipeptides, or dipeptide amides, which excludes some peptidases. The specificity to a limited number of dipeptides was only tentative (116). As suggested by Robinson & Shaw (99), it is best to regard intestinal hydrolysis of dipeptides as the simultaneous action of a number of enzymes until a specific intestinal dipeptidase is highly purified and extensively characterized.

Physiological Approach to Peptide Hydrolysis

Another approach to intestinal peptidases has included the hydrolysis of peptides and proteins by the intact digestive system of man (12, 21, 22) and animals (26, 27, 30), isolated in vivo loops of intestine (14, 46, 140), isolated sacs of intestine (1, 85–87, 135), and everted intestinal rings (129). These general areas have been reviewed (136, 137).

Peptidases that hydrolyze glycylleucine and leucyltyrosine rapidly diffuse from intestinal sac preparations (135) and human small-bowel biopsies (78), whereas the hydrolysis of glycylglycine is not diffusible (85, 135).

PEPTIDASES IN CELIAC DISEASE

Celiac disease in children and nontropical sprue in adults are diseases of the small intestine in which malabsorption is prominent. One of the etiologic theories is a decrease or absence of an intestinal peptidase that allows a toxic peptide to escape hydrolysis and injure the mucosa (37, 65, 77, 131). The hydrolysis of several peptides has been determined in small-bowel biopsies from normal children and patients with celiac disease. There was no difference between normal and celiac children (78). Peptic-tryptic digests of gliadin incubated with biopsy homogenates from celiac patients and normal persons have shown different peptide maps (93).

Investigation of the possible role of peptidases of the small intestine in celiac disease should yield additional information on intestinal peptidases.

INTESTINAL CARBOXYPEPTIDASES

This group of enzymes hydrolyzes carboxy-terminal amino acids of peptides. Purified pancreatic carboxypeptidase does not hydrolyze leucylglycine or leucylglycylglycine; d- and l-leucyltyrosine are hydrolyzed at equally low rates. Acylation of N-terminal leucine of leucyltyrosine greatly increases hydrolysis. Glycylleucine is hydrolyzed at about the same rate as l-leucyltyrosine (143). Tissue carboxypeptidases may have a broader specificity.

Folic (Pteroyl-γ-Glutamic) Acid Conjugase

A folic (pteroylglutamic) acid conjugase has been described in hog intestinal homogenates. Pteroyl-polyglutamic acid may have two to seven carboxy-terminal glutamyl residues, and these forms require the hydrolysis of one to six glutamyl residues to yield pteroylglutamic acid. Formylation or methylation of pteroyl nitrogens is also required for full activation.

The intestinal peptidase activity was inhibited by DNA and RNA but not by the products of the enzymatic reaction (81).

Biotinidase

Crude homogenates of rat small intestine contain an enzymatic activity that hydrolyzed biocytin (γ-N-biotinyl-l-lysine) at the biotinyl-lysine linkage in phosphate buffer at pH 7.0. This enzyme has been purified 700-fold from Streptococcus faecalis (strain 10Cl); it hydrolyzed biotinylamide and biotinyl-methylester. Biocytin was not hydrolyzed by the purified bacterial enzyme (62).

Chloracetyl-l-Tyrosine Hydrolysis

Chloracetyl-l-tyrosine is hydrolyzed by purified pancreatic carboxypeptidase A. Two separate activities have been described in supernates of intestinal homogenates that also hydrolyze this substrate. One enzyme required cysteine for maximal hydrolytic rates and was inhibited by resuspending the precipitate with the supernate. The other activity was inhibited by cysteine and not by resuspending the precipitate in the supernate (33).

Chloracetyldehydroalanine Hydrolysis (Acylase)

The hydrolysis of chloracetyldehydroalanine has been reported in intestinal mucosal homogenates. This hydrolysis was relatively low in the intestine and most other tissues, whereas the liver and kidney were, respectively, 7–11 times as active as the intestine (45). This type of activity has been further purified and more extensively characterized from hog kidney, and it hydrolyzes a number of di-, tri-, and dehydro-peptides (11, 95).

Catheptic Carboxypeptidases of Beef Spleen

A tissue carboxypeptidase has been separated from cathepsin B fractions from beef spleen. CBZ-l-glutamyl-l-tyrosine was maximally hydrolyzed at pH 4.0 or less. The activity was enhanced by cysteine and inhibited by zinc and iodoacetic acid. The activity required a free carboxy-terminal carboxyl group, for esters and amides were not hydrolyzed. Leucinamide, glycylglycylglycine, and chloracetyltyrosine were not hydrolyzed (44).

Intestinal carboxypeptidases have been little explored. Whether intestinal carboxypeptidases are separate, related to other exopeptidases, or associated with lysosomal cathepsins remains to be determined.

GLUTAMINASE AND ARGINASE

Glutaminase

Rat small-intestine homogenates deamidate glutamine to yield glutamic acid and ammonia. This activity is primarily in the precipitate, there being little or no activity in the supernatant. The duodenum contained maximal activities, whereas the midgut activity was 50% of the duodenum and the ileum was 30% of the duodenum. The stomach and colon contained less than 25% of the duodenal activity. This activity was localized to the mucosa (126).

Arginase

This enzymatic activity hydrolyzes arginine to ornithine and urea. In mouse intestine the activity was more pronounced at pH 9.0 than at pH 7.0, was enhanced by manganese, and was inhibited by l-ornithine (64). In the mouse enzymatic activity is maximal in the liver and next greatest in the intestine (61).

INTESTINAL AMINO ACID-NAPHTHYLAMIDASES

Another approach to the study of peptidases of the small intestine began in 1954 when Gomori reported glycyl- and alanyl-β-naphthylamide hydrolysis by intestinal homogenates and histochemically localized this activity to the epithelial cell (42). Shortly thereafter, the leucyl derivative was synthesized and also hydrolyzed by intestinal homogenates (35).

Leucyl-β-naphthylamide hydrolysis was associated with particulate and supernatant fractions in the intestine and hydrolyzed a number of amino acid-naphthylamides (53). Alanyl-β-naphthylamide was hydrolyzed twice as rapidly as the leucyl derivative (4, 53, 90). The activity from human jejunum was partially inhibited by l-methionine, and the supernatant activity was contained in three bands on starch-gel electrophoresis (108).

Relation of Leucylnaphthylamidase and Peptidases

The leucylnapthylamidase activity can be separated from most of the peptidase activity by several methods.

TABLE 5. *Enzymes from Hamster Brush-Border Subfractions*

Cumulative ml Down Gradient	Fractions	Protein, mg	Specific Activity, μmoles/ min/mg	
			Alkaline phosphatase	Maltase
2	A	0.5	0	0
5	B	1.2	0	0
10		0.7	0.3	2.0
20	C*	1.8	4.8	14.0
27		0.2	0.4	2.0
30	D	1.8	2.1	4.0

* Electron micrographs demonstrated microvillus membranes in C fraction (Figs. 1 and 2).

From Eichholz & Crane (32).

Human jejunal supernatants from deoxycholate-treated homogenates have been separated on starch gel. The distributions of leucylnaphthylamide, leucinamide, and leucylglycine hydrolysis were different (83).

Fraction of human small-intestine supernatants separated by column chromatography contained similar distributions of amino acid-naphthylamide and dipeptide hydrolysis. However, these activities were separated by different characteristics. Leucyl-β-naphthylamide hydrolysis was enhanced by cobalt, was maximal at about pH 6.0, and was inhibited by puromycin. Leucylglycine hydrolysis was enhanced by manganese and magnesium, was maximal at pH 9.0, and was not inhibited by puromycin. d-Leucylglycine was not hydrolyzed (4).

Fractions of guinea pig and rabbit intestine separated by density-gradient centrifugation showed different distributions for leucylnaphthylamidase and lysosomal hydrolyases (56).

It is evident that intestinal leucylnaphthylamide hydrolysis may be due to several enzymes and can be separated from most of the peptidase activity.

Cellular Localization

Leucyl-β-naphthylamide hydrolysis has been histochemically localized to the brush border of intestinal epithelial cells (82). Isolated hamster brush borders contained about 75% of the activity in association with comparable amounts of invertase, maltase, and alkaline phosphatase (52, 80). Of the total leucyl-β-naphthylamidase from guinea pig intestine, 83% was associated with a brush border and nuclear fraction; 45% of the total activity in rabbit intestine was similarly located (56).

Papain-treated brush borders yield small particles that contain disaccharidases and a leucylnaphthylamidase. These particles originate from the luminal surface of the membranes of the microvilli (89).

The microvillus membrane has recently been isolated from hamster brush borders and contained most of the alkaline phosphatase and maltase [(32); Table 5]. These membranes were characterized by electron micrographs [(88); Figs. 1 and 2].

These isolated microvillus membranes [see recent study by Rhodes and colleagues (95a)] hydrolyzed 8 di- and tripeptides and leucyl-β-naphthylamide at appreciable rates. d-Leucylglycine and N-CBZ-leucylglycine and several proteins were not hydrolyzed. The isolated membranes contained less than 10% of the

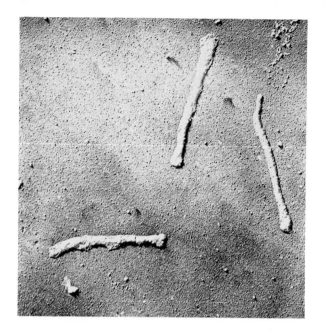

FIG. 1. Electron micrograph of isolated hamster microvillus membranes by shadow casting, × 18,000. [Photograph kindly contributed by Overton et al. (88).]

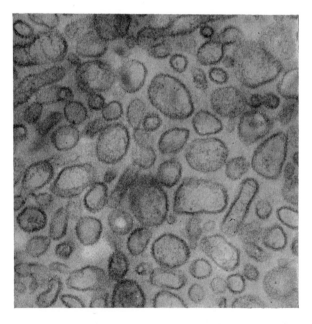

FIG. 2. Electron micrograph of sections from isolated hamster microvillus membranes, × 44,000. [Photograph kindly contributed by Overton et al. (88).]

total peptidase activity of the intestinal mucosa. Non-specific adsorption of the activity was excluded by deoxycholate treatment. The rate of hydrolysis of some tripeptides was about half of the invertase activity. On the basis of the localization, association

with disaccharidases, and relatively high activity, it was concluded that this peptidase activity may have a role in the terminal digestion of protein at the peptide level (95a).

One can conclude that leucylnaphthylamide hydrolysis by intestinal epithelial cells is primarily localized to the brush borders. The activity is further localized to the microvillus membrane and to smaller particles nearer the lumen. The isolated microvillus membrane hydrolyzes di- and tripeptides and could participate in terminal protein digestion at the peptide level. The total microvillus membrane activity is only a small part of the total mucosal exopeptidase activity.

An amino acid-naphthylamidase has been purified 2,650-fold from a human liver particulate fraction that did not hydrolyze leucinamide or leucylglycine (107).

SOME FACTORS INVOLVED IN INTESTINAL
PEPTIDASE DETERMINATIONS

It is evident that no intestinal peptidases have been extensively purified and therefore have not been reliably characterized. Their functions remain essentially unknown. The significance of the relatively high concentrations and high activities for some peptidases remains an interesting and unexplained phenomenon.

Some current problems in peptidases of the small intestine are peculiar to the intestine whereas others may be applicable to peptidases in general.

Small-intestine mucus hampers the separation of intracellular organelles by entrapping these organelles, which may precipitate as larger particles or float to the top of the centrifuge tube. The problem of mucus may partially explain the lack of a standard fractionation methodology (56, 93, 106). The use of a "balance sheet" as discussed by De Duve (28) may prove useful. In the case of liver fractionation, a previous discussion was associated with significant advances in this tissue (104). The "balance sheet" is being more frequently employed in the study of intestinal peptidases (32, 52, 54, 56, 80, 98).

The presence of the active small-intestine aminopeptidase in extracts must always be considered (121). This enzyme hydrolyzes a wide variety of peptides at variable rates. If present in high concentration, this enzyme could hydrolyze a peptide at appreciable rates even if the affinity was quite low. Hence the presence of aminopeptidase(s) may be mistaken for a dipeptidase, especially if only dipeptides are used as substrates.

"No activity" with a particular substrate is a relative term and is largely dependent on the effort expended to detect the hydrolysis of the substrate. The careful work of Smith and his associates is an example of the value of intensive efforts to detect possible activity (25, 119). It is preferable, when possible, to substitute for "no activity" the lowest levels of activity that would be detected in a given experiment.

CHARACTERISTICS OF SOME HIGHLY PURIFIED PEPTIDASES

Earlier concepts of the characteristics of some peptidases (116) may require reemphasis or modification in the light of subsequent information. Factors briefly considered include: *1*) homogeneity, *2*) substrates, *3*) buffers, *4*) pH curves, *5*) divalent cations, and *6*) inhibitors.

Homogeneous Enzymes

It is difficult to establish reliably a completely homogeneous peptidase, since other, contaminating peptidases may have a number of similar characteristics. A purified hog kidney, carnosinase, hydrolyzes leucinamide, which is considered a specific substrate for leucine-aminopeptidase. It was calculated that 0.15% contamination by the well-known aminopeptidase could account for the observed rate of leucinamide hydrolysis (100). Therefore it is always possible to explain the results by assuming the presence of another enzyme with suitable properties. This difficulty can be solved only by extensive purification and characterization.

The methodological advances in protein and particle fractionation have been considerable in recent years. These newer separation techniques are beginning to be applied more extensively to small-intestine peptidases.

Substrates

Some investigators assume that certain peptides are hydrolyzed, largely or exclusively, by a specific peptidase. Current evidence is most compatible with the general hypothesis that most intracellular peptidases hydrolyze a number of peptides at widely variable rates. Although low hydrolytic rates may have little or no biological significance, they are essential to characterize more fully a particular enzyme (15, 96, 119). This may rule in or out an endopeptidase, aminopep-

tidase, tripeptidase, dipeptidase, and perhaps a carboxypeptidase. If a protein is not hydrolyzed, one may assume that an endopeptidase is excluded. The usefulness of the alpha and beta chains of insulin as endopeptidase substrates has been previously mentioned. Cathepsins may also have esterase or transamidase activity that may occur at a pH different from the maximum pH for hydrolysis (79). Aminopeptidases generally do not hydrolyze N-terminal amino acids of the d-configuration or those in which the carbobenzoxy group is in the N-terminal position (119). There may be an exception to this generalization (96). Tripeptidases should not hydrolyze dipeptides and dipeptidases do not hydrolyze tripeptides. Carboxypeptidases are generally unable to hydrolyze carboxyterminal amides. Intracellular "carboxypeptidases" may be an exception. The use of dibasic, neutral, and aromatic amino acids in the N-terminal and carboxyterminal positions may lead to more extensive subclassification. The use of a number of different substrates can also provide relative hydrolytic rates for comparing similar peptidases. Subsequent studies may clarify current tentative concepts of substrate specificity.

Early investigators spent considerable time and effort on the synthesis of substrates that are now commercially available at reasonable cost.

Buffers

Various buffers may have enhancing or inhibiting effects independent of the pH (96), and pH curves may vary depending on the buffer (96, 138). Citrate may inhibit some peptidases and this may be attributed to chelation (119).

Different buffers may have an effect on the methods used to measure the enzymatic activity. For example, certain buffers may enhance absorption when activity is measured at 210–230 mμ (60). Tris may enhance the color development when the ninhydrin method is used to measure liberated amino acids (74).

pH Curves

The use of pH curves for peptidase characterization provides useful information. Catheptic endopeptidases are usually more active in hydrolysis at pH 2.5–5.7, whereas some associated transamidase reactions occur most rapidly at pH 7.5 (39, 79). Other peptidases have pH maxima in the more neutral range of pH 6.0–8.0, and still others are most active at a pH of 7.5–10.0. The pH for the maximal hydrolysis of one substrate might be different from the maximal pH for quite another substrate (96). The configuration of the pH curves can be altered.

Divalent Cations

Various divalent cations may enhance, inhibit, stabilize, or have no effect on some peptidases. These effects may vary with enzyme and cation concentration and time (96, 119).

Carboxypeptidase A and B contain 1 mole of zinc per mole of enzyme that may be removed without significantly altering several physical properties, but the ability to hydrolyze peptides is lost. If cobalt is then added, the activity is restored and enhanced while kinetics are altered, as are the relative rates of peptide hydrolysis (19, 36, 130, 138). Cadmium replacement enhances the esterase activity and markedly reduces peptide hydrolysis (130, 138). The hydrolysis of some dipeptides by a zinc-containing dipeptidase is also enhanced by cobalt and inhibited by cadmium (15).

Cobalt has complex effects on a 2,000-fold-purified hog kidney particulate aminopeptidase preparation. The activity may be enhanced, suppressed, or unaffected, depending on the concentration of cobalt and the particular substrate. The pH maximum may be varied and may be substrate dependent (96).

Another highly purified hog kidney aminopeptidase is stabilized and enhanced by manganese, but activity is reduced by prolonged incubation. A higher concentration of magnesium was required for comparable rates, but the kinetics were different and the pH curves were somewhat altered. However, relative rates of substrate hydrolysis were not altered by different divalent cations (51). In cruder preparations a longer preincubation time was required for maximal activity (117–119).

It is apparent that divalent cations may have profound effects on some peptidases but only minor alterations on other peptidases. A particular pair of substrate and divalent cation does not always "measure" a particular enzyme.

In crude peptidase preparations, the possibility of the activation of a contaminating peptidase with resulting destruction of the enzyme of interest might result in an apparent decrease in activity. A contaminating peptidase may also contribute to the apparent activity, if the contaminating enzyme is also enhanced by the divalent cation.

In view of these possible complex effects of divalent cations, it would appear desirable to avoid their use. However, some peptidases require the metal for stabilization. A divalent cation is helpful under these circumstances.

Inhibitors

Peptidases can be classified on the basis of inhibiting agents. Some peptidases require a sulfhydryl group for activity and are inhibited by agents that alter this group, such as iodoacetamide, *p*-mercuribenzoate, or *N*-ethylmaleimide. Some cathepsins are inhibited by these agents.

Other peptidases contain or require a divalent cation for maximal activity or stability. These enzymes, such as aminopeptidase, are inhibited by metal-chelating agents or dialysis that may remove a tightly bound or loosely associated metal.

Another group of peptidases is inhibited by organophosphorus compounds, such as diisopropylphosphofluoridate, by binding of a serine hydroxyl group. This group of enzymes may not be inhibited by sulfhydryl group or metal-type poisons (116).

It is unlikely that all the above considerations are applicable to all intestinal peptidases. On the other hand, these considerations may be helpful in understanding intestinal peptidases and should be considered in the interpretation of experimental data.

REFERENCES

1. AGAR, W. J., F. J. R. HIRD, AND G. S. SIDHU. The active absorption of amino acids by the intestine. *J. Physiol., London* 121: 255–263, 1953.
2. AGREN, G. The purification of aminopolypeptidase from hog's pyloric mucosa II. *Acta Physiol. Scand.* 9: 255–268, 1945.
3. AGREN, G. The purification of aminopolypeptidase from the hog's pyloric mucosa III. *Acta Physiol. Scand.* 9: 269–275, 1945.
4. BEHAL, F. J., B. ASSERSON, F. DAWSON, AND J. HARDMAN. A study of human tissue aminopeptidase components. *Arch. Biochem. Biophys.* 111: 335–344, 1965.
5. BELOFF, A., AND C. B. ANFINSEN. The products of proteolysis of some purified proteins. *J. Biol. Chem.* 176: 863–872, 1948.
6. BERGER, J., AND M. J. JOHNSON. Metal activation of peptidases. *J. Biol. Chem.* 130: 641–654, 1939.

7. BERGER, J., AND M. J. JOHNSON. The occurrence of leucylpeptidase. *J. Biol. Chem.* 133: 157–172, 1940.

8. BERGER, J., AND M. J. JOHNSON. The activation of dipeptidases. *J. Biol. Chem.* 133: 639–640, 1940.

9. BERGMANN, M. A classification of proteolytic enzymes. *Advan. Enzymol.* 2: 49–68, 1942.

10. BERGMANN, M., AND J. S. FRUTON. On proteolytic enzymes. XII. Regarding the specificity of aminopeptidase and carboxypeptidase. A new type of enzyme in the intestinal tract. *J. Biol. Chem.* 117: 189–202, 1937.

11. BIRNBAUM, S. M. Aminoacylase. In: *Methods in Enzymology*, edited by S. P. Colowick and N. O. Kaplan. New York: Acad. Press, 1955, vol. II, p. 115–119.

12. BORGSTRÖM, B., A. DAHLQVIST, G. LUNDH, AND J. SJÖVALL. Studies of intestinal digestion and absorption in the human. *J. Clin. Invest.* 36: 1521–1536, 1957.

13. BOUMA, J. M. W., AND M. GRUBER. Intracellular distribution of cathepsin B and cathepsin C in rat liver. *Biochim. Biophys. Acta* 113: 350–358, 1966.

14. CAJORI, F. A. The enzyme activity of dogs' intestinal juice and its relation to intestinal digestion. *Am. J. Physiol.* 104: 659–668, 1933.

15. CAMPBELL, B. J., Y. C. LIN, R. V. DAVIS, AND E. BALLEW. The purification and properties of a particulate renal dipeptidase. *Biochim. Biophys. Acta* 118: 371–386, 1966.

16. CHEN, M. L., Q. R. ROGERS, AND A. E. HARPER. Observations on protein digestion in vivo. IV. Further observations on the gastrointestinal contents of rats fed different dietary proteins. *J. Nutr.* 76: 235–241, 1962.

17. CHRISTENSEN, H. N. Conjugated amino acids in portal plasma of dogs after protein feeding. *Biochem. J.* 44: 333–334, 1949.

18. COHNHEIM, O. Die Umwandlung des Eiweiss durch die Darmwand. *Z. Physiol. Chem.* 33: 451–465, 1901.

19. COLEMAN, J. E., AND B. L. VALLEE. Metallocarboxypeptidases: stability constants and enzymatic characteristics. *J. Biol. Chem.* 236: 2244–2249, 1961.

20. CRANE, C. W. Studies on the absorption of ^{15}N-labeled yeast protein in normal subjects and patients with malabsorption. In: *The Role of the Gastrointestinal Tract in Protein Metabolism*, edited by H. N. Munro. Philadelphia: Davis, 1964, p. 333–347.

21. CRANE, C. W., AND A. NEUBERGER. Absorption and elimination of ^{15}N after administration of isotopically labeled yeast protein and yeast protein hydrolysate to adult patients with coeliac disease. 2. Elimination of isotope in the urine and feces. *Brit. Med. J.* 2: 888–894, 1960.

22. CRANE, C. W., AND A. NEUBERGER. The digestion and absorption of protein by normal man. *Biochem. J.* 74: 313–323, 1960.

23. DANNENBERG, A. M., AND E. L. SMITH. Action of proteinase I of bovine lung. Hydrolysis of the oxidized B chain of insulin; polymer formation from amino acid esters. *J. Biol. Chem.* 215: 55–66, 1955.

24. DAVIS, N. C., AND E. L. SMITH. Partial purification and specificity of iminopeptidase. *J. Biol. Chem.* 200: 373–384, 1953.

25. DAVIS, N. C., AND E. L. SMITH. Purification and some properties of prolidase of swine kidney. *J. Biol. Chem.* 224: 261–275, 1956.

26. DAWSON, R., AND E. S. HOLDSWORTH. An investigation into protein digestion with ^{14}C-labeled protein. 1. The general pattern of ^{14}C incorporation in body tissues and fluids of the rat up to 3 hours after feeding. *Brit. J. Nutr.* 16: 13–25, 1962.

27. DAWSON, R., E. S. HOLDSWORTH, AND J. W. G. PORTER. The digestion and absorption of protein in the rat. In: *The Role of the Gastrointestinal Tract in Protein Metabolism*, edited by H. N. Munro. Philadelphia: Davis, 1964, p. 293–307.

28. DE DUVE, C. Principles of tissue fractionation. *J. Theoret. Biol.* 6: 33–59, 1964.

29. DE DUVE, C., AND R. WATTIAUX. Functions of lysosomes. *Ann. Rev. Physiol.* 28: 435–492, 1966.

30. DENT, C. E., AND J. A. SCHILLING. Studies on the absorption of proteins: the amino acid pattern in the portal blood. *Biochem. J.* 44: 318–333, 1949.

31. DESNUELLE, P. Trypsin. In: *The Enzymes*, edited by P. D. Boyer, H. Lardy, and K. Myrback. New York: Acad. Press, 1960, p. 119–132.

32. EICHHOLZ, A., AND R. K. CRANE. Studies on the organization of the brush border in intestinal epithelial cells. I. Tris disruption of isolated hamster brush borders and density gradient separation of proteins. *J. Cell Biol.* 26: 687–691, 1965.

33. FEINSTEIN, R. N., AND J. C. BALLIN. Carboxypeptidase in mammalian tissues. *Proc. Soc. Exptl. Biol. Med.* 83: 10–14, 1953.

34. FLOREY, H. W., R. D. WRIGHT, AND M. A. JENNINGS. The secretions of the intestine. *Physiol. Rev.* 21: 36–69, 1941.

35. FOLK, J. E., AND M. S. BURSTONE. Chromogenic leucyl substrates for aminopeptidase and papain. *Proc. Soc. Exptl. Biol. Med.* 89: 473–476, 1955.

36. FOLK, J. E., E. C. WOLFF, AND E. W. SCHIRMER. The kinetics of carboxypeptidase B activity II. Kinetic parameters of the cobalt and cadmium enzyme. *J. Biol. Chem.* 237: 3100–3104, 1962.

37. FRAZER, A. C., R. SCHNEIDER, D. B. MORGAN, H. G. SAMMONS, AND M. HAYWARD. Gluten-induced enteropathy and protein digestion. In: *The Role of the Gastrointestinal Tract in Protein Metabolism*, edited by H. N. Munro. Philadelphia: Davis, 1964, p. 349–356.

38. FRIEDRICH, M., R. NOACK, AND G. SCHENK. Zur Lokalisation von peptidatischen und proteolytischen Aktivitäten in isolierten Burstensäumen aus der Mucosa des Rattendünndarmes. *Biochem. Z.* 343: 346–353, 1965.

39. FRUTON, J. S. Cathepsins. In: *The Enzymes*, edited by P. D. Boyer, H. Lardy, and K. Myrback. New York: Acad. Press, 1960, p. 233–241.

40. GAILEY, F. B., AND M. J. JOHNSON. The dipeptidases of intestinal mucosa. *J. Biol. Chem.* 141: 921–929, 1941.

41. GITLER, C. Protein digestion and absorption in nonruminants. In: *Mammalian Protein Metabolism*, edited by H. N. Munro and J. B. Allison. New York: Acad. Press, 1964, vol. I, p. 35–66.

42. GOMORI, G. Chromogenic substrates for aminopeptidase. *Proc. Soc. Exptl. Biol. Med.* 87: 559–561, 1954.

43. GREENBAUM, L. M., A. HIRSHKOWITZ, AND I. SHOICHET. The activation of trypsinogen by cathepsin B. *J. Biol. Chem.* 234: 2885–2890, 1959.

44. GREENBAUM, L. M., AND R. SHERMAN. Studies on catheptic carboxypeptidase. *J. Biol. Chem.* 237: 1082–1085, 1962.

45. GREENSTEIN, J. P., AND F. M. LEUTHARDT. Dehydro-

peptidase activity in tissues. *J. Biol. Chem.* 162: 175–176, 1946.

46. GUPTA, J. D., A. M. DAKROURY, AND A. E. HARPER. Observations on protein digestion in vivo. I. Rate of disappearance of injected protein from the gastrointestinal tract. *J. Nutr.* 64: 447–456, 1958.

47. HALDANE, J. B. S. *Enzymes.* Cambridge, Mass.: MIT Press, 1965, p. 107–116.

48. HANSON, H. T., AND E. L. SMITH. Carnosinase: an enzyme of swine kidney. *J. Biol. Chem.* 179: 789–801, 1949.

49. HAUROWITZ, F., AND F. BURSA. The linkage of glutamic acid in protein molecules. *Biochem. J.* 44: 509–512, 1949.

50. HILL, R. L., AND W. R. SCHMIDT. The complete enzymic hydrolysis of proteins. *J. Biol. Chem.* 237: 389–396, 1962.

51. HILL, R. L., AND E. L. SMITH. Leucine aminopeptidase. VI. Inhibition by alcohols and other compounds. *J. Biol. Chem.* 224: 209–223, 1957.

52. HOLT, J. H., AND D. MILLER. The localization of phosphomonoesterase and aminopeptidase in brush borders isolated from intestinal epithelial cells. *Biochim. Biophys. Acta* 58: 239–243, 1962.

53. HOPSU, V. K., U. M. KANTONEN, AND G. G. GLENNER. A peptidase from rat tissues selectively hydrolyzing N-terminal arginine and lysine residues. *Life Sci.* 3: 1449–1453, 1964.

54. HSU, L., AND A. L. TAPPEL. Lysosomal enzymes of rat intestinal mucosa. *J. Cell Biol.* 23: 233–240, 1964.

55. HSU, L., AND A. L. TAPPEL. Lysosomal enzymes and mucopolysaccharides in the gastrointestinal tract of the rat and pig. *Biochim. Biophys. Acta* 101: 83–89, 1965.

56. HUBSCHER, G., G. R. WEST, AND D. N. BRINDLEY. Studies on the fractionation of mucosal homogenates from the small intestine. *Biochem. J.* 97: 629–642, 1965.

57. JOHNSON, M. J. Specificity of intestinal aminopolypeptidase. *J. Biol. Chem.* 122: 89–97, 1937.

58. JOHNSON, M. J., AND J. BERGER. Enzymatic properties of peptidases. *Advan. Enzymol.* 2: 69–92, 1942.

59. JOHNSON, M. J., G. H. JOHNSON, AND W. H. PETERSON. The magnesium activated leucyl peptidase of animal erepsin. *J. Biol. Chem.* 116: 515–526, 1936.

60. JOSEFSSON, L., AND T. LINDBERG. Intestinal dipeptidases. II. Distribution of dipeptidases in the small intestine of the pig. *Biochim. Biophys. Acta* 105: 162–166, 1965.

61. KOCHAKIAN, C. D. The effect of castration and various steroids on the arginase activity of tissues of the mouse. *J. Biol. Chem.* 155: 579–589, 1944.

62. KOIVUSALO, M., C. ELORRIAGE, Y. KAZINO, AND S. OCHOA. Bacterial biotinidase. *J. Biol. Chem.* 238: 1038–1042, 1963.

63. KORNER, A. Protein biosynthesis in mammalian tissues. In: *Mammalian Protein Metabolism,* edited by H. N. Munro and J. B. Allison. New York: Acad. Press, 1964, vol. I, p. 177–242.

64. KOTAKE, Y., AND M. MABUTI. XXXVI. Studien über Darmarginase, insbesondere des kanichens. *Z. Physiol. Chem.* 270: 90–96, 1941.

65. KOWLESSAR, O. D., AND M. H. SLEISENGER. The role of gliadin in the pathogenesis of adult celiac disease. *Gastroenterology* 44: 357–362, 1963.

66. KUNITZ, M. J. Purification and concentration of enterokinase. *J. Gen. Physiol.* 22: 447–450, 1939.

67. LAPRESLE, C., AND T. WEBB. The purification and properties of a proteolytic enzyme, rabbit cathepsin E,

and further studies on rabbit cathepsin D. *Biochem. J.* 84: 455–462, 1962.

68. LASKOWSKI, M. Trypsinogen and trypsin. In: *Methods in Enzymology,* edited by S. P. Colowick and N. O. Kaplan. New York: Acad. Press, 1955, vol. II, p. 26–36.

69. LEBLOND, C. P., AND B. E. WALKER. Renewal of cell populations. *Physiol. Rev.* 36: 255–276, 1956.

70. LEVENSON, S. M., H. ROSEN, AND H. L. UPJOHN. Nature and appearance of protein digestion products in upper mesenteric blood. *Proc. Soc. Exptl. Biol. Med.* 101: 178–180, 1959.

71. LICHTENSTEIN, L. M., AND J. S. FRUTON. Studies on beef spleen cathepsin A. *Proc. Natl. Acad. Sci. U.S.* 46: 787–791, 1960.

72. LIPKIN, M. Cell replication in the gastrointestinal tract of man. *Gastroenterology* 48: 616–624, 1965.

73. MALMSTROM, B. G., AND A. ROSENBERG. Mechanism of metal ion activation of enzymes. *Advan. Enzymol.* 21: 131–167, 1959.

74. MATHESON, A. T., AND B. L. TATTRIE. A modified Yemm and Cocking ninhydrin reagent for peptidase activity. *Can. J. Biochem.* 42: 95–103, 1964.

75. MATHESON, A. T., AND C. S. TSAI. A ribosomal peptidase from Escherichia coli. *Can. J. Biochem.*: 43: 323–329, 1964.

76. MEISTER, A. *Biochemistry of the Amino Acids.* New York: Acad. Press, 1965, p. 473–482.

77. MESSER, M., C. M. ANDERSON, AND L. HUBBARD. Studies on the mechanism of destruction of the toxic action of wheat gluten in coeliac disease by crude papain. *Gut* 5: 295–303, 1964.

78. MESSER, M., C. M. ANDERSON, AND R. R. W. TOWNLEY. Peptidase activity of biopsies of the duodenal mucosa of children with and without coeliac disease. *Clin. Chim. Acta* 6: 768–775, 1961.

79. METRIONE, R. M., A. G. NEVES, AND J. S. FRUTON. Purification and properties of dipeptidyl transferase (cathepsin C). *Biochemistry* 5: 1597–1604, 1966.

80. MILLER, D., AND R. K. CRANE. The digestive function of the epithelium of the small intestine. II. Localization of disaccharide hydrolysis in the isolated brush border portion of intestinal epithelial cells. *Biochim. Biophys. Acta* 52: 293–298, 1961.

81. MIMS, V., M. E. SWENDSEID, AND O. D. BIRD. The inhibition of pteroylglutamic acid conjugase and its reversal. The effect of nucleic acid and sulfhydryl-combining reagents. *J. Biol. Chem.* 170: 367–377, 1947.

82. NACHLAS, M. M., B. MONIS, D. ROSENBLATT, AND A. M. SELIGMAN. Improvement of the histochemical localization of leucine aminopeptidase with a new substrate L-leucyl-4-methoxy-2-naphthylamide. *J. Cell Biol.* 7: 261–264, 1960.

83. NAKAGAWA, S., AND H. TSUJI. Electrophoretic separation of aminopeptidase and leucyl-B-naphthylamide-splitting enzyme. *Clin. Chim. Acta* 10: 572–573, 1964.

84. NEUBERGER, A., AND F. F. RICHARDS. Protein biosynthesis in mammalian tissues. II. Studies on turnover in the whole animal. In: *Mammalian Protein Metabolism,* edited by H. N. Munro and J. B. Allison. New York: Acad. Press, 1964, p. 271–275.

85. NEWEY, H., AND D. H. SMYTH. The intestinal absorption of some dipeptides. *J. Physiol., London* 145: 48–56, 1959.

86. NEWEY, H., AND D. H. SMYTH. Intracellular hydrolysis of

dipeptides during intestinal absorption. *J. Physiol., London* 152: 367–380, 1960.

87. NEWEY, H., AND D. H. SMYTH. Cellular mechanisms in intestinal transfer of amino acids. *J. Physiol., London* 164: 527–551, 1962.

88. OVERTON, J., A. EICHHOLZ, AND R. K. CRANE. Studies on the organization of the brush border in intestinal epithelial cells. II. Fine structure of fractions of tris disrupted hamster brush borders. *J. Cell Biol.* 26: 693–706, 1965.

89. ODA, T., AND S. SEKI. Molecular structure and biochemical function of the microvilli membrane of intestinal epithelial cells with special emphasis on the elementary particles. *J. Electronmicroscopy* 14: 210–217, 1965.

90. PANVELIWALLA, D. K., AND D. W. MOSS. Kinetic properties of aminoacyl-β-naphthylamide hydrolyases from human tissues. *Biochem. J.* 96: 73, 1965.

91. PERAINO, C., Q. R. ROGERS, M. YOSHIDA, M. L. CHEN, AND A. E. HARPER. Observations on protein digestion in vivo. II. Dietary factors affecting the rate of disappearance of casein from the gastrointestinal tract. *Can. J. Biochem.* 37: 1475–1491, 1959.

92. PITTMAN, F. E., C. R. DENNING, AND H. G. BARKER. Albumin metabolism in cystic fibrosis. *Am. J. Diseases Children* 108: 360–365, 1964.

93. PITTMAN, F. E., AND R. J. POLLITT. Studies of jejunal mucosal digestion of peptic-tryptic digests of wheat protein in coeliac disease. *Gut* 7: 368–371, 1966.

94. PRESS, E. M., R. R. PORTER, AND J. CEBRA. The isolation and properties of a proteolytic enzyme, cathepsin D, from bovine spleen. *Biochem. J.* 74: 501–514, 1960.

95. RAO, K. R., S. M. BIRNBAUM, AND J. P. GREENSTEIN. Enzymatic susceptibility of comparable N-acylated L-, D-, and dehydroamino acids. *J. Biol. Chem.* 203: 1–8, 1953.

95a. RHODES, J. B., A. EICHHOLZ, AND R. K. CRANE. Studies on the organization of the brush border in intestinal epithelial cells. IV. Aminopeptidase activity in microvillus membranes of hamster intestinal brush borders. *Biochim. Biophys. Acta* 135: 959–965, 1967.

96. ROBINSON, D. S., S. M. BIRNBAUM, AND J. P. GREENSTEIN. Purification and properties of an aminopeptidase from kidney cellular particulates. *J. Biol. Chem.* 202: 1–26, 1953.

97. ROBINSON, G. B. The hydrolysis of dipeptides by rat intestinal extracts. *Biochim. Biophys. Acta* 44: 386–387, 1960.

98. ROBINSON, G. B. The distribution of peptidases in subcellular fractions from the mucosa of the small intestine of the rat. *Biochem. J.* 88: 162–168, 1963.

99. ROBINSON, G. B., AND B. SHAW. The hydrolysis of dipeptides by different regions of rat small intestine. *Biochem. J.* 77: 351–356, 1960.

100. ROSENBERG, A. Purification and some properties of carnosinase of swine kidney. *Arch. Biochem. Biophys.* 88: 83–93, 1960.

101. ROVERY, M., AND P. DESNUELLE. Sur les aminoacides liberis pardant l'hydrolyse de la globine de chaval par la pepsine, la trypsine et la chymotrypsine cristallisees. *Biochim. Biophys. Acta* 8: 450–458, 1952.

102. SANGER, F., AND E. O. P. THOMPSON. The amino acid sequence of the glycyl chain of insulin. 2. The investigation of peptides of enzymatic hydrolysates. *Biochem. J.* 53: 366–374, 1953.

103. SANGER, F., AND H. TUPPY. The amino acid sequence in the phenylalanyl chain of insulin. *Biochem. J.* 49: 481–490, 1951.

104. SCHNEIDER, W. C., AND G. H. HOGEBOOM. Cytochemical studies of mammalian tissues: the isolation of cell components by differential centrifugation: a review. *Cancer Res.* 11: 1–22, 1951.

105. SCHWERT, R., AND R. HEINTZ. Protein synthesis. *Ann. Rev. Biochem.* 35, part II: 723–758, 1966.

106. SHAPIRO, B. IV. Experiments with cytoplasmic fractions of intestinal mucosa. *Methods Med. Res.* 9: 293–297, 1961.

107. SMITH, E. E., J. T. KAUFMAN, AND A. M. RUTENBERG. The partial purification of an amino acid naphthylamidase from human liver. *J. Biol. Chem.* 240: 1718–1721, 1965.

108. SMITH, E. E., AND A. M. RUTENBERG. Starch-gel electrophoresis of human tissue enzymes which hydrolyze l-leucyl-β-naphthylamide. *Science* 152: 1256–1257, 1966.

109. SMITH, E. L. Manganese and *l*-leucine-aminoexopeptidase. *J. Biol. Chem.* 163: 15–27, 1946.

110. SMITH, E. L. The peptidases of skeletal, heart, and uterine muscle. *J. Biol. Chem.* 173: 553–569, 1948.

111. SMITH, E. L. The glycyl-glycine dipeptidases of skeletal muscle and human uterus. *J. Biol. Chem.* 173: 571–584, 1948.

112. SMITH, E. L. Studies on dipeptidases. II. Some properties of the glycyl-*l*-leucine dipeptidases of animal tissues. *J. Biol. Chem.* 176: 9–19, 1948.

113. SMITH, E. L. Studies on dipeptidases. III. Hydrolysis of methylated peptides; the role of cobalt in the action of glycyl-glycine dipeptidase. *J. Biol. Chem.* 176: 21–32, 1948.

114. SMITH, E. L. The specificity of certain peptidases. *Advan. Enzymol.* 12: 191–257, 1951.

115. SMITH, E. L. Aminopeptidases, leucine aminopeptidase, and dipeptidases. In: *Methods in Enzymology*, edited by S. P. Colowick and N. O. Kaplan. New York: Acad. Press, 1955, vol. II, p. 83–109.

116. SMITH, E. L. Peptide bond cleavage (survey). In: *The Enzymes*, edited by P. D. Boyer, H. Lardy, and K. Myrback. New York: Acad. Press, 1960, vol. IV, p. 1–10.

117. SMITH, E. L., AND M. BERGMANN. The activation of intestinal peptidases by manganese. *J. Biol. Chem.* 138: 789–790, 1941.

118. SMITH, E. L., AND M. BERGMANN. The peptidases of intestinal mucosa. *J. Biol. Chem.* 153: 627–651, 1944.

119. SMITH, E. L., AND R. L. HILL. Leucine aminopeptidase. In: *The Enzymes*, edited by P. D. Boyer, H. Lardy, and K. Myrback. New York: Acad. Press, 1960, vol. IV, p. 37–62.

120. SMITH, E. L., AND W. J. POLGLASE. The specificity of leucine aminopeptidase. II. Optical and side chain specificity. *J. Biol. Chem.* 180: 1209–1223, 1949.

121. SMITH, E. L., AND N. B. SLONIN. The specificity of leucine aminopeptidase. *J. Biol. Chem.* 176: 835–841, 1948.

122. SMITH, E. L., AND D. H. SPACKMAN. Leucine aminopeptidase. V. Activation, specificity and mechanism of action. *J. Biol. Chem.* 212: 271–299, 1955.

123. SMITH, E. L., D. H. SPACKMAN, AND W. J. POLGLASE. The specificity of leucine aminopeptidase. III. Action of diastereoisomers. *J. Biol. Chem.* 199: 801–817, 2952.

124. SPACKMAN, D. H., E. L. SMITH, AND D. M. BROWN. Leucine aminopeptidase. IV. Isolation and properties of

the enzyme from swine kidney. *J. Biol. Chem.* 212: 255–269, 1955.

125. SPENCER, R. P., AND W. E. KNOX. Comparative enzyme apparatus of the gut mucosa. *Federation Proc.* 19 (4): 886–897, 1960.

126. SPENCER, R. P., AND N. ZAMCHECK. Presence of glutaminase I in rat intestine. *Gastroenterology* 40: 423–426, 1961.

127. SYMONS, L. E. A., AND W. O. JONES. The distribution of dipeptidase activity in the small intestine of the sheep. *Comp. Biochem. Physiol.* 18: 71–82, 1966.

128. TSUBOI, K. K., Z. J. PENEFSKY, AND P. B. HUDSON. Enzymes of the human erythrocyte. III. Tripeptidase, purification and properties. *Arch. Biochem. Biophys.* 68: 54–68, 1957.

129. UGOLEV, A. M., N. N. IESUITOVA, N. M. TIMOFEEVA, AND I. N. FEDIUSHINA. Location of hydrolysis of certain disaccharides and peptides in the small intestine. *Nature* 202: 807–809, 1964.

130. VALLEE, B. L. The "active catalytic site," an approach through metalloenzymes. *Federation Proc.* 20, Suppl. 10: 71–80, 1961.

131. VAN DE KAMER, J. H., AND H. A. WEIJERS. Malabsorption syndrome. *Federation Proc.* 20, Suppl. 7: 335–344, 1961.

132. WALDSCHMIDT-LEITZ, E. Enzymes. *Ann. Rev. Biochem.* 1: 69–88, 1932.

133. WATTIAUX-DE CONINCK, S., M. J. RUTGEERTS, AND R. WATTIAUX. Lysosomes in rat-kidney tissue. *Biochim. Biophys. Acta* 105: 446–459, 1965.

134. WEISSMANN, G. Labilization and stabilization of lysosomes. *Federation Proc.* 23, Suppl. 5: 1038–1044, 1964.

135. WIGGANS, D. S., AND J. M. JOHNSTON. The absorption of peptides. *Biochim. Biophys. Acta* 32: 69–73, 1959.

136. WILSON, T. H. *Intestinal Absorption*. Philadelphia: Saunders, 1962, p. 72–73.

137. WISEMAN, G. *Absorption From the Intestine*. New York: Acad. Press, 1964, p. 51–54.

138. WOLFF, E. C., E. W. SCHIRMER, AND J. E. FOLK. The kinetics of carboxypeptidase B activity. *J. Biol. Chem.* 237: 3094–3099, 1962.

139. WOOD, T. Carnosine and carnosinase in rat tissue. *Nature* 180: 39–40, 1957.

140. WRIGHT, R. D., M. A. JENNINGS, H. W. FLOREY, AND R. LIUM. The influence of nerves and drugs on secretion by the small intestine and an investigation of the enzymes in intestinal juice. *Quart. J. Exptl. Physiol.* 30: 73–120, 1940.

141. YAMASHIMA, I. The action of enterokinase on trypsinogen. *Biochim. Biophys. Acta* 20: 433–434, 1956.

142. YAMASHIMA, I. Studies on enterokinase. II. The further purification. *Arkiv Kemi* 9: 225–229, 1956.

143. YANARI, S., AND M. A. MITZ. The mode of action of pancreatic carboxypeptidase. I. Optical and structural specificity. *J. Am. Chem. Soc.* 79: 1150–1153, 1957.

CHAPTER 122

Pancreatic proteolytic enzymes

PATRICIA J. KELLER | *Department of Oral Biology, University of Washington, Seattle, Washington*

CHAPTER CONTENTS

I. INTRODUCTION

THE MODERN ERA of pancreatic proteases began in the 1930s with the now classic studies of Northrop, Herriott, Anson, and their colleagues at the Rockefeller Institute of Medical Research. During that decade these productive investigators isolated, in crystalline form, nine pancreatic proteins concerned with digestion, including trypsin, several chymotrypsins, and carboxypeptidase. They established the protein nature of the digestive enzymes and showed that the enzymes were elaborated in the form of inactive precursors called zymogens. In addition they elucidated the manner in which the respective zymogens were converted to enzymes. The results of these investigations are presented in the monograph entitled *Crystalline Enzymes* (150).

The wealth of information accumulated by these earlier investigators sustained interest in the pancreatic enzymes and zymogens during ensuing decades. These proteins have thus become prototypes for studies going far beyond physiological function. The investigations have included elucidation of the events of zymogen activation at the molecular level (47, 144, 146); isolation of the "active sites" and study of their role in the mechanism of enzyme action (151), determination of the amino acid sequences of several pancreatic proteins, and consideration of the evolutionary implications of the homologies observed (84, 192). More recently still, the pancreatic proteases have been studied with respect to the synchronism of their appearance during early differentiation of pancreatic acinar cells (112, 113, 168, 169).

This review attempts to emphasize the physiological aspects of the pancreatic enzymes, notably their respective roles in the digestion of dietary protein. Examples that illustrate current knowledge of the molecular nature of the pancreatic enzymes and zymogens as well as significant species variations are cited.

The proteolytic enzymes of the pancreas are hydrolytic: they lyse their target bonds with the elements of water. They can be divided into two classes: the endopeptidases and the exopeptidases (13). Endopeptidases attack the protein aiming primarily at centrally located peptide bonds, whereas exopeptidases cleave only the terminal bonds of proteins or peptides. The major endopeptidases of the pancreas are the trypsins, the chymotrypsins, and the elastases; the major exopeptidases are the carboxypeptidases A and B. As we shall see later, the specificity requirements of the endopeptidases are quite complementary, and the specificities of the carboxypeptidases are well matched to the action of the endopeptidases. Thus, through the concerted action of the complex of enzymes, a protein can be degraded first to polypeptide fragments and these can be sequentially hydrolyzed to free amino acids. Undegraded fragments no doubt remain after the action of the pancreatic enzymes, and some of these can be digested further by enzymes secreted by, or present in, the mucosa of the small intestine.

All pancreatic proteolytic enzymes known to date are synthesized in the acinar cells and secreted into the duodenum in the form of inactive precursors. The enzyme enterokinase secreted by the intestinal mucosa potentiates the complex of enzymes by activation of trypsinogen to trypsin. The newly formed trypsin then acts autocatalytically to produce more trypsin and also catalyzes the activation of all the other pancreatic zymogens. All the enzymes appear to be maximally active at pH 7.5 or above.

The early studies with pancreatic proteases were usually carried out with proteins such as hemoglobin, casein, or gelatin as substrates. Digestion of the proteins was followed by measurement of the concentration of acid-soluble split products (150). However, at about the same time that many of the pancreatic enzymes became available in purified form, Bergmann & Fruton (14) noted that these enzymes could hydrolyze small synthetic peptides and peptide derivatives. This observation showed that trypsin and chymotrypsin were endopeptidases rather than obligate proteinases as formerly believed and led ultimately to major advances in our understanding of the specificity requirements of each enzyme. Utilizing relatively simple synthetic substrates of known chemical compositions and quantitative measurements based on specific bonds split, Bergmann & Fruton (14) were able to define many of the specificity requirements of the respective pancreatic proteases.

In the 1940s Schwert et al. (174) found that the susceptible peptide bonds could be replaced by an ester bond and that such esterases were hydrolyzed even more rapidly than the corresponding peptide, provided the remaining structural requirements were fulfilled. Although Warburg had noted the hydrolyses of amino acid esters by pancreatic extracts as early as 1905 (194), proof that the hydrolyses were catalyzed by proteolytic enzymes had to await their purification.

The amino acid derivatives hydrolyzed by the endopeptidases can be represented by the general formula:

$$R-\overset{O}{\overset{||}{C}}-NHCH\overset{O}{\overset{||}{C}}-R''$$
$$\underset{R'}{|}$$

Those hydrolyzed by the carboxypeptidases can be represented by the general formulas:

$$R-\overset{O}{\overset{||}{C}}-NH-\underset{\underset{R'}{|}}{CH}-COOH \quad \text{and} \quad R-\overset{O}{\overset{||}{C}}-O-\underset{\underset{R'}{|}}{CH}-COOH$$

peptide substrates   ester substrates

All the pancreatic proteolytic enzymes are stereochemically specific for the L-form of the amino acid contributing to the susceptible bond.

The precise nature of the $R-\overset{O}{\overset{||}{C}}$, R', and R'' groups preferred by the individual enzymes, as well as the effects of modification of these groups, has been studied in depth and reviewed extensively (74, 149). No attempt is made to present these findings in detail here, but several representative synthetic substrates for each of the enzymes are cited.

Techniques for assay of the pancreatic enzymes have also been described in several comprehensive reviews (42, 74), and the reader is referred to these for details. Some examples of procedures currently in use include the colorimetric ninhydrin procedure to follow hydrolysis of peptides and modifications of the microdiffusion procedure of Conway for determination of ammonia released from amides. The more popular procedures, however, are those based on the esterase activity of these enzymes. This is due both to the relatively high affinity and reaction rates observed with the pancreatic enzymes and esters of the appropriate composition and to the relative ease of assay of esterase action. Hydrolysis of an ester bond at pH 8 liberates a fully ionized carboxyl group that can be measured by null-point titrimetric assays either manually or automatically (93, 163, 174). Alternatively, hydrolysis of many of the ester substrates can be followed by very sensitive spectrophotometric procedures based on differences in the absorption characteristics of the substrate and its hydrolysis products (59, 91, 175).

In recent years enzymologists have returned to the intact protein in their studies of the specificity of proteolytic enzymes, but at a more advanced level. The use of polypeptide chains of known amino acid sequence, such as the A and B chains of oxidized insulin, glucagon, oxytocin, and bovine pancreatic ribonuclease, and the availability of refined techniques for determining the number and nature of bonds split have led to further steps forward in the understanding of the specificity of pancreatic enzymes.

Early workers in the field of pancreatic proteases employed beef pancreas almost exclusively as their starting material, and until a decade ago almost all knowledge of the pancreatic proteases was derived from studies of bovine pancreatic enzymes and zymogens. More recently the pancreatic proteases of various mammals (16, 132–134), those of avian origin (170), and those from such phylogenetically distant species as the Chinook salmon (38) and Pacific spiny dogfish (154) have been examined. Endopeptidase activities typical of trypsin and chymotrypsin as well as carboxypeptidase activities have been found to be widely distributed in nature. The respective enzymes and zymogens show both common molecular features and discrete species differences. In describing the structural and functional features of the pancreatic enzymes and zymogens here, the best-characterized member of each family is used as a model and, where possible, pertinent species differences are noted.

II. ENDOPEPTIDASES

A. Chymotrypsins

The nomenclature surrounding pancreatic chymotrypsins is complicated by a profusion of Greek and English letters, prefixes, and Roman numerals. A brief retracing of the chronological emergence of the several families of chymotrypsins may help to clarify the relations and facilitate study of the vast literature concerning the pancreatic chymotrypsins.

In 1930 Northrop et al. (150) crystallized a basic protein from beef pancreas that was catalytically inactive but could be activated by trypsin to give a protease with milk-clotting ability. Accordingly, the enzyme was called chymotrypsin and the zymogen, chymotrypsinogen. They noted, however, that on standing the enzyme gave rise to several additional forms of enzymes with the same catalytic properties but different solubility properties and crystal habits. They called the first enzyme α-chymotrypsin and those formed subsequently β- and γ-chymotrypsins. The zymogen was designated α-chymotrypsinogen.

Later Kieth et al. (108) and Brown et al. (25), in Laskowski's laboratory, isolated and crystallized another enzyme and its zymogen from beef pancreas. The enzyme had qualitatively the same enzymatic specificity

(65) as the chymotrypsins of Northrop, Kunitz, and Herriott but was a more acidic protein. The enzyme was designated chymotrypsin B and the zymogen, chymotrypsinogen B. The zymogen has recently been purified further in two different laboratories (50, 78, 79, 161).

More recently Gjessing & Hartnett (67) isolated and crystallized an acidic esteroproteolytic enzyme from pork pancreas. The catalytic properties of this enzyme suggest that it is closely related to or identical with a protease subsequently isolated from pig pancreas by Folk & Schirmer (62) that they designated chymotrypsin C. Both groups have isolated the zymogen from their respective enzymes and studied some of the catalytic and molecular properties (56, 138). An anionic porcine chymotrypsinogen different from chymotrypsinogen B was also observed by Charles (26).

In this review the cationic forms of chymotrypsinogen and chymotrypsins typified by the proteins of Kunitz, Northrop, and Herriott are designated as members of the A family. The anionic forms typified by the bovine proteins studied in Laskowski's laboratory are considered members of the B family, and the porcine proteins described in the preceding paragraph are considered to constitute a third family, namely the chymotrypsins C.

Chymotrypsinogens of the A type have been isolated recently from pork pancreas (27, 161) and from the pancreas of the Pacific spiny dogfish (154), and it appears at the present time that there may be a bovine counterpart of the chymotrypsin C family in the form of the so-called "Fraction II" of the bovine procarboxypeptidase A complex (21, 24, 62).

I. ZYMOGEN–ENZYME RELATIONSHIPS. *a. Chymotrypsinogens A.* Chymotrypsinogen A can be activated in vitro by trypsin and also by several bacterial and mold proteinases. Activation by trypsin has been the most extensively studied and is the most physiologically significant mechanism; accordingly it is described here. Activation of chymotrypsinogen A by trypsin can give rise to a number of enzymatically active products depending on the conditions used. Northrop et al. (150), in their pioneer studies of zymogen activation, used conditions that are presently described as "slow activation," namely incubation of chymotrypsinogen A with trypsin in a ratio of 10,000:1 at 4 C for 24 hours. Under these conditions chymotrypsinogen A was converted to α-chymotrypsin and subsequently to β- and γ-chymotrypsins, all of which they isolated in crystalline forms (150).

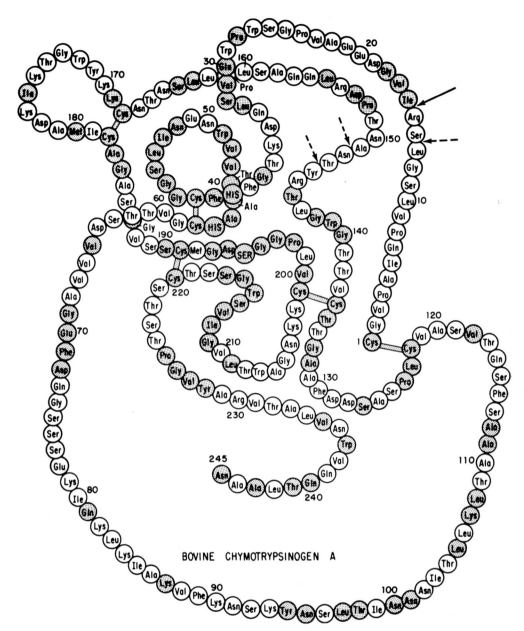

FIG. 1. Model of the structure of bovine chymotrypsinogen A, based on the amino acid sequence[1] as determined by Hartley (83) and the localization of disulfide bridges by Brown & Hartley (23, 24).[2] *Solid arrow* indicates the peptide bond hydrolyzed by trypsin during conversion of chymotrypsinogen A to π-chymotrypsin; *dotted arrows* indicate specific cleavages catalyzed by π-chymotrypsin, resulting in other chymotrypsins or the neochymotrypsinogens. *Shaded circles* indicate amino acid residues that are identical in bovine trypsinogen and chymotrypsinogen A. (The model was made available to us through the courtesy of Dr. James R. Brown.[3])

Approximately 10 years later Jacobsen (92) carried out a kinetic study of the activation of chymotrypsinogen A using conditions presently designated as

"rapid activation." Higher amounts of trypsin were used in this study, namely 1 part in 70, and the activation rate was correspondingly higher. In addition

---

[1] Abbreviations used for amino acids are those recommended by the IUPAC-IUP Combined Commission on Nomenclature in the Revised Tentative Rules of 1965 (*J. Biol. Chem.* 241: i, 1966). Glx indicates that a residue is either glutaminyl or glutamyl; Asx indicates either an asparaginyl or an aspartyl.

[2] Some minor corrections of this model have been reported by

Hartley & Kauffman (84, 85). A similar structure has been reported by Keil and his associates in Czechoslovakia (102, 103).

[3] Present address: Clayton Foundation Biochemical Institute and Department of Biochemistry, University of Texas, Austin, Texas.

the specific enzymatic activity attained during rapid activation was higher than that observed previously. This observation suggested that rapid activation was forming hitherto unknown chymotrypsins more active than α-chymotrypsin itself. Jacobsen proposed the following sequence: chymotrypsinogen A is converted by trypsin into π-chymotrypsin by the cleavage of one peptide bond. The π-chymotrypsin is further degraded to give either δ-chymotrypsin, in the case of rapid activation, or α-chymotrypsin, in the case of slow activation.

Although certain details of Jacobsen's scheme of activation have required revision, these studies paved the way for the final elucidation of the molecular events associated with chymotrypsinogen activation by Neurath's group in the United States and Desnuelle's group in France. The latter group has also described the manner in which bovine chymotrypsinogen A gives rise to altered but still activatable forms designated "neochymotrypsinogens A" (166).

The relation of bovine chymotrypsinogen A to its daughter enzymes, π-, δ-, and α-chymotrypsins, and to the neochymotrypsinogens is best illustrated through the use of a model of chymotrypsinogen. Such a model, shown in Figure 1, is possible as a result of the determination of the complete amino acid sequence by Hartley et al. (83–85) and the localization of disulfide bonds in the molecule by Brown & Hartley (22, 23).

During rapid activation bovine chymotrypsinogen A is converted to π-chymotrypsin by the cleavage of a single peptide bond between arginine-15 and isoleucine-16. The active enzyme can then act proteolytically on itself in certain discrete regions, e.g. between leucine-13 and serine-14 to give the dipeptide seryl-arginine and δ-chymotrypsin (49, 165).

During slow activation several additional reactions are possible: *1*) δ-chymotrypsin can autolyze to α-, β-, and γ-chymotrypsins; or *2*) the chymotrypsin formed can specifically cleave two bonds (one between tyrosine-146 and threonine-147 and another between asparagine-148 and alanine-149) in the chymotrypsinogen not yet activated by trypsin to give inactive neochymotrypsinogens A. On tryptic activation the neochymotrypsinogens A produce α-chymotrypsin directly (43). These sites of cleavage are shown in Figure 1.

Porcine chymotrypsinogen A is activated by a similar mechanism involving cleavage of an arginine-isoleucine bond in position 15. The amino-terminal sequence of this protein differs from that of the bovine zymogen only in the substitution of proline for glycine in position 7 (160).

Bovine chymotrypsinogen A can be activated by a proteolytic enzyme obtained from *Streptomyces griseus* as a by-product of streptomycin production (7). The rate and extent of activation are comparable to tryptic activation of the zymogen with δ-chymotrypsin, the main product.

b. Chymotrypsinogens B. Bovine chymotrypsinogen B contains between 243 and 250 residues (79) whereas bovine chymotrypsinogen A contains 245 residues (84). The sequence of the first 17 residues of chymotrypsinogen A and B are identical except for the replacement of serine by alanine in position 14 of chymotrypsinogen B (78). As described above for chymotrypsinogen A, the activation of chymotrypsinogen B by trypsin involves cleavage of a peptide bond between arginine and isoleucine in the 15th position in the chain (78). However, this cleavage is considerably more rapid in the case of chymotrypsinogen B. Furthermore, the π-form of this family of chymotrypsins does not autolyze, and therefore no δ-type chymotrypsin is seen in the B family (79, 110). Neochymotrypsinogens B, analogous to those in the A family, have been reported (80).

c. Chymotrypsinogens C. Little is known about the primary structure of chymotrypsinogen C or the molecular events of its activation. Present indications are that the porcine chymotrypsinogen C has a half-cystine residue at its amino terminal and that activation may involve the splitting of an arginyl-valine bond (62).

Table 1 presents a comparison of some molecular properties of chymotrypsinogens of various sources.

2. SUBSTRATE SPECIFICITY OF CHYMOTRYPSINS. *a. Synthetic substrates.* The catalytic specificity of the chymotrypsins has been determined with both synthetic substrates and proteins of known amino acid composition. Chymotrypsins of the bovine A family have been the most thoroughly studied. As a result of an early observation that α-chymotrypsin hydrolyzed carbobenzoxy-L-tyrosyl-glycineamide at a rapid rate, Bergmann & Fruton suggested in 1941 (14) that the enzyme was specific for aromatic residues. The prescience of this suggestion is revealed in Table 2, which presents a representative list of substrates for bovine chymotrypsins of the A family (74, 149). The enzyme attacks substrates containing the aromatic amino acids tyrosine, tryptophan, and phenylalanine and, to a lesser extent, those containing methionine. Esters composed of these residues are hydrolyzed faster than the corresponding peptides.

Several assay procedures for chymotrypsin are in use today based on the activity of the enzyme on synthetic esters. The activity against *N*-acetyl-L-tyrosine ethyl ester can be measured by the manual titrimetric

TABLE 1. *Comparison of Chymotrypsinogens of Various Sources*

	Bovine A	Porcine A	Bovine B	Dogfish*	Porcine C†
Isoelectric point	9.1 (111)	7.2 (161)	5.2 (111)	8.7	Anionic
Molecular weight	25,761 (83)	22,700 (161)	26,000 (79)	24,500	31,800
N-terminal residue	Cys (15)	Cys (161)	Cys (96, 161)	Cys	Cys
C-terminal residue	Asn (153, 164)	Asn (160)	Asn (96)		
Bond cleaved during activation	Arg-Ile (162)	Arg-Ile (160)	Arg-Ile (110, 160)	Arg-Val	Arg-Val
	15 16	15 16	15 16		
Amino acid composition	Wilcox et al. (196)	Rovery et al. (161)	Smillie (177)	Prahl & Neurath (154)	Folk & Schirmer (62)
	Hartley (83)		Guy et al. (79)		

* All data reported here for dogfish chymotrypsinogen were taken from Prahl & Neurath (154).

† All data reported here for porcine chymotrypsinogen C were taken from Folk & Schirmer (62).

procedure described by Rovery et al. (163), and the same conditions may be used for automatic titration in the pH-stat (93). The esterase activity can also be measured by the spectrophotometric procedure of Schwert & Takenaka (175) using the same substrate. The specificity and sensitivity of the spectrophotometric procedure can be increased by the use of N-benzoyl-L-tyrosine ethyl ester as described by Hummel (91). This is the recommended substrate for assay of chymotrypsin in the presence of large amounts of trypsin since it is apparently completely resistant to tryptic action, whereas N-acetyl-L-tyrosine ethyl ester is hydrolyzed by trypsin at a very slow rate.

Chymotrypsins A and B hydrolyze N-acetyl-L-tyrosine ethyl ester at about the same rate. They are equivalent against benzoyl-L-phenylalanine ethyl ester (62) and have approximately the same activity against acetyl-L-tryptophan ethyl ester in the presence of low amounts of methanol. However, the presence of 30% methanol in the assay mixture significantly lowers the activity of chymotrypsin B against the latter substrate but has little effect on the activity of chymotrypsin A. This difference in the response of the two forms of the enzyme has been a useful tool for distinguishing between them (47, 105).

The studies of Folk & Schirmer (62) on the specificity of chymotrypsin C have shown that although it is qualitatively similar to chymotrypsins A and B in its ability to hydrolyze N-acetyl-L-tyrosine ethyl ester, it differs from them in its increased ability to hydrolyze peptide, ester, and amide bonds involving the carboxyl group of leucine. Thus chymotrypsin C can be distinguished from chymotrypsins A and B by the high ratio of its activity against N-benzoyl-L-leucine ethyl ester relative to N-acetyl-L-tyrosine ethyl ester.

b. Protein substrates. The point of attack of the three chymotrypsins against glucagon, a pancreatic hormone containing 29 amino acid residues in known sequence (17, 19, 51, 56), is shown in Figure 2. These

TABLE 2. *Representative Substrates for Bovine Chymotrypsin A*

Substrate	K_m, $M \times 10^3$	$k_3 \times 10^3$*
N-acetyl-L-tyrosine amide†	27	3
N-acetyl-L-tyrosine ethyl ester	32	2600
N-acetyl-L-tryptophan amide‡	5.3	0.5
N-acetyl-L-tryptophan ethyl ester	1.7	320
N-benzoyl-L-phenylalanine ethyl ester	6.0	390
N-benzoyl-L-methionine ethyl ester	0.8	8

All assays were performed in phosphate buffer containing 30% methanol except where indicated.

* k_3 is expressed as millimoles substrate hydrolyzed per minute per milligram of enzyme nitrogen.

† In phosphate buffer without methanol.

‡ In tris(hydroxymethyl)aminomethane hydrochloride buffer.

From Green & Neurath (74).

studies corroborate the findings with synthetic substrates and show that chymotrypsin A is the most specific of the three enzymes in that it splits only phenylalanine, trytophan, and tyrosine bonds; chymotrypsin B attacks these and an additional leucine bond; chymotrypsin C, the least specific, splits all the bonds attacked by chymotrypsins A and B and, in addition, glutamine and methionine bonds.

B. Trypsins

I. ZYMOGEN-ENZYME RELATIONSHIPS. Trypsin is secreted by the acinar cells of the pancreas as an inactive precursor, trypsinogen. Northrop et al. (150) crystallized the zymogen from beef pancreas and studied many of its properties; they demonstrated that trypsinogen could be converted to trypsin by alternative mechanisms. The physiological trigger is enterokinase, a proteolytic enzyme secreted by the intestinal mucosa.

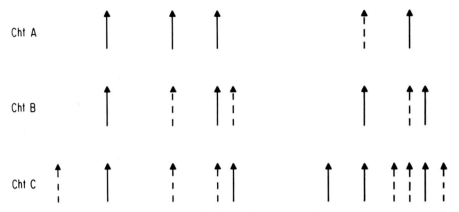

His-Ser-Gln-Gly-Thr-Phe-Thr-Ser-Asp-Tyr-Ser-Lys-Tyr-Leu-Asp-Ser-Arg-Arg-Ala-Gln-Asp-Phe-Val-Gln-Trp-Leu-Met-Asn-Thr
1 2 3 4 5 6 7 8 9 10 11 12 13 14 15 16 17 18 19 20 21 22 23 24 25 26 27 28 29

Cht A

Cht B

Cht C

FIG. 2. Amino acid sequence of glucagon and sites of action of the chymotrypsins. *Solid arrows* indicate major sites of cleavage; *dashed arrows* indicate minor sites of cleavage by chymotrypsins A (17, 51), B (51), and C (56), respectively.

However, trypsinogen can be converted autocatalytically to trypsin and can be activated also by several mold proteases. The first- and best-characterized activation system is the autocatalytic activation of bovine trypsinogen. Accordingly, this system is described and an attempt is made to relate the features of this system with those catalyzed by other enzymes or occurring in other species.

a. Autocatalytic activation. Northrop et al. (150) showed that, at neutral pH in the presence of calcium ions, trypsinogen was converted to trypsin quantitatively in a unimolecular, autocatalyzed reaction. They observed that less than half as much active trypsin was formed in the absence of calcium ions; the authors ascribed this to a secondary reaction by which some of the trypsinogen was converted by trypsin to an inert protein. Little is known of the nature of this inert protein, or even if it is a discrete entity, but present indications are that the inert protein arises from indiscriminate self-digestion and that calcium ions protect against this (44, 46, 150).

As the result of experiments carried out by Desnuelle and co-workers and by Neurath and his associates, the molecular events of the autocatalytic activation of bovine trypsinogen have been elucidated. These can be described best by reference to the model of bovine trypsinogen shown in Figure 3. Activation has been shown to consist in the cleavage of a single peptide bond, namely between lysine in position 6 and isoleucine in position 7 of the zymogen, resulting in the release of the hexapeptide and the appearance of a new amino-terminal group, isoleucine (40, 163). Concomitant with appearance of enzymatic activity

and the release of the hexapeptide, the molecule undergoes significant changes in the specific optical rotation in the direction usually indicative of greater helicity (148, 203).

b. Other activations. 1) Activation by enterokinase. Yamashina studied the activation of bovine trypsinogen, using partially purified preparations of enterokinase from duodenal juice (202). The exact mechanism of activation is difficult to define precisely since enterokinase activates trypsinogen in a pH range at which autoactivation also proceeds at a significant rate. Nonetheless the same trypsin seems to be formed in both cases.

2) Activation by mold proteinases. The strain of penicillium responsible for the activation of trypsinogen at pH 3 that was observed originally by Kunitz (114) is believed to have been lost, and no precise information is available concerning the mechanism of this reaction. However, Hofmann & Shaw (89) have reported that activation of trypsinogen to trypsin is catalyzed by an enzyme from *Penicillium janthinellum*, and the pH optimum and stability of the enzyme suggest that this penicillium kinase is very similar to, if not identical with, Kunitz's enzyme. The trypsin formed at pH 3.4 in citrate buffer by this enzyme has the same specific enzymatic activity as that formed by autoactivation.

Gabeloteau & Desnuelle (66) have studied the activation of trypsinogen by a crystalline enzyme from *Aspergillus saitoi*. Activation proceeds very rapidly at pH 4.5 and 0 C, giving rise to a trypsin with the same specific activity as that produced by

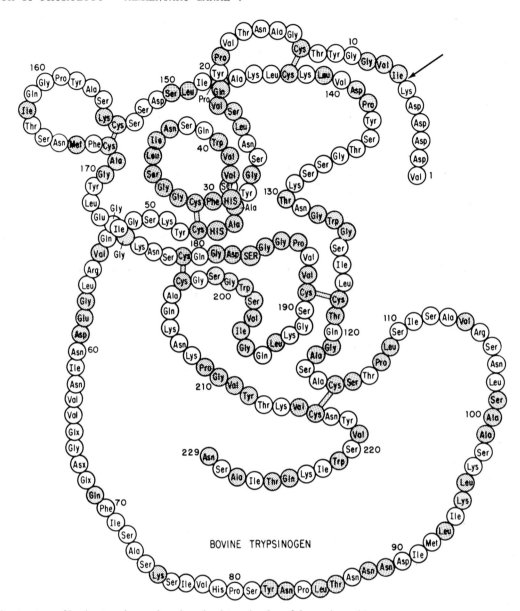

FIG. 3. Model of the structure of bovine trypsinogen based on the determination of the amino acid sequence by Walsh et al. (191) and the localization of disulfide bridges by Kauffman (100).[4] *Arrow* indicates the bond hydrolyzed during the autocatalytic activation of trypsinogen to trypsin. *Shaded circles* indicate amino acid residues that are identical in bovine trypsinogen and chymotrypsinogen A. (The model was made available to us through the courtesy of Dr. James R. Brown.)

the autocatalytic activation. The mechanism of activation seems to be the same as that of autoactivation and involves rupture of the peptide bond between lysine in position 6 and isoleucine in position 7.

[4] The covalent structure of bovine trypsinogen has been determined also by members of the Czechoslovak Academy of Science (90, 139). The sequence proposed by them is essentially the same as shown here but differs in the placement of several amino acids and in the presence of amides in positions 58, 67, 68, and 151 (140).

Nakanishi (141) has described a trypsinogen kinase from Takadiastase, a preparation derived from wheat-bran cultures of *Aspergillus oryzae*. Activation by this enzyme is optimum at pH 3.5 and appears to proceed by the usual mechanism to produce a trypsin that is identical with autoactivated trypsin in its enzymatic activity (142).

The latter reactions catalyzed by the mold proteinases are probably not of physiological importance. However, they have provided alternative means of activating trypsinogen under conditions in which autolysis does not occur and the inert protein is not formed. Moreover, interference by other pancreatic enzymes is held to a minimum under the acidic conditions of activation. They have thus been important tools in studies that do have a more immediate physiological significance.

2. SUBSTRATE SPECIFICITY. *a. Synthetic substrates.* The action of trypsin on synthetic substrates has been extensively reviewed (74, 149) and has been shown to be rather narrowly limited to those bonds involving basic amino acids, in particular to peptides, amides, and esters in which arginine or lysine contributes the carboxyl moiety. The activity of trypsin against several representative substrates is shown in Table 3 (74, 149).

Numerous methods are available for the assay of trypsin, including spectrophotometric methods employing *N*-benzoyl-L-arginine ethyl ester (175) or the more specific substrate recommended by Hummel (91), α-*p*-toluenesulfonyl-L-arginine methyl ester. The latter substrate has greater affinity for trypsin than does *N*-benzoyl-L-arginine ethyl ester and, unlike the latter, is not hydrolyzed by chymotrypsin (91). Titrimetric procedures employing these substrates have also been described (163, 174).

b. Protein substrate. The restricted specificity of trypsin is evidenced also in its action on several protein substrates. Its attack on the oxidized B chain of insulin is shown in Figure 4, demonstrating that only those bonds involving an arginine (position 22) or a lysine (position 29), or both, are hydrolyzed (172) It splits glucagon (see Fig. 2) only at lysine-12 and at the two arginine residues in positions 17 and 18 (18).

3. OTHER TRYPSINS. *a. Porcine pancreatic trypsinogen and trypsin.* Trypsinogen has been isolated from acid extracts of porcine pancreas and purified by chromatography on carboxylmethylcellulose (161). In 1963 Charles et al. (27) further characterized porcine trypsinogen and found that it undergoes autoactivation at the same rate as the bovine zymogen, achieves the same level of specific activity against *N*-benzoyl-L-arginine ethyl ester, and that calcium has the same protective effect on the trypsin formed. They also studied the molecular events of activation and found that activation involves the cleavage of a lysyl-isoleucine bond and elimination of a peptide from the amino-terminal end of the molecule (27). In this instance, however, the peptide released is an octapeptide whose structure is shown in Table 4 together with other molecular properties of the zymogens and enzymes from beef and pork.

TABLE 3. *Representative Substrates for Bovine Trypsin*

Substrate	K_m, $M \times 10^3$	$k_3 \times 10^{3*}$
N-benzoyl-L-arginine amide	2.1	2.2
N-benzoyl-L-arginine ethyl ester		280
α-*p*-Toluenesulfonyl-L-arginine methyl ester		1800
L-Lysine ethyl ester†		110

Reactions were carried out in phosphate buffer, pH 7.8 except where indicated.

* k_3 is expressed as millimoles substrate hydrolyzed per minute per milligram of enzyme nitrogen.

† pH 5.8.

From Green & Neurath (74).

FIG. 4. Sites of action of trypsin (172), chymotrypsin A (172), and elastase (143) on the B chain of insulin. *Solid arrows* indicate major sites of cleavage; *dashed arrows* indicate minor sites of cleavage.

TABLE 4. *Some Molecular Properties of Trypsinogens and Trypsins*

Property	Bovine		Porcine	
	Trypsinogen	Trypsin	Trypsinogen*	Trypsin
Isoelectric point	9.3 (74)	10.1 (74)	7.5	10.8 (183)
Molecular weight	24,000 (87)	23,800 (39)	25,100	23,400 (183)
N-terminal residue	Val (163)	Ile (163)	Phe	Ile (27)
C-terminal residue	Asn (191)	Asn (191)	Asn	Asn (27)
Activation peptide	Val-(Asp)₄-Lys (40, 163)		Phe-Pro-Thr-(Asp)₄-Lys	
Amino acid composition	Hofmann (87)		Charles et al. (27)	

* All data for porcine trypsinogen taken from Charles et al. (27).

Other species have been examined to determine the presence and nature of the trypsinogen present. These studies have shown that pancreatic juice from dog contains a trypsinogen that is a basic protein similar to the zymogens from beef and hog (133). However, in several other species [rat (134), salmon (38), and man (104)] zymogens are present that have the potential enzymatic activity typical of trypsin but differ in their molecular properties. Although they have the potential capacity to hydrolyze both N-benzoyl-L-arginine ethyl ester and α-p-toluenesulfonylarginine methyl ester, substrates usually regarded as specific for trypsin among the pancreatic proteases, their chromatographic behavior indicates that they are acidic proteins.

C. Elastases

Less is known about pancreatic elastase than the other pancreatic endopeptidases. Although studies of this enzyme date back at least 70 years, progress has been slowed by the lack of a standard substrate, impure enzyme preparations, as well as the wide variety of assay procedures employed by different investigators. Some of the discrepancies in the extensive literature on elastase and their possible causes have been reviewed by Loeven (130).

Elastin is the constituent protein of the elastic fibers that are abundant in the walls of the large arteries and in certain ligaments, e.g. the ligamentum nuchae. However, since the elastic fibers occur together with mucopolysaccharides as well as collagen fibers, and other protein and cellular elements, and since elastin itself is extremely insoluble, the elastin must be prepared by selective removal of the other constituents. In the past, different investigators have used different procedures for the preparation of elastin, and the carbohydrate content of the substrate has varied accordingly.

Using a substrate that contained a relatively high proportion of polysaccharides, Hall (81) concluded that elastase is a mixture of two elements: a proteolytic component and a synergistic mucolytic component that together have come to be called the "elastase complex." The complex exhibits both mucolytic and proteolytic action against native elastin, the proteolytic effect being mediated by the so-called "real elastase" or "elastoproteinase" and the mucolytic effect being mediated by an "elastomucase" or "elastomucoproteinase."

The elastase complex may well be important for the degradation of native elastin, but Partridge & Davis (152) have shown that the action of elastase on purified preparations of elastin containing less than 0.2% carbohydrates is entirely proteolytic. Accordingly, in this review the term "elastase" is used exclusively to describe the proteolytic enzyme capable of degrading purified preparations of elastin.

Banga (8) in 1952 prepared elastase from beef pancreas in crystalline but still relatively impure form. Lewis et al. (128) isolated crystalline elastase from pork pancreas and purified the crystalline product further by preparative electrophoresis. The electrophoretically homogeneous elastase of Lewis did not exhibit the restricted substrate specificity implicit in the name elastase but catalyzed the hydrolysis of albumin, hemoglobin, casein, fibrin, and soybean protein although not hair keratin or native collagen. Grant & Robbins (71) achieved a partial purification of porcine elastase by adsorption of the enzyme onto its substrate, elastin. The partially purified preparation also showed strong proteolytic action on proteins other than elastin and had a relatively high activity against typical synthetic substrates for chymotrypsin, for example, N-acetyl-L-tyrosine ethyl ester.

In 1961 two groups independently applied chromatographic procedures to the purification of elastase. Naughton & Sanger (143) used carboxymethylcellulose and showed that crystalline elastase prepared from pork pancreas by the procedure of Lewis et al.

(128) was contaminated with two nonelastolytic components that were eluted from the column earlier than active elastase. Their most highly purified fractions exhibited no detectable tryptic activity as judged by assay against N-benzoyl-L-arginine ethyl ester, but did show slight activity against the chymotrypsin substrate, N-acetyl-L-tyrosine ethyl ester; the authors considered this to be an inherent property of elastase rather than due to contaminant chymotrypsin. Lamy et al. (120) used chromatography on Amberlite IRC-50 to resolve two elastolytic peaks, the second of which was more specific for elastin than the first.

Thus at the present time it appears that elastases prepared without a chromatographic step are heavily contaminated by an enzyme resembling chymotrypsin This activity can be significantly reduced by chromatographic procedures, but to date even the most highly purified preparations retain a nonelastolytic proteolytic activity and possibly are still contaminated with other pancreatic endopeptidases. Conversely, it appears that elastin is not acted on by purified preparations of trypsin or chymotrypsin.

Pancreatic elastase (70) occurs in fresh pancreatic juice as a proenzyme called "proelastase." Lamy & Tauber (121) have achieved 40-fold purification of proelastase from hog pancreas, but their product is still contaminated with chymotrypsinogen although not with trypsinogen. The activation of proelastase to elastase requires active trypsin. The molecular events of activation are not well known and will have to await the preparation of pure proelastase.

Naughton & Sanger (143) tested their purified preparations of elastase on the B chain of oxidized insulin. They reported a broad specificity different from and complementary to the action of trypsin and chymotrypsin as is illustrated in Figure 4.

D. Active Centers and Molecular Homologies of Pancreatic Endopeptidases

The active center of an enzyme is generally considered to be the part of the enzyme that comes into contact with the substrate and to consist of a specificity site as well as a catalytic site. The center may include amino acid residues that are separated widely along the polypeptide chain but are brought into spatial proximity through disulfide bridges or any of a number of configurational influences

Pancreatic trypsins, chymotrypsins, and elastase belong to the class of endopeptidases known as "serine proteinases," all of which possess a serine residue at the active site (82). This residue is acylated transiently during catalysis by the carboxyl moiety of the bond hydrolyzed and it also reacts specifically with the so-called "nerve gas," diisopropylphosphofluoridate, to give the diisopropylphospho enzyme labeled at the active site. The reactive serine is in position 195 in bovine chymotrypsinogen A and position 183 in bovine trypsinogen (see Figs. 1 and 3).

Other so-called "substrate analogue reagents" have been used to demonstrate that histidine is another component of the active centers of the endopeptidases. Thus, p-toluenesulfonyl-*phenylalanine*-chloromethylketone (TPCK) and p-toluenesulfonyl-*lysine*-chloromethylketone (TLCK), resembling respectively the natural substrates for chymotrypsin (173) and trypsin (135), react specifically and irreversibly with a histidine residue in these enzymes and completely inhibit the enzymes. The peptide sequences containing the active serines are the same for all the pancreatic endopeptidases tested—for bovine trypsin, bovine chymotrypsin A, bovine chymotrypsin B, and porcine elastase (151). In addition, it has been shown recently that in these enzymes the active histidine is linked in homologous sequences to another histidine (178). The sequences around the active serine and that of the so-called "histidine loop" are shown in Table 5.

More recently it has been observed that the primary amino groups of the amino-terminal residues of these molecules are involved in the active centers of the respective pancreatic endopeptidases (119). Isoleucine is the amino-terminal residue of both trypsin and chymotrypsin (162, 163), and valine is the amino-terminal residue of elastase (D. L. Kauffman, B. S. Hartley, and J. R. Brown, personal communication). Enzymatic activity is lost in direct proportion to the loss of the primary amino groups of the residues by reaction with sodium nitrite (88).

III. EXOPEPTIDASES

Carboxypeptidases are exopeptidases that catalyze the hydrolysis of peptide bonds adjacent to the terminal carboxyl group of proteins and peptides. In 1937 Anson (6) isolated a carboxypeptidase in crystalline form from exudates of autolyzed beef pancreas. He noted that the enzyme was present in fresh tissue as a proenzyme which he called procarboxypeptidase. During the ensuing years the substrate specificity of Anson's enzyme has been defined

TABLE 5. *Amino Acid Sequences Involved in Active Centers*

Pancreatic Endopeptidase	"Serine" Sites (82)	"Histidine" Sites (179)
Bovine trypsin	Gly-Asp-Ser*-Gly	Gly-Tyr-His-Phe-Cys-Gly-Gly-Ser-Leu Ala-Ala-His*-Cys-Tyr-Lys 27 28 29 30 31 32 33 34 35 44 45 46 47 48 49
Bovine chymotrypsin A	Gly-Asp-Ser*-Gly	Gly-Phe-His-Phe-Cys-Gly-Gly-Ser-Leu Ala-Ala-His*-Cys-Gly-Val 38 39 40 41 42 43 44 45 46 55 56 57 58 59 60
Bovine chymotrypsin B	Gly-Asp-Ser*-Gly	His-Phe-Cys-Gly-Gly-Ser-Leu Ala-Ala-His*-Cys-Gly-Val
Porcine elastase	Asp-Ser*-Gly	Ala-His-Thr-Cys-Gly-Gly-Thr-Leu Ala-Ala-His*-Cys-Val-Asp

* "Active serines" and "active histidines" are marked with asterisks.

(149), and a second form of pancreatic carboxypeptidase with different specificity characteristics has been observed (53). Accordingly, Anson's enzyme has come to be known as carboxypeptidase A and the form observed more recently as carboxypeptidase B.

A. Carboxypeptidase A

I. ZYMOGEN-ENZYME RELATIONSHIPS. Procarboxypeptidase A was purified from acetone powders of beef pancreas by Keller et al. (105, 107). The purified zymogen, although homogeneous by the criteria of electrophoresis, column chromatography, and ultracentrifugation, was observed to be the zymogen for two enzymes: *1*) an exopeptidase with the specificity characteristics of carboxypeptidase A and *2*) an endopeptidase that catalyzed the hydrolysis of the synthetic substrate *N*-acetyl-L-tyrosine ethyl ester. The events of activation suggested at that time are summarized in this equation:

$$\text{Procarboxypeptidase A} \xrightarrow[5.9\ S]{\left[\substack{\text{low}\\ \text{trypsin}}\right],\ 0\ \text{C}}$$

$$\underset{5.9\ S}{\substack{\text{chromotrypsin-like}\\ \text{endopeptidase}}} \xrightarrow[\ ]{\left[\substack{\text{high}\\ \text{trypsin}}\right],\ 37\ \text{C}} \text{fragments} + \underset{3.1\ S}{\text{carboxypeptidase A}}$$

Thus, procarboxypeptidase was converted rapidly by low concentrations of trypsin at 0 C to an endopeptidase with chymotrypsin-like activity and the same sedimentation behavior as the zymogen. On incubation at 37 C with higher concentrations of trypsin, the endopeptidase was extensively degraded and a carboxypeptidase with approximately one-third the chemical mass of the parent zymogen was formed (107).

More extensive studies by Brown et al. (21, 24), Yamasaki et al. (201), and Cox et al. (36) have clarified the complex relation between bovine car-boxypeptidase A and its precursor. These workers observed that procarboxypeptidase A exists in two forms, distinguishable by their sedimentation coefficients. Procarboxypeptidase A-*S*6 denotes the zymogen studied earlier by Keller et al. (107) with a revised sedimentation coefficient of 6.1 Svedberg units (201). Procarboxypeptidase A-*S*5 is another form of the zymogen characterized by a sedimentation coefficient of 5 Svedberg units (24).

Procarboxypeptidase A-*S*6 is a complex composed of three parts designated Subunits I, II, III. The complex can be disaggregated by alternative procedures such as incubation at 22 C for 24 hours in aqueous buffers at pH 10.5 (21), incubation in solutions containing urea at concentrations greater than 5 M (21), and succinylation (147). The first two procedures are accompanied by considerable denaturation of the subunits whereas the last is not. The fractions produced by disaggregation can be separated from each other by chromatography on DEAE-cellulose and have been designated Fractions I, II, and III, respectively. Present indications, based on amino acid composition, end-group analyses, and potential enzymatic activity, indicate that Fraction I is the zymogen for carboxypeptidase A and Fraction II is the zymogen for the chymotrypsin-like endopeptidase activity (21, 147). To date no enzymatic activity has been attributed to Fraction III. The revised view of the events of activation and of disaggregation of the procarboxypeptidase A complex is summarized schematically in Figure 5.

Procarboxypeptidase A-*S*5 can be dissociated by a similar means into two Fractions, I and II, which appear to be identical to Fractions I and II from procarboxypeptidase A-*S*6 (24). Procarboxypeptidase A*S*-5 appears to lack a third subunit. Some molecular characteristics of procarboxypeptidase A-*S*5 and A-*S*6 are presented in Table 6.

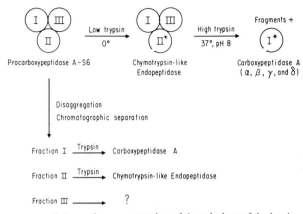

FIG. 5. Schematic representation of the relations of the bovine procarboxypeptidase A complex to carboxypeptidase A and to the chymotrypsin-like endopeptidase.

TABLE 6. *Some Molecular Properties of Bovine Procarboxypeptidases A-S5 and A-S6*

	Procarboxypeptidase A - S6*	Procarboxypeptidase A - S5†
Subunits	I, II, III	I, II
Molecular weight		
Chemical		67,500
Sed., diff.	87,080	
Sed., equil.	84,100	72,500
$S_{20,w}$	6.12	5.0
$\bar{V}$	0.72	
$D_{20,w}$	6.23×10^{-7} cm² sec⁻¹ (105)	
Amino acid composition	Yamasaki et al. (201)	Brown et al. (24)
Zn content	1 g atom/mole (185)	
Amino terminals		
Subunit I	Lysine	Lysine
Subunit II	½ Cystine	½ Cystine
Subunit III	Aspartic or asparagine	

* Except where indicated all data taken from Yamasaki et al. (201).

† All data taken from Brown et al. (24).

Crystalline bovine pancreatic carboxypeptidase A has been prepared by a variety of isolation procedures and from a spectrum of starting materials, including exudates of thawing glands (6, 155), aqueous extracts of acetone powders of pancreatic glands (1), and purified (103) or partially purified procarboxypeptidase A (36). Different molecular forms of the enzyme have resulted from the different starting materials and conditions of activation, and the Greek letters α, β, γ, and δ have been used to denote the various forms of bovine carboxypeptidase A (9,

171). The respective enzymes differ in their amino-terminal groups whereas asparagine is the carboxyl-terminal residue in all four (10). All the enzymes appear to have the same specific enzymatic activity (146). The precise interrelations of the several forms of carboxypeptidase A and their structural relation to procarboxypeptidase A are not yet known completely. Provisional schemes have been advanced by Sampath-Kumar et al. (171), Neurath (146), and Bargetzi et al. (10).

Although the activation scheme for bovine carboxypeptidase A is the best characterized to date, it may not be, in fact, representative of other species. Marchis-Mouren et al. (133) showed in 1961 that porcine pancreatic juice was a good source of procarboxypeptidase A, and subsequent studies by Charles (26) and by Folk & Schirmer (62) have shown that, in contrast to the bovine, the porcine zymogen does not exist as a complex containing potential endopeptidase activity. Although the charge properties of porcine procarboxypeptidase A are similar to those of porcine chymotrypsinogen C, the two zymogens are separable by ordinary fractionation procedures such as chromatography or disc electrophoresis (26, 62). However, multiple forms of the active porcine carboxypeptidase designated carboxypeptidase A_1, A_2, and A_3 analogous to bovine carboxypeptidase A_α, A_β, and A_γ appear to exist (54, 62).

2. SUBSTRATE SPECIFICITY. *a. Synthetic substrates.* The substrate specificity of bovine carboxypeptidase A has been extensively reviewed (74, 149) and is not covered here. Representative examples of peptide and ester substrates hydrolyzed readily by the enzyme are shown in Table 7.

Peptides and esters containing aromatic amino acids are the most sensitive substrates followed by

TABLE 7. *Some Representative Substrates for Bovine Carboxypeptidase A*

Substrate	K_m, M $\times 10^3$	$k_3 \times 10^3$*
Carboxybenzoxyglycyl-L-phenylalanine	33	2,100
Hippuryl-L-phenylalanine	11	2,000
Hippuryl-β-L-phenyllactic acid	0	1,720

* k_3 is expressed as millimoles substrate hydrolyzed per minute per milligram of enzyme nitrogen.

These data were taken from Green & Neurath (74). The kinetic measurements were performed in 0.04 M phosphate buffer, pH 7.5, containing 0.1 M LiCl. Somewhat different values obtained with different buffers and higher ionic strengths have been reported (33, 131, 137).

those containing residues with aliphatic side chains, such as leucine, alanine, and isoleucine. It is of interest to compare the kinetic constants for the specific peptide substrate hippuryl-L-phenylalanine with those for the specific ester substrate hippuryl-L-phenyllactic acid. Whereas the specific rate constants, k_3, are nearly identical for these two substrates, carboxypeptidase A has a much higher affinity for the ester than for the corresponding peptide as evidenced by the respective Michaelis constants.

b. Protein substrates. Among the factors influencing the action of carboxypeptidase A on proteins is the nature of the amino acid in the carboxyl-terminal position. The enzyme is sensitive to the presence of charged groups in the vicinity. Some charged groups, such as arginine and lysine, effectively stop the action of the enzyme (145). Others, such as histidine or glutamic acid, *can* be removed but the reaction proceeds at significant rates only at pH's at which the charge on the residue is suppressed. Thus, histidine is released very slowly from β-lactoglobulin at pH 7.6 but relatively rapidly at pH 9.2 (41), and the optimum pH of the action of carboxypeptidase on polyglutamic acid is 5.5 (73).

The nature of the residue in the penultimate position is also influential, and the imino acid proline in this position will block the action of the enzyme (180).

In keeping with these considerations it has been seen that alanine is the only amino acid released from the terminal sequence Pro-Lys-Ala of the B chain of oxidized insulin (127) (see Fig. 4) whereas 11 amino acids (residues 19–29) were released to an appreciable extent from glucagon during a 24-hour incubation [(20); see Fig. 2].

The tertiary structure of a protein often protects it from carboxypeptidase A action. Many proteins, such as the pancreatic chymotrypsinogens, are resistant to the action of the enzymes in their native configuration but susceptible after denaturation or rupture of disulfide bonds (153).

B. Carboxypeptidase B

In 1956 Folk (53) reported the presence in autolyzed bovine pancreas of a second form of carboxypeptidase with a substrate specificity complementary to that of bovine carboxypeptidase A. In the same report it was stated that the enzyme, designated carboxypeptidase B, exists in fresh pancreas as an inactive precursor, which could be activated by trypsin. The zymogen, designated procarboxypep-

tidase B, has been studied subsequently by Pechère et al. (153), Wintersberger et al. (198), and Cox et al. (37).

An active carboxypeptidase B was isolated by Folk et al. (60) from porcine pancreas. Some of the chemical and molecular characteristics of porcine carboxypeptidase B, but not the events of activation, have been reported (55, 60).

I. ZYMOGEN-ENZYME RELATIONSHIPS. Bovine procarboxypeptidase B has been isolated and purified (198) and is the only well-characterized species in terms of events of activation (37, 198). The purified zymogen is homogeneous by the criteria of chromatography, sedimentation analysis, moving-boundary electrophoresis, and potential enzymatic activity (198). On activation it gives rise to carboxypeptidase B, which has been isolated in crystalline form. Activation of the zymogen is mediated by trypsin and appears to occur in two steps: an initial fast reaction leading to the appearance of 60–70 % of the maximal enzymatic activity without significant change in the sedimentation coefficient of the protein, 4 S, and a second phase resulting in full enzymatic activity and formation of a protein with a lower sedimentation coefficient, 3.1 S. The appearance of activity during the initial stage of activation appears to coincide with the hydrolysis of a single arginyl-threonine bond in the zymogen (37). There is no indication that bovine procarboxypeptidase B exists as a complex analogous to bovine procarboxypeptidase A.

2. SUBSTRATE SPECIFICITY. *a. Synthetic substrates.* The distinguishing characteristic of carboxypeptidase B is its ability to hydrolyze substrates with a basic amino acid in the carboxyl-terminal position. Hippuryl-L-lysine is a sensitive substrate (53) as is hippuryl-L-arginine (57) and its ester analogue, hippuryl-L-argininic acid (58). Carbobenzoxyglycyl-L-histidine, however, is not attacked by the enzyme, and, like carboxypeptidase A, the action of carboxypeptidase B is slowed markedly by the presence of the imino acid proline in a penultimate position (145).

The action of bovine carboxypeptidase B, however, is not restricted to basic substrates but extends to substrates once considered to be specific for carboxypeptidase A (198). It can hydrolyze hippuryl-L-phenyllactic acid at the same rate and carbobenzoxyglycyl-L-phenylalanine at one-fifth the rate of the A enzyme (198). In contrast, bovine carboxypeptidase A does not hydrolyze to any significant degree the basic substrates typical for carboxypeptidases B (69, 149). Thus, the activities of the two enzymes are complementary but not mutually exclusive and can best be distinguished through the use of competitive inhibitors (198).

The specificity of porcine carboxypeptidase B appears to be more restrictive (60, 198).

b. Protein substrates. Carboxypeptidase B liberates lysine from poly-L-lysine and from the C-terminal position of meromyosin-L (68); it liberates arginine from salmine (68). By itself, or in conjunction with the A form of carboxypeptidase, it has proved useful for elucidation of the carboxyl-terminal sequences of proteins and peptides.

C. Active Centers of Exopeptidases

In a classic series of experiments, Vallee and his associates and Neurath and co-workers demonstrated that the bovine carboxypeptidase A exhibits the characteristics of a metalloenzyme (187, 188). The enzyme prepared from bovine pancreatic glands was shown to contain 1 g atom of firmly bound zinc per molecule of enzyme protein, and several lines of evidence were advanced indicating that zinc occurs naturally in the enzyme and not as an artifact of purification. These included the observation that the zinc content and enzymatic activity of carboxypeptidase A increased parallelly during purification and crystallization and remained constant during recrystallization, whereas other metals initially present decreased to stoichiometrically insignificant quantities (188). Furthermore, ^{65}Zn-labeled carboxypeptidase A could be isolated from bovine pancreatic juice after the administration of ^{65}Zn to the animal (167).

These same investigators showed that the metal was firmly bound to the protein but could be removed by dialysis against buffers of pH's under 5.5 or against solutions containing complexing agents such as 1,10-phenanthroline (189). Under either condition enzymatic activity was lost in direct proportion to the loss of zinc. On exposure of the zinc-free apoenzyme to approximately equimolar concentrations of zinc ions, enzymatic activity was restored to the initial level and reactivation was directly proportional to the amount of zinc bound (189). However, other metals are capable of substituting for zinc, and this leads to the formation of a series of metallocarboxypeptidases, each containing 1 g atom of metal per mole and each with enzymatic activity characteristic of the specific metal. Co^{++}, Ni^{++}, Mn^{++}, Fe^{++}—all metals of the first transition period—restored both esterase and peptidase activities to the apoenzymes (31, 32, 189). However, the relative rates of enzymatic activity varied with the specific substrate used. Enzymatic activity against carbobenzoxyglycyl-L-phenylalanine, a commonly used peptide substrate for carboxypeptidase A, was found to be in the order: Co^{++} $Ni^{++} > Zn^{++} > Mn^{++} > Fe^{++}$ (31, 32), but the order differed when other peptide substrates were used (32, 184). Replacement of zinc with Cd^{++} or Hg^{++}—group II B metals—resulted in carboxypeptidases that were active esterases but no longer hydrolyzed peptides (32, 184). These and other aspects of the active center of carboxypeptidase A have been reviewed recently by Vallee (185), who writes: "Thus, solely through the replacement of one metal atom the initial dual specificity of the enzyme is curtailed such that it is only an esterase."

Chemical modifications also increase esterase and decrease peptidase activities, and these changes appear to be related to the modification of two reactive tyrosyl groups in the active center of carboxypeptidase A (185).

Most of the studies on the metallocarboxypeptidases have been made with either carboxypeptidase A_γ or carboxypeptidase A_δ, both of which have amino-terminal asparagine residues. A number of experimental approaches have all led to the conclusion that in carboxypeptidase A_δ the metal atom is bound to the α-amino group of the N-terminal residue and to the sulfur atom of the molecule's only cysteine residue (32, 34, 35, 186, 190). The zinc-binding peptide has been isolated from bovine carboxypeptidase A_α, and the preliminary report of its amino acid sequence has been published (193).

Analogously, carboxypeptidases B from bovine pancreas (199) or from porcine pancreas (60) contain 1 g atom of zinc per mole of enzyme, and the metal is essential for the catalytic function of these enzymes. Wintersberger et al. (197, 199) have demonstrated that, as in the case of bovine pancreatic carboxypeptidase A, zinc is bound to bovine pancreatic carboxypeptidase B through a single thiol group. A peptide containing the thiol group was isolated by Wintersberger and its amino acid sequence was determined (197). These studies revealed that despite similarities in the mechanism of action of carboxypeptidases A and B, the zinc-binding peptides from the respective enzymes were quite different in their composition and amino acid sequence. This lack of structural correspondence was surprising in the light of observations made with other proteolytic enzymes, e.g. the so-called "serine enzymes." Wintersberger writes: "The lack of homology between the cysteinyl amino peptides of carboxypeptidases A and B may suggest that these two enzymes have evolved independently. . . . Alternatively it might be suggested that the difference in amino acid sequence in region of the zinc binding thiol is of no moment as this group merely serves as a support for the crucial metal atom but itself is not part of the active site." A clarification of the possible homologies between carboxypeptidases A and B must await the elucidation of the entire amino acid sequence of both enzymes.

IV. DIGESTIVE ACTION OF COMPLEX OF PANCREATIC PROTEOLYTIC ENZYMES

In the preceding sections the individual endopeptidases and exopeptidases were discussed as separate entities. In this section an attempt is made to relate the separate events and to assess the full effect of the complex of pancreatic enzymes in digestion.

Protein digestion begins in the stomach, where the acidic conditions favor denaturation of any dietary protein not already denatured by cooking. Here pepsin, released from its precursor by gastric hydrochloric acid, acts on protein to produce polypeptides of varying sizes. Pepsin activity, which is optimum around pH 2, stops when the gastric contents are mixed in the duodenum with the alkaline pancreatic juice. The pH of the duodenal contents is around 6.5 and favorable for continued digestion by the pancreatic enzymes. The pancreatic enzymes involved in protein digestion are all secreted from the pancreas in enzymatically inactive forms. They travel by way of the pancreatic juice into the duodenum, where trypsinogen becomes activated by the enterokinase secreted by the intestinal mucosa. The newly formed trypsin then acts autocatalytically on the remaining trypsinogen to produce more trypsin and also catalyzes the activation of all the other pancreatic zymogens.

The activated endopeptidases and exopeptidases act in concert to continue the process of protein digestion begun in the stomach, with the endopeptidases acting to prepare substrates for the exopeptidases. Trypsin attacks peptide bonds in the interior of the protein molecules to produce peptides with basic amino acids in the carboxyl-terminal position, which are well-tailored substrates for carboxypeptidase B action. Similarly, the chymotrypsins and elastase produce peptides with aromatic or nonpolar amino acids as the carboxyl-terminal groups, which are the preferred substrates for carboxypeptidase A. These relationships are summarized in Figure 6.

Aminopeptidases and other peptidases produced by the intestinal mucosa further complement and extend the action of the pancreatic enzymes, and in this manner the dietary protein can be hydrolyzed to free amino acids, which are the major products of intestinal digestion. Although it is recognized that protein digestion in vitro is facilitated by cleavage of

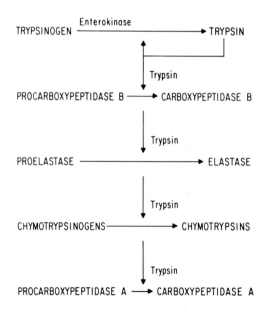

FIG. 6. Summary of the activation and digestive action of the pancreatic proteolytic enzymes.

the disulfide bridges, the manner in which the disulfide bonds of dietary protein are dealt with remains unknown at the present time.

Most of the earlier investigators interested in the proteolytic enzymes of the pancreas used tissue minces and extracts as starting materials. During the last decade, however, a number of investigators have studied the enzymes present in pancreatic juice collected directly by cannulation of the pancreatic duct. In bovine pancreatic juice the proteolytic zymogens—trypsinogen, the chymotrypsinogens A and B, and procarboxypeptidase A-S6—account for approximately two-thirds of the total protein secreted by the acinar cells (106). These proteins from pancreatic juice were shown to conform closely in physicochemical properties and enzymatic behavior to their counterparts previously isolated from acid or aqueous extracts of minced pancreas (106, 107, 150). Members of Desnuelle's group in France have shown that proportions of the respective digestive enzymes and zymogens are different for different species (133, 134) and can be altered by diet (11, 12, 134, 156–158). Marchis-Mouren (132) has reviewed the salient differences in the enzymatic composition of pancreatic juices of beef, pig, rat, and dog. More recently Keller & Allan (104) have reported preliminary observations made with human pancreatic juice.

V. INHIBITORS

A number of relatively simple organic compounds are powerful inhibitors of the pancreatic proteolytic enzymes. These include the organophosphates and substrate analogue inhibitors described earlier that react specifically and irreversibly at the active sites of the endopeptidases, as well as the chelating agents that complex the essential metals of the exopeptidases. They include also a wide spectrum of compounds that compete with the natural substrates for the respective enzymes and inhibit by virtue of their competition. The latter have been discussed extensively in several review articles on the pancreatic endopeptidases and exopeptidases (74).

In addition, trypsin inhibitors of a protein nature are widely distributed in nature. Inhibitors have been isolated in crystalline form from a variety of legumes, such as soybean (115, 116), lima bean (63, 182), field bean and double bean (181), and mung bean (29, 30); from plasma (72); from urine (176); from colostrum (122, 123, 125); from ovomucoid (64, 129); and from pancreas (101, 117). Laskowski and his associates have systematically studied a variety of these inhibitors including those from plasma (126), ovomucoid (124), soybean (124), colostrum (123, 125), and pancreas (124). Laskowski & Laskowski (124) have written a comprehensive review on the naturally occurring trypsin inhibitors. More recently Chü et al. (29) reviewed the properties of a number of trypsin inhibitors in their reports on the inhibitor from mung bean. Further review of the field at this time would be repetitive and beyond the scope of this chapter. Rather, an attempt is made to review recent developments concerning the pancreatic inhibitors.

Two trypsin inhibitors have been isolated from bovine pancreatic glands. Kunitz & Northrop (117) prepared a crystalline trypsin inhibitor from bovine pancreas in 1936. They showed that the inhibitor combined stoichiometrically with trypsin in the pH range 3–7 to form an inactive complex, which they isolated in crystalline form. In 1948 a second trypsin inhibitor from bovine pancreas was discovered and crystallized by Kazal et al. (101). The two forms of pancreatic inhibitor, presently designated the Kunitz inhibitor and the Kazal inhibitor, respectively, have some properties in common: both are crystalline proteins of low molecular weight, and both are soluble and still active after exposure to 2.5% TCA for 5 min at 80 C. However, the Kunitz inhibitor is a homogeneous protein, whereas preparations of the Kazal inhibitor contain three electrophoretic components, at least two of which are active. Moreover, the Kunitz inhibitor is a basic protein (75), whereas all the components of Kazal's preparation have acidic isoelectric points (101). The inhibitors show functional differences as well. Kunitz's preparation inhibits bovine chymotrypsins A and B as well as trypsin, whereas the Kazal inhibitor does not (200). The Kazal inhibitor is susceptible to tryptic digestion in the presence of calcium resulting in a temporary inhibition, whereas the Kunitz inhibitor, in its native state, resists inactivation by trypsin (126). Some of the properties of the two proteins are shown in Table 8.

Although the Kunitz inhibitor has a longer history and is the better characterized of the two forms, present indications are that the Kazal inhibitor is the secreted form. Thus the pancreatic juices of rat (77), dog (94), beef (76), and man (104) all contain trypsin inhibitors with kinetic properties resembling those of Kazal's preparation.

Moreover, Kunitz's inhibitor has been observed recently to be related to the so-called "kallikrein

TABLE 8. *Comparison of Properties of Two Bovine Pancreatic Trypsin Inhibitors, Kunitz and Kazal Inhibitors*

Property	Kunitz Inhibitor (117)	Kazal Inhibitor (101)
Purity	Crystalline (117)	Crystalline (101); three components, A, B and C (101)
Isoelectric point	>8.7 (125)*; >10 (75)†	A, 5.9; B, 5.2; and C, 4.8 (101)*
Molecular weight	6,513 (99)‡	9,600 (124)§
Amino acid composition	(99)	Not known
Type of inhibition of bovine trypsin (17)	Nontemporary (126)	Temporary (126)
Inhibition of chymotrypsin Aα	Yes (200)	No (200)
Inhibition of chymotrypsin B	Yes (200)	No (200)

* Determined by moving-boundary electrophoresis.
† Determined by filter-paper electrophoresis.
‡ Minimum molecular weight calculated from amino acid composition.
§ Estimated from activity of the inhibitor as assayed by the method of Kunitz (116).

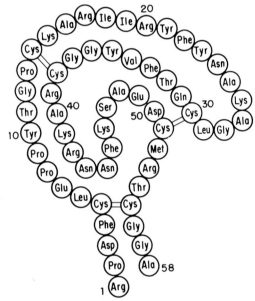

FIG. 7. Model of the structure of bovine pancreatic trypsin inhibitor, based on the amino acid sequence as determined by Kassell (97).

inactivators." Kallikrein is the Greek word for pancreas used to describe certain proteolytic enzymes of glandular origin, but found also in plasma, which act on plasma α-2 globulins to release hypotensive peptides. The inactive precursors of the hypotensive peptides, which are usually isolated as α-2 globulins, have been designated bradykininogen and kallidinogen, respectively. Bradykininogen is converted by kallikrein, as well as by snake venom and trypsin, to a nonapeptide named bradykinin, a powerful smooth muscle hypotensive agent (159); kallidinogen is converted by kallikrein to a decapeptide with physiological properties similar to those of bradykinin,

named kallidin. The structure of these peptides is shown below (86):

bradykinin: Arg-Pro-Pro-Gly-Phe-Ser-Pro-Phe-Arg
kallidin: Lys-Arg-Pro-Pro-Gly-Phe-Ser-Pro-Phe-Arg

Kallidin differs from bradykinin only by the presence of one lysine residue at the amino-terminal end of the peptide chain and can be converted to bradykinin by trypsin. Removal of the carboxyl-terminal arginine by carboxypeptidase B inactivates the peptides (52). The structure and function of bradykinin, kallidin, and some of their congeners have been reviewed in a recent monograph (195).

Kunitz's pancreatic trypsin inhibitor is a kallikrein inactivator and appears to be identical in all respects to other kallikrein inhibitors, for example, those from bovine lung or parotid gland. The primary structure of the pancreatic inhibitor has been investigated recently in three different laboratories (24, 48, 97, 98), and slightly different linear sequences have been reported for the protein. Figure 7 presents the amino acid sequence and disulfide bridging as determined by Kassell et al. (97). Recently Kraut & Bhargava (109) and Anderer & Hornle (2-4) have shown that crystalline kallikrein inhibitors from bovine lung and parotid glands have structures identical to that shown in Figure 7.

However, at the present time our understanding of the precise physiological roles and importance of the respective pancreatic inhibitors is incomplete.

I am greatly indebted to Miss Elaine Cohen and Miss Barbara Allan for their assistance in the preparation of this manuscript. Their contributions to the content and form of the chapter have been numerous and valuable and are deeply appreciated.

REFERENCES

1. ALLAN, B. J., P. J. KELLER, AND H. NEURATH. Procedures for the isolation of crystalline bovine pancreatic carboxypeptidase A. I. Isolation from acetone powders of pancreas glands. *Biochemistry* 3: 40–43, 1964.

2. ANDERER, F. A. Strukturuntersuchungen am kallikrein-inactivator aus Rinderlunge. II. Bestimmung der Aminosäuresequenz. *Z. Naturforsch.* 20b: 462–472, 1965.

3. ANDERER, F. A. Zur Identitat des kallikrein-inactivators aus rinderlunge und rinderparotis. *Z. Naturforsch.* 20b: 499–501, 1965.

4. ANDERER, F. A., AND S. HÖRNLE. Strukturuntersuchungen am kallikrein-inactivator aus Rinderlunge. I. Molekulargewicht, Endgruppenanalyse und Aminosäure-Zusammensetzung. *Z. Naturforsch.* 20b: 457–462, 1965.

5. ANDERER, F. A., AND S. HÖRNLE. The disulfide linkages in kallikrein inactivator of bovine lung. *J. Biol. Chem.* 241: 1568–1571, 1966.

6. ANSON, M. L. Carboxypeptidase. I. The preparation of crystalline carboxypeptidase. *J. Gen. Physiol.* 20: 663–669, 1937.

7. AWAD, W. M., JR., AND P. E. WILCOX. The activation of chymotrypsinogen A by a protease from *Strepomyces griseus*. *Biochim. Biophys. Acta* 73: 285–292, 1963.

8. BANGA, I. Isolation and crystallization of elastase from the pancreas of cattle. *Acta Physiol. Acad. Sci. Hung.* 3: 317–324, 1952.

9. BARGETZI, J-P., K. S. V. SAMPATH-KUMAR, D. J. COX, K. A. WALSH, AND H. NEURATH. The amino acid composition of bovine pancreatic carboxypeptidase A. *Biochemistry* 2: 1468–1474, 1963.

10. BARGETZI, J-P., E. O. P. THOMPSON, K. S. V. SAMPATH-KUMAR, K. A. WALSH, AND H. NEURATH. The amino- and carboxyl-terminal residues and the self-digestion of bovine pancreatic carboxypeptidase A. *J. Biol. Chem.* 239: 3767–3774, 1964.

11. BEN ABDELJLIL, A., A. M. VISANI, AND P. DESNUELLE. Adaptation of the exocrine secretion of rat pancreas to the composition of the diet. *Biochem. Biophys. Res. Commun.* 10: 112–116, 1963.

12. BEN ABDELJLIL, A., AND P. DESNUELLE. Sur l'adaptation des enzymes exocrines du pancréas à la composition du régime. *Biochim. Biophys. Acta* 81: 136–149, 1964.

13. BERGMANN, M. A classification of proteolytic enzymes. *Advan. Enzymol.* II: 49–68, 1942.

14. BERGMANN, M., AND J. S. FRUTON. The specificity of proteinases. *Advan. Enzymol.* I: 63–98, 1941.

15. BETTLEHEIM, F. R. Amino terminal group in chymotrypsinogen. *J. Biol. Chem.* 212: 235–239, 1955.

16. BRICTEUX-GREGOIRE, S., R. SCHYNS, AND M. FLORKIN. Structure des peptides libérés au cours de l'activation du trypsinogène de mouton. *Biochim. Biophys. Acta* 127: 277–279, 1966.

17. BROMER, W. W., L. G. SINN, AND O. BEHRENS. The amino acid sequence of glucagon. II. The hydrolysis of glucagon with chymotrypsin. *J. Am. Chem. Soc.* 79: 2798–2801, 1957.

18. BROMER, W. W., L. G. SINN, AND O. BEHRENS. The amino acid sequence of glucagon. III. The hydrolysis of glucagon by trypsin. *J. Am. Chem. Soc.* 79: 2801–2805, 1957.

19. BROMER, W. W., L. G. SINN, AND O. BEHRENS. The amino acid sequence of glucagon. V. Location of amide groups, acid degradation and summary of sequential evidence. *J. Am. Chem. Soc.* 79: 2807–2810, 1957.

20. BROMER, W. W., A. STAUB, E. R. DILLER, H. L. BIRD, L. G. SINN, AND O. K. BEHRENS. The amino acid sequence of glucagon. I. Amino acid composition and terminal amino acid analyses. *J. Am. Chem. Soc.* 79: 2794–2798, 1957.

21. BROWN, J. R., R. N. GREENSHIELDS, M. YAMASAKI, AND H. NEURATH. The subunit structure of bovine procarboxypeptidase A-S6. Chemical properties and enzymatic activities of the products of molecular disaggregation. *Biochemistry* 2: 867–876, 1963.

22. BROWN, J. R., AND B. S. HARTLEY. The disulfide bridges of chymotrypsinogen-A. *Biochem. J.* 89: 59P, 1963.

23. BROWN, J. R., AND B. S. HARTLEY. Location of disulfide bridges by diagonal paper electrophoresis. The disulfide bridges of bovine chymotrypsinogen A. *Biochem. J.* 101: 214–228, 1966.

24. BROWN, J. R., M. YAMASAKI, AND H. NEURATH. A new form of bovine pancreatic procarboxypeptidase A. *Biochemistry* 2: 877–886, 1963.

25. BROWN, K. D., R. E. SHUPE, AND M. LASKOWSKI. Crystalline activated protein B (chymotrypsin B). *J. Biol. Chem.* 173: 99–107, 1948.

26. CHARLES, M. Nouvelles recherches sur le chymotrypsinogène B. Evaluation quantitative et essai d'identification chez porc. *Biochim. Biophys. Acta* 92: 319–327, 1964.

27. CHARLES, M., M. ROVERY, A. GUIDONI, AND P. DESNUELLE. Sur le trypsinogène et la trypsine de porc. *Biochim. Biophys. Acta* 69: 115–129, 1963.

28. CHAUVET, J., G. NOUVEL, AND R. ACHER. Structure primaire d'un inhibiteur pancréatique de la trypsine (inhibiteur de Kunitz et Northrop). *Biochim. Biophys. Acta* 92: 200–201, 1964.

29. CHÜ, H.-M., AND C.-W. CHI. The isolation and crystallization of two trypsin inhibitors of low molecular weight from mung bean (Phaseolus aureus Roxb.). *Sci. Sinica, Peking* 14: 1441–1453, 1965.

30. CHÜ, H.-M., S.-S. LO, M.-H. JEN, C.-W. CHI, AND T.-C. TSAO. The relationship between trypsin inhibitors A and B from mung bean (Phaseolus aureus Roxb.) and some chemical characteristics of the inhibitors. *Sci. Sinica, Peking* 14: 1454–1463, 1965.

31. COLEMAN, J. E., AND B. L. VALLEE. Metallocarboxypeptidases. *J. Biol. Chem.* 235: 390–395, 1960.

32. COLEMAN, J. E., AND B. L. VALLEE. Metallocarboxypeptidases: stability constants and enzymatic characteristics. *J. Biol. Chem.* 236: 2244–2249, 1961.

33. COLEMAN, J. E., AND B. L. VALLEE. Apocarboxypeptidase-substrate complexes. *J. Biol. Chem.* 237: 3430–3436, 1962.

34. COOMBS, T. L., AND Y. OMOTE. Chemical constitution of the active center of carboxypeptidase A. *Federation Proc.* 21: 234, 1962.

35. COOMBS, T. L., Y. OMOTE, AND B. L. VALLEE. The zinc-binding groups of carboxypeptidase A. *Biochemistry* 3: 653–662, 1964.

36. COX, D. J., F. C. BOVARD, J-P. BARGETZI, K. A. WALSH, AND H. NEURATH. Procedures for the isolation of crystalline bovine pancreatic carboxypeptidase A. II. Isolation

of carboxypeptidase Aα from procarboxypeptidase A. *Biochemistry* 3: 44-47, 1964.

37. COX, D. J., E. WINTERSBERGER, AND H. NEURATH. Bovine pancreatic procarboxypeptidase B. II. Mechanism of activation. *Biochemistry* 1: 1078-1082, 1962.

38. CROSTON, C. B. Endopeptidases of salmon ceca: chromatographic separation and some properties. *Arch. Biochem. Biophys.* 112: 218-223, 1955.

39. CUNNINGHAM, L. W., JR. Molecular-kinetic properties of crystalline diisopropyl-phosphoryl trypsin. *J. Biol. Chem.* 211: 13-19, 1954.

40. DAVIE, E. W., AND H. NEURATH. Identification of a peptide released during the autocatalytic activation of trypsinogen. *J. Biol. Chem.* 212: 515-529, 1955.

41. DAVIE, E. W., C. R. NEWMAN, AND P. E. WILCOX. Action of carboxypeptidase on β-lactoglobulin. *J. Biol. Chem.* 234: 2635-2641, 1959.

42. DAVIS, N. C., AND E. L. SMITH. Assay of proteolytic enzymes. In: *Methods of Biochemical Analysis*, edited by D. Glick. New York: Interscience, 1955, vol. II, p. 215-257.

43. DESNUELLE, P. Chymotrypsin. In: *The Enzymes*, edited by P. D. Boyer, H. Lardy, and K. Myrbäck. New York: Acad. Press, 1960, vol. 4, p. 93-118.

44. DESNUELLE, P. Trypsin. In: *The Enzymes*, edited by P. D. Boyer, H. Lardy, and K. Myrbäck. New York: Acad. Press, 1960, vol. 4, p. 119-132.

45. DESNUELLE, P., AND C. FABRE. Sur le sequence N-terminale due trypsinogène et son ablation pendant l'activation de ce zymogen. *Biochim. Biophys. Acta* 18: 49-57, 1955.

46. DESNUELLE, P., AND C. GABELOTEAU. Sur le rôle du calcium pendant l'activation du trypsinogène par la trypsine. *Arch. Biochem. Biophys.* 69: 475-485, 1957.

47. DESNUELLE, P., AND M. ROVERY. The proteins of the exocrine pancreas. *Advan. Protein Chem.* 16: 139-195, 1961.

48. DLOUHA, V., D. POSPISILOVA, B. MELOUN, AND F. SORM. On proteins XCIV. Primary structure of basic trypsin inhibitor from beef pancreas. *Collection Czech. Chem. Commun.* 30: 1311-1325, 1965.

49. DREYER, W. J., AND H. NEURATH. The activation of chymotrypsinogen A. *J. Biol. Chem.* 217: 527-539, 1955.

50. ENEKEL, A. G., AND L. B. SMILLIE. Preparation and purity of chymotrypsinogen B. *Biochemistry* 2: 1445-1448, 1963.

51. ENEKEL, A. G., AND L. B. SMILLIE. Specificity of chymotrypsin B toward glucagon. *Biochemistry* 2: 1449-1454, 1963.

52. ERDOS, E. G., AND E. M. SLOANE. An enzyme in human blood plasma that inactivates bradykinin and kallidins. *Biochem. Pharmacol.* 11: 585-592, 1962.

53. FOLK, J. E. A new pancreatic carboxypeptidase. *J. Am. Chem. Soc.* 78: 3541-3542, 1956.

54. FOLK, J. E. The porcine pancreatic carboxypeptidase A system. II. Mechanism of the conversion of carboxypeptidase A_1 to carboxypeptidase A_2. *J. Biol. Chem.* 238: 3895-3898, 1963.

55. FOLK, J. E., R. C. BRAUNBERG, AND J. A. GLADNER. Carboxypeptidase B. V. Amino- and carboxyl-terminal sequences. *Biochim. Biophys. Acta* 47: 595-596, 1961.

56. FOLK, J. E., AND P. W. COLE. Chymotrypsin C. II. Enzymatic specificity toward several polypeptides. *J. Biol. Chem.* 240: 193-197, 1965.

57. FOLK, J. E., AND J. A. GLADNER. Carboxypeptidase B. I. Purification of the zymogen and specificity of the enzyme. *J. Biol. Chem.* 231: 379-391, 1958.

58. FOLK, J. E., AND J. A. GLADNER. Carboxypeptidase B. III. Specific esterase activity. *Biochim. Biophys. Acta* 33: 570-572, 1959.

59. FOLK, J. E., AND J. A. GLADNER. Cobalt activation of carboxypeptidase A. *J. Biol. Chem.* 235: 60-63, 1960.

60. FOLK, J. E., K. A. PIEZ, W. R. CARROLL, AND J. A. GLADNER. Carboxypeptidase B. IV. Purification and characterization of the porcine enzyme. *J. Biol. Chem.* 235: 2272-2277, 1960.

61. FOLK, J. E., AND E. W. SCHIRMER. The porcine pancreatic carboxypeptidase A system. I. Three forms of the active enzyme. *J. Biol. Chem.* 238: 3884-3894, 1963.

62. FOLK, J. E., AND E. W. SCHIRMER. Chymotrypsin C. I. Isolation of the zymogen and the active enzyme: preliminary structure and specificity studies. *J. Biol. Chem.* 240: 181-192, 1965.

63. FRAENKEL-CONRAT, H., R. C. BEAN, E. D. DUCAY, AND H. S. OLCOTT. Isolation and characterization of a trypsin inhibitor from lima beans. *Arch. Biochem. Biophys.* 37: 393-407, 1952.

64. FREDERICQ, E., AND H. Z. DEUTSCH. Studies of ovomucoid. *J. Biol. Chem.* 181: 499-509, 1949.

65. FRUTON, J. S. Specificity of chymotrypsin B. *J. Biol. Chem.* 173: 109-110, 1948.

66. GABELOTEAU, C., AND P. DESNUELLE. Sur l'activation du trypsinogène de boeuf par une protéinase crystallisée d' *Aspergillus saitoi*. *Biochim. Biophys. Acta* 42: 230-237, 1960.

67. GJESSING, E. C., AND J. C. HARTNETT. Crystallization and characterization of an esteroproteolytic enzyme from porcine pancreas. *J. Biol. Chem.* 237: 2201-2206, 1962.

68. GLADNER, J. A., AND J. E. FOLK. Carboxypeptidase B. II. Mode of action on protein substrates and its application to carboxyl terminal group analysis. *J. Biol. Chem.* 231: 393-401, 1958.

69. GLADNER, J. A., AND H. NEURATH. Carboxyl terminal groups of proteolytic enzymes. I. Activation of chymotrypsinogen to α-chymotrypsin. *J. Biol. Chem.* 205: 345-360, 1953.

70. GRANT, N. H., AND K. C. ROBBINS. Occurrence and activation of an elastase precursor in pancreas. *Proc. Soc. Exptl. Biol. Med.* 90: 264-265, 1955.

71. GRANT, N. H., AND K. C. ROBBINS. Studies on porcine elastase and proelastase. *Arch. Biochem. Biophys.* 66: 396-403, 1957.

72. GRAY, J. L., S. G. PRIEST, W. J. BLATT, U. WESTPHAL, AND J. JENSON. Isolation and characterization of a proteolytic inhibitor from bovine blood. *J. Biol. Chem.* 235: 56-59, 1960.

73. GREEN, M., AND M. A. STAHMANN. Synthesis and enzymatic hydrolysis of glutamic acid polypeptides. *J. Biol. Chem.* 197: 771-782, 1952.

74. GREEN, N. M., AND H. NEURATH. Proteolytic enzymes. In: *The Proteins*, edited by H. Neurath and K. Bailey. New York: Acad. Press, 1954, vol. II, part 13, p. 1057-1198.

75. GREEN, N. M., AND E. WORK. Pancreatic trypsin inhibitor. I. Preparation and properties. *Biochem. J.* 54: 257-266, 1953.

76. GREENE, L. J., D. S. FACKRE, AND M. RIGBI. A trypsin inhibitor from bovine pancreatic juice. *Federation Proc.* 25: 790, 1966.

77. GROSSMAN, M. I. Some properties of trypsin inhibitor of

pancreatic juice. *Proc. Soc. Exptl. Biol. Med.* 99: 304–306, 1958.

78. GUY, O., M. ROVERY, AND P. DESNUELLE. Etude comparée des séquences N-terminales des chymotrypsinogène A et B. *Biochim. Biophys. Acta* 69: 191–193, 1963.

79. GUY, O., D. GRATECOS, M. ROVERY, AND P. DESNUELLE. Contribution à l'étude du chymotrypsinogen B de boeuf. *Biochim. Biophys. Acta* 115: 404–422, 1966.

80. GUY, O., M. ROVERY, AND P. DESNUELLE. Formation and activation of neochymotrypsinogen B. *Biochim. Biophys. Acta* 124: 402–405, 1966

81. HALL, D. A. Studies on the complex nature of the elastin-elastase system. *Biochem. J.* 55: 35P, 1953.

82. HARTLEY, B. S. Proteolytic enzymes. *Ann. Rev. Biochem.* 29: 45–72, 1960.

83. HARTLEY, B. S. Amino acid sequence of bovine chymotrypsinogen. *Nature* 201: 1284–1287, 1964.

84. HARTLEY, B. S., J. R. BROWN, D. L. KAUFFMAN, AND L. B. SMILLIE. Evolutionary similarities between pancreatic proteolytic enzymes. *Nature* 207: 1157–1159, 1965.

85. HARTLEY, B. S., AND D. L. KAUFFMAN. Corrections to the amino acid sequence of bovine chymotrypsinogen A. *Biochem. J. Biochem. J.* 101: 229–231, 1966.

86. HOFMANN, K., AND P. G. KATSOYANNIS. Synthesis and function of peptides. In: *The Proteins* (2nd ed.), edited by H. Neurath. New York: Acad. Press, 1963, vol. I, p. 54–188.

87. HOFMANN, T. The purification and properties of fragments of trypsinogen obtained by cyanogen bromide cleavage. *Biochemistry* 3: 356–364, 1964.

88. HOFMANN, T., A. GERTLER, AND S. T. SCRIMGER. The involvement of the N-terminal groups in the activity of elastase and trypsin. *Proc. Can. Fed. Biol. Soc.* 9th Annual Meeting, 1966, p. 11.

89. HOFMANN, T., AND R. SHAW. Proteolytic enzymes of *Penicillium janthinellum*. I. Purification and properties of a trypsinogen-activating enzyme (peptidase A). *Biochim. Biophys. Acta* 92: 543–557, 1964.

90. HOLEYSOVSKY, V., V. TOMASEK, O. MIKES, A. S. DANILOVNA, AND F. SORM. On proteins. XCVIII. The disulfide bonds of bovine DIP-trypsin. *Collection Czech. Chem. Commun.* 30: 3936–3952, 1965.

91. HUMMEL, B. C. W. A modified spectrophotometric determination of chymotrypsin, trypsin and thrombin. *Can. J. Biochem. Physiol.* 37: 1393–1399, 1959.

92. JACOBSEN, C. F. The activation of chymotrypsinogen. *Compt. Rend. Trav. Lab. Carlsberg, Ser. Chim.* 25: 325–437, 1947.

93. JACOBSEN, C. F., AND J. LÉONIS. A recording auto-titration. *Compt. Rend. Trav. Lab. Carlsberg, Ser. Chim.* 27: 333–339, 1951.

94. KALSER, M. H., AND M. I. GROSSMAN. Secretion of trypsin inhibitor in pancreatic juice. *Gastroenterology* 29: 35–45, 1955.

95. KASSELL, B., AND M. LASKOWSKI. Comparison of chymotrypsinogen α and B. *Federation Proc.* 19: 332, 1960.

96. KASSELL, B., AND M. LASKOWSKI, JR. Terminal amino acids of chymotrypsinogen B. *J. Biol. Chem.* 237: 413–417, 1962.

97. KASSELL, B., AND M. LASKOWSKI. The basic trypsin inhibitor of bovine pancreas. V. The disulfide linkages. *Biochem. Biophys. Res. Commun.* 20: 463–468, 1965.

98. KASSELL, B., M. RADICEVIC, M. J. ANSFIELD, AND M. LASKOWSKI. The basic trypsin inhibitor of bovine pancreas. IV. The linear sequence of the 58 amino acids. *Biochem. Biophys. Res. Commun.* 18: 255–258, 1965.

99. KASSELL, B., M. RADICEVIC, S. BERLOW, R. J. PEANASKY, AND M. LASKOWSKI. The basic trypsin inhibitor of bovine pancreas. I. An improved method of preparation and amino acid composition. *J. Biol. Chem.* 238: 3274–3279, 1963.

100. KAUFFMAN, D. L. The disulfide bridges of trypsin. *J. Mol. Biol.* 12: 929–932, 1965.

101. KAZAL, L. A., D. S. SPICER, AND R. A. BRAHINSKY. Isolation of a crystalline trypsin inhibitor-anticoagulant protein from pancreas. *J. Am. Chem. Soc.* 70: 3034–3040, 1948.

102. KEIL, B., Z. PRUZIK, AND F. SORM. Disulphide bridges and a suggested structure of chymotrypsinogen. *Biochim. Biophys. Acta* 78: 559–561, 1963.

103. KEIL, B., AND F. SORM. On the structure of chymotrypsinogen A. In: *Structure and Activity of Enzymes*, edited by T. W. Goodwin, J. I. Harris, and B. S. Hartley. London: Acad. Press, 1964, p. 37–46.

104. KELLER, P. J., AND B. J. ALLAN. The protein composition of human pancreatic juice. *J. Biol. Chem.* 242: 281–287, 1967.

105. KELLER, P. J., E. COHEN, AND H. NEURATH. Purification and properties of procarboxypeptidase. *J. Biol. Chem.* 223: 457–467, 1956.

106. KELLER, P. J., E. COHEN, AND H. NEURATH. The proteins of bovine pancreatic juice. *J. Biol. Chem.* 233: 344–349, 1958.

107. KELLER, P. J., E. COHEN, AND H. NEURATH. Procarboxypeptidase. II. Chromatographic isolation, further characterization, and activation. *J. Biol. Chem.* 230: 905–915, 1958.

108. KIETH, C. A., A. KAZENKO, AND M. LASKOWSKI. Studies on proteolytic activity of crystalline protein B prepared from beef pancreas. *J. Biol. Chem.* 170: 227–238, 1947.

109. KRAUT, H., AND N. BHARGAVA. Versuche zur isolierung des kallikreininaktivators, V. Isolierung eines kallikrein-inaktivators aus rinderlunge und seine identifizierund mit dem inaktivator aus rinderparotis. *Z. Physiol. Chem.* 338: 231–237, 1964.

110. KREHBEIL, A., B. KASSELL, AND M. LASKOWSKI, SR. Activation of chymotrypsinogen B. *Biochim. Biophys. Acta* 92: 312–318, 1964.

111. KUBACKI, V., K. D. BROWN, AND M. LASKOWSKI. Electrophoresis and solubility of chymotrypsinogen B and chymotrypsin α. *J. Biol. Chem.* 180: 73–78, 1949.

112. KULKA, R. G., H. HELLER, AND U. MARCHAIM. Secretion of digestive enzymes by the embryonic chick pancreas, *in vitro*. In: *Secretory Mechanisms of Salivary Glands*, edited by L. H. Schneyer and C. A. Schneyer. New York: Acad. Press, 1967, p. 254–263.

113. KULKA, R. G., AND U. YALOVSKY. Secretion of α-amylase by the embryonic chick pancreas *in vitro*. *J. Cell Biol.* 29: 287–292, 1966.

114. KUNITZ, M. Formation of trypsin from trypsinogen by an enzyme produced by a mold of the genus penicillium. *J. Gen. Physiol.* 21: 601–620, 1938.

115. KUNITZ, M. Crystalline soybean trypsin inhibitor. *J. Gen. Physiol.* 29: 149–154, 1946.

116. KUNITZ, M. Crystalline soybean trypsin inhibitor. II. General properties. *J. Gen. Physiol.* 30: 291–310, 1947.

117. KUNITZ, M., AND J. H. NORTHROP. Isolation from beef pancreas of crystalline trypsinogen, trypsin, a trypsin inhibitor, and an inhibitor-trypsin compound. *J. Gen. Physiol.* 19: 991–1007, 1936.

118. LABOUESSE, B., K. CARLSSON, H. L. OPPENHEIMER, AND G. P. HESS. Characterization of a residue controlling the activity and conformation of chymotrypsin. In: *Structure and Activity of Enzymes*, edited by T. W. Goodwin, J. I. Harris, and B. S. Hartley. London: Acad. Press, 1964, p. 71–73.

119. LABOUESSE, B., H. L. OPPENHEIMER, AND G. P. HESS. Conformational changes accompanying the formation of chymotrypsin-substrate complexes. Evidence for the involvement of an N-terminal α-amino group in the activity and the conformation of the enzyme. *Biochem. Biophys. Res. Commun.* 14: 318–322, 1964.

120. LAMY, F., C. P. CRAIG, AND S. TAUBER. Assay and properties of elastase. *J. Biol. Chem.* 236: 86–91, 1961.

121. LAMY, F., AND S. TAUBER. Partial purification and properties of activation of proelastase. *J. Biol. Chem.* 238: 939–944, 1963.

122. LASKOWSKI, M., B. KASSELL, AND G. HAGERTY. A crystalline trypsin inhibitor from swine colostrum. *Biochim. Biophys. Acta* 24: 300–305, 1957.

123. LASKOWSKI, M., JR., AND M. LASKOWSKI. Crystalline trypsin inhibitor from colostrum. *J. Biol. Chem.* 190: 563–573, 1951.

124. LASKOWSKI, M., AND M. LASKOWSKI, JR. Naturally occurring trypsin inhibitors. *Advan. Protein Chem.* IX: 203–242, 1954.

125. LASKOWSKI, M., JR., P. H. MARS, AND M. LASKOWSKI. Comparison of trypsin inhibitor from colostrum with other crystalline trypsin inhibitors. *J. Biol. Chem.* 198: 745–752, 1952.

126. LASKOWSKI, M., AND F. C. WU. Temporary inhibition of trypsin. *J. Biol. Chem.* 204: 797–805, 1953.

127. LENS, J. The terminal carboxyl groups of insulin. *Biochim. Biophys. Acta* 3: 367–370, 1949.

128. LEWIS, L. J., D. E. WILLIAMS, AND N. G. BRINK. Pancreatic elastase: purification, properties, and function. *J. Biol. Chem.* 222: 705–720, 1956.

129. LINEWEAVER, N., AND C. W. MURRAY. Identification of the trypsin inhibitor of egg white with ovomucoid. *J. Biol. Chem.* 171: 565–581, 1947.

130. LOEVEN, W. A. The enzymes of the elastase complex. *Intern. Rev. Connective Tissue Res.* 1: 183–240, 1963.

131. LUMRY, R., E. L. SMITH, AND R. R. GLANTZ. Kinetics of carboxypeptidase action. I. Effect of various extrinsic factors on kinetic parameters. *J. Am. Chem. Soc.* 73: 4330–4340, 1951.

132. MARCHIS-MOUREN, G. Mémoires. Etude comparée de l'équipment enzymatique du suc pancréatique de diverses espèces. *Bull. Soc. Chim. Biol.* 42: 2207–2217, 1965.

133. MARCHIS-MOUREN, G., M. CHARLES, A. BEN ABDELJLIL, AND P. DESNUELLE. Sur l'équipment en enzymes du suc pancréatique de porc et chien. *Biochim. Biophys. Acta* 50: 186–188, 1961.

134. MARCHIS-MOUREN, G., L. PASÉRO, AND P. DESNUELLE. Further studies on amylase biosynthesis by pancreas of rats fed on a starch-rich or a casein-rich diet. *Biochem. Biophys. Res. Commun.* 13: 262–266, 1963.

135. MARES-GUIA, M., AND E. SHAW. The irreversible inactivation of trypsin by the chloromethyl ketone derived from N-tosyl-L-lysine. *Federation Proc.* 22: 528, 1963.

136. McCANN, S. F., AND M. LASKOWSKI. Determination of trypsin inhibitor in blood plasma. *J. Biol. Chem.* 204: 147–152, 1953.

137. McCLURE, W. O., H. NEURATH, AND K. A. WALSH. The reaction of carboxypeptidase A with hippuryl-DL-β-phenyllactate. *Biochemistry* 3: 1897–1901, 1964.

138. McCONNELL, B., AND E. C. GJESSING. Isolation and crystallization of an esteroproteolytic zymogen from porcine pancreas. *J. Biol. Chem.* 241: 573–579, 1966.

139. MIKES, O., V. HOLEYSOVSKY, V. TOMASEK, AND F. SORM. Covalent structure of bovine trypsinogen. The position of the remaining amides. *Biochem. Biophys. Res. Commun.* 24: 346–352, 1966.

140. MIKES, O., V. TOMASEK, V. HOLEYSOVSKY, AND F. SORM. Covalent structure of bovine trypsinogen. *Biochim. Biophys. Acta* 117: 281–284, 1966.

141. NAKANISHI, K. Trypsinogen-kinase in *Aspergillus oryzae*. III. Purification of trypsinogen-kinase and its relation to acid protease. *J. Biochem.* 46: 1263–1270, 1959.

142. NAKANISHI, K. Trypsinogen-kinase in *Aspergillus oryzae*. V. On the mechanism of activation. *J. Biochem.* 46: 1553–1558, 1959.

143. NAUGHTON, M. A., AND F. SANGER. Purification and specificity of pancreatic elastase. *Biochem. J.* 78: 156–163, 1961.

144. NEURATH, H. The activation of zymogens. *Advan. Protein Chem.* XII: 319–386, 1957.

145. NEURATH, H. Carboxypeptidases A and B. In: *The Enzymes*, edited by P. D. Boyer, H. Lardy, and K. Myrbäck. New York: Acad. Press, 1960, vol. 4, p. 11–36.

146. NEURATH, H. Mechanism of zymogen activation. *Federation Proc.* 23: 1–7, 1964.

147. NEURATH, H., AND J. H. FREISHEIM. Activation of procarboxypeptidase A. *Federation Proc.* 15: 408, 1966.

148. NEURATH, H., J. A. RUPLEY, AND W. J. DREYER. Structural changes in the activation of chymotrypsinogen and trypsinogen. Effect of urea on chymotrypsinogen and delta-chymotrypsin. *Arch. Biochem. Biophys.* 65: 243–259, 1956.

149. NEURATH, H., AND G. W. SCHWERT. The mode of action of the crystalline pancreatic proteolytic enzymes. *Chem. Rev.* 46: 69–153, 1950.

150. NORTHROP, J. H., M. KUNITZ, AND R. M. HERRIOTT. *Crystalline Enzymes* (2nd ed.). New York: Columbia Univ. Press, 1948.

151. OOSTERBAAN, R. A., AND J. A. COHEN. The active site of esterases. In: *Structure and Activity of Enzymes*, edited by T. W. Goodwin, J. I. Harris, and B. S. Hartley. London: Acad. Press, 1964, p. 87.

152. PARTRIDGE, S. M., AND H. F. DAVIS. The chemistry of connective tissues. 3. Composition of the soluble proteins derived from elastin. *Biochem. J.* 61: 21–30, 1955.

153. PECHÈRE, J.-F., G. H. DIXON, R. H. MAYBURY, AND H. NEURATH. Cleavage of disulfide bonds in trypsinogen and α-chymotrypsinogen. *J. Biol. Chem.* 233: 1364–1372, 1958.

154. PRAHL, J. W., AND H. NEURATH. Pancreatic enzymes of the Pacific spiny dogfish. I. Cationic chymotrypsinogen and chymotrypsin. *Biochemistry* 5: 2131–2146, 1966.

155. PUTNAM, F. W., AND H. NEURATH. Chemical and enzymatic properties of crystalline carboxypeptidase. *J. Biol. Chem.* 166: 603–619, 1946.

156. REBOUD, J. P., A. BEN ABDELJLIL, AND P. DESNUELLE. Variations de la teneur en enzymes du pancréas de rat en fonction de la composition des régimes. *Biochim. Biophys. Acta* 58: 326–337, 1962.

157. REBOUD, J. P., G. MARCHIS-MOUREN, L. PASÉRO, A. COZZONE, AND P. DESNUELLE. Adaptation de la vitesse de biosynthèse de l'amylase pancréatique et du chymotrypsinogène à des régimes riches en amidon ou en protéines. *Biochim. Biophys. Acta* 117: 351–367, 1966.

158. REBOUD, J. P., L. PASÉRO, AND P. DESNUELLE. On chymotrypsinogen and trypsinogen biosynthesis by pancreas of rats fed on a starch-rich or a casein-rich diet. *Biochem. Biophys. Res. Commun.* 17: 347–351, 1964.

159. ROCHA E SILVA, M., W. T. BERALDO, AND G. ROSENFELD. Bradykinin, a hypotensive and smooth muscle stimulating factor released from plasma globulin by snake venoms and by trypsin. *Am. J. Physiol.* 156: 261–273, 1949.

160. ROVERY, M. Les chymotrypsinogènes et trypsinogènes. *Bull. Soc. Chim. Biol.* 46: 1757–1775, 1964.

161. ROVERY, M., M. CHARLES, O. GUY, A. GUIDONI, AND P. DESNUELLE. Purification de nouveaux précurseurs protéolytiques du pancréas. *Bull. Soc. Chim. Biol.* 42: 1235–1245, 1960.

162. ROVERY, M., AND P. DESNUELLE. Sur l'existence probable d'une chymotrypsine dépourvue d'alanine N-terminale. *Biochim. Biophys. Acta* 13: 300–301, 1954.

163. ROVERY, M., C. FABRE, AND P. DESNUELLE. Etude de l'activation du chymotrypsinogène et du trypsinogène de boeuf par déterminations des résidus n-termineaux dans les protéins et les enzymes correspondants. *Biochim. Biophys. Acta* 12: 547–550, 1953.

164. ROVERY, M., C. GABELOTEAU, P. DI VERNEJOUL, A. GUIDONI, AND P. DESNUELLE. Extrémitiés N et C-terminales du chymotrypsinogène de boeuf. *Biochim. Biophys. Acta* 32: 256–258, 1958.

165. ROVERY, M., M. POILROUX, A. CURNIER, AND P. DESNUELLE. Formation de sérylarginine pendant l'activation du chymotrypsinogène de boeuf. *Biochim. Biophys. Acta* 16: 590–591, 1955.

166. ROVERY, M., M. POILROUX, A. YOSHIDA, AND P. DESNUELLE. Sur le degradation du chymotrypsinogène par le chymotrypsine. *Biochim. Biophys. Acta* 23: 608–620, 1957.

167. RUPLEY, J. A. *Studies on Carboxypeptidase* (Ph.D. Thesis.). Seattle: Univ. of Washington, 1959, p. 102.

168. RUTTER, W. J., W. D. BALL, W. S. BRADSHAW, W. R. CLARK, AND T. G. SANDERS. Macromolecular changes during pancreatic development. In: *Secretory Mechanisms of Salivary Glands*, edited by L. H. Schneyer and C. A. Schneyer. New York: Acad. Press, 1967, p. 239–253.

169. RUTTER, W. J., N. K. WESSELLS, AND G. GROBSTEIN. Control of specific synthesis in the developing pancreas. In: *Metabolic Control Mechanisms in Animal Cells*, edited by W. J. Rutter. Washington, D.C.: Inst. Monograph 13, 1964, p. 51–66.

170. RYAN, C. A., AND Y. TOMIMATSU. A crystalline avian pancreatic protein. *Arch. Biochem. Biophys.* 111: 461–466, 1965.

171. SAMPATH-KUMAR, K. S. V., K. A. WALSH, J-P. BARGETZI, AND H. NEURATH. Chemical relationships among various forms of bovine pancreatic carboxypeptidase A. *Biochemistry* 2: 1475–1479, 1963.

172. SANGER, F., AND H. TUPPY. The amino-acid sequence in the phenylalanyl chain of insulin. 2. The investigation of peptides from enzymic hydrolysates. *Biochem. J.* 49: 481–490, 1951.

173. SCHOELLMANN, G., AND E. SHAW. Direct evidence for the presence of histidine in the active center of chymotrypsin. *Biochemistry* 2: 252–255, 1963.

174. SCHWERT, G. W., H. NEURATH, S. KAUFMAN, AND J. E. SNOKE. The specific esterase activity of trypsin. *J. Biol. Chem.* 172: 221–239, 1948.

175. SCHWERT, G. W., AND A. TAKENAKA. A spectrophotometric determination trypsin and chymotrypsin. *Biochim. Biophys. Acta* 16: 570–575, 1955.

176. SHULMAN, N. R. A proteolytic inhibitor with anticoagulant activity separated from human urine and plasma *J. Biol. Chem.* 213: 655–671, 1955.

177. SMILLIE, L. B., A. G. ENEKEL, AND C. M. KAY. Physicochemical properties and amino acid composition of chymotrypsinogen B. *J. Biol. Chem.* 241: 2097–2102, 1966.

178. SMILLIE, L. B., AND B. S. HARTLEY. Histidine sequences in the active centers of some serine enzymes. *J. Mol. Biol.* 10: 183–185, 1964.

179. SMILLIE, L. B., AND B. S. HARTLEY. Histidine sequences in the active centers of some "serine" proteinases. *Biochem. J.* 101: 232–241, 1966.

180. SMITH, E. L. Specificity of certain peptidases and their use in the study of peptide and protein structure. In: *The Chemical Structure of Proteins*, edited by G. E. W. Wolstenholme and M. P. Cameron. Boston: Little, Brown, 1952, p. 109–128.

181. SOHONIE, K., AND K. S. AMBE. Crystalline trypsin inhibitors from the Indian field bean and the double bean. *Nature* 175: 508–509, 1955.

182. TAUBER, H., B. B. KERSHAW, AND R. D. WRIGHT. Studies on the growth inhibitor fraction of lima beans and isolation of a crystalline heat-stable trypsin inhibitor. *J. Biol. Chem.* 179: 1155–1161, 1949.

183. TRAVIS, J., AND I. E. LIENER. The crystallization and partial characterization of porcine trypsin. *J. Biol. Chem.* 240: 1962–1966, 1965.

184. VALLEE, B. L. The "active catalytic site," an approach through metalloenzymes. *Federation Proc.* 20, Suppl. 10: 71–80, 1961.

185. VALLEE, B. L. Active centers of carboxypeptidase A. *Federation Proc.* 23: 8–17, 1964.

186. VALLEE, B. L., T. L. COOMBS, AND F. L. HOCH. The "active site" of bovine pancreatic carboxypeptidase A. *J. Biol. Chem.* 235: PC46, 1960.

187. VALLEE, B. L., AND H. NEURATH. Carboxypeptidase, a zinc metalloprotein. *J. Am. Chem. Soc.* 76: 5006–5007, 1954.

188. VALLEE, B. L., AND H. NEURATH. Carboxypeptidase, a zinc metalloenzyme. *J. Biol. Chem.* 217: 253–261, 1955.

189. VALLEE, B. L., J. A. RUPLEY, T. L. COOMBS, AND H. NEURATH. The role of zinc in carboxypeptidase. *J. Biol. Chem.* 235: 64–69, 1960.

190. VALLEE, B. L., R. J. P. WILLIAMS, AND J. E. COLEMAN. Nitrogen and sulfur at the active center of carboxypeptidase A. *Nature* 190: 633–634, 1961.

191. WALSH, K. A., D. L. KAUFFMAN, K. S. V. SAMPATH-KUMAR, AND H. NEURATH. On the structure and function of bovine trypsinogen and trypsin. *Proc. Natl. Acad. Sci. U.S.* 51: 301–308, 1964.

192. WALSH, K. A., AND H. NEURATH. Trypsinogen and

chymotrypsinogen as homologous proteins. *Proc. Natl. Acad. Sci. U.S.* 52: 884–889, 1964.

193. WALSH, K. A., K. S. V. SAMPATH-KUMAR, J.-P. BARGETZI, AND H. NEURATH. Approaches to the selective chemical labeling of the acive site of carboxypeptidase A. *Proc. Natl. Acad. Sci. U.S.* 48: 1443–1448, 1962.

194. WARBURG, O. Spaltung des leucin-äthylesters durch pankreasferment. *Chem. Ber.* 38: 187–188, 1905.

195. WHIPPLE, H. E., AND S. SILVERZWEIG (editors). Structure and function of biologically active peptides: bradykinin, kallidin, and congeners. *Ann. N.Y. Acad. Sci.* 104: 1–464, 1963.

196. WILCOX, P. E., E. COHEN, AND W. TAN. Amino acid composition of α-chymotrypsinogen, including asparagine and glutamine. *J. Biol. Chem.* 228: 999–1019, 1957.

197. WINTERSBERGER, E. Isolation and structure of an active-center peptide of bovine carboxypeptidase B containing the zinc-binding sulfhydryl group. *Biochemistry* 4: 1533–1536, 1965.

198. WINTERSBERGER, E., D. J. COX, AND H. NEURATH. Bovine pancreatic procarboxypeptidase B. 1. Isolation, properties and activation. *Biochemistry* 1: 1069–1078, 1962.

199. WINTERSBERGER, E., H. NEURATH, T. L. COOMBS, AND B. L. VALLEE. A zinc-binding thiol group in the active center of bovine carboxypeptidase B. *Biochemistry* 4: 1526–1532, 1965.

200. WU, F. C., AND M. LASKOWSKI. Action of the naturally occurring trypsin inhibitors against chymotrypsin α and B. *J. Biol. Chem.* 213: 609–619, 1955.

201. YAMASAKI, M., J. R. BROWN, D. J. COX, R. N. GREEN-SHIELDS, R. D. WADE, AND H. NERUATH. Procarboxypeptidase A-S6. Further studies of its isolation and properties. *Biochemistry* 2: 859–866, 1963.

202. YAMASHIMA, I. The action of enterokinase on trypsinogen. *Acta Chem. Scand.* 10: 739–743, 1956.

203. YANG, J. T., AND P. DOTY. The optical rotatory dispersion of polypeptides and proteins in relation to configuration. *J. Am. Chem. Soc.* 79: 761–775, 1957.

CHAPTER 123

Pancreatic lipase

P. DESNUELLE | *Institut de Chimie Biologique, Faculté des Sciences, Marseille, France*

CHAPTER CONTENTS

GENERAL CONSIDERATIONS

MOST DIETARY PRODUCTS ingested by higher animals must be hydrolyzed before absorption via the intestinal mucosa. Their hydrolysis is initiated and advanced by various enzymes secreted into the digestive tract from several specialized tissues or glands; of these the pancreas plays an important role. The acinar cells of the pancreas synthesize one or several enzymes for each class of dietary products, namely a number of proteolytic enzymes for proteins, an amylase for carbohydrates, two nucleases for nucleic acids, a phospholipase A for phospholipids, and a lipase for triglycerides. Since triglycerides constitute a large part of the diet of human beings and many animals, an active synthesis of lipase is obviously needed.

According to Palade et al. the enzymes of the exocrine secretion of pancreas are separated from other cellular proteins immediately after their formation, concentrated in vacuoles of the endoplasmic reticulum, and stored in zymogen granules. Stimulation of the secretion induces the coalescence of the smooth membrane of the granules with the wall of the secretory ducts and the transfer of the enzyme into the duct lumen from where it is carried to the duodenum by pancreatic juice. One of the most significant discoveries of recent years in pancreatic biochemistry was that the proteins of bovine pancreatic juice are exclusively, or almost exclusively, enzymes of the exocrine secretion (15, 16). Lipase is present in bovine zymogen granules (15) and in the pancreatic juice of all species investigated so far (15, 19). This does not mean that all species synthesize the same lipase. However, an enzyme with lipolytic activity has been found in each. Its level is especially high in porcine, rat, and human juice (13).

Before entry into the duodenum, carbohydrates and proteins are attacked by salivary amylase and gastric pepsin. The intestinal mucosa is involved in their further degradation by the action of glycosidases and peptidases. In contrast, the existence of a gastric lipase is very unlikely. One or several lipases are present in the intestine, but their activity is relatively weak and their role during intraluminar digestion is still uncertain. Thus most of the chemical transformations occurring in triglyceride molecules during the intraluminar phase of digestion are achieved by pancreatic lipase.

When a cell synthesizes large amounts of a hydrolase for secretory purposes, protection of some kind must be provided against self-digestion. For proteolytic enzymes, efficient protection is afforded by the synthesis of "precursors" or "zymogens" (chymotrypsinogen, trypsinogen, procarboxypeptidases, etc.) that remain inactive as long as they are in the cell. Activation occurs later in the duodenum. It has been claimed (34) that porcine pancreas contains an inactive "prolipase" that may be activated by a boiled extract or by serum, but this postulation has not been confirmed (18). Thus the pancreas probably forms an active lipase directly. Localization alone of the enzyme in zymogen granules appears to protect cellular triglycerides against hydrolysis.

PURIFICATION AND MOLECULAR PROPERTIES

The development of new procedures for the purification of an enzyme requires the use of a quantitative test for the determination of enzymatic activity in a number of fractions. Its success largely depends on the validity of the test. This principle is well illustrated by the case of pancreatic lipase. As already pointed out, the natural substrates of lipase are long-chain triglycerides that are insoluble in water. When they are employed, lipase activity is measured using a heterogeneous emulsion and not, as for other enzymes, a homogeneous solution of the substrate. Some investigators claim that this is an unnecessary complication and they prefer to use aqueous solutions of short-chain esters for the determination of lipase. Figure 1 gives a first indication, confirmed later, that lipase normally acts on emulsions. Ester solutions are hydrolyzed by a group of other pancreatic enzymes with "esterase" activity. A convenient technique for lipase is to use a triglyceride emulsion in gum arabic and to titrate continuously for a few minutes with a recording pH-stat the fatty acids liberated by the enzyme (20). Linear kinetics are obtained from which the amount of lipase in the sample can easily be calculated.

Once this test became available, reliable techniques were developed for the purification of porcine pancreatic lipase. According to one of them (20, 27), lipase is extracted by water from an acetone powder of pancreas and concentrated by selective precipitation by ammonium sulfate and acetone. It is further purified by high-voltage electrophoresis of long duration in a starch column at pH 5.2 or 8.0. In another technique (28) the starting material is an aqueous extract of fresh pancreas. In these homogenates, lipase is completely or partly bound to lipid micelles that, as shown in the left part of Figure 2, are excluded from Sephadex G-200. After delipidation by an alcohol-ether mixture, lipase appears in the free form, and it is retarded by Sephadex G-200. Further purification can be achieved by chromatography on DEAE-cellulose at pH 8.0 in an ionic-strength gradient.

Both procedures give preparations of high purity. The peaks obtained by electrophoresis or chromatography are symmetrical, and their fractions have nearly the same specific activity. Filtration through

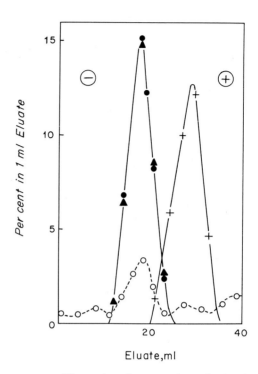

FIG. 1. Electrophoretic separation of the "lipase" and "esterase" activities of porcine pancreas. The extract containing both activities is submitted to high-voltage electrophoresis for 40 hours in a starch column equilibrated with 0.025 M acetate buffer. The esterolytic activity of each fraction is measured with *1*) emulsions of water-insoluble esters [triolein (*black circles*) and methyloleate or *p*-nitrophenyl laurate (*black triangles*)] and *2*) aqueous solutions of methylbutyrate or *p*-nitrophenylacetate (*crosses*). All activities against emulsions are under the lipase peak, which is isoelectric at pH 5.2. Activities against solutions are located under another well-separated peak moving toward the anode. *Open circles* and *dashed line*, total proteins of the fractions (Lowry). [From Sarda & Desnuelle (26).]

Sephadex G-100 indicates a molecular weight of the protein ranging from 35,000 to 42,000 (11, 14, 28). The isoelectric point determined by zone electrophoresis on starch is 5.2. Rat and human lipases are basic proteins that should be able to be purified on cation exchangers.

MODE OF ACTION OF PANCREATIC LIPASE
ON ITS SUBSTRATES

Effect of Bile Salts and Calcium Ions

Incubation of triglycerides with pancreatic lipase is usually performed in the presence of calcium ions and bile salts. When optimal concentrations of these substances are added, the rate of hydrolysis remains constant for a relatively long period and large

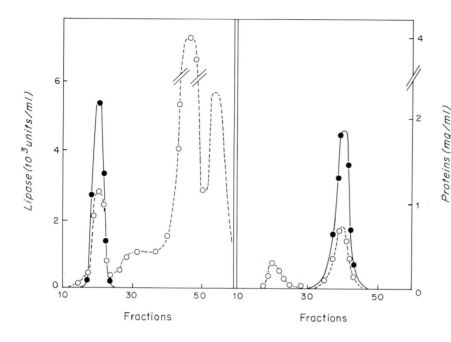

FIG. 2. Chromatography of porcine lipase on Sephadex G-200 before and after delipidation. The column (150 × 0.9 cm) is equilibrated and eluted with a solution 0.75 M in NaCl and 0.025 M in CaCl₂. *Solid line*, lipase activity. *Dashed line*, total proteins (Lowry). *Left*, chromatography of an aqueous extract of fresh pancreas. *Right*, same chromatography after delipidation of the lipase peak obtained during the first run. The fast-moving lipase-lipid association does not exist in pancreatic juice. The lipase peak emerges as indicated by the *right* diagram when juice is filtered through Sephadex. [From Sarda et al. (28).]

amounts of fatty acids are liberated. Moreover, lipase does not act on triglyceride emulsions in arabic gum unless bile salts are added. If the emulsions are prepared in dilute bile salts, calcium ions are necessary. These observations suggest pancreatic lipase activity requires calcium ions and bile salts, but it can be demonstrated (Benzonana and Desnuelle, unpublished observations) that lipase is active on triglycerides in the complete absence of calcium and bile salts. The hydrolysis rate is quite high at the beginning, but it decreases very early and becomes almost negligible after a few minutes. This is readily explained by the fact that lipase is inhibited by the free fatty acids accumulating at the interface during lipolysis. The role of bile salts and calcium is not essentially to "activate" lipase, but to prevent inhibition, probably by combining with the free fatty acids and carrying them into the aqueous phase.

In addition, calcium ions increase the thermal stability of pancreatic lipase (32). The association constant of lipase with calcium ions is 10^3 moles^{-1}.

Physical State of Lipase Substrates

Most enzyme reactions occur in water in which enzyme molecules (E) and substrate molecules (S) are dispersed in a single homogeneous phase. A widespread concept is that the enzyme reversibly absorbs its substrate to form a primary enzyme-substrate complex (ES) that by further degradation regenerates the free enzyme and gives rise to the products. For a fixed amount of enzyme and fixed experimental conditions, the concentration of ES and consequently the reaction rate increase with the substrate concentration. When the equilibrium E + S ⇌ ES is very much in favor of ES, the rate reaches a maximal value that is proportional to the amount of enzyme.

This concept cannot be directly applied to lipase, which is able to act rapidly on water-insoluble substrates in spite of its high solubility in water. These substrates are not dispersed in water. They form emulsified aggregates of varying size that contain a large number of molecules and are separated from water by an interface. Then a first assumption is that the insoluble substrates are in some way "solubilized," for instance by bile salts. This, however, is not supported by experimental data. Conversely it may be assumed that lipase is adsorbed by the particles. In this case only the substrate molecules lying at the interface would be available to the enzyme and the area of this interface would be of importance.

When a substrate is insoluble its molar concentration cannot be defined. However, more or less concentrated emulsions can be prepared by varying the amount of emulsified phase for a constant volume of water. When the same number of lipase units is added to each emulsion, the rate of lipolysis is found to vary with the concentration in exactly the same way as in the ordinary case. The rate increases at first and then reaches a maximum value that is strictly proportional to the amount of enzyme. This

FIG. 3. Lineweaver-Burk plots of lipase activity on emulsified triglycerides. The particles in a triglyceride-water emulsion are separated by differential centrifugation into two groups, one of smaller size (*open circles*) and one of larger size (*black circles*). The initial rate of lipolysis (*v*) is measured for the same quantity of lipase in the presence of various amounts of both types of particles in the same volume of buffer. *Left*, Lineweaver-Burk plot of ($1/v$) versus the reciprocal value of the substrate weight ($1/W$). *Right*, same plot versus the reciprocal value of the area of the interface ($1/I$). [From Benzonana & Desnuelle (3).]

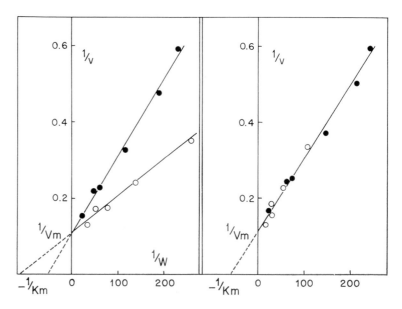

observation is consistent with the idea that lipase is partitioned between water and the emulsified particles. When more particles are present, more lipase is adsorbed and becomes active. The rate is maximal when the adsorption of lipase is complete. Thus the primary mechanism on which lipase action depends is the same as that of enzymes acting in an aqueous solution. In both cases the curve relating enzyme activity to substrate concentration would be an adsorption isotherm. But lipase would be adsorbed by substrate particles instead of absorbing substrate molecules. This theory is fully confirmed when the amounts of lipase remaining in the aqueous phase after centrifugation of the emulsions are measured (3). In the presence of varying quantities of emulsified phase, a precise relationship can be demonstrated between lipase activity and the absorption of the enzyme by the particles.

Moreover, Figure 3 gives Lineweaver-Burk representations of lipase activity as a function of the concentration of the emulsion. Two emulsions are employed, one with larger and the other with smaller triglyceride particles. When the activity is plotted against the weight of the substrate, two different straight lines are obtained. The maximal rate is the same in both cases, since the amount of lipase is the same. But the K_m is higher when the emulsion contains larger particles and, for a fixed weight of substrate, the experimental rate is consequently lower. In contrast, a single straight line is obtained when activity is plotted against the area of the interface. This demonstrates convincingly that lipase activity is controlled by the area of the interface separating

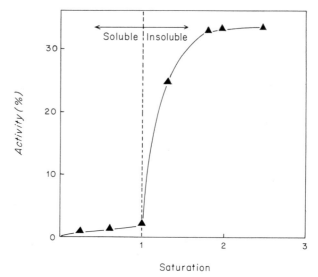

FIG. 4. Action of pancreatic lipase on dissolved or emulsified triacetin. *Ordinate*, activity in % of maximal activity on triolein emulsions. *Abscissa*, saturation of the solution in %. [Sarda & Desnuelle (26).]

the insoluble substrate and water. Other possible factors are the charge of the emulsified particles as well as the number and the packing of the substrate molecules at the interface.

Another interesting property of lipase is its probable inability to split ester bonds in isolated molecules dissolved in water (26). Figure 4 shows that pure lipase either does not hydrolyze triacetin or hydrolyzes it at a very low rate as long as the substrate is dissolved. When the substrate concentration is increased, a point is reached at which the solution is saturated.

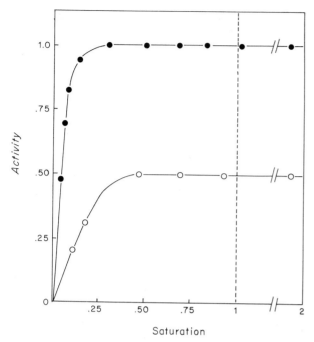

FIG. 5. Action of horse liver esterase on triacetin or methyl-butyrate. The activity of horse liver esterase on methylbutyrate (*black circles*) and triacetin (*open circles*) is expressed in units (10^{-6} substrate equivalents hydrolyzed per minute). *Abscissa*, saturation of the substrate solution. [Sarda & Desnuelle (26).]

no effect on lipase as long as they are dissolved in water. But lipase is readily inhibited by emulsions of diethyl-*p*-nitrophenylphosphate (25).

Positional Specificity of Pancreatic Lipase

When lipase is incubated with an emulsion of long-chain triglycerides at pH 8, lipolysis occurs in three distinct steps. During the first step, which is very fast, triglycerides are converted into diglycerides. Then diglycerides give rise to monoglycerides. Further conversion in vitro of monoglycerides to free glycerol is very slow so that, in contrast with earlier claims, the main product of triglyceride lipolysis in vitro is monoglycerides rather than glycerol. Figure 6 shows that, when two-thirds of the triglyceride ester bonds are cleaved, 75% of the glyceride components are monoglycerides (8). Large amounts of monoglycerides are also found in the intestine during digestion of dietary triglycerides (1, 5, 10, 23).

It will be shown later that monoglycerides as a whole are poor substrates for lipase. But an additional factor explaining their high stability during lipolysis is the positional specificity of the enzyme.

A first indication that the rate at which triglyceride

Beyond this point (indicated in Fig. 4 by a vertical dashed line) a part of the substrate begins to appear in an emulsified form and lipase becomes active. The relation of this activity to the concentration of the emulsion is similar to that already mentioned for insoluble substrates.

Figure 5 shows that the activity of purified horse liver esterase is high in dilute solutions of methyl-butyrate and triacetin. This activity is not affected by oversaturation of the solution. Hence, carboxyl esterase and lipase specificities are quite different. The first group of enzymes hydrolyzes ester molecules dissolved in water. Lipase also hydrolyzes ester bonds, but it apparently requires from its substrate a certain level of multimolecular organization existing in emulsions, micelles, and aggregates. Furthermore, emulsified triglycerides should be in a liquid state at the temperature of the assay. Saturated triglycerides with high melting points are poor substrates for lipase.

The behavior of lipase toward specific inhibitors is very similar to its behavior toward substrates. Organophosphates such as diethyl-*p*-nitrophenyl-phosphate and diisopropylfluorophosphate, which inactivate many esterases by fixation of a stable organophosphoryl radical on a serine residue, have

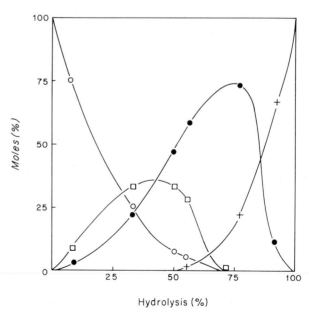

FIG. 6. Three steps of triglyceride hydrolysis by pancreatic lipase. Pure triolein is incubated for various periods with different amounts of lipase at pH 8.0 and 37 C. Triglycerides (*circles*), diglycerides (*squares*), monoglycerides (*black circles*), and free glycerol (*crosses*) are estimated by conventional techniques and expressed in % of the total number of triglyceride molecules at the beginning of the experiment. [Constantin et al. (8).]

ester bonds are cleaved by lipase strongly depends on their position in the molecule was given several years ago when the diolein formed by lipolysis of triolein in vitro was isolated and found to behave like the 1.2 isomer[1] during chromic acid oxidation (6). Moreover, when a mixture of triolein and ^{14}C-palmitic or oleic acid was incubated with rat pancreatic juice, exchange between free and esterified fatty acids mostly occurred on the external positions (7). This suggested a low reactivity of the internal chain.

However, the first direct evidence in favor of a positional specificity of pancreatic lipase was obtained by experiments in vivo (23). Monoglycerides isolated from rat intestine after triolein ingestion were found to contain mostly 2-monoolein. When rats were fed on synthetic 2-oleyldipalmitin, the iodine value of the free fatty acid fraction in the intestine was low, whereas it was as high in the monoglycerides as in monoolein. Thus the cleavage of external chains in triglycerides by pancreatic lipase is more rapid than for the internal chain. This observation was fully confirmed in more detailed investigations carried out in several laboratories (21, 22, 30, 31) with the four possible glycerides containing palmitic and oleic chains. In all cases the free acids appeared to originate mostly from the external positions and the remaining monoglycerides to contain mostly the internal chain.

By use of a synthetic triglyceride labeled with radioactive carbon in the internal chain, it was later possible to show that the positional specificity of pancreatic lipase toward external chains is absolute (29). This means that the internal chain is not cleaved at all by the enzyme. However, the formed 2-monoglycerides partly isomerize in the presence of water at alkaline pH (24), so that sizable amounts of 1-monoglycerides exist at the end of lipolysis in vivo and in vitro. These 1-monoglycerides are slowly hydrolyzed to glycerol. The main pathway of triglycerides hydrolysis in intestinal lumen appears to be:

$$\text{triglycerides} \rightarrow \text{1.2-diglycerides} \rightarrow$$
$$\text{2-monoglycerides}$$
$$\Updownarrow$$
$$\text{1-monoglycerides} \rightarrow \text{glycerol}$$

Penetration of 2-monoglycerides into intestinal mucosa is assumed to require the formation of mixed micelles with free fatty acids and bile salts. The mucosa contains three enzymes—acyl-CoA synthetase, monoglyceride transacylase, and diglyceride transacylase—that induce the resynthesis of triglycerides at the expense of ATP. Finally, the reformed triglycerides are carried away by lymph. The sequence of events occurring in intestinal lumen and mucosal cells can be summarized as shown in the accompanying chart.

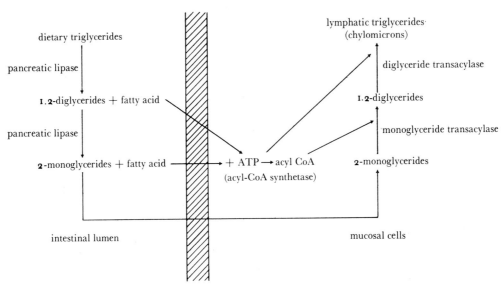

---

[1] Two carbons of glycerol carry primary alcohol groups and are said to occupy external positions in the molecule. They are the 1 and 3 or α and α carbons. The third carbon (α' or β) carries a secondary alcohol group and is said to occupy an internal position.

The short-chain triglycerides (4–10 carbon atoms) behave in a different way. Their hydrolysis by pancreatic lipase in the intestine is more complete, and the shorter fatty acids are not activated in the mucosal cells by acyl-CoA synthetase. Hence, they remain in the free form and are led directly to the liver by portal blood.

The positional specificity of pancreatic lipase is often used for the determination of the structure of natural triglycerides (22, 31). A recent extensive survey (29) has shown that several mold lipases have the same specificity as the pancreatic enzyme. Others cleave the three chains of triglycerides at nearly the same rate. This latter group readily converts triglycerides into free glycerol and fatty acids.

Substrate Specificity

The preceding discussion strongly suggests that the main factors controlling cleavage of fatty chains by pancreatic lipase are the physical state of the substrate and the position of the chains in triglyceride molecules. However, the chemical nature of the substrate, namely the nature of the fatty acyl radical and of the alcohol moiety, is also important.

FATTY ACYL RADICAL. Natural triglycerides contain chains of different length and saturation. In order to study the possible influence of these factors, the positional specificity of lipase should be eliminated. A preliminary technique is to compare the rates at which a series of emulsified triglycerides with three identical chains (tributyrin and triolein, for instance) are hydrolyzed by lipase. Variations in melting point and affinity may complicate the interpretation of such experiments. A more satisfactory technique is to use a single substrate containing two different external chains. Analysis of the liberated fatty acids will show whether one chain is cleaved faster than the other. A last possibility is to prepare a triglyceride mixture in which different chains are distributed at random on external and internal positions (interesterification). Results obtained with these techniques (12, 33) have shown that the saturation of the chain (number of double bonds) is not a factor, except for its well-known effect on the melting point of the triglycerides. In contrast, the chain length appears to be important. The rate of hydrolysis is low for acetyl chains (C_2). It increases sharply and becomes maximal for propionyl (C_3) and butyryl (C_4) chains. Then it decreases and takes a constant value from lauryl (C_{12}) and longer chains. If this value is equal to 1, the rate for acetyl chains is 0.2 and for propionyl and butyryl chains about 2.5.

A mold lipase from *Geotrichum candidum* has been reported to split preferentially unsaturated chains (29).

ALCOHOL MOIETY. The specificity of pancreatic lipase toward the alcohol moiety of its ester substrates has not been investigated in much detail. The data quoted in the past are not conclusive because the enzyme preparations were grossly impure and the conditions of assay were not correct. It is known, however, that propyleneglycol distearate is hydrolyzed by crude lipase in vitro and in the intestine of the rat (17). Fatty acid esters of sucrose are also hydrolyzed by a crude preparation from porcine pancreas (34).

More precise information is available for the fatty acyl esters of monoalcohols. The maximal rate at which these esters are hydrolyzed by purified lipase is much lower than in the case of the external chains of triglycerides. The first chain of triacetin is split 10 times as quickly as methylbutyrate. The ratio is 25 and 50 when triolein is compared with methyloleate (26) and tributyrin with ethylbutyrate (33), respectively.

It has been stressed before that considerable amounts of diglycerides and monoglycerides accumulate during triglyceride lipolysis in vitro and in vivo. The slower hydrolysis of diglycerides and monoglycerides is partly explained by the positional specificity of lipase. The enzyme can cleave two external chains in triglycerides, only one in 1,2-diglycerides, and none in 2-monoglycerides. But some experiments (33) suggest that, even if the preparation used contains a majority of isomers with external chains (1,3-diglycerides and 1-monoglycerides), the rate is definitely lower than for the corresponding triglycerides (tripropionin, 1; 1,3-dipropionin, 0.6; 1-monopropionin, 0.2; tributyrin, 1; 1-monobutyrin, 0.5). The reason for this low activity of lipase toward diglycerides and monoglycerides is not known.

A number of other esters have been used for lipase assays. Some of them are phenol esters (p-nitrophenyl or β-naphtyl esters for instance). According to Figure 1, they are probably true lipase substrates provided they are employed in a heterogeneous system. The main advantage of this class of compounds is that it permits colorimetric determinations that are more sensitive than titrimetry. This may compensate, at least in part, for the lower rate at which they are hydrolyzed by lipase.

Finally, highly purified lipase will hydrolyze the

external chain of phospholipids at quite an appreciable rate (9). Thus, the joint action of pancreatic lipase and phospholipase A would result in the cleavage of the two fatty chains of dietary phospholipids.

REFERENCES

1. AHRENS, E. H., JR., AND B. BORGSTRÖM. Exchange of free fatty acids and glyceride fatty acids during fat digestion in the human intestine. *J. Biol. Chem.* 219: 665–675, 1956.

2. ALFORD, J. A., D. A. PIERCE, AND F. G. SUGGS. Activity of microbial lipases on natural fats and synthetic triglycerides. *J. Lipid Res.* 5: 390–394, 1964.

3. BENZONANA, G., AND P. DESNUELLE. Etude cinétique de l'action de la lipase pancréatique sur des triglycerides en émulsion. Essai d'une enzymologie en milieu hétérogène. *Biochim. Biophys. Acta* 105: 121–136, 1965.

4. BERRY, J. F., AND D. A. TURNER. The enzymatic hydrolysis and tissue oxidation of fatty acid esters of sucrose. *J. Am. Oil Chemists' Soc.* 37: 302–305, 1960.

5. BORGSTRÖM, B. On the action of pancreatic lipase on triglycerides in vivo and in vitro. *Acta Physiol. Scand.* 25: 328–347, 1952.

6. BORGSTRÖM, B. On the mechanism of the hydrolysis of glycerides by pancreatic lipase. *Acta Chem. Scand.* 7: 557–558, 1953.

7. BORGSTRÖM, B. On the mechanism of pancreatic lipolysis of glycerides. *Biochim. Biophys. Acta* 13: 491–504, 1954.

8. CONSTANTIN, M. J., L. PASÉRO, AND P. DESNUELLE. Quelques remarques complémentaires sur l'hydrolyse des triglycérides par la lipase pancréatique. *Biochim. Biophys. Acta* 43: 103–109, 1960.

9. DE HAAS, G. H., L. SARDA, AND J. ROGER. Positional specific hydrolysis of phospholipids by pancreatic lipase. *Biochim. Biophys. Acta* 106: 638–640, 1965.

10. DESNUELLE, P., AND M. J. CONSTANTIN. Formation de glycérides partiels pendant la lipolyse des triglycérides dans l'intestin. *Biochim. Biophys. Acta* 9: 531–537, 1952.

11. DOWNEY, W. K., AND P. ANDREWS. Gel filtration applied to the study of lipases and other esterases. *Biochem. J.* 94: 642–650, 1965.

12. ENTRESSANGLES, B., L. PASÉRO, P. SAVARY, L. SARDA, AND P. DESNUELLE. Influence de la nature des chaines sur la vitesse de leur hydrolyse par la lipase pancréatique. *Bull. Soc. Chim. Biol.* 43: 581–591, 1961.

13. FIGARELLA, C., AND P. DESNUELLE. Premier essai de comparaison entre l'équipement enzymatique du pancréas humain et celui du pancréas de diverses espèces animales. *Compt. Rend. Soc. Biol.* 156: 699–702, 1962.

14. GELOTTE, B. Separation of pancreatic enzymes by gel filtration. *Acta Chem. Scand.* 18: 1283–1291, 1964.

15. GREENE, L. J., C. H. W. HIRS, AND G. E. PALADE. On the protein composition of bovine pancreatic zymogen granules. *J. Biol. Chem.* 238: 2054–2070, 1963.

16. KELLER, P. J., E. COHEN, AND H. NEURATH. The proteins of bovine pancreatic juice. *J. Biol. Chem.* 233: 344–349, 1958.

17. LONG, C. L., F. J. DOMINGUES, V. STUDER, J. R. LOWRY, B. R. ZEITLIN, R. R. BALDWIN, AND R. THIESSEN, JR. Studies on absorption and metabolism of propylene glycol distearate. *Arch. Biochem. Biophys.* 77: 428–439, 1958.

18. MARCHIS-MOUREN, G. *Contribution à l'étude de la purification de la lipase de porc et à l'étude de l'équipement enzymatique du suc pancréatique de diverses espèces* (Dr. Sc. Thesis.) Marseille: Univ. of Marseille, 1959.

19. MARCHIS-MOUREN, G., M. CHARLES, A. BEN ABDELJLIL, AND P. DESNUELLE. Sur l'équipement en enzymes du suc pancréatique de porc et de chien. *Biochim. Biophys. Acta* 50: 186–188, 1961.

20. MARCHIS-MOUREN, G., L. SARDA, AND P. DESNUELLE. Purification of hog pancreatic lipase. *Arch. Biochem. Biophys.* 83: 309–319, 1959.

21. MATTSON, F. H., AND L. W. BECK. The digestion in vitro of triglycerides by pancreatic lipase. *J. Biol. Chem.* 214: 115–125, 1955.

22. MATTSON, F. H., AND L. W. BECK. The specificity of pancreatic lipase for the primary hydroxyl groups of glycerides. *J. Biol. Chem.* 219: 735–740, 1956.

23. MATTSON, F. H., J. H. BENEDICT, J. B. MARTIN, AND L. W. BECK. Intermediates formed during the digestion of triglycerides. *J. Nutr.* 48: 335–329, 1952.

24. MATTSON, F. H., AND R. A. VOLPENHEIN. Synthesis and properties of glycerides. *J. Lipid Res.* 3: 281–296, 1962.

25. SARDA, L., G. AILHAUD, AND P. DESNUELLE. Inhibition de la lipase pancréatique par le diéthyl-*p*-nitrophényl phosphate en émulsion. *Biochim. Biophys. Acta* 37: 570–571, 1960.

26. SARDA, L., AND P. DESNUELLE. Action de la lipase pancréatique sur les esters en émulsion. *Biochim. Biophys. Acta* 30: 513–521, 1958.

27. SARDA, L., G. MARCHIS-MOUREN, AND P. DESNUELLE. Nouveaux essais de purification de la lipase pancréatique de porc. *Biochim. Biophys. Acta* 30: 224, 1958.

28. SARDA, L., M. F. MAYLIÉ, J. ROGER, AND P. DESNUELLE. Comportement de la lipase pancréatique sur Sephadex. Application à la purification et à la détermination du poids moléculaire de cet enzyme. *Biochim. Biophys. Acta* 89: 183–185, 1964.

29. SARI, H., B. ENTRESSANGLES, AND P. DESNUELLE. On the positional specificity of pancreatic lipase. *Biochim. Biophys. Acta* 125: 597–600, 1966.

30. SAVARY, P., AND P. DESNUELLE. Etude chromatographique de l'action de la lipase sur les triglycérides mixtes. *Compt. Rend.* 240: 2571–2573, 1955.

31. SAVARY, P., AND P. DESNUELLE. Sur quelques éléments de spécificité pendant l'hydrolyse enzymatique des triglycérides. *Biochim. Biophys. Acta* 21: 349–360, 1956.

32. WILLS, E. D. The relation of metals and -SH groups to the activity of pancreatic lipase. *Biochim. Biophys. Acta* 40: 481–490, 1960.

33. WILLS, E. D. Studies of the purification and specificity of pancreatic lipase. In: *The Enzymes of Lipid Metabolism*, edited by P. Desnuelle. New York: Pergamon, 1961, p. 13–19.

34. WOODHOUSE, D. L. Investigations in enzyme action directed towards the study of the biochemistry of cancer. The activation of pancreatic pro-lipase. *Biochem. J.* 26: 1512–1527, 1932.

CHAPTER 124

Pancreatic amylase

G. SEMENZA | *Biochemisches Institut der Universität Zürich, Zürich, Switzerland*

DISTRIBUTION AND BIOSYNTHESIS

PANCREATIC TISSUE and juice of all vertebrates investigated contain an amylase[1] which has similar if not identical catalytic properties in all species (4, 85).

Intracellular Location

Cell fractionation (41, 61, 62, 110) and immunofluorescence (116) techniques indicate that most of the pancreatic α-amylase is localized in the zymogen granules of acinar cells, although sizable amounts are also found outside these structures. In contrast, chymotrypsinogen and trypsinogen are localized almost exclusively in zymogen granules.

Biosynthesis and Secretion

In vitro synthesis of amylase has been obtained in slices of pancreas (40, 103), in cell-free systems (103–105), and, recently, in preparations of microsomes (89). Failure in previous attempts is ascribed to the

---

[1] α-1,4-Glucan-4-glucanohydrolase (EC 3.2.1.1). Pancreatic amylase and related subjects have been discussed extensively in previous reviews. The present chapter, therefore, does not discuss in detail the work covered by the reviews quoted.

high RNase activity of pancreas homogenates. Identity of the amylase synthesized in vitro by microsomes with pancreatic α-amylase was established by a number of stringent criteria (89). The acellular amylase-synthesizing system shows the same requirements (Mg^{++}, pH 5 enzymes, etc.) as other protein-synthesizing systems.

It is suggested that amylase is synthesized in (or on) the ribosomes [the specific radioactivity of amylase is higher in ribosomes than in any other fraction at any time (89)], and transferred, as it is synthesized, into the microsomal vesicles, that is, into the cisternal space of the endoplasmatic reticulum (97). The time course of incorporation of radioactive leucine into amylase in the various fractions (Fig. 1) is compatible with and supports this view.

From the cisternal space, amylase (or at least most of it) is transferred into the zymogen granules. It is not known in detail how this transfer takes place. Probably large vacuoles of the Golgi zone are progressively filled with amylase, zymogens, and others; they become "zymogen granules" and migrate away from the Golgi area (82, 98–100). Recent immunochemical electron-microscopic investigations are consistent with this scheme (117).

Various areas of this scheme, however, are still unsettled. For example, a part of the synthesis or a modification of the enzyme molecules may take place in the vacuoles of the Golgi apparatus (98) or in the "mitochondrial fraction" (103–105) or both (see reviews, refs. 82, 98).

The zymogen granules have an optimum stability at pH 5.5 and liberate their content if exposed to hypotonic solutions, detergents, or to neutral or slightly alkaline pH (41, 45). The last mentioned observation indicates that the intracellular pH in the neighborhood of the granules is likely slightly acidic; and it

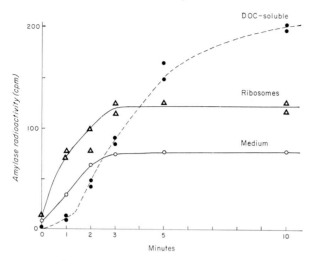

FIG. 1. Time course of incorporation of L-leucine-4,5-³H into amylase of ribosomes, deoxycholate-(DOC)-soluble fraction (i.e., of cisternal spaces), and incubation media. The system was fractionated after incubation. [From Radman et al. (89).]

further suggests that if the zymogen granules are extruded intact, they dissolve simply on coming into contact with the alkaline pancreatic juice (41).

Cholinergic agents and some hormones, notably gastrin and pancreozymin, stimulate the output of pancreatic amylase as well as of other enzymes contained in the zymogen granules (43, 49). This effect of cholinergic agents on amylase output depends on energy production (40, 59) and on Ca⁺⁺ (42), and it is accompanied by a marked stimulation of ³²P incorporation into phosphoinositides. Secretin, which has no effect on the output of amylase in vivo or in vitro, also does not have this effect on phospholipid turnover (43).

The hormonal and nervous control of pancreas secretion is reviewed elsewhere in this *Handbook* (Chapters 53–56) and has been discussed in a number of recent reviews (30–35, 44, 52).

In parotid glands the secretion of amylase is stimulated by epinephrine and norepinephrine (3, 5) via 3′5′-cylic AMP (6, 95).

The rate of synthesis of pancreatic amylase depends on the diet. Fasting animals have low amylase levels (69). Rats fed a carbohydrate-rich diet synthesize amylase at a rate some eight times greater than that of rats fed a protein-rich diet [(7, 87, 88); Fig. 2] (see also 29, 45a, 75).² An acinar cell of a carbohydrate-rich pancreas is able to synthesize some 2.4 × 10⁶ amylase molecules per min.

² Amylase biosynthesis in the parotid glands is unaffected by either diet or diabetes [rat (83)].

It seems very probable that this dietary stimulation of amylase synthesis in the pancreas is mediated by insulin. In fact, alloxan-diabetic animals produce less amylase than the controls, and insulin administration brings the amylase synthesis in the pancreas to normal levels. The chain of events in carbohydrate-stimulated amylase synthesis is therefore likely to be: absorption of glucose—insulin secretion—increased amylase synthesis (8).² Vagotomy does not prevent the response of amylase synthesis to diet (75). Pancreozymin is reported to enhance the synthesis of pancreatic amylase (91) (but see ref. 43).

Development

Amylase synthesis begins in embryonic life. In vitro and in vivo studies on rudiments of pancreas of mice have shown that amylase levels are low until about the twelfth to thirteenth day and increase sharply thereafter (Fig. 3). Ribosomal aggregates, cisternae and prozymogen and zymogen granules appear in sequence, in agreement with the chain of events suggested for amylase synthesis (82, 99, 100) and intracellular transfer (see above). The trigger for the formation of acinar clusters and of amylase is in mesenchymal tissue and appears around the thirteenth day of embryonic life (92). In chick embryo the major step in morphological differentiation and in amylase synthesis takes place at about the nineteenth day, that is, shortly before hatching. Small amounts of amylase, however, can be secreted by pancreatic rudiments much earlier, both spontaneously and under the action

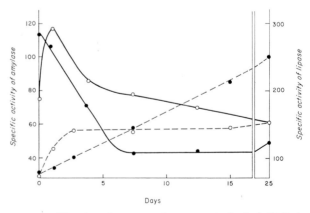

FIG. 2. Kinetics of response of pancreas to food; (*solid line*), rats passing from a carbohydrate-rich to a protein-rich diet; (*dashed line*), rats passing from a protein-rich to a carbohydrate-rich diet. ●, Specific activity of amylase in pancreatic tissue (*left scale*); ○, specific activity of lipase in pancreatic tissue (*right scale*). On the abscissa, time, in days, from the moment of change in diet. [From Ben Abdeljlil & Desnuelle (7).]

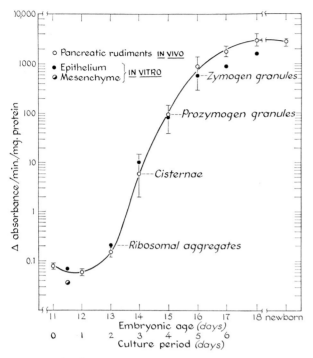

FIG. 3. Amylase activity in the developing pancreas of mice in vivo and in vitro cultures and correlation with intracellular structures. Kallman's observations (53) of the approximate time of the appearance of intracellular structures—ribosomal aggregates, cisternae, prozymogen granules, and zymogen granules—are indicated by *circles*. [From Rutter et al. (92).]

of cholinergic agents (58, 59). A "differentiation phase," therefore, precedes the "maturation phase."

At birth the amounts of α-amylase in the pancreas and duodenal juice are still far less than those at maturity [in rats (84); in piglets (48, 54, 111); Fig 4); in calves (47), as well as in man (2, 23, 55)]. Adult levels are only attained some 22 days after birth in rats (84) or 12 months after birth in man (23, 55). A similar pattern is reported for the development of pancreatic amylase in the chick (64).

MOLECULAR AND CATALYTIC PROPERTIES

Throughout the years a number of reviews have appeared giving account of the progress in these aspects. Some reviews are particularly noteworthy (10, 14, 27, 63, 79, 80, 114).

Salivary amylase is identical with the pancreatic amylase of the same species in a number of properties, including molecular weight, turnover number, stability, solubility (11), and antigenic specificity (67,

70). They may be identical proteins (see, however, refs. 37, 81).

Amylase has been isolated from the pancreas or the pancreatic juice of the hog (15, 24, 36, 65, 72), rat (38, 109), man (26), and from human saliva (73, 76, 77, 96). Hog pancreatic amylase has a molecular weight of 45,000 (17) [or of 49,600 (27)][3] with an axial ratio of 1.14. Human salivary amylase has a molecular weight of 55,200 (76). These amylases do not contain sugars (16, 25) or lipids; their amino acid composition accounts fairly well for the molecular weights as measured by ultracentrifugation techniques (27, 76). The N-terminal residue in porcine amylases may be acetylated (65).

A noteworthy component of α-amylases is calcium. One mole of amylase can bind much more than one mole of the metal. Prolonged exhaustive dialysis

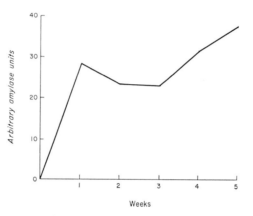

FIG. 4. Development of pancreatic amylase in the pig after birth. [From Walker (111).]

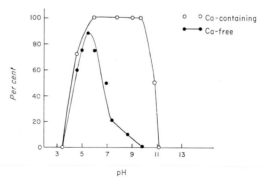

FIG. 5. Stability of Ca++-containing and Ca++-free amylase from hog pancreas. The enzymes were incubated for 20 hours at 25 C at various pHs, then tested for activity in the presence of Ca++. [From Fischer & Stein (27).]

[3] According to later reports, hog pancreas actually contains two (65) or more (105a) amylases, which may be at least in part interconvertible (105a).

against complexing agents is required to remove calcium completely (27, 102, 108). "Calcium-free" amylases show a very high affinity for the metal, the apparent association constants ranging from 10^{12} to 10^{15} (27). Calcium-replete α-amylases are much more stable than the calcium-free enzymes against elevated temperature, alkaline pH values [(27); Fig. 5], organic solvents, urea (36), and proteolytic enzymes, including trypsin (101). The stabilizing role of the metal has an obvious physiological importance.

Calcium-free amylases are catalytically inactive and can be restored to full activity by the addition of one gram atom of Ca^{++} per mole of protein (46). This does not mean that the metal participates directly in the catalysis or in the formation of the enzyme-substrate complex; very probably it stabilizes the protein in the catalytically active configuration (27, 46).

Despite a large amount of first-class work, very little is known about the functional groups of this enzyme. From the pH dependence of amylase activity the participation of two ionizable groups has been suggested, the one having a pK of 4.22 (ΔH, 2 kcal/mole), the other a pK of 7.55 (ΔH, 4 kcal/mole) (27). Slightly different apparent pK values have been reported by another group (106): namely, 4.6 and 6.7 for the chloride-free and 5.3 and 7.8 for the chloride-activated enzyme. These data are compatible with the participation of a carboxyl group and an imidazole group (for discussion, see refs. 21, 27, 60). One or more primary amino groups are necessary for amylase to be catalytically active (9, 68, 86). Contrary to earlier reports pancreatic amylase has recently been shown to contain masked sulfhydryl groups which are necessary for full enzymatic activity (94). Kinetic studies in ^2H_2O rule out an acid-catalyzed step as rate limiting (28).

Pancreatic and salivary amylases are activated by Cl^- and by a number of other anions. This phenomenon was noticed several decades ago and was reported in a number of papers, some of which have become classic (74, 78). The pH activity curve changes with the type of anion present. The anions compete with each other for the same site(s) and have a larger affinity for it (them) at low rather than at high temperature. For example, the Cl^- dissociation constant at 0 C is 2.5×10^{-5} M, at 40 C, 1.2×10^{-3} M (27). It is not clear which chemical groups occur in the "anion site(s)." Because the apparent K_m for starch is not affected by these anions, the anion site(s) is certainly not the same as the substrate site (78).

Substrate Specificity and End Products

Pancreatic and salivary amylases split 1,4-α-glucosidic bonds only.[4] The 1,4 bonds occurring at the end of the polysaccharide chains are not hydrolyzed (hence these amylases are classified as "endoamylases"), nor are those in the immediate neighborhood of 1,6 bonds. Disregarding these exceptions, the susceptible bonds are attacked apparently at random[5] (13, 71). This does not mean that they are attacked at the same speed; in general, polysaccharides are better substrates than oligosaccharides. Maltotetraose is still hydrolyzed, whereas maltose is not hydrolyzed to any detectable extent. Whether maltotriose is split by amylase has been a matter of controversy throughout the years. According to the present view (113), it is split but at a rate of some order of magnitude lower than the rate at which maltotetraose and starch are split. Thus one can distinguish two stages in the degradation of nonbranched 1,4-α-glucosidic chains: the first is fast, leading to maltose and maltotriose, and the second much slower, during which maltotriose is converted into glucose and maltose. Therefore, the composition of the mixture obtained after exhaustive amylolysis depends on the moment which is regarded as "final." At the end of the first stage, amylose has yielded maltose and maltotriose at a molar ratio (2.39:1) in good agreement with the ratio calculated for a random attack (2.35:1) (13, 115).

Amylopectin and glycogen yield, in addition to maltose and maltotriose, a mixture of branched oligosaccharides (the "limit dextrins") containing one or more 1,6 bonds in addition to 1,4 bonds. Their size depends on the number and distribution of 1,6 bonds in the original polysaccharide; they contain from 5 up to 50–330 glucose units (39, 90).

Other substrates of amylase include cyclic Schardiger dextrins (1) as well as synthetic maltosides (50). These latter substrates are hydrolyzed more poorly than the polysaccharides.

Unlike most intestinal disaccharidases (see Chapter 119), pancreatic amylase does not possess detectable transglycosidase activity.

Pancreatic amylase splits the glycosidic bond be-

[4] This substrate specificity may be less strict than formerly believed (12).

[5] This view has been challenged recently and it has been suggested that the enzyme-substrate complex does not immediately dissociate once the first bond is hydrolyzed; the substrate would instead slide on the enzyme surface and would bring another susceptible linkage into position for subsequent attack (1).

tween the C_1 and the oxygen (66). The glycosidic carbon retains its original α-configuration in the products (57, 106) (hence the name "α-amylase").[6] Two possible reaction mechanisms have been suggested to account for these observations and for the possible participation of carboxyl, imidazole, and amino groups (see above). In one mechanism (66) the α-configuration is retained because of the steric restriction imposed by the surface of the enzyme. In the other mechanism (56) a double displacement ultimately brings back the original α-configuration of C_1.

DIGESTION OF STARCH AND GLYCOGEN IN THE GUT

In ruminants, digestion of carbohydrates takes place mostly in the rumen. The major end products are the lower volatile fatty acids, acetic, propionic, and butyric acids. Little or no glucose is absorbed (22). Except for the case of the ruminants, however, pancreatic amylase is by far the most important enzyme for the digestion of starch and glycogen in the alimentary canal.

The detailed picture of starch or glycogen degradation in the gut is not available yet. Even the kinetics of amylase alone, which acts on new substrates as they arise, apparently at random but with less and less activity as the molecular weight decreases, is far too complicated to be predicted accurately. Furthermore, a number of other factors act on amylase in vivo. In addition to anions which affect amylase activity (see above), and which can occur in the digestive secretions or in the food, the following factors are worth mentioning.

Intermediary products of starch degradation by α-amylase are poorer substrates for this enzyme (14, 114), and maltose itself is an inhibitor (19). Intestinal mucosal oligo- and disaccharidases, in particular glucoamylase, isomaltase, and other maltases (see Chapter 119), hydrolyze these intermediary products and maltose to glucose. This monosaccharide does not inhibit amylase significantly (19) and, at any rate, is rapidly absorbed from the gut lumen.

Intestinal mucosa easily adsorbs pancreatic amylase (20, 51). It further possesses at least one amylase of its own, glucoamylase (see Chapter 119). Starch can, therefore, be digested at the surface of small-intestinal mucosa ("membrane digestion," 107). The limiting factor in membrane digestion is often the diffusion of substrate molecules from the medium onto the membrane surface. Membrane digestion of large-molecular-weight substances is, therefore, generally less efficient than membrane digestion of small-molecular-weight substances (107). It seems very appropriate, therefore, that large molecules, such as starch, glycogen, and proteins, are mainly split by enzymes present in the lumen ("cavital digestion"), whereas their degradation products diffuse onto the membrane to be split further there.

The result of the interplay of some of these factors, and possibly of some others as yet ill-defined, is that the digestion of starch in the gut lumen (i.e., in the presence of intestinal mucosa) proceeds at a faster rate than in vitro (18, 107).

Amylase does not degrade intact potato-starch granules, but it does degrade intact maize-starch granules. The existence of a separate enzyme attacking intact starch granules (which has been suggested earlier) seems unlikely. The amylolytic degradation of maize-starch granules is enhanced by detergents, such as bile, deoxycholate (112), and others (93). This effect of detergents requires the presence of phosphates (93, 112) and is due to the disruption of the granules, rather than to an effect on amylase itself. In fact, detergents do not enhance the hydrolysis of soluble substrates.

The author is greatly indebted to Dr. E. A. Stein, Geneva, for critically revising this manuscript.

REFERENCES

1. ABDULLAH, M., D. FRENCH, AND J. F. ROBYT. Multiple attack by α-amylases. *Arch. Biochem. Biophys.* 114: 595–598, 1966.

2. AURICCHIO, S., D. DELLA PIETRA, AND A. VEGNENTE. Studies on intestinal digestion of starch in man. II. Intestinal hydrolysis of amylopectin in infants and children. *Pediatrics* 39: 853–862, 1967.

3. BABAD, H., R. BEN-ZVI, A. BDOLAH, AND M. SCHRAMM. The mechanism of enzyme secretion by the cell. 4. The effects of inducers, substrates and inhibitors on amylase

[6] This conclusion, reached by Kuhn in 1925 (57) by polarimetry, has been confirmed recently by gas chromatography of the reaction products (G. Semenza, H. C. Curtius, and M. Müller, 1967, to be published).

secretion by rat parotid slices. *European J. Biochem.* 1: 96–101, 1967.

4. BARRINGTON, E. J. W. The alimentary canal and digestion. In: *The Physiology of Fishes*, edited by M. E. Brown. New York: Acad. Press, 1957, vol. 1, p. 109–161.

5. BDOLAH, A., R. BEN-ZVI, AND M. SCHRAMM. The mechanism of enzyme secretion by the cell. II. Secretion of amylase and other proteins by slices of rat parotid gland. *Arch. Biochem. Biophys.* 104: 58–66, 1964.

6. BDOLAH, A., AND M. SCHRAMM. The function of 3′5′ cyclic AMP in enzyme secretion. *Biochem. Biophys. Res. Commun.* 18: 452–454, 1965.

7. BEN ABDELJLIL, A., AND P. DESNUELLE. Sur l'adaptation des enzymes exocrines du pancréas à la composition du régime. *Biochim. Biophys. Acta* 81: 136–149, 1964.

8. BEN ABDELJLIL, A., J. C. PALLA, AND P. DESNUELLE. Effect of insulin on pancreatic amylase and chymotrypsinogen. *Biochim. Biophys. Res. Commun.* 18: 71–75, 1965.

9. BENNER, K., AND K. MYRBÄCK. Inactivation of saccharase and salivary amylase by 1-fluoro-2,4-dinitrobenzene. *Arkiv Kemi* 4: 7–10, 1952.

10. BERNFELD, P. Enzymes of starch degradation and synthesis. *Advan. Enzymol.* 12: 379–428, 1951.

11. BERNFELD, P., F. DUCKERT, AND E. H. FISCHER. Propriétés de l'α-amylase de pancréas humain. Comparaison avec les autres α-amylases cristallisées. Sur les enzymes amylolytiques XV. *Helv. Chim. Acta* 33: 1064–1070, 1950.

12. BINES, B. J., AND W. J. WHELAN. Chemical synthesis of "6-deoxy-amylose" and "3,6-anhydro-amylose." *Chem. Ind., London*, p. 997–998, 1960.

13. BIRD, R., AND R. H. HOPKINS. The action of some α-amylases on amylose. *Biochem. J.* 56: 86–99, 1954.

14. CALDWELL, M. L., AND M. ADAMS. Action of certain α-amylases. *Advan. Carbohydrate Chem.* 5: 229–268, 1950.

15. CALDWELL, M. L., M. ADAMS, J. T. KUNG, AND G. C. TORALBALLA. Crystalline pancreatic amylase. II. Improved method for its preparation from hog pancreas glands and additional studies of its properties. *J. Am. Chem. Soc.* 74: 4033–4035, 1952.

16. CALDWELL, M. L., N. LARSON, AND B. HUSTON. Absence of meso inositol in purified amylase preparations from different sources. *Cereal Chem.* 29: 463–469, 1952.

17. DANIELSSON, C. E. Molecular weight of α-amylase. *Nature* 160: 899, 1947.

18. DE LAEY, P. Die Membranverdauung der Stärke. 1. Mitt. Der Einfluss von Seiten der Perfusionsgeschwindigkeit und der amylolytischen Aktivität des Pankreassaftes auf die "In vivo"-Verdauung der Stärke. *Die Nahrung* 10: 641–648, 1966.

19. DE LAEY, P. Die Membranverdauung der Stärke. 3. Mitt. Der Einfluss von alimentären Komponenten des Chymus auf die Membranverdauung der Stärke. *Die Nahrung* 10: 655–663, 1966.

20. DE LAEY, P. Development of the intestinal digestion mechanism of starch as a function of age in rats. *Nature* 212: 78–79, 1966.

21. DIXON, M., AND E. C. WEBB. *Enzymes* (1st ed.). London: Longmans, Green, 1958, p. 148–150.

22. DOUGHERTY, R. W., R. S. ALLEN, W. BURROUGHS, N. L. JACOBSON, AND A. D. MCGILLIARD (editors). *Physiology of Digestion in the Ruminant.* London: Butterworths, 1965.

23. FARBER, S., C. L. MADDOCK, AND H. SHWACHMANN. Quoted in C. A. Smith, *The Physiology of the Newborn Infant* (3rd ed.). Springfield, Ill.: Thomas, 1959, p. 246.

24. FISCHER, E. H., AND P. BERNFELD. Sur les enzymes amylolytiques. VIII. L'α-amylase de pancréas de porc cristallisée. *Helv. Chim. Acta* 31: 1831–1839, 1948.

25. FISCHER, E. H., AND P. BERNFELD. Sur les enzymes amylolytiques. XII. Absence d'inositol dans l'α-amylase. *Helv. Chim. Acta* 32: 1146–1150, 1949.

26. FISCHER, E. H., F. DUCKERT, AND P. BERNFELD. Sur les enzymes amyolytiques. XIV. Isolement et cristallisation de l'α-amylase de pancréas humain. *Helv. Chim. Acta* 33: 1060–1064, 1950.

27. FISCHER, E. H., AND E. A. STEIN. α-Amylases. In: *The Enzymes* (2nd ed.), edited by P. D. Boyer, H. Lardy, and K. Myrbäck. New York: Acad. Press, 1960, vol. 4, p. 313–343.

28. FLASHNER, M., AND A. LUKTON. The effect of ^2H_2O on the activity of α-amylase. *Biochim. Biophys. Acta* 146: 596–598, 1967.

29. FOMINA, L. S. Effect of nutritional patterns upon the pancreatic secretory activity. *Vopr. Pitan.* 25: 27–32, 1966.

30. GREGORY, R. A. Secretory mechanisms of the digestive tract. *Ann. Rev. Physiol.* 27: 395–414, 1965.

31. GROSSMAN, M. I. Nervous and hormonal regulation of pancreatic secretion. In: *The Exocrine Pancreas: Ciba Foundation Symposium*, edited by A. V. S. de Reuck and M. P. Cameron. London: Churchill, 1962, p. 208–224.

32. GROSSMAN, M. I. The digestive system. *Ann. Rev. Physiol.* 25: 165–194, 1963.

33. GROSSMAN, M. I. (Editor). *Gastrin*: UCLA Forum in Medical Sciences No. 5, Berkeley and Los Angeles. Univ. California Press, 1966.

34. HARPER, A. A. A gastric phase of pancreatic secretion? *Gastroenterology* 45: 279–281, 1963.

35. HARPER, A. A., E. L. BLAIR, AND T. SCRATCHERD. The distribution and physiological properties of pancreozymin. In: *The Exocrine Pancreas: Ciba Foundation Symposium*, edited by A. V. S. de Reuck and M. P. Cameron. London: Churchill, 1962, p. 168–185.

36. HATFALUDI, F., T. STRASHILOV, AND F. B. STRAUB. Effect of urea and Ca ions on pancreatic amylase. *Acta Biochim. Biophys. Acad. Sci. Hung.* 1: 39–44, 1966.

37. HAYASHI, S., R. L. SEARCY, AND N. C. HIGHTOWER, JR. Differentiation of parotid and pancreatic amylase in human serum. *Am. J. Digest. Diseases* 11: 695–701, 1966.

38. HEATLEY, N. G. Spontaneous crystallization of amylase from pancreatic juice of the rat. *Nature* 181: 1069–1070, 1958.

39. HELLER, J., AND M. SCHRAMM. α-Amylase limit dextrins of high molecular weight obtained from glycogen. *Biochim. Biophys. Acta* 81: 96–100, 1964.

40. HOKIN, L. E. The synthesis and secretion of amylase by pigeon pancreas *in vitro. Biochem. J.* 48: 320–326, 1951.

41. HOKIN, L. E. Isolation of the zymogen granules of dog pancreas and a study of their properties. *Biochim. Biophys. Acta* 18: 379–388, 1955.

42. HOKIN, L. E. Effects of calcium omission on acetylcholine-stimulated amylase secretion and phospholipid synthesis in pigeon pancreas slices. *Biochim. Biophys. Acta* 115: 219–221, 1966.

43. HOKIN, L. E., AND M. R. HOKIN, Studies of pancreatic tissue *in vitro*. *Gastroenterology* 36: 368–376, 1959.

44. HOKIN, L. E., AND M. R. HOKIN. The synthesis and secretion of digestive enzymes by pancreas tissue *in vitro*. In: *The Exocrine Pancreas: Ciba Foundation Symposium*, edited by A. V. S. de Reuck and M. P. Cameron. London: Churchill, 1962, p. 186–207.

45. HOLTZER, R. L., J. L. VAN LANCKER, AND H. SWIFT. Release of amylase from zymogen granules and microsomes. *Arch. Biochem. Biophys.* 101: 439–444, 1963.

45a. HOWARD, F., AND J. YUDKIN. Effect of dietary change upon the amylase and trypsin activities of the rat pancreas. *Brit. J. Nutr.* 17: 281, 1963.

46. HSIU, J., E. H. FISCHER, AND E. A. STEIN. Alpha-amylases as calcium-metalloenzymes. II. Calcium and the catalytic activity. *Biochemistry* 3: 61–66, 1964.

47. HUBER, J. T., N. L. JACOBSON, AND R. S. ALLEN. Digestive enzyme activities in the young calf. *J. Dairy Sci.* 44: 1494–1501, 1961.

48. HUDMAN, D. B., D. W. FRIEND, P. A. HARTMAN, G. C. ASHTON, AND D. V. CATRON. Digestive enzymes of the baby pig. I. Pancreatic and salivary amylase. *J. Agr. Food Chem.* 5: 691–693, 1957.

49. ICHIKAWA, A. Fine structural changes in response to hormonal stimulation of the perfused canine pancreas. *J. Cell Biol.* 24: 369–385, 1965.

50. JANSEN, A. P., AND P. G. A. B. WYDEVELD. α-(p-Nitrophenyl)maltoside as a substrate for the assay of amylase. *Nature* 182: 525–526, 1958.

51. JESUITOVA, N. N., P. DE LAEY, AND A. M. UGOLEV. Digestion of starch *in vivo* and *in vitro* in a rat intestine. *Biochim. Biophys. Acta* 86: 205–210, 1964.

52. JORPES, E., AND V. MUTT. Gastrointestinal hormones. In: *The Hormones*, edited by G. Pincus, K. V. Thimann, and E. B. Astwood. New York: Acad. Press, 1964, vol. V, p. 365–385.

53. KALLMAN, P. Data quoted in reference 92.

54. KITTS, W. D., C. B. BAILEY, AND A. J. WOOD. The development of the digestive enzyme system of the pig during its preweaning phase of growth. A. Pancreatic amylase and lipase. *Can. J. Agr. Sci.* 36: 45–50, 1956.

55. KLUMPP, T. G., AND A. V. NEALE. Gastric and duodenal contents of normal infants and children: duodenal enzyme activities and gastric and duodenal reactions. *Am. J. Diseases Children* 40: 1215–1229, 1930.

56. KOSHLAND, D. A. Group transfer as an enzymatic substitution mechanism. In: *A Symposium on the Mechanism of Enzyme Action*, edited by W. D. McElroy and B. Glass. Baltimore: The Johns Hopkins Univ. Press, 1954, p. 608–641.

57. KUHN, R. Der Wirkungsmechanismus der Amylasen; ein Beitrag zum Konfigrationsproblem der Stärke. *Ann. Chem.* 443: 1–71, 1925.

58. KULKA, R. G., AND D. DUKSIN. Patterns of growth and α-amylase activity in the developing chick pancreas. *Biochim. Biophys. Acta* 91: 506–514, 1964.

59. KULKA, R. G., AND U. YALOVSKY. Secretion of α-amylase by the embryonic chick pancreas in vitro. *J. Cell Biol.* 29: 287–292, 1966.

60. LAIDLER, K. J. The influence of pH on the rates of enzyme reactions. Part 3. Analysis of experimental results for various enzyme systems. *Trans. Faraday Soc.* 51: 550–561, 1955.

61. LAIRD, A. K., AND A. D. BARTON. Protein synthesis in rat pancreas. I. Intracellular distribution of amylase. *Biochim. Biophys. Acta* 25: 56–62, 1957.

62. LAIRD, A. K., AND A. D. BARTON. Protein synthesis in rat pancreas. II. Changes in the intracellular distribution of pancreatic amylase during the secretory cycle. *Biochim. Biophys. Acta* 27: 12–15, 1958.

63. MANNERS, D. J. Enzymic synthesis and degradation of starch and glycogen. *Advan. Carbohydrate Chem.* 17: 371–430, 1962.

64. MARCHAIM, U., AND R. G. KULKA. The non-parallel increase of amylase, chymotrypsinogen and procarboxypeptidase in the developing chick pancreas. *Biochim. Biophys. Acta* 146: 553–559, 1967.

65. MARCHISMOUREN, G., AND L. PASÉRO. Isolation of two amylases in porcine pancreas. *Biochim. Biophys. Acta* 140: 366–368, 1967.

66. MAYER, F. C., AND J. LARNER. Substrate cleavage point of the α- and β-amylases. *J. Am. Chem. Soc.* 81: 188–193, 1959.

67. MCGEACHIN, R. L. Immunochemical characterization of amylase isozymes. *Ann. N. Y. Acad. Sci.* 103: 1009–1013, 1963.

68. MCGEACHIN, R. L., AND J. H. BROWN. Amino terminal amino acids of hog pancreatic amylase and their relationship to its enzymic activity. *Arch. Biochem. Biophys.* 110: 303–308, 1965.

69. MCGEACHIN, R. L., AND N. K. FORD, JR. Distribution of amylase in the gastrointestinal tract of the rat. *Am. J. Physiol.* 196: 972–974, 1959.

70. MCGEACHIN, R. L., J. M. REYNOLDS, AND J. I. HUDDLESTON, JR. Relationships among amylases determined by rabbit antisera to human salivary amylase. *Arch. Biochem. Biophys.* 93: 387–391, 1961.

71. MEYER, K. H., AND P. BERNFELD. Recherches sur l'amidon, XIX. Sur la dégradation de l'amylose par l'α-amylase. *Helv. Chim. Acta* 24: 359E-369E, 1941.

72. MEYER, K. H., E. H. FISCHER, AND P. BERNFELD. Sur les enzymes amylolytiques (I). L'isolement de l'α-amylase de pancréas. *Helv. Chim. Acta* 30: 64–78, 1947.

73. MEYER, K. H., E. H. FISCHER, A. STAUB, AND P. BERNFELD. Sur les enzymes amylolytiques. X. Isolement et cristallisation de l'α-amylase de salive humaine. *Helv. Chim. Acta* 31: 2158–2164, 1948.

74. MICHAELIS, L., AND H. PECHSTEIN. Die Wirkungsbedingungen der Speicheldiastase. *Biochem. Z.* 59: 77–99, 1914.

75. MORISSET, J., AND J. DUNNIGAN. Exocrine pancreas adaptation in vagotomized rats. *Rev. Can. Biol.* 26: 11–16, 1967.

76. MUTZBAUER, H., AND G. V. SCHULZ. Die Bestimmung der molekularen Konstanten von α-Amylase aus Humanspeichel. *Biochim. Biophys. Acta* 102: 526–532, 1965.

77. MUUS, J. Studies on salivary amylase with special reference to the interaction with chloride ions. *Compt. Rend. Trav. Lab. Carlsberg, Ser. Chim.* 28: 317–334, 1953.

78. MYRBÄCK, K. Ueber Verbindungen einiger Enzyme mit inaktivierenden Stoffen. II. *Z. Physiol. Chem.* 159: 1–84, 1926.

79. MYRBÄCK, K., AND G. NEUMÜLLER. Amylases and the hydrolysis of starch and glycogen. In: *The Enzymes* (1st

ed.), edited by J. B. Sumner and K. Myrbäck. New York: Acad. Press, 1950, vol. 1, p. 653–724.

80. MYRBÄCK, K., AND G. NEUMÜLLER. Stärke und Glycogen. Enzymatische Synthese und Hydrolyse. *Ergeb. Enzymforsch.* 12: 1–88, 1951.

81. NØRBY, S. Electrophoretic non-identity of human salivary and pancreatic amylases. *Exptl. Cell Res.* 36: 663–702, 1964.

82. PALADE, G. E., P. SIEKEVITZ, AND L. G. CARO. Structure, chemistry and function of the pancreatic exocrine cell. In: *The Exocrine Pancreas: Ciba Foundation Symposium*, edited by A. V. S. de Reuck and M. P. Cameron. London: Churchill, 1962, p. 23–55.

83. PALLA, J. C., A. BEN ABDELJLIL, AND P. DESNUELLE. Comparative study of the control of amylase biosynthesis in rat pancreas and parotid glands. *Biochim. Biophys. Acta* 136: 563–565, 1967.

84. PROCHÁZKA, P., P. HAHN, O. KOLDOVSKÝ, M. NOHYNEK, AND J. ROKOS. The activity of α-amylase in homogenates of the pancreas of rats during early postnatal development. *Physiol. Bohemoslov.* 13: 288–291, 1964.

85. PROSSER, C. L. (editor). *Comparative Animal Physiology*. Philadelphia: Saunders, 1950, p. 144–186.

86. RADICHEVICH, I., M. M. BECKER, M. EITINGON, V. H. GETTLER, G. C. TORALBALLA, AND M. L. CALDWELL. Essential groups of porcine pancreatic amylase and of taka amylase. Acetylation with acetic anhydride. *J. Am. Chem. Soc.* 81: 2845–2851, 1959.

87. REBOUD, J. P., G. MARCHIS-MOUREN, A. COZZONE, AND P. DESNUELLE. Variations in the biosynthesis rate of pancreatic amylase and chymotrypsinogen in response to a starch-rich or a protein-rich diet. *Biochem. Biophys. Res. Commun.* 22: 94–99, 1966.

88. REBOUD, J. P., G. MARCHIS-MOUREN, L. PASÉRO, A. COZZONE, AND P. DESNUELLE. Adaptation de la vitesse de biosynthèse de l'amylase pancréatique et du chymotrypsinogène à des régimes riches en amidon ou en protéines. *Biochim. Biophys. Acta* 117: 351–367, 1966.

89. REDMAN, C. M., P. SIEKEVITZ, AND G. E. PALADE. Synthesis and transfer of amylase in pigeon pancreatic microsomes. *J. Biol. Chem.* 241: 1150–1158, 1966.

90. ROBERTS, P. J. P., AND W. J. WHELAN. The mechanism of carbohydrase action. 5. Action of human salivary α-amylase on amylopectin and glycogen. *Biochem. J.* 76: 246–253, 1960.

91. ROTHMAN, S. S., AND H. WELLS. Enhancement of pancreatic enzyme synthesis by pancreozymin. *Am. J. Physiol.* 213: 215–218, 1967.

92. RUTTER, W. J., N. K. WESSELLS, AND C. GROBSTEIN. Control of specific synthesis in the developing pancreas. *Natl. Cancer Inst. Monograph* 13: 51–65, 1964.

93. SANDSTEDT, R. M., AND R. L. GATES. Raw starch digestion: a comparison of the raw starch digestion capabilities of the amylase system for four α-amylase sources. *Food Res.* 19: 190–199, 1954.

94. SCHRAMM, M. Unmasking of sulfhydryl groups in pancreatic α-amylase. *Biochemistry* 3: 1231–1234, 1964.

95. SCHRAMM, M., R. BEN-ZVI, AND A. BDOLAH. Epinephrin-activated amylase secretion in parotid slices and leakage of the enzyme in the cold. *Biochem. Biophys. Res. Commun.* 18: 446–451, 1965.

96. SHAINKIN, R., AND Y. BIRK. Isolation of pure α-amylase from human saliva. *Biochim. Biophys. Acta* 122: 153–156, 1966.

97. SIEKEVITZ, P., AND G. E. PALADE. Distribution of newly synthetized amylase in microsomal subfractions of guinea pig pancreas. *J. Cell Biol.* 30: 519–530, 1966.

98. SJÖSTRAND, F. S. The fine structure of the exocrine pancreas cells. In: *The Exocrine Pancreas: Ciba Foundation Symposium*, edited by A. V. S. de Reuck and M. P. Cameron. London: Churchill, 1962, p. 1–22.

99. SJÖSTRAND, F. S., AND V. HANZON. Membrane structures of cytoplasm and mitochondria in exocrine cells of mouse pancreas as revealed by high resolution electron microscopy. *Exptl. Cell Res.* 7: 393–414, 1954.

100. SJÖSTRAND, F. S., AND V. HANZON. Function of the Golgi apparatus in the exocrine pancreas cell. *Science* 134: 1434, 1961.

101. STEIN, E. A., AND E. H. FISCHER. The resistance of α-amylases towards proteolytic attack. *J. Biol. Chem.* 232: 867–879, 1958.

102. STEIN, E. A., J. HSIU, AND E. H. FISCHER. Alpha-amylases as calcium-metalloenzymes. 1. Preparation of calcium-free apoamylases by chelation and electrodialysis. *Biochemistry* 3: 56–61, 1964.

103. STRAUB, F. B. Formation of amylase in the pancreas. In: *The Biological Replication of Macromolecules* (XIIth Symposium of the Society for Experimental Biology). Cambridge, England: Cambridge Univ. Press, 1958, p. 176–184.

104. STRAUB, F. B. In: *Proceedings of the Fifth International Congress of Biochemistry, Moscow, 1961*, edited by O. Lindberg. New York: Pergamon Press, 1963, vol. II, p. 176–182.

105. STRAUB, F. B., A. ULLMANN, AND P. VENETIANER. Ribonucleic acid and the formation of amylase in cell free preparations from pigeon pancreas. *Biochim. Biophys. Acta* 43: 152–162, 1960.

105a. SZABO, M. T., AND F. B. STRAUB. Chromatographic behaviour of pancreatic amylase. *Acta Biochim. Biophys. Acad. Sci. Hung.* 1: 379–387, 1966.

106. THOMA, J. A., J. WAKIM, AND L. STEWART. Comparison of the active sites of α- and β-amylases. *Biochem. Biophys. Res. Commun.* 12: 350–355, 1963.

107. UGOLEV, A. M. Membrane (contact) digestion. *Physiol. Rev.* 45: 555–595, 1965.

108. VALLEE, B. L., E. A. STEIN, W. N. SUMERWELL, AND E. H. FISCHER. Metal content of α-amylases of various origins. *J. Biol. Chem.* 234: 2901–2905, 1959.

109. VANDERMEERS, A., AND J. CHRISTOPHE. α-Amylase et lipase du pancréas de rat. Purification chromatographique, recherche du poids moléculaire et composition en acides aminés. *Biochim. Biophys. Acta* 154: 110–129, 1968.

110. VAN LANCKER, J. L., AND R. L. HOLTZER. Tissue fractionation studies of mouse pancreas. Intracellular distribution of nitrogen, deoxyribonucleic acid, ribonucleic acid, amylase, acid phosphatase, deoxyribonuclease, and cytochrome oxidase. *J. Biol. Chem.* 234: 2359–2363, 1959.

111. WALKER, D. M. The development of the digestive system of the young animal. II. Carbohydrase enzyme development in the young pig. *J. Agr. Sci.* 52: 357–363, 1959.

112. WALKER, G. J., AND P. M. HOPE. The action of some

α-amylases on starch granules. *Biochem. J.* 86: 452–462, 1963.

113. WALKER, G. J., AND W. J. WHELAN. The mechanism of carbohydrase action. 7. Stages in the salivary α-amylolysis of amylose, amylopectin and glycogen. *Biochem. J.* 76: 257–263, 1960.

114. WHELAN, W. J. Starch and similar polysaccharides. *Encyclopedia Plant Physiol.* 6: 154–240, 1958.

115. WHELAN, W. J., AND P. J. P. ROBERTS. The mechanism of carbohydrase action. Part II. α-Amylolysis of linear substrates. *J. Chem. Soc.* 1953, p. 1298–1304.

116. YASUDA, K., AND A. H. COONS. Localization by immuno-fluorescence of amylase, trypsinogen and chymotrypsinogen in the acinar cells of the pig pancreas. *J. Histochem. Cytochem.* 14: 303–313, 1966.

117. YASUDA, K., T. SUZUKI, AND K. TAKANO. Distribution of the pancreatic amylase around Golgi area, demonstrated by means of immuno-electron microscopic method. *Okaiimas Folia Anat. Japon.* 43: 87–101, 1967.

Physi

R. S. C

I. A.

D. H.

CHAPTE

INTRODUC

THE COMP

extreme n

CHAPTER 125

Physiological anatomy of the ruminant stomach

R. S. COMLINE

I. A. SILVER

D. H. STEVEN

Physiological Laboratory, University of Cambridge, Cambridge, England
Anatomy School, University of Cambridge, Cambridge, England

CHAPTER CONTENTS

INTRODUCTION

THE COMPOUND STOMACH of the ruminant represents an extreme modification of the embryonic gastric spindle to meet the needs of an animal with a preference for plant food. The complexity of the structure has been a source of curiosity and confusion to many since first described by Aristotle (10), and although advances in the knowledge of its physiology have been great, especially during the last twenty years, many of its structures remain ill-defined. This paper attempts to consolidate present knowledge of the structure of the ruminant stomach and to present a guide to this complex organ.

ANATOMY OF THE ADULT STOMACH

Esophagus

In ruminants the esophagus is relatively distensible and thin walled, and unlike the stomach both muscle layers have a spiral arrangement. In the ox the esophagus is composed of striated muscle (68), but in the sheep some smooth muscle is present at the distal end. The esophagus enters the rumino-reticular sac at the cardia, where the esophageal musculature blends with that of the atrium dorsally and the reticulum ventrally and becomes arranged into circular and longitudinal layers. The lumen is lined with stratified squamous epithelium and is devoid of papillae or glands at the caudal end.

The ruminant esophagus lacks obvious cardiac and precardiac "diaphragmatic" sphincters such as those which have been described in other species. Nevertheless, cineradiographs (19) have shown the presence of constrictions both at the cardia and immediately caudal to the heart. The presence of these sphincters in the ruminant esophagus must therefore depend on the differential contraction of the striated muscle at these points.

Stomach

Detailed accounts of the anatomy of the ruminant stomach have been published (8, 29, 53, 60). The general structure is similar but not identical in the sheep and ox, and only those variations between the two species which may be of experimental or functional significance will be mentioned in this review.

The ruminant stomach is subdivided into four compartments which are clearly distinguishable in the 30-mm embryo. An important feature of the ruminant stomach, and indeed of the abdominal cavity, is the tough consistency of the serous peritoneal lining. The peritoneum is also extremely resistant to infection, and these properties greatly facilitate abdominal surgery and in particular the preparation of gastric fistulas.

RETICULUM. The division of the stomach most craniad, the reticulum, is the smallest compartment in the ox but is relatively larger in the sheep. It is not a distinct organ in the camel (8). Its form is that of a pear suspended by the narrow neck and compressed between the liver and diaphragm cranially and the rumen, omasum, and abomasum caudally. It is clearly separated from the rumen by a groove ventrally and laterally but is continuous with the dorsal sac of the rumen dorsally. The reticulum joins the rumen at the atrium ventriculi, a saccular region surrounding the cardia.

Internally, the reticulum has a number of important features. It has three openings, the largest being its communication with the dorsal sac of the rumen through the atrium. This orifice is bounded by a muscular constriction, the rumino-reticular fold, which is prominent ventrally but becomes less obvious medially and laterally and cannot be distinguished behind the cardia. The second opening in the reticulum, from the esophagus at the cardia, is in the form of a narrow slit at the upper end of the esophageal (reticular) groove. The position of the esophageal opening in relation to the rumino-reticular fold is such that heavy foreign bodies leaving the cardia tend to fall into the reticulum, that is, craniad to the fold. The rounded reticulo-omasal orifice is at the lower end of the esophageal groove and is surrounded by the muscular reticulo-omasal pillars. The esophageal groove thus runs between the cardia and the reticulo-omasal orifice. The lips of the groove may form a pas-

sive valvelike mechanism in the reticulo-omasal orifice in cases of muscular paralysis induced by section of the vagus nerves (30).

The mucosa of the reticulum is raised into a honeycomb pattern and is covered with small conical papillae. The walls of this honeycomb are low (2–3 mm) in the sheep and young calf but much higher (1 cm) in the adult ox. Their free borders are reinforced by bands of smooth muscle which represent the muscularis mucosae in this organ. The change from the honeycomb pattern of mucosa to the typical papillae of the rumen takes place at the cranial entrance to the atrium.

RUMEN. This is the largest compartment of the stomach in the adult but is relatively larger in the ox than in the sheep and has a somewhat different external form in the two species.

The rumen has a roughly ovoid shape with its long axis craniocaudal; it is compressed laterally and divided into a dorsal and ventral part by a horizontal groove which is particularly marked at the caudal extremity. The groove provides an external indication of the position, left and right, of the cranial (anterior) and caudal (posterior) longitudinal pillars. Left and right coronary grooves arise from the caudal groove on the appropriate sides and these grooves indicate the sites of the internal coronary pillars. The coronary grooves also mark the limits of the dorsal and ventral posterior blind sacs. The anterior blind sacs lie craniad and, respectively, dorsolaterally and ventrally to the cranial longitudinal groove.

Internally, the cavity of the rumen is partially divided by shelflike projections, the pillars. It has a single opening cranially and dorsally on the right (medial) side which communicates through the atrium with the reticulum. The whole of the internal surface is covered with papillae which vary from simple conical through short, thick tonguelike forms to large flattened leaf-shaped structures which, in the ox, often reach 1 cm in length. In the sheep they are mostly shorter and thicker than in the ox. The distribution of papillae is not uniform. In the ox the dorsal and ventral blind sacs are the most densely papillated regions and also contain the largest papillae. On the other hand, the borders of the pillars, the central part of the dorsal sac, and the medial wall of the atrium bear widely separated and very small papillae; the lateral region of the atrium and the rumino-reticular fold are thickly covered with discrete papillae. In the sheep the papillae of the dorsal sac are usually much smaller than those in the ventral sac. Smooth muscle (muscularis mucosae) is absent in the subepithelial zone of this organ.

OMASUM. This compartment lies on the right side of the stomach and is relatively larger in the ox than in the sheep. It has two openings which are found close together on its medial aspect at each end of the lesser curvature. The cranial opening is the reticulo-omasal orifice which is guarded by the reticulo-omasal pillars and is continuous with the esophageal groove. The caudal opening is the omaso-abomasal orifice, the walls of which are reinforced by the muscular omasal pillar and the cavity of which contains folds of abomasal mucosa. The omasal sulcus is a groove that runs between the two openings; it is homologous with part of the gastric canal of the simple stomach and is derived from the ventral part of the primitive stomach spindle. A number of large papillae that point in the direction of the abomasum are found on the floor of this sulcus.

The most distinctive feature of the omasum is the large number of folds or septa within the organ. The septa are attached to the greater curvature; the free borders lie parallel with the lesser curvature, and they vary in size from those with free edges that almost reach the omasal sulcus to others which are mere ridges on the inside of the greater curvature. The free borders of these laminae bear long horny papillae which are directed toward the abomasum. The surfaces of the laminae bear smaller horny papillae which are less clearly orientated but which, in general, point toward the omaso-abomasal orifice. The arrangement of the papillae is therefore such as to encourage the movement of food material in the omasum toward the abomasum, whatever form of muscular activity may occur.

ABOMASUM. This compartment is derived from the most caudal part of the stomach spindle and in the adult most nearly resembles the simple stomach of non-ruminants. It is attached by secondary adhesion to both the reticulum and the omasum. In the ox it is normally found entirely to the right of the rumen, but in the sheep, where it is relatively larger than it is in the ox, it often extends below the reticulum, craniad to the ventral sac of the rumen, and may emerge to come into contact with the left body wall.

The mucosa of the abomasum is divided into a small region of cardiac glands adjacent to the omaso-abomasal orifice, a much larger cranial fundic zone,

and a narrower, tubular pyloric zone. The fundic zone contains at least 12 spirally arranged folds which run craniocaudally and which disappear at the constriction which separates the fundic from the pyloric zone. The omaso-abomasal valves at the orifice are folds of abomasal fundic mucosa in the sheep and the goat; in the ox, however, the valves are covered with stratified epithelium (68).

Musculature of the Stomach

RUMEN. The surface of the rumen is covered by peritoneum except at its attachment to the dorsal body wall, to the spleen, and to the omasum. The thinner of the two muscular layers is adjacent to this serous coat, and most of the fibers in it run craniocaudally and blend with the outer muscle coat of the esophagus at the atrium (Figs. 1 and 2).

The deep muscle coat of the rumen (Figs. 1, 2) is thicker than the superficial layer, and the fibers run in a circular direction. It is thickened to form the pillars of the rumen that constitute the boundaries of the various anatomical subdivisions. In the region of the atrium the deep muscle layer is continuous with the inner layer of the esophageal musculature, which, particularly in the ox, is composed chiefly of striped muscle.

RETICULUM. The smooth muscle of the reticulum, like that of the rumen, is also arranged in two layers. These are orientated with respect to the esophageal groove, and both are arranged so that the fibers run in an obliquely circular direction (Figs. 1, 2).

The esophageal groove itself is formed in the deep layer of muscle. Its outer wall is partly derived from the outer muscle coat of the esophagus but consists principally of two layers of oblique fibers. The lips of the groove are thick and are formed from dorso-ventrally running muscles that are continuous with the inner layer of the esophageal musculature. The fibers of the right lip are continuous with the inner reticular muscle and those of the left lip with the inner omasal muscle coat. In the adult, unlike the embryo, the free edges of the lips are twisted in a long spiral. In the upper part, the cranial (left) lip overlaps the caudal (right), whereas in the middle both are of equal size; ventrally the caudal lip overlaps the cranial (Fig. 3).

OMASUM. The omasum has a thin outer longitudinal muscle layer that runs parallel to the greater curvature

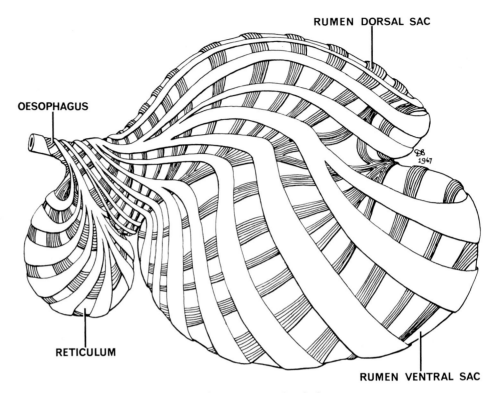

FIG. 1. Arrangement of deep (*shaded*) and superficial musculature of the rumen and reticulum (*left side*). Both layers are present as continuous sheets in life, but are presented here, and in Fig. 2, as strips so that they can be seen in relation to each other.

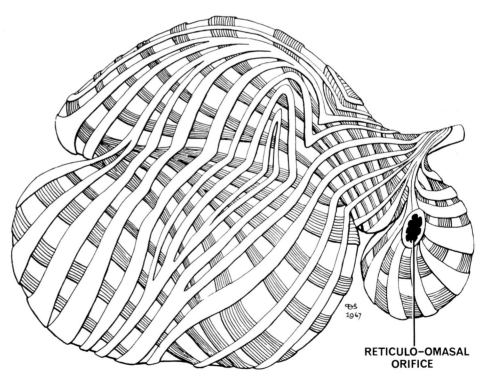

FIG. 2. Deep and superficial musculature of the rumen and reticulum (*right side*). The omasum and abomasum have been removed.

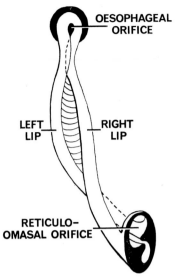

FIG. 3. Diagram showing the spiral arrangement of the lips of the esophageal (reticular) groove.

and a thick inner circular layer that is reinforced at the omasal sulcus by oblique fibers. The largest omasal leaves contain a central band of muscle that is continuous with the inner layer of the wall and extends almost to the free border of the laminae. They also contain a marginal band of muscle in the free border, and a superficial layer on each side that is part of the muscularis mucosae.

INNERVATION

The nerves that supply the ruminant stomach originate in a manner similar to those that supply the simple stomach. The major components of the innervation are derived from the esophageal vagus nerves, which contain both efferent and afferent fibers. In addition, there are large contributions from the sympathetic system via the celiaco-mesenteric plexus.

Many descriptions of the gross innervation of the ruminant stomach have been published (8, 20, 25, 27, 29, 30, 38, 47), and many aspects of the nerve supply to the ruminant stomach have been reviewed by Habel (30). The dorsal and ventral vagus nerves of the simple-stomached animal pass on the visceral (caudal) and parietal (cranial) faces, respectively, of the lesser curvature of the stomach, that is, on either side of the embryonic ventral midline. Habel (30) pointed out that in the ruminant the main vagal trunks follow a similar course along either side of the embryonic ventral aspect of the stomach. The dorsal vagus runs to the embryonic right side of the pylorus and the ventral vagus runs to the embryonic left side. The general distribution of the two vagus nerves also accords in the main with that of the same nerves to the homologous parts of the simple stomach. Thus the greater part of the rumen (embryologically dorsal) and the left aspects of the adult omasum and abomasum (embryologically right) are supplied by the dorsal vagus, whereas most of the reticulum and the adult right side of the omasum and abomasum (embryologically left) are innervated via the ventral vagus. This would be expected if the majority of fibers in the dorsal abdominal vagus were derived from the right, and those in the ventral abdominal vagus from the left thoracic vagus nerve.

The nerves terminate in a rich plexus of fibers and ganglia that lie between the two muscle layers of all regions of the stomach (12, 30). This plexus is also continuous with that on the walls of the arteries. This submucosal plexus is composed almost entirely of fibers which are presumably postganglionic, except in the abomasum in which the ganglion cells of Auerbach's plexus are readily recognized.

Esophagus

Both motor and sensory innervation of the esophagus is derived from the left and right vagus nerves. The upper part of the cervical esophagus is supplied by a proximal branch of the vagus, the pharyngoesophageal nerve. This forms an anastomosis with the esophageal division of the recurrent (caudal) laryngeal nerve. There are additional anastomoses between branches of the cranial laryngeal nerve (internal and external laryngeal) and the pharyngoesophageal and recurrent nerves, details of which vary between species and individuals.

The caudal cervical esophagus receives branches from the recurrent nerves, either directly or via an esophageal division of the nerve.

The thoracic esophagus receives its innervation from both left and right vagus nerves and, after their division and realignment into dorsal and ventral vagus nerves, particularly from the dorsal vagus.

Stimulation of nerves to the esophagus suggests that the motor pathways are as follows (18): *1*) The pharyngoesophageal nerves are motor to the cranial cervical esophagus, the cranial esophageal sphincter, and in some cases, to the caudal cervical esophagus. *2*) The recurrent laryngeal nerves are motor to the cranial thoracic and sometimes the caudal cervical esophagus. *3*) The dorsal vagus nerve is motor to the caudal thoracic esophagus and cardia.

Stomach

DISTRIBUTION OF VAGUS AND SYMPATHETIC NERVES. In the course of their passage through the thorax a variable number of anastomoses occur between the left

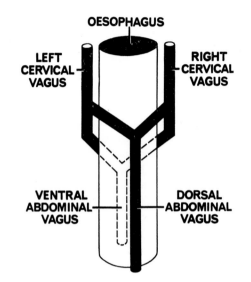

and right vagus nerves (Fig. 4A). The final anastomosis results in a rerouting of the vagus nerves into a dorsal and a ventral position in relation to the esophagus, and this position is retained as they follow the esophagus through the diaphragmatic hiatus to the stomach.

The ventral vagus, which is usually the smaller of the two nerve trunks, contributes to a plexus of nerve fibers on the cranial aspect of the reticulum, just below the esophagus. This plexus extends over the surface of the reticulum from its junction with the esophagus and gives off a dorsal branch on the left side, which accompanies the cranial reticular artery (Figs. 4B, 5) for part of its course to reach a point dorsal to the esophagus, where it joins the dorsal vagus in contributing to the celiac plexus.

The main ventral nerve runs caudoventrally after

FIG. 4. *A (left):* diagram of the anastomoses between the left and right vagus nerves on the thoracic esophagus of the sheep. [Modified from Duncan (20).]. *B (below):* diagrammatic view from the right side of the innervation of the ruminant stomach.

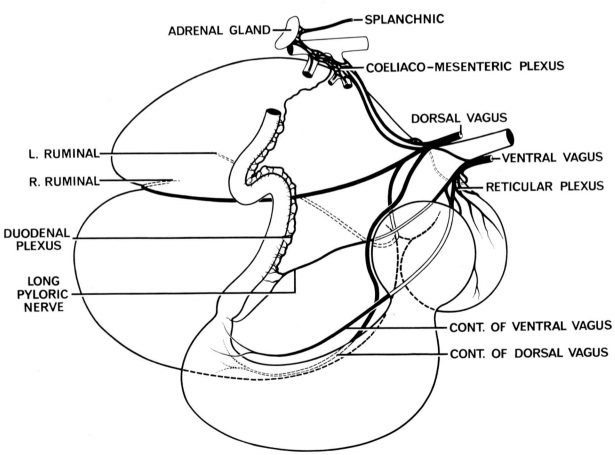

leaving the reticular plexus, first in relation to the right (lesser) curvature of the reticulum and then in the edge of the lesser omentum along its attachment to the omasum and abomasum. It terminates on the right side of the pyloric region of the abomasum. In its course, the ventral vagus gives off the following: *a)* Branches that appear to be mostly afferent from the ventral vagal plexus to the cardia, reticulum, reticulo-omasal junction, atrium ventriculi, and esophageal groove. *b)* The long pyloric nerve that arises from the right part of the vagal reticular plexus and runs caudally in the lesser omentum close to the liver, to reach the duodenum. At this point it becomes involved in the formation of the duodenal plexus, but its trunk can be followed to the pyloric region of the abomasum. *c)* Branches from the main gastric nerve, to the reticulum, omasum, and abomasum. *d)* A terminal branch to the pyloric region.

The dorsal vagus nerve is the larger of the two nerve trunks and runs first on the dorsal aspect of the esophagus and then dorsal to the reticulum to join the celiaco-mesenteric plexus around the roots of the celiac and cranial mesenteric arteries. It gives off a number of branches to the stomach before it joins the celiac plexus.

The main trunk of the nerve on the stomach runs ventrally to the right onto the greater curvature of the omasum, where it continues along the dorsocaudal border in company with the dorsal omaso-abomasal artery (Figs. 4B, 5). Eventually, still following the artery, it reaches the left (visceral) side of the pylorus via the lesser curvature of the abomasum. In its course this main gastric trunk of the dorsal vagus gives off the following branches: *a)* nerves to the reticulo-omasal junction, atrium ventriculi, and omasum; *b)* nerves to the visceral and parietal surfaces of the omasum; *c)* nerves to the visceral surface of the abomasum. Several other major branches of the dorsal vagal trunk supply the stomach. There are a large and variable number of small filaments innervating the dorsal sac of the rumen that arise in series with the larger right ruminal nerve. This right ruminal nerve runs from the left side of the celiac artery along the gastrosplenic artery into the right longitudinal groove of the rumen. Here it continues caudally in company with the right ruminal artery and passes around the caudal groove into the left longitudinal groove (Fig. 4B). In its course it gives off many branches which form the major nerve supply to the rumen.

The left side of the rumen is also innervated by the dorsal vagus nerve by way of fibers from the celiac plexus and one or more branches that come directly from the main nerve. They form a ruminal plexus and are distributed along the left ruminal artery.

The nerves derived from the dorsal vagus which supply the omasum and abomasum consist of the long abomasal nerve and also branches from the celiac plexus. The latter follow the omaso-abomasal arteries together with sympathetic fibers from the plexus. The long abomasal nerve runs ventrally from the main dorsal trunk, between the reticulum and omasum craniad to their junction, in company at first with the common omaso-abomasal artery and after the division of the latter, with the ventral omaso-abomasal artery. It lies on the right (parietal) side of the greater curvature of the abomasum and its terminal branches supply this region of the stomach, which is embryologically a dorsal derivative of the stomach spindle (see Fig. 7).

Effects of Stimulation and Section of Gastric Nerves

Since the principal nerves to the ruminant stomach contain both afferent and efferent fibers, the motor nerve supply cannot be identified solely on the basis of the anatomical distribution. In addition, stimulation of the peripheral ends of the nerves after cutting may give misleading results, since contractions follow stimulation of both the vagus (7, 47) and splanchnic nerves (14); thus the only effective test is the examination of the movements in the conscious animal after previous section of nerves. All reports agree that the typical propulsive movements of the first three compartments are abolished when both vagus nerves have been cut either at the cardia or on the posterior third of the thoracic esophagus (20, 47), and that section of the splanchnic nerves is not followed by any apparent abnormality of the normal movements of the stomach (20). The efferent motor nerve supply to the smooth muscle of the ruminant stomach consists of cholinergic postganglionic parasympathetic nerves that synapse with preganglionic fibers in the vagus nerves. Abomasal contractions are not completely eliminated after section of both vagus nerves (20), and the retention of movements and the propulsion of material through the pyloric sphincter may be related to the presence of ganglia in the submucosa of this compartment in contrast to their absence in the subepithelial tissue of the rumen, reticulum, and omasum (30).

Less consistent results have been reported after section of one of the thoracic vagus nerves or the branches of them to the different compartments. If the dorsal vagus nerve is cut, the effects are largely confined to the elimination of the contractions of the rumen and of the esophageal groove and, to a lesser extent, those of the reticulum. On the other hand, section of the ventral vagus nerve has given widely different results in different laboratories varying between cessation of the propulsive movements and death to the relative absence of any signs of deficiency (20, 24, 47). Most reports agree, however, that after section of either the dorsal or the ventral thoracic vagus nerves the normal cycle of contractions may return, although the period required for recovery is variable (20, 24). The reason for this comparatively transient change after a major connection with the central nervous system has been eliminated is not yet fully understood. Many suggestions have been made to account for the restoration of apparently normal movements, such as the overlapping of areas supplied by both the dorsal and the ventral vagus nerves (20), an increased sensitivity of the denervated smooth muscle (20, 76), or the presence of multisynaptic pathways and association neurons of a myenteric plexus which has its synaptic connection with the vagus nerves in the region of the esophageal groove and reticulo-omasal orifice (52). Definitive evidence which would differentiate between these possibilities is not yet available.

Some of the contradictory reports on the effects of section of one vagus nerve or of its branches may be ascribed to the variation of the distribution of the smaller branches of the vagus nerves between different individuals and different species. Since the rate of growth of the rumen, reticulum, and omasum after birth is dependent to a large extent on the diet, some variation in the distribution of these nerves may be expected, for it is not known whether the development of the motor innervation always coincides with that of the musculature of the first three compartments.

The routes taken by the afferent sensory nerves to the medullary centers have been identified largely by the effect of section or stimulation at various levels on the reflex responses of either the ruminant stomach itself or the secretion of the parotid glands. In general, excitatory stimuli to the reflex centers are mediated through the vagus nerves and inhibitory stimuli via fibers that enter the spinal cord in the thoracic and lumbar regions (23, 66, 67). Some inhibitory effects, however, may persist after section of the splanchnic nerves (23).

VASCULAR SYSTEM

Arterial Supply

The major blood supply to all regions of the stomach is derived from the celiac artery. Anastomoses between peripheral branches of the celiac with esophageal arteries derived from the bronchoesophageal trunk and mediastinal arteries and the pancreatico-duodenal branches of the cranial mesenteric artery may provide an alternative blood supply if other sources are interrupted.

The celiac artery (Fig. 5), after giving branches to the diaphragm and liver, supplies left and right ruminal arteries and a splenic artery and continues as the omaso-abomasal artery. These branches are not always given off separately or in the order stated. The major arteries terminate in very small branches on the walls of the stomach which they penetrate to join a) the vascular plexus between the muscle layers and b) the very extensive subepithelial vascular network.

RUMEN. The largest vessel is usually the right ruminal artery, which descends on the right side of the stomach to the right longitudinal groove, where it continues caudally to its anastomosis, usually through small vessels, with the left ruminal artery in the left groove. In its course it supplies branches to the pancreas, to the great omentum where it arises from the longitudinal groove of the rumen, and to both left and right aspects of the rumen. Large branches enter the coronary grooves.

The left ruminal artery arises from the celiac on the right of the dorsal sac. It runs downward on this sac to reach the right longitudinal groove, where it turns cranially and passes between reticulum and rumen and emerges into the left longitudinal groove, which it follows until its anastomosis with the right ruminal artery. In the groove it lies deep to the attachment of the great omentum and gives numerous branches to the rumen wall.

RETICULUM. There is always at least one artery specifically supplying the reticulum. This may arise directly from the celiac trunk or, as in Figure 5, from the base of the left ruminal artery. The main vessel runs at first over the dorsal part of the atrium under the spleen, and then enters and descends in the left rumino-reticular groove, where it lies beneath the superficial muscle layer. It gives off branches cranially to the region on the left of the cardia, and distally to the

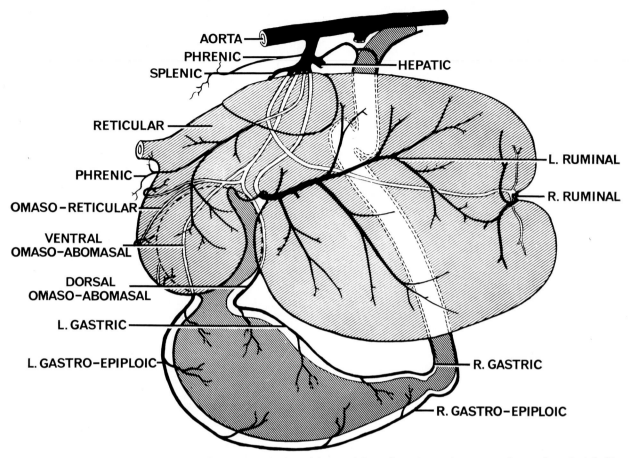

FIG. 5. Diagrammatic view of the arterial supply to the ruminant stomach, seen from the left side

left wall of the reticulum. This latter branch continues around the cranial and ventral aspect of the organ. The artery to the cardia supplies the atrium and, in addition, passes to the right of the reticulum below the esophagus, and finally it anastomoses with terminations of the omasal arteries. Branches from this artery also anastomose with esophageal arteries and send filaments to supply the caudal face of the diaphragm. In sheep, this supply to the reticulum may arise separately from the celiac trunk.

A separate supply to the right wall of the reticulum is derived in the sheep from the omaso-reticular branch of the ventral omaso-abomasal artery. A second branch from the omaso-abomasal artery sometimes supplies the caudal wall of the reticulum.

OMASUM AND ABOMASUM. The terminal branch of the celiac artery runs down the right wall of the rumen to a point above the omasum where it divides into dorsal and ventral branches. The dorsal branch follows and supplies the greater curvature of the omasum and then

runs in the lesser omentum along the lesser (dorsal) curvature of the abomasum which it supplies. On the surface of the omasum it gives branches that penetrate the wall to enter the base of each omasal leaf. In the region of the pylorus it anastomoses with the right gastric branch of the hepatic artery.

The ventral omaso-abomasal artery lies between the omasum and reticulum, and in the sheep gives off a cranial branch to the reticulum and cranial wall of the omasum. The main artery continues ventrally to reach the abomasum. There it enters the attachment of the great omentum and runs along the greater curvature of the abomasum where it anastomoses with a second branch of the hepatic artery (the right gastroepiploic).

Venous Drainage

In general, the veins are satellites of the arteries. Veins from the right side of the rumen form a long right ruminal vein which also receives a tributary from the spleen. The left ruminal vein unites the veins draining the reticulum, omasum, and abomasum. Left and right ruminal veins then combine to form a large common trunk, the gastric vein, which is joined by the gastroduodenal vein, a satellite of the right gastric and right gastroepiploic arteries. Before entering the porta of the liver, the gastric vein joins the cranial mesenteric vein.

Lymphatic Drainage

The ruminant stomach is drained by an extensive network of lymphatic channels, which pass through several rather loosely defined groups of lymph nodes. The channels lie superficially in the walls of the stomach (Fig. 6).

The lymphatics of the left wall of the rumen drain both cranially and caudally. When present, lymph nodes are located in the left ruminal groove. Efferent lymphatic vessels run cranially and caudally from these nodes. The caudal, efferent lymphatics pass along the right ruminal artery to join the drainage of the right side. The cranial efferent channel leads to the anterior group of ruminal nodes, which are located in the anterior groove of the rumen.

The right side of the rumen drains into the right ruminal group of nodes, which also receive the efferent vessels from the anterior group of nodes. The right ruminal nodes are located in the right ruminal groove, and efferents from these nodes run foward to the reticulum and to the gastric efferent lymphatic trunk.

The lymphatic drainage of the reticulum runs to the group of nodes that is situated at the reticulo-omasal junction.

The majority of omasal lymphatics drain into either the reticular group of nodes or to the omasal nodes that are found along the omasal part of the dorsal omaso-abomasal artery. The efferent vessels from these

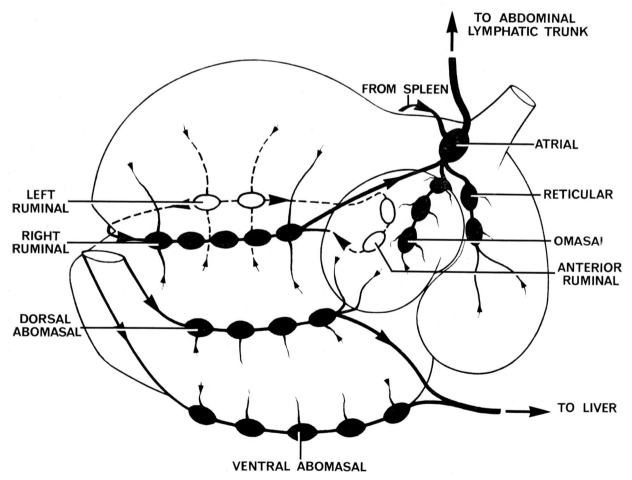

FIG. 6. Diagram showing the position of the major lymph nodes and direction of lymph flow on the ruminant stomach. Note that the major drainage is via the atrial nodes, but there is a separate channel via the liver from the abomasum (right).

nodes run to the atrial nodes. There is a distinct alternate drainage from the ventral part of the omasum through the dorsal abomasal nodes.

The abomasum is drained chiefly to dorsal lymph nodes in the edge of the lesser omentum. These efferent vessels pass in the omentum to join the hepatic lymphatics. The ventral part of the abomasum has a secondary drainage via a ventral group of nodes that also project to the hepatic lymph vessesls. Lymph from the duodenum runs to the abomasal nodes.

The lymph nodes of the atrium ventriculi receive the major effluent drainage from the ruminant stomach. Thus these nodes drain the dorsal parts of the reticulum and rumen directly and also receive efferent vessels from the spleen, but a very large proportion of the lymph flow through this region is derived from the distant regions, that is, the efferent vessels from reticular, right, and anterior ruminal, omasal, and dorsal abomasal nodes. The major efferent vessels from the stomach arise from the atrial nodes and usually join to run as a satellite of the celiac artery. This common efferent duct joins the mesenteric lymphatic trunk.

EMBRYOLOGY

The development of the ruminant stomach has been studied sporadically and has been the subject of disagreement as to whether the forestomachs develop from the embryonic gastric spindle. On the basis of comparative studies in reptiles and amphibia (where only fundic and pyloric glands are found), the suggestion was once made (77) that the cardiac glands of mammals are derived from embryonic esophageal glands. Furthermore, it was claimed that cardiac, and therefore esophageal, glands were present in the esophageal groove of the sheep, and it was inferred from this that the forestomachs should be regarded as diverticuli of the esophagus. This view has also held wide currency on the grounds that the stratified epithelium of the esophagus is similar to that of the forestomachs (60). However, there is a general tendency in many simple-stomached herbivores toward a suppression of gastric glands and their replacement by stratified epithelium. This occurs in such diverse groups as monotremes, rodents, and equidae and is dissociated from subdivisions of the stomach which could be considered as esophageal diverticuli.

The early development of the stomach has been studied primarily by Pernkopf (57), and a number of less exhaustive investigations have also been made

(4, 28, 45, 72, 74, 75). Pernkopf showed that there was no involvement of the esophagus in the development of the ruminant stomach and that all the compartments of the adult stomach were derived from the primitive gastric spindle.

Early Development

In ox and sheep the development in the early embryonic stages is very similar, although small differences appear later.

Up to the 7-mm stage the development of the stomach spindle is similar to that in a simple-stomached animal (Fig. 7A), but shortly after this a dorsal prominence appears at the cranial end of the spindle. By the 9-mm stage there is not only a dorsal prominence, but an indication of the position of the esophageal groove has appeared ventrally along the left of the lesser curvature (Fig. 7B). This groove may be homologous with the gastric canal of the lesser curvature of the simple-stomached animal.

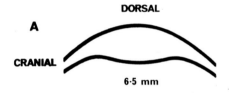

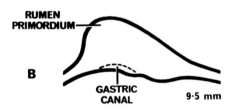

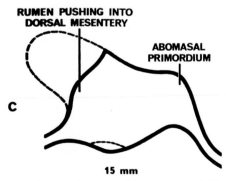

FIG. 7. Outline drawings of the stomach spindle of the ox at (A) 6.5 mm, (B) 9.5 mm, and (C) 15 mm, reconstructed from serial sections. *Dotted line* indicates direction of future growth of the rumen.

Further differentiation of the stomach spindle follows, and by the 12- to 15-mm stage all the parts of the adult stomach can be distinguished (Fig. 7C); the reticulum is the last compartment to differentiate. At

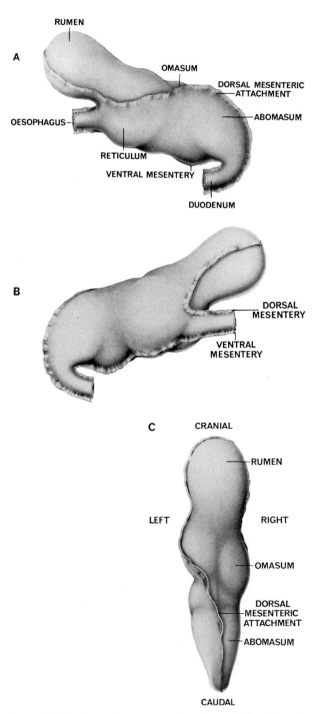

FIG. 8. Drawings of a reconstruction from serial sections of the stomach of a 28-mm ox embryo, showing the attachments of the mesenteries. A: from the left; B: from the right; C: from above.

this stage the stomach is still somewhat flattened, and the dorsal and ventral mesenteries are rather thick; but as the stomach develops further it elongates, with the greatest increase in size occurring in the rumen, which pushes upward and forward into the dorsal mesentery and then undergoes a rotation of 90° on its long axis (Fig. 8A–C).

During the next period of growth further differentiation of the other compartments may be seen, and the divisions between the various regions become more obvious. Internally the esophageal groove is identifiable ventrally, but the characteristic arrangement of the epithelium of the different compartments has not yet developed except in the case of the omasum and abomasum. In the former the first folds can be distinguished ventrally and the omasal sulcus is also present dorsally. Rumen, reticulum, and omasum are lined with a thick, stratified, polygonal epithelium which is neither squamous nor keratinized. The abomasum shows a number of longitudinal folds in the mucosa similar to those in the adult; the epithelium is columnar but nonglandular.

Further development results in still more clearly marked division of the compartments, together with changes within each part of the stomach. A shelf of muscular tissue appears at the blind end of the rumen which divides it into a dorsal and ventral part and then extends laterally to form the longitudinal pillars.

Obvious muscular development occurs around the omaso-abomasal opening with great enlargement of the esophageal groove and precocious growth of its right lip. This early enlargement of the groove may be a prelude to the development of reflexes involved in the swallowing of amniotic fluid (2, 21).

The adult mucosal pattern begins to be established by about the 50-mm stage, when for the first time the typical "honeycomb" of the reticulum can be distinguished and the secondary leaves appear in the omasum. The abomasum retains a nonglandular stratified columnar epithelium.

During this period of internal and external differentiation, the whole stomach undergoes a series of rotational movements. The first of these affects the rumen. It consists of a rotation of the compartment on its long axis through 90°, so that its original dorsal midline comes to lie laterally on the left, and its original midventral line comes into a right lateral position (Figs. 8 and 9A, B). This rotation has the effect of pulling the attachment of the main part of the dorsal mesentery ventrally over the left side of the rumen. It also pulls the region of the dorsal mesentery, which is trapped between the esophagus and the

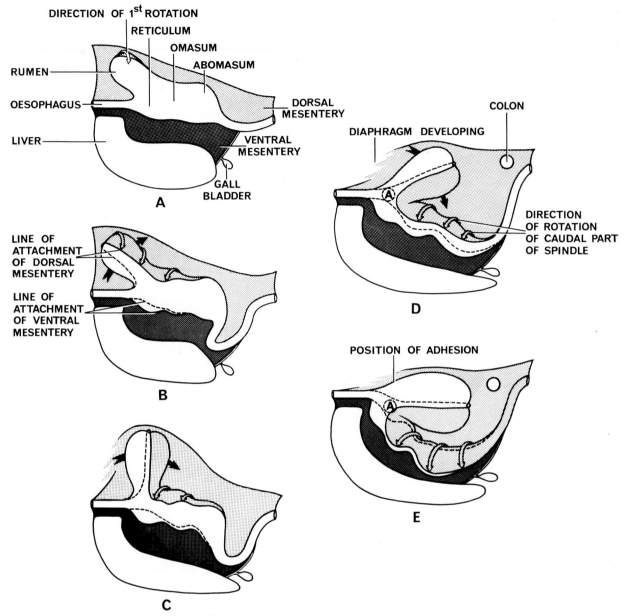

FIG. 9. Diagrams constructed from serial sections, showing the rotations of the ruminant stomach and the effects on the mesenteries. *A–B:* primary rotation of rumen (*open arrow*), *C–D–E:* secondary rotation of rumen (*black arrow*) and rotation of caudal part of gastric spindle (*open arrows*). In *D* and *E* dotted circle (*A*) indicates position of adhesion of omasum to the rumen in the adult.

rumen, around to the right side of the rumen. The rotation continues beyond the rumen and affects the cranial part of the stomach spindle to result in the displacement of the mesenteric attachments, as shown in Fig. 9*A, B.*

After completing the 90-degree rotation on its long axis the rumen begins a second rotation on a transverse axis which eventually continues through about 150°. The axis of rotation is situated at a point slightly be-

hind the entrance of the esophagus (Fig. 9*C*). By the 50-mm stage in the ox, the rotation of the rumen is almost half completed, so that the position of the blind end of the rumen has changed from pointing dorso-cranially to directly dorsally. Simultaneously with this second ruminal rotation, the rest of the stomach begins a belated primary rotation on its longitudinal axis, that is, the same axis as served for the primary rotation of the rumen (Fig. 9*C, D*). The direction of rotation is also the same as that seen previously in the first rotation of the rumen, that is, the dorsal region rotates to the left. This is similar to the primary rotation of the simple stomach, but whereas the primary rotation of the rumen stops after 90°, the primary rotation of the other parts continues through 180°. This rotation of the caudal parts of the stomach finishes before the secondary rotation of the rumen on its transverse axis is completed (see Fig. 9D, E).

Growth of the rumen now displaces the rest of the stomach to the right side of the fetus, and this results in the various compartments reaching the positions they occupy in the adult (Figs. 10–12).

The effect on the stomach of these movements is as follows: a) The primitive dorsal cranial aspect of the rumen becomes left, ventral, and caudal. b) The primitive left dorsal aspects of omasum and abomasum become right ventral. c) The esophageal groove, which

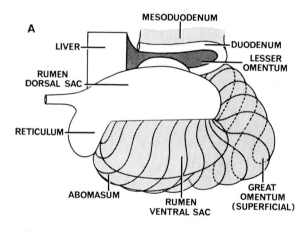

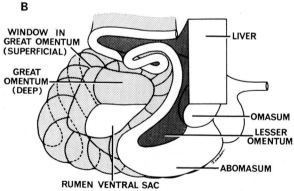

FIG. 10. Diagrams showing the definitive arrangement of the ruminant stomach together with the attachments of the gastric mesenteries, (A) from the left side, (B) from the right side. In B the deep layer of the great omentum has been foreshortened to expose the ventral sac of the rumen, and a "window" has been made in the right caudal part of the superficial layer of the omentum which allows a view of the inside of the omental bursa.

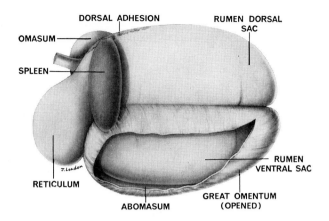

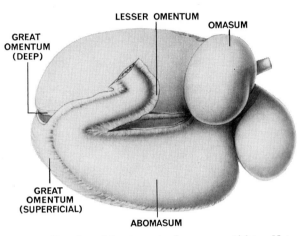

FIG. 11. Drawing of the stomach of a 23-cm calf fetus. Note that the proportions of the stomach are almost the same as in the adult. A (upper): left side; B (lower): right side. A "window" has been cut in the great omentum on the left to expose the ventral sac of the rumen.

developed as a left ventral structure, becomes right dorsal.

The stomach of the adult is supported from the dorsal wall of the abdominal cavity by a large area of adhesion between the dorsal sac of the rumen and the crura of the diaphragm. This adhesion forms toward the end of the second rotation of the rumen; it serves as a pathway for gastric blood and lymphatic vessels together with nerves from the celiaco-mesenteric plexus.

The later fetal development of the stomach consists of differential growth of the various compartments without major changes in position. Initially the rumen is the largest part of the stomach, and both sheep and ox pass through a fetal stage at which the different regions of the stomach are very similar in proportion to those of the adult. Figures 11 and 12 illustrate the species differences to be seen at this stage. Subsequently there is a rapid enlargement of the abomasum and a relatively slower growth of the other regions (Fig. 13). This differential growth may well be due to development of swallowing reflexes and redirection of fluid by the esophageal groove into the abomasum (2, 21).

Gastric Mesenteries

The effects of the movements on the mesenteries is very complex, and this complexity is increased by the secondary attachments that form between the rumen and body wall dorsally, and between the omasum and the right wall of the rumen.

The embryological dorsal mesentery of the stomach becomes the greater omentum, and the embryological ventral mesentery becomes the lesser omentum, which

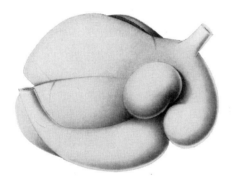

FIG. 12. Drawing of the stomach of a 70-day sheep fetus (viewed from the right). Compare the proportions with those shown in Fig. 11 for calf stomach at a similar stage of development.

is similar to that found in simple-stomached animals. The lesser omentum runs from the deep surface of the liver to the omasum, abomasum, and duodenum (along the ventral line of the gastric spindle). The greater omentum in the ruminant is double, because of the extension of the rumen into it during development. The superficial part of the greater omentum runs from the left groove of the rumen, under the ventral sac, to attach to the greater curvature of the abomasum (which was originally dorsal) and the first part of the duodenum. Around the caudal groove of the rumen it is continuous with a deep part of the greater omentum which runs from the right longitudinal groove of the rumen primarily to the medial side of the mesoduodenum, and secondarily, by adhesion, to the pancreas, colon, and liver. The two parts of the greater omentum together form a double-layered envelope around the small intestine and spiral colon. The rotations of the various parts of the stomach together with the consequent effects on the mesenteries are shown diagrammatically in Figure 9A–E. During the stages represented by Figure 9C–E, the dorsal mesentery in the region of the transverse septum (in which the liver is developed) becomes involved in the formation of the diaphragm. Caudal to the diaphragm the now considerably stretched dorsal part of the dorsal mesentery of the stomach becomes incorporated by adhesion into the mesenteries of the duodenum and colon, so that the greater omentum now runs from the duodenum to the left and right grooves of the rumen (Fig. 10A, B). The rapidly developing small intestine invaginates the deep part of the omentum from above.

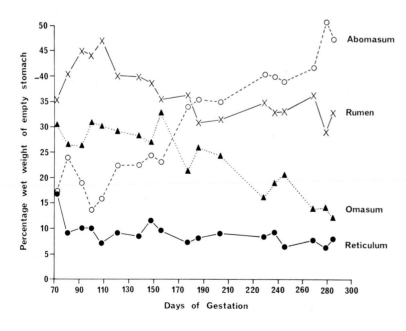

FIG. 13. Graph showing the rapid increase in relative and absolute size of the abomasum after midterm. [Constructed from data of Becker et al. (4).]

This part of the omentum extends from the right ruminal groove to the duodenum and is stretched until it is pressed against the superficial part, which passes from the left ruminal groove to the greater curvature of the abomasum and comes to lie on the floor of the abdominal cavity. Changes in the ventral mesentery (lesser omentum) are less complicated, and are mainly the result of the migration of the liver from the ventral position, as seen in Figure 9*A–E*, to the right dorsal position seen in Figure 10*A, B*. This movement of the liver carries the lesser omentum upward and forward, and the caudal part of the abomasum and first part of the duodenum are pulled in the same direction.

EPITHELIUM OF STOMACH

The keratinized nonglandular epithelium which lines the reticulum, rumen, and omasum is very different both in appearance and structure from either the stratified squamous epithelium of the esophagus or the typical secretory gastric epithelium of the abomasum. The transition between the different types of epithelium is abrupt both at the cardia and at the omaso-abomasal junction.

The main impetus to study the epithelium of the ruminant stomach was provided when it was recognized that products of microbial digestion are absorbed across these epithelial layers. Most investigations have been concerned primarily with the epithelium of the rumen since it can be studied more easily and changes are more readily produced. It has usually been assumed that the epithelium of the reticulum and of the omasum is similar to that of the rumen.

The keratinized epithelium of these three compartments has frequently been compared to the skin, and the same conventions have been used to describe the layers of cells and keratinized material. Certain differences in nomenclature are found in the literature (17, 34, 69), but it is generally agreed that four layers can by identified in the rumen epithelium (68); they are often classified in the following manner:

Stratum basale, which consists of columnar cells often closely packed and sometimes arranged in a single layer. It is separated from underlying connective tissue by a basement membrane. In some regions, especially at the tips of the papillae, the cells of this basal layer may be cuboidal rather than columnar.

Stratum spinosum, in which conspicuous intercellular bridges can be identified, analogous to those of the "prickle" cells of the skin.

Stratum granulosum, a thin layer of cells filled with irregular basophilic granules.

Stratum corneum, the superficial layers of which are in contact with the rumen fluid and which usually show signs of damage and sloughing. There is also considerable variation in the number of layers of keratinized material present in different parts of the rumen, presumably due to differential sloughing of the superficial keratinized material. This layer may vary in depth in different regions. In many parts of the rumen a further layer of swollen cells can be identified on the deep surface; these have been differentiated from the true stratum corneum as a layer of primary swelling (34) and are usually covered by a particularly dense zone of closely packed cells.

Electron micrographs have shown wide intercellular spaces in the outer layers and confirmed the presence of abundant mitochrondria in the basal and central layers (39). The analogy with the structure of the skin or of other stratified squamous epithelia is, however, far from complete, and many morphological peculiarites have been described in the rumen epithelium. Thus, the stratum lucidum of the skin is absent and the different layers of cells are not sharply delineated but rather merge into one another without distinct boundaries. Indeed, the outer layers of the epithelium show many signs typical of parakeratosis (34).

A detailed description of the different layers is given by Dobson et al. (17) and also by Henriksson & Habel (34), who suggest that the stratum granulosum and the outer layer of primary swelling might be described as the stratum transitionale.

It is doubtful whether a comparison between the rumen epithelium and skin will continue to be useful or relevant. The paradox originally noted by Barcroft et al. (3) between the absorption of large amounts of volatile fatty acids and the nature of the epithelium is largely resolved when it is recognized that the keratinized layers are derived from columnar cells that originate embryologically from the gastric spindle. Keratinization can probably be regarded as a reaction of the epithelial cells to the anaerobic rumen contents and especially to the products of microbial digestion, such as the volatile fatty acids. Butyric and propionic acids in particular are known to stimulate papillary and epithelial growth in the young animal, and cytological changes such as vacuolation, especially in the ventral rumen, have been attributed to the varying salt concentrations of the rumen fluid (34). The intensity of keratinization, the thickness of the epithelium, and even papillary growth can therefore be expected to vary among different species and also with age, diet, and the situation in the rumen. Some of the contradictory reports in the literature (17, 31, 32) on whether substances such as glycogen or lipids can be identified histologically in the rumen epithelium of the adult may be due to differences in technique, but more probably should be attributed to variation in the diets and in the conditions under which the tissue samples were taken. It may be significant that the presence of glycogen granules in the lamina propria was more apparent immediately after a change from milk to a diet of hay and grain (32), a time at which the rumen epithelium might be expected to react in many different ways to the stimulating or even damaging effects of the rumen contents.

Considering its importance in absorption, surprisingly few studies have been carried out on the rate of regeneration or replacement of these epithelial cells. The results of preliminary experiments, in which cell division was inhibited by colchicine, indicate that the rate of cell division is much slower in the rumen than in either the abomasum or the small intestine (unpublished observations).

The closely packed columnar cells of the basal layer from which the epithelium of the rumen, reticulum, and omasum are derived are probably responsible for the many reactions associated with absorption from these organs. The presence of mitochondria orientated toward the long axes of these cells has been associated with their ability to maintain active transport of sodium against an electrochemical gradient (16, 17). Many of the enzymes responsible for cellular oxidation and glycolysis have also been demonstrated in the epithelium by histochemical techniques (15, 32). All these results reinforce evidence from other sources (see Chapter 132) which indicates that the rumen, reticulum, and omasum are covered by a highly active epithelium which can react to the composition of the rumen fluid in a variety of ways, one of them appearing to be the extent to which the layers become keratinized.

The epithelium cannot, however, be regarded as a uniform layer of cells interposed between the contents and the tissue fluid. The papillae of the rumen, and to a certain extent those of the reticulum and omasum, consist of a core of densely packed collagen fibers that extend into numerous papillary processes on which the deeper layers of the epithelium are irregularly arranged (Fig. 14). The processes are especially prominent at the tips of the papillae. They have been compared with the papillary bodies of the skin (17), but recent investigations (9) have shown that instead

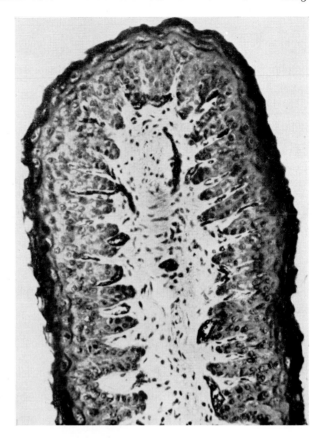

FIG. 14. Longitudinal section of a rumen papilla in which capillaries have been injected with India ink. Note the folding of the inner layer of epithelium on the connective tissue processes. × 50. [From Dobson et al. (17).]

they represent a system of interconnecting grooves on the deep surface of the epithelium (Fig. 15A, B). These grooves may expand the area of the inner vascular surface to almost twice that of the lumen side and possibly reduce the effective thickness of the epithelium by at least one-half. Similar but shallower grooves are also present in the basal layer of the epithelium of the reticulum and omasum.

The epithelium of all three compartments has a rich vascular supply derived from arteries and veins that penetrate the layers of smooth muscle and then form a complex system of anastomosing vessels, both arterial and venous, which ramify in the subepithelial connective tissue (Fig. 16). This prominent subepithelial network is similar in appearance and position to the submucous vascular plexus of the small intestine, and the blood supply to each rumen papilla is derived from it by arterioles that usually run toward the tip to supply a dense capillary network lying in close apposition to the basal layer of the epithelium [(9, 46); Fig. 16].

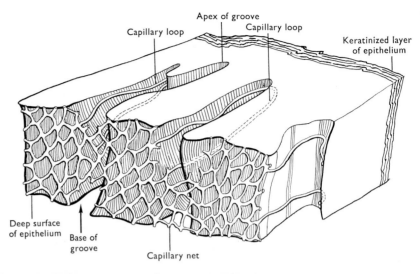

FIG. 15. *A (right):* diagrammatic reconstruction of the capillary blood supply to the deep surface of the rumen epithelium. [From Cheetham & Steven (9).] *B (lower):* photograph showing the grooves on the deep surface of the rumen epithelium.

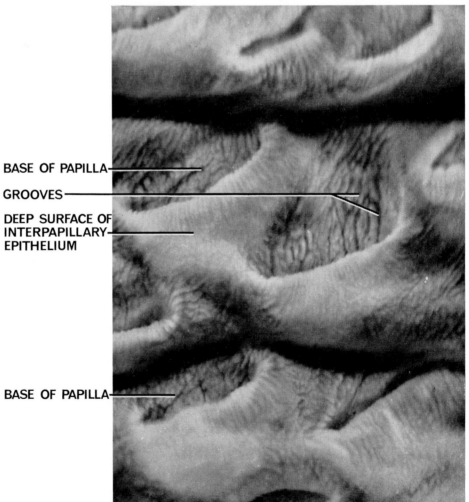

Slender loops that arise from this capillary bed enter and leave the system of interconnecting grooves, previously known as papillary bodies, on the deep surface of the epithelium [Fig. 15*A*; (9)].

Lymph vessels have been identified in the central core of rumen papillae after the subepithelial injection of India ink (17). The fine structure and microscopic distribution of the lymphatic vessels of the walls

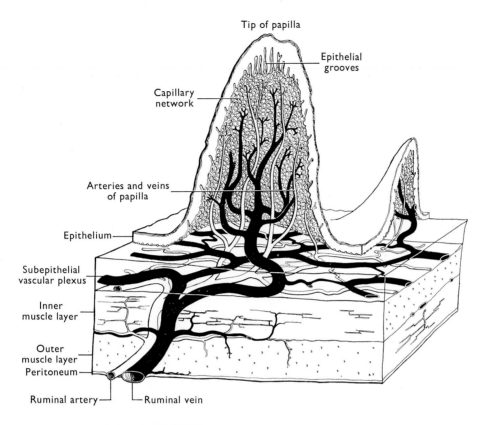

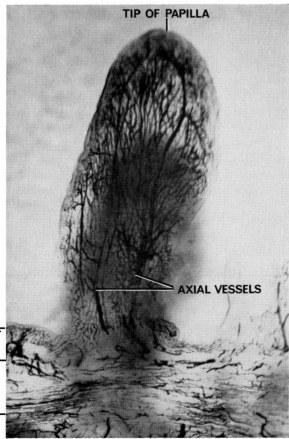

FIG. 16. *A (upper):* diagrammatic reconstruction of the blood supply to a ruminal papilla. [From Cheetham & Steven (9).] *B (left):* photomicrograph of a cleared rumen papilla with the blood vessels injected with Micropaque (colloidal barium sulfate).

of the first three compartments have yet to be described in detail.

The vascular supply to the epithelium of the reticulum and omasum is similar to that of the rumen: both have a well-developed subepithelial plexus and a dense capillary network adjacent to the basal layer of epithelial cells. The leaves of the omasum have a particularly profuse blood supply from arteries that run radially from the base to the free edge. These radial vessels give off a number of tangential branches that freely anastomose with one another and supply an extensive subepithelial capillary bed. Each omasal papilla is supplied by a central arteriole, and the capillary bed drains through one or two venules at its base (unpublished observations).

The abomasal mucosa is analogous to the secretory epithelium of the stomach of other species. As such it does not call for special comment here, but it should be noted that the area of fundic glands is greatly enlarged by the presence of numerous spiral folds. The blood vessels to the abomasal mucosa also resemble those of the simple stomach. A fine plexus of subepithelial capillaries is supplied from a coarse network of larger blood vessels in the connective tissue beneath the gastric epithelium.

INNERVATION AND NERVE ENDINGS

Much remains to be discovered about the fine structure and distribution of nerves and their endings in the wall of the ruminant stomach. Both the motor and sensory innervation require further study before definitive correlations can be made between structures and the many actions and responses that have been demonstrated by other means. In fact, the same gap exists, as in other viscera, between the physiological and pharmacological evidence of function and the knowledge of the fine structure.

The results of investigations using silver impregnation techniques have been extensively reviewed by Habel (30), who also showed that the density of the nervous tissue and endings in the smooth muscle is uneven. Certain areas, such as the cardia, the margin of the reticulo-omasal orifice, and the omasal pillar, appear to be more densely innervated than others (30).

Motor Innervation

The finer details of the motor innervation of the ruminant stomach have not yet been traced, and there is little known about the mechanisms or structures involved in the compensation which occurs after cutting one of the major vagus nerves in the thorax or at the esophageal hiatus.

More specific information on the nature of the autonomic nerve supply to the different effector organs such as the smooth muscle of the rumen or the blood vessels can be obtained by the use of histochemical methods for the identification of acetylcholinesterase or of catecholamines. By such means preganglionic and postganglionic nerve fibers and ganglia have been identified in all the compartments of the sheep stomach (12, 51). Each muscle fasciculus appears to be innervated by its own particular set of cholinergic nerve fibers; again, the density of innervation does not appear to be uniform throughout the stomach, but the muscle fibers of the anterior and posterior pillars are reported to be particularly well supplied (12).

The submucosal plexus of arteries and veins in the rumen is surrounded by a network of both cholinergic and adrenergic nerves. In particular, the proximal third of the central arteriole to each papilla is especially densely innervated by both types of nerve fibers (51). All these nerves, both cholinergic and adrenergic, probably produce vasomotor effects, but other evidence suggests that their influence on blood flow is small in comparison with the effects of the introduction of CO_2 or butyrate into the rumen (59). They may, however, be responsible for the initial rise in blood flow in the ruminal artery that coincides with feeding.

The innervation of the striated muscles of the esophagus has also been demonstrated by the cholinesterase technique. Motor end plates, arranged in groups or clumps, can readily be recognized, but they are only about one-quarter to one-third the size of the typical motor end plates of skeletal muscle. In addition, some of the esophageal striated muscle is innervated by multiple small nerve endings arranged in series along the length of the muscle fibers in a manner that is typical of the innervation of other slow muscle fibers such as those in the extraocular muscles of the mammal (12).

Sensory Endings

The absence of any readily recognizable sensory nerve endings is one of the more puzzling features of the ruminant stomach. There is much evidence from reflex responses and recordings of the activity in afferent nerves that discrete stimuli such as touch, stretch, and reduction of the pH in the abomasum can be distinguished experimentally and lead to separate responses when applied to various compartments (23, 40, 41, 66, 67). Yet, in spite of diligent searching, no definitive structures have been found in these viscera which can be clearly identified as sensory receptors (30).

Myelinated nerve fibers have been reported by several investigators in close proximity to the epithelium, and in the absence of other structures they have been implicated as sensory receptors (30). There are also several reports that fine nonmyelinated nerve fibers end within the epithelium of the reticulum and rumen. Some of these may be cholinergic, but variable results have been obtained with the cholinesterase technique (12, 51). In addition, it is not certain that these endings actually penetrate between the epithelial cells, since they may run in adjacent interconnecting grooves or papillary bodies that are hidden in the histological sections by overlying epithelial cells. A complex system of free nerve endings stained after perfusion with methylene blue has been described in the immature rumen and reticulum of newborn lambs and kids. The distribution of these endings appears to correspond with those areas in the two compartments that are especially responsive to sensory stimulation (36). Whether it is justifiable to apply these results to the fully developed stomach of the adult remains a matter for conjecture.

A solution to the problem of sensory receptors is necessary for the understanding of the functions and movements of all the compartments of the ruminant stomach. Several explanations can be put forward for the failure to identify receptors. Structures serving as receptors may not be susceptible to staining by the methods commonly used to identify sensory receptors. Alternatively, there is the possibility that in the rumen certain nonmyelinated endings may possess the capacity to distinguish between the different modalities, as appears to be the case in the skin (42). Meanwhile, much information is available concerning the reactions of the presumed sensory receptors (41), their adaptation (40, 66), and their sensitivity to adrenaline (22, 43, 66) which may serve as a useful basis in the search for their position.

GROWTH OF RUMINANT STOMACH

The pronounced changes in the ruminant stomach that occur between birth and weaning are largely confined to the reticulum, rumen, and omasum. In contrast, the abomasum, which is by far the largest compartment at birth (Fig. 13), shows little change either in its size or its shape during this critical period.

A study of the histology of the ruminal and abomasal epithelium of the newborn animal serves as a convenient basis to illustrate the differences between the neonatal stomach and that of the adult. At birth, the rumen is filled with a clear, highly viscous fluid. The papillae, although regular in shape, are relatively undeveloped and are joined for the first third of their length (69) so that the adjacent columns of cells form cords or pegs (65) in the submucosa. The basal layers of epithelium consist of closely packed polygonal cells with large, oval, granular nuclei (69), and in the calf the prickle cells of the rumen and reticulum, but not of the omasum, contain considerable amounts of glycogen (32). The appearance of the stratum corneum depends on the species. In the calf it is vestigial (65), whereas in the lamb it is readily recognizable (69). Such slight differences between the calf and the lamb may well be related to variations in the degree of their development at birth and be similar to those in other organs (13). The abomasal epithelium at birth also appears to be immature. The chief cells contain only a few zymogen granules, and the parietal cells are small and sparsely distributed (65).

A number of the postnatal changes occur remarkably rapidly. Thus, within a week of birth the glycogen disappears from the cells of the rumen epithelium, and the cells of the abomasal glands are by that time similar to those of the adult (65); indeed, there may even be an increase in the number of parietal cells (35) within 72 hours of birth. These developments form only part of the series of comparatively rapid and complex adjustments that occur immediately after birth and as such are not directly relevant to the present review.

The growth and development of the first three compartments are much slower. It was shown independently and almost simultaneously in two laboratories (6, 73) to be related to the diet and especially to the establishment of an active microbial digestion. The problem has been investigated by means of a variety of techniques such as the measurement of the size, displacement volume of the reticulum and rumen (5, 73), the changes in organ weights (26, 73), observations of the topographical changes in the relations of the stomach within the abdomen (33, 64), and examination of papillary and epithelial development, especially of the rumen (6, 33, 64, 65). In the calf all the experimental observations confirm the general conclusion that fibrous lignified material, typical of

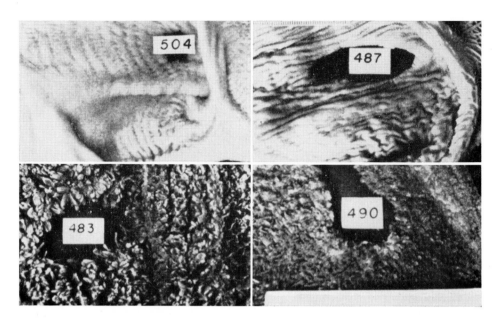

FIG. 17. Photographs showing the effect of diet on the development of the papillae in the central part of the cranial dorsal sac of the rumen. *504*, Newborn; *487*, milk fed to 13 weeks; *483*, grain fed to 13 weeks; *490*, hay fed to 13 weeks. [From Warner et al. (73).]

roughage, is responsible only for increasing the capacity of the rumen and reticulum and possibly for the development of the musculature in response to stretching. Similar but possibly less pronounced changes (70) in the rumen have been reported in the lamb and the kid. Growth of the omasum is also related to the diet, and the feeding of either hay or concentrates to growing calves has been shown to cause a rapid development of both the volume and the weight of omasal tissue (5, 33).

Papillary development in the rumen requires the stimulus of the end products of microbial digestion and in particular certain volatile fatty acids. The analysis of the factors concerned with the growth of the rumen papillae has depended, in most experiments, on the marked retardation of their development in animals fed on milk alone (Fig. 17). Various estimates have been made of the efficiency with which milk is diverted into the abomasum by closure of the esophageal groove, but measurements based on the volume of rumen fluid suggest that only a small proportion (about 5% of a pure milk diet) enters the rumen (61). Under these conditions the fluid contained in the rumen and reticulum is largely derived from isotonic parotid saliva which does not stimulate papillary growth. Furthermore, the introduction into the rumen of bulky inert materials such as plastic or cellulose sponges or simple salt solutions such as sodium and potassium chloride or bicarbonate is equally ineffective (26, 58, 64). Large quantities o

milk given directly into the rumen merely lead to sloughing of the epithelium and its invasion by leukocytes (64, 65). Volatile fatty acids, especially butyrate and propionate, are the only substances that have been shown to be effective in causing growth of papillae comparable with that found when the animals are fed on diets that encourage the growth of the rumen microbial population.

The effect of these two acids, however, depends on the exposure of the epithelium to a critical concentration over a period of weeks if it is to mimic the effects of high-energy diets of readily digestible food. Because of the variation in the experimental conditions in different laboratories, it is difficult to establish precise requirements either for the concentration of acid or for the period of contact that is necessary before the appearance of changes on the entire surface of the rumen or reticulum. It is clear, however, that infrequent dosage or low concentrations may fail to stimulate papillary growth or may lead only to a limited development within a small area of the rumen adjacent to the fistula through which acids were administered (26).

The fundic glands of the abomasum also respond to the effects of different diets, although the changes are less spectacular. Growth of the fundic glands and shortening of the excretory ducts have been reported in calves fed on a diet that rapidly established an active microbial digestion in the rumen. A diet of milk alone had no effect, but the growth of the glands was stimulated when volatile fatty acids were introduced into the rumen of these animals. The amount of these acids which was required appeared to be smaller than that needed to elicit marked papillary growth in the rumen (65).

Continuous stimulation from the volatile fatty acids formed by active microbial digestion also appears to be essential for the maintenance of the hypertrophied papillae of the rumen, at least in the young growing animal. A change from a diet of hay and grain to milk, without access to bedding, leads to regression of the large papillae already developed and a reversion to the minute papillae typical of a milk diet [(33); Fig. 17]. The absence of papillary development in calves that had been given rumen contents from adult animals in addition to milk over a period of time, a finding which has been attributed to insufficient stimulation (26), may also indicate that the concentration of acid required for the maintenance of the rumen epithelium and papillae is lower than that necessary for stimulation of papillary growth.

The volatile fatty acids, especially butyric and propionic, therefore appear to act as specific stimulants to the growth and development of the epithelium and the submucosa of the rumen and the other compartments of the stomach of the young animal. The precise mechanism by which they act so specifically on the epithelium is, however, far from certain. Most suggestions (50, 58, 64) are based on their preferential disappearance by their absorption across the rumen epithelium (44) and their active metabolism by the epithelium in vitro (54–56, 62, 63). Certainly their presence can radically increase the rate of absorption of acetate within 24 hours (1), but the stimulation of metabolism they may produce does not entirely explain the much longer period of exposure to solutions of above a critical concentration that is necessary to induce growth of the rumen wall. In many respects their effects on the growth of the keratinized epithelium of the forestomachs resembles those attributed to abrasion on stratified squamous epithelium at other sites, such as the tongue or esophagus (48, 49). It is, however, difficult to make this comparison until the rates of cell division and replacement of the epi-

thelial cells of the rumen are known, but possible deleterious effects of either butyrate or propionate during its transit across the rumen epithelium warrant further study. Chronic inflammatory changes in the abomasal mucosa of the adult have already been tentatively ascribed to the possible effects of the volatile fatty acids (37) which are in lower concentration in this organ than in the rumen and reticulum.

For the first two or three weeks after birth, the young ruminant cannot be forced to eat plant food (71) and is almost entirely maintained on milk, so that, in practice, the growth of the rumen is probably adjusted to the general development of the young animal. The duration of this neonatal period appears to be similar in both calves and lambs, and the abrupt rise in the volatile fatty acid concentration of the rumen contents found in grazing lambs at about two weeks of age (71) should provide an adequate stimulus thereafter for the growth of the epithelium of the first three compartments.

The rumen, however, appears to be as dependent as any other tissue on the endocrine background for its growth and development. Hypophysectomy or thyroidectomy of the very young calf or goat retards development of the rumen and especially the epithelial and submucosal layers (11). This finding could, in part, be explained by the extension of the neonatal period on a milk diet which occurs after such procedures, but the effect persists after weaning and may be evident after one year of age. Under these conditions, the rumen increases in volume, but the walls remain very thin and the epithelium and the papillae are poorly developed. An abnormal development of the forestomachs may also be implicated in the frequency with which ruminal tympany follows weaning after complete thyroidectomy of the very young calf (unpublished observations with A. V. Edwards). Further work is required before the influence of the endocrine background on the development of the rumen in the normal animal can be assessed, particularly in determining whether the endocrine factors can limit the rate of growth of the stomach and its absorptive capacity, in young calves receiving an easily digestible diet, to encourage the establishment of an active microbial digestion.

REFERENCES

1. ARMSTRONG, D. G., K. L. BLAXTER, AND N. M. GRAHAM. The heat increments of steam-volatile fatty acids in fasting sheep. Brit. J. Nutr. 11: 392–408, 1957.

2. BARCROFT, J., AND D. H. BARRON. The development of behaviour in foetal sheep. J. Comp. Neurol. 70: 477–502, 1939.

3. BARCROFT, J., R. A. McANNALLY, AND A. T. PHILLIPSON. The absorption of sodium ortho-iodo-hippurate from the rumen of lambs. *J. Exptl. Biol.* 20: 132–133, 1944.

4. BECKER, R. B., P. T. DIX ARNOLD, AND S. P. MARSHALL. Development of the bovine stomach during fetal life. *J. Dairy Sci.* 34: 329–332, 1951.

5. BLAXTER, K. L., M. K. HUTCHESON, J. M. ROBERTSON, AND A. L. WILSON. The influence of diet on the development of the alimentary tract of the calf. *Brit. J. Nutr.* 6: i–ii, 1952.

6. BROWNLEE, A. The development of rumen papillae in cattle fed on different diets. *Brit. Vet. J.* 112: 369–375, 1956.

7. BRUNAUD, M., AND J. NAVARRO. Modifications, sous l'influence de substances ganglioplégiques, de l'action du nerf vague sur les estomacs du mouton. *J. Physiol., Paris* 46: 272–276, 1954.

8. CHAUVEAU, A., AND S. ARLOING. *The Comparative Anatomy of the Domesticated Animals* (2nd ed.), edited by G. Fleming. London: Churchill, 1891.

9. CHEETHAM, S. E., AND D. H. STEVEN. Vascular supply to the absorptive surfaces of the ruminant stomach. *J. Physiol., London* 186: 56–58P, 1966.

10. COLE, F. J. *A History of Comparative Anatomy.* Macmillan: London, 1949.

11. COMLINE, R. S., AND A. V. EDWARDS. The growth and development of the calf after hypophysectomy. *J. Physiol., London* 180: 5–6P, 1965.

12. COMLINE, R. S., AND M. A. MESSAGE. Neuromuscular physiology of the ruminant stomach. In: *Physiology of Digestion in the Ruminant,* edited by R. W. Dougherty. Washington, D.C.: Butterworths, 1965, p. 78–87.

13. COMLINE, R. S., AND M. SILVER. Development of the activity in the adrenal medulla of the foetus and new-born animal. *Brit. Med. Bull.* 22: 16–20, 1966.

14. COMLINE, R. S., AND D. A. TITCHEN. Contractions of the reticulum of the young goat. *J. Physiol., London* 115: 24P, 1951.

15. DE LAHUNTA, A. Dehydrogenase histochemistry of bovine ruminal epithelium with comparisons to esophageal epithelium and epidermis. *Am. J. Vet. Res.* 26: 1013–1025, 1965.

16. DOBSON, A. Active transport through the epithelium of the reticulo-rumen sac. *J. Physiol., London* 146: 235–251, 1959.

17. DOBSON, M. J., W. C. B. BROWN, A. DOBSON, AND A. T. PHILLIPSON. A histological study of the organisation of the rumen epithelium of sheep. *Quart. J. Exptl. Physiol.* 41: 247–253, 1956.

18. DOUGHERTY, R. W., R. E. HABEL, AND H. E. BOND. Esophageal innervation and the eructation reflex in sheep. *Am. J. Vet. Res.* 19: 115–128, 1958.

19. DOUGHERTY, R. W., AND C. D. MEREDITH. Cinefluorographic studies of the ruminant stomach and of eructation. *Am. J. Vet. Res.* 16: 96–100, 1955.

20. DUNCAN, D. L. The effects of vagotomy and splanchnotomy on gastric motility in the sheep. *J. Physiol., London* 119: 157–169, 1953.

21. DUNCAN, D. L., AND A. T. PHILLIPSON. The development of motor responses in the stomach of the foetal sheep. *J. Exptl. Biol.* 28: 32–40, 1951.

22. DUSSARDIER, M. Action *in vivo* de l'acétylcholine et de l'adrénaline sur la motricité gastrique des ruminants. *J. Physiol., Paris* 46: 777–797, 1954.

23. DUSSARDIER, M. Controle nerveux du rythme gastrique des ruminants. *J. Physiol. Pathol. Gen.* 47: 170–173, 1955.

24. DUSSARDIER, M. Effets de la vagotomie intrathoracique partielle sur la survie et la croissance du mouton. *Ann. Biol. Animale Biochim. Biophys.* 1: 141–144, 1961.

25. ELLENBERGER, W., AND H. BAUM. *Handbuch der Vergleichenden Anatomie der Haustiere* (3rd ed.). Berlin: Hirschwald, 1912.

26. FLATT, W. P., R. G. WARNER, AND J. K. LOOSLI. Influence of purified materials on the development of the ruminant stomach. *J. Dairy Sci.* 41: 1593–1600, 1958.

27. FOUST, H. L. A dissection of the nerve supply to the gastric compartments of the ruminant (bovine). *J. Am. Vet. Med. Assoc.* 27: 1052–1059, 1928–1929.

28. GREEN, W. W., AND L. M. WINTERS. *Prenatal Development of the Sheep.* Minn. Agr. Exptl. Station Tech. Bull. 169, 1945.

29. HABEL, R. E. *Guide to the Dissection of the Cow.* Ithaca, N.Y.: Cornell Co-op Soc., 1949.

30. HABEL, R. E. A study of the innervation of the ruminant stomach. *Cornell Vet.* 46: 555–627, 1956.

31. HABEL, R. E. The presence of lipids in the epithelium of the ruminant forestomach. *Am. J. Vet. Res.* 20: 337–341, 1959.

32. HABEL, R. E. Carbohydrates, phosphatases and esterases in the mucosa of the ruminant forestomach during post-natal development. *Am. J. Vet. Res.* 24: 199–211, 1963.

33. HARRISON, H. N., R. G. WARNER, E. G. SANDER, AND J. K. LOOSLI. Changes in the tissue and volume of the stomachs of calves following the removal of dry feed or consumption of inert bulk. *J. Dairy Sci.* 43: 1301–1312, 1960.

34. HENRIKSSON, K., AND R. E. HABEL. The morphology and sulfhydryl and disulfide reactions of the epithelium of the bovine forestomach during postnatal development. *Anat. Record* 139: 499–507, 1961.

35. HILL, K. J. Gastric development and antibody transference in the lamb, with some observations on the rat and guinea-pig. *Quart. J. Exptl. Physiol.* 41: 421–432, 1956.

36. HILL, K. J. Nervous structures in the reticulo-rumenal epithelium of the lamb and kid. *Quart. J. Exptl. Physiol.* 44: 222–228, 1959.

37. HILL, K. J. Abomasal secretory function in the sheep. In: *Physiology of Digestion in the Ruminant,* edited by R. W. Dougherty. Washington, D.C.: Butterworths, 1965, p. 221–230.

38. HOFLUND, S. Untersuchungen über Störungen in den Funktionen der Wiederkäuermagen, durch Schädigungen des N. vagus verusacht. *Svensk Vet. Tidskr.* 45: Suppl. 15, 1–322, 1940.

39. HYDÉN, S., AND I. SPERBER. Electron microscopy of the ruminant forestomach. In: *Physiology of the Digestion in the Ruminant,* edited by R. W. Dougherty. Washington, D.C.: Butterworths, 1965, p. 51–60.

40. IGGO, A. Tension receptors in the stomach and the urinary bladder. *J. Physiol., London* 128: 593–607, 1955.

41. IGGO, A. Central nervous control of gastric movements in sheep and goats. *J. Physiol., London* 131: 248–256, 1956.

42. IGGO, A. Cutaneous mechanoreceptors with afferent C fibres. *J. Physiol., London* 152: 337–353, 1960.

43. KAY, R. N. B. The effects of stimulation of the sympathetic nerve and of adrenaline on the flow of parotid saliva in sheep. *J. Physiol., London* 144: 476–489, 1958.

44. KIDDLE, P., R. A. MARSHALL, AND A. T. PHILLIPSON.

A comparison of the mixtures of acetic, propionic and butyric acids in the rumen and the blood leaving the rumen. *J. Physiol., London* 113: 207–217, 1951.

45. LAMBERT, P. S. The development of the stomach in the ruminant. *Vet. J.* 104: 302–310, 1948.

46. LAMBRECHTS, H. B. The microscopic vascular pattern of the ruminal wall in *Ovis aries. Onderstepoort J. Vet. Res.* 33: 233–238, 1966.

47. MANGOLD, E., AND W. KLEIN. *Bewegungen und Innervation des Wiederkäuermagens.* Leipzig: Thieme, 1927.

48. MARQUES-PEREIRA, J. P., AND C. P. LEBLOND. Mitosis and differentiation in the stratified squamous epithelium of the rat esophagus. *Am. J. Anat.* 117: 73–90, 1965.

49. MARTIN, B. F. Cell renewal in the guinea-pig tongue. *J. Physiol., London* 182: 18–19P, 1966.

50. MCGILLIARD, A. D., N. L. JACOBSON, AND J. D. SUTTON. Physiological development of the ruminant stomach. In: *Physiology of Digestion in the Ruminant,* edited by R. W. Dougherty. Washington, D.C.: Butterworths, 1965, p. 39–50.

51. MESSAGE, M. A. The innervation of the blood supply to the papillae of the rumen of the sheep. *J. Physiol., London* 187: 17P, 1966.

52. MORRISON, A. R., AND R. E. HABEL. A quantitative study of the distribution of vagal nerve endings in the myenteric plexus of the ruminant stomach. *J. Comp. Neurol.* 122: 297–309, 1964.

53. NICKEL, R., A. SCHUMMER, AND E. SEIFERLE. *Lehrbuch der Anatomie der Haustiere. II. Eingeweide.* Berlin: Parey, 1960.

54. PENNINGTON, R. J. The metabolism of short-chain fatty acids in the sheep. 1. Fatty acid utilization and ketone body production by rumen epithelium and other tissues. *Biochem. J.* 51: 251–258, 1952.

55. PENNINGTON, R. J. The metabolism of short-chain fatty acids in the sheep. 2. Further studies with rumen epithelium. *Biochem. J.* 56: 410–417, 1954.

56. PENNINGTON, R. J., AND T. M. SUTHERLAND. The metabolism of short-chain fatty acids in the sheep. 4. The pathway of propionate metabolism in rumen epithelial tissue. *Biochem. J.* 63: 618–628, 1956.

57. PERNKOPF, E. Die Entwicklung des Verderdames, inbesondue des Magens der Wiederkauer. *Z. Anat. Entwicklungsgeschichte* 94: 490–622, 1931.

58. SANDER, E. G., R. G. WARNER, H. N. HARRISON, AND J. K. LOOSLI. The stimulatory effect of sodium butyrate and sodium propionate on the development of rumen mucosa in the young calf. *J. Dairy Sci.* 42: 1600–1605, 1959.

59. SELLARS, A. F., C. E. STEVENS, A. DOBSON, AND F. D. MCLEOD. Arterial blood flow to the ruminant stomach. *Am. J. Physiol.* 207: 371–377, 1964.

60. SISSON, S., AND J. D. GROSSMAN. *The Anatomy of the Domestic Animals.* Philadelphia: Saunders, 1953.

61. SMITH, R. H. The development and function of the rumen in milk-fed calves. *J. Agric. Sci.* 52: 72–78, 1959.

62. SUTTON, J. D., A. D. MCGILLIARD, AND N. L. JACOBSON. Functional development of rumen mucosa. 1. Absorptive ability. *J. Dairy Sci.* 46: 426–436, 1963.

63. SUTTON, J. D., A. D. MCGILLIARD, M. RICHARD, AND N. L. JACOBSON. Functional development of rumen mucosa. II. Metabolic activity. *J. Dairy Sci.* 46: 530–537, 1963.

64. TAMATE, H., A. D. MCGILLIARD, N. L. JACOBSON, AND R. GETTY. Effect of various dietaries on the anatomical development of the stomach in the calf. *J. Dairy Sci.* 45: 408–420, 1962.

65. TAMATE, H., A. D. MCGILLIARD, N. L. JACOBSON, AND R. GETTY. The effect of various diets on the histological development of the stomach in the calf. *Tohuko J. Agri. Res.* 14: 171–193, 1964.

66. TITCHEN, D. A. Reflex stimulation and inhibition of reticulum contractions in the ruminant stomach. *J. Physiol., London* 141: 1–21, 1958.

67. TITCHEN, D. A. The production of rumen and reticulum contractions in decerebrate preparations of sheep and goats. *J. Physiol., London* 151: 139–153, 1960.

68. TRAUTMANN, A., AND J. FIEBIGER. *Fundamentals of the Histology of the Domestic Animals,* edited by R. E. Habel and E. L. Biberstein. London: Baillière, 1952.

69. WARDROP, I. D. Some preliminary observations on the histological development of the fore-stomachs of the lamb. I. Histological changes due to age in the period from 46 days of foetal life to 77 days of post-natal life. *J. Agri. Sci.* 57: 335–341, 1961.

70. WARDROP, I. D. Some preliminary observations on the histological development of the fore-stomachs of the lamb. II. The effects of diet on the histological development of the fore-stomachs of the lamb during post-natal life. *J. Agri. Sci.* 57: 343–346, 1961.

71. WARDROP, I. D., AND J. B. COOMBE. The development of rumen function in the lamb. *Australian J. Agri. Res.* 12: 661–680, 1961.

72. WARNER, E. D. The organogenesis and early histogenesis of the bovine stomach. *Am. J. Anat.* 102: 33–63, 1958.

73. WARNER, R. G., W. P. FLATT, AND J. K. LOOSLI. Dietary factors influencing the development of the ruminant stomach. *J. Agri. Food Chem.* 4: 788–792, 1956.

74. WINTERS, L. M., AND G. FEUFFEL. Studies on the physiology of reproduction in the sheep. IV. *Foetal Development.* Minn. Agr. Exptl. Station Tech. Bull. 118, 1936.

75. WINTERS, L. M., W. W. GREEN, AND R. E. COMSTOCK. *Prenatal Development of the Bovine.* Minn. Agr. Exptl. Station Tech. Bull. 151, 1942.

76. WEISS, K. E. Physiological studies on eructation in ruminants. *Onderstepoort J. Vet. Res.* 26: 251–283, 1953.

77. ZIMMERMAN, A., AND J. SAL. *Beitrag zur Histologie des Pansens. Deut. Z. Tiermedizin* 1894.

CHAPTER 126

Ruminant digestion and evolution

R. J. MOIR | *Institute of Agriculture, University of Western Australia, Nedlands, Western Australia*

CHAPTER CONTENTS

INTRODUCTION

IN 1885, Pasteur (109) mused that it would be interesting to feed a germ-free animal on pure sterile food and stated "Sans vouloir rien affirmer, je ne cache pas que j'entreprendais cette étude, si j'en avais le temps, avec la pensée préconçue que la vie, dans cette conditions, deviendrait impossible." The imaginative germ-free work at the Lobund Institute (120), and at other centers, has discounted Pasteur's preconceived idea. Yet certain features of these germ-free studies, such as the nutrition of the animals, the grossly enlarged cecum of germ-free rabbits and guinea pigs, and the remarkable response of this organ to "infection" by microorganisms, raise, instead, questions of the interaction between mammals and bacteria through long association. The special developments of the alimentary tract in herbivores, the cecum and colon of nonruminants, and the rumen and rumenlike stomach of other herbivores have undoubtedly evolved through such associations and the ecological advantages these associations have conferred. The ubiquitous distribution of bacteria, together with the essentially similar composition of all plants used for food, suggests the possibility of many experiments in the development of symbiotic accommodation within the various phyletic lines. There is, for example, little doubt that marsupials are an entirely separate phyletic line to the Eutheria (121, 130), yet within the marsupials the general development of the gastrointestinal tract of the different dietary groups—the insectivores, carnivores, omnivores, and herbivores—parallel those of equivalent eutherians closely. Considerable conservatism of genetic potential is indicated.

The gradual evolution of the higher plants, and the resultant changing nutritional environment, must inevitably have set the framework within which animals developed and evolved (66). That this environment has changed little, if at all, chemically is suggested by the essential similarity of the nutritional requirements of all animals, and of their digestive and biochemical characteristics; from ciliate to primate, nutritional needs are similar. If the animal biomass has been expanding, this must have been achieved by more efficient energy utilization, by a greater turnover of available resources, or by utilization of a wider range of energy-yielding substrates. As the autotrophic animal has not yet evolved, and in view of the limited digestive range of animals, increasing complexity of the digestive system is necessary to achieve exploitation and colonization of new and more "difficult" nutritive environments (153).

Cellulose and similar plant structural polymers constitute a vast source of energy not directly available to animals, except to a few cellulase-producing protozoa, snails, and beetles. Cellulose digestion is, however, a relatively common phenomenon among the bacteria, and herbivores of all types have adopted cellulolytic bacteria as their source of cellulase. The stomach of ruminants and the cecum and large intestines of all herbivores offer an ideal environment for anaerobic mesophilic bacteria and, together, the bacteria and the host animal constitute a complex system with a wider range. The rapid adaptability of the microbial inhabitants of the gut to new substrates, and greater synthetic capacity of the bacteria, in addition to the normal digestive process of the animal make the total system less directly dependent on the dietary supply of the more readily digested, conventional metabolic requirements. Thus it is possible to satisfy the ruminant system entirely with a diet consisting only of cellulose, urea, minerals, and the fat-soluble vitamins (74). The fermentation in the rumen, following ingestion of the diet, yields fatty acids, protein, and vitamins sufficient to satisfy the metabolic needs of the fastidious mammalian host. These metabolic requirements, if they differ at all, differ only in degree from those of the more commonly studied laboratory animals and man.

RUMINANT ENERGY METABOLISM

The central role of glucose in metabolism and the features of glucose regulation in mammalian systems are well established. Omnivores and simple-stomached herbivores obtain substantial amounts of glucose from food, and the liver is well equipped to convert glucose to glycogen and to release sugar to the blood. On the other hand, carnivores and insectivores under feral conditions receive insignificant amounts of glucose from the alimentary tract and must rely upon gluconeogenesis for glucose. Although the diet of adult ruminants is similar to, and may be identical with, that of other herbivores, the ruminal fermentation, preceding digestion and absorption, removes hexose from the ingesta. Under normal conditions the fermentation is so effective that it has been estimated that only 5–6 g of glucose per day is available for intestinal absorption in a hay-fed sheep (73). This hexose is largely derived from storage polysaccharide contained in the bacteria flowing from the rumen.

Alimentary hyperglycemia is, therefore, an exceptional occurrence.

The livers of most adult animals contain two hexokinases—a nonspecific hexokinase, and glucokinase, specific to glucose and mannose. Glucokinase has a high Michaelis constant for glucose which would permit enzymatic control over glucose phosphorylation in response to changes in blood glucose within the normal range. This enzyme is absent in adult sheep liver (15); under physiological conditions it is unlikely in them that direct transformation of blood glucose into liver glycogen ever occurs. Glycogen probably acts as a store for glucose derived from gluconeogenesis. The liver of ruminants is well equipped enzymatically to synthesize glucose and to release glucose into the blood (16). In keeping with the situation in the sheep, the cow, ruminant-like marsupials, and also carnivores, such as the cat, all lack glucokinase, and the activity of the nonspecific liver hexokinase is low in each of these species (14).

Although it had been known since the 1880s that the ruminal fermentation produced mainly acetic, propionic, and butyric acid, knowledge of the carbohydrate metabolism of ruminants remained confused until 1944, when Barcroft et al. (17) showed that these acids were readily absorbed and metabolized. The range and proportions of the acids produced by rumen fermentation under a number of conditions are shown in Table 1. As acetate and butyrate are metabolized by way of the tricarboxylic cycle (6, 35, 36), they cannot contribute to net carbohydrate synthesis (148). Acetate, as the major component, contributes substantially to energy requirement and is important in milk fat synthesis (113). Butyrate is metabolized to β-hydroxybutyrate by the ruminal epithelium (112) and as the main metabolite of that membrane plays an important role in the full development of the mucosa when fermentation is initiated in the rumen (146).

Propionate is the main source of glucose to the ruminant. Inspection of Table 1 shows that the proportion of propionic acid produced on high-cellulose diets is very low. The amount of glucose from this source may therefore be limited. Nevertheless it has been estimated from labeled glucose infusions that the rate of utilization of glucose by ruminants is quite comparable to that of nonruminants (8). Lindsay (93) concludes that ". . . the carbohydrate economy of ruminants is precarious—changes either in quality of the diet or in demands for carbohydrate can readily alter carbohydrate balance from the normal to the pathological."

TABLE I. *Volatile Fatty Acid Proportion in the Stomach of Ruminants*

Animal	Type of Diet	Concn, mmoles/L. VFA	Molar Proportions							Ref.
			Formic	Acetic	Pro-pionic	n-Butyric	i-Bu-tyric	n-Va-leric	i-Va-leric + 2 Methyl Butyric	
Sheep	Hay, before feeding	47	0	66	28	5	1	0	0	5
	Hay, 3 hours after	94	0	58	29	7	2	1	3	5
	Hay—portal blood 3 hours after	1.75	4	75	21	tr.	0	0	0	5
	Hay—carotid blood 3 hours after	0.71	5	92	3	0	0	0	0	5
	Semipurified 20% cellulose	100		49	36	12	0.1	1.7	0.0	74
	Semipurified 44% cellulose	94		51	33	7	0.4	1.1	0.6	74
	Semipurified 70% cellulose	99		67	22	7	0.6	0.7	0.8	74
	Semipurified 85% cellulose	100		77	19	2	0.3	0.4	0.4	74
	Grazing 31% protein	216		51	25	17	3	4[a]		88
Cattle	Grazing grass	137		64	21.9	11.9		2.2[a]		26
	Hay + concentrates	129		61.5	20.1	9.5		8.9[b]		13
	Ground hay + concentrates	133		49.0	32.1	11.9		7.0[b]		13
Camel		134		77.1	16.4	6.5[c]			.	149
Quokka (*Setonix*)	Mixed grazing	101		85.0	4.2	8.5	1.0	0.5	0.9	d
	Mixed grazing	137		71.2	11.0	17.1	tr.	1.2	tr.	e
Monkey										
Presbytis cristatus		110	3.7	59.6	26.7	7.6		1.9	0.7	60
Procolobus verus		181	0.8	70.5	16.7	9.9		2.5		60

[a] C_5 acids.

[b] Higher acids.

[c] Butyric + higher acids.

[d] R. J. Moir, R. E. Hungate, and J. Kinnear; personal communication.

[e] A. Ramsay; personal communication.

Newborn ruminants have a blood sugar level in the "normal" range, but this decreases gradually to the low value typical of adult ruminants (99). The blood sugar levels of juvenile and adult ruminants, camels, ruminant-like animals, and of the better known nonruminant herbivores, rodents, and man are given in Table 2. Notwithstanding the very low values of adult ruminants (118), it is difficult to reduce the level by starvation, and adult ruminants, but not newborn animals (86), show great tolerance to reduced blood sugar level after intravenous insulin injection, and to the reactions usually associated with this condition (119). Raggi & Kronfeld (116) have recently shown that the K_m for sheep brain hexokinase is considerably lower than that for rat brain. They suggest that this is an adaptation to the normally low blood sugar level (2.5 mM) of the ruminant compared with that of the rat (5 mM), and further, that as a result of the greater affinity of the sheep hexokinase for glucose, the sheep brain is able to obtain sufficient glucose to avoid the usual consequences of insulin-induced hypoglycemia.

RUMINANT NITROGEN METABOLISM

Although ruminants are apparently well adapted to low blood sugar levels, their total glucose utilization rates are close to those of other species. As propionate, the main alimentary gluconeogenic product, provides only 50–60% of the total glucose requirement (7), substantial amounts of protein must be deaminated to fulfill the remainder. As a consequence, the urinary nitrogen output of ruminants should exceed that of other mammals. The minimal urinary nitrogen excretion, determined by the conventional device of feeding nitrogen-free (or -low) diets, does not, on the surface at least, support this hypothesis. On the contrary, the minimal excretion is frequently substantially below the standard mam-

TABLE 2. *Normal Blood Glucose Levels*

Animal	Glucose, mg/100 ml	Ref.
Domestic ruminants		
Lamb, 2–4 weeks	70–108	99
Lamb, 6–9 weeks	60–65	99
Sheep, adult	34.8±3.1	118
Calf, 8 days	105	99
Calf, 31 days	83	99
Cow, adult	42–55	115
Wild ruminants		
Aoudad, 14 days	90	99
Aoudad, adult	56	99
Mouflon, 56 days	63	99
Mouflon, adult	57	99
Addax antelope, 1 year	49–63	99
White-tailed deer, 1 year	47	99
Eland, adult	65	99
Indian black buck	42	99
Camels		
Arabian camel, adult	75–99	99
Llama	72–121	99
Alpaca, 1 month	121	141
Alpaca, 3–5 years	99	141
Ruminant-like		
Quokka (*Setonix*), young	40–79	18
Quokka (*Setonix*), adult	15–78	102
Presbytis spp., adult	62–99	90
Tree sloth	59–62	97
Nonruminant		
Horse, adult	66–100	1
Rabbit, adult	79–99	67
Guinea pig, adult (pregnant)	49–106	67
Rat, adult	89–112	84
Pig, adult	72	67
Man, adult	78–97	133

TABLE 3. *Urinary Nitrogen Excretion of Ruminants*

Species	Mean Minimum Urinary N, mg/kg$^{0.73}$ per day	Ref.
Mice—elephant (mean)	146	45
Sheep, 25–36 kg (N-free diet)	79 (54–94)	63
Cattle (0.8% N)	95.6	62
Macropod marsupials (0.5–0.8% N)	34 (21–48)	47
Camel A, hay + dates	15 (mg/kg)	127

malian value of 146 mg/kg$^{0.73}$ per day (45) (Table 3). The conventional method of determination, however, cannot give legitimate values. Urea nitrogen constitutes a substantial proportion (60–70%) of the nitrogen in the copious parotid saliva (132). Further, because of the bacterial ureases present in the rumen (117), the urea concentration in this organ is always extremely low and urea diffuses from the blood down a gradient into the rumen (81, 83). Extensive feeding experiments have demonstrated that urea is an adequate nitrogen source for the ruminal bacteria, many of which require ammonia, since they are unable to absorb most amino acids (48). On protein-free or low-protein diets, considerable amounts of endogenous urea may be upgraded to protein and removed from the urinary cycle. This "protein regeneration cycle" (81) may, however, be minimized by inadequacies in bacterial nutrients. Thus the ratio of recycled nitrogen to recycled sulfur is of the order of 70–80:1, whereas the ratio required for optimal bacterial cell protein synthesis is of the order of 10:1 (44). The extent of the contribution of protein to gluconeogenesis and the influence this has on nitrogen metabolism remain to be determined.

Under normal circumstances, dietary protein is also largely fermented and the nitrogen appears as ammonia (100). The ammonia may be utilized by bacteria (48) or absorbed through the rumen wall (100), transported to the liver, and converted to urea. It has been estimated, however, that almost the whole of the amount of nitrogen in the dietary protein may be converted to microbial protein, in the form of bacterial and protozoal cells (101). Irrespective of the source of animal nitrogen supply—from ingested protein or nonprotein nitrogen, or from recycled endogenous urea—the ruminant protein supply is, therefore, substantially or completely presented as microbial protein. Despite variations in the microbial population of the rumen, the component organisms have very similar amino acid constitutions; consequently, the biological value of the protein available for absorption will always be approximately the same (114). Ruminant tissues, as distinct from the whole ruminant system, have the same limited ability to synthesize amino acids as other mammalian tissue (37, 59) and require the "essential" amino acids commensurate with their physiological condition.

Microbial cells have a very high nucleic acid content, and 13–18% of the total microbial nitrogen is in the form of polynucleotide nitrogen (64). The purine excretion of ruminants is, therefore, substantially higher than that of other mammals (39). Further, due to the absorption of degradation products of the lignin in the diet, hippuric acid excretion is also high; a sheep may require 0.5 g of nitrogen a day to detoxify these absorbed benzoic acid products. Despite this additional "endogenous" nitrogen cost, the amino acids synthesized by the ruminal micro-organisms from recycled urea under adverse dietary nitrogen conditions may more than compensate these losses and substantially increase survival time. Problems of ruminant protein nutrition are related largely to the amount of protein synthesized by the ruminal bacteria and protozoa; the animal is fully protected against amino acid imbalance and similar problems.

DIGESTA FLOW PATTERNS

Brandt & Thacker (43) in a study of the rate of passage of digesta through the gut of the rabbit derived equations that supported the concept of a flow pattern through a system with a single reservoir. Using the data of Balch et al. (12) for cattle, they showed that in this case the flow pattern was consistent with that for two reservoirs. The equations derived were essentially similar to those derived by Blaxter et al. (38) for sheep. The increase in retention time of digesta is an important component in the effective fermentation of the more refractory food components. The cecum of ruminants is simple and reduced, relative to other herbivores, and rather simpler than that of the pig. In pigs the mean retention time varies between 32.3 and 25.9 hours from half to twice normal intake levels (52). Castle (51) has shown that the retention time of particles introduced into the duodenum of goats was of the order of 13.2 hours, values very similar to those for particles introduced into the abomasum of cattle (11). On the other hand, the mean retention time for hay fed to cattle may vary from 40 to 100 hours, depending on the level of intake, the nature of the food, and other dietary conditions. The rumen is, therefore,

an effective delay mechanism because of its capacity (Table 4) and its bypassed nature.

ORGANOGENESIS AND STRUCTURE OF STOMACH OF TYPICAL RUMINANT

Although in older literature the ruminant is often stated to be polygastric, to have four stomachs, and occasionally, because of the squamous or "esophageal"-type epithelium of the first three chambers, to have proventriculi, such views and terms are inadmissible: the ruminant has a single, albeit multilocular, stomach. Lewis (92), in a short note on the comparative embryology of the stomach of the cat, rat, pig, and sheep, indicates that the simple embryological stomach spindle of the sheep yields the rumen from the fundus, the reticulum from the body of the stomach, the omasum from the lesser curvature, and the abomasum, including both vestibule and antrum, from the pars pylorica. Warner (144) has investigated the development of the bovine stomach, and from both the organogenesis and histogenesis of the stomach he refutes any suggestion of esophageal origin and confirms Lewis's views of the development of the various compartments. The position of the chambers in the adult (Figs. 1 and 2) is due to migration and rotation. Figure 3 illustrates the stomach of the adult sheep in the embryological configuration. Thus the expansion of the fundus, which gives the dorsal sac of the rumen, shifts dorsad, caudad, and slightly to the right, whereas the dorsally developing region of the fundus moves caudad, ventrad, and more to the left to become the ventral sac of the rumen. The reticu-

TABLE 4. *Weight and Proportion of Stomach Contents in Ruminant-Like Animals*

Animal	Diet Regimen	Body Wt, kg	Stomach Contents		Cecum		Colon		Ref.
			Kg	Ratio/body wt	Kg	Ratio/body wt	Kg	Ratio/body wt	
Suni		3.69	0.29	0.08	0.029	0.008	0.017	0.004	85
Thompson's gazelle		23.7	3.16	0.13	0.11	0.005	0.24	0.010	85
Zebu	Grass pasture	237	36.3	0.15	1.4	0.006	0.9	0.004	85
Camel		331	56.1	0.17	0.9	0.003	3.4	0.01	85
Sheep	Hay + concentrates	58	7.75	0.15	0.9	0.15	0.4	0.07	42
Cow	Hay + beet pulp	498	66.4	0.14			1.6*	0.003	96
Procolobus badius (monkey)	Leaves	7.3	0.95	0.13					90
Setonix brachyurus (macropod marsupial)	Grass, herbs, shrub	3.16	{0.08 {0.485	{0.04 {0.15	0.035†	0.011			102
Bradypus	Leaves			0.25					69
Elephant		3,600			120	0.034	277	0.077	85

* Large intestine total.   † Cecum + upper one-third colon.

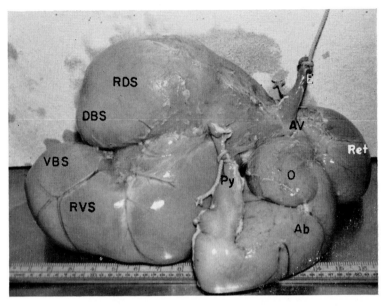

FIG. 1. Rumen of the adult sheep (inflated) as viewed from the right side. *AV*, atrium ventriculi; *Ab*, abomasum; *E*, esophagus; *DBS*, dorsal blind sac; *O*, omasum; *Py*, pyloris; *RDS*, dorsal rumen; *RVS*, ventral rumen; *VBS*, ventral blind sac.

lum, first apparent as a swelling on the greater curvature of the stomach, becomes distinct externally from the rumen and omasum by the development of grooves. This chamber moves gradually forward and to the left. Internally the reticular (esophageal) groove, originally horizontal, becomes vertical and slightly spiral. The lips of this groove are formed from dorsal and ventral mesodermal ridges of the early embryonic stomach, and the groove is, therefore, properly called ventricular groove, rather than the esophageal groove, as it has a purely stomach origin. The omasum develops into a nearly spherical compartment from the lesser curvature of the stomach with progressive separation from the reticulum and abomasum. Concurrently it develops the typical array of laminae and migrates to the right anterior position of the stomach. The omasal sulcus is continuous with, and of common origin to, that of the reticulum. The abomasum meanwhile bends increasingly on the longitudinal axis, and the angular incisura becomes more acute; the pyloric region beyond the incisura extends at first ventrally then to the right and cephalad. The cardiac region expands both in length and diameter, and primary and secondary folds in the mucosa develop. Warner also showed that epithelial differentiation occurs first in the esophagus and is followed by differentiation in the reticular groove area, a small area of the omasum near the reticulo-omasal orifice, the whole of the rumen, reticulum, and omasum, and finally the abomasum, in that order. The abomasum is the only secretory region of the stomach, and according to Hill (77) three histological regions may be differen-

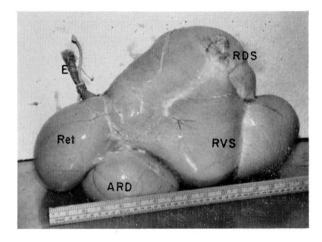

FIG. 2. Left view of adult sheep rumen. *E*, esophagus; *Ret*, reticulum; *RVS*, ventral rumen; *RDS*, dorsal rumen; *ARD*, anterior sac dorsal rumen.

tiated in the abomasum of the goat. The cardiac region forms a very narrow band at the omaso-abomasal junction with typical tubular mucous glands and occasional parietal cells. The peptic region with its mucosal folds extends 10–12 cm and is followed by almost smooth pyloric region with typical pyloric glands. Within the peptic region the concentration of both parietal and peptic cells increases to a maximum 2–3 cm from the cardiac region, then decreases toward the pyloric region.

The various chambers of the adult rumen, the dorsal and ventral sacs with their posterior blind sacs, and the reticulum are clearly defined and are separated externally by distinct grooves, which internally are thickened to form strong muscular pillars projecting into the rumen. While these pillars are important in the mixing of the bulk of material in the very large reticulo-rumen, they may also play a part as baffles to stabilize the large volume of digesta (normally the reticulo-rumen contents weigh 15% of body weight) in these swift and sometimes agile beasts. The rumino-reticular fold separates the anterior dorsal sac and reticulum. Externally this is marked by a deep groove on the ventral and left aspects, but dorsally and to the right there is no demarcation between the two, and the esophagus at this point enters the atrium ventriculi (131). The reticular groove begins at the cardia, and passes slightly (10–12 cm) forward in the bovine but slightly behind in the ovine, to the reticulo-omasal orifice. The honeycomb-like raised cells of the reticulum and the laminae of the omasum are developed early and remain relatively unchanged throughout the life of the animal. The ruminal mucosa, however, does vary in structure. At birth, and while the animal is on a milk diet, the mucosa is relatively smooth, having

papillae less than 1 mm in height. The papillae develop rapidly with the onset of fermentation into dense tonguelike projections that increase the surface area of the rumen enormously. This development may be induced in milk-fed calves by infusing solutions of volatile fatty acids into the rumen; the effectiveness of these is in the order butyrate > propionate > acetate. Glucose, sodium, and potassium chlorides or carbonates are ineffective (124). The ruminal epithelium is known to metabolize these acids, butyrate being the favored energy source (112).

Sucking or drinking milk reflexly closes the reticular groove, thus bypassing the rumen and directing the milk through the omasum to the abomasum (147). At birth, the reticulo-rumen is only about half the size of the abomasum, and the omasum appears contracted and functionless (131). Access to fermentable fodder results in rapid development of the reticulo-rumen to adult proportions (145). The development of the functional rumen is coordinated with changes in other anatomical and physiological features. Of these, the development of the parotid salivary gland and its secretion is basic, as the alkaline parotid saliva is the main buffer source to the rumen. The development of the parotid lags when an animal is milk fed. Purified diets, which stimulate ruminal development but do not cause rumination, provide minimal stimulus; hay feeding or grazing produces maximal development. Wood shavings, which cause increase in rumen size but little epithelial development, result in full parotid development (150). In this case, as for rumen capacity, physical factors appear dominant, whereas chemical or nutrient factors derived from the microbial fermentations are essential for ruminal epithelial development. Thus the full expression of genotype is due to interaction with environmental factors.

STOMACH VARIATION

Typical Ruminants

There is a continuous and defined series of developments in the stomachs of the typical ruminants. Cordier (53) made a substantial study of the comparative anatomy of the stomachs of a wide range of ruminants. *Hyemoschus* (water chevrotain) and other tragulids have an extended ventral blind sac giving the rumen an almost S-shaped tubular aspect compared with the normal globular, but grooved, typical rumen. The reticulum is large, and the omasum, if present, has no more than two small leaves and is

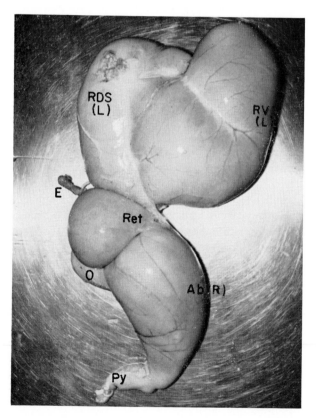

FIG. 3. Adult sheep rumen in embryonic configuration prior to rotation. *Ab (R)*, right abomasum; *E*, esophagus; *O*, omasum; *Py*, pyloris; *Ret*, reticulum; *RVS (L)*, ventral rumen (left); *RDS (L)*, dorsal rumen (left).

continuous with the tubular abomasum (see Fig. 7, *12*). All the true ruminants have a distinct omasum. This organ, however, is not as well developed in the deer and antelopes (see Fig. 7, *13*); indeed, in some it is poorly separated from the abomasum and has only seven or eight leaves. It reaches its full expression in the Giraffidae and in the Bovidae (see Fig. 7, *14*), as does the rumen. The reticular (ventricular) groove is more primitive in the tragulids. The internal muscle layer forming the lips of the groove in the true ruminants is cut off quite sharply and does not cover the floor of the groove; in the tragulids there is a slight excursion of this muscle layer into the floor of the groove (53).

It is possibly significant that the depot fat of the Cervidae has a much higher linoleic-linolenic acid content than the ruminants which have more highly developed stomachs (76); this suggests a less complete fermentation. The difference may be due to a more rapid rate of passage of food because of the lesser development of the omasum. Evidence on this point is lacking.

"Conventional" Herbivores

As outlined earlier, the rumen, by permitting fermentation prior to normal digestion and absorption, modifies many aspects of the nutrition and associated physiology of the ruminant animal. This type of digestive system is, however, not unique to the suborder Ruminantia, the true ruminants; there are many parallel and convergent systems in other families and orders, many phylogenetically distant or distinct.

Within the herbivorous order Perissodactyla, the stomach is always simple, but the cecum and colon are capacious and well sacculated. A substantial part of the stomach mucosa is, however, of stratified squamous epithelium and devoid of glands. This esophageal part constitutes one-third to two-fifths of the mucosal surface in the horse; a narrow band of mucous cardiac glands follows, then the extensive area of fundus and pyloric glands (131). The tapir and rhinoceros in the same order have similar epithelial arrangements (34), but other herbivores such as the elephant and the hyrax have only small areas of stratified epithelium at the cardia. The hyrax has long been reputed to chew the cud (Leviticus 11:5). Beddard (27) considered this to be a fallacy, but continues to state that ". . . the traveller Bruce kept one in captivity to see if it did really chew the cud, and found that it did!" Hendrichs (75) confirms

that "rumination" occasionally occurs in the hyrax (*Procavia capensis*) when fed hay. The stomach is not unusually large but is constricted into two unequal parts. The larger cardiac portion is muscular and has an epithelium of cardiac glands, whereas the smaller pyloric region is richly glandular. The cecum is very large and normally situated, but in addition there is a pair of ceca, without valves, farther along the colon (69). The Hyracoidea is an ancient group (130) and displays many peculiarities; whether it is ruminant-like, apart from its possible "ruminating" habit, has not been ascertained.

Suiformes

The Suiformes generally have relatively simple stomachs; a few have a simple conical diverticulum, but the peccaries have a three-chambered stomach (53) (see Fig. 7, *6*). The globular central chamber has simple nonpapillated stratified pavement epithelium except for a crescentic area of short cardiac glands on the anterior floor. The broad anterior sac, communicating freely with the central chamber, has a similar cardiac gland epithelium. These glandular areas are bordered by a roll of pavement epithelium and show signs of being subdivided into reticulum-like "cells." The pyloric region, the smallest of the three chambers, is separated by a constriction. About 1 cm beyond this pillar, pyloric glands commence. Cordier found only pyloric glands in this chamber despite a careful search of his material, but Edelmann (61) found both fundus and pyloric glands. A ventricular groove, rudimentary in its form and development, runs from the cardia to the third chamber. Evidence of fermentation in the stomach of the peccari is lacking, but the possibility that it could occur in some species appears high.

The hippopotamuses lack a cecum but have an enormous and complex stomach (69). The esophagus discharges into a vestibule which communicates freely with a pair of large but unequal anterior diverticula and with the tubular body of the stomach (see Fig. 7, *7*). These three compartments all have projecting folds with numerous small papillae and are lined by a stratified epithelium (104). The central chamber, leading to the well-separated pyloric portion, carries a ventricular groove along its lesser curvature and an unusual series of incomplete septa on its greater curvature. These septa are at right angles to the gastric canal, similar to a series of dams in a stream, and must substantially impede the flow of digesta in the gastric canal.

The size and conformation of the stomach, the nonglandular nature of the major portion, the presence of a defined ventricular groove, and the nature of the depot fat (76), all suggest a substantial degree of fermentation of the digesta, although not necessarily as complete as in ruminants.

RUMINANT-LIKE CONVERGENCE

Tylopoda

The camels have frequently been classified together with the Ruminantia because of their ruminating habit. Rumination per se is quite inadequate to establish phylogenetic relationships and, on more conventional fossil evidence, Simpson (130) places them in a separate suborder, the Tylopoda Illiger, considering that the differentiation of even the most ancient of the extinct ruminants, from the primitive Tragulina, occurred after the separation of these from the Tylopoda.

Many earlier authors readily made homologies between the various parts of the ruminant and camel stomachs, although Cordier (53) states vehemently that they are totally different and he draws parallels between the stomachs of camels and those of peccaries on histological similarities. Modern authors (41, 71) treat these homologies with caution. It is nevertheless convenient and functionally apt to use the ruminant stomach terminology in discussing tylopod digestion. Embryological studies would be valuable in defining the homologies.

Externally, all tylopod stomachs differ quite strikingly in detail from those of ruminants (see Fig. 7, 11). The relative lack of grooves and the rather smooth ovoid shape heighten the presence of the two glandular sac areas (the water cells of the older literature) which characterize the tylopod stomach (41). The omasum with the abomasum forms a single long tube in the camel (71), llama (53), guanaco, vicuna (41), and alpaca (141). The lack of anatomical separation of omasum and abomasum led to the idea that camels lacked the omasum or that it was confined to a very restricted region near the reticulum.

Internally, the differences between ruminant and tylopod stomachs are equally striking. In the tylopod the esophagus discharges only into the rumen instead of at a vestibule between rumen and reticulum (41). The ventricular groove is not as well developed as in ruminants (53), and although it is similar in form in the camel (71), Bohlken (41) states that there is only

a single lip to the groove in the New World forms. Nevertheless, Vallenas (141) gives the impression that in the alpaca, at least, there are two lips. The rumen wall is devoid of papillae and has a smooth stratified epithelium except in the lower portions of the glandular sac areas. The free borders and sides of the partitions between the sacs are similar to those in the rumen, but the epithelium changes abruptly to simple columnar with tubular glands of a cardiac form within the sacs (71). The reticulum is similar to the glandular sac areas except that the stratified epithelium is less extensive. Boas (40) states that a small area of stratified epithelium extends into the omasal region, but this is not mentioned by recent authors, who generally agree that the cardiac gland mucosa of the omasal region is thrown into a series of low, parallel ridges in all species. This is in accord with the relationship Cordier (53) considered to exist between the degree of flexure between omasum and abomasum and the complexity and development of the omasal leaves. The abomasum has a small fundus gland area, but the glands are exceptionally deep and are more tortuous and branched than is normal in other mammals (71).

The motility pattern of the alpaca rumen differs substantially from that of the typical ruminant. Whereas the cycle of contractions in ruminants is relatively stable, occurring about once a minute according to time after feeding, the alpaca shows characteristically five to eight contractions in approximately 1.2 min followed by a quiescent period of 0.8 min. When food is given, the rate increases and contractions become continuous and more frequent (141). The response of both the motility of the stomach and salivation to drugs is similar in camels and in ruminants. The salivary glands of the camel appear to be similar in size and in function to those of ruminants except that the ventral buccal gland, which is morphologically similar to the parotid, is much larger (142). It is possible that the mucosa of the glandular sac areas may also contribute a buffer (71). The fermentation in the rumen yields acetic acid, propionic acid, butyric acid (149), CO_2, and methane at rates, and in proportions, comparable with those in typical ruminants (85). The colony count of cellulolytic organisms is high (85), but little other work has been done on the nature and extent of the bacterial flora. The fauna of the rumen has received some attention, and according to Lubinski (94) the ciliate Caloscolex camelinus, from the rumen of camels, is a very advanced phylogenetic form of the Ophryoscolecidae, which is largely confined to ruminants.

Although the blood glucose level of the camel is similar to that of nonruminants [see Table 2; (99, 141)], the extent and nature of the fermentation in the rumen suggests that the energy metabolism of this group would follow a pattern substantially similar to that of the true ruminant. The depot fats of the camel are very similar to those of the sheep and ox, but there is, as in the hippopotamus, a larger amount of unsaturated C_{18} dienoic and trienoic acids (76) than in the true ruminants. These unsaturated acids of food origin are largely hydrogenated to *trans* isomers in the rumen of the sheep (129), and appear in the depot fat in that form; the hydrogenation process, therefore, appears to be less complete but further information is necessary to resolve this difference.

After earlier reports that the urea content of camel urine could be extremely low, it has been shown that when growing camels are fed low-nitrogen, but adequate-energy diets, urea from endogenous sources and also a very high proportion of injected urea (259 and 475 mmole) apparently are retained (127). This is consistent with the recycling of endogenous urea to the rumen (81, 132) and the conversion of urea nitrogen to protein nitrogen by the ruminal microorganisms. As there are no fundamental reasons why the camel's amino acid requirement should differ from that of other mammals, nor that the amino acid constitution of the camel's ruminal bacteria should differ from that of bacteria in the sheep's rumen, substantial conservation of nitrogen could be expected on low nitrogen intakes where dietary conditions permit adequate growth of the ruminal population and protein "regeneration" from endogenous urea.

The extent to which vitamins are synthesized in the tylopod stomach is not recorded, as far as the author is aware. It appears entirely likely that the pattern is also similar to that of ruminants. Since, however, the camel stomach contains extensive areas of cardiac glands in the rumen, reticulum, and omasum, it may, like the macropod marsupials, be less susceptible to the induced vitamin B_{12} deficiency of low-cobalt status to which the domestic ruminants, at least, are prone (140).

Edentata

Salmi (122) has advanced the interesting hypothesis that the giant sloth [*Mylodon* (= *Neomylodon*) *listai*] became extinct partly through copper and cobalt deficiency. This followed climatic changes that caused loss of trees and deterioration of available grazing. Unlike the relatively simple stomach of the insectivorous edentates, that of the Bradypoididae, the leaf-eating tree sloths, is extremely large and complex (see Fig. 7, *10*). When filled with food it represents 20–30% of the body weight of the animal (69); the similarity to a rumen has been noted by many authors (69, 104). The main body of the stomach consists of three chambers which are well divided internally by pillars. It has a stratified epithelium. The right or anterior chamber is extended into a large blind conical diverticulum with cardiac glands throughout. A short ventricular groove along the left chamber passes through a small chamber with cardiac and fundus glands to the pyloric stomach (89). Although bizarre, the general development is broadly similar to that in the camel, though the presence of pillars more closely resembles typical ruminants.

Some aspects of the metabolism in the stomach of sloths have recently been investigated (87). Stomach contents from the "rumen" of *Choloepus hoffmanni* Pet. contain a cellulase that releases sugar from carboxymethylcellulose; as cultural methods reveal a rich microbial flora including cellulolytic organisms and as neither chitinolytic nor cellulolytic activity is found in epithelial extracts from either the rumen or the abomasal area, the functional analogy to the ruminant has been, in part, confirmed. The fermentation products have not been described, nor have rumination and other ruminant-like features been recorded.

The marine herbivorous mammals, the manatee and dugong of the order Sirenia, although having some anatomical complications of the stomach, have such highly unsaturated depot fats (76) that fermentation in the foregut appears improbable. The stomach is, in fact, less complex than that of the carnivorous Cetacea which Owen (106) suggests bear ". . . a closer resemblance to the ruminant stomach; it is divided for example, into a greater number of receptacles, and has the first cavity, like the rumen, lined with cuticle; while in the dugong, on the contrary, the stomach is properly divided into two parts only (of which the second more closely resembles intestine) and both are lined with a mucous membrane."

Macropod Marsupials

The possibility of ruminant-like digestion in the macropod marsupials may have been inferred from the earliest descriptions of the anatomy of these animals by Home (80) and Owen (105), both of whom raised the analogy to ruminants on the grounds of the size and complexity of the stomach, the presence of an esophageal groove (107), and the simplicity of the cecum and colon. As with most of the early studies cited here, interpretation of anatomical detail remained limited in the absence of the basic concepts of rumen microbiology, the fermentation processes within the rumen, and the influence of these on the physiology of the ruminant or ruminant-like animal. With these concepts, in addition to the anatomical facts, ruminant-like digestive physiology has been demonstrated in the small marsupial macropod *Setonix brachyurus* by Moir et al. (102).

The stomach of the macropods is a long tubular

FIG. 4. Ventral view of the stomach of the quokka (*Setonix brachyurus*). *E*, esophagus; *C*, cul-de-sac; *P*, pyloris; *D*, duodenum. (Photograph courtesy of G. Ward.)

colonlike organ which may measure as much as 1 m along the greater curvature in the larger kangaroos. In *Setonix*, a small (3.5 kg) wallaby, the contents of the replete stomach may constitute almost 15% of total body weight, a proportion similar to that found in the ruminants (see Table 4). The stomach, in situ, fills the ventral abdominal region (Fig. 4). The cul-de-sac, occupying the medial position, and the left descending limb are deeply sacculated along the greater curvature. The sacculations diminish on the ascending limb, and the pyloric region is smooth, as is the entire lesser curvature (Fig. 5). Internally, a well-defined ventricular groove extends from the cardia toward the nonsacculated region along the lesser curvature, its length and definition varying with different species. The immediate area of the groove invariably has a smooth stratified epithelium; in some, for example, *Macropus*, the stratified epithelium extends slightly beyond the groove area and the cardia into the sacculated region; in others, such as *Dorcopsis*, most of the upper half of the stomach is invested by this type of membrane (125). The remainder of the sacculated area has cardiac glands which terminate at the thick-walled portion of the stomach carrying fundus glands. This region, 5–10 cm in length, is followed by a pyloric region of about the same length but of lesser diameter and wall thickness (125).

The parotid gland of the kangaroo is large (95), and the pH of the saliva is high (8.4) (102). Whether saliva is the sole source of buffer to the stomach is not known, but the volume produced, 0.5–5.8 ml/kg per hour (8), is comparable with that of ruminants (147). The possibility exists, however, that the extensive cardiac glands of the stomach may contribute buffer. It has been suggested that the cardiac glands of the glandular sac areas of the camel may possibly share this function (71).

The stomach carries a dense population of bacteria and, under grazing conditions at least, of protozoa. Quantitatively the population of bacteria is similar to that of the ruminant (10^{10} per ml), and the proportion of cellulolytic bacteria is also of the same order (R. E. Hungate, personal communication). The ciliate population, which may exceed 10^6 per ml of contents, is strikingly different from that of the true ruminants.

The fermentation in the stomach of grazing macropod marsupials produces volatile fatty acids, ammonia, and gas. The proportion of acetic acid found in the two studies conducted so far is much higher than is usual in grazing ruminants, and the propionic

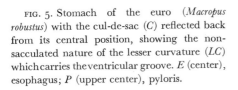

FIG. 5. Stomach of the euro (*Macropus robustus*) with the cul-de-sac (*C*) reflected back from its central position, showing the non-sacculated nature of the lesser curvature (*LC*) which carries the ventricular groove. *E* (center), esophagus; *P* (upper center), pyloris.

acid is lower (Table 1). The rate of production of acid in the quokka (*Setonix brachyurus*), 20.3 μmole/g per hour, is of the same order of magnitude as that in larger ruminants, but is lower than in the small antelope, the suni, of comparable body weight [(85) and R. J. Moir, R. E. Hungate, and J. Kinnear, personal communication]. Possibly the quokka selects a lower quality diet than the suni; the ability of the kangaroo to utilize low-quality diets successfully has been demonstrated (65). The gas produced soon after the fermentation has commenced has a much higher hydrogen content and a lower methane content than the rumen gas of cattle.

The volatile fatty acids produced by fermentation are absorbed directly from the stomach and are metabolized in the liver and body (18, 102); clearance rates for both acetate and propionate are high. Injected propionate gives a sharp rise in blood glucose, but injected acetate shows no such effect. Like ruminants, the macropod marsupials lack hepatic glucokinase, an indication that little glucose is received from the gut. The rate of glucose incorporation into glycogen by the liver is also very low—less than 4 % of the rate found in rat liver (14). It is clear that liver function is directed toward producing glucose by gluconeogenesis rather than by removing glucose rapidly from the portal blood. Although little glucose is available from the gut (18, 102), the blood glucose level (25–78 mg glucose per 100 ml blood) rises and falls rapidly after feeding. Despite this rapid rise and fall, which does not occur readily in ruminants (118), the macropods show considerable tolerance to the effects of massive intravenous insulin injections, although their blood sugar levels are substantially reduced (18). Their response under these

conditions is very similar, indeed, to that of the sheep (119).

The motility of the macropod stomach and its control has not been investigated, nor have the secretory mechanisms and controls. The emptying rate of the stomach of *Setonix* is approximately linear (136), and the retention time is much shorter in macropod marsupials than in ruminants (49, 65). Nevertheless, food is retained for a sufficient length of time to enable appreciable digestion of cellulose; 25–32 % of alfalfa crude fiber is digested (49, 65).

The digestive efficiency of the red kangaroo (*Macropus rufus*) and sheep has recently been compared (65). Sheep eat slightly more alfalfa hay than the kangaroos (g per kg$^{0.73}$) and digest more of it, but the kangaroos maintain a relatively better intake of oat straw (0.64 % N) than sheep and are able to maintain body weight on this diet, whereas sheep lose weight.

Consistent with the carbohydrate digestive pattern, the nitrogen metabolism of the kangaroo tribe also shows ruminant-like characteristics. Brown (46) found that the minimum urinary nitrogen excretion is extraordinarily low in the euro (*Macropus robustus*), being only 34 mg per kg$^{0.73}$ compared with the value of 146 mg per kg$^{0.73}$ generally found for mammals (47). Urea is returned to the stomach by the saliva and also directly through the stomach epithelium (47). Like camels and sheep (81, 127, 132), the quokka and euro retain a high proportion of injected urea. The ability of the bacteria of the stomach to utilize this urea nitrogen and to convert it to protein to the advantage of the animal must be accepted in view of the extraordinarily low minimal nitrogen excretion of these animals.

Little is known of eructation in the kangaroos

although copious gas formation occurs during fermentation. Food is generally well masticated, but there are some reports of food regurgitation. This regurgitatory process has been reviewed by Barker et al. (19), who concluded that the process is not analogous to rumination in ruminants. From their own observations, and from earlier reports, regurgitation in kangaroos appears to be an infrequent and difficult process, occurring with "... a vigorous heaving movement of its chest and abdomen" (151). In the light of the evidence, assumption of a true rumination process does not appear to be justified, but whether the observed regurgitation represents a form of vomiting, an aberrant eructation, or a partial development of a ruminatory process deserves investigation.

The presence of *trans* acids in the depot fat of macropods supports the view that they approach ruminants in their digestive physiology. However, there is also a considerable di- and polyunsaturated fatty acid content indicating a lesser degree of hydrogenation (72). While the lower digestibility of fodder constituents may well be explained in terms of the shorter retention time in macropods compared with domestic ruminants, the evidence from the lipid constituents and the stomach gases indicates differences in degree in the fermentative processes. Other aspects of marsupial physiology have been reviewed recently (143).

Colobid Monkeys

The stomach of the leaf-eating monkeys of the subfamily Colobinae has long been recognized as being "singularly complicated" (54). Ayer (9) quotes Schwalbe as suggesting that "... the stomach in *Semnopithecus* is capable of providing for rumination," but states that rumination does not occur in these animals and that the sacculated stomach is not comparable to the ruminant stomach. Hill (78) also considers, with reservations, such comparisons unfortunate, but this view is based on the erroneous belief that the first three compartments of the ruminant stomach are of esophageal origin. Comparison, however, of stomach morphogenesis in Colobidae (79) and in the ox (144), together with the recent work drawing attention to the fermentation in the stomach of the Colobinae, leaves no room for doubt of the functional similarity between the stomachs of the colobid monkeys and those of the ruminants (60, 90).

The anatomy of various colobid stomachs has recently been described in considerable detail by several authors (19, 78, 90). The stomach of *Procolobus* has four parts—the sacculated and expanded presaccus and saccus, the long tubus gastricus, and the short pars pylorica (90). The saccus and presaccus, which in some species communicate only by narrow slits, are considered together by Ayer and by Hill as a single entity (9, 78); but both authors were making analogies with a simple tripartite primate stomach. From the esophagus, a well-defined ventricular groove (*Magenstrasse* or gastric canal) runs down the lesser curvature of the tubus toward the pyloric region. The lips of the groove are strongly muscular and have a rich nerve supply. The mucosa immediately surrounding the cardia forms a shield of dense stratified epithelium. The remainder of the mucosa of the upper stomach is of cardiac glands, and it is not until the terminal third of the tubular stomach that parietal cells appear, abruptly. This region is followed by one of typical pyloric glands (Fig. 6).

The stomach in some species is somewhat similar in form to that of the macropods; the cecum, too, is reduced, and the small intestine is typically long. Early authors considered this capacious stomach [600 ml in *Procolobus* and 2,200 ml in *Trachypithecus obscurus* (78)] as a substitute for cheek pouches which are absent in the Colobinae monkeys. Kuhn (90) demonstrated a substantial bacterial population but did not find ciliates; nor was he able to isolate any of the bacteria present. The upper stomach has a relatively neutral reaction, pH values of 6.95 having been measured in *Procolobus*, but the pH of stomach contents in vitro, and soon after death in situ, falls quickly to about 5.5, at which point fermentation ceases (90). Although the salivary glands are relatively extensive (78), Kuhn considers that, as rumination does not occur, saliva may not be an important buffer source, but that secretions from the cardiac mucosa of the stomach may well be.

Fermentation studies (90) revealed rates of fermentation very similar to those for small ruminants (85). The volatile fatty acids formed, and their proportions, are very similar to those for grazing ruminants (60), except that formic acid was present in small quantities and isobutyric acid was not found. From the low concentration in the pyloric region, it is clear that the fatty acids are absorbed directly from the stomach. Methane and carbon dioxide were the main gases produced. The pH is reduced rapidly in the pyloric region to between 2 and 3, and Kuhn raises the question of the fate of the carbon dioxide which must be liberated by this reduction in pH, and suggests that the ventricular groove may be used to drain off the gas formed. It appears possible, however, that the more caudal region of the tubus may, like the omasum of ruminants, absorb considerable bicarbonate (108); this would reduce the gas formed as well as economize in the amount of HCl necessary for enzyme activation in the pyloric region.

The blood sugar level of *Presbytis* spp. was found to be 62–99 mg per 100 ml (90), values comparable with those for the tylopods but higher than for macropods or true ruminants. However, though some advantages may accrue from low blood sugar levels, and whereas they are normal in true ruminants, the rate of gluconeogenesis and the activity of the phosphorylating enzymes are functionally more important. Ruminants are well equipped in this respect, as are the macropods; whether the Colobinae follow the same pattern of hepatic enzymes is not known, but one could confidently predict similarities, not only in this group but also the camel family and other ruminant-like animals.

Eructation occurs frequently, and it is estimated that fermentation in the stomach of an adult *Procolobus*

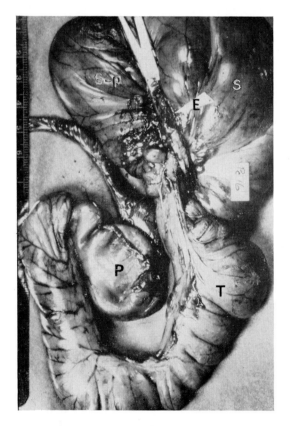

FIG. 6. Stomach of the Malayan langur monkey (*Presbytis cristatis*), showing the presaccus (*S-p*) (upper center), saccus (*S*) (upper right), tubus (*T*), and smooth pyloric region (*P*). Esophagus (*E*) is closed off by forceps.

badius would yield 300–1,000 cc of gaseous products per hour (90). The author is unaware of any studies on the mechanism of eructation in these animals or of the movements of the stomach.

The stomach form in this group of monkeys, rather than being a simple form of tripartite primate stomach as Ayer (9) concludes, is clearly a highly evolved ruminant-like stomach which has advanced to the point where these animals have a facility enabling them to invade ecological niches difficult or even impossible for other primates.

There are several losses in energy associated with the ruminant and ruminant-like digestion which are inescapable. Fermentation losses, as heat and hydrogen, may be limiting factors making the other ecological advantages of a ruminant fermentation inaccessible to very small animals. However, calculation of the caloric yield of the fermentation products in the rumen of a range of animals (85) in relation to metabolic requirement shows that the ratio of these parameters for well-fed animals remains relatively constant within the ruminants down to a body weight of 3 kg. In view of the greater selective ability of very small animals, it does not seem improbable that the range of ruminant-like animals could not extend to much smaller animals, such as rodents, without penalty.

COPROPHAGY AND STOMACH
FERMENTATION IN RODENTS

The long and successful history of the rodents, the vast numbers of species, and their variability and mutability are well known (126). Most rodents have simple stomachs but well-developed ceca and large intestines. Coprophagy, or fecal reingestion, in rodents and rabbits, is a normal, highly developed, nutritional device, long known but only recently appreciated. The nitrogen balance of rabbits prevented from reingesting the so-called "soft feces," which have a much higher protein content than the hard feces (which are not eaten), is reduced by almost 50% (138). Recently, it has been clearly demonstrated that urea is "recycled" or diffuses into the cecum of rabbits, where it is utilized by the microbial population and results in an improved nitrogen balance following reingestion of the soft feces. The improved nitrogen balance on low-nitrogen diets is further enhanced by injected urea, and by water restriction, which reduces urea excretion; but the addition of antibacterial agents to the diet inhibits bacterial growth in the large intestine and results in reduced nitrogen retention and increased urinary urea excretion (82). The undoubted importance of coprophagy in the vitamin nutrition of the rat is now well established and has been put on a very sound basis by the admirable work of Barnes and his colleagues (20, 21, 23, 25). Recently, the same group has raised important questions of detoxification and of amino acid economy in rats in relation to this phenomenon (22, 24). Griffiths & Davies (70) have shown that the reingested "soft" fecal pellets consisting largely of bacteria enveloped in a membrane remain as biological entities for 12 or more hours in the stomach of the rabbit and are capable of continued fermentation as a result of their structure and composition. These workers conclude that "... the fundus of the rabbit stomach, loaded with soft pellets, is analogous to the rumens of sheep and cattle in that it is a region of the stomach maintained at a high pH and capable of breaking down carbohydrate of high molecular weight."

There are many genera among the Myomorpha, however, that display a constricted stomach, the cardiac pouch often being of considerable size, lined by squamous epithelium and without glands (34). The degree of separation of the two sacs is variable. Thus in *Cricetomys gambianus*, the cardiac sac (7.5 x 3 cm), into which the esophagus discharges, is separated from the smaller pyloric portion (3.5 x 2.5 cm) by a constriction approximately 1 cm in diameter (50). In the mouse there is little effective separation although the anterior sac has, like *Cricetomys*, a stratified epithelium (34). Camain and co-workers (50) found a felt of microorganisms over the surface of the epithelium in the cardiac sac of the gambian rat. Unlike the very diverse population in the rumen, only members of the one genus, *Bacillus*, were found by their cultural techniques. Further investigation of the microbiology is required. A stomach similar to that of *Cricetomys* is found in the golden hamster. These animals are able to utilize and retain the nitrogen of urea when fed with barley flour, and to improve body weight significantly, whereas the common white laboratory rat fails to do so and instead excretes the added urea quantitatively in the urine (98).

Many of the small desert rodents are able to survive for years when fed only dry grain (126), and queries have been raised on the nutritional requirements of these animals. Schmidt-Nielsen (128) also quotes the ability of the pack rats (*Neotoma* spp.) to use foodstuffs high in oxalate content successfully.

Several species of *Neotoma* have quite large stomachs with a developed cardiac sac (A. R. Main, personal communication). Exploratory dissection of *Dipodomys deserti* and *Dipodomys hermani* indicates that the cardiac horn of the stomach of the former species is large, is well separated from the pyloric region, has a high pH (about 6.5), and carries a substantial microbial population, whereas the stomach of *D. hermani* is relatively simple and has a low pH (2–3) throughout (Fig. 7, 3, and 4). Both had well-developed ceca. Several possibilities arise. First, the stomach development may enhance the coprophagic mechanism by permitting continuing fecal pellet fermentation; second, it may permit continuing fermentation independent of fecal pellets, partially or entirely replacing coprophagy. Although the buffering capacity of the rumen is largely due to the salivary bicarbonate and minimally to phosphate (139), the phosphate content of fecal pellets is high and in the stomach may yield a buffer solution capable of maintaining the pH above 5.5 for considerable periods (70). Fermentation in many systems ceases at this point (90), and phosphate ceases to be an effective buffer as it is almost 98% ionized (139). The pH may then be readily reduced in the pyloric portion of the stomach. In simple systems, where provision for reabsorption of buffer is absent or minimal, phosphate would appear as an ideal buffer. Apart from fecal reingestion, which is known to supply phosphate, stomach sacs with cardiac glands may possibly recycle phosphate and thus reduce dependence on coprophagy or enable an independent fermentation. As coprophagy is an observed phenomenon in *Dipodomys* (128) it is probable that, if stomach fermentation occurs at all, it varies from being pellet dependent, as in the rabbit and other species without adequate anatomical separation, to being dependent on fecal recycling of buffer to maintain a continuing fermentation by a virtually independent flora. In the latter case, though coprophagy would still be essential, the system would approach that of the ruminant in its ability to cope with new or unusual substrates.

EVOLUTION

Complex Stomach

The range of ordinal groups in which ruminant-like fermentation occurs, and the range of stomach forms and functions, preclude the possibility of development from some single complex form. The

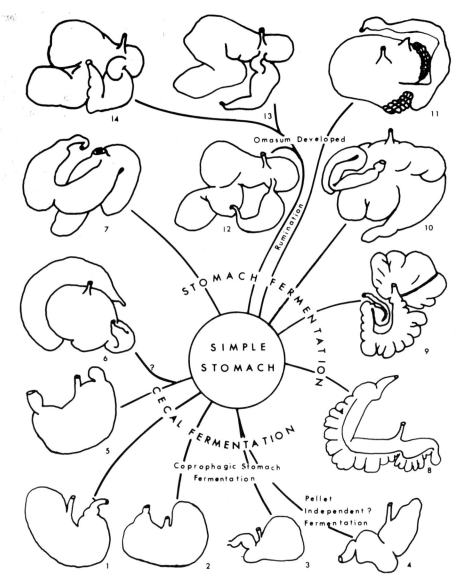

FIG. 7. The radiation of stomach forms from the simple stomach. 1, *Equus* [after Bensley (34)]; 2, *Lepus* [after Bensley (34)]; 3, *Dipodomys hermani*; 4, *Dipodomys deserti*; 5, *Sus* [after Bensley (34)]; 6, *Tayassu* (=dicotyles) [after Cordier (53)]; 7, hippopotamus [after Grasse (69)]; 8, *Macropus*; 9, *Presbytis*; 10, *Bradypus* [after Grasse (69)]; 11, *Camelus* [after Cordier (53)]; 12, *Hyemoschus* [after Cordier (53)]; 13, antelope [after Cordier (53)]; 14, *Ovis*.

various developments that provide functional separation of the fermentative chamber, or chambers, from the simple digestive chamber must have evolved on many different occasions from the simple stomach. Diverticula of the simple stomach occur as a constant feature in the domestic pig (see Fig. 7, *5*) (131), and congenital diverticula occur in humans (123). Most congenital diverticula occur around the cardioesophageal junction; occasionally they appear in the pyloric region. Larger diverticula arise on rarer occasions from the body of the stomach. Samuel

(123) states that these "... distort the lumen of the stomach and the diverticulum comes into the direct line of the ingested food with the result that the diverticulum becomes filled first and the stomach only fills by spill over from the diverticulum." Although rare, this phenomenon may well indicate adequate initial genetic potential for the development of the known ruminant and ruminant-like stomachs. The range of stomach forms depicted in Figure 7 indicates at least some of the occasions when the stomach has been developed as a fermentative

chamber. Most have probably arisen *de novo* from the simple form. Some may have a close origin, but only the ruminants show a progressive development.

Two devices have been used to accommodate bulky food and the microbial symbionts: first, elongation of the body of the stomach with sacculation of the greater curvature, as in the macropods and in the Colobidae; second, enlargement and modification of the cardiac region with constriction across the gastric canal, as occurs in all other forms. The hippopotamuses have achieved this in a rather unusual manner with the transverse septa along the body of the stomach. Whether this unusual septate chamber is analogous to the omasum has not been investigated, but the omasum of typical ruminants, increasing in complexity and size through the ruminant series, represents an intriguing evolutionary development still awaiting full clarification.

The modification of the epithelium in ruminant and ruminant-like stomachs, particularly the extensive areas of stratified epithelium, was the subject of considerable discussion by early workers (34), which led to misconceptions about the origin of the ruminant stomach. Mechanical effects, due to the sometimes harsh nature of the food, its great bulk, and prolonged stay in the stomach, appear to have played a dominant role in the replacement of the cardiac gland membranes with the more resistant stratified epithelium. The situation in the macropods, in which the area of stratified epithelium varies in different types (125), is probably a direct reflection of food preference (34). The intensity and frequency of stomach movement may well be an additional factor affecting not only the epithelium but also the mucosal adornments. Thus the stratified epithelial areas of the camel stomach are smooth, whereas those of ruminants have a papillated surface typical of the particular species and its nutritional state. The frequency of stomach contraction in the alpaca is much greater than that of the ruminant, and three to five contractions a minute have been recorded after feeding compared with one contraction every 50–60 sec in the sheep (141). Though it is not known whether the motility pattern is similar in all tylopods, the smooth nature of the epithelium in all species strongly supports this possibility and also the influence of motility on the epithelium. On the other hand, the lack of papillae would substantially reduce the absorptive area of the rumen. If absorption of the volatile fatty acids from the rumen of camels is as great as in typical ruminants, then the absorptive

function of the glandular sac areas is strongly supported (71).

Rumination

Without rumination, the rate of passage of coarse fodder through the alimentary tract of ruminants is reduced very substantially and may adversely influence intake (111). The ruminating habit, well known in ruminants and camels, has been extensively investigated (30), and the many features of its development (137), mechanisms (4, 28, 32, 134), central and peripheral nervous control (29, 31, 33, 110), and physiological effects (10, 68) are well documented.

The origin of rumination is not clearly defined. Bell (30) states that "In the process of rumination, a series of reflex acts occur, namely regurgitation, re-mastication, re-insalivation and deglutition. It is only the regurgitatory phase (a form of controlled vomition) which is unique and peculiar to ruminant digestion...." It is widely thought that adult ruminants do not vomit and that a vomition center is lacking (3). However, we have observed vomiting in both sheep and cattle on several occasions among our experimental animals. Bell suggests that, because of the similarity of the regurgitatory phase of rumination to vomition, the neural mechanisms are closely linked (30). Recent work supports this view. Parenteral injections of Veratrum alkaloid extracts result in stimulation of eructation or, in larger doses, marked vomition in adult cattle. Intense rumination follows (103). Further limited experiments indicate that the alkaloids have considerable ruminatoric activity (58). Although it has been considered that the rumination center is a special area unrelated to the vomiting center (91), the emerging evidence strongly supports Bell's suggestion (30) of a controlled vomition. Voluntary and controlled vomition, or merycism, may occur in many animals including man; Young (152), for example, found the ability of his friend Mitchell to "ruminate" very valuable in his work on the digestive process. The evolutionary development of the potential of merycism into the highly coordinated rumination process would appear probable.

COLONIZATION AND NUTRITIONALLY "DIFFICULT" ENVIRONMENTS

The environment within which the ruminant system developed may be reconstructed with some certainty; similar conditions probably apply to the tylopods and also to the macropod marsupials in their isolated Australian environment. The conditions resulting in the colobid development are not as readily perceived, but, when accepted, may contribute to the understanding of the ecology of these monkeys.

Paleobotanical evidence strongly supports the view that the woody habit among angiosperms is ancestral and that the herbaceous mode is derived, probably on many occasions, by reduction. Although the number of species in the two great groups is approximately equal, trees and shrubs predominate in the tropics, and herbs in more temperate regions (56). Fossil evidence shows that herbs become more frequent from the Tertiary onward than they had been in previous eras. Up to and including the Eocene, the landscape had been dominated by forest, and it was not until the Miocene that large areas of herb and grass developed, favored by the cooler and drier climates of the time. By late Miocene, grasslands were extensive (135).

During the Eocene the dominant herbivores were perissodactyls, which continued to be abundant and varied until the Pliocene. However, by late Eocene there had been an upsurge of artiodactyls, and they had become the dominant group. The Suiformes were the major forms at that time, but subsequent to the Oligocene, ruminants have completely dominated the ungulate herbivores (130). There can be little doubt of the correlation between climatic changes and development of the grasslands and the grazing ruminant. The adoption of bacteria as cellulase-producing tissue, the modification of the stomach to accommodate this "tissue," and the necessary bulk of poor fodder, together with metabolic adjustments and the reuse by cycling of sodium, phosphate, and nitrogen, have enabled ruminants to colonize successfully the high-fiber, low-nitrogen environments.

Whereas cellulose digestion is basically important in the radiation of ruminants, the presence of a bacterial population in the stomach offers possibilities of colonizing other plant environments normally dangerous to mammals. If movement into these environments is gradual, some portion of the bacterial population quickly adapts to, and metabolizes, toxic substances to harmless substances, although occasionally toxic products are produced from relatively harmless sub-

strates. Dodson (57) has investigated the toxicity of *Oxalis cernua* to sheep and cattle. This plant in certain areas constitutes the diet of sheep and cattle, and although it may contain up to 14.5% of oxalate, adapted cattle are apparently never affected and sheep only rarely so. It is significant that, prior to the annual growth under the seasonal Mediterranean climate of South Australia, the ruminal population has very limited ability to metabolize oxalate, but within two weeks this substance is so rapidly broken down in the rumen that negligible quantities are presented to the animal for absorption. The sheep is susceptible to much lower quantities of oxalate if this is injected or infused into the abomasum. Similarly, ruminants are unharmed by the gossypol of cottonseed when this is fed (55) and are extremely resistant to aflatoxins (2). Kuhn (90), in discussing the diet of the leaf-eating monkeys, reports that one of these animals, *Colobus guereza caudatus*, favored a species of *Rauwolfia*, plants well known for their alkaloids. Investigation would undoubtedly reveal many excursions into difficult environments by ruminants and ruminant-like animals as a result of the activities of their microbial symbionts.

The ascending dominance of ruminants over the nonruminant herbivores since the Oligocene attests the superiority of fermentation in the stomach over that of the cecum. While cecal fermentation, together with coprophagy, has remained a successful nutritional device in the rodents, even within this group there has been some move toward maintaining an independent stomach fermentation, even though this remains highly dependent on the coprophagic habit. In larger herbivores, direct coprophagy is impracticable; on highly fibrous diets of low digestibility, it would restrict even further the marginal energy intake and render other possible advantages useless.

As Young (153) has stated in relation to the evolution of vertebrates in general, "If we have interpreted the situation correctly, there can be said to be an evolutionary path that is progressive, in the sense of enabling life to be lived under wider and wider conditions." The development of the ruminant and other ruminant-like digestive systems is surely a progressive evolutionary pathway enabling life to be lived under wider, more difficult, and even inhospitable nutritional environments.

REFERENCES

1. ALEXANDER, F. Factors affecting the blood sugar concentration in horses. *Quart. J. Exptl. Physiol.* 40: 24–31, 1955.
2. ALLCROFT, R., H. ROGERS, G. LEWIS, J. NABNEY, AND P. E. BEST. Metabolism of aflatoxin in sheep: excretion of the milk toxin. *Nature* 209: 154–155, 1966.
3. AMADON, R. S. An experimental study of drugs stimulating

the motility of the ruminant stomach. *J. Am. Vet. Med. Assoc.* 76: 65–74, 1930.

4. ANDERSSON, B., R. KITCHELL, AND N. PERSSON. A study of rumination induced by milking in the goat. *Acta Physiol. Scand.* 44: 92–102, 1958.

5. ANNISON, E. F., K. J. HILL, AND D. LEWIS. Studies on the portal blood of sheep. 2. Absorption of volatile fatty acids from the rumen of the sheep. *Biochem. J.* 66: 592–599, 1957.

6. ANNISON, E. F., R. A. LENG, D. B. LINDSAY, AND R. R. WHITE. The metabolism of acetic acid, propionic acid and butyric acid in sheep. *Biochem. J.* 88: 248–252, 1963.

7. ANNISON, E. F., AND R. R. WHITE. Glucose utilization in sheep. *Biochem. J.* 80: 162–169, 1961.

8. ARMSTRONG, D. G. Carbohydrate metabolism in ruminants and energy supply. In: *Physiology of Digestion in the Ruminant,* edited by R. W. Dougherty et al. Washington, D.C.: Butterworths, 1965, p. 272–282.

9. AYER, A. A. *The Anatomy of Semnopithecus entellus.* Madras, India: The Indian Publishing House, 1948.

10. BAILEY, C. B., AND C. C. BALCH. Saliva secretion and its relation to feeding in cattle. 1. The composition and rate of secretion of parotid saliva in a small steer. *Brit. J. Nutr.* 15: 371–382, 1961.

11. BALCH, C. C. Factors affecting the utilization of food by dairy cows. 1. The rate of passage of food through the digestive tract. *Brit. J. Nutr.* 4: 361–388, 1950.

12. BALCH, C. C., D. A. BALCH, S. BARTLETT, V. W. JOHNSON, S. J. ROWLAND, AND J. TURNER. Studies on the secretion of milk of low fat content by cows on diets low in hay and high in concentrates. IV. The effect of variations in the intake of digestible nutrients. *J. Dairy Res.* 21: 305–317, 1954.

13. BALCH, D. A., AND S. J. ROWLAND. Volatile fatty acids and lactic acid in the rumen of dairy cows receiving a variety of diets. *Brit. J. Nutr.* 11: 288–298, 1957.

14. BALLARD, F. J. Glucose utilization in mammalian liver. *Comp. Biochem. Physiol.* 14: 437–443, 1965.

15. BALLARD, F. J., AND I. T. OLIVER. The effect of concentration on glucose phosphorylation and incorporation into glycogen in foetal and adult rat and sheep liver. *Biochem. J.* 92: 131–136, 1964.

16. BALLARD, F. J., AND I. T. OLIVER. Carbohydrate metabolism in liver from foetal and neonatal sheep. *Biochem. J.* 95: 191–200, 1965.

17. BARCROFT, J., R. A. McANALLY, AND A. T. PHILLIPSON. Absorption of volatile fatty acids from the alimentary tract of the sheep and other animals. *J. Exptl. Biol.* 20: 120–129, 1944.

18. BARKER, J. M. The metabolism of carbohydrate and volatile fatty acids in the marsupial *Setonix brachyurus. Quart. J. Exptl. Physiol.* 46: 54–68, 1961.

19. BARKER, S., G. D. BROWN, AND J. H. CALABY. Food regurgitation in the Macropodidae. *Australian J. Sci.* 25: 430–432, 1963.

20. BARNES, R. H., AND G. FIALA. Effects of the prevention of coprophagy in the rat. II. Vitamin B12 requirement. *J. Nutr.* 65: 103–114, 1958.

21. BARNES, R. H., G. FIALA, AND E. KWONG. Decreased growth rate resulting from prevention of coprophagy. *Federation Proc.* 22: 125–128, 1963.

22. BARNES, R. H., G. FIALA, AND E. KWONG. Prevention of coprophagy in the rat and the growth-stimulating effects

of methionine, cystine and penicillin when added to diets containing unheated soybeans. *J. Nutr.* 85: 127–131, 1965.

23. BARNES, R. H., G. FIALA, B. McGEHEE, AND A. BROWN. Prevention of coprophagy in the rat. *J. Nutr.* 63: 489–498, 1957.

24. BARNES, R. H., AND E. KWONG. Effect of soybean trypsin inhibitor and penicillin on cystine biosynthesis in the pancreas and its transport as exocrine protein synthesis in the intestinal tract of the rat. *J. Nutr.* 86: 245–252, 1965.

25. BARNES, R. H., E. KWONG, AND G. FIALA. Effects of the prevention of coprophagy in the rat. IV. Biotin. *J. Nutr.* 67: 599–610, 1959.

26. BATH, I. H., AND J. A. F. ROOK. The effect of stage of growth of S23 perennial rye-grass on the production of volatile fatty acids in the rumen of the cow. *Proc. Nutr. Soc.* 20: XV, 1961.

27. BEDDARD, F. E. *Mammalia.* London: Macmillan, 1909, p. 234.

28. BELL, F. R. The mechanism of regurgitation during the process of rumination in the goat. *J. Physiol., London* 142: 503–515, 1958.

29. BELL, F. R. The electroencephalogram of conscious goats and its association with the ruminant state. *J. Physiol., London,* 143: 46P–47P, 1958.

30. BELL, F. R. Some observations on the physiology of rumination. In: *Digestive Physiology and Nutrition of Ruminant,* edited by D. Lewis. London: Butterworths, 1961, p. 59.

31. BELL, F. R., AND A. M. LAWN. Localization of regions in the medulla oblongata of sheep associated with rumination. *J. Physiol., London* 128: 577–592, 1955.

32. BELL, F. R., AND A. M. LAWN. The pattern of rumination behaviour in housed goats. *Brit. J. Animal Behaviour* 5: 85–89, 1957.

33. BELL, F. R., AND A. M. LAWN. Disturbance of rumination in the goat after oblation of the orbito-frontal lobes of the cerebral cortex. *Brit. J. Animal Behaviour* 5: 125–130, 1957.

34. BENSLEY, R. R. The cardiac glands of mammals. *Am. J. Anat.* 2: 105–165, 1902.

35. BLACK, A. L., AND M. KLEIBER. The tricarboxylic acid cycles as a pathway for transfer of carbon from acetate to amino acids in the intact cow. *Biochem. Biophys. Acta* 23: 59–69, 1957.

36. BLACK, A. L., M. KLEIBER, AND A. M. BROWN. Butyrate metabolism in the lactating cow. *J. Biol. Chem.* 236: 2399–2403, 1961.

37. BLACK, A. L., M. KLEIBER, AND A. H. SMITH. Carbonate and fatty acids as precursors of amino acids in casein. *J. Biol. Chem.* 197: 365–370, 1952.

38. BLAXTER, K. L., N. McC. GRAHAM, AND F. W. WAINMAN. Some observations on the digestibility of food by sheep, and related problems. *Brit. J. Nutr.* 10: 69–91, 1956.

39. BLAXTER, K. L. AND A. K. MARTIN. The utilization of protein as a source of energy in fattening sheep. *Brit. J. Nutr.* 16: 397–407, 1962.

40. BOAS, J. E. V. Zur Morphologie des Magens der Cameli den und der Tragulider und uber die Systematische Stellung Letzterer Abtheilung. *Morphol. Jahrb., Leipzig* 16: 494–524, 1890. (Cited in reference 71.)

41. BOHLKEN, H. Remarks on the stomach and the systematic

position of tylopoda. *Proc. Zool. Soc., London* 134: 207–215, 1960.

42. BOYNE, A. W., R. M. CAMPBELL, J. DAVIDSON, AND D. P. CUTHBERTSON. Changes in composition of the digesta along the alimentary tract of sheep. *Brit. J. Nutr.* 10: 325–333, 1956.

43. BRANDT, C. S., AND E. J. THACKER. A concept of rate of food passage through the gastro-intestinal tract. *J. Animal Sci.* 17: 218–223, 1958.

44. BRAY, A. C. *Sulphur Metabolism in Sheep* (Ph.D. Thesis), University of Western Australia, 1965.

45. BRODY, S. *Bioenergetics and Growth.* New York: Reinhold, 1945, p. 369. (Reprinted by Hafner, New York, 1964.)

46. BROWN, G. D. *The Nitrogen Requirement of the Euro Macropus robustus* [B.Sc. (Honours) Thesis], University of Western Australia, 1959.

47. BROWN, G. D. *The Nitrogen Requirements of Macropod Marsupials* (Ph.D. Thesis), University of Western Australia, 1964.

48. BRYANT, M. P., AND I. M. ROBINSON. Apparent incorporation of ammonia and amino acid carbon during growth of selected species of ruminal bacteria. *J. Dairy Sci.* 46: 150–154, 1963.

49. CALABY, J. H. Studies in marsupial nutrition. II. The rate of passage of food residues and digestibility of crude fibre and protein by the quokka, *Setonix brachyurus* (Quoy and Gaimard). *Australian J. Biol. Sci.* 11: 571–580, 1958.

50. CAMAIN, R., A. QUEMUM, J. KERREST, AND S. GOUEFFON. Considerations sur l'estomac de *Cricetomys gambianus. Bull. Mem. Ecole Nat. Med. Pharm., Dakar* 8: 134–142, 1960.

51. CASTLE, E. J. The rate of passage of foodstuffs through the alimentary tract of the goat. *Brit. J. Nutr.* 10: 15–23, 1956.

52. CASTLE, E. J., AND M. E. CASTLE. Further studies of the rate of passage of food through the alimentary tract of pigs. *J. Agr. Sci.* 49: 106–112, 1957.

53. CORDIER, J. A. Recherches sur l'anatomie comparée l'estomac des ruminants. *Annal. Sci. Nat. Zool.* 16: Ser. 7, 1–128, 1894.

54. CUVIER, BARON GEORGES. *The Animal Kingdom.* London: Henry Bohn, 1863, p. 46.

55. DANKE, R. J., R. J. PANCIERA, AND A. D. TILLMAN. Gossypol toxicity studies with sheep. *J. Animal Sci.* 24: 1199–1201, 1965.

56. DARRAH, W. C. *Principles of Paleobotany* (2nd ed.). New York: Ronald, 1960, p. 214–215.

57. DODSON, M. E. Oxalate ingestion studies in sheep. *Australian Vet. J.* 35: 225–233, 1959.

58. DOUGHERTY, R. W., C. H. MULLENAX, AND M. J. ALLISON. Physiological phenomena associated with eructation in ruminants. In: *Physiology of Digestion in the Ruminant,* edited by R. W. Dougherty et al. Washington, D.C.: Butterworths, 1965, p. 159–170.

59. DOWNES, A. M. On the amino acids essential for the tissues of sheep. *Australian J. Biol. Sci.* 14: 254–259, 1961.

60. DRAWERT, F., H.-J. KUHN, AND A. RAPP. Reaktions—Gaschomatographie. III. Gaschomatographische Bestimmung der Niederfluchtigen Fettsauren im Magen von Schlankaffen (*Colobinae*). *Z. Physiol. Chem.* 329: 84–89, 1962.

61. EDELMANN, R. Vergleichend Anatomische und Physiologische Untersuchungen uber une Besondere Region der Magenschleimhaut (Cardiacdrusenregion) bei den Saug-

etieren Deutsche. *Z. Thier. Med.* 15: 165–214, 1889. (Cited in reference 34.)

62. ELLIOTT, R. C. AND J. H. TOPPS. Nitrogen metabolism of African cattle fed diets with an adequate energy, low protein content. *Nature* 197: 668–670, 1963.

63. ELLIS, W. C., G. B. GARNER, M. E. MUHRER, AND W. H. PFANDER. Nitrogen utilization by lambs fed purified rations containing urea, gelatin, casein, blood fibrin and soybean protein. *J. Nutr.* 60: 413–425, 1956.

64. ELLIS, W. C., AND W. H. PFANDER. Rumen microbial polynucleotide synthesis and its possible role in ruminant nitrogen utilization. *Nature* 205: 974–975, 1965.

65. FOOT, J. Z., AND B. ROMBERG. The utilization of roughage by sheep and the red kangaroo, *Macropus rufus* (Desmarest). *Australian J. Agr. Res.* 16: 429–436, 1965.

66. GOOD, R. H. *Features of the Evolution in the Flowering Plants.* London: Longmans, Green, 1956, p. 355.

67. GOODWIN, R. F. W. The distribution of sugar between red cell and plasma: variations associated with age and species. *J. Physiol., London* 134: 88–101, 1956.

68. GORDON, J. G. The act of rumination. *J. Agr. Sci.* 50: 34–42, 1958.

69. GRASSE, P. P. *Traité de Zoologie Mammifères.* Paris: Masson, 1955, vol. 17, p. 515, 886, 1215.

70. GRIFFITHS, M., AND D. DAVIES. The role of soft pellets in the production of lactic acid in the rabbit stomach. *J. Nutr.* 80: 171–180, 1963.

71. HANSEN, A., AND K. SCHMIDT-NIELSEN. On the stomach of the camel with special reference to the structure of its mucous membrane. *Acta Anat.* 31: 353–375, 1957.

72. HARTMAN, L., F. B. SHORLAND, AND I. R. C. McDONALD. The trans-unsaturated acid contents of the fats of ruminants and non-ruminants. *Biochem. J.* 61: 603–607, 1955.

73. HEALD, P. J. The assessment of glucose-containing substance in microorganisms during a digestion cycle in sheep. *Brit. J. Nutr.* 5: 84–93, 1951.

74. HEMSLEY, J. A. *Roughage Utilization by Sheep* (Ph.D. Thesis), University of Western Australia, 1965.

75. HENDRICHS, H. Wiederkauen bei Klippschliefern und Kanguruks. *Naturwissenschaften* 50: 454–455, 1963.

76. HILDITCH, T. P. *The Chemical Constitution of Natural Fats* (3rd ed.). London: Chapman and Hall, 1956, p. 93–94, 458.

77. HILL, K. J. The glands of the mucous membrane of the goat abomasum. *J. Anat.* 85: 215–220, 1951.

78. HILL, W. C. O. The external and visceral anatomy of the olive colobus monkey (*Procolobus verus*). *Proc. Zool. Soc., London* 122: 127–186, 1952.

79. HILL, W. C. O. Ontogenetic changes in the mesogastric viscera of monkeys of the family Colobidae. *Proc. Zool. Soc., London* 124: 163–183, 1954.

80. HOME, E. *Lectures on Comparative Anatomy.* London: Bulmer, 1814, vol. I, p. 153.

81. HOUPT, T. R. Utilization of blood urea in ruminants. *Am. J. Physiol.* 197: 115–120, 1959.

82. HOUPT, T. R. Urea utilization by rabbits fed a low-protein ration. *Am. J. Physiol.* 205: 1144–1150, 1963.

83. HOUPT, T. R., AND K. A. HOUPT. Movement of urea across the epithelium of a rumen pouch. *Federation Proc.* 23: 262, 1964.

84. HRUBETZ, M. C., AND L. B. DOTTI. Liver glycogen, with a

note on the blood sugar level. *J. Biol. Chem.* 107: 731–733, 1934.

85. HUNGATE, R. E. G. D. PHILLIPS, A. McGREGOR, D. P. HUNGATE, AND H. K. BUECHNER. Microbial fermentation in certain mammals. *Science* 130: 1192–1194, 1959.

86. JARRETT, I. G., AND B. J. POTTER. Insulin tolerance and hypoglycaemic convulsions in sheep. *Australian J. Exptl. Biol. Med. Sci.* 31: 311–318, 1953.

87. JEUNIAUX, C. Recherche de polysaccharidases dans l'estomac d'un Paresseux, *Choloepus hoffmanni* Pet. (Mammifère Edenté). *Arch. Intern. Physiol. Biochim.* 70: 407–410, 1962.

88. JOHNS, A. T. Pasture quality and ruminant digestion. II. Levels of volatile acids and ammonia in the rumen of sheep on a high-production pasture. *New Zealand J. Sci. Technol.* 37: 323–331, 1955.

89. KLINCKOWSTRÖM, A. Zur Anatomie der Edentaten. I. Beiträge zur Anatomie des Magens. *Aus. Zootom Inst. Univ. Stockholm, Zool. Hahrb,* 1895. (Cited in reference 104.)

90. KUHN, H.-J. Zur Kenntnis von Bau und Funktion des Magens der Schlankaffen (Colobinae). *Folia Primat.* 2: 193–221, 1964.

91. KUZMIN, P. M. The rumination centre and its functional links in cattle. *Fiziol. Zh. SSSR Sechenova* 49: 346–359, 1963; *Nutr. Abstr. Rev.* (Abstr. 4367) 33: 730, 1963.

92. LEWIS, F. T. Comparative embryology of the mammalian stomach. *Anat. Record* 9: 102, 1915.

93. LINDSAY, D. B. The significance of carbohydrate in ruminant metabolism. *Vet. Rev.* 5: 103–128, 1959.

94. LUBINSKI, G. Studies on the evolution of the ophryoscolecidae (Ciliata: Oligtricha). III. Phylogeny of the ophryoscolecidae based on their comparative morphology. *Can. J. Zool.* 35: 141–159, 1957.

95. MACKENZIE, W. C., AND W. J. OWEN. *The Glandular System in Monotremes and Marsupials.* Melbourne, Australia: Jenkin, Buxton, 1919.

96. MÄKELÄ, A. On the influence of diet on the retention time of food in the digestive tract of cows. *J. Sci. Agr. Soc., Finland* 32: 39–51, 1960.

97. MARVIN, H. N., AND B. R. SHOOK. Hematological studies on the two-toed sloth, *Choloepus didactylus. Comp. Biochem. Physiol.* 8: 187–189, 1963.

98. MATSUMOTO, T. Nutritive value of urea as a substitute of feed protein. I. Utilization of urea by the golden hamster. *Tohoku J. Agr. Res.* 6: 127–131, 1955.

99. McCANDLESS, E. L., AND J. A. DYE. Physiological changes in intermediary metabolism of various species of ruminants incident to functional development of rumen. *Am. J. Physiol.* 162: 434–446, 1950.

100. McDONALD, I. W. The absorption of ammonia from the rumen of sheep. *Biochem. J.* 42: 584–587, 1948.

101. McDONALD, I. W., AND R. J. HALL. The conversion of casein into microbial proteins in the rumen. *Biochem. J.* 67: 400–405, 1957.

102. MOIR, R. J., M. SOMERS, AND H. WARING. Studies on marsupial nutrition. I. Ruminant-like digestion in a herbivorous marsupial *Setonix brachyurus* (Quoy and Gaimard). *Australian J. Biol. Sci.* 9: 293–304, 1956.

103. MULLENAX, C. H., W. B. BUCK, R. F. KEELER, AND W. BINNS. Stimulation eructation and vomition in normal and bloated ruminants with alkaloid extracts from *Veratrum. Am. J. Vet. Res.* 27: 211–222, 1966.

104. OPPEL, A. *Lehrbuch der Vergleichenden microskopischen Anatomie der Wirbeltiere.* Erster Teil-Der Magen. Jena: Gustav Fischer, 1896.

105. OWEN, R. Notes on the anatomy of a new species of kangaroo *Macropus parryi* Benn. *Proc. Zool. Soc., London,* Part 3: 152, 1834.

106. OWEN, R. On the anatomy of the dugong. *Proc. Zool. Soc., London,* Part 6: 28–46, 1838.

107. OWEN, R. Marsupialia. In: *The Cyclopaedia of Anatomy and Physiology,* edited by R. B. Todd. London: Longman, Brown, Green, Longmans, and Roberts, vol. 3, 1839–1847, p. 301.

108. OYAERT, W., AND J. H. BOUCHAERT. A study of the passage of fluid through the sheep's omasum. *Res. Vet. Sci.* 2: 41–52, 1961.

109. PASTEUR, L. Observations relatives à la note précédente de M. Duclaux. *Compt. Rend.* 100: 68, 1885.

110. PEARCE, G. R. Rumination in sheep. IV. The investigation of some possible control mechanisms. *Australian J. Agr. Res.* 16: 837–853, 1965.

111. PEARCE, G. R., AND R. J. MOIR. Rumination in sheep. I. The influence of rumination and grinding upon the passage and digestion of food. *Australian J. Agr. Res.* 15: 635–644, 1964.

112. PENNINGTON, R. J. The metabolism of short-chain fatty acids in the sheep. I. Fatty acid utilization and ketone body production by rumen epithelium and other tissues. *Biochem. J.* 51: 251–258, 1952.

113. POPJAK, G., T. H. FRENCH, AND S. J. FOLLEY. Utilization of acetate for milk-fat synthesis in the lactating goat. *Biochem. J.* 48: 411–416, 1951.

114. PURSER, D. B., AND S. M. BEUCHLER. Amino acid composition of rumen organisms. *J. Dairy Sci.* 49: 81–84, 1966.

115. RADLOFF, H. D., L. H. SCHULTZ, AND W. G. HOEKSTRA. Relationship of plasma free fatty acids to other blood components in ruminants under various physiological conditions. *J. Dairy Sci.* 49: 179–182, 1966.

116. RAGGI, F., AND D. S. KRONFELD. Higher glucose affinity of hexokinase in sheep brain than in rat brain. *Nature* 209: 1353–1354, 1966.

117. RAHMAN, S. A., AND P. DECKER. Comparative study of the urease in the rumen wall and rumen content. *Nature* 209: 618–619, 1966.

118. REID, R. L. Studies on the carbohydrate metabolism of sheep. I. The range of blood sugar values under several conditions. *Australian J. Agr. Res.* 1: 182–199, 1950.

119. REID, R. L. Studies on the carbohydrate metabolism of sheep. III. Blood glucose during insulin hypo-glycaemia. *Australian J. Agr. Res.* 2: 132–145, 1951.

120. REYNIERS, J. A. The pure culture concept of gnotobiotics in germfree vertebrates: present status. *Ann. N. Y. Acad. Sci.* 78: 3–16, 1959.

121. RIDE, W. D. L. Evolution of Australian mammals. In: *The Evolution of Living Organisms,* edited by G. W. Leeper. Melbourne, Australia: Univ. of Melbourne Press, 1962, p. 281–306.

122. SALMI, M. Additional information on the findings in the Mylodon Cave at Ultima Esperanza. *Acta Geog.* 14: 314–333, 1955.

123. SAMUEL, E. Gastric diverticula. *Brit. J. Radiol.* 28: 574–578, 1955.

124. SANDER, E. G., R. G. WARNER, H. N. HARRISON, AND J. K. LOOSLI. The stimulatory effect of sodium butyrate and sodium propionate on the development of rumen mucosa in the young calf. *J. Dairy Sci.* 42: 1600–1605, 1959.

125. SCHAFER, E. A., AND D. J. WILLIAMS. On the structure of mucous membrane of the stomach in the kangaroo. *Proc. Zool. Soc., London*, p. 165–177, 1876.

126. SCHMIDT-NIELSEN, B., AND K. SCHMIDT-NIELSEN. A complete account of the water metabolism in kangaroo rats and an experimental verification. *J. Cellular Comp. Physiol.* 38: 165–181, 1951.

127. SCHMIDT-NIELSEN, B., K. SCHMIDT-NIELSEN, T. R. HOUPT, AND S. A. JARNUM. Urea excretion in the camel. *Am. J. Physiol.* 188: 477–484, 1957.

128. SCHMIDT-NIELSEN, K. *Desert Animals.* Oxford: Clarendon Press, 1964, p. 146–149.

129. SHORLAND, F. B., R. O. WEENINK, AND A. T. JOHNS. Effect of the rumen on dietary fats. *Nature* 175: 1129–1130, 1955.

130. SIMPSON, G. G. The principles of classification and a classification of mammals. *Bull. Am. Museum Nat. Hist.* 85: 1–350, 1945.

131. SISSON, S., AND J. D. GROSSMAN. *The Anatomy of the Domestic Animals* (4th ed.). Philadelphia: Saunders, 1953, 1964, p. 456, 490.

132. SOMERS, M. Factors influencing the secretion of nitrogen in sheep saliva. 4. The influence of injected urea on the quantitative recovery of urea in the parotid saliva and the urinary excretion of sheep. *Australian J. Exptl. Biol.* 39: 145–156, 1961.

133. SOMOGYI, M. Studies of arteriovenous differences in blood sugar. 1. Effect of alimentary hyperglycemia on the rate of extrahepatic glucose assimilation. *J. Biol. Chem.* 174: 189–200, 1948.

134. STEVENS, C. F., AND A. F. SELLERS. Pressure events in bovine esophagus and reticulo rumen associated with eructation, deglutition and regurgitation. *Am. J. Physiol.* 199: 598–602, 1960.

135. STIRTON, R. A. *Time, Life and Man.* New York: Wiley, 1959, p. 315–356.

136. STORR, G. M. Estimation of dry matter intake in wild herbivores. *Nature* 197: 307–308, 1963.

137. SWANSON, E. W., AND J. D. HARRIS. Development of rumination in the young calf. *J. Dairy Sci.* 41: 1768–1776, 1958.

138. THACKER, E. J., AND C. S. BRANDT. Coprophagy in the rabbit. *J. Nutr.* 55: 375–386, 1955.

139. TURNER, A. W., AND V. E. HODGETTS. Buffer systems in the rumen of sheep. 11. Buffering properties in relationship to composition. *Australian J. Agr. Res.* 6: 125–144, 1955.

140. UNDERWOOD, E. J. *Trace Elements in Human and Animal Nutrition* (2nd ed.). New York: Acad. Press, 1962, p. 131–147.

141. VALLENAS, P. A. Some physiological aspects of digestion in the alpaca (*Lama pacos*). In: *Physiology of Digestion in the Ruminant*, edited by R. W. Dougherty et al. Washington, D.C.: Butterworths, 1965, p. 147–158.

142. VAN LENNEP, E. W. The glands of the digestive system in the one-humped camel, *Camelus dromedarius L.* 1. The salivary glands. *Acta Morphol. Neerl.-Scand.* 1: 286–292, 1958.

143. WARING, H., R. J. MOIR, AND C. H. TINDALE-BISCOE. Comparative physiology of marsupials. In: *Advances in Comparative Physiology and Biochemistry*, edited by O. Lowenstein. New York: Acad. Press, 1966, vol. 2, p. 237–376.

144. WARNER, E. D. The organogenesis and early histogenesis of the bovine stomach. *Am. J. Anat.* 102: 33–64, 1958.

145. WARNER, R. G., AND W. P. FLATT. Anatomical development of the ruminant stomach. In: *Physiology of Digestion in the Ruminant*, edited by R. W. Dougherty et al. Washington, D.C.: Butterworths, 1965, p. 24–28.

146. WARNER, R. G., W. P. FLATT, AND J. K. LOOSLI. Dietary factors influencing the development of the ruminant stomach. *Agr. Food Chem.* 4: 788–792, 1956.

147. WATSON, R. Studies on deglutition in sheep. 1. Observations on the course taken by liquids through the stomach of the sheep at various ages from birth to maturity. *Council Sci. Ind. Res. Bull.* 180: 7–94, 1944.

148. WEINMAN, E. O., E. H. STRISOWER, AND I. L. CHAIKOFF. Conversion of fatty acids to carbohydrates: application of isotopes to this problem and the role of Krebs cycle as a synthetic pathway. *Physiol. Rev.* 37: 252–272, 1957.

149. WILLIAMS, V. J. Rumen function in the camel. *Nature* 197: 1221, 1963.

150. WILSON, A. D. The effect of diet on the secretion of parotid saliva by sheep. *Australian J. Agr. Res.* 14: 680–689, 1963.

151. WOOD-JONES, F. *The Mammals of South Australia*, part 1. Adelaide, Australia: Government Printer, 1923, p. 59.

152. YOUNG, J. R. *An Experimental Inquiry into the Principles of Nutrition and the Digestive Process* (M. D. dissertation), University of Pennsylvania, 1803. Facsimile reprint by Univ. of Illinois Press, Urbana, 1959.

153. YOUNG, J. Z. *The Life of Vertebrates* (2nd ed.). London: Oxford Univ. Press, 1962.

CHAPTER 127

Physiology of eructation in ruminants

ROBERT W. DOUGHERTY | *National Animal Disease Laboratory, Animal Disease and Parasite Research Division, Agricultural Research Service, U. S. Department of Agriculture, Ames, Iowa*

CHAPTER CONTENTS

GAS PRODUCTION in the first three compartments of the ruminant stomach is continuous with fluctuations associated with feeding (16). It increases after eating and decreases slowly until the next feeding. Most of the gas is produced in the first two compartments of the stomach as a result of microbial digestion of simple and complex carbohydrates. It has been estimated that 1.2–2 liters of gas are formed per minute in the rumen and reticulum of a thousand-pound cow (16). The rate of production fluctuates according to the kinds and quantities of substrates available to the bacteria. Although most of the gas is the result of bacterial action and CO_2 liberation from salivary bicarbonate, the work of Oxford indicates that rumen protozoa may also produce gas (20).

The principal gases present in the ruminant stomach and their relative proportions, reported by McArthur & Miltmore (19), are: 65.35% CO_2, 26.76% CH_4, 7% N_2, 0.56% O_2, 0.18% H_2, and 0.01% H_2S. Ammonia is produced during ruminal fermentation (18). The volatile base methylamine was present soon after feeding but disappeared some hours later (15). Before the work of Hill and Mangan conventional methods of analysis did not distinguish methylamine from ammonia. The method of McArthur & Miltmore (19) did not measure ammonia

or methylamine. It must be emphasized that the proportions of the different gases are subject to individual, species, and diurnal variations. The large volumes of gas formed are mainly eliminated by eructation. Lesser amounts are absorbed from the digestive tract and are either eliminated from the lungs or incorporated into various metabolic schemes (5). Some gas may be carried through the digestive tract with the feces. Unless gas elimination equals gas production, death may occur in domestic ruminants.

MOTILITY OF ESOPHAGUS DURING ERUCTATION

Dougherty et al. (8) and Hill (14) describe eructation in sheep as a complex phenomenon involving a series of well-coordinated events. Ordinarily, gas accumulates mainly in the caudal part of the dorsal sac of the rumen. In the quiescent state of the ruminant stomach, ingesta fill the reticulum and may cover the cardia. Before eructation can occur the reticulum and cardia must be cleared of liquid contents to ensure proper mechanical and normal neurophysiological functioning of the eructation mechanism.

Eructation begins with a forward-moving contraction of the rumen, first described by Weiss (23) and later confirmed by Titchen & Reid (22). Dougherty et al. (4) described a complicated maneuver of the reticulum, rumino-reticular fold, and surrounding rumino-reticular wall which clears the reticulum and area around the cardia of ingesta. The forward-moving contraction may contribute to forcing the gas into the cleared area. Because rumino-reticular movements are complicated and must be coordinated, and because the movements are difficult to record in their entirety and in proper sequence in conscious animals, much research remains to be done in this area.

ANATOMICAL STRUCTURES INVOLVED IN ERUCTATION REFLEX

Eructation is a complicated reflex involving a number of anatomical structures. It has been studied by Dzuik & Sellers (13), Dougherty et al. (5–8, 12), Stevens & Sellers (21), Weiss (23), Titchen & Reid (22), and others.

The tunica muscularis of the esophagus of the ruminant is composed of striated muscle (8). The pharyngoesophageal sphincter is well developed and has been described in detail (7). Action of the diaphragmatic sphincter and cardia during eructation has been studied by cinefluorographic techniques (10). The motor fibers of the cephalic part of the ruminant esophagus are supplied by the pharyngoesophageal nerves, the middle part by the recurrent nerves, and the caudal part mainly by the dorsal thoracic vagus. These are all branches of the vagus nerves. The esophagus can be paralyzed by injections of curare (7).

Receptors

The eructation reflex is initiated by receptors in the caudal part of the dorsal sac of the rumen (23), the wall adjacent to the cephalic fold of the rumen (21), and a limited area around the cardia (8). Although these are the receptor areas that have been described, it is probable that receptors also exist in other parts of the rumeno-reticulum.

Iggo (71) recorded afferent impulses in fibers of the cervical vagus and found tension receptors near the junction of the reticular groove. He suggested that the receptors were in series with the ruminal muscle. He did not find evidence of "volume" receptors. Stevens & Sellers (21), with special electrodes and cuffs implanted on and around the thoracic dorsal vagal trunk, using electrical stimuli, were able to increase the rate of rumen contractions. Moderate electrical stimuli increased the eructation rate. No publications have been found describing classic receptors in the mucosa of the rumeno-reticulum revealed by present histochemical methods. The large number of afferent fibers in the vagus nerves and the large number of reflexes initiated from the ruminant stomach indicate an efficient and varied receptor system.

Cole et al. (1), Dougherty (3), and a number of other workers have stimulated eructation by gaseous distention of the rumeno-reticulum with several gases and combinations of gases (4, 6, 21, 23). Insufflating gases included CO_2, N_2, O_2, and a CO_2-CH_4 mixture. It has also been demonstrated that eructation is associated with reticular and ruminal motor activity. Weiss (24) was the first to describe a return or antiperistaltic wave of contraction associated with eructation. This has been confirmed recently by Titchen & Reid (22), who used different recording techniques.

Inhibition of Eructation

Because acute distention of the first two compartments of the ruminant stomach has important economic implications, for it sometimes causes much loss of life and productivity of cattle and sheep, detailed studies of eructation were begun about 1950 in a number of laboratories. In the course of these studies, one group (8) demonstrated not only receptors around the cardia that initiated the eructation reflex when stimulated by gaseous distention, but also receptors in the same area that inhibited eructation when stimulated by the presence of foam, liquids, or ordinary rumen ingesta. This means that complicated and coordinated movements of the reticulum, the rumino-reticular fold, the anterior pillar, and adjacent structures must first clear the cardia and adjacent mucosa so that gases can be forced forward and down into this area. Tests also showed that failure to clear the cardia area inhibited or decreased the efficiency of eructation. The protective nature of this inhibitory reflex became obvious when later work by Colvin et al. (2) and Dougherty et al. (9) demonstrated that the glottis remains open during eructation.

Rumen gases first appear as countless microscopic bubbles. Normally these coalesce to form progressively larger bubbles until the gas accumulates in a large mass overlying the ingesta. Eructation and gas absorption normally keep pace with gas formation. Occasionally, surface tension phenomena prevent the liberation of gas from the small bubbles and the ingesta become a foamy mass which may completely fill and distend the rumeno-reticulum. This is commonly known as "frothy bloat." Inability to clear the cardia of this frothy mass causes stimulation of the eructation-inhibitory reflex.

PULMONARY ABSORPTION OF ERUCTATED GAS

It has been shown by Dougherty et al. (6, 12) that a large percentage of eructated gas in cows and sheep reaches the lungs and that components of these gases are absorbed into the blood (5, 12). Radioactive carbon from $^{14}CO_2$ and $^{14}CH_4$ introduced into the rumen was demonstrated in the blood and saliva of sheep and the blood and milk of a goat. Off-flavors in milk have been shown to be introduced into the milk via eructated gases through the lungs and the bloodstream at a faster rate and more efficiently than by direct absorption from the digestive tract (11).

Recent work (10a) has demonstrated that a small amount of the radioactive methane introduced into the blood stream of unanesthetized sheep was oxidized. Radioactive carbon dioxide was exhaled soon after the radioactive methane was introduced. Under the conditions of the experiments, only about 0.1 % of the total amount of radioactivity introduced as methane was recovered in the form of radioactive carbon dioxide. One experiment in which $^{14}CH_4$ was infused into a pig showed that this simple-stomached animal could also oxidize a small amount of introduced radioactive methane, although the amount of radioactive carbon in the exhaled CO_2 was less than in ruminants under similar experimental conditions.

In summary, the eructation reflex in cattle and sheep involves the following features:

1. Most of the gas produced by microbial action in the rumeno-reticulum is eliminated by eructation.

2. Eructation is initiated by gaseous distention of the rumeno-reticulum; the receptors concerned have been demonstrated in various areas of the rumen wall.

3. The area around the cardia is first cleared of ingesta by a complicated series of movements of the reticulum, rumino-reticular fold, anterior fold, and the adjacent wall areas.

4. An antiperistaltic wave starting in the caudal dorsal sac of the rumen moves gas forward and downward into the cleared area around the cardia and in the reticulum.

5. Relaxation of the cardia and diaphragmatic sphincters fills the esophagus with rumino-reticular gas, which is then trapped there because of closure of the pharyngoesophageal sphincter.

6. The cardia and diaphragmatic sphincters close, the pharyngoesophageal sphincter relaxes, and an extremely rapid wave of orad-moving esophageal contraction forces the gas into the pharynx. The antiperistaltic esophageal wave of contraction travels at 160 cm per sec.

7. The nasopharyngeal sphincter closes, the mouth remains partly closed, the glottis open. This maneuver forces more than half the eructated gas into the lungs, where some of its volatile components are absorbed.

8. It has been shown by the use of $^{14}CO_2$ and $^{14}CH_4$ that $^{14}CO_2$ placed in the rumen is incorporated in the bicarbonate of saliva, the lactose of milk, and in the carbon skeleton of other tissues and that a small amount of $^{14}CH_4$ is oxidized.

9. Receptors which inhibit the eructation reflex have been identified physiologically in a restricted area around the cardia. They are stimulated when this area is covered with fluid, ingesta, or foam, and eructation inhibited or made less efficient. The area must be cleared to ensure efficient eructation.

10. Gas elimination must keep pace with its formation. Any reduction in gas elimination or its complete cessation will reduce the productivity of the animal and may endanger its life.

REFERENCES

1. COLE, H. H. Physiology of the ruminant stomach in relation to bloat and feed consumption. *Calif. Vet.* 3: 19–22, 1950.

2. COLVIN, H. H., P. T. CUPPS, AND H. H. COLE. Eructation studies in cattle. In: *Rept on Conf. on Rumen Function, U.S. Dept. Agr., ARS* 24–25, 1956.

3. DOUGHERTY, R. W. Physiological studies of induced and natural bloat in dairy cattle. *J. Am. Vet. Med. Assoc.* 96: 43–46, 1940.

4. DOUGHERTY, R. W. The physiology of eructation in ruminants. In: *Digestive Physiology and Nutrition of the Ruminant*, edited by R. W. Dougherty, R. S. Allen, W. Burroughs, N. L. Jacobson, and A. D. McGilliard. London: Butterworths, 1961, p. 79–87.

5. DOUGHERTY, R. W., M. J. ALLISON, AND C. H. MULLENAX. Physiological disposition of C^{14}-labeled rumen gases in sheep and goats. *Am. J. Physiol.* 207: 1181–1188, 1964.

6. DOUGHERTY, R. W., AND H. M. COOK. Routes of eructated gas expulsion in cattle—a quantitative study. *Am. J. Vet. Res.* 23: 997–1000, 1962.

7. DOUGHERTY, R. W., AND R. E. HABEL. The cranial esophageal sphincter, its action and its relation to eructation in sheep as determined by cinefluorography. *Cornell Vet.* 45: 459–464, 1955.

8. DOUGHERTY, R. W., R. E. HABEL, AND H. E. BOND. Esophageal innervation and the eructation reflex in sheep. *Am. J. Vet. Res.* 19: 115–128, 1958.

9. DOUGHERTY, R. W., K. J. HILL, F. L. CAMPETI, R. C. MCCLURE, AND R. E. HABEL. Studies of pharyngeal and laryngeal activity during eructation in ruminants. *Am. J. Vet. Res.* 23: 213–219, 1962.

10. DOUGHERTY, R. W., AND C. D. MEREDITH. Cinefluoro-

graphic studies of the ruminant stomach and of eructation. *Am. J. Vet. Res.* 16: 96–100, 1955.

10a. DOUGHERTY, R. W., J. J. O'TOOLE, AND M. J. ALLISON. Oxidation of intra-arterially administered carbon[14]-labelled methane in sheep. *Proc. Soc. Exptl. Biol. Med.* 124: 1155–1157, 1967.

11. DOUGHERTY, R. W., W. F. SHIPE, G. V. GUDNASON, R. A. LEDFORD, R. D. PETERSON, AND R. SCARPELLINO. Physiological mechanisms involved in transmitting flavors and odors to milk. I. Contribution of eructated gases to milk flavor. *J. Dairy Sci.* 45: 472–476, 1962.

12. DOUGHERTY, R. W., W. E. STEWART, M. M. NOLD, M. S. LINDAHL, C. H. MULLENAX, AND B. F. LEEK. Pulmonary absorption of eructated gas in ruminants. *Am. J. Vet. Res.* 23: 205–212, 1962.

13. DZUIK, H. E., AND A. F. SELLERS. Physiological studies of the vagal nerve supply to the bovine stomach. II. Studies of the eructation mechanism in adult cattle. *Am. J. Vet. Res.* 16: 499–504, 1955.

14. HILL, K. J. Pressure changes in the oesophagus of the sheep during eructation. Quoted in: *Physiology of Digestion in the Ruminant*, edited by R. W. Dougherty, R. S. Allen, W. Burroughs, N. L. Jacobson, and A. D. McGilliard. Washington: Butterworths, 1965, p. 159–170.

15. HILL, K. J., AND J. L. MANAGAN. The formation and distribution of methylamine in the ruminant digestive tract. *Biochem. J.* 93: 39–45, 1964.

16. HUNGATE, R. E., D. W. FLETCHER, R. W. DOUGHERTY, AND B. F. BARRENTINE. Microbial activity in the bovine rumen: Its measurement and relation to bloat. *Appl. Microbiol.* 3: 161–173, 1965.

17. IGGO, A. Spontaneous and reflexly elicited contractions of reticulum and rumen in decerebrate sheep. *J. Physiol., London* 115: 74–75, 1951.

18. MANGOLD, E., AND C. SCHMITT-KRAMER. Die stickstoffverteilung im pansen der wiederkäuer bei fütterung und hunger und ihre beziehung zie der pansen-infresorien. *Biochem. Z.* 191: 411–422, 1927.

19. McARTHUR, J. M., AND J. E. MILTMORE. Rumen gas analysis by gas-solid chromatography. *Can. J. Animal Sci.* 41: 187–196, 1961.

20. OXFORD, A. E. Rumen ciliate protozoa: Their chemical composition, metabolism, requirements for maintenance and culture, and physiological significance for the host. *Exptl. Parasitol.* 4: 569, 1955.

21. STEVENS, C. E., AND A. F. SELLERS. Physiological studies of the vagal nerve supply to the bovine stomach. III. Procaine effects on the dorsal vagal trunk. *Am. J. Vet. Res.* 17: 588–593, 1956.

22. TITCHEN, D. A., AND C. S. W. REID. The reflex control of the motility of the ruminant stomach. In: *Physiology of Digestion in the Ruminant*, edited by R. W. Dougherty, R. S. Allen, W. Burroughs, N. L. Jacobson, and A. D. McGilliard. Washington, D.C.: Butterworths, 1965, p. 68–77.

23. WEISS, K. E. Physiological studies on eructation in ruminants. *Onderstepoort J. Vet. Res.* 26: 251–283, 1953.

24. WEISS, K. E. *Studies on the Pathogenesis of Acute Bloat in Ruminants* (Ph.D. Thesis). Univ. of Pretoria, Onderstepoort, Republic of South Africa, 1953.

CHAPTER 128

Rumination

C. E. STEVENS

A. F. SELLERS

Department of Physiology, New York State Veterinary College, Cornell University, Ithaca, New York

A COW spends about seven hours a day in rumination (25). Ingesta are regurgitated to the mouth at regular intervals for further mastication. After regurgitation, the remastication, reinsalivation, and redeglutition phases of the rumination act occur in sequence. The time spent ruminating is reduced by grinding of roughage before feeding (21).

Coarse material (grass, hay) floating in the rumen and reticulum is regurgitated specifically (see below), resulting in finer subdivision than when first ingested. Such plant material tends to be eaten hurriedly and is incompletely masticated. Although remasticated material may undergo more than one cycle of rumination (25), it tends to sink in the rumen and is then more readily hydrolyzed by the microorganisms. This increases the utilization of roughage (24).

Regurgitation is a reflex superimposed on cyclic, sequential contractions of the reticulum and rumen (Fig. 1). It occurs at the beginning of a rumino-reticular cycle, and its frequency corresponds in general to that of rumino-reticular contractions. These occur about once a minute. Thus, the regurgitation-remastication-redeglutition sequence lasts about a minute.

A preliminary "regurgitation contraction" of the reticulum, occurring just before the regular reticular contractions, floods the cardia with ingesta from the reticulum and anterior rumen. An aspiratory effort of the thorax occurs simultaneously with this submersion of the cardia and with dilation of the caudal esophageal sphincter. Ingesta as a consequence enter the lower esophagus. An antiperistaltic wave of esophageal contraction carries the mass to the pharynx and oral cavity. The presence of food in the mouth is the stimulus for mastication and increased saliva flow. Fluid squeezed from the mass by the first few masticatory movements is swallowed. At the conclusion of remastication deglutition occurs.

The physical character of the swallowed bolus largely determines its future course (25). Light boli (cured hay, roughage) tend to float on the surface of the rumen liquid. In cattle, approximately the upper third of the semifluid mass in the rumen consists of coarse, floating material. As a result of regurgitation-remastication-reinsalivation, the moisture content and specific gravity of the material increase, and being less buoyant, some of it sinks. Following further bacterial digestion in the ventral rumen, the more finely subdivided material is segregated into the cranial dorsal sac. The contents of the cranial dorsal sac are then dumped into the reticulum at the onset of each succeeding rumino-reticular cycle. Much ruminated material thus finds its way into the reticulum, and thence to the omasum and abomasum.

DESCRIPTION OF RUMINATION

Historical

The regurgitation phase of rumination was first carefully studied during the nineteenth century by French workers, whose results form the basis of the

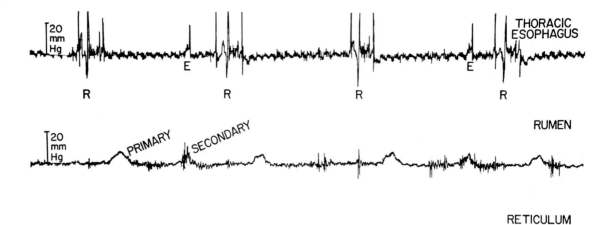

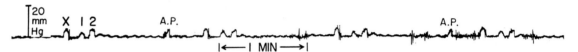

FIG. 1. Three complete cycles of rumino-reticular contraction during rumination. The double reticular contraction, *1* and *2*, and a primary and secondary rumen contraction are labeled for the first cycle. The extra reticular contraction associated with regurgitation (*X*) is also labeled. The esophageal pressure changes during regurgitation are labeled (*R*) and consist of a small positive-pressure wave, followed by the negative deflection due to inspiration against a closed glottis and then, immediately, the large positive deflection due to antiperistaltic esophageal contraction. Regurgitation is usually soon followed by deglutition (unlabeled) of the fluid expressed from the bolus at the beginning of mastication. A wave of deglutition, carrying the bolus to the rumen, is also seen on the esophageal trace at the end of each cycle of rumination and just before the next regurgitation. Note the close integration of the rumination and rumino-reticular cycles. Eructation (*E*) is also labeled, and the associated increase in pressure due to abdominal press can be seen on the reticular trace (*A.P.*) and also superimposed on the secondary wave of rumen contraction.

present description and interpretation of this phase. Flourens (16) in 1833 demonstrated that surgical fixation of the reticulum to the abdominal wall did not prevent regurgitation, and in 1854 Colin (8) showed that the lips of the reticular groove were not involved. Colin (9) later concluded that reticular contraction was the primary force that moved digesta into the esophagus, but that contraction of the diaphragm might also be involved. In 1875 Toussaint (28) recorded intratracheal pressure during regurgitation and concluded that digesta were aspirated into the esophagus as a result of inspiration against a closed glottis.

Wester (30), in 1926, showed that regurgitation could be induced in the unanesthetized cow by manual manipulation, through a rumen fistula of the cranial rumino-reticular epithelial wall. He concluded that a contraction of longitudinal esophageal muscles decreased the intraesophageal pressure and opened the cardia, and neither rumen contraction nor abdominal press was involved in the movement of digesta into the esophagus. He described the movement of digesta up the esophagus as due to an antiperistalic

wave, which he believed to be a continuation of a wave of antiperistaltic contraction passing through the rumen as its secondary contraction.

Regurgitation Mechanism

The contribution made by the development of negative pressure in the thorax to the passage of digesta into the esophagus is well corroborated. Esophageal dilation can be observed fluoroscopically (10), and the negative pressure can be recorded in both the thoracic cavity (4) and the esophagus (27). Although Winship and co-workers (31) recorded an initial positive rather than negative pressure wave in their esophageal recordings, there is some question whether their recordings are those of eructation rather than regurgitation. Eructation gives a wave form almost identical to those they reported. Since eructation also occurs regularly with each rumino-reticular cycle but at a different stage than regurgitation, their separation is best accomplished by simultaneous recording of rumino-reticular motility.

The contribution made by the development of a

positive pressure in the rumen antrum to the passage of digesta into the esophagus is less certain. Some authors feel that the extra reticular contraction at the time of regurgitation serves to flood the cardia with more fluid digesta and to help force these into the esophagus. Bell (3) concluded that in the goat, reticular contraction provides an important contribution to the movement of digesta. However, in the cow a negative intrathoracic esophageal pressure of 40 mm Hg can be recorded at the time of regurgitation, whereas reticular contraction is accompanied by only a 5- to 6-mm Hg rise of pressure at the base of the reticulum, and essentially no positive pressure is recorded within the rumen antrum near the cardia (27). This suggests that, at least in the cow, aspiration is the primary force moving digesta into the esophagus.

A difference may exist among ruminants between the relative contributions made by rumen and esophageal pressures to the act of regurgitation. But accurate recordings of the amplitude of reticular and esophageal pressure waves are difficult to obtain from these animals. The faithful reproduction of the form and therefore the amplitude of a pressure wave requires a superior system capable of recording faithfully other pressure waves of at least one-sixth the duration of the primary wave. Since the pressure waves to be measured last about one second, the recording system should faithfully reproduce pressure waves having a duration of one-sixth of a second. The ability to do this is limited by the devices used to sense the pressure change, the transducer used to translate this to a recorder, and the characteristics of the intervening pressure transmitting system. The use of open-tipped, fluid-filled, polyethylene catheters and of strain gauges has made it possible to record these pressure waves with the required fidelity in cattle, but the catheters needed for these large animals require special attention to length and diameter and use of a solution of greater specific gravity than water to transmit the pressure waves to the strain gauges (27).

In their fluoroscopic studies Czepa & Stigler (10) observed that after influx of digesta into the esophagus, it became constricted and forced its contents orally; they concluded that this was due to a marked expiratory effort. However, Downie (12) was unable to show a marked positive pressure within the trachea at this time, and tandem recordings within the esophagus have since shown that the digesta aspirated into the thoracic esophagus are carried orally by an antiperistaltic wave of esophageal contraction (Fig. 2). These waves pass over the esophagus at more than twice the rate of those recorded during deglutition.

Regurgitation is thus accomplished in two stages. First, rumen contents are aspirated into the thoracic esophagus by the marked negative pressure developed by inspiration against a closed glottis, then carried

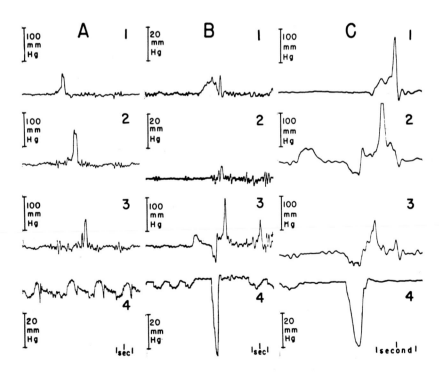

FIG. 2. Pressure events associated with deglutition (A series) and regurgitation (C series) were recorded in the esophagus and pleural cavity. Numbers of the traces in these two series represent 1) cervical esophagus 70 cm cranial to cardia, 2) thoracic esophagus 40 cm cranial to cardia, 3) thoracic esophagus 10 cm cranial to cardia, and 4) pleural cavity. Note peristaltic deglutition wave (series A) with no associated change in respiratory cycle, compared with regurgitation (series C), which shows the marked drop of pressure in the pleural cavity and thoracic esophagus followed by the antiperistaltic wave of esophageal contraction. Center series (B) were also taken during regurgitation and represent 1) base of the reticulum, 2) rumen antrum 4 cm caudal to cardia, 3) thoracic esophagus 40 cm cranial to cardia, and 4) pleural cavity. Note that there is no evidence of a substantial increase in rumen antrum pressure (trace 2) during the extra reticular contraction. [From Stevens & Sellers (27).]

orally by antiperistalsis. Although esophageal constrictions have been observed radiographically in both the cranial cervical and the distal vestibular esophagus of sheep (11), as with other species anatomical evidence of sphincters at these sites is lacking. However, there is physiological evidence for the presence of a sphincter in the cranial cervical esophagus which opens just prior to passage of either the peristaltic or the antiperistaltic wave of contraction (27).

Although it is tempting to consider the first stage of rumination as a controlled variation of the emesis seen in other species, this does not appear to be the case. Vomiting by the simple-stomached animal is accompanied by a) contraction of the duodenum and pyloric sphincter, b) relaxation of the stomach, cardia, and esophagus, and c) abdominal press. None of these have been found to occur during rumination, and there is no evidence of an antiperistaltic wave during emesis. Inspiration against a closed glottis appears to be their only common characteristic. Furthermore it has been shown that the cow does eject or vomit abomasal contents into its forestomach under conditions that simulate emesis in other species, i.e., abomasal torsion (15) or duodenal obstruction (19). This has been demonstrated radiographically and by measuring the appearance of polyethylene glycol in rumen contents following its addition to the abomasum. These conditions were also accompanied by an increase in Cl concentration of rumen contents and resulted in a decrease in plasma Cl and alkalosis similar to that seen with persistent vomiting in the simple-stomached animal. Therefore it appears that although the vomited HCl remains in the digestive tract of the ruminant, it is not reabsorbed rapidly enough to prevent a net accumulation in the forestomach.

Ruminants rarely eject digesta from the mouth, although this can occur in cases of reticulitis and with functional stenosis of the reticulo-omasal orifice or pylorus (20). It can also be induced by mechanical manipulation of the epithelial wall near the reticulo-omasal orifice. Mullenax and co-workers (23) produced a projectile vomition in cattle, with an associated drop in intratracheal pressure and marked rise in intraruminal pressure, after the injection of alkaloidal extracts of *Veratrum* species. They also described a simultaneous distention of the paralumbar fossa which, considered with the observed intraruminal pressures of up to 90 mm Hg in the sheep and 200 mm Hg in the cow, suggests an accompanying contraction of abdominal muscles. The presence of abdominal press suggests emesis, but the projectile

vomition may have been due to the high intraruminal pressures rather than either the characteristic regurgitation of ruminants or the emesis of simple-stomached animals. The foregoing indicates that emesis and the regurgitation phase of rumination differ in a number of respects and, in the ruminant, are independent in characteristics and control.

Completion of Rumination Act

During rumination, regurgitation is followed by a methodical mastication for about one minute. The first few jaw movements are accompanied by swallowing of the expressed fluid. Saliva is again added to the bolus during mastication. At the end of the cycle of rumination the entire bolus is swallowed, and this is followed almost immediately by regurgitation of another bolus (Fig. 1). The cycle of rumination is closely integrated with the cycle of rumino-reticular contraction, regurgitation occurring during an extra contraction of the reticulum. This extra contraction always occurs just before the double reticular contraction that normally marks the beginning of a rumino-reticular contraction. The contraction cycles during rumination thus differ from those during rest in the additional reticular contraction, in the relative number of secondary rumen contractions, and in a somewhat longer duration of the rumino-reticular cycle. This relationship between forestomach motility and rumination requires a close integration of a series of complex events and raises the question whether this phenomenon is due to a single, well-integrated reflex or to a series of reflexes. The studies of Bost (5, 6) suggest that although the reticular and respiratory phases of regurgitation are closely integrated with rumino-reticular contraction, antiperistalsis and mastication may be separately mediated reflexes. However, experimental distention of the thoracic esophagus produces peristaltic rather than antiperistaltic waves of esophageal contraction (26, 31). Since the durations of the cycles of rumination and rumino-reticular contraction are equal, it appears that these two series of events are integrated within the central nervous system rather than by the overlapping of a series of independent reflexes.

NERVOUS CONTROL

Regurgitation can be stimulated by friction, pressure, or traction on the lining of the rumen and reticulum (2, 25), particularly the cardia area, the reticular groove, and the rumino-reticular fold. It is probable that the desire to ruminate is related to the volume of the contents of the rumen and reticulum and to tactile stimuli from coarse floating ingesta in the region of the cardia. If the ruminating animal is disturbed by external conditions, rumination will usually be suspended or stopped.

Integrity of either the dorsal or the ventral trunk of the abdominal vagus is necessary for regurgitation (14, 18, 20, 22, 29). Section of the vagi abolishes rumination, probably by cutting the paths that mediate the desire to ruminate, as well as cutting efferents necessary for reticular motility.

The efferent nerves of rumination are the motor nerves to the muscles concerned: inspiratory, laryngeal, esophageal, masticatory, and reticular (13). Rumination can occur, although with difficulty, when the phrenic nerves are cut (17). Under such conditions, the inspiratory muscles other than the diaphragm produce the necessary negative pressure.

Rumination proceeds normally in decorticate sheep (7). A "rumination center" has not been located, although the rostral hypothalamic area (7) and medulla oblongata (1) have been suggested.

COMMENTS

Obviously serious gaps exist in the information available on rumination. For example, more detailed studies are needed as to types and locations of receptors subserving the rumination act and the cyclic rumino-reticular contractions. The afferent arms of the reflex(es) initiating the uniquely coordinated extra reticular contraction, inspiratory effort, dilation of the cardia, and antiperistaltic contraction of the esophagus are not well defined. The integration of the several contributing parts of the rumination act with each other and with ongoing cyclic motor events of the rumeno-reticulum indicates central control. However, the existence, location, interrelation, and control of such centers have been explored only in part. It is apparent that the emesis phenomenon in ruminants, which results in sequestration of water and electrolyte in the large-volume rumino-reticular compartment, also requires more intensive study.

REFERENCES

1. ANDERSSON, B., R. L. KITCHELL, AND N. PERSSON. A study of central regulation of rumination and reticuloruminal motility. *Acta Physiol. Scand.* 46: 319–338, 1958.

2. BALCH, C. C. Factors affecting the utilization of food by dairy cows. 6. The rate of contraction of the reticulum. *Brit. J. Nutr.* 6: 366–375, 1952.

3. BELL, F. R. The mechanism of regurgitation during the process of rumination in the goat. *J. Physiol., London* 142: 503–515, 1958.

4. BERGMAN, H. D., AND H. H. DUKES. An experimental study of the mechanism of regurgitation in rumination. *J. Am. Vet. Med. Assoc.* 69: 600–612, 1926.

5. BOST, J. Sur les phénomènes mécaniques de la rumination. *J. Physiol., Paris* 50: 174–179, 1958.

6. BOST, J. Sur la coordination des actes réflexes de la rumination. *J. Physiol., Paris* 50: 180–184, 1958.

7. CLARK, C. H. The nerve control of rumination and reticuloruminal motility. *Am. J. Vet. Res.* 14: 376–384, 1953.

8. COLIN, G. *Traité de Physiologie Comparée des Animaux Domestiques.* Paris: Baillière, 1854, vol. I.

9. COLIN, G. *Traité de Physiologie Comparée des Animaux* (2nd ed.). Paris: Baillière, 1871.

10. CZEPA, A., AND R. STIGLER. Der Verdauungstrakt des Wiederkäuers im Röntgenbilde. II. Mitteilung. *Fortschr. Naturw. Forsch.* 6: 1–71, 1929.

11. DOUGHERTY, R. W., AND C. W. MEREDITH. Cinefluorographic studies of the ruminant stomach and eructation. *Am. J. Vet. Res.* 16: 96–100, 1955.

12. DOWNIE, H. G. Photokymographic studies of regurgitation and related phenomena in the ruminant. *Am. J. Vet. Res.* 15: 217–223, 1954.

13. DUKES, H. H. *The Physiology of Domestic Animals* (7th ed.). Ithaca, N. Y.: Comstock, 1955.

14. DUNCAN, D. L. The effects of vagotomy and splanchnotomy on gastric motility in the sheep. *J. Physiol., London* 119: 156–169, 1953.

15. ESPERSEN, G., AND SIMESEN, M. G. Alkalose ved højresidig løbedilatation. *Nord. Vet. Med.* 13: 147–159, 1961.

16. FLOURENS, P. *Acad. Sci., Paris, Mém.* 12, 1833, p. 483, 531.

17. FLOURENS, P. Expériences sur le mécanisme de la rumination. *Mém. Anat. Physiol. Comp., Paris,* 1844.

18. HABEL, R. E. A study of the innervation of the ruminant stomach. *Cornell Vet.* 46: 555–633, 1956.

19. HAMMOND, P. B., H. E. DZIUK, E. A. USENIK, AND C. E. STEVENS. Experimental intestinal obstruction in calves. *J. Comp. Pathol. Therap.* 74: 210–222, 1964.

20. HOFLUND, S. Untersuchungen über Störungen in den Functionen der Wiederkäuermagen, durch Schädigungen des N. Vagus Verursacht. *Svensk. Vet., Suppl. 45,* 1940.

21. KICK, C. H., P. GERLAUGH, A. F. SCHALK, AND E. A. SILVER. The effect of mechanical processing of feeds on the mastication and rumination of steers. *J. Agr. Res.* 55: 587–597, 1937.

22. MANGOLD, E., AND W. KLEIN. *Bewegungen und Innervation des Wiederkäuermagens.* Leipzig: Thieme, 1927.

23. MULLENAX, C. H., W. B. BUCK, R. F. KEELER, AND W.

BINNS. Stimulating eructation and vomition in normal and bloated ruminants with alkaloid extracts from *Veratrum* spp. *Am. J. Vet. Res.* 27: 211–222, 1966.

24. PEARCE, G. R., AND R. J. MOIR. Rumination in sheep. I. The influence of rumination and grinding upon the passage and digestion. *Australian J. Agr. Res.* 15: 635–644, 1964.

25. SCHALK, A. F., AND R. S. AMADON. Physiology of the ruminant stomach. *N. Dakota Agr. Expt. St., Bull.* 216, 1928.

26. SELLERS, A. F., AND D. A. TITCHEN. Responses to localized distension of the oesophagus in decerebrate sheep. *Nature* 184: 645–646, 1959.

27. STEVENS, C. E., AND A. F. SELLERS. Pressure events in bovine esophagus and reticulorumen associated with eructation, deglutition and regurgitation. *Am. J. Physiol.* 199: 598–602, 1960.

28. TOUSSAINT, H. Application de la méthode graphique à la détermination du mécanisme de la rejection dans la rumination. *Arch. Physiol. Normal. Pathol.* 2: 141–176, 1875.

29. WEISS, K. E. Physiological studies on eructation in ruminants. *Ondersteepoort J. Vet. Res.* 26: 251–283, 1953.

30. WESTER, J. *Der Physiologie und Pathologie der Vormägen beim Rinde.* Berlin: Schoetz, 1926.

31. WINSHIP, D. H., F. F. ZBORALSKE, W. N. WEBER, AND K. H. SOERGEL. Esophagus in rumination. *Am. J. Physiol.* 207: 1189–1194, 1964.

CHAPTER 129

Nervous control of motility of the forestomach of ruminants

D. A. TITCHEN | *Department of Veterinary Preclinical Sciences, University of Melbourne, Parkville, Victoria, Australia*

CHAPTER CONTENTS

IN RUMINANTS the movements of the more orad parts of the stomach are under the control of the central nervous system. Contractions of the esophageal groove, of the reticulum, of the rumen in association with contractions of the reticulum, and of the rumen independently of those of the reticulum have all been obtained as reflex responses in decerebrate preparations. These medullary reflex responses have been evoked by stimulation of different parts of the alimentary tract: they are modified and coordinated by higher parts of the central nervous system.

Contractions of the reticulum and rumen have

been implicated in the mixing of digesta in these parts of the stomach, the movement of digesta from them into the omasum (the next part or division of the ruminant stomach), the regurgitation of digesta to be subjected to remastication and ensalivation in the course of the process of rumination, and also in the removal of gases evolved during the fermentative digestion of plant material in the rumen and reticulum. A structure within the reticulum, the esophageal groove, is responsible for the more direct passage of fluid swallowed by young suckling ruminants into the abomasum (the last and only truly secretory part of the stomach).

In ruminants there appears to be a clearer dependence of the control and coordination of gastric motility on the central nervous system than in many other mammals. In an earlier contribution to this *Handbook* series, Eliasson (39) commented on the scant evidence of basic relations between the central nervous system and the digestive system. It is not possible here to offer comparative evidence on the phylogenetic development of the systems, evidence that Eliasson suggested would contribute to a better understanding of their interrelations. Studies on the nervous control of the motility of the ruminant stomach have added and will continue to add understanding to the relations between the nervous system and the gastrointestinal tract of mammals.

Ruminants develop the ability to utilize ingested plant materials as a source of nutrients; it is not a capacity with which these animals are born. It depends on the establishment after birth of a population of symbiotic microorganisms in the more orad divisions of the stomach, the development of these divisions into an ample "fermentation vat," and the development of the capacity of the animals themselves to maintain favorable conditions for this fermentative type of digestion by contributing sufficient salivary secretion to support microbial fermentation. At birth, and until these capacities have been developed, gastric digestion is limited to that which takes place in the abomasum and which is due to the HCl and proteolytic enzyme secreted by it. Ruminants continue to suckle for some time after they have started to ingest plant material and after a fermentative type of digestion has been established in the reticulum and rumen. Under these conditions food may be first exposed to gastric digestion in either the rumen and reticulum or in the abomasum. Suckled milk takes a direct course to the abomasum; plant material passes into the reticulum and rumen.

ESOPHAGEAL GROOVE

The passage of suckled milk directly to the abomasum depends on the functioning of the esophageal groove. The anatomical disposition of the esophageal groove and the presence of milk in only the abomasum of calves slaughtered shortly after suckling suggested to Faber [cited by Peyer (65)] that the esophageal groove serves to direct swallowed milk to the abomasum without any sojourn in, or even passage into, the reticulum and rumen. This has now been amply confirmed by experimental observations of both a direct and an indirect nature. The esophageal groove or gutter (*gouttière oesophagienne*) forms a channel from the esophagus, through the reticulum, to the reticulo-omasal orifice. Briefly it consists (in the calf, lamb, and kid) of two well-defined "lips" flanking a "floor" which passes from the esophagus to the reticulo-omasal orifice. The lips are so disposed that if they become approximated they make a functional extension of the esophagus to the reticulo-omasal orifice.

Watson (91) in 1944 wrote the most comprehensive and critical review of earlier literature on the stimulation and function of the esophageal groove. He classified evidence provided by studies on the functioning of the esophageal groove according to the methods employed and indicated the application of the indicator slaughter, indicator excretion methods of study, and of observations *per fistulam*, and recognized the value of radiographic techniques.

Faber's conclusions about the esophageal groove

were reached by deduction of function from structure and by the simplest application of the indicator-slaughter technique. Later applications of this technique have involved detection of the destination in the alimentary tract of a dye or marker added to the ingested material (76, 95). A recent development of the technique has been to combine it with absorption studies (76). Glucose has been used for this purpose. Ingested glucose is absorbed as such in adult ruminants and causes a postprandial hyperglycemia only if it passes directly to the abomasum and thus escapes breakdown by the rumen microorganisms (76). In the indicator excretion technique the time between ingestion of a marker and its appearance in the feces is used to indicate whether the material first entered the abomasum or the rumen.

The passage of fluid through the esophageal groove and omasal canal directly to the abomasum of a kid goat was recognized in the first published account of a radiographic study of the ruminant stomach (24). Ample confirmation of this original observation has been provided in subsequent radiological studies in lambs, calves, and kids (10, 91). An indication of the application of the radiographic technique in the determination of the route taken by suckled fluid is provided in Figure 1a. Watson (91) included a study on the route taken by fluid suckled by lambs from their dams; this was made possible by the injection of radiopaque material into the mammary glands of ewes before the lambs were permitted to suckle. Watson clearly differentiated between the route taken into or through the stomach by fluid according to whether it was ingested as a response in the satiation of thirst or in association with suckling. In adult ruminants, water swallowed normally passes into the rumen and reticulum. In this connection it is relevant to recall that Schalk & Amadon (77) established in one cow a preference for drinking milk; in this animal the esophageal groove contracted when it drank milk and none of the milk passed into the rumen or reticulum. It has also been reported that simply the sight (or smell) of milk, without actual ingestion, might lead to contraction of the esophageal groove (94).

A number of workers have concluded that contraction of the esophageal groove occurs as a reflex response; for example, Schalk & Amadon (77) wrote "The phenomena of the function [esophageal groove contraction] appear to be governed by a reflex mechanism." Sixteen years later Watson (91) marshaled a considerable body of evidence supporting the proposition that contraction occurs as a reflex response to physical or chemical stimulation of buccal or pharyngeal receptors. He admitted of other possibilities and wrote "There is, of course, a remote possibility that the excitation of functional activity of the O.G. [oesophageal groove] mechanism might have been achieved by a purely humoral mechanism." Contraction of the esophageal groove as a reflex response to buccopharyngeal stimulation has been demonstrated. Evidence has been obtained that the effector mechanism is established in the lamb by the 110th day of fetal life (30).

Decerebrate Preparations

Esophageal groove contraction has been obtained as a reflex response in decerebrate (intercollicular section) calves and lambs (21). Decerebration was performed under ether anesthesia, and the observations and recordings were made during a period when the effects of the anesthetic agent had largely worn off. The sensitivity of the reflex to anesthesia is emphasized by studies in fetal lambs in which anesthetic administered to the mother depressed the responses of the fetus to swallowing and suckling (30).

The observations on esophageal groove contraction being obtained as a reflex response in decerebrate preparations provide a *prima facie* case for locating the reflex center in the medulla oblongata (21).

Nerve stimulation studies in decerebrate preparations of calves have revealed that the majority of effector nerve fibers to the esophageal groove reach it in the dorsal vagus nerve trunk. The contraction of the esophageal groove obtained with stimulation of this nerve was greater than that produced by stimulation of the ventral trunk. The response of the esophageal groove to vagus nerve stimulation in the decerebrate calf was blocked by atropine administered intravenously in doses of 80–200 µg per kg (21).

A profusion of ganglion cells in association with the muscle of the esophageal groove and degeneration of pericellular nerve terminations after section of the vagus nerves have been demonstrated (40). This evidence and that of the blocking action of atropine (21) make it reasonable to conclude that the esophageal groove receives postganglionic (muscarinic) cholinergic innervation via the vagus. Confirmation that the majority of the preganglionic fibers distributed to its ganglion cells are contained in the dorsal vagal trunk has been obtained from nerve section studies; a failure of the esophageal groove to contract was observed in conscious lambs in which the dorsal vagus nerve trunk had been previously cut in the abdomen (28). It can be seen by comparing Figures 1a and b

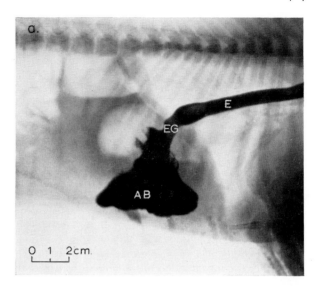

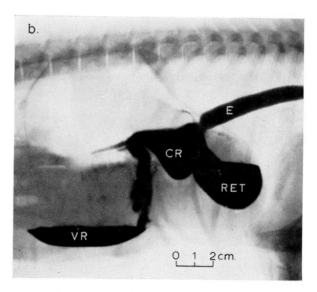

FIG. 1. Radiographs of the same lamb taken during suckling *a*, before, and *b*, 24 hours after both dorsal and ventral vagus nerve trunks had been cut in the abdomen just below the diaphragm. In *a*, suckled fluid (a suspension of barium sulfate in milk) passed via the esophageal groove to the abomasum; in *b*, suckled fluid passed into the reticulum and cranial dorsal sac of the rumen and can be seen spilling over the cranial pillar into the ventral sac of the rumen. The esophageal groove failed to contract after the vagus nerves had been cut. Key to location of radiopaque material: *E*, esophagus; *EG*, esophageal groove; *AB*, abomasum; *RET*, reticulum; *CR*, cranial dorsal rumen (between reticulo-ruminal fold and cranial pillar); *VR*, ventral sac of the rumen. (J. C. Newhook and D. A. Titchen, unpublished data).

that the passage into the abomasum of suckled fluid depends on the integrity of the vagus nerves.

The afferent stimulation used to evoke contraction of the esophageal groove in decerebrate preparations

FIG. 2. Decerebrate calf—records from above downward: esophageal groove, laryngeal movement in swallowing, blood pressure, signal indicating stimulation of central end of abomasal nerve (A), signal indicating stimulation of central end of superior laryngeal nerve (S). Time marked in 5-sec intervals. a: Stronger stimulation of abomasal nerve (coil at 10 cm) than in b (coil at 12 cm). Note long-persisting inhibition with stronger stimulation of abomasal nerve in a. [From Comline & Titchen (21).]

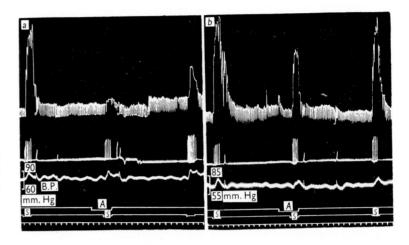

was either the introduction of water into the posterior mouth cavity or stimulation of the central end of the superior laryngeal nerve (21). Swallowing and esophageal groove contraction were the usual but not invariable responses to these stimuli. Esophageal groove contraction without swallowing has been observed in preparations in which the stimulus was apparently subliminal for swallowing (23). This observation might provide an indication that, normally, in the young suckling ruminant, esophageal groove contraction occurs as one of a series of reflex responses, including buccopharyngeal and esophageal movements of swallowing, esophageal and perhaps reticuloomasal sphincter relaxation, and coordination of respiratory movements, and that each of these individual components of the complete response might be obtained separately.

Properties of Esophageal Groove Reflex

Studied in detail in decerebrate preparations of calves, the properties of the esophageal groove reflex revealed (21) included latency, summation of individually inadequate stimuli, fatigue, afterdischarge, and inhibition. The latency was of the order of 2–4 sec. Long latencies have been a characteristic of all of the reflex responses of the stomach studied in ruminants; that exhibited by the esophageal groove reflex is among the shortest. It was frequently observed that when the introduction of water into the mouth or stimulation of afferent fibers of the superior laryngeal nerve was ineffective in evoking swallowing or esophageal groove contraction, the simultaneous delivery of the two stimuli elicited both responses.

Inhibition of the reflex response of the esophageal groove, but not of swallowing, was obtained with stretch of the abomasum or reticulum or with stimula-

tion of the central end of a major abomasal branch of the vagus nerve. This inhibition was prolonged (Fig. 2). Obtained in preparations in which the splanchnic nerves had been cut, it was judged to be central. Inhibition due to abomasal distention possibly explains the failure of the esophageal groove to contract in conscious animals toward the end of a dose of contrast medium or when the abomasum is filled with radiopaque material (24).

Inhibition of both esophageal groove contraction and swallowing was observed in decerebrate preparations on stimulation of the central end of the glossopharyngeal nerve; expiratory efforts were also observed with this stimulation (21). This observation has its parallel in one made in conscious animals. With clumsy swallowing of fluid there was coughing and the esophageal groove failed to contract (24).

The esophageal groove of the calf may apparently be directly inhibited, for inhibition follows the intravenous injection of epinephrine and stimulation of the peripheral end of the splanchnic nerves (21). In decerebrate preparations of calves in which the splanchnic nerves had been cut, there was usually a stronger and more sustained contraction in response to each salvo of reflex stimulation than in those preparations in which the splanchnic nerves remained intact. However, esophageal groove contraction has been stimulated by epinephrine administered intravenously (in doses of 2–5 μg per kg) in lambs anesthetized with chloralose or decerebrated under halothane (B.P.) anesthesia (J. C. Newhook and D. A. Titchen, unpublished data). In conscious lambs the passage of suckled fluid to the abomasum was detected at times when epinephrine administered intravenously would be presumed to be still exerting an effect, judged by studies made in decerebrate preparations. Thus, detailed observations on effector mechanisms made in one species of ruminant are not necessarily referable to another species.

Esophageal Groove Contraction in Adult Animals

The esophageal groove does not normally contract in adult ruminants when water is swallowed. Interest in provoking it to contract in adult conscious animals arose from a realization that the efficiency of orally administered anthelminthic agents would be increased by their passage, not into the rumen and reticulum, but through the esophageal groove into the abomasum. Copper salts in sheep (92) and sodium salts in cattle (76) have the effect, in a high proportion of adult animals, of causing the esophageal groove to contract. Copper sulfate in a concentration of 0.40 M was found to be most effective in sheep. Copper salts were relatively ineffective in cattle but sodium salts caused contraction. Sodium bicarbonate was more effective than was sodium chloride: cattle of 6–11 months of age were used in the study and in 93% of them 60 ml of 10% sodium bicarbonate administered orally led to a closure of the esophageal groove (76). Taste probably played an important part in these studies. It has been reported that the oral administration of glucose solutions leads in some sheep and cattle to closure of the esophageal groove (76, 91). Earlier work is cited in references (21, 76, 91, 92, 95).

The many reports of the action of these metallic salts in causing contraction of the esophageal groove confirm that in a majority of adult animals the esophageal groove can be stimulated to contract and that it does not regress.

The esophageal groove affords an interesting example of adaptation of structure to function. The esophageal groove provides a means by which ingested food may be subjected initially to acid-peptic enzymatic digestion or to fermentative digestion, depending on the route taken by it after swallowing. The route is affected by the buccal or pharyngeal stimulation caused by the ingested material.

CONTRACTIONS OF RETICULUM AND RUMEN

Characteristically, the reticulum exhibits diphasic contractions that recur at relatively regular intervals. The frequency of these contractions varies, depending on whether the animals are fed, feeding, or fasted. A varying degree of relaxation occurs between the two phases of contraction. These features of reticulum contractions have been recognized by direct palpation of the reticulum (77) and recorded by balloon manometers or pressure systems (66, 73, 77, 80), level records (of the floor of the reticulum) in cows (72), or by potential changes associated with reticulum contractions (50). They have been observed radiographically in sheep and goats (10, 24, 27) and photographed and recorded from partial exteriorizations of the reticulum prepared in sheep and cattle (70, 71, 74, 83, 86).

The two phases of contraction of the reticulum are of about equal duration (2–3 sec). Their total duration is 4–6 sec. An added phase is observed normally in association with regurgitation during rumination. This additional contraction precedes the diphasic contraction, and at the height of this additional phase of the reticulum contraction there is an inspiratory effort against a closed glottis; these two events lead to the development of a substantial pressure differential between the reticulo-rumen and the terminal thoracic esophagus (8). Monophasic contractions of the reticulum have been observed and recorded in conscious sheep when first fed (70) after a period of fasting and in sheep during the inhibition of reticulo-ruminal motility associated with intraduodenal infusion of oleic acid or of triglyceride (88).

The reticulum, rumen, and omasum are poorly developed in fetal and newly born animals when compared with the abomasum and with their adult proportions (30, 90). The increase in the capacity of the reticulum, rumen, and omasum and the development of their epithelium and muscle toward the form of proportions characteristic of the adult ruminant have been associated with the establishment of a fermentative type of digestion (14, 90). In response to electrical stimulation of the peripheral end of a vagus nerve cut in the neck, contractions of the reticulum and rumen have been obtained at the 70th day of fetal life in the lamb (30), and of the reticulum within the first few days after birth in the kid (20). It has been reported that contractions of the reticulum occur in young suckling calves; but it was suggested, "A regular cycle of contraction, however, sets in when solid food is eaten" (10). A clear difference between the force and regularity of contractions of the reticulum and rumen was established in calves restricted to a milk diet and in others given, in addition, access to hay (37, 61). There was a greater force of reticulo-ruminal contractions obtained with vagus nerve stimulation in young animals having access to hay than in those limited to milk (37).

Form of Rumen Contractions

Two different forms of sequential contractions of the rumen have been recognized. The first occurs in association with, and following, contractions of the reticulum. In general terms it successively involves the cranial, middle, and then the caudal regions of first the dorsal and then the ventral sac of the rumen (70, 71, 87). The intensity of the contractions of any one part of the rumen during this sequence of contraction and the rapidity with which it sequentially involves individual parts of the rumen differ markedly according to whether an animal is being fed or fasted (70, 71). The whole sequence of contraction in fasted animals is more rapid, shorter in individual parts of the rumen, and weaker or simpler in its form than in fed animals (86, 87). An indication of these differences is provided in Figure 3.

The contractions of the rumen associated with those of the reticulum were described by Schalk & Amadon (77) as ". . . peristaltic in nature, the advancing wave of contraction being preceded by a wave of inhibition." This peristaltic form of contraction has not been confirmed. The contraction of one part of the rumen may, in causing a translocation of contents of the stomach, produce a dilatation of another part of the stomach; but inhibition of a preexisting tonic contraction has not been identified. This form of rumen contraction which characteristically precedes diphasic contractions of the reticulum is referred to as the "A sequence" of contraction. Other terms that have been used are "primary" and "mixing" cycles of contraction. The terminology used here is that employed by a number of workers (70, 79); it has been adopted because it has the advantage of being devoid of any inference or implication as to the nature of the contractions.

Schalk & Amadon (77) also referred to a "secondary peristaltic wave" of contraction which successively involved different parts of the rumen and with which there was neither an associated reticulum contraction nor any association with reticulum contractions. These contractions have also been termed "antiperistaltic," "secondary," or "extraruminal"; they sequentially involve the caudal ventral blind sac of the rumen, the caudal dorsal, cranial dorsal, and finally the main ventral sac of the rumen (70, 87). This sequential involvement of these regions of the wall of the rumen has been defined by study of the contractions of exteriorizations prepared in the left lateral wall of the rumen. In these investigations (71) the term "B sequence" was applied to these contractions and it is used in this report. The sequential in-

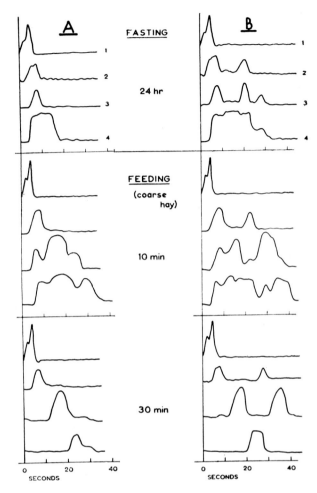

FIG. 3. Contractions of the reticulum in a Welsh Mountain sheep: (*1*), cranial dorsal rumen (*2*), cranial ventral rumen (*3*), and caudal ventral blind sac (*4*) recorded from exteriorizations prepared in the left lateral wall of these structures. *A:* typical A sequences of contraction in this animal after being fasted for 24 hours (top panel), 10 min after first being given food, and (bottom panel) 30 min after being fed. Note the abrupt and simple form of the A sequence in the fasted state and the changes in the form and temporal relations of the contractions of the rumen with feeding, in this case coarse meadow hay. *B:* B sequences of contractions following A sequences in the same animal and under the same conditions. As in *A* at the stage between fasting and feeding (10 min after starting to feed) very complex movements are seen in the rumen. Eructation commonly occurs at the time the cranial dorsal sac of the rumen is involved in the B sequence of contraction. [After Reid (70).]

volvement of different regions of the left lateral wall of the rumen of the sheep in the B sequence is also illustrated in Figure 3. Eructation commonly occurs in association with the B sequence of contraction—at the time the contraction involves the cranial regions of the dorsal sac of the rumen. More detailed accounts of the A and B sequences of contractions are provided elsewhere (70, 71, 87).

Efferent Innervation of Reticulum and Rumen

Orderly sequential movements of the reticulum and rumen cease after the vagus nerves have been cut (28, 40) or after atropine has been administered (29). Habel (40) has described the distribution of the vagus nerves to the ruminant stomach and the effects on stomach movements of section of these nerves; he has reviewed earlier literature on these topics and on the effects of stimulation of these nerves. Degeneration studies indicate that the efferent fibers in the cervical and thoracic vagus nerve trunks are preganglionic. This conclusion is supported by pharmacological observations on the action of ganglionic-blocking agents (16).

Two forms of rumen contraction have been obtained with different frequencies of stimulation of the peripheral end of the vagus nerve cut in the neck (75). With higher frequencies caudally progressing contractions of the dorsal sac of the rumen were observed, and associated with them were contractions of the reticulum and a marked bradycardia. Lower frequencies of stimulation evoked cranially progressing contractions of the dorsal sac of the rumen without associated reticulum contractions and without marked bradycardia. In the cat, two groups of vagal efferent fibers, one of low and one of high threshold, have been implicated in the mediation of the different gastric effector responses. Secretory responses, vasodilatation, and inhibition of motility obtained with vagus nerve stimulation were related to stimulation of fibers exhibiting a higher threshold; the enhanced motility observed with efferent vagal stimulation was associated with the stimulation of vagal efferent fibers exhibiting a low threshold (58). Such studies have yet to be done in the ruminant stomach. The observations of Reid & Titchen (75) that different forms of rumen contraction occur with different frequencies of vagus nerve stimulation suggest that different groups of efferent fibers are involved in the two forms of rumen contraction. Studies by direct recording (48, 49) of action potentials in efferent vagal nerve fibers and by indirect means using the technique of vagophrenic anastomosis (33) support the proposition that different groups of fibers may be involved in different contraction sequences. These at present, however, must remain indications. It is possible nevertheless to establish a firm association between medullary neuron (7) and efferent vagal fiber activity (48) and reticulum contractions.

In the case of the reticulum, an inhibitory effect of efferent vagus nerve stimulation has been recognized (20, 23). This effect, which is apparent as a diminution of tonus of the reticulum in spinal or anesthetized preparations or as an inhibition of a sympathetically induced contraction of the reticulum, persists after the excitatory actions of the vagus have been eliminated by atropine (Fig. 4). Inhibitory effects of vagus nerve stimulation on the stomach have been recognized in animals with a simpler form of stomach. In the cat, after the administration of atropine, the inhibitory effect on the stomach persists (59), without release of epinephrine (57); this is also true of the reticulum of the ruminant. The possibility of 5-hydroxytryptamine being a vagal transmitter substance must be considered.

Acetylcholine and other choline esters may either stimulate or inhibit contractions of the reticulum and rumen (29, 31, 36). The effect obtained depends on the experimental conditions. Inhibitory effects have been related to the central actions of acetylcholine (31) and to the inhibitory actions of catecholamines secreted by the adrenal medulla stimulated by it (29). Direct evidence for the excitatory action of acetylcholine has been obtained from both in vitro and in vivo studies (29, 31, 36). These observations and those on the blocking action of atropine support the conclusion that the rumen and reticulum receive a postganglionic muscarinic parasympathetic excitatory innervation via the vagus nerves (28, 40).

Both excitatory and inhibitory effects of sympathomimetic amines on reticulum and rumen motility have been reported (20, 29, 31, 36). In spinal and decerebrate preparations and in anesthetized animals, with and without the vagus nerves intact, epinephrine injected intravenously evoked contractions of the reticulum (20). Contractions of the reticulum have been produced by efferent stimulation of the left splanchnic and right thoracic sympathetic nerve trunks (20); the responses to sympathetic nerve stimulation are blocked by sympatholytic agents (20, 31). These experimental observations contrast markedly with earlier views that the sympathetic exerts a purely inhibitory action on gastric motility of the ruminant. In decerebrate preparations an inhibitory effect of epinephrine has been demonstrated on reflexly stimulated contractions of the reticulum. Two other effects have also been observed in these preparations: namely, a sympathetic contraction of the reticulum and a sympathetic contraction succeeded by a series of characteristic diphasic contractions of the reticulum. This has been interpreted as arising from central facilitation (31) or receptor sensitization (51, 84).

Bilateral splanchnotomy appears to have no effect on contractions of the reticulum and rumen in conscious animals in which observations were made some time after the nerves had been cut (28). This is not a definitive procedure, at least in terms of sympathetic denervation in toto. From stimulation studies it is clear that not all the sympathetic fibers to the reticulum, at least, are contained in the splanchnic nerves—some appear to take a course from the thoracic sympathetic nerve trunk of the right side without passage into the right splanchnic nerve (20). Sympathetic nerve trunk section results in some deafferentation of the viscera receiving the innervation, a phenomenon on that intensifies the difficulty of defining the effects of nerve section. The demonstration that rhythmic orderly contractions of the reticulum and rumen continue

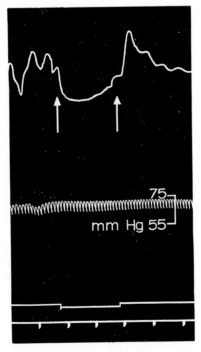

FIG. 4. Kid anesthetized with chloralose. Inhibitory effect of stimulation of peripheral end of cervical vagus after atropine. Note decrease in tone of reticulum slip preparation (upper record) and absence of cardiac inhibition. *Signal* and *arrows* indicate period of stimulation of the vagus nerve (induction coil). Time in 5-sec intervals, bottom trace. Blood pressure recorded from carotid artery. [Comline & Titchen (20), unpublished record.]

after some sympathetic nerves have been sectioned cannot be regarded as evidence that sympathetic nerves play no part in stimulation, regulation, or even initiation of contractions of the reticulum and rumen. The route taken to the reticulum and rumen by sympathetic fibers and their effects needs further investigation.

Localized contractions of the reticulum and rumen have been observed and recorded in spinal, decerebrate (20, 84), anesthetized, and conscious animals [(28, 29); Fig. 4]. Tonic activity was prominent in some conscious sheep after vagotomy (28); it may be inhibited by either epinephrine or acetyl and others of the choline esters and by histamine (29). Increases in tone have also been observed after the administration of long-acting choline esters.

Increased tonic activity of the reticulum is frequently observed in anesthetized, decerebrate, and conscious animals for a period of 5 sec or more before the occurrence of diphasic contractions (70, 84). Long-lasting tonic changes have been observed in the reticulum in sheep subjected to intraduodenal infusions of oleic acid and triglyceride [C. S. W. Reid and D. A. Titchen, unpublished observations; and McLeay (62)]. Whether tonic activity is purely intrinsic in origin and a reflection of neuromuscular excitability or is also affected by the extrinsic innervation and also influenced by gastrointestinal hormones remains to be defined. Evidence has been obtained that the synthetic gastrin preparation pentagastrin modifies reticulum and rumen motility (62).

Reflex Centers

The medullary location of reflex centers controlling contractions of the reticulum and rumen has been indicated by studies in decerebrate preparations (33, 46, 84) by observation of the effect of intramedullary stimulation in anesthetized and conscious animals (1, 8, 35) and by studies concerned with the recording of potentials from the medulla oblongata (7).

Three different types of response to direct medullary stimulation have been obtained:

1. Production of contractions of the reticulum and rumen when none were present previously.

2. An acceleration of an already existing series of contractions of the reticulum and rumen.

3. Deceleration or disappearance of previously existing reticulum and rumen contractions during the period of stimulation, succeeded by an acceleration after the stimulus was withdrawn.

These effects, in the order of their enumeration, have been interpreted as (33) due to:

1. Stimulation of the dorsal motor vagal nuclear cells of preganglionic fibers which in turn excite postganglionic neurons supplying the reticulum and rumen

2. Stimulation of sensory fibers influencing the efferent vagal nuclear cells in an excitatory sense

3. Stimulation of inhibitory neurons.

A strict viscerotopic representation has not been found in the efferent neurons in the medulla oblongata, although a distinct localization of effect has been observed, so that rumen contractions without, for example, esophageal contractions have been recorded on stimulation of the medulla oblongata, when the volume of brain tissue stimulated was estimated to be in the order of 0.5 mm^3 (8). Observations of medullary stimulation have led to the conclusion that discrete areas in the medulla oblongata control the motility of the individual compartments of the ruminant stomach, and that one such area is concerned with the overall coordination of the responses.

Contractions of the reticulum and of the rumen have been obtained in decerebrate preparations under conditions indicating that the responses are reflex in nature. Contractions of the reticulum and rumen have been evoked by afferent stimulation in decerebrate preparations with the medulla and pons intact (33, 34, 46, 75, 84) in preparations with transection between the pons and medulla (46), in decerebellated decerebrate preparations (84), and in decerebrate preparations with high cervical spinal cord transection (46, 75, 84, 85). It is reasonable to conclude that the reflex centers are situated in the medulla oblongata.

This conclusion is supported by evidence of a relationship between potential changes recorded from neurons in the dorsal nucleus of the vagus. The time course of these potentials and their regular association with reticulum contractions (spike discharge preceding reticulum contraction by 0.48–0.96 sec.) are both compatible with the suggestion that there is a causal relationship between dorsal vagal neuron potentials recorded and reticulum contractions (7, 33).

Efferent Vagal Fiber Activity

A direct association between contractions of the reticulum and rumen and impulses in vagal efferent preganglionic neurons has been indicated by the application of two techniques. In conscious animals, Dussardier (33) applied the technique of vagophrenic nerve anastomosis to detect, from the reinnervated

part of the diaphragm, vagal efferent preganglionic nerve impulses. In anesthetized animals direct recording of action potentials in single vagal preganglionic efferent fibers has been accomplished (48, 49, 56). In both cases a relationship between impulses in efferent preganglionic vagal fibers and reticulum and rumen contractions has been established. It must be stated that preganglionic efferent nerve fiber activity is an indirect indication of stimulation of the smooth muscle of the reticulum and rumen by postganglionic vagal fibers and that the relation between efferent vagal fiber impulses and reticulum or rumen contractions has been, necessarily, of an inferential nature.

With these techniques preganglionic fibers thought to be concerned in the innervation of the reticulum showed activity only immediately preceding and during contractions of the reticulum. Preceding the contraction there was a rapidly increasing number of impulses which occurred either in two distinct groups (Fig. 5) or showed two periods of peak frequency when diphasic contractions of the reticulum occurred. With the technique of vagophrenic anastomosis the maximum frequency of impulses recorded was 20 per sec; usually the greatest frequency was about 12 per sec. Up to 60 impulses per sec were detected in studies with direct recording from vagal efferent fibers. Delays between peak impulse frequency recorded from vagal fibers in the neck and the time at which contractions reached their height were found to be in the order of 2–3 sec. Most of the delay apparently occurs at a postganglionic site, since the preganglionic fibers concerned have conduction velocities in the range of 5–15 m per sec (49). The form and duration of contractions of the reticulum and rumen are most likely determined by the efferent vagal discharge. Brunaud (15) has imitated the form of a diphasic contraction of the reticulum by delivering two separate salvos of stimuli to efferent vagal nerve fibers. The observation that the duration of the discharge recorded in efferent vagal fibers destined for the rumen was longer than

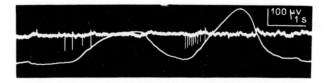

FIG. 5. Electromyogram (upper record) recorded from part of the diaphragm innervated by nerve fibers involved in a vagophrenic nerve anastomosis. Lower record contraction of reticulum. Time, 1 sec. Note two bursts of action potentials preceding each peak of contraction of the reticulum. [After Dussardier (33).]

that in fibers destined for the reticulum provides an indication that the variations in form of rumen contractions observed in fed and fasted animals are due to differences in efferent vagal fiber activity and are largely determined centrally.

Iggo & Leek (49) have classified vagal efferent fibers destined for abdominal visceral structures into seven groups. Their work involved recording from these efferent fibers in the neck. Their observations were made in sheep anesthetized with halothane. Under these experimental conditions rumen contractions, and particularly of the ventral sac, were weaker than normal. This made it difficult to associate the efferent fibers with characteristic reticulo-ruminal activity except in the case of one group of fibers that displayed activity in association with reticulum contractions and another group whose discharges were related to contraction of the dorsal sac of the rumen.

With the technique of direct recording of impulses in vagal efferent fibers in anesthetized animals, no evidence was obtained of a tonic or constant discharge of impulses in fibers judged to be destined to innervate the reticulum or rumen. Dussardier (33) detected a constant impulse traffic in some fibers that had been involved in vagophrenic anastomosis; the interpretation was offered that the fibers concerned would have innervated the rumen, but clear-cut relations between motility and the efferent impulses were not apparent. Dussardier (33) also found two bursts of impulses in fibers believed to be ruminal efferents; one occurred in association with an A sequence of rumen contraction, the other with a B sequence. Insufficient evidence is available to allow comment on the possible significance of the different frequency and duration of the impulses in the two bursts. As yet no evidence is forthcoming from other workers on different vagal efferent discharges which may be related to the two forms of rumen contraction.

AFFERENT STIMULATION OF CONTRACTIONS
OF RETICULUM AND RUMEN

Buccal, pharyngeal, esophageal, gastric, and intestinal stimulation have all been shown to increase the frequency of contractions of the reticulum and rumen. Both excitatory and inhibitory effects of changes in conditions in some parts of the alimentary tract have been demonstrated. Nerve stimulation, section, and recording experiments have added to an understanding of how stimulation of the gut may modify reticulum and rumen motility. Observations

have been made in conscious animals and in anesthetized and decerebrate preparations. An attempt will be made here to relate observations made under different experimental conditions.

Buccal and Pharyngeal Stimulation

Afferent stimulation of the mandibular and maxillary branches of the trigeminal nerve will initiate and maintain reticulum contractions in lambs and sheep anesthetized with chloralose (11). The effects of trigeminal nerve stimulation may be analogous to those of buccal mucosal stimulation (11). Attention has been drawn to the greater buccal stimulation developed when ingested food is chewed for the first time than that occurring with mastication of material regurgitated from the stomach. This difference has been offered as an explanation for the different frequencies of reticulum and rumen contractions observed during feeding and rumination.

Concurrent contractions of the reticulum, esophageal groove, and reticulo-omasal orifice observed in lambs anesthetized with chloralose may be, as suggested (12), of general significance or related to the use of chloralose. Confirmation of an association of the motility of the reticulum, esophageal groove, and reticulo-omasal orifice has not been reported under other experimental conditions. The relative importance of buccal, pharyngeal, esophageal, and gastric stimulation in contributing to the increased frequency of reticulum and rumen contractions when animals feed cannot be assessed with the evidence available at present.

Esophageal Stimulation

Tactile and stretch stimulation of the esophagus produces both sialogogic effects and increased frequency of contractions of reticulum and rumen. These responses have not been obtained with equal facility from all regions of the esophagus. Tactile stimulation proved most efficacious in provoking or increasing reticulum contractions and salivary secretion when delivered to the most caudal part of the thoracic esophagus (18).

Generalized distention of the esophagus (52), the stimulus accorded by the movement of a balloon down the esophagus (78), and stretch resulting from distention of a balloon retained in either the most caudal or most cranial regions of the thoracic esophagus (78) stimulate reticulum and rumen contractions in decerebrate preparations and anesthetized animals.

Responses to localized distention of the esophagus were obtained after esophageal contractions had been blocked by a curarizing agent (78). Whether the receptors involved in these responses are also sensitive to contraction of the esophagus remains to be defined. Inhibitory effects of greater degrees of esophageal stimulation have also been recognized. The afferent pathways involved in the responses of the reticulum and rumen to esophageal stimulation have not been defined. It has been shown that excitatory effects of esophageal stimulation of salivary secretion depend on the integrity of the vagus nerves (18, 52).

Stimulation of Reticulum

Evidence has been obtained that suggests that stimulation of receptors in either the reticulum muscle or the mucosa may modify the motility of the reticulum, rumen, and other parts of the alimentary tract in ruminants. Stretch of the reticulum reflexly stimulates contractions of the reticulum. This has been defined in decerebrate preparations and in anesthetized animals (32, 84). The response is abolished by section of the vagus nerves (46, 84, 85), or by the administration of atropine (49, 84, 85) or ganglionic-blocking agents (49). Reflex contractions of the reticulum have also been evoked by electrical stimulation of afferent fibers in the vagus nerves (7, 33, 46, 84). These observations, together with the observation that contractions of the reticulum in response to its stretch may be obtained in decerebrate preparations in which the spinal cord had been cut in the upper cervical region (84), suggest that the response is a vago-vagal reflex.

Evidence obtained from studies on impulse traffic in afferent vagal fibers suggests that the reticulum is provided with mechanoreceptors responsive to both passive stretch of the reticulum and to contraction of the reticulum (45, 46, 49). These receptors have been characterized as slowly adapting "in series" tension receptors. By direct mechanical stimulation most of the receptors were found to be situated close to the ventral part of the esophageal groove, that is, in the medial and caudal walls of the reticulum. The receptive area of mechanoreceptors associated with a single afferent fiber was 1–2 cm². The threshold for initiation of afferent fiber impulses was a balloon pressure of about 7.5 mm Hg; beyond this pressure the frequency of impulses increased by 0.7 impulses/sec per mm Hg distention pressure. Impulses in mechanoreceptor vagal afferent fibers from reticulum increased during contractions of the reticulum. When reticulum contractions were stimulated and recorded under iso-

metric conditions, a considerable increase in afferent impulses occurred with each contraction; with isotonic recording conditions, a lesser discharge was recorded with each reticulum contraction [(46, 48, 49, 56); B. F. Leek, unpublished data].

In decerebrate preparations the reflex responses of the reticulum to its maintained stretch display long latencies, susceptibility to central inhibition, and facilitation by afferent stimulation of other parts of the gut; they continue for a relatively long time (30–50 min) as a series of contractions (84). The first of such a series of reflex contractions may be monophasic in decerebrate or anesthetized preparations (7, 84); later contractions are diphasic. Once a series of reflex contractions of the reticulum in response to a given degree of stretch has ceased, another series may be initiated by greater stretch (84). Both the latency and the duration of the response to reticulum stretch vary according to the experimental conditions. In circumstances associated with a constant inhibitory stimulus, the response may be late and short lived.

Both excitatory and inhibitory effects of stretch of the reticulum on parotid salivary secretion have been recognized (4, 22). Inhibitory effects of stretch of the reticulum on B sequences of rumen contraction have been identified in conscious animals (70) and decerebrate preparations (75). When this inhibition was evident, there were at the same time excitatory effects on reticulum contractions. The reduction in the force and frequency of B sequences of rumen contractions was accompanied by an increased threshold for eructation. The possibility of mechanical embarrassment to the passage of gas from the rumen into the esophagus was precluded (75). Increased frequency of contractions of the caudal thoracic esophagus resulting from stretch of the reticulum has been reported in decerebrate preparations (78); an inhibition of esophageal contractions by reticulum stretch has also been reported. It is probable that at least some of the inhibitory effects of reticulum stretch are mediated by vagal afferents.

Evidenced by responses obtained in conscious animals, tactile receptors occur in the reticulum. A relatively evanescent response to a stimulus, likely to have been tactile, has been obtained as an increased frequency of reticulum (4) and associated A sequences of rumen contractions (70) and of parotid salivary secretion (4). This form of stimulation may also induce rumination (4, 70, 77). In conscious sheep with chronic transection of the lower cervical spinal cord, the responses to tactile stimulation were found to be short lived by comparison with those obtained with stretch of the reticulum (70). Possibly tactile receptors in the reticulum are rapidly adapting, whereas its "in series" tension receptors are slowly adapting. Structures believed to be sensory receptors in the reticulum have been described by both Hill (41) and Habel (40).

Stimulation of Reticulo-Ruminal Fold

Both tactile and stretch stimulation of the reticulo-ruminal fold have been implicated in modification of motility of reticulum, rumen, and esophagus and in the stimulation of parotid salivary secretion (4, 22, 78). Excitatory effects of stretch of the reticulo-ruminal fold have been obtained in decerebrate preparations in which the spinal cord was cut in the upper cervical regions (85) and in conscious animals in which the spinal cord had been chronically transected in the lower cervical region (70). It appears probable that the afferents concerned are contained in the vagus nerves. It has been commented, "The responses to stretch of the reticulo-ruminal fold in addition to stretch of the reticulum usually exhibited a shorter latent period, reached a maximum sooner, provoked a greater response in terms of force and frequency of contractions of the rumen and reticulum and of parotid salivary flow and endured longer than did the response to stretch of the reticulum alone" (23). A comparison of the responses of the reticulum and rumen to distention of a balloon confined to the reticulum, projecting from the reticulum

through the reticulo-ruminal orifice and located in the cranial regions of the dorsal sac of the rumen, can be made by reference to the kymograph record shown as Figure 6. The contractions of the rumen evoked, in decerebrate preparations, by stretch of both the reticulum and the reticulo-ruminal fold appear to be analogous to those associated with contractions of the reticulum in conscious animals and called "A sequences of contraction."

Similar excitatory effects have been observed with stretch of the reticulo-ruminal fold in conscious animals. An inhibitory effect of stretch of the reticulo-ruminal fold has also been observed in conscious animals as an abrupt termination of rumination with distention of a balloon located in the reticulo-ruminal orifice. Stimulation, apparently of a tactile nature delivered specifically to the reticulo-ruminal fold, causes an increase in the frequency of reticulum and associated A sequences of contractions in conscious animals, promotes an increased secretion of parotid saliva, and may initiate rumination (4, 70).

Definition of the sensitivity of the reticulo-ruminal fold to stretch and tactile stimulation is important. This is emphasized by an action of the reticulo-ruminal fold that has been demonstrated in cineradiographic studies (27). When the reticulo-ruminal fold remains contracted after the completion of the second phase of the diphasic contraction of the reticulum, it serves for a time to hold back ingesta from the reticulum in the rumen. After this temporary retention of ingesta in the cranial region of the rumen, there is

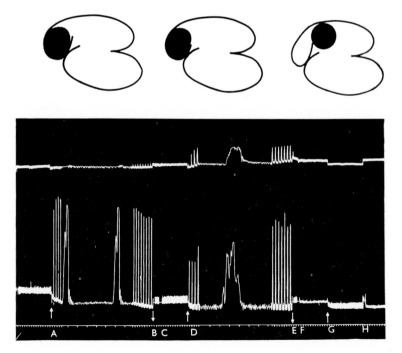

FIG. 6. Decerebrate sheep—kymograph records of uppermost contraction of middorsal sac of rumen (lever record), trace from water manometer connected to balloon distended in the three positions indicated by diagrams above tracing. Time marker 60 sec during slow drum speeds, 10 sec during fast speeds. A, introduction of 250 ml of water into balloon confined to reticulum, removed at B. C, movement of balloon into reticulo-ruminal orifice. D, introduction of 250 ml of water into balloon when projecting into reticulo-ruminal orifice and stretching reticulo-ruminal fold. Water removed at E, F, balloon moved into cranial dorsal sac of rumen. G, introduction of 250 ml of water into balloon now in cranial dorsal sac of rumen, water removed at H. Distention of the balloon in the reticulum (A–B) stimulated reticulum contractions. Distention of the balloon when it stretched the reticulo-ruminal fold (D–E) stimulated reticulum and rumen contractions. [After Titchen (84).]

first a gradual and then a more rapid flow of material from the rumen back into the reticulum. In this way tactile and stretch stimuli may be repeatedly delivered to the fold.

Stimulation of Rumen

Stimuli delivered to the rumen affect gastric and esophageal motility, salivary secretion, and rumination. Both excitatory and inhibitory effects have been observed. The effective forms of stimulation include tactile stimulation, generalized and localized distention, and changes in the chemical composition of ruminal contents. A comprehensive review of the many reports of the effects of ruminal stimulation is not attempted here. Observations are cited that illustrate the nature of the stimuli, their effects, and conditions under which they may be demonstrated.

Tactile stimulation of the mucosa appears to be most effective when applied to certain regions of the rumen. In view of its action in the initiation of rumination, in increasing the frequency of reticulum and associated rumen contractions (A sequences), and in the stimulation of parotid salivary secretion, the regions of the rumen most sensitive to tactile stimulation are the more cranial parts of its dorsal sac, the reticuloruminal fold, the cranial pillar, and, to lesser extent, the caudal pillar (4, 70, 71). Tactile stimulation of the rumen has been shown to modify the frequency of reticulum and rumen contractions and also the form of rumen contractions. This has been demonstrated in conscious sheep with chronic transection of the lower cervical spinal cord. In those fasted for 18–24 hours, tactile stimulation, particularly of the regions of the rumen already mentioned, changed the form of A sequences of rumen contraction from that characteristic of fasted animals to one more typical of the recently fed or feeding animal (70).

Both excitatory and inhibitory effects of distention of a discrete region of the rumen have been recognized. In a preparation in which the most cranial regions of the rumen adjacent to the esophagus were isolated, gaseous distention evoked eructation, whereas aqueous distention did not. The failure of eructation to occur was due to a persistent contraction of the cranial esophageal sphincter and was thus in effect a specific excitatory response (of the sphincter) which caused an "inhibition" (of eructation). The inhibition of eructation was abolished by the application of a solution of local anesthetic to the mucosa in this region of the rumen; this procedure had no effect on the excitatory action of gaseous distention. It was suggested that the inhibitory effects were mediated by superficially situated receptors and the excitatory effects by more deeply placed receptors (26). It was recognized that receptors in the more cranial regions of the rumen were not the only ones involved in the evocation of eructation; the superficially located receptors were thought to signal whether the region of the cardia was free of or cleared of liquid ingesta (26). Sharma has considered alimentary tract receptor mechanisms in Volume I of this Section of the *Handbook*. Reference should be made to his discussion for a more complete account of some features of receptor responses.

Tactile stimulation has been interpreted as summating with stimulation of the rumen by distention in the production of B sequences of rumen contraction and eructation in decerebrate preparations (75). The inclusion of scabrous material in diets, which is likely to lead to high levels of gas production during the course of fermentative digestion, was suggested as a desirable feature (19).

Gaseous distention of the rumen stimulated eructation (25, 38) and B sequences of contractions in conscious animals (70, 93) and in decerebrate preparations (75). It has been suggested that this results specifically from the stimulation of receptors located in the caudal regions of the dorsal sac of the rumen (93). Stretch applied to the ventral part of the caudal dorsal blind sac of the rumen or stretch by traction in a dorsal direction of the caudal pillar of the rumen evoked and maintained a series of B sequences of rumen contractions in fasted conscious sheep (70). In these studies responses were also observed in sheep in which the spinal cord had been chronically transected in the lower cervical regions. Gaseous distention of the rumen stimulated eructation and B sequences of rumen contractions in decerebrate preparations placed at 45 degrees to the horizontal so that the insufflation of gas into the ventral rumen resulted in an accumulation of gas in the dorsal sac of the rumen [(75); Fig. 7]. These responses in decerebrate (intercollicular section) preparations were observed after high cervical spinal cord transection. The evidence suggests that gaseous distention of the dorsal sac of the rumen stimulates B sequences of rumen contractions and eructation as a vago-vagal reflex response. The craniad movement of gas in the rumen has been detected with cineradiography [(27); Akester and Titchen, unpublished observations]. Whether eructation occurs with the craniad movement of this gas cap is determined by the summed effects of gaseous distention, tactile stimulation, the stimulus delivered by the forward movement of the gas cap, and conditions in the orad regions of the rumen adjacent to the esophagus.

Inhibitory effects of greater degrees of distention of the rumen have been detected in conscious (25), anesthetized (52, 68), and decerebrate preparations (85). At least in the case of salivary responses, the inhibitory effects are believed to be mediated by vagal afferents (52, 68). The inhibitory effects recognized include a reduction in parotid salivary secretion, an inhibition of eructation, a reduction in the frequency and force of reticulum and rumen contractions, and a cessation of rumination (70). Distention of either the dorsal or the ventral sacs of the rumen and

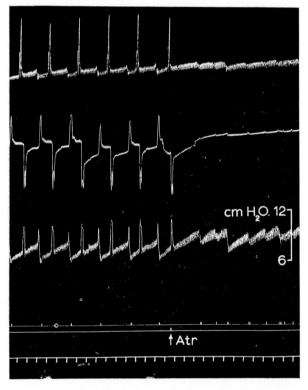

FIG. 7. Decerebrate sheep—records from above downward: reticulum contractions (balloon manometer record); mid-dorsal sac of rumen (upward deflection indicates forward movement of contraction, downward deflection backward movement); dorsal rumen gas pressure; signal indicating eructation; signal indicating injection of 0.1 mg/kg of atropine sulfate (Atr); time in 30 sec. Throughout record CO₂ was insufflated into rumen at 150 ml/min. Before administration of atropine, eructation occurred only in association with the forward-moving contractions of the rumen (those occurring without associated reticulum contraction). Reticulum and rumen contractions were abolished by atropine, after which eructation still occurred although at a higher threshold (in terms of dorsal rumen gas pressures). [After Reid & Titchen (75).]

stretch of the pillars of the rumen have been found to lead to a reduced frequency of contractions of the reticulum (4).

Inhibition of contractions of the reticulum and rumen has been demonstrated in both conscious and anesthetized sheep upon introduction of acids into the rumen (2, 17, 79). Lactic acid and the short-chain fatty acids—acetic, butyric, and propionic—produced these effects; mineral acids did not. The effects of the fatty acids were thought to be independent of changes in their concentrations in the blood; they were related specifically to stimulation of neural elements in the rumen wall (2). The inhibition was obtained in animals with an extensive sympathectomy; it appeared that the effects arose from central inhibition, initiated by afferent nerve fibers contained in the vagus nerves (2). These inhibitory effects following introduction of shorter-chain fatty acids into the rumen (2, 4, 80) and their excitatory effects on parotid salivary secretion (4) may be due to a nonspecific stimulation of receptors; the potency of acetic acid in the stimulation of skin receptors is well known.

The effects of chemical stimulation of the rumen cited are difficult to relate to normal circumstances because of the low pH at which they have been obtained; those of tactile stimulation and stretch are more readily equated with circumstances that arise with and after the ingestion of food. The ingestion of food material results in both tactile and distention stimulation of the rumen. A further distention arises with the increased evolution of gas during the microbial fermentation of the ingested material.

Omasal Stimulation

The passage of ingesta from the reticulo-rumen into the omasum appears to depend on both the integrity of the vagus nerves and the coordinated motility of the reticulum and reticulo-omasal orifice (5, 6, 63, 64, 67, 81). The reticulo-omasal orifice is an area of particular sensitivity to both stretch and tactile stimulation, to judge by the efficacy of such stimuli in the evocation of rumination (4), the promotion of increased reticulo-ruminal motility, and the stimulation of parotid salivary secretion (4). The effects on salivary secretion depend on the continued integrity of the vagus nerves.

In sheep, an estimate has been made that 5.8–18 liters of material may pass out of the reticulum in 24 hours (44), the amount varying according to the nature of the food. It has been suggested that the important factors determining what particles pass through the reticulo-omasal orifice are their size and specific gravity (5, 6). Associated with these ideas is one that the reticulo-omasal orifice serves, in some fashion, as a filter, or to impede the passage of grosser particulate material (6, 81) between the reticulum and the omasum. These considerations, together with the demonstrated sensitivity of the reticulo-omasal orifice to stretch and tactile stimuli and the effects of these on reticulo-ruminal motility, indicate the role the sensory innervation of this orifice plays in regulating the motility of the ruminant stomach and the passage of ingesta through it.

Omasal canal stimulation increased both the force and frequency of reticulum contractions in decerebrate preparations. This stimulation resulted from inflation of a balloon in the omasal canal; in addition, deformation of the body of the omasum that occurred on squeezing it stimulated reticulum contractions (84). These effects were abolished by section of the ventral abdominal vagus nerve trunk. A change of rumen contractions to a more complex form has been observed in a decerebrate preparation with omasal stimulation (85).

Inhibitory effects of omasal stimulation have been recognized. Cessation of rumination and reduced frequency and force of reticulum and rumen contractions and of those of the omasum and abomasum were reported in conscious animals with gross distention of the reticulo-omasal orifice (77).

Abomasal Stimulation

Excitatory effects of the introduction of acid into the abomasum have been recognized on reticulum and rumen contractions in decerebrate (84, 85) and anesthetized (48) preparations and in conscious animals (2). An excitatory effect of tactile stimulation of the abomasal mucosa has also been detected (84); both excitatory and inhibitory effects of abomasal distention on reticulum and rumen contractions (33, 66, 84, 85, 93) and inhibition of esophageal groove motility (21) have been reported.

In sheep and goats it was found that both abomasal acid secretion and reticulum contractions waned in an apparently related fashion over a period of 30–150 min after decerebration (84). This discovery led to a study of the effects of the introduction of acid into the abomasum (82, 84). Hydrochloric acid was shown to stimulate contractions of the reticulum when introduced at a concentration approximately that at which it is secreted by the oxyntic cells. Acid receptors intimately associated with oxyntic cells were postulated.

Electrophysiological studies indicated the existence of acid receptors in the cat's stomach (47). The reflex response of the reticulum to the introduction of acid into the abomasum has also been obtained in anesthetized animals in which both reticulum contractions and reticulum efferent vagal fiber impulses have been studied [(48); Fig. 8].

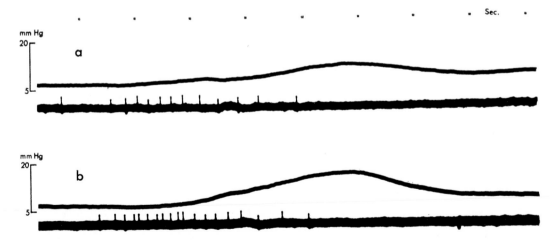

FIG. 8. Sheep in halothane anesthesia. Increased force of reticulum contraction and increase in impulses in efferent vagal preganglionic fibers (destined for the reticulum) after introduction of 50 ml 0.2 N HCl into the abomasum. Upper record: a control reflex contraction of the reticulum and impulses in vagal preganglionic fibers. In the lower record can be seen increases in both, recorded 90 sec after introduction of HCl into the abomasum. [After A. Iggo & B. F. Leek (48)]

Increased force and frequency of reticulum contractions have been observed in conscious animals with the introduction of acetic acid into the abomasum (2). The latency of this response in conscious animals was of the same order as the response to HCl in decerebrate preparations (i.e., 60–90 sec). The time course of the response to the introduction of acetic acid into the abomasum suggests that the acetic acid stimulates receptors directly and not indirectly by exciting acid

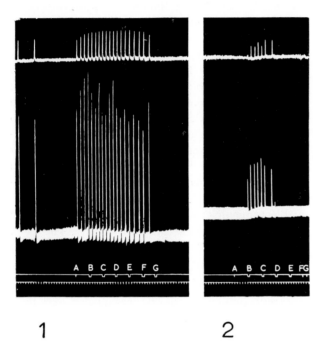

FIG. 9. Records of decerebrate sheep preparation. Summated effects of stretch of the reticulum and the introduction of acid into the abomasum. Records from above downward: contractions of the middorsal sac of the rumen (movement of wall recorded with a string lever system); reticulum contractions (balloon water manometer system); signal; 60-sec time marker. In both tracings, A signals the introduction of 50 ml of 0.2 N HCl into the abomasum isolated from the rest of the stomach by ligatures tied round the pylorus and the omaso-abomasal junction. Samples of abomasal contents were taken at B, C, D, E, F, and the acidity determined by titration was:

	Panel 1	Panel 2
B	0.186 N	0.175 N
C	0.162 N	0.173 N
D	0.134 N	0.158 N
E	0.128 N	0.142 N
F	0.110 N	0.112 N

The abomasum was washed out with saline at G in both cases. Panel 1: the reticulum balloon contained 250 ml water; panel 2: the reticulum balloon contained 15 ml water. The first contraction of the reticulum in panel 2 occurred after manipulation of the abomasal cannula for the withdrawal of sample B. [After Titchen (85).]

secretion. It has not been shown whether the same receptors are stimulated by the introduction of HCl and acetic acid into the abomasum. It is unlikely that the reticulo-ruminal responses to the introduction of acetic acid into the abomasum were due to the stimulation of gastric HCl secretion. But acetic acid introduced into either the rumen or the abomasum serves as a potent stimulus to the secretion of HCl from the abomasum (3, 42, 43).

Frequently, in decerebrate and anesthetized preparations, acid introduced into the abomasum may stimulate contractions of both the reticulum and the rumen by its summation with other stimuli. Such a summation is evident in Figure 9.

Responses to tactile stimulation of the abomasum have been detected in decerebrate preparations of both sheep and goats. It was found that either touching the abomasal mucosa with a glass rod or manipulating a cannula tied into the abomasum may stimulate one or more contractions of the reticulum (84).

Both excitatory and inhibitory effects of distention of the abomasum have been recognized in conscious animals and in anesthetized and decerebrate preparations (33, 66, 84, 85). In conscious sheep it was found that distention of a balloon in the abomasum led to a reduction in the force and frequency of reticulum and associated rumen contractions (A sequences) and no change (66) in B sequences of rumen contractions. In decerebrate preparations the effects of abomasal distention on A sequences of rumen contractions have been uniformly inhibitory. In contrast reflexly stimulated contractions of the reticulum are not necessarily inhibited by abomasal distention. An absolute inhibition of them may arise, or there may be a reduction in the force of reticulum contractions with an increase in their frequency. Excitatory effects of abomasal distention have also been recognized as an increase in the frequency of reticulum contractions which were not reduced in force. These excitatory effects on the reticulum have been obtained during periods of absolute inhibition of the normally associated contractions of the rumen (A sequences) [(85); Fig. 10]. In studies in decerebrate preparations the effects of abomasal distention on B sequences of rumen contraction were equivocal. It was not possible consistently to demonstrate an excitatory or inhibitory effect. Excitatory effects of abomasal distention were obtained, but it was impossible to distinguish whether these were truly responses to abomasal distention or were due to transfer of pressure to the rumen (75). A major difficulty in experiments in decerebrate preparations has been the inhibition that becomes a particularly dominant feature when more extensive dissections are undertaken. Such extensive dissections proved necessary in experiments aimed at an analysis of the effects of abomasal stimulation on B sequences of rumen contractions (75). The ease with which inhibition follows dissection or other procedures has also been commented on by Iggo & Leek (49), who encountered this problem in their experiments at even the deepest planes of anesthesia.

Afferent nerve fibers that mediate the effects of abomasal distention appear to take their courses to the central nervous system either in the vagus nerves or in sympathetic nerve trunks, particularly the splanchnic nerves (33, 84). Both inhibitory and excitatory effects of stimulation in an afferent sense of a large abomasal branch of the ventral vagus nerve trunk have been recognized (33, 60, 84). It is possible to interpret results obtained with abomasal distention before and after section of the splanchnic nerves as an indication that three groups of afferent nerve fibers are concerned—splanchnic afferent fibers from the abomasum whose receptors have a low threshold to distention and which mediate inhibitory effects, vagal afferent fibers whose receptors have high thresholds for distention and whose effects are inhibitory, and low-threshold excitatory vagal fibers.

An association between the activities of the abomasum and those of the reticulum and rumen is achieved through the sensitivities of each of these parts of the stomach to conditions in the others. The importance of this, particularly in another regard—the control of abomasal secretion—has been discussed elsewhere (3, 42, 43). The result of this complex interrelation between forestomach and abomasal activity is that the ruminant stomach functions as a closely coordinated unit and not as a series of independent compartments.

Enteric Stimulation

Distention of the duodenum of conscious sheep has been shown to inhibit contractions of the reticulum and rumen. Similar effects were not obtained simply with the flow through the duodenum of abomasal contents (67). It has been found that the removal of duodenal contents serves to increase outflow from the abomasum, and it was concluded that ". . . distention of the duodenum therefore has a controlling effect on the outflow from the abomasum in exactly the same way as the volume of material in the abomasum influences flow from the abomasum" (67).

Abomasal acid secretion, reticulum and rumen contractions, and outflow of digesta from the abomasum can all be inhibited by the infusion of long-chain fatty acids into the duodenum; which, if any, of these effects is the primary one has not been defined. The rapidity with which the inhibition of reticulo-ruminal motility develops during the infusion of, for example, oleic acid into the duodenum (88) makes it tempting to suggest that the effect is either primarily on abomasal acid secretion or on reticulo-ruminal motility. It has been suggested that these effects of infusions of oil into the duodenum are due to the release of enterogastrone (43). The intravenous infusion of 0.1 ml per kg of oleic acid has a profound inhibitory effect on both acid secretion and reticulo-ruminal motility [(88); McLeay and Titchen, unpublished observations]. It is interesting to observe that, during the later stages of the inhibition of reticulum and ruminal motility after infusions of long-chain fatty acids into the duodenum, B sequences of rumen contractions remain although A sequences disappear completely (62, 88). Differential effects of abomasal distention on the different forms of contractions of the rumen have been recognized in conscious sheep. A delay in abomasal emptying during intraduodenal infusions of oil has been reported (43).

FIG. 10. Records of decerebrate goat preparation. Excitatory effects on the reticulum, inhibitory effects on the rumen of distention of the abomasum (with 250 ml of saline indicated by *A*). Records from above downward: middorsal sac of rumen (string lever record); reticulum (balloon water manometer trace); signal; 60-sec time marker. Stimulus to reticulum and rumen contractions, distention (with 200 ml) of balloon extending through reticulo-ruminal orifice. [After Titchen (85).]

Conditions in the lower regions of the alimentary tract may also influence reticulum and rumen motility. This was identified by Weiss (93) who found a reduction in reticulum and associated A sequences of rumen contractions during the distention delivered to the cecum by insufflation of air into it. Lesser effects on B sequences of rumen contractions were observed. There may be a parallel between these effects and those described in animals with a simpler stomach as the "enterogastric reflex."

Coordination of Motility of Ruminant Stomach

Emphasis has been directed in this presentation to the reflex control exerted at a medullary level over the motility of the reticulum and rumen. Increased frequency of reticulum and associated A sequences of rumen contractions have been observed in fasted animals while preparations were being made to feed them (69). Rumination may cease if animals are disturbed. Reductions in the frequency of contractions of the reticulum and rumen have also been observed in experimental animals when disturbed. It has been suggested from a study of the effects of the ablation of the orbitofrontal lobes of the cerebral cortex in goats (9) that the cortex may exert a controlling influence over those regions of the medulla oblongata in which the basic reflex centers are believed to be situated.

Stimulation studies have provided some evidence of an influence of the hypothalamus over these medullary centers (53).

Changes in the motility of the reticulum and rumen associated with hyperglycemia and hypoglycemia (13, 55, 89) with alterations in the CO_2-combining capacity of the blood (93) and with alterations in blood concentrations of the short-chain volatile fatty acids (54) have been recorded. Where and how these changes exert their influence have not been defined. It is conceivable that such changes may lead to alterations in the excitability of the neurons of the medullary centers directly or indirectly by effects originating elsewhere. The frequency and form of contractions of different parts of the ruminant stomach are determined by the efferent discharge from medullary centers. These centers are influenced by a wide spectrum of afferent impulses, many but not all of which are initiated by stimulation of receptors in the alimentary tract. These centers are in turn affected by influences from higher parts of the central nervous system; their excitability and that of the sensory receptors and of effector organs may be directly or indirectly influenced hormonally, and by their immediate chemical environment due either to changes in the composition of the blood or to local metabolic activities.

REFERENCES

1. ANDERSSON, B., R. KITCHELL, AND N. PERSSON. A study of central regulation of rumination and reticulo-rumenal motility. *Acta Physiol. Scand.* 46: 319–338, 1959.
2. ASH, R. W. Inhibition and excitation of reticulo-rumen contractions following the introduction of acids into the rumen and abomasum. *J. Physiol., London* 147: 58–73, 1959.
3. ASH, R. W. Acid secretion by the abomasum and its relation to the flow of food material in the sheep. *J. Physiol., London* 156: 93–111, 1961.
4. ASH, R. W., AND R. N. B. KAY. Stimulation and inhibition of reticulum contractions, rumination and parotid salivary secretion from the forestomach of conscious sheep. *J. Physiol., London* 149: 43–57, 1959.
5. BALCH, C. C., AND R. C. CAMPLING. Rate of passage of digesta through the ruminant digestive tract. In: *Physiology of Digestion in the Ruminant*, edited by R. W. Dougherty. Washington, D. C.: Butterworths, 1965, p. 108–123.
6. BALCH, C. C., A. KELLY, AND G. HEIM. Factors affecting the utilization of food by dairy cows. 4. The action of the reticulo-omasal orifice. *Brit. J. Nutr.* 5: 207–216, 1951.
7. BEGHELLI, V., G. BORGATTI, AND P. L. PARMEGGIANI. On the role of the dorsal nucleus of the vagus in the reflex activity of the reticulum. *Arch. Ital. Biol.* 101: 365–384, 1963.

8. BELL, F. R., AND A. M. LAWN. Localisation of regions in the medulla oblongata of sheep associated with rumination. *J. Physiol., London* 128: 577–592, 1955.
9. BELL, F. R., AND A. M. LAWN. Disturbance of rumination in the goat after ablation of the orbito-frontal lobes of the cerebral cortex. *Brit. J. Animal Behavior* 5: 125–130, 1957.
10. BENZIE, D., AND A. T. PHILLIPSON. *The Alimentary Tract of the Ruminant.* Edinburgh: Oliver, 1957.
11. BORGATTI, G., AND R. MATSCHER. Voies et signification du réflexe oral du réseau. *Arch. Ital. Biol.* 96: 38–57, 1958.
12. BORGATTI, G., AND R. MATSCHER. La fonction du sphincter réseau-feuillet étudiée chez l'agneau à alimentation lacteo-végétale en rapport avec l'activité rhythmique du réseau et l'activité de déglutition de la gouttière oesophagienne. *Arch. Ital. Biol.* 96: 58–77, 1958.
13. BOWEN, J. M. Effects of insulin hypoglycemia on gastrointestinal motility in the sheep. *Am. J. Vet. Res.* 23: 948–954, 1962.
14. BROWNLEE, A. The development of rumen papillae in cattle fed on different diets. *Brit. Vet. J.* 112: 369–375, 1956.
15. BRUNAUD, M. Méthode d'étude de l'action du nerf pneumogastrique sur les estomacs du mouton. *Bull. Acad. Vet. France* 26: 375–380, 1953.
16. BRUNAUD, M., AND J. NAVARRO. Modifications sous l'in-

fluence de substances ganglioplégiques de l'action du nerf vague sur les estomacs du mouton. *J. Physiol., Paris* 46: 272–276, 1954.

17. CLARK, R., AND B. A. LOMBARD. Studies on the alimentary tract of the merino sheep in South Africa. XXII. The influence of the pH of the ruminal contents on ruminal motility. *Onderstepoort J. Vet. Sci.* 25: 79–92, 1951.

18. CLARK, R., AND K. E. WEISS. Reflex salivation in sheep and goats initiated by mechanical stimulation of the cardiac area of the fore stomachs. *J. S. African Vet. Med. Assoc.* 23: 163–165, 1952.

19. COLVIN, H. W., P. T. CUPPS, AND H. H. COLE. Dietary influences on eructation and related phenomena in cattle. *J. Dairy Sci.* 41: 1565–1579, 1958.

20. COMLINE, R. S., AND D. A. TITCHEN. Contractions of the reticulum of the young goat. *J. Physiol., London* 115: 24P, 1951.

21. COMLINE, R. S., AND D. A. TITCHEN. Reflex contractions of the oesophageal groove in young ruminants. *J. Physiol., London* 115: 210–226, 1951.

22. COMLINE, R. S., AND D. A. TITCHEN. Reflex contractions of the reticulum and rumen and parotid salivary secretion. *J. Physiol., London* 139: 24P, 1957.

23. COMLINE, R. S., AND D. A. TITCHEN. Nervous control of the ruminant stomach. In: *Digestive Physiology and Nutrition of the Ruminant*, edited by D. Lewis. London: Butterworths, 1961, p. 10–22.

24. CZEPA, A., AND R. STIGLER. Der wiederkauermagen im rontgenbild. *Arch. Ges. Physiol.* 212: 300–356, 1926.

25. DOUGHERTY, R. W. Physiological studies of induced and natural bloat in dairy cattle. *J. Am. Vet. Med. Assoc.* 96: 43–46, 1940.

26. DOUGHERTY, R. W., R. E. HABEL, AND H. E. BOND. Esophageal innervation and the eructation reflex in sheep. *Am. J. Vet. Res.* 19: 115–128, 1958.

27. DOUGHERTY, R. W., AND C. D. MEREDITH. Cinefluorographic studies of the ruminant stomach and of eructation. *Am. J. Vet. Res.* 16: 96–100, 1955.

28. DUNCAN, D. L. The effects of vagotomy and splanchnotomy on gastric motility in the sheep. *J. Physiol., London* 119: 157–169, 1953.

29. DUNCAN, D. L. Responses of the gastric musculature of the sheep to some humoral agents and related substances. *J. Physiol., London* 125: 475–487, 1954.

30. DUNCAN, D. L., AND A. T. PHILLIPSON. The development of the motor responses in the stomach of the foetal sheep. *J. Exptl. Biol.* 28: 32–40, 1951.

31. DUSSARDIER, M. Action *in vivo* de l'acétylcholine et de l'adrenaline sur la motricité gastrique des ruminants. *J. Physiol., Paris* 46: 777–797, 1954.

32. DUSSARDIER, M. Controle nerveux du rhythme gastrique des ruminants. *J. Physiol., Paris* 47: 170–173, 1955.

33. DUSSARDIER, M. *Recherches sur la Controle Bulbaire de la Motricité Gastrique Chez Les Ruminants (Thèse Doctorat és Sciences)*. Paris: Institut Nationale de la Recherche Agronomique, 1960.

34. DUSSARDIER, M., AND D. ALBE-FESSARD. Quelque propriétés du centre vagal controlant l'activité réflexe de l'estomac des ruminants. *J. Physiol., Paris* 46: 354–357, 1954.

35. DUSSARDIER, M., J. FLINOIS, AND J. P. ROUSSEAU. Localisation des centres bulbaires qui commandent la motricité gastrique. *J. Physiol., Paris* 52: 90–91, 1960.

36. DUSSARDIER, M., AND J. NAVARRO. Étude in vitro des actions motrices exercéés par l'adrenaline et l'acetylcholine sur les estomacs des bovidés. *J. Physiol., Paris* 45: 569–595, 1953.

37. DZUIK, H. E., AND A. F. SELLERS. Physiological studies of the vagal nerve supply in milk-fed and roughage-fed calves, using a chronic intra-thoracic vagal electrode technique. *Am. J. Vet. Res.* 16: 411–417, 1955.

38. DZUIK, H. E., AND A. F. SELLERS. Physiological studies of the vagal nerve supply to the bovine stomach. II. Studies on the eructation mechanism in adult cattle. *Am. J. Vet. Res.* 16: 499–504, 1955.

39. ELIASSON, S. G. Central control of digestive functioning. In: *Handbook of Physiology. Neurophysiology*, edited by J. Field, H. W. Magoun, and V. E. Hall. Washington, D.C.: Am. Physiol. Soc., 1960, sect. 1, vol. 2, chapt. 45, p. 1164.

40. HABEL, R. E. A study of the innervation of the ruminant stomach. *Cornell Vet.* 46: 555–628, 1956.

41. HILL, K. J. Nervous structures in the reticulo-ruminal epithelium of the lamb and kid. *Quart. J. Exptl. Physiol.* 44: 222–238, 1959.

42. HILL, K. J. The abomasum. *Vet. Rev. Annotations* 7: 83–106, 1961.

43. HILL, K. J. Abomasal secretory function in the sheep. In: *Physiology of Digestion in the Ruminant*, edited by R. W. Dougherty. Washington, D.C.: Butterworths, 1965, p. 221–230.

44. HOGAN, J. P. The digestion of food by the grazing sheep. I. The rate of flow of digesta. *Australia J. Agri. Res.* 15: 384–396, 1964.

45. IGGO, A. Tension receptors in the stomach and the urinary bladder. *J. Physiol., London* 128: 593–607, 1955.

46. IGGO, A. Central nervous control of gastric movements in sheep and goats. *J. Physiol., London* 131: 248–256, 1956.

47. IGGO, A. Gastric mucosal chemoreceptors with vagal afferent fibres in the cat. *Quart. J. Exptl. Physiol.* 42: 398–409, 1957.

48. IGGO, A., AND B. F. LEEK. Reflex regulation of gastric activity. *Acta Neuroveget., Vienna* 28: 353–359, 1966.

49. IGGO, A., AND B. F. LEEK. An electrophysiological study of vagal efferent units associated with gastric movements in sheep. *J. Physiol., London* 191: 177–204, 1967.

50. ITABISASHI, T. Electrophysiological studies on the movement of the ruminant stomach. III. Relations between periodic potential fluctuations and intragastric pressure in goats. *Natl. Inst. Animal Health Quart.* 4: 115–124, 1964.

51. KAY, R. N. B. Rumination in sheep caused by injection of adrenaline. *Nature* 183: 552–553, 1959.

52. KAY, R. N. B., AND A. T. PHILLIPSON. Response of the salivary glands to distension of the oesophagus and rumen. *J. Physiol., London* 148: 507–523, 1959.

53. LARSSON, S. On the hypothalamic organization of the nervous mechanism regulating food intake. *Acta Physiol. Scand.* 32: Suppl. 115, 1954.

54. LE BARS, H., J. LEBRUMENT, R. NITESCU, AND H. SIMONNET. Recherches sur la motricité du rumen chez les petits ruminants. IV. Action de l'injection intraveineuse d'acides gras à courtes chaines. *Bull. Acad. Vet. France* 27: 53–67, 1954.

55. LE BARS, H., R. NITESCU, AND H. SIMONNET. Recherches sur la motricité du rumen chez les petits ruminants. II. Relation entre la motricité et la glycémie. *Bull. Acad. Vet. France* 27: 53–67, 1954.

56. LEEK, B. F. Single unit activity in cervical vagal efferent axons associated with reticulo-ruminal movements. *J. Physiol., London* 169: 5–6P, 1963.

57. MARTINSON, J. The effect of graded stimulation of efferent vagal nerve fibres on gastric motility. *Acta Physiol. Scand.* 62: 256–262, 1964.

58. MARTINSON, J. The effect of graded vagal stimulation on gastric motility secretion and blood flow in the cat. *Acta Physiol. Scand.* 65: 300–309, 1965.

59. MARTINSON, J., AND A. MUREN. Excitatory and inhibitory effects of vagus stimulation on gastric motility in the cat. *Acta Physiol. Scand.* 57: 309–316, 1963.

60. MATSCHER, R., AND V. BEGHELLI. L'influenza dell'attivita abomasale sui prestomaci. Inibizione dell'atrio e del sacco ventrale del rumine per stimulazione elletrica del N. abomasale. *Arch. Sci. Biol.* 42: 251–262, 1958.

61. MCGILLIARD, A. D., AND N. L. JACOBSON. Physiological development of the ruminant stomach. In: *Physiology of Digestion in the Ruminant*, edited by R. W. Dougherty. Washington, D.C.: Butterworths, 1965, p. 39–50.

62. MCLEAY, L. M. *Control of Abomasal Secretion in the Sheep* (M. Agr. Sci. Thesis). Massey University, New Zealand, 1967.

63. OHGA, A., Y. OTA, AND Y. NAKAZATO. The movement of the stomach of the sheep with special reference to the omasal movement. *Japan. J. Vet. Sci.* 27: 151–160, 1965.

64. OYAERT, W., AND J. H. BOUCKAERT. A study of the passage of fluid through the sheep's omasum. *Res. Vet. Sci.* 2: 41–52, 1961.

65. PEYER, J. C. *Merycologia sive de Rumantibus et Ruminatione Commentarius*. Basle, 1685.

66. PHILLIPSON, A. T. The movements of the pouches of the stomach of the sheep. *Quart. J. Exptl. Physiol.* 29: 395–415, 1939.

67. PHILLIPSON, A. T., AND R. W. ASH. Physiological mechanisms affecting the flow of digesta in ruminants. In: *Physiology of Digestion in the Ruminant*, edited by R. W. Dougherty. Washington, D.C.: Butterworths, 1965, p. 97–107.

68. PHILLIPSON, A. T., AND C. S. W. REID. Distension of the rumen and salivary secretion. *Nature* 181: 1722–1723, 1958.

69. QUIN, J. I., AND J. G. VAN DER WATH. Studies on the alimentary tract of Merino sheep in South Africa. v. The motility of the rumen under various conditions. *Onderstepoort J. Vet. Sci.* 11: 361–382, 1938.

70. REID, C. S. W. *The Influence of the Afferent Innervation of the Ruminant Stomach on Its Motility* (Ph.D. Thesis). Cambridge: Univ. of Cambridge, 1962.

71. REID, C. S. W. Diet and motility of the forestomachs of the sheep. *Proc. New Zealand Soc. Animal Prod.* 23: 169–188, 1963.

72. REID, C. S. W., AND J. B. CORNWALL. The mechanical activity of the reticulo-rumen of cattle. *Proc. New Zealand Soc. Animal Products* 19: 23–35, 1959.

73. REID, C. S. W., A. W. MELVILLE, AND J. B. CORNWALL. A technique for recording pressure changes in the reticulo-rumen of cattle using small electrical pressure transducers and a four channel recorder. *New Zealand J. Agr. Res.* 3: 41–62, 1960.

74. REID, C. S. W., AND D. A. TITCHEN. Activity of the partially exteriorized reticulum and rumen in conscious sheep. *J. Physiol., London* 149: 14P, 1959.

75. REID, C. S. W., AND D. A. TITCHEN. Reflex stimulation of

76. RIEK, R. F. The influence of sodium salts on the closure of the oesophageal groove in calves. *Australian Vet. J.* 30: 29–37, 1954.

77. SCHALK, A. F., AND R. S. AMADON. Physiology of the ruminant stomach. *N. Dakota Agr. Expt. Sta. Bull. 216*, 1928.

78. SELLERS, A. F., AND D. A. TITCHEN. Responses to localised distension of the oesophagus in decerebrate sheep. *Nature* 184: 645, 1959.

79. SHINOZAKI, K. Studies on experimental bloat in ruminants. 5. Effects of various volatile fatty acids introduced into the rumen. *Tohoku J. Agr. Res.* 9: 237–250, 1959.

80. STEVENS, C. E., AND A. F. SELLERS. Studies on the reflex control of the ruminant stomach with special reference to the eructation reflex. *Am. J. Vet. Res.* 20: 461–482, 1959.

81. STEVENS, C. E., A. F. SELLERS, AND F. A. SPURRELL. Function of the bovine omasum in ingesta transfer. *Am. J. Physiol.* 198: 449–455, 1960.

82. TITCHEN, D. A. Reflex contractions of the reticulum. *J. Physiol., London* 122: 32P, 1953.

83. TITCHEN, D. A. Partial exteriorization of the reticulum in sheep. *J. Physiol., London* 139: 24P, 1958.

84. TITCHEN, D. A. Reflex stimulation and inhibition of reticulum contractions in the ruminant stomach. *J. Physiol., London* 141: 1–21, 1958.

85. TITCHEN, D. A. The production of rumen and reticulum contractions in decerebrate preparations of sheep and goats. *J. Physiol., London* 151: 139–153, 1960.

86. TITCHEN, D. A., AND C. S. W. REID. The nervous control of the ruminant stomach. *New Zealand Vet. J.* 12: 81–87, 1964.

87. TITCHEN, D. A., AND C. S. W. REID. The reflex control of the motility of the ruminant stomach. In: *Physiology of Digestion in the Ruminant*, edited by R. W. Dougherty. Washington, D.C.: Butterworths, 1965, p. 68–77.

88. TITCHEN, D. A., C. S. W. REID, AND P. VLIEG. Effects of intra-duodenal infusions of fat on the food intake of sheep. *Proc. New Zealand Soc. Animal Products* 26: 36–51, 1966.

89. VALLENAS, G. A. Effects of the glycemic levels on rumen motility in the sheep. *Am. J. Vet. Res.* 17: 78–89, 1956.

90. WARNER, R. G., AND W. P. FLATT. Anatomical development of the ruminant stomach. In: *Physiology of Digestion in the Ruminant*, edited by R. W. Dougherty. Washington, D.C.: Butterworths, 1965, p. 24–38.

91. WATSON, R. H. Studies on deglutition in sheep. 1. Observations on the course taken by liquids through the stomach at various ages from birth to maturity. *Bull. Australian Council Sci. Industrial Res.* 180: 1–94, 1944.

92. WATSON, R. H., AND I. G. JARRETT. Studies on deglutition in sheep 2. Observations on the influence of copper salts on the course taken by liquids into the stomach of sheep. *Bull. Australian Council Sci. Industrial Res.* 180: 95–126, 1944.

93. WEISS, K. E. Physiological studies on eructation in ruminants. *Onderstepoort J. Vet. Res.* 26: 251–283, 1953.

94. WISE, G. H. Factors affecting the reactions of the esophageal groove of dairy calves. *J. Dairy Sci.* 22: 465, 1939.

95. WISE, G. H., AND G. W. ANDERSON. Factors affecting the passage of liquids into the rumen of the dairy calf. 1. Method of administering liquids: drinking from open pail versus sucking through a rubber nipple. *J. Dairy Sci.* 22: 697–705, 1939.

movements of the rumen in decerebrate sheep. *J. Physiol., London* 181: 432–448, 1965.

CHAPTER 130

Ruminal fermentation[1]

R. E. HUNGATE | *University of California, Davis, California*

CHAPTER CONTENTS

THE RUMEN contains a mass of moist, often-replenished plant material held at a constant temperature in a medium devoid of oxygen. These features favor the growth of a very large number of anaerobic protozoa and bacteria of many kinds, each fermenting some component of the digesta and together producing the microbial bodies and volatile fatty acids used as

[1] More complete accounts are contained in: *Physiology of Digestion in the Ruminant*, edited by R. W. Dougherty, Washington, D. C.: Butterworths, 1965; R. E. Hungate, *The Rumen and Its Microbes*, New York: Acad. Press, 1966.

food by the host. There are undoubtedly viral agents in the rumen, but only a preliminary account of one virus has been reported (10).

The association between the ruminant and the rumen protozoa must be very ancient. There are at present no free-living, close relatives of the rumen protozoa. Only those descendants have survived that modified as their rumen habitat evolved. Free-living relatives have disappeared or evolved in such a direction that a relationship is no longer easily discernible.

The evidence is not nearly so conclusive for a restriction of specific bacteria to the rumen habitat. Some kinds of rumen bacteria also occur in the alimentary tract of other mammals (18). To the extent that each ruminant has its specific and characteristic rumen conditions, it supports a composite population characteristic for the particular species. This population may include some very specific bacteria, as well as less specific types that occur in the alimentary tracts of other animals. It is relatively easy to isolate and maintain ruminants free of protozoa; it is much more difficult to isolate and maintain them free of typical rumen bacteria (28). If germ-free ruminants become available, it may be possible to explore the question of bacterial specificity more precisely.

In analyzing the rumen it is important to select significant measurements of the system. The composition of the rumen microbiota is one of these.

BACTERIA OF THE RUMEN

Careful simulation of the rumen environment in culture media (32) has permitted the isolation and characterization of a wide variety of rumen bacteria

TABLE I. *Substrates and Fermentation Products of Some Bacteria of the Rumen*

Organism	Substrates	Products
Bacteroides succinogenes	Cellulose, cellobiose, glucose, CO_2	Succinate, acetate, formate
Ruminococcus	Cellulose, cellobiose, xylan, CO_2	Succinate, lactate, acetate, formate, ethanol, H_2
Butyrivibrio	10–20 Carbohydrates, varying among strains	Butyrate, lactate, ethanol, formate, CO_2, and sometimes acetate and propionate
Bacteroides ruminicola	Many sugars, CO_2	Succinate, acetate, formate
Bacteroides amylophilus	Starch, maltose, CO_2	Succinate, acetate, lactate, ethanol
Succinimonas amylolytica	Starch, maltose, CO_2	Succinate, acetate, propionate
Succinivibrio dextrinosolvens	Dextrin, maltose, xylose, pectin, CO_2	Acetate, succinate, lactate
Lachnospira multiparus	Pectin, esculin, salicin, cellobiose, glucose, fructose	Formate, acetate, lactate, ethanol, CO_2, H_2
Peptostreptococcus elsdenii	Lactate, glucose, fructose-maltose, mannitol, sorbitol	2–6 C fatty acids, H_2, CO_2
Selenomonas ruminantium	7–13 Carbohydrates, esculin, sometimes salicin, glycerol, mannitol	Acetate, propionate, CO_2, and often formate, butyrate, lactate, succinate
Streptococcus bovis	10–14 Sugars, starch, esculin, salicin	Lactate
Eubacterium	Glucose, cellobiose, and 4–6 other sugars	Formate, lactate, acetate, butyrate, CO_2, H_2
Methanobacterium	CO_2, H_2, formate	CH_4 and H_2O

(11). Use of a bicarbonate-carbon dioxide buffer, strict anaerobiosis, inclusion of rumen fluid as part of the medium, and direct dilution into agar cultures without previous liquid dilution were initially key factors in the successful isolation of rumen bacteria (31). With the knowledge subsequently gained, defined growth factors in many cases can substitute for rumen fluid (13).

Although a thorough description of the rumen bacteria cannot be given in this review, some of the main features will assist in understanding rumen fermentation. Insofar as carbohydrates are concerned, the rumen microflora exhibit two extremes. Certain species live on one or a very few of the carbohydrate components of a forage, whereas others can use a great many. Between these extremes are a number of intermediate types. Among the rumen bacteria that show considerable specificity in substrate selection are certain cellulose-digesting bacteria, namely *Bacteroides succinogenes*, *Ruminococcus flavefaciens*, and *R. albus*, and the starch-digesting *Bacteroides amylophilus*. These species degrade the indicated polysaccharide and its split components but in many cases not the monose. Most *Ruminococcus* strains can use cellobiose but not glucose, and *Bacteriodes amylophilus* uses maltose but not glucose. This extends also to some of the hemicelluloses; xylan is used by *Ruminococcus* but xylose is not.

At the opposite end of the nutritional spectrum is the genus *Butyrivibrio*; many strains digest starch, some attack cellulose, and numerous sugars can be fermented.

Examples of rumen bacteria and the substrates they utilize are shown in Table 1. In it are also shown the fermentation products formed by pure cultures. There are widely diverse fermentation types. A single type may be exhibited by a number of different species, whereas other fermentations are unique. The production of methane appears to be restricted to *Methanobacterium ruminantium* (54) and a recently isolated strain (48a). Similarly, the homofermentation of sugar to lactate occurs in *Streptococcus bovis*, a bacterium present in small numbers in animals on many kinds of feed.

The chief final products of the rumen fermentation of carbohydrates are carbon dioxide, methane, and acetic, propionic, and butyric acids. The products of pure cultures of rumen bacteria include also ethanol, lactate, succinate, formate, and hydrogen, which are not found as final fermentation products in the rumen. This could be due to a difference in metabolism of an organism in pure culture from its metabolism in the mixed rumen population or to a production of these molecules in the rumen and their rapid conversion to one or more of the final products.

Studies (39, 45) have shown that lactate and ethanol are not important intermediates in the rumen fermentation, but that succinate (7), formate (15), and hydrogen (34a) are. It had originally been assumed that lactate was the precursor of rumen

TABLE 2. *Nutritional Requirements of Some Bacteria of the Rumen*

	CO_2	One or More Volatile Fatty Acids	NH_3	Vitamins
Bacteroides succinogenes	E*	E	E	Biotin E, p-aminobenzoic acid (PBA) + to −
Ruminococcus	E	E	E	Biotin E, folic acid or PAB E, pyridoxamine E to −, thiamine + or −, riboflavin + or −
Butyrivibrio	+ to −	E to −	E to −	Biotin E, PAB E, pyridoxal E
Bacteroides ruminicola	E	E to −	+ to −	Some B vitamins E
Bacteroides amylophilus	E	−	E	None required
Succinimonas amylolytica	E	E	E	
Succinivibrio dextrinosolvens	+	−	+	
Lachnospira multiparus		Acetate +	−	
Peptostreptococcus elsdenii	−	Acetate +	−	
Selenomonas ruminantium	+ to −	E to −	−	
Streptococcus bovis	+	+ to −	+ to −	Biotin E, thiamine +, pantothenic acid + or −
Eubacterium		E to −	E	
Methanobacterium	E	E	E	B_{12} E, unknown factor E

* E indicates essential, + indicates degree of stimulation, − indicates not stimulatory.
Modified from Hungate (34).

propionate, but if it does not occur as an important intermediate and is not present in the feed, it is obvious that it cannot be a chief precursor of rumen propionate. Turnover studies with succinate (7) have indicated it is the propionate precursor. Table 1 shows that succinate is indeed produced by many pure cultures of bacteria. One of the mysteries of the bovine rumen is the identity of the organisms responsible for the conversion of succinate to propionate.

The relative importance of formate and hydrogen as intermediates in the rumen fermentation has been difficult to assess because of the rapid exchange between these materials. A small concentration of hydrogen can be demonstrated in rumen gas (42), and hydrogen incubated with rumen contents rapidly disappears, with an increase in methane production. The same increase is observed with formate. Measurements of dissolved hydrogen and formate and their relation to rates of methane production indicate that hydrogen rather than formate is the immediate precursor of rumen methane (34a).

The unimportance of lactate and ethanol in the mixed rumen fermentation can be explained by the fact that their production entails the sacrifice of a potential adenosine triphosphate (ATP) molecule. The pyruvate, precursor of lactic acid in microbial fermentations, could yield acetyl-CoA and ATP if it were not reduced to lactate. Similarly, acetyl-CoA, the normal precursor of ethanol in microbial fermentations, could yield an ATP if it were converted

to acetate rather than to ethanol. In the intense competition within the rumen soluble carbohydrate is limiting. An organism capable of deriving more ATP per carbohydrate molecule would have an advantage. The ATP sacrifice selects against lactate and ethanol as repositories for hydrogen atoms that must be transferred during the fermentation. Sequential use of a sugar by two species, one forming lactate or ethanol and the other using it, would not compete effectively with use by a single strain to form the same end products. The single strain could produce more cells than would either of the associated strains from the same substrate.

Nutrition of Rumen Bacteria

The nutritional requirements of some rumen bacteria are shown in Table 2. Among the nutrients required by some rumen bacteria are the straight and branched 4- to 6-carbon fatty acids (12). These arise during the breakdown of amino acids in the rumen (52). Many strains of bacteria require one or more of these acids in various combinations.

Some rumen bacteria require biotin, thiamine, p-aminobenzoic acid, folic acid, pyridoxin, and possibly additional vitamins. These do not need to be supplied in the feed since many of the rumen microorganisms produce them. The rumen synthesis of vitamins occurs to a greater or lesser extent, depending on the quantity of the vitamin in the feed. If the vitamins are in very low quantity in the feed but there is a sufficient supply of fermentable carbohydrate and nitrogenous nutrients, vitamins will be synthesized to a level adequate for the metabolism of both the rumen microbiota and the host. If they occur in the feed to a considerably greater extent than is normal in the rumen, they may be degraded or at least are not synthesized.

Many rumen bacteria utilize ammonia for the synthesis of cell material even in the presence of amino acids. Some bacteria utilize amino acids as a source of nitrogen and, in some cases, can be shown to assimilate peptides preferentially (49). Between these extremes are intermediate types of rumen bacteria for which ammonia may or may not be essential, amino acids may or may not be essential, and various other combinations of nutritional requirements occur.

Attachment to Digesta

In general the rumen bacteria have not been shown to be closely associated with the plant fibers in the digesta, although early reports (3) indicated that beds digested out of the plant material could be detected surrounding adherent cocci. *Bacteroides succinogenes* is more abundant on the fibers than it is in the medium as a whole. It is quite probable that *Lachnospira* also penetrates within the fibers. When the solid materials in the rumen contents of cattle fed alfalfa hay are macerated, a considerably greater proportion of colonies of *Lachnospira* is obtained than if rumen liquid is used as inoculum. The *Lachnospira* is capable of digesting pectin and may penetrate the intercellular lamellae.

Ruminococcus and *Butyrivibrio* are no more abundant on the fibers than in the liquid medium. Even in liquid media, however, they attain some sort of preferential position with relation to the fiber undergoing digestion. This is inferred from the following observations: In low serial dilutions of rumen contents into cellulose agar the dilutions containing 10^{-3} or 10^{-4} ml of rumen contents show little evidence of digestion of the cellulose suspended in the agar. In contrast, parallel liquid tubes show rapid and complete cellulose digestion. When a pure culture of *Ruminococcus* or *Butyrivibrio* is inoculated into cellulose agar, the cellulose is completely digested in all dilutions. The cellulolytic organisms cannot grow in the presence of accompanying forms in agar, whereas they can grow with accompanying forms in liquid medium. In agar the sugars formed by action of the cellulase are intercepted by the numerous contaminants to such an extent that the cellulase-elaborating cell receives no return from its product and cannot grow. In liquid it moves in some fashion to compete with neighbors for the sugar formed by its enzymes.

In high dilutions (10^5–10^7) of a cellulose agar medium inoculated with rumen contents, small clear spots can be seen in which the cellulose has been digested. These never become large, because as digestion increases the distance between the cellulose and the cellulolytic colony, accompanying noncellulolytic forms have an ever-increasing chance to capture the sugars.

Number of Bacteria in the Rumen

The number of total bacteria in rumen contents is best determined by direct count, particularly if the ruminant is on a forage ration. For animals on rations high in concentrate, the culture count approximates the direct count, but for forage diets the culture count is usually less than 20 % of the count detectable by direct microscopic examination. The reason for this difference is not known. A large fraction of the rumen bacteria may be dead, but more likely the culture conditions necessary to demonstrate all the rumen bacteria have not yet been discovered.

In general the number of bacteria per milliliter of rumen contents increases as the digestibility of the ration increases. The size of the microbial population is a function of the quantity of fermentable material and other nutrients: the greater the digestibility the greater is the concentration of bacteria.

An increased food intake will hardly affect the size of the microbial population if other factors remain constant, because the degree of digestion of the ration decreases only slightly with more rapid passage of the digesta. If the increase in the rate of rumen passage is due to greater salivary secretion the bacterial concentration would decrease.

Another generalization can be made with regard to the numbers of bacteria in relationship to time of feeding. The highest concentration of bacteria—i.e., the largest number of cells per milliliter of rumen content—is usually found just before feeding, and the number drops after feeding. This is due to dilution of organisms in the rumen by the feed and saliva. In contrast, the rate of fermentation is lower just before feeding. Thus diurnal variations due to infrequent feeding will show the highest concentration of bacteria when the fermentation rate is lowest, and vice versa.

With a ration high in concentrate, the number of

bacteria demonstrable by direct count may be as high as 10^{11} cells per ml. On poorer rations the count may be as low as 6×10^9. Brief periods of inanition do not greatly depress the bacterial population, but an extended period can cause a very considerable drop. Even after prolonged starvation, the rumen fermentation returns to normal within a day or two after feed is again supplied. This is due to the retention of rumen contents, both liquid and solid, to the extent of about 50% of normal, even in animals dying of starvation. Some bacteria survive within these digesta.

With young calves separated from the rest of the herd it is sometimes recommended that they be given rumen contents by mouth to provide a favorable microbiota. This may be of value under rare circumstances, but normally the rumen protozoa and bacteria are transferred from one individual to another by grazing the same area or by grooming with the tongue. Rumination moves the microorganisms to the mouth.

Rate of Growth

Relatively few careful studies have been made on the rates at which rumen bacteria can grow. Under favorable in vitro conditions *Streptococcus bovis* can divide as often as once in 20 min, and division rates as high as this may occur in the rumen when starch is fed to animals previously on a hay ration. But this high rate of division is exceptional, and most rumen organisms grow relatively slowly. Food is normally limiting in the rumen, and the bacteria cannot grow at their maximum potential rate.

A high net growth rate is not required for maintenance of a strain within the rumen. If the numbers of a particular kind of bacterium remain constant, the net rate of cell production can only be as great as the turnover rate constant for passage out of the rumen. A lower net rate of cell production would cause numbers to fall, and a higher rate would cause the population to increase. The time between divisions must be 0.69 of the turnover time in order for the rate of cell production to equal the turnover rate constant in a continuous fermentation system. Since turnover rate constants of between 1 and 3 per day are normal for rumen contents, the net growth rate requires an average division time for the bacteria in the rumen between 5 and 16 hours. The frequency of division must be greater than this if some of the bacteria die or are used as food by the protozoa. When feed is intermittent, the division frequency may be

greater for a short period after feeding, followed by a compensatory slower division.

PROTOZOA

Most of the rumen protozoa are ciliates. Some very small flagellates usually do not increase greatly in numbers unless the ciliate protozoa are removed, in which case the flagellates may become abundant.

The rumen ciliates are of two main types, the holotrichs and the entodiniomorphs. The surface of the holotrich is evenly covered with cilia, whereas in the entodiniomorphs zones of syncilia (membranelles) are found only around the mouth and in some genera on the dorsal region of the body.

Holotrichs

The holotrichs in cattle and sheep include two genera, *Isotricha* and *Dasytricha*, with three species, *I. prostoma*, *I. intestinalis*, and *D. ruminantium*. *Dasytricha* is smaller than *Isotricha*.

The holotrichs (46, 47) normally utilize sugars as a source of carbohydrates and absorb them rapidly when feed first enters the rumen. The sugars are fermented in part as they are absorbed, but if the concentration in the rumen is sufficiently high a fairly large fraction is stored as reserve starch within the protozoa. These starch grains are very small and are reported to be chemically identical with the starch grains of higher plants (22). When sugars are no longer available these starch grains are gradually digested within the protozoa. This arrangement extends the period of ready availability of energy.

If carbohydrates are too abundant in the rumen, starch storage may continue to the point that the protozoa burst (17, 26). They do not appear to have a mechanism for controlling starch storage in the presence of sugar. With most feeds this is not a handicap, but in some instances with lush legume feeds it may be important, as is mentioned later in AB-NORMALITIES IN THE RUMEN MICROBIAL FERMENTATION.

The holotrichs have been reported to consume bacteria, and it is assumed that they use them as food along with the carbohydrates. The species of *Iso-tricha* may on occasion ingest very small starch grains. This is relatively rare and is peculiar in that the iso-trichs are not able to utilize maltose whereas the smaller *Dasytricha* can, yet do not ingest starch. Sugars utilized by these protozoa include glucose, fructose, sucrose, and raffinose. *Dasytricha* also uses cellobiose and to a slightly less extent (30) galactose, amygdalin, and salicin.

Entodiniomorphs

The entodiniomorphs include the genus *Entodinium* in which the syncilia or adoral membranelles occur only around the mouth. They serve as organelles of locomotion and also for the ingestion of food. The food of the entodinia consists chiefly of starch grains and bacteria. Both are ingested rapidly, and in animals fed a high quantity of unheated starch in the diet the numbers of entodinia often become very high. In one case the nitrogen in the protozoa constituted a minimum of 40% of the nitrogen in the entire rumen contents, and most of the protozoa were *Entodinium*.

There are a great many species of *Entodinium* (19), and on almost all types of feed individuals of *Entodinium* are more numerous than any other protozoan genus. The various species of *Entodinium* are identified by their size and shape and also by the position, size, and shape of the macronucleus. This can be easily stained with methyl green in acetic acid. The micronucleus occurs on the inside of the macronucleus in *Entodinium*, in contrast to the other entodiniomorph genera, in which it is outside, toward the dorsal cell surface. Some entodinia have caudal spines, which often assist in the identification of species but vary widely.

The remaining genera of entodiniomorphs have the adoral syncilia plus a second ciliary band on the dorsal side, the dorsal membranelles. The genus *Diplodinium* is very large. It includes those species of protozoa in which the dorsal membranelles are about as far anterior as are the oral membranelles. *Diplodinium* is divided into the subgenera *Diplodinium*, *Eudiplodinium*, *Polyplastron*, *Elytroplastron*, *Ostracodinium*, and *Enoploplastron*. These are distinguished on the basis of the skeletal plates, the shape and position of the macronucleus, the size of the cell, the location and number of contractile vacuoles, and the spines at the posterior part of the body. As in the case of *Entodinium*, spination is a variable feature.

Members of the genus *Diplodinium* avidly ingest starch as well as bacteria. In addition a number of species ingest the fragments of plant fibers and digest the cellulose and hemicellulose. It is the members of the genus *Diplodinium* that normally contain the plant particles noted by so many investigators. The capacity of these protozoa to digest cellulose has been much discussed, but it now appears definite that they are capable of this activity. It is still possible that the actual digestion is due to bacteria living symbiotically within the protozoa, but this lacks experimental demonstration.

Some members of this genus are carnivorous on other protozoa (19), and very interesting specific relationships between certain species have been established (20). *Epidinium* and *Eudiplodinium maggii* were never found in the same rumen with *Polyplastron multivesiculatum*. This is due to the consumption of the two genera by *Polyplastron*. *Diplodinium affine* tended to be associated with *Polyplastron*. Other investigators have confirmed these observations.

The genus *Epidinium* has a much more slender and cylindrical shape than does *Diplodinium*, and in addition the dorsal membranelles are displaced a little more posteriorly than in *Diplodinium*. *Epidinium* may have from one to six caudal spines; the feature is not constant. Epidinia have been reported to be extremely abundant in cattle in New Zealand fed on red clover. They readily ingest starch and also use bacteria as food.

The genus *Ophryoscolex* is the most complex of the rumen ciliates. The body surface contains a great many small spines that may be variously arranged and are also variable in their number and development. The dorsal membranelle zone lies about one-third back from the anterior end of the animal and is so elongated that it almost completely encircles the cell. *Ophryoscolex* becomes abundant in animals fed on alfalfa and may often be seen to contain particles of ingested chlorophyll. These cells also consume starch readily.

Cultivation of Protozoa

Representatives of most of the genera of the rumen ciliates have been cultured in vitro, with the exception of *Isotricha*, which has been kept alive for only 40–50 days. Cultures of *Diplodinium*, *Entodinium*, and *Ophryoscolex* have been started with single cells and maintained over very long periods. It is probable that diligent attention to the other species would permit obtaining them also in clone culture, which is highly desirable for studying the morphological features of some of the genera occurring in several forms.

The in vitro cultures of the protozoa contain innumerable bacteria, and thus far it has not been possible to obtain gnotobiotic cultures, i.e., with known bacteria. Further work along these lines is needed in order to answer the question of specificity or non-specificity in the food relationships between the rumen bacteria and protozoa. Fluctuations in the kinds and numbers of the protozoa have been noted but not explained.

The fermentation of sugars, starch, and cellulose by the rumen protozoa results in the production of carbon dioxide, hydrogen, and various acids, of which acetic, butyric, and lactic are the most important. *Entodinium* produces a little propionic acid and formic acid but very little lactic acid. *Ophryoscolex* does not appear to produce any lactic acid. The visible gas production by the protozoa separated from the bacteria provides graphic evidence of their important fermentative activity, an observation supported by quantitative manometric measurements.

Number of Protozoa

The number of protozoa may range as high as 10^6 per ml or even more depending on the nature of the food, but their relatively large size causes them to be much more important in relation to bacteria than would be indicated by the number alone.

On certain types of feed in which the rumen becomes quite acid, the protozoa are killed. A normal number and variety of protozoa are the best indices for a healthy rumen and can be easily and quickly ascertained by direct microscopic examination of fresh material.

NATURE OF THE RUMEN FERMENTATION

One of the most important features of the rumen fermentation is its more or less continuous operation. To a greater or less extent, depending on the feeding regimen, the rumen fermentation is constant.

Use of a continuous fermentation model facilitates a number of quantitative estimates and comparisons of rumen function. When ruminants are fed only once or twice a day the actual functioning of the rumen departs significantly from the continuous fermentation model, but the average can be considered as continuous without too great an error, and with measurements made at a particular time each day the model is exactly applicable even if feeding is restricted to once per day, provided the time of feeding is always the same.

The continuous nature of the rumen fermentation is an important factor in the very high fermentation rate of the rumen. In a continuous system it is possible to maintain the high concentration of organisms required for a rapid fermentation.

Several features of a continuous fermentation system can be noted. The rate of addition and removal of materials must not exceed the net rate at which the microorganisms can grow or they will wash out. The rate of feed—that is, the fraction of the rumen volume or dry matter added per hour—must be less than the maximal growth rate unless the microbes have some means of avoiding spillover. In consequence the rumen microorganisms are growing at less than their maximum potential rate and must be regarded as in a more or less starved condition. This feature of the normal rumen is most easily demonstrated by addition of fresh food to rumen contents in vitro. Addition causes a marked increase in the fermentation rate, which indicates that the concentration of food in the rumen was limiting.

Occasionally, for example, when the rumen becomes acid because of too much available food, the accumulation of fermentation products limits the rumen fermentation. Too great an accumulation may exert deleterious effects on the host. Under most conditions, and almost universally when roughage is consumed, absorption of products keeps pace reasonably well with the rate of fermentation and the acidity ranges between about pH 5.8 and 6.8.

The symbiotic fermentation by the myriads of rumen microorganisms permits the ruminant to utilize components of forages not digested by other mammals. Mammals themselves do not secrete enzymes capable of digesting the hemicellulose and cellulose that may compose more than half the dry weight of forage. The rumen microorganisms can elaborate such enzymes. The best postulate to explain the evolution of the rumen microbial symbiosis is that it has conferred a survival advantage on the host able to utilize the otherwise indigestible food components.

Whereas the usual aerobic metabolism of animals leads to carbon dioxide and water as the primary products of carbohydrate degradation, anaerobic conversions such as those in the rumen lead to some products more oxidized and some more reduced than the initial carbohydrate material. In the rumen fermentation, the most oxidized fermentation product is carbon dioxide, and a very large fraction of the substrate carbon appears in this form. Measurement of the carbon dioxide arising in the rumen and that in the whole animal (38) indicated that the CO_2 production of the rumen was about one-third that of the host itself. All the other chief final products of the rumen fermentation are either at the same oxidation-reduction state as carbohydrates or are somewhat more reduced. Acetate has the same relative composition of carbon, hydrogen, and oxygen but propionate, butyrate, and methane are more reduced than carbohydrate. The acetic, propionic, and butyric acids are absorbed and oxidized by the host, serving as a source of energy.

MAGNITUDE OF THE RUMEN FERMENTATION

The magnitude of the fermentation is one of the important rumen parameters. Rates can be given in terms of disappearance of total substrate or individual components, in terms of the rate of formation of total or individual fermentation products, or as the rate of heat production. The productivity of the rumen fermentation in terms of microbial cells constitutes another important parameter, with again a possibility for splitting this parameter into subunits according to individual cell types.

Of all the possible measurements one of the most feasible is that of the total fermentation. This was initially approached (5) by studying the rate of absorption of volatile fatty acids from the rumen, a process treated in a subsequent section of this volume.

Another approach has been to measure the rate of heat production, which is based on the fact that in the fermentative conversion of substrate there is an inefficiency in energy conversions that results in evolution of heat. This inefficiency, characteristic of all metabolic processes, is of sufficient magnitude to be precisely measurable with sensitive techniques. This has been done (56) with a double calorimeter containing killed rumen contents in a control chamber and viable contents in a paired experiment. The conditions for mixing and maintenance of anaerobiosis are similar to those in the rumen, and precise rate measurements can be obtained.

The isotope-dilution techniques for measuring the rate of volatile fatty acid production consist in adding a known quantity of radioactive acetate, butyrate, or propionate to the rumen or a sample of the rumen contents and determining the rate at which it is diluted (25). If suitable corrections are made for the exchange of label between acetate and butyrate, the method gives results comparable with those obtained by other means.

The rate of formation of fermentation products can be measured by the zero-time rate method (15, 38) in which a sample of rumen contents is removed and immediately incubated in vitro under conditions resembling those in the rumen. The time during removal of the sample to an anaerobic jar in a constant-temperature water bath (39 C) must be very short, preferably no more than a minute. At the instant the sample is removed from the rumen, a subsample is killed with acid or alkali and saved for analysis for volatile fatty acids. Subsamples are subsequently removed at 30- to 40-min intervals from the fermenting mass, and these are similarly killed and analyzed. The increase in concentration of each volatile fatty acid is plotted against time, and the slope of this curve, measured by graphic approximation, indicates the rate of production of the acid in vitro. The slope of this curve at zero time represents the rate of production of the acid at the instant the sample was removed and therefore represents also the rate of production in the rumen.

Studies on milking cows at the University of California at Davis in collaboration with Professors Kleiber and Black (38) disclosed that the major part of the respiratory carbon dioxide and the carbon in the cow's milk could be accounted for by the rate of volatile fatty production. The pertinent results are shown in Figure 1 and Table 3. The values for carbon supplied the host in these tables do not take account of the carbon in the bodies of the microorganisms presumably absorbed by the host. These would increase the measured values by roughly 10%. Approximately 85–90% of the carbon requirements of the host were supplied by the microbial fermentation in these experiments.

The zero-time rate method involves not only the errors of analysis, increased because the increment involves two separate analyses, but also is affected by variations in the volume of rumen content and by inaccuracies in sampling. By including materials taken from several portions of the rumen, experienced investigators can obtain representative samples with a variability of less than 5%. It is very important that the sample contain the proportion of solids characteristic of the entire rumen, since the substrate supporting the fermentation is chiefly within the solids. The rumen material is rather difficult to handle and subsample because of the large content of solids, but with experience it can be done with a satisfactory degree of reproducibility. In subsampling the contents should not be stirred up much since this permits oxygen to penetrate the fibrous material and also cools by evaporation.

Rates of fermentation can be measured with rumen contents in large Warburg vessels with manometers containing mercury for measuring pressure changes.

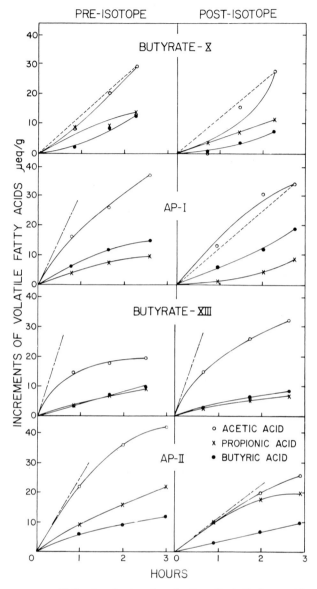

PRE-ISOTOPE   POST-ISOTOPE

BUTYRATE-X

AP-I

BUTYRATE-XIII

AP-II

○ ACETIC ACID
× PROPIONIC ACID
● BUTYRIC ACID

INCREMENTS OF VOLATILE FATTY ACIDS μeq/g

HOURS

FIG. 1. Estimates of rates of production of volatile fatty acids in rumen contents from milking cows. Butyrate-*X*, AP-I, etc., are simply the designations for that particular experiment. [From Hungate et al. (38).]

TABLE 3. *Rates of Carbon Utilization by Milking Cow and Volatile Fatty Acid Production in the Rumen*

Experiment	Butyr-ate-X*	AP-I	Butyrate XIII	AP-II
C in milk	4.35†	3.58	3.63	3.90
C in respiratory CO_2	6.20	6.76	8.00	5.46
Total	10.55	10.34	11.63	9.36
C in fermentation acids	5.65	6.54	6.77	7.83
C in fermentation CO_2, estimated	1.49	1.76	2.12	1.99
Total	7.14	8.30	8.89	9.82
Host C metabolism accounted for by fermentation acids, %	68	80	76	105
Respiratory CO_2 accounted for by fermentation CO_2, %	24	26	23	36

* Butyrate-X, AP-I, etc., are simply the designations for that particular experiment.

† All rates are in terms of gram atoms per hour.

A very simple method for measuring relative rates of the rumen fermentation (52) is to remove a sample of 100 or 200 g to a wide-mouth jar gassed with CO_2. It is immediately stoppered with a rubber stopper and placed in a water bath at 39 C. A 10-ml hypodermic syringe, well lubricated with water, is thrust through the center of the stopper where it has been partially bored to leave a rubber thickness of about ¼ inch. As fermentation gases are produced, the barrel of the syringe is displaced. The gas volume is read at fixed intervals, the syringe withdrawn, discharged, and reinserted. In this fashion precise curves to show rates of gas production have been obtained. As with the Warburg technique, if there is an insufficiency of bicarbonate the true rate of acid production will not be obtained.

Sufficient bicarbonate to accommodate the acid must be included. This can be accomplished by adjusting the pH to 6.7 with sodium bicarbonate in a medium equilibrated with an atmosphere of CO_2. The time involved in setting up the respirometric method makes it a little less precise than the zero-time rate method. Also, to obtain the true amount of volatile fatty acid corresponding to the CO_2 released from bicarbonate, it is necessary to measure release of CO_2 from bicarbonate by known quantities of fatty acids in a control vessel.

STOICHIOMETRY OF SOME RUMEN PARAMETERS

When carbohydrate is the substrate for a rumen fermentation, the stoichiometry between the fermentation products and the carbohydrate fermented can be calculated on the assumption that the sugar is broken initially to triose, then to pyruvate, and that the acetic, propionic, and butyric acids are derived from pyruvate by the usual biochemical mechanisms.

In one experiment [butyrate-X experiment (38)] 20.25 μmoles of acetic acid, 7.1 μmoles of propionic acid, 5.25 μmoles butyric acid, 18.8 μmoles carbon dioxide, and 7.66 μmoles of methane were formed.

These acids could be derived from hexose as follows:

$$10.125\ C_6H_{12}O_6 + 20.25\ H_2O \rightarrow$$

$$20.25\ CH_3COOH + 20.25\ CO_2 + 81\ H$$

$$3.55\ C_6H_{12}O_6 + 14.2\ H \rightarrow$$

$$7.1\ CH_3CH_2COOH + 7.1\ H_2O$$

$$5.25\ C_6H_{12}O_6 \rightarrow 5.25\ CH_3CH_2CH_2COOH$$

$$+ 10.5\ CO_2 + 21\ H$$

$$\overline{}$$

$$18.925\ C_6H_{12}O_6 + 13.15\ H_2O \rightarrow 20.25\ HAc$$

$$+ 7.1\ HPr + 5.25\ HBut + 30.75\ CO_2 + 87.8\ H \quad (1)$$

According to these pathways there is a net production of hydrogen. This hydrogen is converted to methane, but the methane is less than that expected from equation 1 because the microbial cells contain a greater proportion of hydrogen than does carbohydrate.

The weight of microbial cells synthesized in the rumen has been estimated from a number of experiments (see NITROGEN METABOLISM) to be about 10% of the weight of carbohydrate fermented; i.e., for each 10 g of carbohydrate fermented 1 g dry weight of microbial cells is formed.

On the assumption that these cells would have the approximate percentage composition 53 C, 10 H, 20 O, 10.5 N, and 6.5 minerals, the C, H, O atomic ratios would be $C_6H_{13.6}O_{1.7}$ for 83% of the cell weight. This fraction (the C, H, and O) of the cell weight is derived from carbohydrate. It has a molecular weight of 112.8 as compared to 180 for the carbohydrate from which it was derived. Thus $(180/112.8) \times 0.083 = 0.132$ of the carbohydrate used would be required to account for the C in the cells. The carbon in the remaining fraction (0.868) of the carbohydrate used would appear in the fermentation products shown in equation 1. To produce these products, and also cells weighing 0.1 of the weight of the fermented carbohydrate, would require 18.925/0.868 μmoles = 21.81 μmoles total carbohydrate, of which 2.88 would provide carbon for the synthesis of cells equal in weight to 2.181 μmoles carbohydrate, that is, 392 μg. Of this weight 83% (325 μg), or 2.88 μmoles, would have the composition $C_6H_{13.6}O_{1.7}$ (mol wt 112.8).

Transformation of carbohydrate with a molecular composition of $C_6H_{12}O_6$ into cells with a composition of $C_6H_{13.6}O_{1.7}$ would require the removal of O and addition of H according to the following equation:

$$2.88\ C_6H_{12}O_6 + 29.368\ H \rightarrow$$

$$(2.88\ C_6H_{13.6}O_{1.7}) + 12.384\ H_2O \quad (2)$$
$$\text{cells}$$

Addition of equations 1 and 2 gives

$$21.81\ C_6H_{12}O_6 + 0.766\ H_2O \rightarrow (2.88\ C_6H_{13.6}O_{1.7})$$
$$\text{cells}$$

$$+ 20.25\ HAc + 7.1\ HPr + 5.25\ HBut$$

$$+ 30.75\ CO_2 + 58.432\ H \quad (3)$$

If the hydrogen is converted to methane

$$58.432\ H + 7.304\ CO_2 \rightarrow 7.304\ CH_4 + 14.608\ H_2O \quad (4)$$

Addition of equations 3 and 4 gives

$$21.81\ C_6H_{12}O_6 \rightarrow (2.88\ C_6H_{13.6}O_{1.7}) + 20.25\ HAc$$
$$\text{cells}$$

$$+ 7.1\ HPr + 5.25\ HBut + 23.45\ CO_2$$

$$+ 7.3\ CH_4 + 13.94\ H_2O \quad (5)$$

Comparison with the found values of 20.25 μmoles acetate, 7.1 μmoles propionate, 5.25 μmoles butyrate, 18.8 μmoles CO_2, and 7.66 μmoles CH_4 shows that when production of cell material is taken into account the found quantity of methane is about that expected, but the carbon dioxide is less.

From equation 5 the theoretical ratios between fermentation products and the carbohydrates utilized can be calculated. Per micromole of carbohydrate fermented, 1.5 μmoles of acid and 0.35 μmoles of methane would be expected. In 22 averaged measurements (Table VI-1 in ref. 34) 0.42 μmoles of methane were found per micromole of food digested. D. A. Balch (4) found only 1.27 μmoles acid per μmole of food digested, as compared to the theoretical 1.5 from equation 5. Part of the latter difference is due to the fact that some of the digested food is protein rather than carbohydrate.

For a particular rumen and a certain ration, if the ratios between the food digested, the fermentation acids, and the methane are determined in vitro, the amount of methane formed in vivo can be used to calculate the quantity of fatty acids formed or food fermented in the animal. Measurement of the rumen methane affords an index to the rate of the fermentation, and this can be compared to the amount of food digested, that is, to the feed-feces difference. This estimate from methane is not subject to the errors of rumen volume measurement nor to the sampling problems that arise with the zero-time rate method. The method is valid only if the ratio of the acids to CO_2 and methane remains constant, and this is not strictly so since there is a tendency for the proportion of methane to be lower after feeding (37). However, this is not a large error.

If the methane production in the entire animal is measured, there is also involved the error in the production of methane in the large intestine and cecum. This latter is usually not a very large fraction (36), and if only the elimination of methane from the mouth is measured, some of the error due to methane production in the posterior tract is eliminated. Methane production as an index of the fermentation rate is particularly useful in that it can be performed without the necessity for stomach tubes, fistulas, or otherwise disturbing the animals' nutrition.

RELATIONSHIPS BETWEEN CONTINUOUS-
FERMENTATION PARAMETERS

One method for testing hypotheses of rumen function is to examine the various parameters to see how they are quantitatively related. On the basis of a continuous-fermentation model, a number of parameters can be compared, some of them significant in understanding rumen fermentation.

In using measured rates of fermentation by rumen contents to calculate total production of volatile fatty acids, methane, or carbon dioxide, it is desirable to know how many daily feeds are represented in the rumen contents. This can be calculated from the turnover rate constant and the daily feed according to the relationship, daily feed/k = amount feed represented in the rumen, in which k is the turnover rate constant (see equation 6).

If there were no digestion of food components in the rumen, the dry weight of the daily food divided by the dry weight of the food in the rumen would equal the dilution or feed rate in terms of the number of turnovers per day. Since the food is digested, the acid fermentation products are absorbed, and the CO_2 is eliminated, the rumen dry matter is less than that expected on the basis of feed intake and rumen turnover rate. In order to calculate the turnover of dry matter directly from the dry weight of the feed and of the rumen contents it is necessary to know the degree to which the dry matter of the food has undergone digestion in the rumen.

An attempt to evaluate the expected extent of digestion in the rumen can be made by examining the rate of fermentation of the feed by an excess of mixed rumen microorganisms (34). The result of a 40-hour experiment of this sort with alfalfa hay is shown in Figure 2.

It is assumed that the initial rapid rate of fermen-

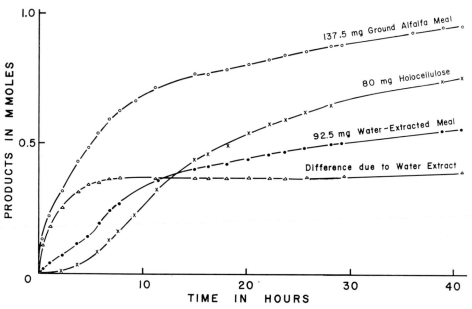

FIG. 2. Time course of fermentation of alfalfa hay preparations by 20 ml rumen liquid in round-bottom Warburg flasks with mercury manometers. Temperature, 39 C. Holocellulose was prepared by chlorite treatment of 137.5 mg ground alfalfa meal. [From Hungate (34).]

tation during the first 30 min to 1 hour is at the expense of soluble carbohydrates in the feed. The curve in Figure 2 showing fermentation of the soluble materials supports this view, though it shows that there is a tailing off for as long as three to four hours presumably due to gradual utilization of polysaccharide stored from the soluble components of the feed.

There is a second, almost straight-line portion of the curve in Figure 2 that is interpreted as the time during which the effect of the soluble sugars is diminishing and the attack on the fibrous material in the feed is increasing. Whatever the explanation, the relationship can be treated mathematically as linear for the period between 1 and 6 hours.

After 6 hours there is a gradual decrease in rate that extends over a very long period, with some fermentation in excess of the control even after 40 hours. This extended fermentation, interpreted as attack on fibrous components, is initiated about 3 hours after addition of the feed and accounts for part of the linear rate between 3 and 6 hours. It reaches a maximum after about 6 hours and then diminishes gradually.

This third portion of the curve, representing fiber digestion after 6 hours, can be fitted to a harmonic series based on the postulate that digestion of the fiber extends over a period of 36 hours and that the relative rate of digestion between 6 and 7 hours is 1 and in successive hours $\frac{1}{2}$, $\frac{1}{3}$, $\frac{1}{4}$, and so on up to $\frac{1}{36}$. In Figure 3 are shown actual points for the fibrous material in a grass hay from zero hour and for alfalfa hay from 6 hours after ingestion, as compared with the harmonic-series curve. The agreement is quite good.

These measurements provide an estimate of the rate at which food leaves the rumen due to digestion. It also leaves by passage to the omasum. The net disappearance is due to the simultaneous operation of both processes.

According to the continuous fermentation model, material in the rumen spills into the omasum at a rate proportional to its concentration and to a constant representing the flow or dilution rate, $dx/dt = kx$. The fraction left in the rumen at any time would be

$$x = e^{-kt} \qquad (6)$$

In Figure 4, curve A shows the expected concentration of an inert marker injected into a rumen with a turnover time of 24 hours, that is, a rate of once per day. This curve also shows the composition of the rumen contents at any one time. At zero time the value 1 represents the fraction still present of the material that just entered; it was all still there. Material that had entered the rumen 12 hours previously would be three fifths as abundant as material that had just entered. The material that entered 24 hours previously would be a little more than one third as abundant as that just entered, etc. If this curve were extended to infinity, the area under the curve would equal the total quantity in the rumen and would be equal to the area in the rectangle 0, 1.0, 1, and 24 in Figure 4.

The soluble fraction of the food, x_s, leaves the rumen according to a fermentation rate that is linear for a period of 1 hour ($x_s = 1 - t$, when $t < 1$), and also according to the dilution rate ($x_s = e^{-kt}$). The product of these two equations ($x_s = e^{-kt}(1 - t)$) shows the fraction of the soluble material left in the rumen at any time, curve B in Figure 4.

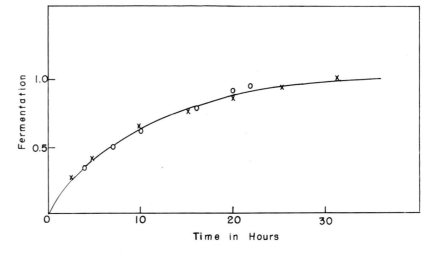

FIG. 3. Curve for harmonic series between 0 and 36 hours fitted to amounts of fermentation products formed from kikuyu grass hay (O——O) after adding it to incubating rumen fluid and from alfalfa hay (×——×) 6 hours after adding it to incubating rumen liquid. [From Hungate (34).]

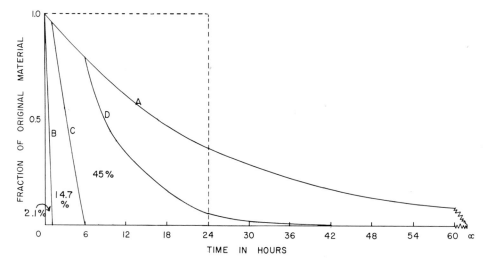

FIG. 4. Curves showing time composition of rumen contents (curve A) and degree of digestion of the digestible materials in soluble (*curve B*), 1-6 hour (*curve C*), and fiber (*curve D*) fractions of alfalfa hay.

The ared under curve B divided by the area of the rectangle, 24, is the fraction of soluble materials not fermented. This fraction would spill over into the omasum. The area under curve B is only 2.1 % of the total area under curve A. This represents the fraction of the soluble material that would escape fermentation if the sugars from a given bite of feed lasted in the rumen as long as 1 hour. The true value is probably even less, because with most feeds the soluble material is used in less than an hour. The calculation indicates that the utilization of dissolved sugars is almost 100 %.

Similarly, the material fermented between 1 and 6 hours, x_i , leaves the rumen according to the dilution rate and the linear rate of utilization from 1 to 6 hours. The amount of this fraction in the rumen between 0 and 1 hour will be governed only by the relationship $x_i = e^{-kt}$, with $t < 1$, because any digestion of this fraction has already been included with the linear rate in the first hour. The fraction of this component left in the rumen at the end of 1 hour will be 0.96, and the area under this portion of the curve will be 0.98, or 4 % of the area of the square. The amount of this component after the first hour will be governed by the relationship $x_i = 0.96\ e^{-kt}$ $(1 - t_i/5)$, with $t_i = t - 1$, for values of t between 1 and 6.

Calculation shows the area under this part of curve C to be 10.7 % of the area of the rectangle. With the 4 % escaping in the first hour, 14.7 % of this component will be in the rumen material and enter the omasum; 85.3 % will be utilized.

Finally, it is possible to combine the harmonic

series with turnover rate and plot the fraction of the digestible fibrous material expected in the rumen when it disappears due to digestion and to passage to the omasum. Curve D in Figure 4 shows the fraction of the digestible fibrous material in alfalfa hay that would be left in the rumen. Here we find that about 22.5 % of the material (the area under curve A between 1 and 6 hours) leaves the rumen in the first 6 hours before its fermentation starts, and that 29 % of the remainder ($0.29 \times 0.775 = 22.5\%$ of the total) escapes digestion by leaving the rumen after 6 hours, making a total of 45 % of this component that leaves the rumen before it has been digested. Of the digestible material in the fiber 55 % is digested.[2]

From Figure 2 showing the amount of gas production from the alfalfa hay, the relative quantities of the three fractions of the alfalfa hay can be estimated. The rapid initial fermentation of the sugar accounts for about 0.24 of the pressure increase, the 1- to 6-hour period accounts for 0.34 of the gas, and the fiber for 0.42 of the gas pressure increase. If the fraction for each of these components is multiplied by its extent of digestion, that is, (0.24×0.98) +

[2] In earlier similar calculations (34) digestion of the fibrous portion of the feed was assumed to start at 0 time, with 29% escaping digestion. This was applicable for grass hay, and the harmonic series alone could represent its digestion, but separation of the alfalfa hay curve (Fig. 2) into 3 components more accurately represents its utilization. To the extent that fibrous material moves more slowly through the rumen, digestion of the digestible fiber will be more complete than is indicated by these estimates.

(0.34 × 0.85) + (0.42 × 0.55), the value 0.76 is obtained as the theoretical extent to which the digestible components are digested. If the digestibility of the feed after 36 hours of in vitro incubation was 65%, the feed leaving the rumen would be digested to the extent of 50% (0.76 × 65%). Each 5 lb. of residual dry matter in the rumen would represent 10 lb. (dry wt) of feed consumed. The daily feed, multiplied by 0.5 and divided by the dry weight of the feed residues in the rumen, would represent the turnover rate constant per day of the rumen contents, provided all materials in the rumen were turning over at the same rate.

The daily feed, divided by the turnover rate constant (turnovers per day), measured by means of a liquid marker, should equal the dry matter (VFA and bicarbonate content subtracted) in the rumen divided by 0.5. If essentially all the digestion of foodstuffs occurs in the rumen, the daily dry matter in the feces divided by the rumen turnover rate constant should equal the dry matter in the rumen; or, vice versa, the daily dry matter in the feces divided by the dry matter in the rumen should give the turnover rate constant.

These calculations assume a single dilution rate. This may be valid for rations that have been ground or chopped to a degree of fineness such that the retention mechanism of the omasum does not prevent passage of any of the particles. On diets of coarse forage the rate of passage of small particles is not the same as that for the larger ones. The latter must be retained until they are reduced to a smaller size by rumination and can mix with the pool of finer materials. During this period they undergo additional digestion.

The rate of passage of the fine materials, which include the bacteria and probably most of the protozoa, can be determined by use of polyethylene glycol as a marker. The rate of passage of the coarser materials is perhaps best measured by the lignin content or some other internal marker, though it can also be estimated by external markers such as chromic oxide.

The portion of the rumen contents that is not free to pass into the omasum because of the large particle size can be termed the rumination pool. The solids in the rumen contents of animals on a coarse forage ration consist of two portions, a small-particle liquid pool that turns over and leaves the rumen at a certain rate and a rumination pool that feeds into the first. The small particles produced from the rumination pool become a part of the small-particle liquid pool that leaves the rumen along with the polyethylene glycol. The rate of passage of this small particle and liquid pool is the one most pertinent for the nitrogen nutrition of the ruminant.

Because of the rumination pool, in animals on coarse feeds a difficulty arises in comparisons of dry matter in the rumen with the turnover rate constant. If the rate constant for the liquid small-particle pool is applied to the total rumen dry matter, the calculated daily turnover of dry matter exceeds the dry matter in the daily feed and is obviously erroneous. The daily feed divided by the liquid small-particle turnover rate constant will give the dry weight of the food represented by the liquid small-particle pool in the rumen. Multiplication by the digestibility of the feed (from feed-feces difference) gives the weight of the rumen dry matter in the liquid small-particle pool. The remainder of the rumen dry matter is in the rumination pool.

It should be understood that this discussion of rumen parameters is preliminary and to a considerable extent theoretical. It is a model to be tested and revised in accordance with experimental results. Much of the value of any such model is the extent to which it stimulates experiments leading to a more accurate description.

EFFECTIVENESS OF THE RUMEN FERMENTATION

Although the digestion of the cellulose and hemicellulose of forage fiber provides an advantage to the ruminant in its competition with other animals for food, there are two drawbacks to utilization of these structural elements of forage. First, the digestion of cellulose occurs relatively slowly over a considerable period of time; second, in most forages the digestible cellulose and hemicellulose are combined with considerable amounts of indigestible materials. They diminish the rate of attack by the cellulase enzymes, occupy valuable digestive space, and must be transported through the alimentary tract. The rate of movement of the bulk of indigestible material, dependent on the time required for rumination, limits the rate of transport of food through the alimentary tract. This rate can be increased by grinding and pelleting the food, but since cellulose digestion occurs over a long period of time, cellulose utilization is diminished; there is a greater relative return to the ruminant animal from the water-soluble and 6-hour fractions of the feed than from the fiber part.

A seeming anomaly can occur when rates of passage

of easily digested foods are compared with those less readily digested. When the fiber in concentrate feeds is used as an index for rate of passage, the passage rate is slower than that of fiber in a hay-fed animal (23). The rumen always contains a considerable quantity of solids; it never empties even in starved animals. Many of the microorganisms remain viable and serve to start fermentation when food is next ingested. Since the digestible fiber residues from concentrate feeds are so much less per day, the residue of fiber in the rumen of animals fed concentrates represents more days' ration than when hay is consumed.

It is evident that a considerable improvement in ruminant feed utilization would result from an increase in the digestibility of the feed. This can be accomplished either by feeding more concentrates and easily digestible carbohydrates or by increasing the digestibility of the components of forage fibers. Chlorite treatment to remove lignin increases the total digestibility of the fiber in alfalfa, as can be seen from Figure 2. Unfortunately, in forages there are not large supplies of digestible cellulose and hemicellulose free of proteins and other materials. A few exceptions are the hemicellulose in corn cobs and corn stalks and the material in beet pulp, but in most instances cellulose and hemicellulose occur in conjunction with lignin, which tends to diminish their digestibility.

There is a rough correlation also between the protein and soluble sugar content of a forage and the digestibility of its hemicellulose and cellulose. Older forages become more lignified and have a lesser proportion of nitrogen, phosphorus, and sugars as compared with younger forages, and the fiber is less digestible. Younger forages have a greater quantity of digestible carbohydrate and also more protein and other nitrogenous nutrients.

If improved economy in ruminant feeding is to be achieved through maximum utilization of the capacity for the rumen microorganisms to assimilate cell material, including protein, from inorganic materials, it is obvious that the most digestible forages are least suited because they ordinarily contain more of the protein and other nutrients. A maximum assimilation of microbial cells from simple nitrogenous sources would be possible only with high digestible carbohydrate and low protein in the feed. Such combinations do not commonly occur in natural forages. In theory it should be possible to feed sugar and suitable inorganic nutrients to cattle and to obtain maximal microbial assimilation. Experiments along

these lines have shown that milk production can be maintained in cows using only inorganic materials plus readily digested carbohydrates (55). The cellulose in these experiments was not digested.

NITROGEN METABOLISM

The conversions of nitrogenous materials by the mixed rumen population can be considered from several aspects: *1*) fate of proteins and amino acids, *2*) utilization of inorganic and simple nitrogenous materials, *3*) magnitude of the microbial assimilation, and *4*) adequacy of microbial nitrogen in host metabolism.

Fate of Proteins and Amino Acids

The proteins fed to nonruminants are digested to amino acids that are absorbed and used for body-building purposes by the host, to the extent that the essential amino acids in the food resemble those in the tissues of the host. If adequate supplies of energy (ATP) from carbohydrate are available, most of these amino acids can be assimilated. The situation is quite different in a ruminant. Feed proteins are susceptible to digestion and assimilation, but through fermentation they can also serve as a source of energy. In the intense competition within the rumen environment any organism capable of dissimilating proteins as a source of energy will have a competitive advantage if there are proteins in the feed. In consequence any ingested protein is potentially a substrate for a fermentation in which a significant part of the nitrogen is liberated as ammonia.

Experiments with isotopically labeled amino acids (50, 58) show that breakdown considerably exceeds assimilation. Less than 10% of the labeled nitrogen or carbon in an amino acid added to rumen contents is assimilated into microbial cell material. The rest undergoes conversion into organic acids, carbon dioxide, and ammonia. The greater the proportion of protein in the ration, the greater is the relative extent of fermentation rather than assimilation.

This extensive fermentation of protein can be understood on the basis that soluble proteins can be more rapidly fermented than can the fibrous components of the forage. In consequence, even though the ratio of protein to carbohydrate is optimal in the diet for microbial assimilation, when the two are fed together the lesser availability of part of the carbohydrate creates an initial relative excess of protein and a later deficit. This difficulty is partially alleviated by extending the feeding periods over a longer time so that entering proteins will be more continuously available for organisms growing on the fibrous components.

Studies on pure cultures of *Bacteroides ruminicola* (49) have disclosed a preference of this organism for peptides over amino acids as a source of assimilable nitrogen. In the competition for nitrogenous foods, organisms capable of seizing peptides may have an advantage over others that must wait for conversion to amino acids or ammonia. Absorption of nitrogenous peptides could well be more efficient than absorption of single amino acids. Whatever the explanation, the fact is that in the mixed rumen microbiota the assimilated fraction of peptides exceeds the assimilated fraction of amino acids (57a). But even in this case the fraction of the total protein assimilated as peptides is small.

A practical finding in ruminant nutrition is that the nature of the protein fed is not so important for the growth of the ruminant as for the nonruminant. This can be understood if the proteins are chiefly degraded to ammonia and the ammonia is then assimilated by the rumen microbiota.

Speed of utilization of proteins depends on their solubility (27). Some of the very insoluble proteins pass through the rumen and are digested and absorbed in the succeeding parts of the alimentary tract (43).

Utilization of Simple Nitrogenous Materials

The consequence of microbial fermentation of protein is creation of a pool of ammonia that is readily absorbed into the ruminant. Amounts normally formed are converted into urea, which enters the circulation. A certain proportion of the urea reenters the rumen with the saliva and an additional amount by direct diffusion through the rumen wall. Urea in the rumen is again transformed into ammonia by the enzyme urease, which appears to be formed in small quantities by a large number of rumen microorganisms; at least no abundant active urea splitters have been demonstrated in the rumen. When the nitrogen in the feed is extremely low, this recycling of urea can provide an important part of the nitrogenous materials utilized by the host.

Ammonia is the chief nitrogenous substance used by the microorganisms. Many of them (13) use it even in the presence of amino acids. The rumen thus possesses a rather considerable capacity for assimilation of simple nitrogenous materials. Realization of this capacity for assimilation of inorganic nitrogen depends on supplying to the ruminant the nutrients needed by the rumen microorganisms in addition to digestible carbohydrates and assimilable nitrogen.

Biological Value of Microbial Nitrogen

Analyses indicate a rumen bacterial nitrogen content of about 10.5 % of the dry weight, equivalent to 65 % crude protein. Not all of this is actually protein since the cell envelopes of bacteria contain amino sugars and other nonprotein nitrogenous substances. These nitrogenous wall materials may constitute a fairly large fraction of the total bacterial nitrogen, since as size diminishes the ratio between envelope and weight of cell contents becomes progressively greater.

The nutritional value of rumen microbial cells for the host has been investigated in a number of laboratories with the general finding that both the bacteria and the protozoa of the rumen are fairly good sources of protein for the host. If anything, the balance is slightly in favor of the protozoa over the bacteria. This superiority may explain the greater weight gains by faunated as compared to defaunated lambs (1, 16). It has been pointed out by Moir that the nitrogenous constituents of the bacterial cell envelope might well be less suitable as nitrogenous food for the host than are the amino acids of true protein. Since the bacterial envelope constitutes a relatively larger fraction of the total cell than is the case with the protozoa, it is conceivable that a greater fraction of protozoal nitrogen than of bacterial nitrogen can be assimilated by the ruminant host.

The percentage nitrogen of the rumen protozoa is less than in the bacteria, and because of the stored starch the values are more variable. This lower nitrogen content of the protozoa increases the difficulty of explaining their favorable influence on the host as due to purely a quantitative effect.

Magnitude of Microbial Assimilation

Estimates of the extent of microbial growth in the rumen at the expense of the carbohydrate food materials have been made in various ways. These have included measurements of the weight of microbial cells assimilated in vitro and in vivo at the expense of a given weight of digested feed carbohydrate, measurement of the quantity of microbial protein within the rumen and calculation of the amount supplied the host from the rate of rumen turnover, and estimates based on the measured growth rates of the rumen bacteria. It is also possible to obtain some idea of the optimal proportions of nitrogenous and carbohydrate materials in the feed by comparing the performance of animals on various rations and examining the quantity of nitrogen lost from the rumen.

The quantity of microbial cells formed when a given amount of substrate is fermented depends on the conditions of the experiment, including the substrate used. With sugars as substrate and with limiting quantities of sugars, the amount of microbial cells formed can be as high as 21 % in the case of pure cultures of *Ruminococcus albus* (33) or *Selenomonas* (29). Low values of 8 % (41) and 6.4 % (54) may be due to provision of more sugar than could be utilized. With mixed rumen bacteria, yields of cells as high as 17 % of the substrate have been obtained (8, 9, 53).

Similar estimates can be obtained from experiments in which carbohydrates have been fed to ruminants and a measure of the microbial synthesis obtained. In one of these experiments (2) the cells constituted 8.9 % of the dry matter disappearing. In other experiments (21) the yield of cells was 12.6 % of the carbohydrate digested.

In somewhat similar fashion an estimate of the extent of nitrogen assimilation can be obtained by examining experiments in which the quantity of nitrogen varies. In one experiment (24) only 48 % of the dietary nitrogen entered the omasum when the ration contained 2.9 % nitrogen, 65 % when the ration contained 1.8 % nitrogen, 100 % with 1.1 % nitrogen, and somewhat more than 100 % when the ration contained 0.7 % nitrogen. In this last instance presumably some of the nitrogen reentered the rumen as urea. In other experiments (40) the total nitrogen was 1.2 % of the carbohydrate used. On the assumption of a 92 % digestibility of this nitrogen, the quantity of cells produced would amount to about 18.5 % of the carbohydrate that had fermented in these experiments. Oyaert & Bouckaert (48) obtained an estimate of 14.4 % whereas Moir & Harris (44) found 10.5 %.

These results as a whole indicate that about 13 % of the fermented carbohydrate can be assimilated into cell material (equal in weight to 10 % of the carbohydrate) and that under favorable conditions about 20 % may be assimilated into cells. On a basis of 65 % crude protein in the cells, the protein would constitute a maximum of 13 % of the weight of the carbohydrate fermented. The average value is probably somewhat less than this. As a reasonable estimate the weight of the microbial protein is between 7 and 8 % of the weight of the fermented carbohydrate.

The quantity of nitrogen available to the host can also be estimated by measuring the quantity of microbial nitrogen in the rumen and multiplying by the number of turnovers per day. Various estimates (6, 57) indicate that 47–81 % of the nitrogen in the rumen is microbial. Analyses of the total nitrogen in the rumen indicate that it varies between 0.1 and 0.5 % (w/v) in sheep and cattle under various conditions of feed. This would indicate between 0.63 and 3.2 % (w/v) protein in the rumen. If this be assumed to be 80 % digestible, the digestible protein would amount to 0.5–2.5 % (w/v) of the rumen contents.

A value of 1.25 % (w/v) microbial protein in a 5-liter sheep rumen turning over 1.6 times each day would yield 100 g of protein to the animal. If 80 % digestible, the net would be 80 g of digestible protein. Since in such a sheep the maintenance protein requirement is approximately 45 g, the estimates indicate that the rumen microorganisms can easily provide a large part of the nitrogenous food needed by the host.

The yield of the microorganisms to the host can also be obtained by knowing the content of the microbial cells in the rumen and determining the average growth rate. In such an experiment (52) the average net growth rate of the rumen microorganism approximated the turnover rate constant for passage of digesta from the rumen. This should be the case since any deviation of the average net growth rate of the rumen microbiota from the specific turnover rate of the contents would lead to a greater or lower concentration of these microorganisms. Since they remain relatively constant on a given feed over long periods of time, it is obvious that the average net growth rate and the average rate of passage from the rumen must be identical.

Consumption of bacteria by the protozoa complicates the model by necessitating that consumed bacteria must have a net growth equal to the dilution rate. This net growth dx/dt would be the sum of the true growth rate and the negative growth rate due to consumption by the protozoa. Preliminary information indicates that factors in addition to the protozoa can cause a lysis of bacteria in the rumen (38a).

Adequacy of Microbial Nitrogen in Metabolism

The estimates obtained in the preceding section indicate that weight of the microbial protein synthesized in the rumen constitutes about 7–10% of the weight of the carbohydrate fermented. Not all of this material is in the form of assimilable amino acids, and the true quantity of available protein must be considered as somewhat less. The question then arises, is there any discrepancy between the quantity of assimilable nitrogen for the host and the quantity of energy-yielding materials at its disposal?

Estimates of the degradation of energy during the fermentation process by the rumen microorganisms indicate that as much as 10% of the energy in the food is dissipated as methane and another 10% is assimilated into the bodies of the rumen microbes with an energy content approximately the same as an equal weight of carbohydrate. This leaves approximately 80% of the original energy. If in the process of metabolism and fermentation in the rumen 10% of the initial energy is degraded into heat or other unusable energy, the fermentation acids will contain approximately 70% of the total energy in the initial food. The energy available for synthesis of cellular components in the ruminant is thus approximately 10 times the amount in the food to be assimilated. This is a fairly high ratio between available energy and building materials for growth. It appears quite possible that the concentration of microbial protein supplied to the host, rather than the quantity of volatile fatty acids, is the factor that limits growth. If true, supply of more protein to the ruminant would support faster growth at the expense of the volatile fatty acids produced in the fermentation.

This conclusion does not apply to the dairy animal, which synthesizes a considerable quantity of fat and carbohydrate for its chief product, milk. The protein of milk constitutes roughly only a third of the dry matter formed and on an energy basis only about a fourth of the energy of the dry matter in the milk. Under these circumstances there is little imbalance between the supply of protein and energy materials to the dairy animal, and with a good dairy animal there is little fat stored within the body. With beef animals the reverse is true, with a tendency as the animal matures for very considerable deposition of fat.

ABNORMALITIES IN THE RUMEN
MICROBIAL FERMENTATION

The maintenance within the ruminant of the great mass of rumen microorganisms can on occasion constitute a hazard not experienced by nonruminant mammals.

Addition of readily fermented foods to rumen contents incubated in vitro causes a big increase in fermentation. This means that the very concentrated microbial population of the rumen is partially starved. It is a population that is near maximum concentration for the particular food supply. If a more readily fermentable food is provided to this population in vivo the fermentation increases. On occasion the rate of production exceeds the capacity of the ruminant to accommodate. Acute indigestion and bloat are abnormalities in which products of the rumen microbial fermentation accumulate more rapidly than they can be removed.

Acute Indigestion

This disease occurs when animals that have been on a predominantly forage diet suddenly receive a more readily fermentable substrate such as sugar or starch (35). These foods support an almost explosive development of those rumen organisms able to grow rapidly on the starch or carbohydrate substrate. The particular rumen organism most capable of doing this is *Streptococcus bovis*, and in most animals receiving a sudden excess of sugar or starch there is a tremendous increase in numbers of *S. bovis*. Lactic acid accumulates to the point that the rumen becomes very acid. In many animals the acidity causes atony of the rumen musculature and in severe cases may cause death of the animal. This phenomenon is the basis for only gradually increasing the concentrate ration in the feed lot. Another possible means of prevention of acute indigestion is to provide the new feed continuously at a very slow rate over a considerable part of the day. This would prevent acidity and select a population adapted to the new ration.

The great accumulation of lactate in acute indigestion as opposed to its relative unimportance as an intermediate in the normal rumen fermentation is due to the excess available carbohydrate. As long as carbohydrate is limiting, the fermentation efficiency in ATP production from a given quantity of carbohydrate has competitive survival value and bacteria obtaining more than 2 ATP per sugar can compete successfully with *Streptococcus bovis*. In acute indigestion the great excess of starch or sugar makes carbohydrate no longer limiting. *Streptococcus bovis* can metabolize the carbohydrate faster than competing types that use each molecule more efficiently. The ATP yield of *S. bovis* per molecule of sugar is low, but when carbohydrate is in excess the yield of ATP per unit of time is considerably greater than in competing species.

The animal with acute indigestion loses appetite. The lactic acid is gradually absorbed. When the carbohydrate has been utilized the rumen acidity returns to normal and more efficient producers of ATP compete successfully.

Bloat

There are several causes of bloat in ruminants, but in all cases the swelling associated with this disease is caused by the accumulation of microbial fermentation products. Two of these products, CO_2 and CH_4, are gases. Since bicarbonate is the chief buffer in the rumen, carbon dioxide is released also by the acids. In consequence very large quantities of gas (as much as 2 liters/min) can form within the rumen. Normally the gas is eliminated by belching or eructation. The healthy animal has the capacity to eliminate in this fashion more gas than is ever likely to form in the rumen. Any abnormality preventing the escape of this gas causes bloat. In severe bloat death can ensue within a very short time. Production of even 1 liter of gas per min would in 30 min accumulate gas equal to about half the bovine rumen volume.

In some cases bloat is caused by injury to the cardia that prevents the normal eructation reflex. In other instances it is due to a retention of small bubbles of gas within the rumen digesta; the gas does not collect above the solids as a separate phase that can easily be eliminated.

Bloat occurs fairly commonly in animals fed on fresh legumes. The materials within the rumen compose a viscous mass within which small bubbles of fermentation gases are formed but do not coalesce. The entire mass of rumen contents rises in the same fashion as rising bread dough. Under these circumstances the mass expands to fill and stretch the rumen, ultimately even impairing the circulation and causing

death. The animal is unable to release the digesta by vomition.

The identity of the materials causing the viscous slime in the digesta of bloating animals is obscure. Hypotheses to explain the production of slime within the rumen include: formation by bacteria acting on the sugars in the fresh legume; denaturation of the proteins in legumes; release of nucleic acids by bursting of protozoa, with a resultant great increase in viscosity; peculiarities in the nature and quantity of the saliva secreted by the animal; and the nature of the legume itself as affected by various other factors. None of these has as yet received independent support in a sufficient number of laboratories to assure that it is applicable. Some factors, such as suitable forage, are necessary prerequisites for the operation of other factors.

That microbial factors are concerned is suggested by the effectiveness of certain antibiotics in relieving bloat. The disease can also be alleviated or prevented by the addition of foam-breaking agents.

Another type of bloat occurs in animals on a high grain ration. In this instance the inability to eructate has two explanations: excess acidity with the high starch ration may impair the eructation mechanism or in many cases a slimy type of material is formed that traps the small gas bubbles as in legume bloat.

Ketosis

This is a disease most common in milking cattle and in part affected by the nature of the microbial fermentation. Rumen fermentations that provide a greater proportion of propionic acid among the products tend to diminish the incidence of ketosis. One theory is that the excessive demands of the lactating ruminant for carbohydrate cannot be met unless there is a considerable quantity of propionate available. Propionate is a ready carbohydrate precursor. Lacking a sufficient quantity of propionate, the metabolism of the animal leads to an excess production of ketone bodies.

REFERENCES

1. ABOU AKKADA, A. R., AND K. EL-SHAZLY. Effect of presence or absence of rumen ciliate protozoa on some blood components, nitrogen retention, and digestibility of food constituents in lambs. J. Agr. Sci. 64: 251–255, 1965.
2. AGRAWALA, I. P., C. W. DUNCAN, AND C. F. HUFFMAN. A quantitative study of rumen synthesis in the bovine on natural and purified rations. 1. Protein, dry matter, and non-protein nitrogen. J. Nutr. 49: 29–40, 1953.
3. BAKER, F., AND S. T. HARRISS. Microbial digestion in the rumen (and caecum), with special reference to the decomposition of structural cellulose. Nutr. Abstr. Rev. 17: 3–12, 1947.

4. BALCH, D. A. An estimate of the weights of volatile fatty acids produced in the rumen of lactating cows on a diet of hay and concentrates. *Brit. J. Nutr.* 12: 18–24, 1958.

5. BARCROFT, J., R. A. McANALLY, AND A. T. PHILLIPSON. Absorption of volatile acids from the alimentary tract of the sheep and other animals. *J. Exptl. Biol.* 20: 120–129, 1944.

6. BLACKBURN, T. H., AND P. N. HOBSON. Breakdown of protein and proteolytic activity in the sheep rumen at different times after feeding. *J. Gen. Microbiol.* 22: 290–294, 1960.

7. BLACKBURN, T. H., AND R. E. HUNGATE. Succinic acid turnover and propionate production in the bovine rumen. *Appl. Microbiol.* 11: 132–135, 1963.

8. BLOOMFIELD, R. A., R. P. WILSON, AND G. B. THOMPSON. Influence of energy levels on urea utilization (Abstr.) *J. Animal Sci.* 23: 868, 1964.

9. BOWIE, W. C. *In vitro* studies of rumen microorganisms, using a continuous-flow system. *Am. J. Vet. Res.* 23: 858–867, 1962.

10. BRAILSFORD, M. D. *Isolation and Characterization of Streptococcus bovis Bacteriophages* (M. S. Thesis). Ames, Iowa: Iowa State Univ. 1965.

11. BRYANT, M. P. Bacterial species of the rumen. *Bacteriol. Rev.* 23: 125–153, 1959.

12. BRYANT, M. P., AND R. N. DOETSCH. Factors necessary for the growth of *Bacteroides succinogenes* in the volatile acid fraction of rumen fluid. *Science* 120: 944–945, 1954.

13. BRYANT, M. P., AND I. M. ROBINSON. Some nutritional characteristics of predominant culturable ruminal bacteria. *J. Bacteriol.* 84: 605–614, 1962.

14. CARROLL, E. J., AND R. E. HUNGATE. The magnitude of the microbial fermentation in the bovine rumen. *Appl. Microbiol.* 2: 205–214, 1954.

15. CARROLL, E. J., AND R. E. HUNGATE. Formate dissimilation and methane production in bovine rumen contents. *Arch. Biochem. Biophys.* 56: 525–536, 1955.

16. CHRISTIANSEN, W. C., R. KAWASHIMA, AND W. BURROUGHS. Influence of protozoa upon rumen acid production and live weight gains in lambs. *J. Animal Sci.* 24: 730–734, 1965.

17. CLARKE, R. T. J. Diurnal variation in the numbers of rumen ciliate protozoa in cattle. *N. Z. J. Agr. Res.* 8: 1–9, 1965.

18. DAVIES, M. E. Cellulolytic bacteria in some ruminants and herbivores as shown by fluorescent antibody. *J. Gen. Microbiol.* 39: 139–141, 1965.

19. DOGIEL, V. A. Monographie der Familie Ophryoscolecidae. *Arch. Protistenk.* 59: 1–288, 1927.

20. EADIE, M. J. Inter-relationships between certain rumen ciliate protozoa. *J. Gen. Microbiol.* 29: 579–588, 1962.

21. ELLIS, W. C., G. G. GARNER, M. E. MUHRER, AND W. H. PFANDER. Nitrogen utilization by lambs fed purified rations containing urea, gelatin, casein, blood fibrin, and soybean protein. *J. Nutr.* 60: 413–425, 1956.

22. FORSYTH, C., AND E. L. HIRST. Protozoal polysaccharides. Structure of the polysaccharide produced by the holotrich ciliates present in sheep's rumen. *J. Chem. Soc.* 2132–2135, 1953.

23. FREER, M., AND R. C. CAMPLING. Factors affecting the voluntary intake of food by cows. 5. The relationship between the voluntary intake of food, the amount of digesta in the reticulo-rumen and the rate of disappearance of digesta from the alimentary tract with diets of hay, dried grass or concentrates. *Brit. J. Nutr.* 17: 79–88, 1963.

24. GRAY, F. V., A. F. PILGRIM, AND R. A. WELLER. The digestion of food stuffs in the stomach of the sheep and the passage of digesta through its compartments. 2. Nitrogenous compounds. *Brit. J. Nutr.* 12: 413–421, 1958.

25. GRAY, F. V., R. A. WELLER, A. F. PILGRIM, AND G. B. JONES. The rates of production of volatile fatty acids in the rumen. III. Measurement of production *in vivo* by two isotope dilution procedures. *Australian J. Agr. Res.* 17: 69–80, 1966.

26. HEALD, P. J., AND A. E. OXFORD. Fermentation of soluble sugars by anaerobic holotrich ciliate protozoa of the genera *Isotricha* and *Dasytricha*. *Biochem. J.* 53: 506–512, 1953.

27. HENDERICKX, H., AND J. MARTIN. *In vitro* study of the nitrogen metabolism in the rumen. *Compt. Rend. Rech. Instit. Rech. Sci. Ind. Agr., Bruxelles*, No. 31, 9–66, Dec. 1963.

28. HOBSON, P. N. Reviews of the progress of dairy science. Part 2. Rumen microbiology. *J. Dairy Res.* 30: 288–307, 1963.

29. HOBSON, P. N. Continuous culture of some anaerobic and facultatively anaerobic rumen bacteria. *J. Gen. Microbiol.* 38: 167–180, 1965.

30. HOWARD, B. H. The biochemistry of the rumen protozoa. I. Carbohydrate fermentation by *Dasytricha* and *Isotricha*. *Biochem. J.* 71: 671–675, 1959.

31. HUNGATE, R. E. Studies in cellulose fermentation. III. The culture and isolation of cellulose-decomposing bacteria from the rumen of cattle. *J. Bacteriol.* 53: 631–645, 1947.

32. HUNGATE, R. E. Ecology of bacteria. In: *The Bacteria*, edited by I. C. Gunsalus and R. Y. Stanier. New York: Acad. Press, 1962, vol. IV.

33. HUNGATE, R. E. Polysaccharide storage and growth efficiency in *Ruminococcus albus*. *J. Bacteriol.* 86: 848–854, 1963.

34. HUNGATE, R. E. *The Rumen and Its Microbes*. New York: Acad. Press, 1966, 533 p.

34a. HUNGATE, R. E. Hydrogen as an intermediate in the rumen fermentation. *Arch. Mikrobiol.* 59: 158–164, 1967.

35. HUNGATE, R. E., R. W. DOUGHERTY, M. P. BRYANT, AND R. M. CELLO. Microbiological and physiological changes associated with acute indigestion in sheep. *Cornell Vet.* 42: 423–449, 1952.

36. HUNGATE, R. E., G. D. PHILLIPS, A. MacGREGOR, D. P. HUNGATE, AND H. K. BUECHNER. Microbial fermentation in certain mammals. *Science* 130: 1192–1194, 1959.

37. HUNGATE, R. E., G. D. PHILLIPS, D. P. HUNGATE, AND A. MacGREGOR. A comparison of the rumen fermentation in European and zebu cattle. *J. Agr. Sci.* 54: 196–201, 1960.

38. HUNGATE, R. E., R. A. MAH, AND M. SIMESEN. Rates of production of individual volatile fatty acids in the rumen of lactating cows. *Appl. Microbiol.* 9: 554–561, 1961.

38a. JARVIS, B. D. W. Lysis of viable rumen bacteria in bovine rumen fluid. *Appl. Microbiol.* 16: 714–723, 1968.

39. JAYASURIYA, G. C. N., AND R. E. HUNGATE. Lactate conversions in the bovine rumen. *Arch. Biochem. Biophys.* 82: 274–287, 1959.

40. KLEIN, W., H. SCHMID, E. STUDT, AND R. MÜLLER. Der Strukturwert des aus nichteiweissartigen Verbindungen im pansen erzeugten Bakterieneiweisses auf Grund des festgestellten physiologischen Eiweissminimums. *Z. Tierzucht. Zuchtungsbiol.* 43: 76–119, 1939.

41. KÖHLER, W. Versuche über die zahlenmässige Veränderng der naturlichen Bakterienflora in dem Verdauungsorganen der Wiederkäuer. *Arch. Mikrobiol.* 11: 432–469, 1940.

42. MacARTHUR, J. M., AND J. E. MILTIMORE. Rumen gas

analysis by gas-solid chromatography. *Can. J. Animal Sci.* 41: 187–196, 1961.

43. McDonald, I. W. The role of ammonia in ruminal digestion of protein. *Biochem. J.* 51: 86–90, 1952.

44. Moir, R. J., and L. E. Harris. Ruminal flora studies in the sheep. x. Influence of nitrogen intake upon ruminal function. *J. Nutr.* 77: 285–298, 1962.

45. Moomaw, C. R., and R. E. Hungate. Ethanol conversion in the bovine rumen. *J. Bacteriol.* 85: 721–722, 1963.

46. Oxford, A. E. The conversion of certain soluble sugars to a glucosan by holotrich ciliates in the rumen of sheep. *J. Gen. Microbiol.* 5: 83–90, 1951.

47. Oxford, A. E. A guide to rumen microbiology. *N. Z. Dept. Sci. Ind. Res. Bull.* 160: 1964.

48. Oyaert, W., and J. H. Bouckaert. Quantitative aspects of food digestion in the rumen. *Zentr. Veterinaermed.* 7: 929–935, 1960.

48a. Paynter, M. J. B., and R. E. Hungate. *Methanobacterium mobilis,* sp. n., isolated from the bovine rumen. *J. Bacteriol.* 95: 1943–1951, 1968.

49. Pittman, K. A., and M. P. Bryant. Peptides and other nitrogen sources for growth of *Bacteriodes ruminicola. J. Bacteriol.* 88: 401–410, 1964.

50. Portugal, A. V. *Some Aspects of Amino Acid and Protein Metabolism in the Rumen of the Sheep* (Ph.D. Thesis). Aberdeen, Scotland: Aberdeen Univ., 1963.

51. Shazly, K. el-. Degradation of protein in the rumen of the sheep. 2. The action of rumen microorganisms on amino acids. *Biochem. J.* 51: 647–653, 1952.

52. Shazly, K. el-, and R. E. Hungate. Fermentation capacity as a measure of net growth of rumen microorganisms. *Appl. Microbiol.* 13: 62–69, 1965.

53. Smith, J. A. B., and F. Baker. The utilization of urea in the bovine rumen. 4. The isolation of the synthesized material and the correlation between protein synthesis and microbial activities. *Biochem. J.* 38: 496–505, 1944.

54. Smith, P. H., and R. E. Hungate. Isolation and characterization of *Methanobacterium ruminantium,* n. sp. *J. Bacteriol.* 75: 713–718, 1958.

55. Virtanen, A. I. Milk production of cows on protein-free feed. *Science* 153: 1603–1614, 1966.

56. Walker, D. J., and W. W. Forrest. The application of calorimetry to the study of ruminal fermentation *in vitro. Australian J. Agr. Res.* 15: 299–315, 1964.

57. Weller, R. A., F. V. Gray, and A. F. Pilgrim. The conversion of plant nitrogen to microbial nitrogen in the rumen of the sheep. *Brit. J. Nutr.* 12: 421–429, 1958.

57a. Wright, D. E. Metabolism of peptides by rumen microorganisms. *Appl. Microbiol.* 15: 547–550, 1967.

58. Wright, D. E., and R. E. Hungate. The metabolism of glycine by rumen microorganisms. *Appl. Microbiol.* 15: 152–157, 1966.

CHAPTER 131

Abomasal function

K. J. HILL | *Unilever Research Laboratory, Bedford, England*

CHAPTER CONTENTS

ALTHOUGH the characteristic chambers of the ruminant digestive tract—the rumen, reticulum, and omasum—are present in the newborn animal, they are poorly developed and nonfunctional. The role of the true gastric secretory stomach—the abomasum—is analogous to that of the conventional mammalian stomach since it receives food of animal origin that is attacked and digested under acid conditions by the enzymes of the gastric juice. Except for the presence of a potent milk-curdling enzyme, rennin, in the gastric juice of the suckling ruminant, gastric secretory function does not differ from that of other species. Only with the transition to a herbivorous diet and the onset of fermentative digestion in the forestomachs does the characteristic continuous nature of abomasal function develop.

ABOMASUM OF ADULT RUMINANT

Morphological Considerations

GROSS ANATOMY. The abomasum constitutes the fourth division of the ruminant stomach and corresponds morphologically and functionally to the gastric secretory stomach of other animals. The body region is comparatively wide and communicates cranially with the omasum through the unguarded omaso-abomasal orifice and is succeeded caudally by the long, narrow pyloric region. Estimates of the relative capacities of the various chambers indicate that that of the adult abomasum is about 7 % (bovine) and 12 % (ovine) of the total stomach volume (44).

Blood is supplied to the abomasum by a branch of the celiac artery and the omaso-abomasal artery, which divides into inferior and superior divisions that supply the lesser and greater curvatures, respectively. These vessels are embedded in omental fat and give off numerous branches to the right and left faces of the abomasum. They continue to the pyloric sphincter where the superior omaso-abomasal artery anastomoses with the right gastric artery and the inferior omaso-abomasal artery with the right gastro-epiploic artery. The abomasum is thus assured of a copious blood supply, important in view of the large volume of gastric juice it produces. The abomasal arteries are accompanied by corresponding veins that ultimately drain into the portal system.

Two main nerve trunks derived from the dorsal and ventral vagi pass over the omasum and follow the lesser curvature of the abomasum. Both trunks are embedded in the fat of the lesser omentum and give off branches to the appropriate side of the abomasum. The hepatic-duodenal nerve derived from the ventral

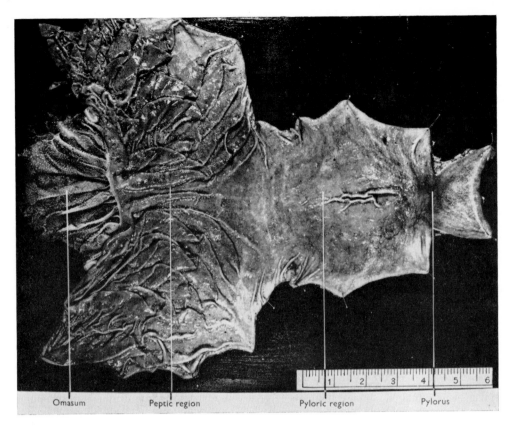

Omasum   Peptic region   Pyloric region   Pylorus

FIG. 1. Goat abomasum opened along greater curvature, showing large mucosal folds in body (*peptic region*).

abdominal vagus nerve runs in the lesser omentum close to the liver and gives off a branch to the pylorus.

The glandular lining of the body region of the abomasum is characterized by large folds which are formed by eversion of the mucosa into the stomach lumen (Fig. 1). They are relatively constant for a given species (34) and begin at the omaso-abomasal junction. Passing caudally, they soon attain their maximum height then gradually become smaller as they approach the antrum or pyloric region. The latter is covered with a smooth mucous membrane which presents a few small rugae. The abomasal folds greatly increase the mucosal secretory area (Table 1).

HISTOLOGY. Transition from omasum to abomasum is sharply defined by the change from stratified to simple columnar epithelium on the lip separating these chambers and by the occurrence of typical gastric glands containing zymogen- and acid-secreting cells (25, 36, 43). A small zone of mucus-secreting glands is often present at the omaso-abomasal junction. Further modification of the gastric glands

TABLE 1. *Surface Area Abomasal Mucosa*
(*Clun Forest Sheep, 56.5 kg.*)

FUNDIC AREA	=	2166 SQ.CM.
PYLORIC AREA	=	133 SQ.CM.
TOTAL AREA	=	2299 SQ.CM.
FUNDIC AREA WITH FOLDS	=	2166 SQ.CM.
FUNDIC AREA WITHOUT FOLDS	=	300 SQ.CM.
AREA OF FOLDS	=	1866 SQ.CM.

occurs at the junction of the body with the antral region where there are glands that consist mainly of mucous cells with occasional parietal or peptic cells.

The mucosa of the pyloric gland area is relatively smooth and composed of typical mucus-secreting pyloric glands. Because of continuous abomasal secretion, the rate of cell renewal in the mucosa may be high, and circumstantial evidence for this is that desquamation and accumulation of cellular debris are frequently seen on microscopic examination.

Entry of Food Material Into Abomasum

The unique arrangement of the ruminant digestive tract, through which food is held and subjected to microbial attack before passage into the abomasum, has brought about considerable modification of abomasal secretory and motor behavior compared to the simple stomach.

In most monogastric animals food passes into the stomach only when meals are eaten, and this is usually at widely separated intervals. In the stomach the food is subjected to the action of saliva and gastric juice and leaves the stomach over a relatively short period. On the other hand, observations on grazing ruminants have shown that these animals may eat for a considerable proportion of each 24 hours and that the reticulo-rumen therefore always contains a considerable amount of food material (21). Even under stall-feeding conditions, in which animals may only be fed once or twice a day, the rumen contains an appreciable amount of digesta and its passage into the abomasum is more or less continuous.

The flow of digesta into the abomasum depends on the nature and physical characteristics of the diet and on the frequency of feeding. Other factors include the volume of material in the reticulo-rumen and in the abomasum itself. Since the abomasal secretory response is markedly influenced by the composition and amount of digesta entering it, studies on abomasal secretion must take into account events occurring in the forestomachs.

General Features of Abomasal Secretion

Much information on the secretory behavior of the simple mammalian stomach has been obtained, with the stomach tube and the simple gastric fistula. The former of these methods is not easily applicable to the study of abomasal function, and as digesta are always present in this organ the simple fistula cannot be used for investigations on pure gastric juice. Thus, gastric juice, free of digesta, can only be obtained from surgically prepared gastric pouches; the special features involved in the construction and use of such pouches have been described (30).

Much of the information on abomasal secretion has been obtained from sheep kept indoors and on a dry diet, usually fed once or twice daily. There is no information on the abomasum of grazing animals. However, it has long been recognized that even under a once-daily feeding regimen the reticulo-rumen is never empty but constitutes a reservoir of

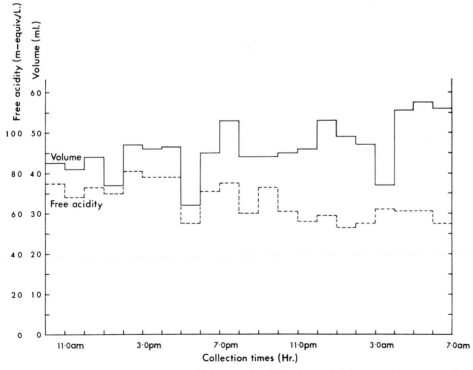

FIG. 2. Volume and acidity of gastric juice secreted by a vagally innervated abomasal pouch in a sheep fed ad libitum with hay and oats.

food material that ensures an uninterrupted flow to the abomasum. Continuous abomasal secretory activity (Fig. 2) is therefore not surprising, a feature noted by several of the earlier workers observing animals that had frequent access to food (6, 9, 19).

Whether continuous secretion was due to the innate ability of the gastric glands to secrete spontaneously or to their constant stimulation by humoral or reflex means was not clear from the earlier work, but it is now known that the glands are much less active after a fast and that when digesta do not enter the abomasum secretion of acid gastric juice ceases (26). Continuous abomasal secretion, in fact, is not due to the innate ability of the glands to secrete spontaneously but to specific stimuli, the most important being the continuous passage of digesta from the reticulo-rumen into the abomasum.

Although the juice is continuously produced, there are minor fluctuations in the volume and acidity; several earlier investigators showed that secretory activity was reduced during a fast and that subsequent feeding was accompanied by increased secretion (6, 9, 19). Other influences on abomasal secretory activity have also been reported. Thus, Krzywanek & Buss (32) found that the acidity of the abomasal content fell to a low level one month before lambing and gradually regained its original level after parturition. Diurnal changes in secretion in ruminating calves and seasonal influences on abomasal secretory activity have been reported (40).

Calculations of the total volume of secretion produced by the entire fundic gland area of the abomasum of sheep and cattle have been made by extrapolation from the volume produced by a gastric pouch of a known surface area. They have provided estimates of 5–6 liters per 24 hours from a 50-kg sheep (28) and 30 liters per 24 hours from a 2-year-old bovine (40).

Secretory Mechanisms of Abomasum

As already indicated, intermittent as opposed to ad libitum feeding is accompanied by a relatively short-lived secretory response of the abomasum which is superimposed on the basal secretion. This is illustrated by the results obtained when a sheep is trained to consume its daily food in 1–2 hours (Fig. 3). A secretory response from a vagally innervated abomasal pouch then develops within 15 min of the start of feeding and may last for several hours before declining to the prefeeding level (28). During feeding there is hypermotility of the forestomach and of the

abomasum, which leads to an increased flow of reticulo-rumen content to and through the abomasum. There is little doubt that this is the major stimulus to the secretion of acid gastric juice by the abomasum, for consumption of a meal when the reticulo-rumen is empty of digesta fails to evoke a secretory response (26).

Earlier workers had inferred that this was so. For example, Grosser (19) was inclined to the view that mechanical factors were responsible for the increased secretion provoked by a meal after a period of fasting, and although he did not commit himself it may be inferred that he had in mind an increased rate of passage of digesta. Belgowski (6), in a series of experiments on calves with abomasal pouches, described the continuous nature of gastric secretion and the secretory response to a meal and concluded that the secretion of juice was closely connected with the reception of food in the stomach. He was unable

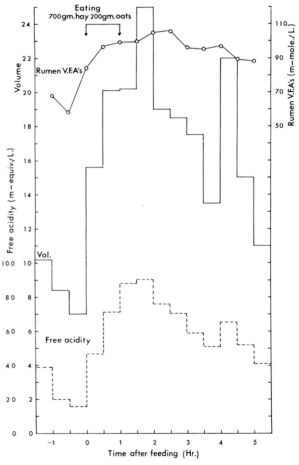

FIG. 3. Effect of a single meal on the secretion of gastric juice by a vagally innervated abomasal pouch in a sheep. V.F.A.'s = volatile fatty acids. [From Hill (28).]

to determine whether there was a relationship be-tween the rate of secretion and the nature of the diet. Popov (37) concluded, from experiments on sheep with abomasal pouches, that the pyloric (gas-trin) phase of secretion was the most important factor in the secretory response, for direct stimulation of the abomasum by the introduction of food through an abomasal fistula was very effective in provoking secretion. Popov's work was subsequently extended by other Russians, who confirmed that abomasal secretion is controlled mainly by humorochemical factors. They did, however, show that a denervated abomasal pouch, although capable of secreting con-tinuously, secreted at a greater rate before denerva-tion; and they believed that the vagi fulfill an adap-tive and trophic function in that they intensify the metabolic processes in the cells of the abomasal glands so that they function better under the influence of humoral and chemical factors (40).

Direct evidence that the flow of digesta through the abomasum constitutes the major stimulus for the secretion of acid gastric juice has been obtained within recent years. Hill (28) demonstrated increased flow from the duodenum during eating and that this corresponded temporally with the increased secretory response from gastric pouches. Ash (3) measured acid secretion by an isolated abomasal pouch and the outflow of digesta from the abomasum simul-taneously and found that both acid secretion and the flow of digesta increased in the first hour after feed-ing, reached a peak between the second and third hours, and thereafter declined. When the daily food intake was increased, the flow of food material, the amount of water drunk, and the secretion of acid were increased. A decrease in food intake had the opposite effect.

Gastric secretion is likewise increased when the flow of digesta through the abomasum is increased by the gastric hypermotility of insulin hypoglycemia. That the secretory response is mainly due to an in-creased flow of digesta and not to direct vagal stimu-lation of the gastric glands is apparent from the greatly reduced response to insulin when the fore-stomachs are emptied prior to its administration. Direct vagal stimulation of the gastric glands does occur during insulin hypoglycemia, but this is shown essentially as an increase in proteolytic enzyme secre-tion (28).

Insofar as acid and water secretion are concerned, intraabomasal factors appear to be mainly involved, and there is evidence to show that both distention of the abomasum and the actual composition of the

digesta are important in stimulating secretion (4, 28). The antral hormone gastrin is known to be liberated by local chemical or mechanical stimula-tion and to provoke the secretion of acid and water but not of pepsin; it is presumably the result of gastrin liberation by distention of the antral and corporal regions of the abomasum which provokes a secretory response. In this context, Anderson et al. (1) have recently isolated histamine-free gastrin from the abomasum of the cow and sheep, and it is note-worthy that they were able to obtain active material from both the pyloric and the body regions of the abomasum and that their extracts exerted their effect for much longer periods than those obtained from nonruminants.

The precise nature of the chemical stimulus respon-sible for causing gastrin release has not been clearly defined, although meat and liver extracts are among the most potent liberators in nonruminant mammals. There is no information on the nature of the gastrin releasers which operate in the ruminant abomasum, although it is possible that bacterial proteins, present in appreciable amounts in the digesta entering the abomasum from the reticulo-rumen, may be in-volved.

Rumen fluid, which contains large numbers of bacteria, certainly stimulates gastric secretion when introduced directly into the abomasum (Fig. 4), but this effect appears to be mainly attributable to its volatile fatty acid content. Short-chain fatty acids are among the major end products of bacterial fer-mentation in the rumen; it has been known for some years that acetic acid, which is produced in greatest quantity during rumen fermentation, stimulates abomasal secretion when placed in the abomasum (4, 37). Ash also showed that buffered solutions con-taining a mixture of acetic, propionic, and butyric acids stimulate abomasal secretion when added to the abomasum, the fatty acids being considered to potentiate the secretory response brought about by the buffer solution itself. Secretion of acid gastric juice in response to fatty acid stimulation continued until the abomasal content was of high acidity, when there was inhibition of secretion. The intro-duction of a solution of pH 1.9–2.8 was also effective in inhibiting secretion. Whether the fatty acids act by provoking the release of gastrin is not known, but as they are normally present in abomasal contents their gastric stimulatory properties must contribute to the secretory activity of the abomasum.

The marked increase in the production of volatile fatty acids in the rumen following the ingestion of

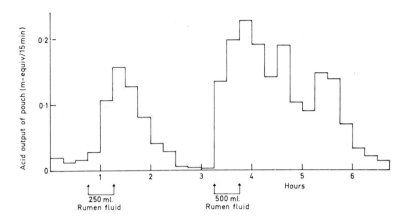

FIG. 4. Effect on acid secretion by a pouch introducing rumen fluid directly into the abomasum (between *arrows*). Conscious sheep with reticulo-rumen empty and free flow from abomasum to duodenum. [From Ash (4).]

food after a fast correlates closely with the increased secretory activity of an abomasal pouch; it is possible that the greater concentration of fatty acid in the material entering the abomasum is responsible for this effect. The addition of fatty acid to the rumen is also effective in stimulating abomasal secretion (Fig. 5), and this again may be attributable to the increased concentration of volatile fatty acids that enter the abomasum. On the other hand, the addition of acetate to the empty rumen in sufficiently small volume to prohibit its passage to the abomasum is equally effective in the stimulation of secretion.

The classic concept of the gastric secretory phases—the nervous, gastric, and intestinal—has often been employed in descriptions of gastric secretion in ruminants; and there has been a general tendency to regard the nervous phase as either absent or of little consequence, for there is manifestly no need for a preparatory rapid outpouring of juice (cephalic phase) to cope with newly ingested food. The relative contributions of the different phases of secretion do vary in different species, and it is true that the cephalic phase in the ruminant is absent as determined by sham-feeding experiments with an esophagostomy or simply by feeding when the reticulo-rumen is empty of digesta (28). Nevertheless, it has become increasingly evident during recent years that there is little point in a rigid separation of nervous and humoral stimulatory mechanisms, since there is considerable functional integration of the two and they are interdependent (2).

The importance of vagal stimulation in pepsin release from the abomasum is shown when insulin hypoglycemia is used to stimulate the vagal centers. When this is done with a full reticulo-rumen, the concurrent hypermotility causes an increased flow of food material to the abomasum which stimulates the flow and acidity of the gastric juice. There is also an

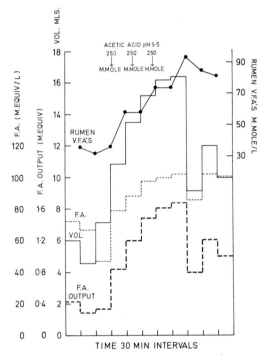

FIG. 5. Effect of adding acetic acid to the rumen on the secretion of gastric juice from an innervated gastric pouch in a sheep. [From Hill (28).]

increase in pepsin output which does not occur during histamine stimulation. Insulin hypoglycemia produces a similar stimulation of pepsin secretion when the reticulo-rumen is empty of digesta, although there is then only a small, accompanying increase in the volume and acidity of the juice. Injection of the cholinergic drug carbachol is equally effective (Fig. 6) in increasing pepsin concentration and output (29).

Although the cephalic phase of vagally stimulated gastric secretion is absent in the adult ruminant, vagal excitation must presumably play a part in the

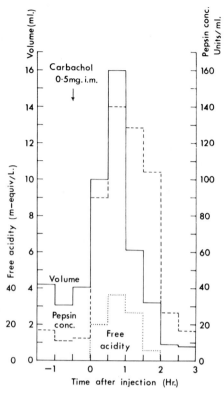

FIG. 6. Secretory response of an abomasal pouch following the intramuscular injection of carbachol. [From Hill (29).]

secretory behavior of the abomasum, since there is an increased output of pepsin from gastric pouches during the secretory response to feeding. There is certainly a basal secretion of pepsin by an abomasal pouch; this must be caused by intrinsic cholinergic mechanisms, for there is no evidence to suggest that pepsin secretion is significantly affected by other than vagal mechanisms. It would appear, therefore, that reflex vagal excitation must occur, if not continuously, at least intermittently throughout each 24 hours.

Several authors have suggested that, in nonruminant animals, afferent impulses from the stomach and intestine might have reflex effects on gastric secretion, and reflex pathways originating in mechanoreceptors in the stomach and duodenum have been shown to cause vagal effects in the stomach (22). Whether there is a similar reflex control of pepsin secretion from the ruminant abomasum or from the reticulo-rumen has not been conclusively demonstrated.

As already indicated, the gastrin phase of secretion is undoubtedly of major significance insofar as the secretion of acid and water by the abomasum is concerned, and as with the monogastric stomach there is little doubt that histamine is involved in the stimula-

tory mechanism. The abomasum is equally responsive to histamine; it secretes copious amounts of highly acid juice after subcutaneous, intramuscular, or intravenous injection of histamine (29). Under histamine stimulation, the acidity, total chloride, and volume rate of secretion show the parallelism found in man and the dog, whereas the total chloride concentration shows a straight-line relationship against acidity. When neutral chloride concentration is plotted against acidity, there is a straight-line relationship with a negative slope, and extrapolation shows that when neutral chloride is zero the acidity is around 167 mEq per liter, which is comparable to figures obtained in other animals (Fig. 7). In practice the maximum acidity observed in abomasal juice after any form of stimulation has not been more than 140 mEq per liter, which compares with 153 mEq per liter reported for the dog.

The sodium concentration in histamine-stimulated juice varies inversely with the acidity, as does the magnesium concentration; this indicates that they are both derived from the alkaline component of gastric juice.

Potassium concentration increases from about 5 mEq per liter before stimulation to around 20 mEq per liter about one hour after histamine stimulation and falls thereafter to the preinjection level (Fig. 8). The relationship of changes in potassium concentration to changes in gastric secretion is not fully understood; and although there is apparent correlation between potassium concentration and acidity in the ruminant as in the dog, other evidence suggests that there may be a general release of potassium under the influence of histamine rather than any specific relationship to the process of hydrochloric acid formation (31).

Inhibition of Abomasal Secretion

Inhibition of gastric secretion by the reduction or blockage of gastrin release when the gastric content is excessively acid has been shown to be one of the controlling mechanisms in monogastric species; a similar mechanism has been shown to operate in the abomasum, for the secretion of juice of high acidity is invariably followed by the secretion of juice of reduced acidity (3, 28). The critical acidity for the inhibition of gastrin release by the abomasum has not been determined but is around pH 2.0.

Under conditions of frequent feeding, the pH of the digesta leaving the abomasum remains within a comparatively narrow range and is evidently the

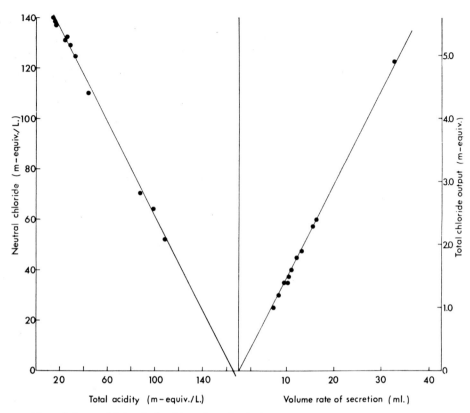

FIG. 7. Variations in ionic composition of abomasal juice during histamine stimulation.

result of the interplay of the stimulation and inhibition of gastrin release. When animals are fed infrequently, however, there is greater fluctuation in accordance with the considerable acid secretory response evoked, and a wave of acidity is observed to pass along the duodenum and jejunum (23).

Inhibitory effects on abomasal secretion also arise from the duodenum; as in nonruminants, the liberation of enterogastrone by the presence of fat in the duodenum is followed by complete or partial cessation of gastric secretion and inhibition of abomasal and forestomach motility. Olive oil added directly to duodenal contents produces these effects very readily, but dietary fats are normally completely hydrolyzed to fatty acids in the rumen so that little triglyceride reaches the abomasum and duodenum.

Atropine produces its characteristic inhibitory effect on abomasal secretion (Fig. 9) by blocking direct vagal stimulatory mechanisms, but as vagal fibers are also implicated in the release of gastrin by local mechanical and chemical stimuli acting on the pyloric mucosa, atropine inhibition must also involve blockage of gastrin release. The vagus is also the efferent pathway for reflexes from the duodenum which inhibit gastric secretion.

Insofar as the adult abomasum is concerned it may be concluded that the volume and acidity of the secretion produced by the abomasum are influenced by the amount and composition of the material which enters it and by the relative degree to which various inhibitory mechanisms from the abomasum itself and from the duodenum participate. The secretion of pepsin is under vagal control and may be influenced by stimulation from the forestomach.

Abomasal Function

When a meal is eaten by a monogastric animal, it is swallowed in a semisolid condition and remains in that state for a comparatively long time and is only gradually penetrated by the gastric juice. In the ruminant, on the other hand, the digesta which enter the abomasum are already in a finely divided state and are immediately immersed in the highly acid abomasal content. The continuous secretion of gastric juice ensures that the contents remain acid and at low pH, and conditions are therefore optimal for gastric proteolysis. The passage of digesta through the abomasum is rapid, but as the pH of the duodenal content is little different from that of the abomasum

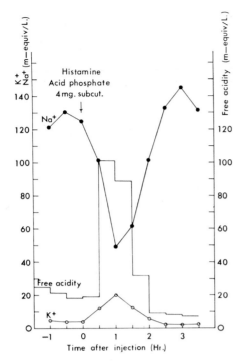

FIG. 8. Changes in the sodium and potassium concentration of gastric juice following the subcutaneous injection of histamine. [From Hill (29).]

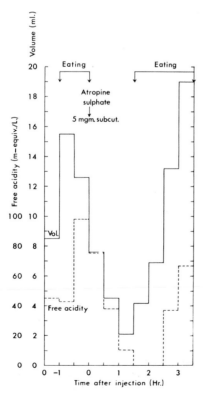

FIG. 9. Inhibitory effect of atropine on the secretory response to a meal of an innervated abomasal pouch in a sheep.

(23) it is obvious that proteolysis does not cease immediately when the digesta leave the abomasum. Backflow of digesta from the duodenum into the abomasum (42) must also increase the time during which digesta are subjected to peptic proteolysis.

Because of the fermentative stage of digestion which takes place in the reticulo-rumen, the substrate normally presented to the abomasum is of comparatively uniform composition, and as the nitrogenous constituents of the food undergo essentially complete microbial conversion, the protein presented for gastric digestion is mainly bacterial. It is generally assumed that the bacteria and protozoa from the rumen are killed in the acid environment of the abomasum and that proteolysis takes place rapidly, although there is little information on the extent of proteolytic digestion in the abomasum of the adult ruminant.

ABOMASUM OF YOUNG RUMINANT

Development of Abomasum

As in monogastric animals the ruminant stomach develops from a simple spindle-shaped enlargement of the primitive digestive tube, the abomasum itself being derived from the area which in nonruminants becomes the pyloric antrum, whereas the reticulum and rumen are derived from what, in the primitive stomach, are the potential fundic and pyloric regions. During fetal life the abomasum develops more rapidly than the other components, so that in the newborn animal it is larger than the reticulo-rumen and remains so provided only milk is consumed. The young ruminant is physiologically a monogastric animal, for the ingested food (milk) passes directly to the abomasum along the esophageal groove and does not undergo prior fermentation in the rumen. With the ingestion of solid food, particularly roughage, the relative capacities of the stomach chambers change, and the reticulo-rumen rapidly attains much greater capacity than the abomasum as befits its role as a fermentation and storage chamber (44).

Histogenesis

In the sheep the primary epithelial lining of the simple stomach spindle consists of a single layer of columnar cells which gradually become folded and so form projections into the lumen of the stomach. The projections, consisting of a core of mesoblast covered with columnar cells, eventually form the large mucosal folds of the adult abomasum. By about 60 days the columnar epithelial lining of the entire stomach is formed into a series of shallow tubular pits—the future gastric glands—and the various cell types of the mature gland are produced by differentiation from the simple columnar cells lining them. In the 75–85-day fetus it is possible to distinguish the future peptic cells; clearly defined zymogen granules are present from 119 days onward. Parietal cells are very infrequent and remain sparse until birth; it is only during the first 24–36 hours of life that a rapid increase takes place in their number (27).

The characteristic milk-coagulating properties of the young ruminant stomach have been recognized for many years. Edkins (14) has suggested that the chief cells of the gastric glands contain the zymogens of both rennin and pepsin. More recent investigations have revealed the existence of several proteolytic enzymes in the gastric juice of man and the dog, and rennin may now be considered as one of a similar range of proteolytic enzymes present in the gastric juice of the young ruminant. It seems probable that the zymogens of all these enzymes are produced by the chief cells.

Passage of Food Material to Abomasum

The first milk obtained after parturition is colostrum, and its composition differs most markedly from that of later milk in the concentration and distribution of the proteins. There may be 17–18% protein in the first colostrum, although this falls rapidly during the first 24 hours after parturition and gradually approaches that of normal milk. Although the high protein concentration of colostrum is of major significance in the transmission of immunity to the young, it is obviously also of considerable nutritional significance; well-developed systems of proteolysis are necessary to ensure its adequate utilization.

The presence of a mechanism whereby the forestomachs are bypassed and ingested milk is directed to the abomasum has been known for many years, but it is only comparatively recently that detailed information on the reflex nature of the esophageal groove mechanism has been obtained (13). Correct functioning of the groove ensures that most of the meal passes to the abomasum; this aspect of abomasal filling has been amply documented (39, 45, 46).

There is, however, comparatively little information on the events which take place in the abomasum after the ingestion of a meal. Clotting or coagulation of the milk takes place rapidly with separation of the whey from the clot, and as the fluid appears in the duodenum within five minutes of feeding (35) it is evident that the passage of the whey, at least, is a rapid process. Mortensen et al. (33) endeavored to determine the rate at which milk left the abomasum by placing milk in this organ through the reticuloomasal opening and palpating the abomasum for the presence of curds. They found that boiled and autoclaved milk (8–12 hours) was usually evacuated faster than raw milk (12–18 hours). Espe & Cannon (15) used the same technique and found that milk which contained up to 6% fat tended to leave the stomach more rapidly than skim milk. They attributed the increased emptying time to differences in the texture of the curd produced when fat was present in the diet. In this work the method of introduction of the milk prevented its admixture with pregastric lipase (38, 47) and may not have stimulated the secretion of gastric juice to the same extent as normal sucking. Both of these events may influence the rate of breakdown of milk clot in the abomasum, and as the act of sucking also stimulates contractions of the abomasum the emptying time may have been longer than normal.

Secretory and Digestive Processes in Abomasum

In the very young ruminant, which suckles frequently, the abomasum is unlikely ever to be completely free of food material and the secretion of gastric juice is probably continuous. There is, in fact, evidence that this is so in calves from 2 weeks of age fed twice daily (Fig. 10). Precisely how this secretion is

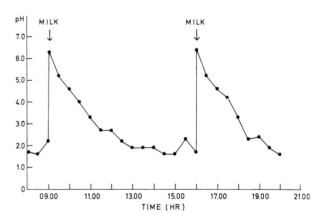

FIG. 10. The pH of the abomasal content of a 14-day-old calf. Note the low pH at the beginning of the experiment when the calf had been fasted for 17 hours and the 4-hour lag period following a meal before the pH had fallen to the prefeeding level.

maintained is not known. Espe & Cannon (16) prepared Pavlov pouches in calves, and from their lack of response to sham-feeding they concluded that the psychic or cephalic phase was of little importance to these animals. Other workers have reported that sham-feeding of esophagotomized calves for 5–10 min stimulated gastric secretion (40).

Ash found that the secretion of acid by innervated abomasal pouches in calves was relatively high in the presucking period, and since the calves were expecting to be fed he considered it possible that there was strong vagal excitation to the gastric mucosa. The patterns of secretion of proteolytic enzymes also provided suggestive evidence of vagal excitation in the presucking period (5).

There is, however, little doubt that the general increase in the volume and acidity of the gastric juice following a meal is due to the flow of food material into the abomasum. Shoptaw and colleagues (41), for example, compared the effect of feeding whole milk and soybean gruel on the secretory activity of gastric pouches in calves and found that both produced a marked secretory response that was maximal 60–90 min after feeding and subsided over the subsequent 90 min to prefeeding levels. Similar responses were obtained by Ash, who noted that the increase in volume of secretion and concentration of acid began within 15 min of sucking; he also showed that the acts of sucking and drinking were not directly responsible for the acid secretory response since the introduction of milk directly into the abomasum was also effective (5). This type of response to feeding compares with that seen in the adult ruminant and is doubtless similarly attributable to the pyloric phase of secretion. Short-chain fatty acids, mainly butyric acid, derived from the action of pregastric esterases (38) and not from fermentation, are also present in the abomasum of the young ruminant, but whether they potentiate gastric secretion is not known.

Although marked variability in the patterns of secretory response occurs among calves, the basic stimulus to secretion is the presence of milk in the abomasum, and it is therefore important to understand the nature of digesta flow into and out of the abomasum before causes for changes in secretory activity can be assigned. One of the most important factors affecting the emptying of the abomasum is the formation of milk clot; although there are many studies on the clotting mechanism and the hydrolysis of casein in vitro (11, 12), there are few on the actual process of clotting in the abomasum.

Studies on extracts of the abomasal mucosa do,

however, abound. There has been a protracted controversy as to whether milk coagulation is caused by a distinct enzyme, rennin, or whether it is the result of peptic activity. This has only been resolved comparatively recently by the preparation of crystalline rennin (7).

Fomin (18) appears to have been the first to show that rennin is present in the gastric juice of the calf and is secreted during feeding; he developed a method for the production of rennin in which young calves with abomasal fistulas were fed milk and the abomasal content was then collected for the preparation of rennin. Berridge and his colleagues (8) repeated this work but found that the yields of rennin were too low to be economical. By feeding whey slowly and collecting it as it emerged from the abomasal fistula they found that there was a lag of about 5 min between the start of feeding and the maximum secretion of rennin. Grosskopf (20) and Ash (5) also noted that the clotting activity of pouch juice increased rapidly during the first 15 min of sucking and then rapidly decreased to less than in the presucking period. No attempt was made to discriminate between rennin and pepsin, and since the time taken for milk to be clotted by the gastric juice was inversely related to the concentration of proteolytic activity it is possible that the clotting activity was entirely attributable to pepsin.

The relationship between the proteolytic enzymes active at low pH and the enzyme rennin, in the gastric juice of the very young calf, has not been completely elucidated, although there are indications that rennin is the only enzyme present at birth and that, provided the animal is maintained on a pure milk diet, only rennin is secreted. Berridge et al. (8) found that in calves maintained on a pure milk diet there was a high ratio of milk-coagulating to proteolytic activity, the latter activity possibly also being due to rennin since the pH optimum was near 4.0. Fish (17) has shown that rennin is a powerful proteolytic enzyme with a pH optimum of 4.0; and since an appreciable time elapses before the pH falls below this after a meal, conditions in the abomasum of the young calf may be more suitable for rennin activity than peptic.

In the dog and man the ratio of milk-clotting to proteolytic activity is apparently independent of the age of the animal; that is, both activities are attributable to proteolytic enzymes active at low pH. This is not so in very young calves, for in them a very high milk-clotting to proteolytic ratio occurs, and it has been claimed that the proteolytic activity increases only during weaning and transfer to solid food (8). Henschel and co-workers (24) were unable to confirm these findings; their results indicated that either pepsin or rennin or both enzymes were secreted in the gastric juice of calves 1–2 weeks old maintained on a milk diet.

The composition of the abomasal secretion of the ruminant during the first week or so of life is unknown. Until modern methods of enzyme separation have been applied to such material from animals maintained on well-defined diets, the present confused situation will remain.

The mechanisms controlling the secretion of enzymes in the gastric juice of the young ruminant are not known, but their rapid increase before and after feeding is indicative of a neural, presumably vagal, mechanism. Reduced output of proteolytic activity after feeding may be due to a decrease in vagal stimulation as a result of satiation of appetite (5).

Abomasal Function

The essential role of the preruminant abomasum appears to be that of a reservoir and control mechanism for the regulation of the passage of food material into the intestine. A certain amount of lipid and protein breakdown takes place as a result of pregastric lipase, rennin, and proteolytic enzyme activity, but it appears to be the markedly efficient milk-clotting mechanism which is of primary importance to the very young ruminant. Clotting of ingested milk appears to be instantaneous, and, although the initial flow of whey and digestive secretions into the duodenum is rapid, the more solid clotted material is only gradually discharged from the abomasum. There is thus a continuous slow provision of food material to the small intestine which may be advantageous to a young animal that has not attained biochemical and physiological maturity of its digestive tract.

Circumstantial evidence for this view is provided by observations on calves in which clot formation was inhibited or prevented by the nature of the diet. In this situation a rapid flow of food material through the abomasum is likely, which results in intermittent accumulation of high concentrations of fermentable materials in the intestine. There is no direct evidence that the enzymatic or absorptive capacity of the gut is exceeded under these conditions, but large amounts of fermentable material certainly occur in the small intestine under these circumstances (10), indicating that the absence of the delaying effect on gastric emptying produced by clot formation is the cause or at least a contributory factor.

REFERENCES

1. ANDERSON, W. R., T. L. FLETCHER, C. L. PITTS, AND H. N. HARKINS. Isolation and assay of ovine gastrin. *Nature* 193: 1286–1287, 1962.
2. ANDERSSON, S., AND L. OLBE. Gastric acid secretory responses to gastrin and histamine in dogs before and after vagal denervation of the gastric pouch. *Acta Physiol. Scand.* 60: 51–56, 1964.
3. ASH, R. W. Acid secretion by the abomasum and its relation to the flow of food material in the sheep. *J. Physiol., London* 156: 93–111, 1961.
4. ASH, R. W. Stimuli influencing the secretion of acid by the abomasum of sheep. *J. Physiol., London* 157: 185–207, 1961.
5. ASH, R. W. Abomasal secretion and emptying in suckled calves. *J. Physiol., London* 172: 425–438, 1964.
6. BELGOWSKI, J. Ein Beitrag zur Lehre von der Labmagenverdauung der Wiederkäur. *Arch. Ges. Physiol.* 148: 319–368, 1912.
7. BERRIDGE, N. J. The purification and crystallisation of rennin. *Biochem. J.* 39: 179–186, 1945.
8. BERRIDGE, N. J., J. G. DAVIES, P. M. KON, S. K. KON, AND F. R. SPRATTLING. The production of rennet from living calves. *J. Dairy Res.* 13: 145–161, 1943.
9. BICKEL, A. Experimentelle Untersuchungen über die Magensaftsekretion der Herbivoren. *Berl. Klin. Wochschr.* 42: 144–145, 1905.
10. BLAXTER, K. L., AND W. A. WOOD. Some observations on the biochemical and physiological events associated with diarrhoea in calves. *Vet. Record* 65: 889–892, 1953.
11. CERBULIS, J., J. H. CUSTER, AND C. A. ZITTLE. Action of rennin and pepsin on β-casein: Insoluble and soluble products. *J. Dairy Sci.* 43: 1725–1730, 1960.
12. CHRISTENSEN, L. R. The action of proteolytic enzymes on casein proteins. *Arch. Biochem. Biophys.* 53: 128–137, 1954.
13. COMLINE, R. S., AND D. A. TITCHEN. Nervous control of the ruminant stomach. In: *Digestive Physiology and Nutrition of the Ruminant*, edited by D. Lewis. London: Butterworths, 1961, p. 10–22.
14. EDKINS, J. S. The chemical mechanism of gastric secretion. *J. Physiol., London* 34: 133–144, 1906.
15. ESPE, D. L., AND C. Y. CANNON. The relation of the fat content of milk to the passage of the milk curd from the stomach of the calf. *J. Dairy Sci.* 18: 141–146, 1935.
16. ESPE, D. L., AND C. Y. CANNON. Gastric secretion in ruminants. *Am. J. Physiol.* 119: 720, 723, 1937.
17. FISH, J. C. Activity and specificity of rennin. *Nature* 180: 345, 1957.

18. FOMIN, D. Cited by N. J. Berridge in *The Enzymes*, edited by J. B. Sumner and K. Myrback. New York: Acad. Press, 1951, vol. 1, part 1.

19. GROSSER, P. Untersuchungen über den Magensaft der Wiederkäuer. *Zbl. Physiol.* 19: 265–266, 1905.

20. GROSSKOFF, J. F. W. Some factors affecting the secretion of abomasal juice in young dairy calves. *Onderstepoort J. Vet. Res.* 28: 133–141, 1959.

21. HAFEZ, E. S. E., AND M. W. SCHEIN. The behaviour of cattle. In: *The Behaviour of Domestic Animals*, edited by E. S. E. Hafez. London: Baillière, 1962, p. 247–296.

22. HARPER, A. A., C. KIDD, AND T. SCRATCHERD. Vago-vagal reflex effects on gastric and pancreatic secretion and gastro-intestinal motility. *J. Physiol., London* 148: 417–436, 1959.

23. HARRISON, F. A., AND K. J. HILL. Digestive secretions and the flow of digesta along the duodenum of the sheep. *J. Physiol., London* 162: 225–243, 1962.

24. HENSCHEL, M. J., W. B. HILL, AND J. W. G. PORTER. The development of proteolytic enzymes in the abomasum of the young calf. *Proc. Nutr. Soc., Engl. Scot.* 20: 40–41, 1961.

25. HILL, K. J. The glands of the mucous membrane of the goat abomasum. *J. Anat.* 85: 215–220, 1951.

26. HILL, K. J. Continuous gastric secretion in the ruminant. *Quart. J. Exptl. Physiol.* 40: 32–39, 1955.

27. HILL, K. J. Gastric development and antibody transference in the lamb, with some observations on the rat and guinea pig. *Quart. J. Exptl. Physiol.* 41: 421–432, 1956.

28. HILL, K. J. Abomasal secretion in the sheep. *J. Physiol., London* 154: 115–132, 1960.

29. HILL, K. J. Abomasal secretory function in sheep. In: *Physiology of Digestion in the Ruminant*, edited by R. W. Dougherty. Washington, D.C.: Butterworths, 1965, p. 221–230.

30. HILL, K. J., AND R. A. GREGORY. The preparation of gastric pouches in the ruminant. *Vet. Record* 65: 647–652, 1951.

31. HOLLANDER, F. The significance of sodium and potassium in gastric secretion. A review of the problem. *Gastroenterology* 40: 477–490, 1961.

32. KRZYWANEK, F. W., AND W. BUSS. Beiträge zur Physiologie der Verdauung beim Wiederkäuer. 1. Saure-und Fermentgehalt im Labmagen des Schates. *Arch. Wiss. Prakt. Tierheilk.* 69: 321–328, 1935.

33. MORTENSEN, F. N., D. L. ESPE, AND C. Y. CANNON. Effect of heating milk on the time which the curds remain in the abomasum of calves. *J. Dairy Sci.* 18: 229–238, 1935.

34. OPPEL, A. Lehrbuch der vergleichenden mikroscopischen Anatomie der Wilbeltiere. In: *Der Magen*. Jena, Germany: Fischer, Teil 1, 1896.

35. PHILLIPSON, A. T. The movements of the pouches of the stomach of sheep. *Quart. J. Exptl. Physiol.* 29: 395–415, 1939.

36. PLENK, H. Der Magen. In: *Handbuch der microscopischen Anatomie der Menschen*. Berlin: Springer, 1932, Bd. 5, p. 1–324.

37. POPOV, A. N. *On the Physiology of the Sheep*. Moscow: Izdanke Eniio, 1932.

38. RAMSEY, H. A., AND J. W. YOUNG. Role of pregastric esterase in the abomasal hydrolysis of milk fat in the young calf. *J. Dairy Sci.* 44: 2227–2231, 1961.

39. SCHALK, A. F., AND R. S. AMADON. *Physiology of the Ruminant Stomach (Bovine)*. Bull. North Dakota Agric. Exptl. Station, 1928.

40. SEREBRYEKOV, P. N. *I. P. Pavlov's Theories and Farm Animal Physiology*. Moscow: Selkhozgiz, 1950.

41. SHOPTAW, L., D. L. ESPE, AND C. Y. CANNON. Gastric digestion of soyabean flour. *J. Dairy Sci.* 20: 117–127, 1937.

42. SINGLETON, A. G. The electromagnetic measurement of the flow of digesta through the duodenum of the goat and the sheep. *J. Physiol., London* 155: 134–147, 1961.

43. SOMMERVILLE, R. I. The histology of the ovine abomasum and the relation of the globule leucocyte to nematode infestations. *Australian Vet. J.* 32: 237–240, 1956.

44. WARNER, R. G., AND W. P. FLATT. Anatomical development of the ruminant stomach. In: *Physiology of Digestion in the Ruminant*, edited by R. W. Dougherty. Washington, D. C.: Butterworths, 1965, p. 24–38.

45. WATSON, R. H. Studies on deglutition in sheep: A resume of observations on the course taken by liquids through the stomach of sheep at various ages from birth to four years. *Australian Vet. J.* 17: 52–58, 1941.

46. WISE, G. H., AND G. W. ANDERSON. Factors affecting the passage of liquids into the rumen of the dairy calf. 1. Method of administering liquids: drinking from open pail versus sucking through a rubber nipple. *J. Dairy Sci.* 22: 697–705, 1939.

47. WISE, G. H., P. G. MILLER, AND G. W. ANDERSON. Changes observed in milk sham-fed to dairy calves. *J. Dairy Sci.* 23: 997–1011, 1940.

CHAPTER 132

Absorption from the ruminant forestomach

ALAN DOBSON | *Department of Physiology, New York State Veterinary College, Ithaca, New York*

A. T. PHILLIPSON | *Department of Veterinary Clinical Studies, School of Veterinary Medicine, Cambridge, England*

CHAPTER CONTENTS

MEASUREMENTS of the gross internal area of the various parts of the stomach and intestine of the ox (17) showed that the rumen, reticulum, and omasum together almost equaled that of the small and large intestine combined. By contrast, the internal area of the intestine of the dog and cat was about four times that of the stomach. These comparisons, though taking into account the laminal projections into the omasum, ignored the intestinal villi, which would increase the intestinal area by a factor of about ten, and the papillae of the rumen, which would make a smaller increase in area. Despite these omissions, the measurements showed that if any absorption occurred from the rumen, reticulum, and omasum, it would likely be extensive.

This was recognized by Ellenberger (29). His studies on the absorptive capacity of isolated parts of the stomach and forestomach led him to suppose that no absorption of water and salts occurred, except insignificant traces from the omasum. Aggazzotti (1), however, found appreciable absorption of water from the omasum of anesthetized calves. Colin (18) thought that little or no absorption occurred through the keratinized epithelium lining the rumen, arguing teleologically that absorption would render the contents too dry to be regurgitated or passed to the omasum. Ellenberger (30) presented the same point of view.

The rapid action of orally administered chloral hydrate on cattle made Wester (115) suspect that it was absorbed from the rumen, but Trautmann (107) produced the first convincing evidence of absorption from this organ. He put small quantities of solutions of pilocarpine into isolated pockets of the rinsed rumen of goats and observed an increase in salivation within minutes. Atropine applied to the rumen epithelium inhibited salivation. Solutions applied to the exposed epithelium soon disappeared and the epithelium became dry unless frequently moistened. In another experiment he showed that after introduction of a little of the azo dye pyridium into the empty rumen the urine became red within 20 min. Later, Barcroft et al. (7) observed that the radiopaque compound sodium o-iodohippurate appeared in the urine when introduced into the rumen of anesthetized lambs from which the exit was closed by ligature. These experiments proved that the rumen epithelium was permeable to a variety of compounds.

METHODS AND CRITERIA

Methods used to study absorption from the rumen are classified in Table 1. Methods using trained conscious animals are preferred since they are free from changes produced by surgical trauma and anesthetics. To assess the reliability of observations on conscious animals, it is important to consider systematic errors of measurements since there is often less control of conditions than during acute experiments. In this respect the isolated "Pavlov" type of pouch of the rumen has much to commend it since measurements can be made on a closed system. It is doubtful, however, whether the epithelium of the pouch acts normally since the papillae of isolated pouches regress in size and practically disappear. There is, however, no evidence suggesting that the events recorded from such pouches are very different from those in the whole rumen, and in a qualitative sense their properties are so far the same.

TABLE 1. *Methods Used in Study of Ruminal Absorption*

		Preparation	Advantages	Limitations
1. Acute		Rumeno-reticulum isolated by ligature of esophagus and reticulo-omasal orifice. A rumen cannula allows organ to be emptied and washed clean.	Closed system gives good control for estimate of gain or loss of solutions in rumen.	Preparation deteriorates with time. Anesthetic and surgical trauma interfere with absorption.
2. Acute or conscious	a)	Comparison of blood drawn from rumen veins with arterial blood.	Simple way of detecting absorbed products of fermentation from normal rumen contents.	Small changes in concentration may be masked by volume of blood flow and by exchange of water. Anesthetic and surgical interference. Reflects metabolism of muscle and epithelium as well as absorption.
	b)	2a together with blood flow measurement.	Semiquantitative measurement of transport.	Burden of flow measurement.
3. Conscious	a)	Use of nonabsorbable, stable marker to determine rumen volume and inflow. May be combined with incubation experiments or infusion of isotopes to determine rates of production and loss.	Minimal disturbance to animal. Repeated observations possible on same animal. Viability of epithelium not prejudiced by procedure.	Slow mixing with rumen contents unless contents are circulated. Salivary contamination may interfere and sampling errors reduce sensitivity.
	b)	Isolated innervated Pavlov-type pouches of the rumen.	Good control of errors and small volumes needed.	Papillae reduced in size. Reduction with time of pouch size.
	c)	Temporarily isolated ventral sac of the cow.	Viability of epithelium not prejudiced by procedure.	Uncertain isolation of experimental solution.
4. Isolated	a)	Perfused rumeno-reticulum.	Recirculation improves sensitivity.	Unstable preparation. Anoxia in setting up may prejudice epithelium. Formation of constrictor substances in perfusing blood or fluid.
	b)	Isolated rumen epithelium in diffusion chambers.	Exact experimental control.	Preparation deteriorates with time. Really fresh tissue is needed for active preparations.

Acute anesthetized preparations and isolated tissues or organs permit much greater control of experimental procedures, but the need for an index of the condition of the epithelium becomes more pressing. In anesthetized sheep in which the rumen is isolated by ligature its absorption rate and blood flow decrease with time. Nevertheless, with normal rumen contents in this preparation, the electrical potential across the rumen epithelium resembles that of conscious sheep. Interruption of the blood supply to the rumen causes a prompt decrease in the potential, which is irreversible unless the supply is restored within a few minutes (23). A similar decline in the potential was reported with sodium chloride in the rumen when a sheep was killed by an overdose of pentobarbital (40). This sensitivity to anoxia makes it important that a criterion such as potential across the epithelium be measured continuously to monitor viability when methods involving perfusion of the rumen are used.

In studies using isolated sheets of epithelium in diffusion chambers similar to those introduced by Ussing (111), when the same solution bathes both sides, the open-circuit potential or the short-circuit current can be used. When solutions of different composition are placed on opposite sides of the tissue, a part of the potential across the epithelium will be generated by diffusion, which may be less sensitive to epithelial damage. Supplementary measurement of conductance might be a useful criterion. The most delicate test of performance in these preparations is probably the ability of the membrane to transfer sodium against its electrochemical gradient. It will, however, be necessary to refine continually the criteria of viability of the epithelium as understanding of its physiology is refined.

SHORT-CHAIN FATTY ACIDS

The rumen liquor of cattle, sheep, and goats usually contains from 50 to 150 mM of short-chain fatty acids. Feeding increases their concentration and fasting reduces it. The reaction of the rumen contents is on the acid side, but the pH seldom falls below 5.5, so that most of each acid is present in the ionized state (80). The principal acids are acetic, propionic, and butyric (31, 44), but isobutyric and isomers of C_5 acids are also present in small concentrations (32, 33, 45, 46). The concentration of short-chain fatty acids in the abomasum is from 5 to 20 mM (68, 82). Increasing the concentration within the rumen of conscious sheep by addition of sodium salts of these acids did not subsequently cause a corresponding increase in the abomasum, although their concentration within the rumen returned to the predosing level within a few hours. An eight-hour incubation of rumen contents in vitro was accompanied by an increase, rather than a decrease, in the amount of volatile acid present. Further proof of absorption was the fact that venous blood leaving the rumen, reticulum, and omasum of fully fed sheep always contained greater concentrations than arterial blood, whereas the concentration of venous blood leaving the abomasum or small intestine was similar to carotid blood. Venous blood from the cecum again contained more volatile acids than arterial blood (6). The concentration of volatile acids in venous blood showed that they were absorbed from the alimentary tract whenever adequate concentrations were present in the gut contents, irrespective of the epithelial lining they had to traverse. This was true of a number of other species—the dog (81), the guinea pig (47), and the small wallaby (Setonix brachyurus) (71).

Ionization and Fatty Acid Absorption

When acidic solutions of the three principal fatty acids were introduced into the empty isolated rumen of anesthetized sheep, the pH rose and it was necessary to add repeated small quantities of acid in order to maintain the pH at its original value (20). The total absorption of acid was greater from acidic than from neutral equimolar solutions in many experiments.

Absorption of the three acids from slightly alkaline solutions was accompanied by an accumulation of total carbon dioxide within the rumen. This gain, which was mainly as bicarbonate, was related in a linear fashion to the loss of acid. The increase equaled about half the acid absorbed (67). This was examined by Ash & Dobson (5) who found that in the absence of fatty acid, carbon dioxide passed through the rumen wall until the partial pressure in the lumen reached a level about 30 % greater than in the plasma. This would be expected from the production of carbon dioxide by the metabolic activity of the rumen wall. Bicarbonate exchanged much more slowly, and equilibrated in the rumen below the concentration in the plasma. During acetate absorption, a depressed steady level of carbon dioxide within the rumen was attained, lower at times than the plasma concentration. At the same time the bicarbonate equilibrated to a level several times that of the plasma, and the

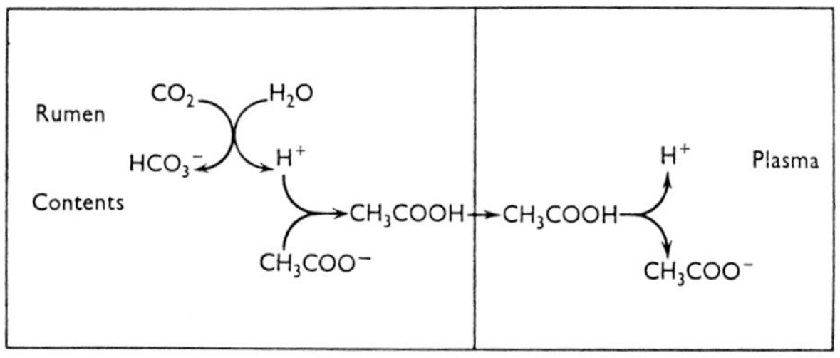

FIG. 1. Effect of the selective absorption of un-ionized acetate upon CO_2 and HCO_3^- in the rumen. The position of the membrane within the layers between plasma and rumen contents is not defined. Un-ionized acetate diffuses through the barrier down its concentration gradient. It ionizes continuously on the plasma side of the membrane to produce hydrogen ions and acetate. On the rumen contents side of the membrane, the reverse process takes place. The supply of hydrogen ion is maintained by the conversion of CO_2 to HCO_3^-. [From Ash & Dobson (5).]

pH within the rumen rose from 7 to about 7.5. These changes would be explained if a substantial fraction of the free acid was absorbed from the rumen solution even at neutral pH. Because less than 1 % would be un-ionized at this pH, a supply of hydrogen ions would be necessary to convert the acetate to acetic acid. This could be supplied by the conversion of carbonic acid to bicarbonate according to the scheme in Figure 1.

It was argued that because of the amount of bicarbonate produced, at least half of the fatty acid leaving neutral solutions in the rumen did so in the un-ionized form. Sodium loss from such solutions approximated to half that of acetate. Since no other anion accompanied this sodium, nor was it replaced by an equivalent amount of cation, the maintenance of bulk electrical neutrality required that half the fatty acid leave as the anion.

The amount of acetate absorbed from the lumen side of isolated rumen epithelium, or transported across the tissue, was markedly increased by an increase in acetate concentration in the lumen bath. When an equivalent electrical potential gradient was imposed in a direction that would tend to increase the electrochemical gradient of the anion, no increase in absorption or transport of fatty acid was noted; this suggested that the preparation was relatively impermeable to the anion (98).

Thus, the un-ionized form of the fatty acid is absorbed in quantity even from neutral solutions, but the extent to which the ionized form penetrates the epithelium is difficult to assess.

Metabolism and Fatty Acid Absorption

It is convenient to describe a loss from the lumen side as absorption, and its appearance on the blood side as transport. Provided accumulation within the epithelium of acid can be ignored, the amount absorbed will then equal the sum of the amounts transported and metabolized. There is evidence of an interconversion of butyrate to acetate by the rumen epithelium (98). Production within the tissue, therefore, may need to be considered.

A discrepancy between the relative amounts of the three fatty acids absorbed and those transported in the blood first suggested that butyrate was removed by the epithelum (61, 67). The rate of absorption of fatty acid increased with chain length (20, 43, 79, 97, 117), whereas the amount transported generally decreased with chain length, as judged by concentration in venous effluent (67) and by in vitro experiments (97, 98). Losses within epithelium were particularly marked with butyrate. It appeared, therefore, that the proportion metabolized increased markedly with chain length. This was clearly shown by Pennington (77) while incubating isolated epithelium in vitro with acetate, propionate, or butyrate.

Formation of ketone bodies accounts for much of the acetic and butyric acid that disappears. The introduction of butyrate solutions into the empty rumen of anesthetized sheep caused an increase in ketone bodies in the venous blood of the rumen greater than the increase in carotid blood, and an accumulation of ketone bodies in the rumen (77). Similar experiments with conscious sheep in which the portal vein was catheterized also showed greater ketone body concentration in the venous as compared with arterial blood after introduction of butyrate into the rumen (3). Ketone bodies contributed, on an energy basis, about 15 % of the fatty acid found in the portal blood of fed ewes, whereas no ketone body was produced in the alimentary tract in starved sheep (84). Propionate metabolism by isolated rumen epithelium gave rise to lactate and carbon dioxide. Isotopic studies with ^{14}C-labeled carbon dioxide or propionate labeled in the carboxyl group showed that fixation of carbon dioxide occurred with the formation of labeled succinate (78). Some absorption of isobutyrate, n-valerate, isovalerate, and methyl butyrate was found from the rumen of anesthetized sheep (4).

An interesting role of metabolism in absorption and transport is suggested by observations made on isolated sheets of epithelium. Anoxia, which sup-

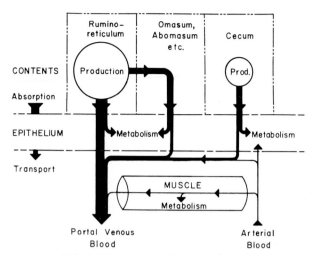

FIG. 2. Relation between production, absorption, metabolism, and transport of the short-chain fatty acids in the alimentary tract of the ruminant.

pressed the conversion of acetate and butyrate to ketone bodies, increased the amount of these acids transported and decreased the amount absorbed (50, 97). Apparently the enhanced absorption and decreased transport of butyrate relative to acetate is largely due to its greater metabolism within the epithelium.

A small quantity of acetate has been reported moving against its electrochemical gradient across the rumen epithelium from the plasma to the lumen side (99). The biological implications of this are obscure.

Quantitative Aspects In Vivo

The major interrelations between production, absorption, and transport of the steam-volatile fatty acids are illustrated in Figure 2. Most of the short-chain acids produced within the rumen are absorbed there. The remainder is absorbed in the omasum or passes to the abomasum and the intestines. The transported fatty acids in the venous effluents from the rumen, omasum, and abomasum combine in the portal vein with a contribution of that transported from the cecum. The portal vein also receives a small concentration of fatty acid from systemic blood, part of which has, however, been modified by metabolism in the parallel blood flow through the gut musculature. Omitted from this diagram are minor pathways such as the entry of fatty acid into the rumen via the saliva, and the negligible removal of transported short-chain fatty acid by the lymph (61).

Methods are available for the measurement of

fatty acid production within the rumen and that transported in the portal vein. As a measure of ruminal production, the initial rate of increase of fatty acids upon incubation of samples of rumen contents can be measured and then extrapolated to the whole contents. A second approach involves measurement of the entry rate of the ruminal pool of each fatty acid by infusion of isotopically labeled material into the rumen. For the measurement of transport, the concentration of fatty acid in the portal vein, corrected for the concentration present in arterial blood, is multiplied by the portal blood flow. Since both the portal blood flow and fatty acid concentration vary with time after feeding (8), this product must be integrated throughout a feeding cycle. Alternatively, the infusion of isotopes into a ruminal vein, with sampling from the portal vein, can be used to measure the entry rate of an acid into the pool draining the gut.

These and other assessments have shown that the short-chain fatty acids are quantitatively important end products of digestion. They are reviewed and criticized by Warner (112). None directly measures the amount of fatty acid absorbed or transported by a single organ. Improved methods will likely produce better estimates shortly, since introducing mechanical mixing of rumen contents reduces the sampling errors to manageable proportions (36, 103) and the introduction of continuous feeding circumvents many experimental difficulties by permitting a steady state to be attained in vivo (10, 72, 104).

In one study the rate of absorption of each short-chain fatty acid from the reticulo-rumen was measured by correcting the production rate for the measured onflow into the omasum (102, 103, 105). The total production observed in a sheep on a maintenance diet was 3.4 mole per day, 12.5% of which flowed into the omasum. Hence 3.0 mole per day was absorbed from the rumen. The absorption coefficient of each acid, calculated as the millimole·hour^{-1} absorbed per millimolar concentration present in the contents at pH 6.3, was found to be 1.58 for acetic, 1.88 for propionic, and 2.08 for butyric. This indicated that the absorption rate under these circumstances tended to increase with chain length.

The entry rate of propionate into the portal blood has been measured by an isotopic dilution method in conscious, continuously fed sheep (11). The mean rate was 0.6 mole per day on a ration that allowed the animals to maintain a constant weight. On half-ration, the propionate entry rate decreased to one half.

How much of the fatty acid absorbed is metabolized by the epithelium is an open question, since no simultaneous measures of absorption and transport on the same ration in the same animal exist.

NITROGENOUS SUBSTANCES

Ammonia and Urea

A convincing demonstration of the absorption of ammonia from normal rumen contents was first made by McDonald (70) by comparing the appreciable concentration in venous blood leaving the rumen with the negligible concentration in arterial blood. This was confirmed in conscious sheep by Lewis and colleagues (65), who showed a close relation between the concentration of ammonia in the rumen contents with that found in the portal blood.

The amount of ammonia absorbed from the rumen increased when either its concentration or the pH within the organ was increased (42, 51, 119). Thus, un-ionized ammonia may be preferentially absorbed. No clear relationship has been found between fatty acids and ammonia absorption, although near neutrality the absorption of fatty acids appeared to increase the rate of absorption of ammonia (51). The mechanism of this interaction has not been examined.

There is a clear relationship between the concentration of ammonia produced in the rumen and the concentration of urea in the blood (64). Ammonia absorbed from the rumen is presumably an important source of blood urea. The ammonia that appeared in the rumen contents and venous blood when the normal contents were initially free of ammonia probably originated from the blood urea (51, 53).

Bacterial ureases are produced in the rumen, and hydrolysis of urea is rapid in the rumen contents of normally fed animals (76). Washing the rumen usually does not remove all urease activity, and the rate of entry of ammonia plus urea into the organ when ammonia-free solutions are introduced has been taken as a measure of the diffusion of urea from blood across the rumen epithelium (5, 53).

The rate of entry of urea into the rumen from the blood is roughly proportional to the concentration in the plasma (37, 59). This has been tested in vivo with pouch and whole forestomach preparations and in vitro with surviving epithelial membranes. The absorption of urea from a pouch containing no urease activity has been demonstrated when concentration gradients were favorable (54). Workers at Hannover (21) have used ^{14}C-urea to calculate the entry of urea

into the rumen. They assume that the main site of urea hydrolysis is in the reticulo-rumen, although there is probably diffusion into the remainder of the alimentary tract, as in other mammals.

The possibility of urea synthesis has been considered seriously since the activity of carbamyl phosphate-ornithine transcarbamylase and arginase is similar in the rumen epithelium to that in the liver. However, the usual mechanism of combining carbon dioxide with ammonia to give carbamyl phosphate is not present, since no carbamyl phosphate synthetase activity can be found in the rumen epithelium (62, 66).

Amines

Methylamine is a normal constituent of the rumen contents at the 1-mM level (49), whereas lower concentrations of tyramine, histamine, methylamine (19), ethylamine (90), isobutylamine, β-phenylethylamine, pyrrolidine, isoamylamine, piperidine, and ethanolamine (41) have been reported. The concentration of some amines in the rumen depended on diet and time after feeding (41, 49), but little is known of their absorption. Since most methods for the estimation of ammonia measure volatile amine, it is possible that some amines, particularly methylamine, have been included with ammonia in experiments where normal rumen contents were present.

Amino Acids

In the perfused rumen it has been shown that amino acids can be transferred from the lumen to the blood (22). However, much of the nonprotein amino acid in rumen contents is associated with bacteria, and the absence of an increased level of amino acids in the portal blood after feeding would suggest that absorption from the rumen under some conditions is unimportant (2).

A concentration in the rumen of some "free" amino acids sufficiently large to give a favorable concentration gradient during a part of the feeding cycle was accompanied by an increase in their concentration in jugular venous plasma (63). It is not clear if these amino acids in the rumen contents were in solution or associated with bacteria; nor does this observation preclude amino acid absorption from the small intestine. It has still to be shown that absorption of amino acids from the rumen contributes significantly to nitrogen metabolism of the sheep.

OTHER ORGANIC SUBSTANCES

Lactic Acid

The absorption of lactic acid from the isolated reticulo-rumen was about ten times less rapid than that of an equimolar solution of the short-chain fatty acids at pH 5. At pH 7.5, the rate of lactate absorption remained unchanged, but absorption of short-chain fatty acids was slower, making lactate absorption only three times less rapid than fatty acids. The presence of fatty acids depressed the absorption of lactate at pH 5, but not at pH 7.5, and the mechanism for this is unknown. Below pH 5, lactic acid was more rapidly absorbed, presumably because much more became un-ionized. D(−)-lactate disappeared from a racemic mixture more rapidly than L(+)-lactate (117).

Carbon Dioxide

The salient features of the equilibration of carbon dioxide and bicarbonate have already been dealt with in discussing its interactions with fatty acid absorption. On a molar basis carbon dioxide is absorbed from normal rumen contents faster than any other solute. Even so, the rapid production of carbon dioxide within the fermenting contents maintains carbon dioxide as 65% of the gas in the space above the rumen contents (69, 114). Hungate (55) estimated that one-fourth to one-third of the carbon dioxide produced was absorbed from the rumen. This was based on the higher proportion of methane in the gas above the rumen contents compared to that produced by in vitro fermentations, and he assumed that no methane was absorbed.

Impermeable Substances

Soluble substances not absorbed from the rumen have become very important since they permit the estimation of rumen volume and outflow. In addition, if a substance disappears faster than a nonabsorbed marker, this is evidence of its absorption from the rumen, provided it is neither destroyed nor concentrated by the particulate matter. Pectin was the first substance used as a nonabsorbed marker when aqueous solutions were introduced into the empty rumen (43), but its susceptibility to destruction limits its use. Phenol red, like many other dyes, is unsatisfactory since it is adsorbed onto the epithelium of the rumen (117).

Polyethylene glycol (PEG) was successfully used as a soluble marker by Sperber et al. (94) in normal animals, and the requirements to be fulfilled by such a marker and the errors involved in its use are discussed by Hydén (56, 57). The sensitivity of the method has been improved by ^{3}H-labeling of the PEG (106), and errors due to mixing have been reduced by mechanical stirring (36, 103). The ^{51}Cr complex of ethylenediamine tetraacetic acid (EDTA) gives results similar to those of PEG (28). Since chromium EDTA has an intense purple color, it may be possible to use the stable chromium isotope under circumstances in which a radioactive marker is difficult to use. Both PEG and chromium EDTA have been used in grazing sheep (52, 109).

Creatinine proved a useful volume marker for acute experiments on the anesthetized sheep (5). In the conscious cow, however, it cannot be used since it is appreciably absorbed (A. Dobson and A. F. Sellers, unpublished data).

Miscellaneous Compounds

Acetone and ethanol disappeared rapidly from the lumen of a rumen pouch (108). Ethanol appeared to distribute itself throughout the total body water of the sheep after its injection into the rumen contents (13). Antipyrine, which is also used for total body water estimations, rapidly traversed the epithelium of the rumen both in vivo and in vitro (37, 116).

ELECTRIC POTENTIAL

The electric potential makes the blood about 30 mv positive to rumen contents in vivo when the rumen contents have high sodium and low potassium concentrations (26). With both dry and grass diets a relationship with considerable scatter between the potential and potassium concentration in the rumen has been observed (88). Potentials as high as 70 mv can be seen in sodium-depleted sheep, but the potential appears to be related to potassium concentration in the rumen rather than the secretion of aldosterone (87).

In anesthetized sheep, similar potentials are observed with artificial solutions in the rumen (24, 26), but it is clear that the lumen potassium concentration is more important than sodium concentration in determining the potential (40). The slope of the plot of potential against log (K+) at constant sodium concentration and tonicity, is about 70% of the theoretical for a potassium electrode with sulfate and 50% with chloride as the major anion. In its response to the lumen potassium concentration, the epithelium of the rumen differs from that of the frog skin, where the potential responds to changes on the outside of concentration of sodium rather than of potassium.

The surviving isolated epithelium of the rumen immersed in Ringer or similar solutions produces an electric potential difference between solutions of the same composition, with the blood side positive. Different observers have recorded mean sustained potentials varying from 8 mv to 18 mv with epithelium from sheep, goats, calves, and cows (23, 37, 39).

The magnitude of the potential is determined by the short-circuit current and the tissue conductance. The slow drop of potential of the isolated epithelium was due largely to the decline in short-circuit current, whereas a low potential observed by tearing the tissue from the muscle rather than dissecting it was related to a high tissue conductance (96). The replacement of chloride ions in the bathing solutions by less permeable sulfate ions not only decreased the conductance but also increased the short-circuit current and this led to higher sustained potentials (39). Other factors implicated include the previous dietary regimen of the animal (39) and the region of the rumen sampled (C. E. Stevens, personal communication). The short-circuit current and potential are markedly reduced by anoxia, removal of sodium, or the addition of ouabain (39).

Since the short-circuit current is less than the net sodium current in the short-circuited skin, at least one other ion must be involved in the generation of the short-circuit current and hence in the open-circuit potential. Some evidence indicates chloride is implicated (96).

INORGANIC IONS

Sodium

Most agree that sodium can be transported by the epithelium against its concentration and electrochemical gradients from the contents of the rumen into the plasma. This was first observed from the rumen pouch of a sheep (93) and since has been demonstrated in the anesthetized and conscious sheep with artificial solutions or normal rumen contents (24, 58). In the isolated, short-circuited epithelium a net transport of sodium can be observed between identical bathing solutions (38, 96) thereby formally establishing the presence of a sodium pump. The net sodium current was, however, about three times the short-circuit current; this indicated that sodium was not the only ion transported. Since the partial conductance of the

tissue to sodium could exceed the total tissue conductance, Stevens (96) suggested that either a neutral NaCl pump was acting or that exchange diffusion of sodium was involved with part of the sodium transported.

The addition of sufficient ammonia or urea to the rumen appeared to interfere with the absorption of sodium (35), whereas an increase in osmotic pressure has been claimed to increase sodium absorption (95).

Sodium transport is a major activity of the rumen epithelium. The net sodium absorbed from the rumen of the sheep was equivalent to a current of about 0.5 amp, and its intensity on the basis of epithelial weight was similar to that of frog skin (24).

Potassium

This ion passed into solutions in the rumen when the concentration was low and was absorbed when the concentration was high. The equilibrium concentration was higher than its concentration in the plasma, as would be expected from the contribution of the electric potential across the epithelium to the electrochemical potential of potassium (58, 93). The leakage of potassium from the isolated epithelium was small and similar to either side if care was taken when dissecting away the muscle layer (96). Any net transfer of potassium through the epithelium under these circumstances could only be small compared with the short-circuit current. In contrast, a net transport of potassium in the opposite direction to sodium was reported when an isolated, short-circuited epithelial preparation was used. The net transport was measured with [42]K on paired tissue samples (38). It is, however, not clear whether the fluxes were measured after a steady state had been reached.

Magnesium

It seems unlikely that any significant net passage of magnesium ions takes place across the epithelium of the rumen of the sheep with concentrations in the range encountered under normal feeding conditions (83), although [28]Mg can be absorbed even when no net passage of magnesium is apparent (14). With sheep receiving magnesium salts, the arteriovenous concentration difference of magnesium has led to the conclusion that magnesium is absorbed from the rumen (100). Since similar effects on the magnesium arteriovenous difference were produced with sodium and calcium salts, it seems more reasonable to ascribe the enhanced concentration of magnesium in the venous blood to the passage of water into the rumen down its osmotic gradient. A similar criticism seems relevant to more recent work (15).

Calcium

The rumen appears to be relatively impermeable to calcium ion (83). Only a fraction of either magnesium or calcium present in the rumen appears ultrafiltrable (101). Part of the ultrafiltrable form may well be un-ionized, but the prospect of absorption from the rumen in chelated form has had no attention.

Chloride

Absorption of chloride against its concentration gradient was first observed from a rumen pouch (93). Hydén's experiments on conscious sheep showed that chloride could be absorbed from concentrations in the rumen as low as 7–8 mM (58). This cannot be accounted for in terms of electrochemical gradient alone, since a potential making the blood more than 100 mv positive to the contents would be required, whereas with the potassium concentration observed it would be unlikely to exceed 50 mv (87, 88). Observations on the isolated, short-circuited epithelium bathed by the same solution on either side have shown that movement of chloride from the lumen to the plasma side of the membrane was greater than movement in the other direction (96). The unidirectional fluxes of ^{36}Cl and ^{82}Br were measured simultaneously, and although the bromide isotope may not have given a precise measure of chloride flux, a net chloride transport was clearly demonstrated.

Results in anesthetized sheep with artificial solutions in the rumen are quite different. The equilibrium chloride concentration in the rumen was about 35 mM (75). The direction of chloride movement is that expected from diffusion down its electrochemical gradient (26). However, a further complication arose with high concentration of potassium and low concentration of sodium in the rumen, since there was evidence of a movement of chloride against its electrochemical gradient into the rumen (24). This was in the opposite direction to its transport in other preparations. Obviously something peculiar is going on in the anesthetized sheep that indicates a gap in our understanding of chloride movements.

Phosphate

That 98% of the phosphate placed in a rumen pouch was recovered after 24 hours indicated a negligible absorption (93). The rumen epithelium is sufficiently impermeable to allow Hydén (58) to use the amount of phosphate appearing in the rumen in selected experiments as a measure of the salivary inflow. An early conclusion that the rumen secretes phosphate (91) was based on underestimates of the secretory capacity of the salivary glands. Radioactive phosphorus has been shown to cross the epithelium in either direction (74, 85, 118), but the fluxes are so small that net transfer would be negligible (73).

WATER

When the osmotic pressure in the rumen was higher than that in the plasma, water passed into the rumen contents, whereas when the osmotic pressure was similar to, or less than, the plasma, water was absorbed from rumen contents (75). In similar acute experiments little net water movement was observed when the solution within the rumen was slightly hypertonic to plasma, but since there was an appreciable net uptake of ions, this observation is not incompatible with the movement of water down its osmotic gradient (24). The osmotic pressure difference across the epithelium was not measured in any of these experiments.

Very large and variable (7–70 liters/day) water exchanges between the rumen contents and plasma have been observed by using tritiated water in the conscious goat with normal rumen contents (34). The flux into the rumen, which included saliva flow, and the flux from the rumen were similar when measured in quick succession. Although the rumen fluid was somewhat hypotonic to plasma, it was claimed that a net passage of water through the epithelium into the rumen took place (35). This was based on estimates of the net liquid inflow into the rumen, defined as the salivary inflow minus that absorbed through the rumen wall. The mean net inflow observed, 8.9 liters per day, was considered to be larger than the possible saliva inflow. However, this would be on the low side of the mean estimate of salivary secretion for a sheep of comparable weight (60). When an esophageal balloon was used to prevent saliva inflow, two experiments showed a small net absorption from the rumen, whereas one showed a passage into the hypotonic rumen contents. Hydén (55a, 57) gives examples of two sources of error in this experimental approach. First, the space penetrated by polyethylene glycol, which was used to estimate net water inflow in rumen contents, increased slightly with time. Second, he observed that small leakages past the esophageal balloon were possible. Although neither of these errors in itself is large, each would tend to bias the estimate of water absorbed in the same direction—that is, make it too low. The claim that water passes into hypotonic rumen contents under normal circumstances has thus not been proved. Nevertheless, the contention of Engelhardt (34), that the observation of water passage in acute experiments under anesthesia are unphysiological, cannot be gainsaid. At this stage one must choose between more controlled observations under unphysiological conditions or possibly biased observations in a conscious normal animal.

The rumen contents of goats (35) and sheep (113) tend to be hypotonic during the later part of a feeding cycle or during starvation even when no drinking is permitted. Immediately after a meal, rumen contents of sheep become hypertonic (75) because of the breakdown of polymers and the liberation of salts, the result being a marked increase in osmotically active particles. There are, however, reactions that lead to a net reduction in osmotically active particles. The neutralization of hydrogen ions by bicarbonate is particularly effective, since the carbon dioxide formed can pass into the gas phase of the rumen and be removed by eructation. If, once the peak of fermentation is passed, processes such as this predominate over those that produce osmotically active particles, then the contents would tend to become slightly hypotonic.

ABSORPTION AND BLOOD FLOW

The anatomy of the veins of the rumen makes it virtually impossible to measure the total venous outflow from the organ. Blood flow has been measured at a point in the right ruminal vein of the sheep which drains 35–45 % of the area of reticulum and rumen together, as judged by epithelial weight This vein can be doubly cannulated and the blood led through a simple bubble flowmeter in the anesthetized, heparinized sheep. In comparing the effects of different solutions in the rumen, isotonic sodium chloride produced a slower blood flow than neutral isotonic solutions of acetate, propionate, or butyrate. Solutions of sodium butyrate caused a more rapid blood flow than those of acetate or propionate. Solutions of these acids at pH 5.5 buffered with phosphate caused the most rapid blood flow, and again the effects of butyrate solution were greater than those of acetate. By contrast, lactic or phosphoric acid buffers at pH 4 caused

no greater blood flow than was obtained with saline solutions.

Acidic solutions of the short-chain acids depressed the pH of the venous blood from the rumen to as low as 6.9; the rapid blood flow could be attributed to local dilatation of vessels in the rumen wall. No such change in pH in the venous blood occurred when lactic or phosphoric acid buffers were in the rumen. Large increases in blood flow were obtained together with depression of the pH of the rumen venous blood if saline solutions were saturated with carbon dioxide or if the rumen was mildly inflated with this gas (25). The stimulus to blood flow thus appears to be the un-ionized acid which is absorbed.

Substantially similar effects of solutions in the rumen upon flow in the right ruminal artery of the conscious cow have been observed with the use of chronically implanted electromagnetic blood flow probes (89). Feeding increased arterial flow by about 50 % through the ruminal and omasal arteries and to a lesser extent through the celiac artery. The effect continued for at least 90 min after feeding, although arterial flow through the posterior mesenteric and hypogastric arteries was unaffected. Removing the contents of the rumen depressed arterial flow to the rumen, whereas reintroducing the contents restored it. Neither the volume in the rumen nor the activity of the musculature played any detectable role in these changes of blood flow, but seeing and smelling the food could produce a psychic stimulation. With rumen contents replaced with saline, the right ruminal blood flow was stimulated only during the act of eating. Thus it appeared that although reflex events may play a part initially in increasing the flow of blood during normal feeding, the continued high level might be attributed to the products of fermentation. Blood flow through the portal vein was higher after feeding (8, 9), but was only slightly depressed on starvation (84). These large variations of portal blood flow associated with feeding show that assessments of the quantities of volatile acids transported to the liver based on average values of portal flow are underestimates.

RUMINAL ABSORPTION AND THE RUMINANT

The major function of the forestomachs is to provide a vat where the ingested food can be fermented to products that the host can assimilate. Absorption plays an important role by removing these products as they are formed, thereby contributing to homeostasis within the rumen particularly with regard to its acidity. The copious secretion of an alkaline saliva neutralizes a part of the acids produced, but the direct absorption of the un-ionized fatty acids plays at least as important a role in maintaining a high pH within the rumen (5). Since un-ionized acid is absorbed in relation to its concentration, this mechanism becomes more effective as the pH deviates further on the acid side of neutrality. Indeed, unless lactic acid is produced and accumulates, it is unusual to find the rumen contents below pH 5.5 (12).

The sheep secretes about 10 liters of saliva per day, most of which is isotonic to plasma (60). With an adequate dietary intake of sodium, perhaps 30 mmole per day, this saliva will contain about 1.2–1.5 mole of sodium, a little more perhaps than is present in the extracellular space. About half this sodium is absorbed from the rumen, whereas the remainder is absorbed from the small and large intestine (24, 58). It may be noted that lithium added to the rumen contents shows a recycling similar to that of sodium (110).

The recycling of nitrogen through the forestomachs, first suggested by McDonald (70), may play an important role in ruminants when their nitrogen intake is low. Under these circumstances sheep retain a greater proportion of circulating urea than when their dietary nitrogen is adequate for their needs (86). Urea entering the rumen in the saliva and by diffusion through the wall is promptly hydrolyzed to ammonia. This ammonia together with suitable carbon skeletons may be incorporated into bacterial protein. Sheep on a low-protein ration which provided 7 g of nitrogen per day were observed to have 11–12 g per day passing the duodenum, and 5 g per day were defecated. Amino nitrogen entering the duodenum under similar circumstances was proportionately greater than that of the diet (16). This increase may be explained partly by the entry of urea into the rumen so that a greater quantity of protein leaves it than is eaten, and partly by the secretion of mucus into the abomasum. (48). Rough calculations indicate that urea entering the rumen is sufficient to account for about half the increase observed and that ruminal diffusion is greater than the salivary contribution (5, 53, 92).

CONCLUSION

Absorption from the rumen has been studied with three main objectives. The first was to determine which substances could be absorbed. The second was to assess the extent to which the water-soluble constituents of the rumen contents are absorbed, and the third objective has been to study transport mechanisms.

A broad generalization is that the epithelium of the rumen permits the absorption of the soluble products of bacterial and protozoan metabolism. Like other natural membranes, it allows the rapid penetration of small molecules such as ammonia urea and lipid-soluble material such as ethanol and the un-ionized fatty acids. Ions, except those for which the epithelium makes special provision, tend to penetrate less rapidly, especially the larger and more highly charged species.

A great deal more work is needed to investigate the transporting systems offered by the rumen mucosa. This keratinized epithelium is reasonably homogeneous since it does not contain goblet or other secretory cells (27). Its simplicity of structure, combined with the ease with which it can be prepared as an isolated membrane with a minimum of subepithelial tissue, commends its use in the study of transport across mammalian alimentary membranes.

REFERENCES

1. AGGAZZOTTI, A. Esperienze sulla funzione assorbenti degli stomaci nei ruminanti. *Clin. Vet.* 33: 54–75, 1910.
2. ANNISON, E. F. Nitrogen metabolism in the sheep. Protein digestion in the rumen. *Biochem. J.* 64: 705–714, 1956.
3. ANNISON, E. F., K. J. HILL, AND D. LEWIS. Studies on the portal blood of sheep. 2. Absorption of volatile fatty acids from the rumen of sheep. *Biochem. J.* 66: 592–599, 1957.
4. ANNISON, E. F., AND R. J. PENNINGTON. The metabolism of short-chain fatty acids in the sheep. 3. Formic, n-valeric and some branched-chain acids. *Biochem. J.* 57: 685–692, 1954.

5. ASH, R. W., AND A. DOBSON. The effect of absorption on the acidity of rumen contents. *J. Physiol., London* 169: 39–61, 1963.
6. BARCROFT, J., R. A. McANALLY, AND A. T. PHILLIPSON. Absorption of volatile acids from the alimentary tract of the sheep and other animals. *J. Exptl. Biol.* 20: 120–129, 1944.
7. BARCROFT, J., R. A. McANALLY, AND A. T. PHILLIPSON. The absorption of sodium ortho-iodo-hippurate from the rumen of lambs. *J. Exptl. Biol.* 20: 132–134, 1944.
8. BENSADOUN, A., O. L. PALADINES, AND J. T. REID. Effect

of level of intake and physical form of the diet on plasma glucose concentration and volatile fatty acid absorption in ruminants. *J. Dairy Sci.* 45: 1203–1210, 1962.

9. BENSADOUN, A., AND J. T. REID. Estimation of rate of portal blood flow in ruminants: effect of feeding, fasting and anesthesia. *J. Dairy Sci.* 45: 540–543, 1962.

10. BERGMAN, E. N, R. S. REID, M. G. MURRAY, J. M. BROCKWAY, AND F. G. WHITELAW. Interconversions and production of volatile fatty acids in the sheep rumen. *Biochem. J.* 97: 53–58, 1965.

11. BERGMAN, E. N., W. E. ROE, AND K. KON. Quantitative aspects of propionate metabolism and gluconeogenesis in sheep. *Am. J. Physiol.* 211: 793–799, 1966.

12. BRIGGS, P. K., J. P. HOGAN, AND R. L. REID. The effect of volatile fatty acids, lactic acid and ammonia on rumen pH in sheep. *Australian J. Agr. Res.* 8: 674–690, 1957.

13. BUDTZ-OLSEN, O. E., J. D. CLEEVE, AND B. A. OELRICHO. Total body water in merino and Romney Marsh sheep estimated by alcohol (ethanol) dilution. *Australian J. Agr. Res.* 12: 681–688, 1961.

14. CARE, A. D. Discussion. In: *Proceedings of the Conference on Hypomagnesaemia, London, 1960.* London: British Veterinary Association, 1961, p. 35.

15. CARE, A. D., AND A. T. VAN'T KLOOSTER. In vivo transport of magnesium and other cations across the wall of the gastro-intestinal tract of sheep. *J. Physiol., London* 177: 174–191, 1965.

16. CLARKE, E. M. W., G. M. ELLINGER, AND A. T. PHILLIPSON. The influence of diet on the nitrogenous components passing to the duodenum and through the lower ileum of sheep. *Proc. Roy. Soc., Ser. B* 166: 63–79, 1966.

17. COLIN, G. *Traité de physiologie comparée des animaux domestiques.* Paris: Baillière, vol. 1, 1854, p. 408.

18. COLIN, G. *Traité de physiologie comparée des animaux* (3rd ed.). Paris: Baillière, vol. 2, 1886, p. 102.

19. DAIN, J. A., A. L. NEAL, AND R. W. DOUGHERTY. The occurrence of histamine and tyramine in the rumen contents of experimentally overfed sheep. *J. Animal Sci.* 14: 930–935, 1955.

20. DANIELLI, J. F., M. W. S. HITCHCOCK, R. A. MARSHALL, AND A. T. PHILLIPSON. The mechanism of absorption from the rumen as exemplified by the behavior of acetic, propionic and butyric acids. *J. Exptl. Biol.* 22: 75–84, 1945.

21. DECKER, P., K. GÄRTNER, H. HÖRNICKE, AND H. HILL. Fortlaufende Messung von Harnstoffbildung und Harnstoffrückfluss in den Pansen in Abhängigkeit vom Harnfluss mit Hilfe von 14C-Harnstoff bei Ziegen. *Arch. Ges. Physiol.* 274: 289–294, 1961.

22. DEMAUX, G., H. LEBARS, J. MOLLÉ, J. RERAT, AND H. SIMONNET. Absorption des acides aminés au niveau du rumen de l'intestine grêle et du cœcum chez le mouton. *Bull. Acad. Vet., France* 34: 85–88, 1961.

23. DOBSON, A. *The Movements of Ions Across the Epithelium of the Reticulo-rumen Sac* (Ph.D. Thesis). Aberdeen: Univ. of Aberdeen, 1956.

24. DOBSON, A. Active transport through the epithelium of the reticulo-rumen sac. *J. Physiol., London* 146: 235–251, 1959.

25. DOBSON, A., AND A. T. PHILLIPSON. The influence of the contents of the rumen upon its blood supply. *J. Physiol., London* 133: 76–77P, 1956.

26. DOBSON, A., AND A. T. PHILLIPSON. The absorption of

27. DOBSON, M. J., W. C. B. BROWN, A. DOBSON, AND A. T. PHILLIPSON. A histological study of the organisation of the rumen epithelium of the sheep. *Quart. J. Exptl. Physiol.* 41: 247–253, 1956.

28. DOWNES, A. M., AND I. W. MCDONALD. The chromium-51 complex of ethylenediamine tetraacetic acid as a soluble rumen marker. *Brit. J. Nutr.* 18: 153–162, 1964.

29. ELLENBERGER, W. Zur anatomie und physiologie des dritten magens der wiederkäuer. *Arch. Wiss. Prakt. Tierheilk.* 7: 17–58, 1881.

30. ELLENBERGER, W. *Vergleichenden Histologie und Physiologie des Haussäugethiere.* Berlin: Paul Parey, vol. 2, 1890, p. 863.

31. ELSDEN, S. R. The fermentation of carbohydrates in the rumen of the sheep. *J. Exptl. Biol.* 22: 51–62, 1945.

32. EL SHAZLY, K. Degradation of protein in the rumen of the sheep. 1. Some volatile fatty acids, involving branched-chain isomers, found *in vivo. Biochem. J.* 51: 640–647, 1952.

33. EL SHAZLY, K. Degradation of protein in the rumen of the sheep. 2. The action of rumen micro-organisms on amino-acids. *Biochem. J.* 51: 647–653, 1952.

34. ENGELHARDT, W. VON. Untersuchungen über die Regulierung des Wasserhaushaltes im Ziegenpansen. 1. Pansenflüssigkeitsvolumen, Flüssigkeitsausfluss in den Psalter, Nettoflüssigkeitszufluss in den Pansen und Flüssigkeitsaustausch durch die Pansenwand. *Arch. Ges. Physiol.* 278: 141–151, 1963.

35. ENGELHARDT, W. VON. Untersuchungen über die Regulierung des Wasserhaushaltes im Ziegenpansen. 2. Beeinflussung des Nettoflüssigkeitszuflusses in den Pansen. *Arch. Ges. Physiol.* 278: 152–161, 1963.

36. ENGELHARDT, W. VON, H. HOELLER, AND H. HOERNICKE. Pump for rapid mixing of rumen contents during experiments with small ruminants. *J. Dairy Sci.* 46: 65–66, 1963.

37. ENGELHARDT, W. VON, AND W. NICKEL. Die Permeabilität der Pansenwand für Harnstoff, Antipyrin und Wasser. *Arch. Ges. Physiol.* 286: 57–75, 1965.

38. FERREIRA, H. G., F. A. HARRISON, AND R. D. KEYNES. Studies with isolated rumen epithelium of the sheep. *J. Physiol., London* 175: 28–29P, 1964.

39. FERREIRA, H. G., F. A HARRISON, AND R. D. KEYNES. The potential and short-circuit current across isolated rumen epithelium of the sheep. *J. Physiol., London* 187: 631–644, 1966.

40. FERREIRA, H. G., F. A. HARRISON, R. D. KEYNES, AND A. H. NAUSS. Observations on the potential across the rumen of the sheep. *J. Physiol., London* 187: 615–630, 1966.

41. FRASER, J. G., AND G. W. BUTLER. Steam volatile amines in rumen liquor from cattle and sheep. *New Zealand J. Agr. Res.* 7: 707–712, 1964.

42. GÄRTNER, K., AND W. VON ENGELHARDT. Untersuchungen über den Resorption-mechanismus von Ammoniak an der Pansenschleimhaut. *Deut. Tieraerztl. Wochschr.* 71: 57–60, 1964.

43. GRAY, F. V. The absorption of volatile fatty acids from the rumen. *J. Exptl. Biol.* 24: 1–10, 1947.

44. GRAY, F. V., AND A. F. PILGRIM. Fermentation in the rumen of the sheep. 2. The production and absorption of volatile acids during the fermentation of wheaten hay and lucerne hay in the rumen. *J. Exptl. Biol.* 28: 83–90, 1951.

45. GRAY, F. V., A. F. PILGRIM, H. T. RODDA, AND R. A.

chloride ions from the reticulo-rumen sac. *J. Physiol., London* 140: 94–104, 1958.

WELLER. Volatile fatty acids in the rumen of the sheep. *Nature* 167: 954, 1951.

46. GRAY, F. V., A. F. PILGRIM, H. J. RODDA, AND R. A. WELLER. Fermentation in the rumen of the sheep. 4. The nature and origin of the volatile fatty acids in the rumen of the sheep. *J. Exptl. Biol.* 29: 57–65, 1952.

47. HAGAN, P., AND K. W. ROBINSON. The production and absorption of volatile acids in the intestine of the guinea pig. *Australian J. Exptl. Biol. Med. Sci.* 31: 99–103, 1953.

48. HARRIS, L. E., AND A. T. PHILLIPSON. The measurement of the flow of food to the duodenum of sheep. *Animal Prod.* 4: 97–116, 1962.

49. HILL, K. J., AND J. L. MANGAN. The formation and distribution of methylamine in the ruminant digestive tract. *Biochem. J.* 93: 39–45, 1964.

50. HIRD, F. J., AND M. J. WEIDEMANN. Transport and metabolism of butyrate by isolated rumen epithelium. *Biochem. J.* 92: 585–589, 1964.

51. HOGAN, J. P. The absorption of ammonia through the rumen of the sheep. *Australian J. Biol. Sci.* 14: 448–460, 1961.

52. HOGAN, J. P. The digestion of food by the grazing sheep. 1. The rate of flow of digesta. *Australian J. Agr. Res.* 15: 384–396, 1964.

53. HOUPT, T. R. Utilization of blood urea in ruminants. *Am. J. Physiol.* 197: 115–120, 1959.

54. HOUPT, T. R., AND K. A. HOUPT. Movement of urea across the epithelium of a rumen pouch. *Federation Proc.* 23: 262, 1964.

55. HUNGATE, R. E. *The Rumen and Its Microbes.* New York: Acad. Press, 1966, p. 181.

55a. HYDÉN, S. Description of two methods for the collection of saliva in sheep and goats. *Kgl. Lantbrukshögskol. Ann.* 24: 55–75, 1958.

56. HYDÉN, S. The use of reference substances and the measurement of flow in the alimentary tract. In: *Digestive Physiology and Nutrition of the Ruminant,* edited by D. Lewis. London: Butterworths, 1961, p. 35–47.

57. HYDÉN, S. Determination of the amount of fluid in the reticulo-rumen of the sheep and its rate of passage to the omasum. *Kgl. Lantbrukshögskol. Ann.* 27: 51–79, 1961.

58. HYDÉN, S. Observations on the absorption of inorganic ions from the reticulo-rumen of the sheep. *Kgl. Lantbrukshögskol. Ann.* 27: 273–285, 1961.

59. JUHÁSZ, B. Endogenous nitrogen cycle in ruminants. *Acta Vet. Acad. Sci. Hung.* 15: 25–34, 1965.

60. KAY, R. N. B. The rate of flow and composition of various salivary secretions in sheep and calves. *J. Physiol., London* 150: 515–537, 1960.

61. KIDDLE, P., R. A. MARSHALL, AND A. T. PHILLIPSON. A comparison of the mixtures of acetic, propionic and butyric acids in the rumen and in the blood leaving the rumen. *J. Physiol., London* 113: 207–217, 1951.

62. KRVAVICA, S., B. KURLEC, AND T. MARTINČIĆ. Enzymatic investigation in the mucosa of the rumen. 3. On the presence of carbamylphosphate synthetase and ornithine transcarbamylase in the mucosa of the rumen. *Vet. Arhiv.* 34: 94–100, 1964.

63. LEIBHOLZ, J. The free amino acids occurring in the blood plasma and rumen liquor of the sheep. *Australian J. Agr. Res.* 16: 973–979, 1965.

64. LEWIS, D. Blood urea concentration in relation to protein utilization in the ruminant. *J. Agr. Sci.* 48: 438–446, 1957

65. LEWIS, D., K. J. HILL, AND E. F. ANNISON. Studies on the portal blood of sheep. 1. Absorption of ammonia from the rumen of the sheep. *Biochem. J.* 66: 587–592, 1957.

66. MARTINČIĆ, T., AND S. KRVAVICA. Enzymatic investigations in the mucosa of the rumen. 2. On the presence of arginase in the ruminal mucosa of cattle. *Vet. Arhiv.* 34: 90–93, 1964.

67. MASSON, M. J., AND A. T. PHILLIPSON. The absorption of acetate, propionate and butyrate from the rumen of sheep. *J. Physiol., London* 113: 189–206, 1951.

68. MASSON, M. J., AND A. T. PHILLIPSON. The composition of the digesta leaving the abomasum of sheep. *J. Physiol., London* 116: 98–111, 1952.

69. McARTHUR, J. M., AND J. E. MILTIMORE. Rumen gas analysis by gas-solid chromatography. *Can. J. Animal Sci.* 41: 187–196, 1961.

70. McDONALD, I. W. The absorption of ammonia from the rumen of the sheep. *Biochem. J.* 42: 584–587, 1948.

71. MOIR, R. J., M. SOMERS, AND H. WARING. Studies on marsupial nutrition. 1. Ruminant-like digestion in a herbivorous marsupial (Setonix brachyurus). *Australian J. Biol. Sci.* 9: 293–304, 1956.

72. MURRAY, M. G., R. S. REID, AND T. M. SUTHERLAND. The rate of passage of digesta from the reticulo-rumen of the sheep. *J. Physiol., London* 164: 26–27P, 1962.

73. PARTHASARATHY, D. *Some Aspects of Digestion in Herbivora* (Ph.D. Thesis), Aberdeen University, 1952.

74. PARTHASARATHY, D., G. A. GARTON, AND A. T. PHILLIPSON. The passage of phosphorus across the rumen epithelium of sheep. *Biochem. J.* 52: xvi–xvii, 1952.

75. PARTHASARATHY, D., AND A. T. PHILLIPSON. The movement of potassium, sodium, chloride and water across the rumen epithelium of the sheep. *J. Physiol., London* 121: 452–467, 1953.

76. PEARSON, R. M., AND J. A. B. SMITH. Utilization of urea in the bovine rumen. 2. Conversion of urea to ammonia. *Biochem. J.* 37: 148–153, 1943.

77. PENNINGTON, R. J. The metabolism of short-chain fatty acids in the sheep. 1. Fatty acid utilization and ketone body production by rumen epithelium and other tissues. *Biochem. J.* 51: 251–258, 1952.

78. PENNINGTON, R. J., AND T. M. SUTHERLAND. The metabolism of short-chain fatty acids in the sheep. 4. The pathway of propionate metabolism in rumen epithelial tissue. *Biochem. J.* 63: 618–628, 1956.

79. PFANDER, W. H., AND A. T. PHILLIPSON. The rates of absorption of acetic, propionic and n-butyric acids. *J. Physiol. London* 122: 102–110, 1953.

80. PHILLIPSON, A. T. The fluctuations of pH and organic acids in the rumen of the sheep. *J. Exptl. Biol.* 19: 186–198, 1942.

81. PHILLIPSON, A. T. The production of fatty acids in the alimentary tract of the dog. *J. Exptl. Biol.* 23: 346–349, 1947.

82. PHILLIPSON, A. T., AND R. A. McANALLY. Studies of the fate of carbohydrates in the rumen of the sheep. *J. Exptl. Biol.* 19: 199–214, 1942.

83. PHILLIPSON, A. T., AND J. E. STORRY. The absorption of calcium and magnesium from the rumen and small intestine of the sheep. *J. Physiol., London* 181: 130–150, 1965.

84. ROE, W. E., E. N. BERGMAN, AND K. KON. Absorption of ketone bodies and other metabolites via the portal blood of sheep. *Am. J. Vet. Res.* 27: 729–736, 1966.

85. SCARISBRICK, R., AND T. K. EWER. The absorption of in-organic phosphate from the rumen of the sheep. *Biochem. J.* 49: lxxix, 1951.

86. SCHMITT-NIELSEN, B., AND H. OSAKI. Renal responses to changes in nitrogen metabolism in sheep. *Am. J. Physiol.* 193: 657–661, 1958.

87. SCOTT, D. The effects of sodium depletion and potassium supplements upon electrical potentials in the rumen of the sheep. *Quart. J. Exptl. Physiol.* 51: 60–69, 1966.

88. SELLERS, A. F., AND A. DOBSON. Studies on reticulo-rumen sodium and potassium concentrations and electrical potentials in sheep. *Res. Vet. Sci.* 1: 95–102, 1960.

89. SELLERS, A. F., C. E. STEVENS, A. DOBSON, AND F. D., McLEOD. Arterial blood flow to the ruminant stomach. *Am. J. Physiol.* 207: 371–377, 1964.

90. SHINOZAKI, K. Studies on experimental bloat in ruminants. 4. Identification of amines from rumen ingesta and passage of histamine across the rumen epithelium. *Tohoku J. Agr. Res.* 8: 149–154, 1957.

91. SMITH, A. H., M. KLEIBER, A. L. BLACK, AND C. F. BAXTER. Transfer of phosphate in the digestive tract. 2. Sheep. *J. Nutr.* 57: 507–527, 1955.

92. SOMERS, M. Factors influencing the secretion of nitrogen in sheep saliva. 1. The distribution of nitrogen in the mixed and parotid saliva of sheep. *Australian J. Exptl. Biol. Med. Sci.* 39: 111–122, 1961.

93. SPERBER, I., AND S. HYDÉN. Transport of chloride through the ruminal mucosa. *Nature* 169: 587, 1952.

94. SPERBER, I., S. HYDÉN, AND J. EKMAN. The use of poly-ethylene glycol as a reference substance in the study of ruminant digestion. *Kgl. Lantbrukshögskol. Ann.* 20: 337–344, 1953.

95. STACEY, B. D., AND A. C. I. WARNER. Balance of water and sodium in the rumen during feeding: osmotic stimula-tion of sodium absorption in the sheep. *Quart. J. Exptl. Physiol.* 51: 79–93, 1966.

96. STEVENS, C. E. Transport of sodium and chloride by the isolated rumen epithelium. *Am. J. Physiol.* 206: 1099–1105, 1964.

97. STEVENS, C. E., AND B. K. STETTLER. Factors affecting the transport of volatile fatty acids across rumen epithelium. *Am. J. Physiol.* 210: 365–372, 1966.

98. STEVENS, C. E., AND B. K. STETTLER. Transport of fatty acid mixtures across rumen epithelium. *Am. J. Physiol.* 211: R 264–R 271, 1966.

99. STEVENS, C. E., AND B. K. STETTLER. Evidence for active transport of acetate across bovine rumen epithelium. *Physiologist* 9: 297, 1966.

100. STEWART, J., AND E. W. MOODIE. The absorption of magnesium from the alimentary tract of sheep. *J. Comp. Pathol. Therap.* 66: 10–21, 1956.

101. STORRY, J. E. Studies on calcium and magnesium in the alimentary tract of sheep. 1. The distribution of calcium and magnesium in the contents taken from various parts of the alimentary tract. *J. Agr. Sci.* 57: 97–102, 1961.

102. SUTHERLAND, T. M. The metabolism of short chain fatty acids in the ruminant. In: *Progress in Nutrition and Allied Sciences*, edited by D. P. Cuthbertson. Edinburgh: Oliver & Boyd, 1963, p. 159–170.

103. SUTHERLAND, T. M., W. C. ELLIS, R. S. REID, AND M. G. MURRAY. A method of circulating and sampling the rumen contents of sheep fed on ground pelleted foods. *Brit. J. Nutr.* 16: 603–614, 1962.

104. SUTHERLAND, R. M., B. N. GUPTA, R. S. REID, AND M. G. MURRAY. Some effects of continuous feeding on digestion in the sheep. In: *Proceedings of the 6th International Congress of Nutrition, Edinburgh, 1963*, edited by C. F. Mills and R. Passmore. Edinburgh: Livingstone, 1964, p. 579–580.

105. SUTHERLAND, T. M., R. S. REID, AND M. G. MURRAY. The rate of production of steam volatile fatty acids in the reticulorumen of sheep fed finely ground pelleted diets. In: *Proceedings of the 6th International Congress of Nutrition, Edinburgh, 1963*, edited by C. F. Mills and R. Passmore. Edinburgh: Livingstone, 1964, p. 580.

106. TILL, A. R., AND A. M. DOWNES. The preparation of tritium-labelled polyethylene glycol and its use as a soluble rumen marker. *Brit. J. Nutr.* 19: 435–442, 1965.

107. TRAUTMANN, A. Beiträge zur Physiologie des Wiederkäuer-magens. 6. Über die Resorption in Wiederkäuermagen. *Arch. Tierenähr. Tierzucht* 9: 178–193, 1933.

108. TSUDA, T. Studies on absorption from the rumen. 2. Absorption of several organic substances from the minia-ture rumen of the goat. *Tohoku J. Agr. Res.* 7: 241–256, 1956.

109. ULYATT, M. J. The use of polyethylene glycol as a marker for measuring rumen water volume and the rate of flow of water from the rumen of grazing sheep. *New Zealand J. Agr. Res.* 7: 713–722, 1964.

110. ULYATT, M. J. The suitability of lithium as a marker for estimating rumen water volume in sheep. *New Zealand J. Agr. Res.* 7: 774–778, 1964.

111. USSING, H. H., AND K. ZERAHN. Active transport of sodium as the source of electric current in the short-circuited isolated frog skin. *Acta Physiol. Scand.* 23: 110–127, 1951.

112. WARNER, A. C. I. Production of volatile fatty acids in the rumen: methods of measurement. *Nutr. Abstr. Rev.* 34: 339–352, 1964.

113. WARNER, A. C. I., AND B. D. STACY. Solutes in the rumen of the sheep. *Quart. J. Exptl. Physiol.* 50: 169–184, 1965.

114. WASHBURN, L. E., AND S. BRODY. Growth and develop-ment. 42. Methane, hydrogen, and carbon dioxide produc-tion in the digestive tract of ruminants in relation to the respiratory exchange. *Missouri Univ. Agr. Expt. Sta. Res. Bull.* No. 263, 1937.

115. WESTER, J. *Die Physiologie und Pathologie der Vormagen beim Rinde*. Berlin: Springer, 1926.

116. WHITING, F., C. C. BALCH, AND R. C. CAMPLING. Some problems in the use of antipyrine and N-acetyl-4-amino-antipyrine in the determination of body water in cattle. *Brit. J. Nutr.* 14: 519–533, 1960.

117. WILLIAMS, V. J., AND D. D. S. MACKENZIE. The absorp-tion of lactic acid from the reticulo-rumen of the sheep. *Australian J. Biol. Sci.* 18: 917–934, 1965.

118. WRIGHT, E. Site of phosphorus absorption in the sheep. *Nature* 176: 351–352, 1955.

119. YOSHIDA, J. Studies on the toxicity of urea and its control. 8. Influence of pH on ammonia absorption from the ru-men. *Japan. J. Zootech. Sci.* 34: 328–335, 1963.

CHAPTER 133

Secretion of plasma proteins into the digestive tract

GRAHAM H. JEFFRIES
MARVIN H. SLEISENGER

Division of Gastroenterology, Department of Medicine, Cornell University Medical College, New York City

CHAPTER CONTENTS

THE FUNCTIONS of the gastrointestinal tract that relate to plasma protein metabolism include: the absorption of intact protein during the neonatal period and the subsequent absorption of products of protein digestion that may be reutilized for plasma protein synthesis; the intestinal synthesis of plasma proteins; and the enteric secretion or leakage (or both) of plasma proteins that contributes to plasma protein catabolism. These functions of the gut are discussed, together with the methods that have been used to study these aspects of plasma protein metabolism in healthy persons and in patients with disease.

PHYSIOLOGY OF ENTERIC METABOLISM OF PLASMA PROTEINS

Enteric Protein Absorption

The intestinal mucosa of neonatal animals has the capacity to absorb intact protein molecules (4, 6, 35). This function has been studied experimentally by observing the incorporation of ferritin or fluorescein-labeled plasma proteins into vacuoles in the apical cytoplasm of intestinal epithelial cells after feeding these proteins (Fig. 1). Ultrastructural studies suggest that this transfer of protein into the epithelial cell is accomplished by microphagocytosis (pinocytosis) (6). This process, which persists for only a few days after birth, is selective; homologous gamma globulin is absorbed more readily than heterologous plasma proteins.

Recent studies have shown that gamma-A globulin (immunoglobulin-A, IgA) is concentrated in colostrum; the maternal protein is conjugated with a "transfer protein" in the mammary gland (39, 42). The absorption of specific antibodies from colostrum during the neonatal period is of major importance in providing immunological protection in some animals (4), but is probably of less significance in the human infant, in whom the period of intestinal pinocytosis is brief and transplacental passage of maternal antibody to the fetus is of greater magnitude.

In the adult animal immunological studies have revealed that trace amounts of protein (or antigenic peptide) may be absorbed from the gut; this has no

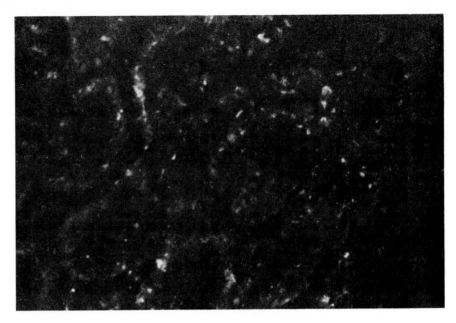

FIG. I. Intestinal absorption of gamma globulin in the neonatal rat. Fluorescein-labeled rabbit gamma globulin was fed by mouth to a 3-day-old rat. Examination of a frozen section of the upper small intestine under ultraviolet illumination shows the presence of labeled protein in intestinal epithelial cells. Intestinal villi are sectioned transversely.

known physiological significance but may occasionally be of pathological importance.

Synthesis of Plasma Proteins

Most plasma proteins are synthesized by the liver parenchymal cells [albumin, alpha and beta globulins, and fibrinogen (32)] and by plasma cells of the lymphoid system (immunoglobulins). Two important plasma proteins are produced in the gastrointestinal mucosa. Beta lipoprotein synthesized in the intestinal mucosal cell during lipid absorption appears necessary for the transfer of triglyceride fat from vacuoles within the cell through the basal and lateral cell membrane to the lymphatics of the lamina propria (10, 20). This protein may be an essential constituent of the chylomicron. In patients with abetalipoproteinemia (an inborn error of metabolism), and in animals treated with puromycin (an inhibitor of protein synthesis), triglyceride fat accumulates in large vacuoles in the cytoplasm of the epithelial cells, and chylomicrons do not appear in the lamina propria, the intestinal lymphatics, or the plasma after a meal containing triglyceride (10).

Immunoglobulins are synthesized by mononuclear cells in the lamina propria of the mucosa. The lymphoid tissue of the gut differs from that of peripheral lymph nodes; whereas plasma cells in peripheral lymph nodes synthesize gamma-G globulin (IgG)

predominantly (the number of cells staining with fluorescein-labeled antisera to the specific immunoglobulins, IgG, IgA, and IgM, is roughly proportional to the plasma concentration of these proteins), IgA is most prevalent in plasma cells infiltrating the lamina propria (7) (Fig. 2). IgA produced in the mucosa may contribute to the circulating pool of protein, but may also have a specific protective function within the mucosa or on mucosal surfaces. Secretions from the nose, bronchi, salivary glands, and stomach contain IgA in excess of other immunoglobulins. In parotid saliva, as in colostrum, this immunoglobulin is combined with a "transfer protein" (39, 42). The mucosal synthesis and selective secretion of IgA at sites of exposure to dietary and microbial antigens may be of considerable immunological importance. Bronchitis, chronic sinusitis, and malabsorption have been attributed to a deficiency of IgA in patients with dysgammaglobulinemia.

Degradation of Plasma Proteins

Plasma proteins of all classes are present in low concentrations in saliva and gastrointestinal secretions from normal subjects (18, 19, 38). These proteins may be detected by immunological methods (immunodiffusion and immunoelectrophoresis) when the secretions are collected and concentrated under conditions that prevent digestion of protein (Fig. 3).

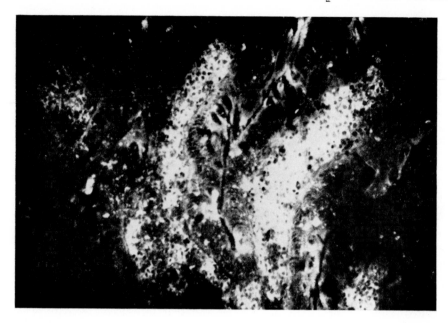

FIG. 2. Distribution of plasma cells containing IgA in normal jejunal mucosa. A frozen section of human jejunal mucosa was incubated with fluorescein-labeled antibody to human IgA. The lamina propria is densely packed with mononuclear cells that contained IgA in their cytoplasm. Ultraviolet illumination; × 200. [From Rubin et al. *J. Clin. Invest.* 44: 475–485, 1965.]

Normally, proteins that enter the lumen of the stomach or intestine are rapidly hydrolyzed to their constituent amino acids, which are reabsorbed in the intestine.

Two important aspects of the physiology of plasma protein degradation by the gut need clarification. One is the process by which plasma proteins pass through the mucosal or glandular epithelia, and the other is the quantitative significance of this phenomenon in relation to total plasma protein catabolism.

HOW DO PLASMA PROTEINS PASS THROUGH THE GASTRO-INTESTINAL MUCOSA? The answer to this question is incomplete. With the exception of IgA, which appears to be actively secreted with a carrier molecule, there is no evidence that plasma proteins are actively transported across the mucosal epithelium from the lamina propria. Furthermore, the apical junctional complex between the lateral cell membranes of intestinal epithelial cells would appear to limit the passage of protein molecules between the cells. The most reasonable hypothesis, which still lacks experimental support, is that lymph escapes from the lamina propria at the apex of the intestinal villi with desquamating cells.

WHAT IS THE QUANTITATIVE SIGNIFICANCE OF NORMAL ENTERIC LOSS OF PLASMA PROTEIN? The final answer awaits the development of methods to measure accurately the quantities of specific plasma proteins that enter the gut lumen each day, as well as the total amount of each protein that is catabolized daily.

Although a number of proteins and macromolecules labeled with radioisotopes have been used to study plasma protein turnover and enteric loss, none are ideal for this purpose. Waldmann (43) has recently defined the characteristics of the labeled macromolecule that would be ideal for measuring enteric loss of plasma protein: "(a) The labeled serum protein should have a normal metabolic behavior, thus permitting the simultaneous determination of rates of endogenous protein catabolism, protein synthesis, and intestinal protein loss. (b) There should be no absorption of the label from the intestinal tract after catabolism of the protein since this would result in an underestimation of the extent of the gastrointestinal protein loss. (c) There should be no excretion of the label into the gastrointestinal tract except when bound to protein. Such secretion of label . . . would result in overestimation of the magnitude of the gastrointestinal protein loss."

Methods for Measuring Gastrointestinal Loss of Plasma Protein

^{131}I-LABELED SERUM PROTEINS. Serum proteins carefully labeled with radioiodine (^{125}I, ^{131}I) (30) have a normal metabolic behavior (2). Thus after an in-

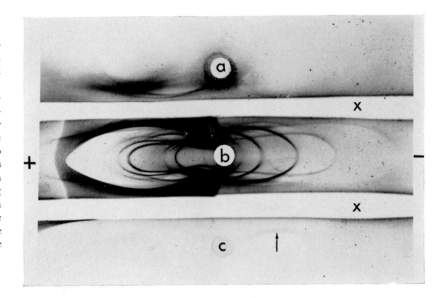

FIG. 3. Immunoelectrophoretic analysis of plasma proteins in concentrated gastric juice and saliva. Wells *a*, *b*, and *c* contained concentrated gastric juice, serum, and concentrated saliva, respectively. The gastric juice had been neutralized by instilling phosphate buffer at pH 7 into the stomach. Both gastric juice and saliva were concentrated 50 times. After electrophoresis the troughs (*x*) were filled with antiserum to human plasma. Precipitin lines corresponding to albumin and several alpha and beta globulins indicated the presence of these proteins in the gastric juice. A single precipitin line (→) demonstrated the presence of IgA in saliva.

travenous injection of radioiodinated albumin or gamma globulin the tracer protein is distributed throughout the intra- and extravascular pools of protein and is catabolized at the same rate as the recipient's protein. Under steady-state conditions (when protein synthesis and degradation are equal) the plasma volume and intravascular and total protein pools can be calculated from the plasma protein concentration and the dilution of labeled protein after complete mixing in the intravascular and total pools, respectively.

After equilibration of the labeled protein in the intravascular and extravascular compartments (after 2–3 days) the decline in plasma radioactivity, corrected for radioactive decay, reflects the degradation of the protein and may be expressed as a percentage of the injected dose degraded daily or as grams of protein degraded per kilogram of body weight (3, 31, 41) (Fig. 4). The slope of the plasma decay curve after initial equilibration parallels the plot of the cumulative urinary excretion of radioiodine (when uptake of radioiodine by the thyroid has been blocked by prior iodine therapy). The daily urinary excretion of radioiodine after initial equilibration has been shown to be a constant function of the plasma pool of labeled protein (1); this supports the contention that plasma protein is catabolized from the plasma pool and that plasma protein catabolism should thus be expressed as a percentage of the plasma pool (31), rather than of the total body pool (3, 41).

Recently Nosslin (33) derived a formula for calculating plasma protein catabolism based on the assumption that newly synthesized protein is distributed initially in the plasma pool after its release from its site of synthesis and that the specific activity of labeled protein at the site of degradation is identical with that in plasma; it is assumed that the turnover and exchange between compartments can be described by exponential functions. The model is independent of the site of degradation and the number of extravascular pools. The amount of protein degraded daily and similarly the amount synthesized daily are each equal to the plasma pool of protein divided by the area under the curve of plasma radioactivity (expressed as a percentage of plasma radioactivity at zero time) from zero time to infinity.

Although plasma proteins labeled with radioiodine are ideal for studying plasma protein kinetics, they are unsuitable for measuring enteric loss. Iodine is concentrated and secreted by salivary glands and by gastric mucosa and is reabsorbed by the intestinal epithelium.

Plasma protein leakage into the gut has been estimated in experimental animals by collecting secretions from isolated segments of the intestine and by measuring their content of injected radioiodinated albumin or gamma globulin (14, 49). These studies have suggested that between 40 and 60 % of plasma protein catabolism takes place in the gut. This is difficult to reconcile with observations in eviscerated animals; removal of the gut prolonged the survival of injected iodinated albumin by less than 10 % (12). Several factors may have contributed to an overestimation of enteric protein loss in animal studies: study periods were short compared to the turnover time of the plasma protein, only short segments of the gut were used at one time, and operative

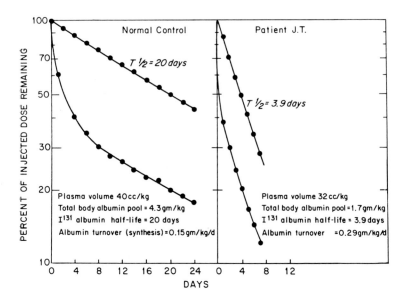

FIG. 4. Turnover of ^{131}I-albumin in a normal subject and in a patient (*J. T.*) with gastrointestinal protein loss secondary to intestinal lymphangiectasia. *Upper curves* represent the decline in total body radioactivity with time. *Lower curves* represent the decline in plasma radioactivity. The total-body albumin pool was much reduced in patient *J. T.* The survival half-life of iodinated albumin was markedly shortened, and the albumin synthetic rate was slightly faster than normal. [From Waldmann (43).]

injury to the gut segment may have caused excessive leakage of plasma or lymph.

In some patients with gastric mucosal disease the measurement of albumin-bound ^{131}I in gastric juice collected after intragastric instillation of neutral buffer solution to prevent proteolysis has been of clinical value in demonstrating an excessive loss of plasma protein (5, 13). With this exception, radioiodinated albumin has not been of value in measuring gastrointestinal protein loss in man.

A technique in which an ion-exchange resin (Amberlite) was given orally in an attempt to chelate ^{131}I that entered the gut after an intravenous injection of labeled protein did not provide a measure of enteric protein loss (24); radioiodine excreted with resin in the feces was derived not only from ^{131}I-albumin leakage, but also from free iodide secreted by salivary glands and stomach (28).

[51]CR-LABELED ALBUMIN. Albumin labeled with $^{51}CrCl_3$ is unsuitable for measuring plasma protein kinetics because of its shortened half-life of survival due to the elution of chromium from the protein. The properties of the ^{51}Cr label, however, make it ideal for enteric studies; chromium salts are neither secreted into nor absorbed from the gastrointestinal tract in significant amounts. Thus ^{51}Cr-albumin loss into the gut is reflected by excretion of ^{51}Cr label in the stool [(43, 44); Fig. 5].

When stools, uncontaminated with urine, are collected for a period of several days after an intravenous injection of ^{51}Cr-albumin, and the daily fecal radioactivity is related to the corresponding plasma radioactivity, the loss of albumin into the gut may be expressed as a fraction of the plasma pool or as milliliters of plasma excreted per day. This clearance of plasma albumin by the gut may be calculated from the formula: gut loss of plasma albumin (ml of plasma/day) = fecal radioactivity during the collection period/mean plasma radioactivity during the collection period × number of days of collection. In normal subjects tested by this procedure between 5 and 25 ml of plasma, or less than 1% of the plasma albumin pool, was cleared daily by the gastrointestinal tract (44).

[67]CU-LABELED CERULOPLASMIN. [67]Cu-labeled ceruloplasmin is an ideal labeled macromolecule for measuring enteric loss (47). The copper is an integral part of the protein molecule, and the radioactive label is not absorbed from the gut. Calculations based on the excretion of [67]Cu in the stools after an intravenous injection of [67]Cu-ceruloplasmin in normal subjects indicated that about 2% of the circulating protein was excreted daily. This accounted for only 10% of the protein degradation, which corresponds to the fraction of catabolized plasma albumin that could be accounted for by enteric degradation in ^{51}Cr-albumin studies. Major disadvantages of [67]Cu-ceruloplasmin that preclude its use in routine studies are the very short half-life of the radioisotope and the expense of its preparation.

OTHER LABELED MACROMOLECULES. ^{131}I-labeled polyvinylpyrrolidone (^{131}I-PVP) has been used in many clinical studies to diagnose excessive enteric loss of

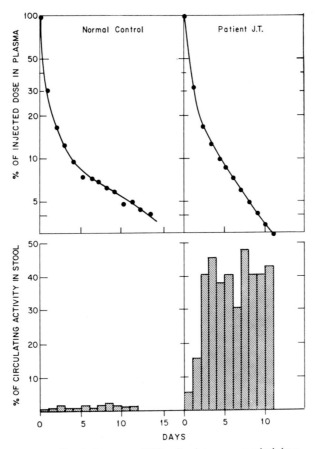

FIG. 5. Fecal clearance of ⁵¹Cr after intravenous administration of ⁵¹Cr-albumin in a normal subject and a patient (*J. T.*) with gastrointestinal protein loss. The normal subject cleared 0.8% of the plasma pool of labeled albumin into the gastrointestinal tract each day, whereas patient *J. T.* cleared more than 30% of the plasma pool into the gastrointestinal tract each day, an indication of severe gastrointestinal protein loss. [From Waldmann (43).]

plasma protein (9, 15, 16, 32, 34). Patients with excessive enteric loss of plasma protein excrete greater amounts of intravenously injected ¹³¹I-PVP than do normal subjects. However, studies with this labeled macromolecule do not yield physiological information. ¹³¹I-PVP is rapidly cleared from the plasma by the reticuloendothelial system and the kidneys, and instability of the iodine-PVP bond with release of free iodide permits both secretion and reabsorption of label in the gut (11).

In summary, the evidence derived from the fecal excretion of intravenously injected ⁵¹Cr-albumin and ⁶⁷Cu-ceruloplasmin indicates that no more than 10% of the catabolism of albumin and ceruloplasmin can be accounted for by enteric loss of the proteins. These values are considerably lower than values estimated from studies of ¹³¹I-labeled plasma protein

clearance in experimental animals, but they probably reflect the physiological state more accurately.

EXCESSIVE ENTERIC LEAKAGE OF PLASMA PROTEIN

Pathophysiology

The common pathological bases for excessive enteric loss of plasma protein (protein-losing enteropathy) are mucosal ulceration, disordered metabolism or turnover of epithelial cells (or both), and lymphatic obstruction (26, 43). Excessive loss of plasma protein may be due to inflammatory exudation through areas of ulceration, increased mucosal permeability to protein because of impaired metabolism or excessive cell desquamation, or direct leakage of lymph from obstructed lacteals.

In patients with protein-losing enteropathy, all serum proteins leak excessively into the gut. The change in concentration and total pool of individual plasma proteins that results from excessive enteric loss will depend on two compensatory mechanisms— increased synthesis and decreased endogenous (non-enteric) catabolism. Levels of proteins that normally have the longest survival (albumin and gamma globulins) tend to be more severely depressed than those of proteins with a relatively short survival (fibrinogen). Excessive enteric loss of protein is reflected by a shortening of the half-life of injected ¹³¹I-albumin, an increase in the fractional catabolic rate of this protein (percent of plasma pool degraded daily), and an increased fecal excretion of injected ⁵¹Cr-albumin (see Figs. 4 and 5).

Clinical Manifestations

Hypoproteinemia due to excessive enteric loss of plasma protein may be manifested by dependent edema due to the lowered colloidal osmotic pressure of plasma, an increased fluid transudation from the capillaries, and secondary hyperaldosteronism with sodium and water retention.

In patients with intestinal lymphatic obstruction the transport of dietary long-chain triglycerides as chylomicrons in the lymph may be impaired, and lymph containing both plasma proteins and triglyceride fat may be lost into the intestinal lumen, with variable steatorrhea (25, 48).

Diseases Associated with Protein-Losing Enteropathy

As noted previously, the diseases that may be associated with excessive enteric loss of plasma protein fall into three categories: *1*) diseases in which there is mucosal ulceration, *2*) diseases in which there is impaired metabolism or turnover of surface epithelial cells or both, and *3*) diseases in which there is obstruction to the flow of intestinal lymph.

Mucosal ulceration may be localized or diffuse and may be associated with either benign (40) or malignant (23) conditions. The severity of the plasma protein leakage into the gut will depend on the extent of ulceration and the degree of associated inflammation or lymphatic obstruction.

Impaired metabolism of surface epithelial cells, which may lead to a change in mucosal permeability to protein or to an increase in cell desquamation, is common to several diseases of the small intestine and is usually associated with a derangement of intestinal absorption. Diffuse disease of the intestinal mucosa may result from infection [viral, bacterial, or parasitic (27, 29)] or a sensitivity to dietary substances [gliadin in celiac disease (17), milk protein in allergic enteritis (45, 50)], or it may be unexplained [mucosal changes

associated with defective synthesis of gamma globulin, particularly IgA (46)].

Obstruction to lymphatic flow from the small intestine may be due to a congenital lymphatic malformation [intestinal lymphangiectasia associated with Milroy's disease (25, 37, 48)], to obstruction of lymphatic vessels by fibrosis or neoplastic infiltration (tuberculosis, lymphoma), or to an increase in the pressure in the superior vena cava [constrictive pericarditis (36), tricuspid valvular disease, congestive heart failure (8)].

For further discussion of the clinical aspects of excessive enteric protein loss the reader is referred to recent reviews (22, 26, 43). The methods used to study protein loss in normal subjects have been applied extensively in studies of protein-losing enteropathy; in spite of their limitations for physiological studies these methods have provided data that have increased understanding of the pathophysiology of derangements of plasma protein metabolism and have provided valuable aids to diagnosis.

REFERENCES

1. ANDERSEN, S. B. Intravascular or extravascular degradation of γ_{ss}-globulin. In: *Physiology and Pathophysiology of Plasma Protein Metabolism.* Berne: Hans Huber, 1964, p. 105–115.

2. BENNHOLD, H., AND E. KALLEE. Comparative studies on the half-life of I^{131}-labeled albumins and non-radioactive human serum albumin in a case of analbuminemia. *J. Clin. Invest.* 38: 863–872, 1959.

3. BERSON, S. A., R. S. YALOW, S. S. SCHREIBER, AND J. POST. Tracer experiments with I^{131}labeled human serum albumin: distribution and degradation studies. *J. Clin. Invest.* 32: 746–768, 1953.

4. BRAMBELL, F. W. R. The passive immunity of the young animal. *Biol. Rev.* 33: 488–531, 1958.

5. CITRIN, Y., K. STERLING, AND J. A. HALSTED. Mechanism of hypoproteinemia associated with giant hypertrophy of gastric mucosa. *New Engl. J. Med.* 257: 906–912, 1957.

6. CLARK, S. L., JR. The ingestion of proteins and colloidal materials by columnar absorptive cells of the small intestine in suckling rats and mice. *J. Biophys. Biochem. Cytol.* 5: 40–50, 1959.

7. CRABBE, P. A., AND J. F. HEREMANS. The distribution of immunoglobulin-containing cells along the human gastro-intestinal tract. *Gastroenterology* 51: 305–316, 1966.

8. DAVIDSON, J. D., T. A. WALDMANN, D. S. GOODMAN, AND R. S. GORDON, JR. Protein-losing gastroenteropathy in congestive heart failure. *Lancet* 1: 899–902, 1961.

9. DAWSON, A. M., R. WILLIAMS, AND H. S. WILLIAMS. Faecal PVP excretion in hypoalbuminaemia and gastrointestinal disease. *Brit. Med. J.* 2: 667–670, 1961.

10. DOBBINS, W. O. An ultrastructural study of the intestinal mucosa in congenital β-lipoprotein deficiency with particu-

lar emphasis upon the intestinal absorptive cell. *Gastroterology* 50: 195–210, 1966.

11. FRENCH, A. B., A. I. RAGINS, H. M. POLLARD, AND B. DICKASON. Distribution of ^{131}I-polyvinylpyrrolidone after oral and intravenous administration. *Federation Proc.* 20: 242, 1961.

12. GITLIN, D., J. R. KLINENBERG, AND W. L. HUGHES. Site of catabolism of serum albumin. *Nature* 181: 1064–1065, 1958.

13. GLASS, G. B. J., AND A. ISHIMORI. Passage of serum albumin into the stomach: its detection by paper electrophoresis of gastric juice in protein-losing gastropathies and gastric cancer. *Am. J. Digest. Diseases* 6: 103–133, 1961.

14. GLENERT, J., S. JARNUM, AND S. RIEMER. The albumin transfer from blood to gastro-intestinal tract in dogs. *Acta Chir. Scand.* 124: 63–74, 1962.

15. GORDON, R. S., F. C. BARTTER, AND T. WALDMANN. Idiopathic hypoalbuminemias. *Ann. Internal Med.* 51: 553–576, 1959.

16. GORDON, R. S., JR. Exudative enteropathy: abnormal permeability of the gastro-intestinal tract demonstrated with labelled polyvinylpyrrolidone. *Lancet* 1: 325–326, 1959.

17. GORDON, R. S., JR. Protein-losing enteropathy in the sprue syndrome. *Lancet* 1: 55–56, 1961.

18. GULLBERG, R., AND B. OLHAGEN. Electrophoresis of human gastric juice. *Nature* 184: 1848–1849, 1959.

19. HOLMAN, H., W. F. NICKEL, JR., AND M. H. SLEISENGER. Hypoproteinemia antedating intestinal lesions, and possibly due to excessive serum protein loss into the intestine. *Am. J. Med.* 27: 963–975, 1959.

20. ISSELBACHER, K. J., AND D. M. BUDZ. Synthesis of lipoproteins by rat intestinal mucosa. *Nature* 200: 364–365, 1963.

21. Jarnum, S. The ^{131}I-polyvinylpyrrolidone (^{131}I-PVP) test in gastrointestinal protein loss. *Scand. J. Clin. Lab. Invest.* 13: 447–461, 1961.

22. Jarnum, S. *Protein-Losing Gastroenteropathy.* Oxford: Blackwell, 1963.

23. Jarnum, S., and M. Schwartz. Hypoalbuminemia in gastric carcinoma. *Gastroenterology* 38: 769–776, 1960.

24. Jeejeebhoy, K. N., and N. F. Coghill. The measurement of gastrointestinal protein loss by a new method. *Gut* 2: 123–130, 1961.

25. Jeffries, G. H., A. Chapman, and M. H. Sleisenger. Low-fat diet in intestinal lymphangiectasia: its effect on albumin metabolism. *New Engl. J. Med.* 270: 761–766, 1964.

26. Jeffries, G. H., H. R. Holman, and M. H. Sleisenger. Plasma proteins and the gastrointestinal tract. *New Engl. J. Med.* 266: 652–660, 1962.

27. Jeffries, G. H., and M. H. Sleisenger. Abnormal enteric loss of plasma protein in gastrointestinal diseases. *Surg. Clin. N. Am.* 42: 1125–1133, 1962.

28. Jones, J. H., and D. B. Morgan. Measurement of plasma-protein loss into gastrointestinal tract using ^{131}I-labeled proteins and oral Amberlite resin. *Lancet* 1: 626–629, 1963.

29. Laster, L., T. A. Waldmann, L. F. Fenster, and J. W. Singelton. Reversible enteric protein loss in Whipple's disease. *Gastroenterology* 42: 762, 1962.

30. McFarlane, A. S. Efficient trace-labelling of plasma proteins with iodine. *Nature* 182: 53, 1958.

31. McFarlane, A. S. The behavior of I[131]-labelled plasma proteins in vivo. *Ann. N. Y. Acad. Sci.* 70: 19, 1957.

32. Miller, L. L., and W. F. Bale. Synthesis of all plasma protein fractions except gamma globulin by liver: use of zone electrophoresis and lysine-ε-C[14] to define plasma proteins by isolated perfused liver. *J. Exptl. Med.* 99: 125–132, 1954.

33. Nosslin, B. Quoted by S. B. Andersen (1).

34. Parkins, R. A. Protein-losing enteropathy in sprue syndrome. *Lancet* 2: 1366–1368, 1960.

35. Payne, L. C., and C. L. Marsh. Absorption of gamma globulin by the small intestine. *Federation Proc.* 21: 909–912, 1962.

36. Petersen, V. P., and J. Hastrup. Protein-losing enteropathy in constrictive pericarditis. *Acta Med. Scand.* 173: 401–410, 1963.

37. Pomerantz, M., and T. A. Waldmann. Systemic lymphatic abnormalities associated with gastrointestinal protein loss secondary to intestinal lymphangiectasia. *Gastroenterology* 45: 703–711, 1963.

38. Soergel, K. H., and F. J. Ingelfinger. Proteins in serum and rectal mucus of patients with ulcerative colitis. *Gastroenterology* 40: 37–46, 1961.

39. South, M. A., M. D. Cooper, F. A. Wollheim, R. Hong, and R. A. Good. The IgA system. 1. Studies of the transport and immunochemistry of IgA in the saliva. *J. Exptl. Med.* 123: 615–628, 1966.

40. Steinfeld, J. L., J. D. Davidson, R. S. Gordon, Jr., and F. E. Greene. Mechanism of hypoproteinemia in patients with regional enteritis and ulcerative colitis. *Am. J. Med.* 29: 405–415, 1960.

41. Sterling, K. Turnover rate of serum albumin in man as measured by I[131] tagged albumin. *J. Clin. Invest.* 30: 1228–1237, 1951.

42. Tomasi, T. B., E. M. Tan, A. Solomon, and R. A. Prendergast. Characteristics of an immune system common to certain external secretions. *J. Exptl. Med.* 121: 101–124, 1965.

43. Waldmann, T. A. Protein-losing enteropathy. *Gastroenterology* 50: 422–443, 1966.

44. Waldmann, T. A. Gastrointestinal protein loss demonstrated by ^{51}Cr-labelled albumin. *Lancet* 2: 121–123, 1961.

45. Waldmann, T. A., R. S. Gordon, Jr., T. F. Dutcher, and P. T. Wertlake. Syndromes of gastrointestinal protein loss. In: *Plasma Proteins and Gastrointestinal Tract in Health and Disease.* Copenhagen: Munksgaard, 1962, p. 156–160.

46. Waldmann, T. A., and L. Laster. Abnormalities of albumin metabolism in patients with hypogammaglobulinemia. *J. Clin. Invest.* 43: 1025–1035, 1964.

47. Waldmann, T. A., A. G. Morell, R. D. Wochner, and I. Sternlieb. Quantitation of gastrointestinal protein loss with copper[67]-labeled ceruloplasmin. *J. Clin. Invest.* 44: 1107, 1965.

48. Waldmann, T. A., J. L. Steinfeld, T. F. Dutcher, J. D. Davidson, and R. S. Gordon, Jr. The role of the gastrointestinal system in "idiopathic hypoproteinemia." *Gastroenterology* 41: 197–207, 1961.

49. Wetterfors, J. Albumin: investigations into the metabolism, distribution and transfer of albumin under normal and certain pathologic conditions, with special reference to the gastrointestinal tract. *Acta Med. Scand.* 177, Suppl. 430: 1–72, 1965.

50. Wilson, J. F., D. C. Heiner, and M. E. Lahey. Milk-induced gastrointestinal bleeding in infants with hypochromic mycrocytic anemia. *J. Am. Med. Assoc.* 189: 568–573, 1964.

CHAPTER 134

Congenital aganglionosis[1]

MURRAY DAVIDSON

Departments of Pediatrics, Bronx Lebanon Hospital Center
and Bronx Municipal Hospital Center, Albert Einstein College of Medicine,
The Bronx, New York

CHAPTER CONTENTS

CONGENITAL AGANGLIONOSIS

Secondary Proximal Dilatation

FOR APPROXIMATELY 60 YEARS after Hirschsprung described congenital megacolon, physicians focused on the dilated colonic segments of these patients. Less than 20 years ago Swenson (25) and Bodian (3), and their associates, pointed out that the histology of the megacolon is normal and that the dilatation is secondary to distal obstruction by an achalasic aganglionic segment (9, 22). Ehrenpreis demonstrated that assisted regular emptying of the proximal colons of young infants with congenital aganglionosis could forestall the secondary dilatation (9). Once dilatation has occurred, relief of the obstruction after surgical correction of the condition leads to gradual return to normal caliber (3, 15, 25).

[1] Preparation of this review and performance of some of the original observations referred to herein were made possible in part by support of Grants RG4460 and A-3432 from the National Institute of Arthritis and Metabolic Diseases, and HD-02032 from the National Institute of Child Health and Human Development, Bethesda, Md.

Muscle Physiology in Dilated Segment

If the disease remains uncorrected for long, the muscular wall of the distended segment becomes thinned out. However, prior to this there is muscular hypertrophy with increase in motor activity, like that observed in other hollow viscera proximal to areas of chronic partial obstruction. Wright & Shepherd (27) showed that isolated strips of muscle from this region display normal spontaneous contractility. In our studies normal resting motility occurred in this segment (8).

Substance P, a biologically active polypeptide which is normally present in intestinal ganglia and which exerts a stimulating force on smooth muscle (13), was found in elevated concentrations in the hypertrophic musculature of the dilated segment (7). Kamijo et al. (17) demonstrated depressed activities for nonspecific and specific cholinesterases in the hypertrophic proximal bowel, suggesting exaggeration of cholinergic responses in this area. Confirmatory observations made with muscle strips from these segments from patients with congenital megacolon showed increased sensitivity to acetylcholine in vitro (27).

In pharmacological studies, when such muscle strips were exposed to nicotine and dimethylphenylpiperazinium (DMPP) (27) their response was identical to muscle from normal colon (28). Both agents initially induce an adrenergic effect (inhibition of contractility) followed by a cholinergic response (contraction). Kern & Almy (19) demonstrated that 50 % of normal adults undergo relaxation and cessation of resting activity in the distal colon after subcutaneous injections of methacholine chloride or after intravenous injections of acetylcholine. They believe that the relaxation of the left colon is necessary so that a concomitant increase of pressure in the right colon might be effective in expelling colonic contents through the area (Fig. 1). Figure 2 illustrates our confirmation of their observations, with motility records from this site in normal children (8). However, our interpretation of the data is somewhat different from theirs. We do not believe that material is simply pushed through the relaxed distal segment, but that the propulsive wave is instead transmitted into this area. It is our impression that the cessation of the intrinsic discoordinate (resting) smooth muscle contractions, which is observed after methacholine, represents suppression of this form of motility in preparation for transmission of a coordinated propulsive response. Occasionally we have been fortunate enough to record both the diminution in resting activity and

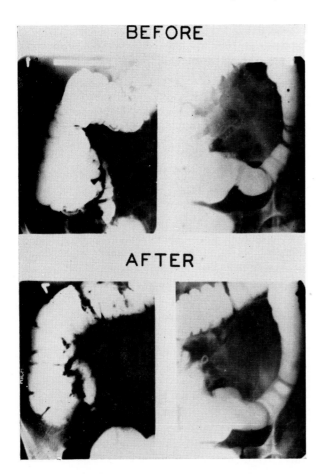

FIG. 1. Roentgenologic appearance of the right and left portions of the colon before infusion of acetylcholine and at the height of the effect of this agent. Note contraction of the right colon and the widening and disappearance of segmental contractions in the distal colon. [From Kern & Almy (19).]

the appearance of the propulsive waves, as in Figure 3 (7). This change from spontaneous smooth muscle activity to integrated peristaltic activity is presumably under nervous control. The finding that this also occurs in the proximal segments of patients with congenital aganglionosis (8) substantiates the general opinion that neural integration is intact in this portion of their colons.

Other observations that propulsive motility of the dilated segment is normal were made with balloons in this segment by Swenson et al. (26), from radiographic studies with contrast agents (18), and in one instance by following the migration of a cork inserted through a colostomy in a patient with congenital aganglionosis (29).

Distal Aganglionic Segment

Intraluminal contents proceed normally only to the upper level of the achalasic segment, corresponding approximately to the zone of transition between histologically normal proximal colon and the distal bowel, in which complete absence or a severe paucity of ganglia in Auerbach's and Meissner's plexuses may be demonstrated. Why interruption of normal propulsion occurs at the upper level of this aganglionic segment is not understood. Two concepts exist. In one the distal area is believed to be so spastic, because of the neurogenic defect, that it impedes free passage of intraluminal material. The second concept visualizes a more passive process in which the abnormal segment is not in spasm but simply fails to propagate peristaltic waves that arrive from above.

Spasm Theory

Hiatt is an advocate of the spasm concept (14). He interpreted the long-duration waves which he recorded from the aganglionic segments of children with congenital megacolon by a balloon-kymograph technique as representing "mass contraction" phenomena which rendered the segment unable to enter into coordinated propulsive motility. He and his co-workers concluded that the hypertrophic neurons of the intestinal wall in this area are cholinergic, from the high levels of activity of specific cholinesterase which they found (17). They also suggested that these nonmyelinated fibers are postganglionic and that the ganglia from which they originate may be outside the colon. They postulated that the pathophysiological defect of congenital megacolon is a paucity of the adrenergic neurons normally present

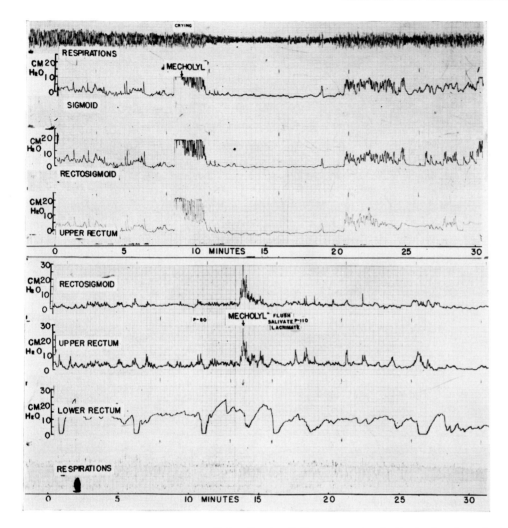

FIG. 2. Relaxation in all three segments of *upper tracing* after subcutaneous methacholine. This reaction is typical of 50% of normal population. No effect of same agent on any segment of patient shown in *lower tracing*. Note typical tonus pattern of rectum in lower tracing. [From Davidson et al. (8).]

as components of centrally situated ganglion cells. Deficiency of adrenergic neurons could result in the net effect of unopposed tonic contractions. Confirmation has been given by histochemical studies with specific fluorescence, from which the adrenergic neurons in animals (23) and in humans (11) have been shown to be distributed mainly to the intramural plexuses, where they make synaptic contacts with parasympathetic ganglion cells. Ehrenpreis (11) found these adrenergic neurons to be normal in proximal hypertrophied segments but not in the narrowed segments of patients with congenital megacolon. Wright & Shepherd (27) were able to elicit the cholinergic effect in isolated muscle strips from the constricted segment, but the adrenergic response was absent; that is, only contraction, rather than the biphasic response of normal muscle, was evoked by addition of nicotine and DMPP to the nutrient medium.

Despite this body of evidence, the view that spasm is the important factor in colonic achalasia is not entirely acceptable. The mass contractions recorded by Hiatt in the distal colon of patients with congenital aganglionosis (14) have the appearance of tonus waves, normally recorded as part of resting motility in studies of the gastrointestinal tract (4). We demonstrated, as shown in Figure 4, that these patterns are present in highest concentration in the rectal segments of normal children (6). This finding applies also in the distal segments of patients with congenital aganglionosis (8). Jorup recorded from the rectums of infants who had colic but who were free of congenital

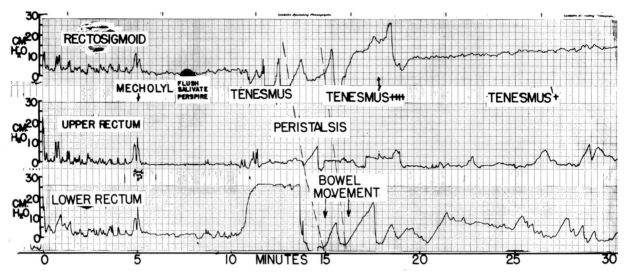

FIG. 3. Relaxation of resting motility following subcutaneous methacholine, followed by onset of propulsive motility. [From Davidson et al. (7).]

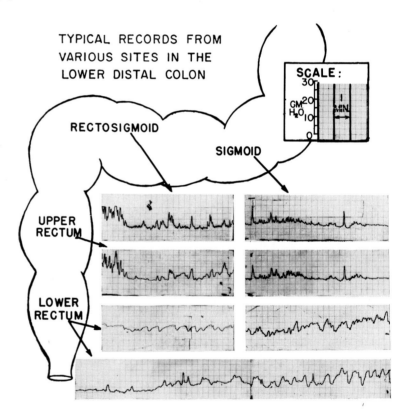

FIG. 4. The *left* and *right upper* sets of records were each obtained simultaneously from the areas indicated from two children. The *lower* record is from a third child. Note the preponderance of tonus activity in the lower rectal tracings. [From Davidson et al. (6).]

megacolon and found that similar waves were prominent (16). A further question with regard to Hiatt's interpretation stems from the fact that he recorded solely from the aganglionic segment (14). It is difficult to distinguish spastic from propulsive contractions under such conditions. Almy & Tulin (1) proctoscoped subjects who were under the stress of con-stricting headbands and observed directly an increase in contractility of the lumen of the rectum. However, since they restricted their observations to this site and could not perceive what was going on in the immediately proximal segments, they were unable to distinguish between spasm and propulsive contractions.

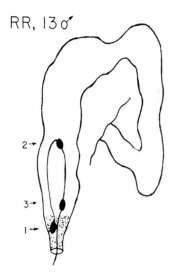

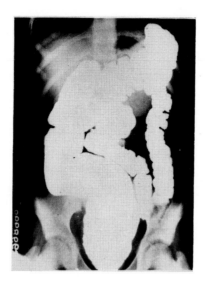

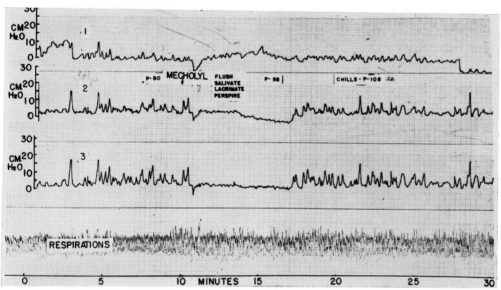

FIG. 5. Catheter tip *1* is coiled and lies in lower portion of rectum below *2* and *3*. Achalasic segment fails to respond to subcutaneous methacholine, whereas more proximal area undergoes relaxation. [From Davidson & Bauer (5).]

Passive Achalasia

An alternative to the spasm theory suggests that the peristaltic wave is stopped at the transition zone between normally innervated and aganglionic bowel; this would cause this level to serve as an "obstruction." In this light, some of the observations referred to above may be interpreted as substantiating a concept of passive achalasia. The lower than normal concentrations of substance P in this segment found by Ehrenpreis and Pernow could lead to lowered sensitivity to propulsive activity (12). The high

cholinesterase activity demonstrated in the segment (17) may also indicate interference with peristalsis because of rapid inactivation of released acetylcholine.

In our motility studies, in patients who displayed a cessation of resting activity in the proximal segments after injection with methacholine, no response occurred to this agent in the aganglionic segment (8). This inconsistent response, never observed in normal subjects, suggests that the nervous integration for coordinated propulsion is interrupted in the aganglionic segment and that peristaltic waves cannot be transmitted into this area. Swenson and colleagues

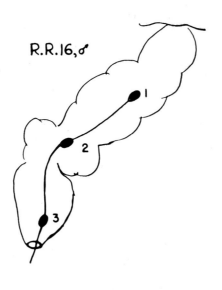

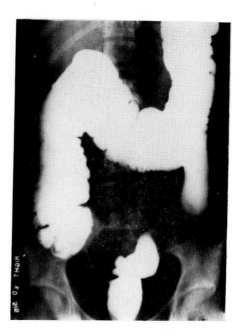

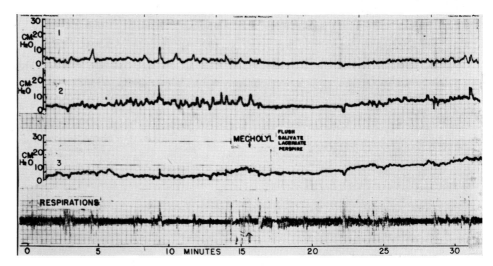

FIG. 6. Postoperative study of patient in Fig. 5. All areas now relax to subcutaneous methacholine. [From Davidson & Bauer (5).]

(26) and others (18, 29) were also unable to observe normal progression of the peristaltic wave into this segment.

Although the segment appears incapable of participating in coordinated propulsion, we have not been impressed that the base-line pressure is higher than that in the dilated segment or than that observed in normal children. Insertion of a sigmoidoscope or finger is not usually met with resistance. From our motility studies we interpret the resting motility of this segment to be normal (8), in agreement with Swenson and co-workers (26). Wright & Shepherd

(27) showed that the resting activity of muscle strips from this segment was normal and indistinguishable from that in strips from control individuals (28) and that the strips demonstrated no hypersensitivity to acetylcholine.

Differences between the spasm theory and the passive concept cannot be resolved by available evidence. Much of one's bias depends on whether cholinergic responses of the colon are seen as resulting solely in propulsion, solely in increases in tone, or in both. We interpret the accumulated observations as indicating that the aganglionic segment is incapable of transmitting the peristaltic wave. The area does not, however, exhibit excessive spasm or active resistance to propulsion.

ACQUIRED AGANGLIONOSIS

Acquired aganglionosis is reported in a number of clinical instances. Chief among these is Chagas' disease, which is caused by *Trypanosoma cruzii* (20, 21). Physiological observations are virtually non-existent, although the clinical symptomatology suggests that these might not be very different from those observed in congenital aganglionosis. Degenerative changes in the ganglia of the colon have also resulted from impairments in the vascular supply to this organ after surgery (2, 10). In other instances, hypoganglionosis has been observed (11). Physiological documentation is equally lacking in these patients.

PSEUDO-HIRSCHSPRUNG'S DISEASE

In another group of patients megacolon has developed secondary to retention of feces within the rectum, but neurohistology of the distal segment is normal (24). Terms such as "pseudo-Hirschsprung's disease" and "idiopathic megacolon" have been applied to such patients (7, 23, 25). We have studied a number of these patients and have found that the colonic motility was entirely normal. We have also described three youngsters with normal ganglia distally but with a somewhat different clinical picture, and have performed motility studies in them before and after surgery (5, 8). Although we were unable to explain the findings, except as possibly related to nervous system abnormalities which are located more centrally than in the myenteric plexuses of the colon, the physiological findings were similar to those in children with congenital aganglionosis. Figure 5, a preoperative tracing in one of these youngsters, demonstrates that before surgery the achalasic segment did not respond to subcutaneous methacholine chloride injections, whereas the more proximal bowel did. After surgery, which consisted of resection of the achalasic area, there was relaxation of all segments after injection of the parasympathomimetic agent, as shown in Figure 6. This is the response observed after resection of the aganglionic segment in congenital Hirschsprung's disease.

REFERENCES

1. ALMY, T. P., AND M. TULIN. Alterations in colonic function in man under stress: experimental production of changes simulating the "irritable colon." *Gastroenterology* 8: 616–626, 1947.
2. BENTLEY, J. F. R., H. H. NIXON, T. EHRENPREIS, B. SPENCER, J. LISTER, B. DUHAMEL, R. PAGES, AND A. KATZ. Seminar on pseudo-Hirschsprung's disease and related disorders. *Arch. Disease Childhood* 41: 143–154, 1966.
3. BODIAN, M., F. O. STEPHENS, AND B. C. H. WARD. Hirschsprung's disease and idiopathic megacolon. *Lancet* 1: 6–11, 1949.
4. CODE, C. F., N. C. HIGHTOWER, AND C. G. MORLOCK. Motility of the alimentary canal in man; review of recent studies. *Am. J. Med.* 13: 328–351, 1952.
5. DAVIDSON, M., AND C. H. BAUER. Studies of distal colonic motility in children. IV. Achalasia of the distal rectal segment despite presence of ganglia in the myenteric plexuses of this area. *Pediatrics* 21: 746–761, 1958.
6. DAVIDSON, M., M. H. SLEISENGER, T. P. ALMY, AND S. Z. LEVINE. Studies of distal colonic motility in children. I. Non-propulsive patterns in normal children. *Pediatrics* 17: 807–819, 1956.
7. DAVIDSON, M., M. H. SLEISENGER, T. P. ALMY, AND S. Z. LEVINE. Studies of distal colonic motility in children. II. Propulsive activity in diarrheal states. *Pediatrics* 17: 820–833, 1956.
8. DAVIDSON, M., M. H. SLEISENGER, H. STEINBERG, AND T.

P. ALMY. Studies of distal colonic motility in children. III. The pathologic physiology of congenital megacolon (Hirschsprung's disease). *Gastroenterology* 29: 803–823, 1955.
9. EHRENPREIS, T. Megacolon in the newborn; a clinical and roentgenological study with special regard to the pathogensis. *Acta Chir. Scand.* 94: Suppl. 112, 114, 1946.
10. EHRENPREIS, T. Acquired megacolon as a complication of of rectosigmoidectomy for Hirschsprung's disease. *Arch. Disease Childhood* 40: 180–185, 1965.
11. EHRENPREIS, T. Some newer aspects on Hirschsprung's disease and allied disorders. *J. Pediat. Surg.* 1: 329–337, 1966.
12. EHRENPREIS, T., AND B. PERNOW. On the occurrence of substance P in the rectosigmoid in Hirschsprung's disease. *Acta Physiol. Scand.* 27: 380–388, 1952.
13. EULER, U. S. VON. Untersuchungen über Substanz P, die atropinfeste darmerregende und gefasserweiternde Substanz aus Darm und Gehirn. *Arch. Exptl. Pathol. Pharmakol.* 181: 181–197, 1936.
14. HIATT, R. B. The pathologic physiology of congenital megacolon. *Ann. Surg.* 133: 313–320, 1951.
15. HIATT, R. B. The surgical treatment of congenital megacolon. *Ann. Surg.* 133: 321–329, 1951.
16. JORUP, S. Colonic hyperperistalsis in neurolabile infants, studies in so-called dyspepsia in breast-fed infants. *Acta Paediat.* 41: Suppl. 85, 110, 1952.
17. KAMIJO, K., R. B. HIATT, AND G. B. KOELLE. Congenital

megacolon. A comparison of the spastic and hypertrophied segments with respect to cholinesterase activities and sensitivities to acetylcholine, DFP and the barium ion. *Gastroenterology* 24: 173–185, 1953.

18. KEEFER, G. P., AND J. F. MOKROHISKY. Congenital megacolon (Hirschsprung's disease). *Radiology* 63: 157–174, 1954.

19. KERN, F., JR., AND T. P. ALMY. The effects of acetylcholine and methacholine upon the human colon. *J. Clin. Invest.* 31: 555–560, 1952.

20. KÖBERLE, F. Die Chagaskrankheit; eine Erkrankung der neurovegetativen Peripherie. *Wien. Klin. Wochschr.* 68: 333–339, 1956.

21. KÖBERLE, F. Megacolon. *J. Trop. Med. Hyg.* 61: 21–24, 1958.

22. LEE, C. M., JR., AND K. C. BEBB. The pathogenesis and clinical management of megacolon with emphasis on the fallacy of the term "idiopathic." *Surgery* 30: 1026–1048, 1951.

23. NORBERG, K. A. Adrenergic innervation of the intestinal wall studied by fluorescence microscopy. *Intern. J. Neuropharmacol.* 3: 379–382, 1964.

24. RAVITCH, M. M. Pseudo-Hirschsprung's disease. *Ann. Surg.* 147: 781–795, 1958.

25. SWENSON, O., E. B. D. NEUHAUSER, AND L. K. PICKETT. New concepts of the etiology, diagnosis and treatment of congenital megacolon (Hirschsprung's disease). *Pediatrics* 4: 201–209, 1949.

26. SWENSON, O., H. F. RHEINLANDER, AND I. DIAMOND. Hirschsprung's disease: new concept of etiology. Operative results in 34 patients. *N. Engl. J. Med.* 241: 551–556, 1949.

26a. VON EULER, U. S. see EULER, U. S. VON (13).

27. WRIGHT, P. G., AND J. J. SHEPHERD. Response to drugs of isolated human colonic muscle from a case of Hirschsprung's disease. *Lancet* 2: 1161–1164, 1965.

28. WRIGHT, P. G., AND J. J. SHEPHERD. Some observations on the response of normal human sigmoid colon to drugs in vitro. *Gut.* 7: 41–51, 1966.

29. ZUELZER, W. W., AND J. L. WILSON. Functional intestinal obstruction on a congenital neurogenic basis in infancy. *Am. J. Disease Childhood* 75: 40–64, 1948.

CHAPTER 135

Gastric secretion in the lower vertebrates and birds

H. SMIT | *Zoology Laboratory, University of Leiden, Leiden, The Netherlands*

CHAPTER CONTENTS

LITTLE ATTENTION has been paid to the secretion of gastric juice in lower vertebrates and birds. Compared with those in mammals, physiological studies on the rate and control of gastric secretion in lower vertebrates are rare. Regulation is complex; the controlling mechanisms are hormonal, nervous, and vascular and are activated by widely differing stimuli (visual, psychic, chemical, mechanical) originating from various sites (the senses, mouth, stomach, intestine). One aspect is specific for the lower vertebrates: their inconstant body temperature, which forms an important controlling factor for secretory and digestive rates. Knowledge of these mechanisms

and their interaction in lower vertebrates and birds is fragmentary.

This review gives limited attention to the anatomy and histology of the stomach. Such practical features as digestibility and caloric value of food and its conversion into live material are not considered. Attention is focused on the composition of gastric juice, the rate of digestion, and secretory control. Hopefully comparisons with gastric secretion in mammals will aid interpretation of the scattered data on the secretory processes in nonmammalian vertebrates. These processes are interesting from an evolutionary point of view, but many gaps in knowledge must be closed before a survey of the evolution of digestive control in vertebrates can be drafted. This article indicates the points between the gaps.

MORPHOLOGY AND HISTOLOGY

The stomach is a storage place where food is subjected to the initial stage of digestion. A true stomach always has gastric juice glands and can be closed by a sphincter at its caudal end. If a stomach is lacking, as in some fishes, the anterior part of the intestine is wider, thus compensating for the loss of the storage capacity of a stomach.

The stomach wall has several layers: *1*) the mucosa, containing the gastric glands, lined by an epithelium; *2*) the submucosa, consisting of connective tissue; *3*) the muscularis, normally consisting of two layers, one circular, the other longitudinal; *4*) the serosa, lining the outer surface. Usually there is a thin muscular layer between the mucosa and submucosa, the muscularis mucosae. Nerve plexuses are situated in the submucosa (submucous plexus) and in the muscularis (myenteric plexus).

In the mammalian gastric gland, pepsin is secreted by the chief cells of the glandular body and acid is produced by the parietal cells. The gastric glands of nonmammalian vertebrates contain one form of granulated cell that is considered to be functionally homologous with both the chief and the parietal cells of mammals. In certain amphibians, gastric acid and pepsinogen are secreted by separate glands. In the neck region of the vertebrate gastric gland are special mucous neck cells, which are lacking in many fishes.

The primary function of the stomach, which becomes evident with the introduction of macrophagous feeding, is that of a food container; the digestive function is acquired secondarily (6). In certain stomachless fishes (e.g., Cyprinidae and Labridae), the absence of gastric glands must be secondary. The stomach of most birds has become differentiated into two parts; the pyloric part has been modified into the muscular gizzard, which has a special grinding function. Gizzard-like stomachs have also evolved in crocodiles and in some fishes (*Mugil, Mormyrus*). The three functions of the stomach—storage, chemical digestion, and mechanical action (digestion)—can be distinguished even in the simple tubiform stomach. Stomachs with a narrow lumen normally have an elastic wall; in other types of stomachs, especially in some fishes, a well-developed blind sac (cecum) supplies a large storage space. In birds the storage function may be partly shifted to the crop (Galliformes, Columbiformes, marabou); it may be confined mostly to the glandular stomach (Psittacidae, Struthionidae, Procellaria), or to the muscular stomach (Phalacrocoracidae, Ciconiidae, Strigidae). The mechanical function is performed by the pyloric part, which can be strikingly well developed in animals in which the stomach has apparently taken over the masticatory function otherwise accomplished by the jaws (some fishes, crocodiles, most birds). In other cases the mechanical digestion is poorly developed, the initial digestion being mainly chemical (amphibians, ophidians, saurians, most fishes, and some birds).

In fishes the stomach is often curved, so both the gastroesophageal junction and the pyloric region are anterior. The stomachal corpus forms a saclike organ that in some fishes extends backward as a cecum. In other species the stomach is spindle shaped (e.g., pike). The cylindrical epithelium of the stomach contains cells that secrete mucus, which forms a lining of the inner surface of the stomach and is supposed to protect the mucosa against mechanical and chemical damage. The glands secreting gastric juice are tubular, simple or branched, and consist of two regions (10). The neck region is lined by surface epithelial cells, although in some fishes neck cells comparable to the mammalian mucoid neck cells have been described (19). The body region contains granular cells, thought to secrete both acid and pepsin. The gastric glands are confined mainly to the corpus, though the chief glands sometimes extend into the pyloric region (*Pleuronectes, Salmo*). The pyloric glands have no granulated cells.

In amphibians the slender stomach is straight or slightly curved. It has a relatively thin elastic wall, allowing rather big lumps of food to be swallowed. When empty the gastric lumen is quite narrow. The epithelial lining of the stomach contains many mucogenic cells. The chief glands of the corpus possess granulated cells and distinct mucoid neck cells. The digestive glands of *Rana* are in the lower esophagus and in the corpus and pylorus. The esophageal glands secrete pepsinogen (56, 93). Zymogenic cells are lacking in the pyloric glands. The esophageal and corpus glands can be considered as gastric chief glands, the frontal and caudal glands secreting mainly pepsinogen and acid, respectively (59). Norris (73) distinguished four zones in the foregut of *Rana pipiens*: *1*) esophagus; *2*) forestomach, a zone approximately 5 mm long located just caudal of the esophagogastric junction, in which the compound tubuloacinous glands of the esophagus change into the simple or branched tubulous glands of the corpus; *3*) the corpus; and *4*) the pyloric portion, in which the glands are shorter. The zymogenic cell is only found in the esophagus and forestomach; a cell with finely granular eosinophilic cytoplasm and resembling the parietal cell of mammals occurs only in the fundic and pyloric regions. Stomachal and esophageal glands are also distinguishable by histochemical methods. The chief cells of the esophageal glands contain much more tryptophan than those of the corpus glands. Tryptophan indicates the presence of pepsin (85). Apparently, in the frog as in some other anurans and urodeles, the glands secreting enzyme and those secreting acid are separated spatially. All glands possess mucoid neck cells.

In reptiles with an elongated body the stomach is usually a straight tube but is sometimes slightly curved at the pyloric end. Tortoise and turtle stomachs have a more compact shape or are strongly bent,

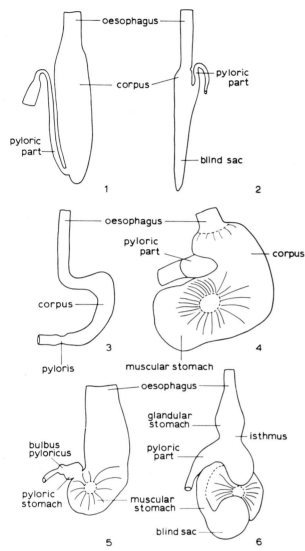

FIG. 1. Examples of stomachs. *1:* Dogfish (*Mustelus laevis*). *2:* Eel (*Anguilla vulgaris*). *3:* Pond turtle (*Emys* sp.). *4:* Alligator *mississipiensis*. *5:* Grey heron (*Ardea cinerea*). *6:* Peacock (*Pavo cristatus*). [Modified from Pernkopf & Lehner (77).]

so that the pyloric part curves to the right and proximally. The gastric apparatus of crocodiles has a strongly developed muscularis, the pyloric part forming a sort of gizzard. As in many birds, the mechanical digestion of food is accomplished in crocodiles through pebbles present in the pyloric cecum.

The gastric mucosa of saurians and ophidians contains simple tubular glands resembling those of fishes and amphibians. Chelonians possess branched corpus glands similar to the glands of the avian glandular stomach. In lizards, cells of the gastric glands other than those producing mucus contain

granules similar in appearance and staining properties to those of the chief cells of the mammalian stomach. No parietal oxyntic cells are recognizable. After secretion, great depletion of the granules of the chief cells can be seen. These cells supposedly secrete both HCl and pepsin (105).

The bird's stomach is more highly differentiated than that of lower vertebrates. In most cases the pyloric part has developed into a distinct muscular stomach (gizzard). Usually a transitory zone (isthmus) is present between the gizzard and the anterior part of the gastric apparatus (glandular stomach or proventriculus), which contains the chief glands. Also, some fish-eating birds have a pyloric stomach (Ciconiidae, Ardeidae, Podicepedidae, Anatidae) (Fig. 1). There is some correlation between the type of food and the development of the gizzard. Carnivorous species normally have a thin-walled gizzard; graminivorous birds have a highly developed muscular stomach. The compound gastric glands of the proventriculus are tubular. There is much variation in the arrangement of glandular elements with regard to the collecting-duct system and also in the distribution of the glands (29). The proventricular glands produce the gastric juice. The granulated cells of the secretory elements secrete both acid and pepsin. The pyloric glands secrete a product that forms a thin elastic coating over the inner surface of the gizzard in carnivorous birds. Cormorants frequently push off the inner lining of their gizzards to envelop the undigested remains of the food; after rejection of this pellet a new lining is formed (21). In graminivorous birds the pyloric glands supply the hard keratinoid lining of the muscular stomach (24).

More detailed information on morphology and physiology of the alimentary tract is given by Barrington (8) for fishes, Reeder (80) for amphibians, Wettstein (104) and Lüdicke (58) for reptiles, and Farner (29) for birds. Comprehensive descriptions of the morphology and histology of vertebrate stomachs are given by Oppel (75), Pernkopf & Lehner (77), and Slijper (87).

INNERVATION

Elasmobranchs possess a well-developed autonomic system containing parasympathetic and sympathetic elements. The abdominal organs are sympathetically innervated by the anterior, median, and posterior splanchnic nerves; parasympathetic innervation is almost entirely confined to the organs in the head

(107). The stomach is the only abdominal organ having a double autonomic innervation—by the right vagus branch and the anterior splanchnicus (67). The functional antagonism between the sympathetic and parasympathetic systems found in mammals appears to be absent in elasmobranchs; both vagal and splanchnic stimulation excite stomachal motility (4, 5), which is also enhanced by acetylcholine and adrenaline (66). A direct nervous influence on gastric secretion has not been demonstrated, though there is some evidence that acetylcholine stimulates secretion in elasmobranchs (95).

In the digestive tract of teleosts the stomach is the only organ that possesses a double innervation. Both the vagus and the sympathetic system are motor to the stomach. No antagonism between vagal and sympathetic fibers has been found; pharmacologically and physiologically, the visceral motor nerves cannot easily be divided into sympathetic and parasympathetic systems (108).

In amphibians, too, the stomach is doubly innervated. Parasympathetic fibers are supplied by the stomachal branches of the intestinal vagal trunk; sympathetic fibers to the stomach run via the splanchnic nerve (9, 23, 57). Some authors have studied the regulating influences of the extrinsic nerve supply on the motility of esophagus and stomach in frogs (1, 12, 15, 20, 31, 38, 44, 46, 76, 84, 109). Nervous control of gastric motility has been investigated by means of vagal or sympathetic stimulation, vagotomy or sympathectomy, and administration of atropine or adrenaline. Results indicate that the vagus has a stimulatory effect on stomachal motility, but the sympathetic is not always inhibitory. There is no distinct antagonism between vagal and splanchnic activities in the stomach. The tone of the plain musculature is governed chiefly by the intrinsic nerve plexuses, which are thought to cause the automatic stomachal contractions, although motility control is partly extrinsic. The intramural plexuses are situated in the submucosa and muscularis (75, 40); they also play a role in the control of secretion (90).

The gastric apparatus of birds is innervated by sympathetic and parasympathetic fibers. Antagonism between the actions of vagal and celiac nerves on gastric motility has not been demonstrated; both vagotomy and celiacotomy reduce the frequency and magnitude of the stomachal contractions; stimulation of the celiac nerves may reduce or enhance the gastric movements (69, 70). The extrinsically denervated chicken gizzard shows automatic contractions generated by the intramural nerve plexus. The glandular stomach and the gizzard have the same frequency of automatic contractions. The rhythm of the proventricular contractions is controlled by nerve fibers originating in the gizzard and passing through the isthmus. There is evidence that the intramural neurons are partly of vagal and partly of sympathetic origin. Gastric motility is also liable to central influences via vagus and splanchnic nerves. The parasympathetic system also plays a role in the control of secretion of pepsin (33) and acid (26).

GASTRIC JUICE

Gastric Acid

Secretion of gastric acid is common to almost all vertebrates. The secretion acidifies the gastric contents, thus promoting the proteolytic action of pepsin. Furthermore, the acid juice kills bacteria and sometimes prey and dissolves calcareous skeletons.

Elasmobranchs have a strongly acid secretion. Sullivan (92) found that the gastric acidity is greatest in sharks and rays when the stomach is filled with partly digested crustaceans. After feeding, total HCl reaches a concentration of 1 % (= 274 mN). The fasting stomach is practically neutral, although the high acidity may be maintained for several days after emptying of the stomach (22). In the bullhead (*Ictalurus*), titration values up to 280 mN HCl have been obtained with pure gastric juice (91). Amphibians also have a good acid production in the stomach. Gastric juice of frogs may have pH values as low as 1.2 (106) or 1.5 (78) and acidity values of 150 mN (89). The pH values of gastric juice of *Necturus* range from 1.0 to 3.5 (34). Lizards and tortoises with vegetable material in their stomachs had a gastric fluid at pH 1.5–2; histamine-stimulated gastric juice of these animals had a pH of 1–2 (105). The pH of avian gastric juice can also be 1–2 (21, 28).

With respect to the acidification of gastric contents, the rate of secretion is more important than the acidity of the secretion. The food often has a strong neutralizing capacity, so that relatively large quantities of gastric juice are needed to acidify the chyme in order to obtain intensive peptic action. The rate of secretion depends greatly on the type of secretory stimulus.

Enzymes

OCCURRENCE OF PEPSIN. A protease with optimum activity at a low pH value is found only in vertebrates and in them its occurrence is the rule, stomachless fishes being the only exception. Pepsin has been found in mucosal extracts and gastric juice of elasmobranchs (4, 11, 22, 92), teleosts (14, 50, 61, 64, 81, 97, 99), amphibians (18, 30, 32, 34, 56, 90, 93), reptiles (48, 56, 105), and birds (33, 41, 43, 61, 86). Pepsin is secreted only in the corpus of the stomach, not in the pyloric part. In several amphibians (*Proteus, Necturus, Rana, Bufo, Pelobates, Triton*) and in *Testudo*, pepsin is secreted mainly by the esophageal glands. Larval anurans lack a true stomach; however, larval urodeles possess a stomach in which pepsin digestion takes place (54). Pepsin does not appear in anurans until the hindlegs develop (7). In stomachless fishes the proteolytic activity is performed by trypsin and "erepsin" (2, 45, 81). Pepsin secretion in birds occurs in the proventriculus (glandular stomach), although the acid proteolytic action may occur mainly in the gizzard.

FACTORS INFLUENCING PEPTIC ACTIVITY. Vonk (96) measured the peptic activity of gastric mucosal extract of *Acanthias* and found an optimum at pH 2.2–2.5 for carmine fibrin as a substrate at a temperature of 18 C. The pH optima of pepsin of *Acanthias*, pike, perch, frog, tortoise, heron, and swine, acting on fibrin, differ but slightly and lie close to pH 2 (61, 97). In enzymatic measurements, the situation of the pH optimum is influenced by the nature and concentration of the substrate, the concentrations of enzyme and electrolytes, the temperature, and the incubation time. For gelatin an optimum at pH 3 has been found for fish pepsin (11); for egg white, the optimum peptic activity of *Rana* lies between pH 1.0 and 1.4 (78). Comparison of the results obtained by various authors is often difficult because experimental conditions differed. In the enzyme-substrate mixture, two factors affecting enzymatic activity are in opposition: at increasing temperature there are 1) an increase of enzyme-reaction velocity and 2) increasing inactivation of the enzyme due to denaturation of the enzymatic protein. The rate of denaturation is dependent on time. The duration also influences the reaction velocity because at long duration the high concentration of reaction products inhibits the velocity. Thus the shape and situation of the activity curve depend on the duration

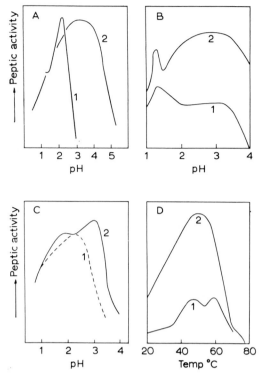

FIG. 2. *A: 1*, peptic activity of gastric mucosa extract of pike (*Esox*). Substrate fibrin; digestion time: 30 min at room temperature. [After Vonk (97).] *2*, pH activity curve of gastric juice of bullhead (*Ictalurus*). Substrate edestin; digestion at 40 C for 10 min. *B:* activity of crystalline salmon (*Oncorhynchus*) pepsin—*1*, in a salt-free medium; *2*, in the presence of 0.1 M NaCl. Substrate hemoglobin; 10-min incubation at 25 C. [After Norris & Elam (71).] *C:* peptic activity of gastric mucosa extract of pig—*1*, substrate horse serum; *2*, substrate edestin. Incubation temperature 40 C. [After Geilenkirchen & Elbers (35).] *D:* peptic activity of gastric mucosa extract of trout (*Salmo trutta fario*). Substrate edestin, pH 3.6. Incubation time: *1*, 1 min; *2*, 5 min. [After Buchs (14).]

of the experiment. Using short incubation periods Buchs (14) obtained an activity curve showing two peaks for the gastric protease of trout. For human gastric juice these two peaks are situated at pH 2.2 and 3.5 for edestin. Such double-peaked curves were also found for fish pepsin [(71); Fig. 2]. The occurrence and situation of the peaks depend on the incubation temperature and kind of substrate. High temperatures shift the peaks to higher pH values or a single-peak curve emerges (35).

COMPARISON WITH MAMMALIAN PEPSIN. The pepsins of lower vertebrates strongly resemble those of mammals with respect to the pH and temperature dependency of the proteolytic activity. The pepsins of all vertebrates have their optimum activity at pH values in the vicinity of 2 (depending on the nature of the substrate). Although exact values of optimum temperatures for peptic activity cannot be given because the optima are so strongly related to experimental conditions, it has nevertheless been found that there are no major differences in this respect between pepsins of poikilotherms and those of homeotherms. Another point of comparison is the thermostability of the enzyme. For example, pike pepsin is more thermolabile than canine pepsin; the gastric protease of frogs is less stable than human pepsin when compared at 50 C; the pepsin of *Testudo* has a thermostability equal to that of mammalian pepsin. On the other hand, fish pepsin has a greater activity at low temperatures than that of homeotherms (61). Comparative studies of enzymatic heat resistance would probably reveal differences between poikilotherm and homeotherm pepsin. Other differences are possibly produced or obscured by the choice of substrate. Differences might be found by a comparative study of enzyme specificity. In this connection, knowledge of the specific activity of the enzyme is important. In such studies, not only reaction velocities but also the quantities of pure pepsin must be measured; if the exact quantity is not known, only the specific activity of the preparation containing the enzyme would be measured. Useful comparisons can be made from experiments using crystalline pepsin (74). For example, synthetic peptides, which are hydrolyzed by mammalian pepsin, are not digested by crystalline salmon pepsin; tuna pepsin has a greater alkali stability and a lower inactivation temperature than swine pepsin (71, 72); chicken pepsin is much less sensitive to alkali than swine pepsin (42). There is also an immunological difference between the pepsins of swine and those of chicken. Swine and bovine pepsins precipitate in swine pepsin antiserum; chicken and shark pepsins do not (86). Differences in structure and configuration between the pepsin molecules of different species are also to be expected. If what occurs with proteins in general also holds for pepsins, pepsin too would exhibit species specificity. Herriott observed that activation of swine pepsinogen with chicken pepsin results in the formation of swine pepsin, and activation of chicken pepsinogen with swine pepsin results in the formation of chicken pepsin. The structure responsible for the species specificity of the enzyme is therefore present in the inactive precursor.

OTHER ENZYMES. Kenyon (50) found a very low amylase activity (tested on starch) in stomach mucosal extracts of pike (*Esox lucius*) and crappie (*Pomoxis sparoides*), bull snake (*Pituophis catenifer sayi*), and snapping turtle (*Chelydra serpentina*). Extracts of the stomach of the eelpout (*Zoarces anguillaris*) possess a strong lipase (60). Gastric juice of cod contains two proteolytic enzymes showing optimum activities at pH 5 and 9, as determined on agar-skim milk substrate. A gastric mucosa extract treated in slightly acid conditions shows only one active principle the optimum pH of which is 5 (55). Activity at pH 9 is probably caused by regurgitated duodenal contents.

In several fishes (herring, trout, eel, European eelpout), good proteolytic action of the gastric juice has been found at pH 4.2 (13). Several authors obtained double-peaked curves when the proteolytic activity of the gastric protease was plotted against pH. Norris et al. (71, 72) found two pH optima for salmon and tuna protease; such double-peaked curves have also been obtained for swine pepsin (35) and human pepsin (14, 94). Some authors consider the second peak to depend on the buffer concentration and the nature of the substrate. As a matter of fact, the shape of the curve depends on the kind of substrate. Another concept is that the proteolytic activity of the gastric protease between pH 3 and 5 is caused by cathepsin (gastricsin).

The occurrence of "catheptic" activity in the gastric juice of some fishes suggests that proteolytic activity at about pH 4 might also be present in the gastric juice of other nonmammalian vertebrates. If so, the digestion rate in general would be less dependent on the pH of the chyme, proteolytic digestion taking place through a wide pH range, from 1 to 5.

GASTRIC DIGESTION

pH of Chyme

Adequate (chemical and mechanical) secretory stimuli are generally initiated from swallowed food. However, not only the quantities of acid and enzyme but also their interrelated activity must be taken into account. In the chyme a gastric juice of high acidity and low pepsin content may have a high digestive ability because the pH is favorable for enzymatic action. On the other hand, the unfavorable pH of a gastric juice of low acidity may be offset by a high pepsin concentration. Since the proteolytic activity of pepsin depends on pH, the concentrations of enzyme and substrate, and the nature of the substrate, it is clear that the amount and kind of food and the amounts of acid and pepsin in the gastric juice will influence the velocity of gastric digestion and emptying time. In addition, body temperature, duration of the sojourn of food in the stomach, and stomachal motility influence digestive activity.

During prolonged presence of food in the stomach and continued acid secretion, the pH will gradually diminish. In a number of carnivorous animals such as the pike, which swallow big pieces of food, digestion first attacks the outer layer of the food, bringing its pH down to a low value, whereas in the deeper layers the pH is much higher. Thus digestion gradually proceeds inward, only the superficial layer of the contents of the stomach having a pH favorable for enzymatic action. Once this layer has been digested and liquefied, it is transported to the pylorus by the stomachal movements, and the mixture of pepsin and acid exerts its action on the following layer.

In sharks the food is exposed to large amounts of strongly acid gastric juice in which the quantity of pepsin is relatively small. There is evidence that in animals that secrete small quantities of pepsin, much acid can be found, and vice versa (99). In frogs and snakes a better accordance exists between the optimum pH for pepsin action and the lowest pH in the chyme. In the frog, pepsin is secreted in the lower part of the esophagus, whereas acid is mainly secreted in the pyloric part. In the cardiac part of the stomach the chyme contains a relatively large amount of pepsin, but an alkaline reaction prevails. In the pyloric part the food is acidified and kneaded; that is, it is chemically and mechanically digested (39). In the stomachs of garter snakes (*Thamnophis sirtalis*) that had swallowed frogs 1–3 hours before being opened, a region of high acidity was observed around the frog (50). In the chyme of carnivorous birds (heron, falcon, owl) Mennega (61) measured pH values higher than 3.5, which is beyond the pH optimum for peptic activity. In a cormorant, van Dobben (21) found a pH of 4.6 in the liquefied chyme 3 hours after feeding a fish meal. The intensive gastric digestion in these animals may be explained by their high body temperature and by the fact that the food, to which pepsin is added in the proventriculus, is kneaded in the gizzard. Thus the muscular stomach functions as a site of peptic digestion. Values as low as pH 0.9 have been found in the muscular stomach of the cormorant. This relates to almost pure gastric secretion, sampled about half an hour after feeding a piece of fish (21). In the gizzard of omnivorous birds, relatively low pH values have

also been observed. Farner (27) reports the following pH values: domestic fowl, 2.14; turkey, 2.19; pheasant, 2.06; pigeon, 2.00; duck, 2.33.

Influence of Temperature on Rate of Digestion

In cold-blooded animals the digestive rate is substantially affected by the environmental temperature. Joly (47) measured the emptying time of the stomachs of newts (*Triturus helveticus*) fed with small crickets. At 15 C the stomachs were empty after 2 days, at 10 C after 4 days, and at 3 C emptying time was 6 days. Scheuring (82) assessed the rate of digestion by measuring the difference in time between food intake and defecation in the pond loach (*Misgurnus fossilis*). He found a semilog relationship between temperature and digestive time (in hours) as follows: 7 C, 36–46; 8 C, 35; 10 C, 25–35; 14 C, 20; 19 C, 8–12; 20 C, 7–10. A semilog relationship has also been demonstrated between the temperature and the rate of gastric digestion in large-mouth bass (*Micropterus salmoides*) (62). The rate of digestion in four predatory fish species (*Lucioperca l.*; *Micropterus salmoides*; *Silurus glanis*; *Perca fluviatilis*) appeared to be 5–10 times faster at 25 C than at 5 C (Fig. 3). This was established using an X-ray method to observe the rate of stomach emptying (25, 63). The relative effect of temperature on the digestion rate is approximately the same for the four species. If the data from Figure 3 are positioned in an Arrhenius plot, straight lines are obtained, from which Fábián et al. (25) calculated the activation energy. It may be assumed that temperature effects on the emptying rate of the stomach are the result of at least three temperature-dependent processes: *1*) rate of secretion of gastric juice, *2*) peptic activity in the chyme, and *3*) gastric motility. Therefore the measurement of rates of gastric digestion cannot be considered an adequate method for investigating enzyme kinetics.

In these experiments test temperatures were identical with acclimation temperatures. Nicholls (65, 66), investigating temperature dependency of digestion rate in killifish (*Fundulus heteroclitus*), obtained a bipartite rate-temperature curve, the two parts having different slopes. His experimental fish were transferred from an intermediate temperature to the lower or higher temperatures immediately before the experiment. Only if experiments were to be carried out at intermediate temperatures were the fish left at their acclimation temperature. Thus high test temperatures were above acclimation level and low test temperatures were below acclimation level. This probably

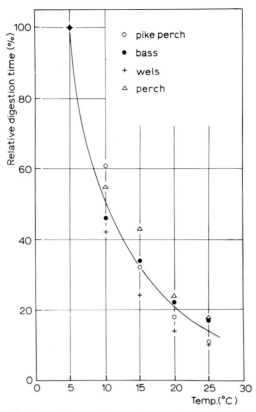

FIG. 3. Relation between temperature and rate of gastric digestion in four predatory fish species (*Lucioperca l.*; *Micropterus salmoides*; *Silurus glanis*; *Perca fluviatilis*). Gastric emptying times at various temperatures are expressed as percent of the 5 C values. [After Fábián et al. (25).]

means that at high and low test temperatures the estimations of digestion rates were too high and too low, respectively. It should be pointed out that in physiological experiments on poikilotherms, not only test temperatures but also acclimation temperatures should be considered.

A rise of body temperature causing an increase of metabolic rate in poikilotherms probably also causes an increased digestion rate. Fast-swimming big fishes such as tunas (Thunnidae), marlins (Istiophoridae), and swordfishes (Xiphiidae), which inhabit warm surface layers, may have body temperatures more than 10 C above ambient temperature owing to their enormous muscular activity, thus approaching the temperature of warm-blooded animals. Reptiles, with their behavioral temperature regulation, may also reach high body temperatures while basking in the sun. Metabolism of the poikilotherm exhibits a distinct temperature adaptation; that is, cold-adapted animals have a higher metabolic rate than warm-adapted animals when both are measured at an intermediate

temperature (79, 83). It is not known whether such an adaptation holds for digestion, but it is suggested that the influence of temperature on digestion rate also depends on the acclimation temperature; that is, the digestion rate might exhibit the phenomenon of temperature adaptation. Evidence for this is offered by the influence of acclimation temperature on gastric-juice secretory rate in *Ictalurus* (see following section).

REGULATION OF GASTRIC JUICE SECRETION

Since secretion of gastric juice is not a continuous process, there must be some mechanism by which it is regulated. Much information about this regulatory mechanism has been collected from mammals. For lower vertebrates, however, knowledge is scanty and scattered.

Elasmobranchs

Almost nothing is known about the mechanism by which gastric secretion in elasmobranchs is regulated. That regulation does exist is indicated by the observations of Sullivan (92), who found the highest acidity in the stomach of the shark when it was filled with partly digested food, whereas the contents of a fasting stomach had a virtually neutral pH. Dobreff (22), on the contrary, found a continuous acid secretion in *Scylliorhinus* and was unable to influence this secretion by means of pilocarpine, acetylcholine, histamine, or atropine. Because he did not succeed in finding any nervous control, Dobreff supposed the gastric secretion to be humorally regulated, since the presence of food in the stomach increased the acidity. Babkin et al. (3, 5) worked with anesthetized rays (*Raja* sp.) in some of which the spinal cord was transected. These animals showed a continuous secretion that could be neither inhibited by vagotomy or atropine injection nor enhanced by distention of the stomach, stimulation of the splanchnic nerves, or administration of adrenaline and histamine. Babkin et al. (3, 5) elicited a "paralytic" secretion by interrupting the connections between the sympathetic system and spinal cord. Since adrenaline, a vasoconstrictor, prevented this secretion, they thought vasodilation would stimulate it, assuming secretion in elasmobranchs to be under vascular or hormonal control. Ungar (95), working with perfused stomachs of sharks (*Squalus* and *Scilliorhinus*) and rays (*Torpedo*), found that histamine and acetylcholine stimulated secretion. The histamine-stimulated secretion could not be inhibited by atropine, whereas the ACh-stimulation was blocked by atropine. The observations of Babkin et al. suggest that vascular influences affect secretion in elasmobranchs. If circulatory adjustments in these fishes are able to exert a strong influence on the gastric secretory rate, which is not at all improbable, anesthetizing the animals or sectioning of the spinal cord or even mere handling of the fish may cause inhibition of secretion to such extent that the effects of other secretory influences are obscured. In Ungar's experiments with perfused stomachs, these influences exerted by histamine and acetylcholine became demonstrable, and they probably can also be shown in intact conscious animals if drugs are applied in adequate doses and care is taken to avoid strong circulatory reactions. Ungar's results show that the gastric nerve plexus plays a role in the secretory control of selachians. No clear demonstration has been made of hormonal control of gastric secretion in elasmobranchs.

Teleosts

There is evidence that gastric secretion in teleosts is under nervous and hormonal control. Krayukhin (53) found in the bullhead (*Ictalurus nebulosus*) that the act of swallowing is accompanied by a copious flow of gastric juice, and he considers this secretion to be evoked by an unconditioned reflex. A conditioned-reflex secretion has also been observed by means of the fistula method (52). The rate of food digestion in the burbot (*Lota l.*) was greatly reduced by vagotomy, indicating that the vagus nerve plays a role in the regulation of secretion of gastric juice (37). Krayukhin (52) observed that digestion of voluminous meals was more intensive than that of smaller ones, and he suggests that the secretory rate was influenced by mechanical stimulation of the stomach wall. The secretory rate also depended on the kind of food introduced through a gastric fistula. These observations indicate that fishes have a cephalic phase and a chemical phase, the first mediated by the vagus nerve, the latter possibly being hormonal. The intrinsic nerves of the stomach may also play a part in the control of secretion. (These Russian publications are known to the author only from summaries in English.)

In the discussion of the influence of temperature on digestion rate, mention was made of the finding of a semilog relationship between rate of gastric digestion in fish and temperature, resulting from the interplay of secretory rate, peptic activity, and gastric motility, which are temperature-dependent processes. A semilog relationship between temperature and the rate of

TABLE 1. *Acid Secretion in Bullhead*

Accl. Temp., °C	Exptl. Temp., °C	Secretory Rate, mEq HCl/hr
20	25	1.05±0.18
25	25	0.81±0.11
30	25	0.30±0.10

34 Experiments; mean body weight 384 g.

gastric acid secretion has also been demonstrated in the bullhead through the range 10–25 C (91). For the burbot Gomazkov (36) has established that at low temperatures decreased enzymatic activity is compensated for by an increased secretory rate. Digestion is most intensive at intermediate temperatures, and it decreases at both higher and lower temperatures. A temperature optimum has also been found for the rate of acid secretion in the bullhead (*Ictalurus nebulosus*), in which the highest secretory rate has been observed at 25 C, the rates at 20 and 30 C being about one-third of that at 25 C (91). The maximum rate (at 25 C), however, depends on the acclimation temperature (Table 1).

Since the fishes acclimated at 20 C show a higher rate of acid secretion than the 30-C fishes when both are measured at the intermediate temperature, the bullhead apparently compensates for temperature changes as far as the rate of gastric acid secretion at the optimal temperature is concerned.

Frogs

Langley (56) observed a substantial decrease in the number of secretory granules in the gastric glands of the frog about 1.5 hours after feeding. This also happened when a sponge was introduced into the stomach. The bigger the sponge (causing greater distention of the stomach wall), the fewer were the number of granules. The number increased again after removal of the sponge. Smirnoff (88) evoked secretion in the frog by placing pieces of cork or rubber in the stomach. The secretory response to this mechanical stimulation was not inhibited by sectioning of the vagi. Smirnoff proposed that secretion depends on sympathetic control. However, Wolvekamp & Tinbergen (106) could not obtain inhibition of mechanically evoked secretion of pepsin when they transected the sympathetic chain and severed the connections between the chain and the spinal cord. Crombach et al. (17) combined vagotomy and sympathectomy and this also failed to abolish the secretion of pepsin in response to distention. They considered the regulation of pepsin secretion to be a local process.

Gastric acid secretion in frogs has been investigated by Klok & Smit (51), who used animals with completely extrinsically denervated stomachs. They also found that acid secretion evoked by distention of the stomach wall is a local process in which no long reflex paths are involved. Double vagotomy did not affect the response of acid secretion to mechanical stimulation, but pepsin output was reduced by approximately 40% (89). Thus pepsin secretion is more sensitive to vagal influences than acid secretion, which corresponds to the situation in mammals. Administration of atropine by injection into the ventral subcutaneous lymph sac inhibits secretion of acid and pepsin to the same extent. Since extrinsic denervation of the stomach does not block the acid secretory response to distention of the stomach wall but atropine does, it may be concluded that secretion of acid is under the control of cholinergic fibers of the intramural nerve plexus. No reflex secretion via the sympathetic system could be demonstrated in *Rana*. Sympathetically induced vasoconstriction, however, lowered the secretory output. This was demonstrated by the administration of sodium nitrite in the ventral lymph sac of frogs (90). Nitrite, which causes relaxation of the smooth muscles of the blood vessels and therefore vasodilation and lowered blood pressure, inhibits gastric secretion in intact frogs. Low blood pressure in the brain can be counteracted by vasoconstriction in the bowels, which is brought about by sympathetic impulses. This mechanism can be disturbed by cutting the sympathetic nerves. Sectioning of the splanchnic nerves followed by the administration of nitrite enhances gastric secretory output (Fig. 4). This shows that the splanchnic nerve can exert an indirect influence on secretion by controlling the blood supply to the stomach. Further evidence that blood supply affects the secretory rate is provided by the following facts. *1*) Destruction of the central nervous system weakens circulation and inhibits secretion. This is not the result of the interruption of a reflex path, because extrinsic denervation of the stomach does not inhibit secretion. *2*) Nembutal, which lowers blood pressure, inhibits gastric secretion. *3*) Disturbance of the frog by electric shocks or fastening the animal in a clamp gives a marked diminution of secretory response to the distention stimulus. It is suggested that excitement increases the adrenosympathetic tone, thus causing a vasoconstrictor effect in the splanchnic area.

The existence of hormonal control of gastric secretion in the frog has not been proved. Histamine stimulates acid secretion strongly and, to a lesser degree, also pepsin secretion. Acid output is increased

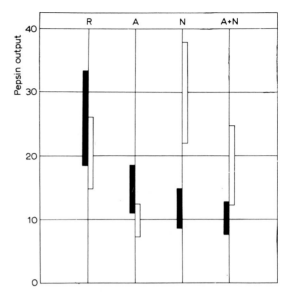

FIG. 4. Pepsin output (arbitrary units) in frogs, in which gastric secretion was evoked by distention of the stomach wall after subcutaneous injection with Ringer solution (*R*), 20 mg atropine/kg (*A*), 15 mg sodium nitrite/kg (*N*), and atropine and nitrite combined (*A* + *N*). *Solid bars:* intact frogs; *open bars:* splanchnectomized frogs. Secretory period 2 hours; temperature 20 C; 160 experiments. [After Smit (89).]

by injection of mammalian gastrin, but pepsin yield is unaffected. The positive reaction to gastrin suggests that in *Rana* a hormonal mechanism comparable to that of mammals might be involved in the regulation of gastric acid secretion, although natural occurrence of a gastric hormone in the frog has not been demonstrated. There is evidence that secretion of acid and pepsin are partly independent processes. Sensitivity to controlling influences is different for acid and pepsin secretions. For example: *1*) intensifying the distention stimulus increases the rate of pepsin secretion more strongly than that of acid; *2*) secretory rates of acid and pepsin may fluctuate in time independently of each other; *3*) vagotomy does not change acid secretion, but pepsin secretion is reduced; *4*) acid secretion is more sensitive to vascular conditions than the secretion of pepsin; *5*) histamine stimulates the rate of acid secretion more strongly than that of pepsin.

From these facts it may be concluded that in the frog, gastric juice secretion is regulated by neurogenic, vascular, and probably hormonal mechanisms.

Reptiles

Very little is known about the regulation of gastric juice secretion in reptiles. Langley (56) observed in the water snake a decrease of secretory granules of the gland cells during digestion. Kahle (48) showed that administration of pilocarpine diminishes the number of granules of the fundic glands in *Testudo*. Kenyon (50) observed high acidity in the stomach of a bull snake (*Pituophis catenifer sayi*) containing the remains of two mice, whereas no acid could be demonstrated in the stomach of a fasting bull snake. In tortoises (*Testudo graeca*) whose stomachs contained small residues of vegetable material, the stomach contents were found to have a pH of 2 (105). The mucosa of empty stomachs had a pH of 7.5–8. Apparently, stimuli eliciting gastric acid secretion originate from the food. Histamine evokes acid secretion in the tortoise, but only at relatively high body temperatures. Combined injection of histamine and pilocarpine greatly decreases the number of secretory granules and produces a viscous juice of pH 1. Vagal stimulation causes a slight secretion with a high pepsin content. Specimens of the Australian lizard *Tiliqua nigro-lutea*, provided with gastric fistulas, secreted a clear juice of high acidity (pH 1) in response to intramuscularly administered histamine. These observations suggest that nervous and humoral influences may control the secretion of gastric juice in reptiles.

Birds

Knowledge of gastric secretory control in birds is also fragmentary. Keeton et al. (49) and Friedman (33) found that histamine provokes secretion in birds. Friedman experimented on chickens supplied with a permanent proventricular fistula. Histamine stimulated the secretion of acid but not of pepsin. The secretory rate after histamine injection could be diminished by administration of adrenaline, which suggests a vascular influence on secretion. The histamine-stimulated secretion was poor in pepsin, but subsequently injected acetylcholine greatly increased the pepsin concentration. Apparently secretion of pepsin is under parasympathetic control. This is also apparent from the observation that the stimulating effect of pilocarpine on secretion is inhibited by atropine. The secretory rate in domestic fowl has been found to respond positively to sham-feeding (16). This finding provides evidence for the existence of a cephalic phase in birds, which is further supported by the experiments of Walter (102) on ducks with gastric fistulas. Walter gave his ducks an auditory stimulus concurrently with feeding. Once the animals were conditioned, the sound of the electric bell evoked a copious flow of gastric juice. The sight of a tray with

food and even that of an empty food tray could elicit secretion. The ducks could not be conditioned to olfactory stimuli (103). The effectiveness of acoustical and optical stimuli indicates the presence of a "psychic" phase of gastric juice secretion in birds.

These results obtained in birds fit well into the picture of secretory control in mammals, but whether all the known features of mammalian control of gastric secretion are present in birds is open to question.

CONCLUSIONS

Acid proteolysis is common to almost all vertebrates and takes place in the stomach, in which chemical and mechanical digestive functions are combined with that of storage. Despite great differences in external appearance, all stomachs have a common construction of the wall, consisting of the mucosa, which contains the gastric glands; the muscularis, which is responsible for motility; and the inner epithelial lining, which produces a protective mucous layer (mucous barrier). The mucosal glands are simple or branched tubular; fishes, amphibians, saurians, and ophidians have more simply built gastric glands than chelonians, crocodiles, and birds; the latter have strongly compound glands. Lower vertebrates and birds possess only one type of granulated cell, which secretes acid and enzyme. In a number of amphibians, acid and pepsinogen are produced by separate glands. The glands have two regions: a neck region containing distinct mucoid neck cells (except in most fishes) and the granulated cells of the body.

The size and shape of the stomach are related mainly to the storage function and mechanical digestion and not to the regulation of secretion. Specially shaped stomachs, fulfilling a special storage function, are found among fishes with a stomachal cecum; specialized stomachs pertaining to mechanical digestion are found in crocodiles whose stomachs have two chambers, the second resembling the gizzard of birds and having a masticatory function.

Stomachal innervation is both parasympathetic and sympathetic and is performed by vagus and splanchnic nerves. Lower vertebrates and birds have no well-defined functional antagonism between the two parts of the autonomic nervous system affecting motility. The automatic contractions are chiefly controlled by the intramural nerve plexus. This plexus also plays a role in the regulation of secretion, although this has not been demonstrated in reptiles.

Except for a number of stomachless fishes, all

vertebrates show proteolytic predigestion of food, brought to a low pH by means of HCl. The gastric juice has a pH of about 1–2, but the actual pH of the chyme depends on the amounts of food and gastric acid. Normally the stomach produces more acid when it contains much food, but this does not mean that all the food is acidified at the same time. In many animals only the outer layer of the food lump is acidified and predigested. After being liquefied, this outer layer is carried off and the next layer becomes acidified. The optimum pH value for the activity of gastric protease is about 2. However, motility and temperature mainly determine the intensity of proteolysis. The gastric protease, normally denoted as pepsin, occurs in several forms, distinguishable by their pH optimum and heat stability, and can be chromatographically and electrophoretically separated. Species specificity probably occurs, and also within one species two or more different pepsins can be found, which together cover a relatively wide pH range, sometimes reaching pH values lower than 1 and higher than 4. As yet there is no conclusive evidence that as a group the pepsins of the lower vertebrates differ greatly from those of mammals. In this context and in view of the sequence of enzymatic activities in the alimentary canal of vertebrates, it may be recalled, as pointed out by Vonk (100), that in both lower and higher vertebrates the gastric protease is always a pepsin (and not a trypsin) and that the pancreatic protease is a trypsin (and not a cathepsin).

The composition of the gastric juice depends on the rate of secretion and on the nature of the secretory stimulus and its duration. Rate and quantity of acid and pepsin secretion need not be correlated; the acidity and pepsin content of gastric juice can diverge widely. The quantity of secreted juice depends, among other things, on the amount of food in the stomach. Emptying time is not necessarily correlated with secretory output. Bulky meals may involve relatively small quantities of gastric juice, and emptying time may be shortened, resulting in incomplete digestion, so digestive efficiency may be lower when food intake is excessive.

In cold-blooded animals temperature is an important determinant of digestive rates. Body temperature influences the rate of output and composition of gastric juice, proteolytic activity, gastric motility and emptying time. Emptying time shows a semilogarithmic relationship with temperature, but it is difficult to assess how much each process contributes to this result. The phenomenon of temperature adaptation may also occur in gastric digestion. If temperature compensation occurs, the digestive rate of cold-adapted animals would be expected to be higher than that of warm-adapted animals when both rates are measured at an intermediate temperature. Such compensation has been demonstrated for the gastric secretory rate in fishes. It is clear that fluctuating environmental temperatures typically complicate comparison of the digestive processes of poikilotherms with those of homeotherms.

Secretion of gastric juice is a discontinuous process, apparently regulated by the intake of food, the presence of food in the stomach, and the digestion of the food. The regulation may be hormonal, nervous, or vascular, or a combination of the three; however, this regulatory mechanism has not yet been completely analyzed for any nonmammalian vertebrate. Observations have failed to demonstrate a regulatory influence of the extrinsic stomachal innervation in elasmobranchs, although they suggest that the gastric nerve plexus plays a part in secretory control. Some evidence suggests that the regulation is mainly hormonal. In teleosts secretion and digestion are under nervous control: vagotomy reduces the rate of digestion; mechanical stimulation of the stomach wall elicits secretion; and secretion is probably also evoked by conditioned and unconditioned reflexes. Since the secretory rate also depends on the chemical composition of the food, the existence of a hormonal mechanism cannot be excluded. Environmental temperatures have a marked influence on digestive and secretory rates. Whether this is achieved via metabolic or circulatory adjustments or otherwise is not known, but it would be interesting to measure the metabolic rate concurrently with secretory output at various temperatures. Nervous control of gastric secretion in amphibians has been established for the frog, in which the cholinergic part of the gastric intramural nerve plexus governs the secretory rate. Furthermore, vascular influences have been demonstrated. The existence of a hormonal regulatory mechanism is probable, since histamine and mammalian gastrin increase secretory output. There is some evidence that gastric secretion in reptiles is under nervous and humoral control. Secretion in birds is stimulated by acetylcholine, sham-feeding, and conditioned reflexes, thus proving that secretion is under nervous control. There is no clear-cut evidence for hormonal regulation of gastric secretory activity in birds, although histamine is effective in stimulating secretion. The secretion of gastric juice in mammals is regulated by neurohormonal mechanisms. Nervous control is exerted by the vagus, whereas hormonal regulation is accomplished by the pyloric antrum. These mechanisms do not act independently, for there is potentiation between them.

If what is known of secretory regulation in non-mammalian vertebrates is compared with that of mammals, no essential deviation from the situation in mammals is evident. For example, in all vertebrates the presence of food in the stomach stimulates gastric secretion strongly; in this mechanism the intramural nerve plexus plays some role; as far as is known, only the parasympathetic neural elements are of direct importance for secretion; histamine stimulates gastric secretion in all vertebrate classes. In general, it can be said that gastric digestion in lower vertebrates is achieved in the same way as in mammals, but temperature is a special factor in poikilotherms. A hormonal regulatory mechanism probably exists in non-mammalians, but has not yet been proved. Inhibition of secretion by gastric acid, which is clearly demonstrable in mammals and by which the gastrin mechanism can be blocked, has not been identified in lower vertebrates or birds, but it is to be expected that some not yet discovered mechanism stops secretion when a certain pH value has been reached. A hormone-releasing organ like the mammalian pyloric antrum has not been found in nonmammalians. For example, in amphibians, in which acid secretion is mainly pyloric, it is not likely that this part of the stomach is also the source of a gastric hormone. Little is known about the part played by the intramural nerve plexuses in the release of gastrin in mammals, and it need hardly be said that virtually nothing is known about the interplay of the gastric nerve plexus and a gastric hormone in lower vertebrates.

REFERENCES

1. AIKAWA, T. On the innervation of the frog's stomach. *Japan. J. Med. Sci.* 2: 91, 1931.

2. BABKIN, B. P., AND D. J. BOWIE. The digestive system and its function in Fundulus heteroclitus. *Biol. Bull.* 54: 254–277, 1928.

3. BABKIN B. P., A. F. CHAISSON, AND M. H. F. FRIEDMAN. Factors determining the course of the gastric secretion in elasmobranchs. *J. Biol. Bd. Can.* 1: 251–259, 1935.

4. BABKIN, B. P., AND M. H. F. FRIEDMAN. The relation of the autonomic nervous system to the motility and secretion of the stomach in elasmobranchs. *Am. J. Physiol.* 109: 3, 1934.

5. BABKIN, B. P., M. H. F. FRIEDMAN, AND M. E. MacKay-SAWYER. Vagal and sympathetic innervation of the stomach in the skate. *J. Biol. Bd. Can.* 1: 239–250, 1935.

6. BARRINGTON, E. J. W. Gastric digestion in the lower vertebrates. *Biol. Rev., Cambridge Phil. Soc.* 17: 1–27, 1942.

7. BARRINGTON, E. J. W. The delayed development of the stomach of the frog (Rana temporaria) and the toad (Bufo bufo). *Proc. Zool. Soc. London* 116: 1–21, 1946.

8. BARRINGTON, E. J. W. The alimentary canal and digestion. In: *The Physiology of Fishes*, edited by M. E. Brown, New York: Acad. Press, 1957, vol. 1, 109–161.

9. BISHOP, G. H., AND J. O'LEARY. Pathways through the sympathetic nervous system in the bullfrog. *J. Neurophysiol.* 1: 442–454, 1938.

10. BLAKE, I. H. Studies on the comparative histology of the digestive tube of certain teleost fishes. *J. Morphol.* 50: 39–70, 1930.

11. BODANSKY, M., AND W. C. ROSE. Digestion in elasmobranchs and teleosts. *Am. J. Physiol.* 62: 482–487, 1922.

12. BOTTAZZI, P. The action of the vagus and the sympathetic on the oesophagus of the toad. *J. Physiol., London* 25: 157–164, 1899.

13. BRAMSTEDT, F. Die Bedeutung der katheptischen Fermente für die proteolytische Verdauung im Tierreich. *Zool. Anz. 14, Suppl. Verhandl. Deut. Zool.* 173–182, 1949.

14. BUCHS, S. Die Proteolyse im Tiermagen. *Z. Vergleich. Physiol.* 36: 165–175, 1954.

15. CARLSON, A. J., AND A. B. LUCKHARDT. Cardiac and vasomotor reflexes induced by visceral stimulation in Amphibia and Reptilia. *Am. J. Physiol.* 55: 31–52, 1921.

16. COLLIP, J. B. The activation of the glandular stomach of the fowl. *Am. J. Physiol.* 59: 435–438, 1922.

17. CROMBACH, J. J. M. L. Some experiments on pepsin secretion in the frog. *Acta Physiol. Pharmacol. Neerl.* 7: 121, 1958.

18. CROMBACH, J. J. M. L., M. I. C. P. DE JONG, AND H. P. WOLVEKAMP. Quelques expériences sur la sécrétion de pepsine de la grenouille verte (Rana esculenta L.) et de la grenouille rousse (Rana temporaria L.) *Acta Physiol. Pharmacol. Neerl.* 7: 78–92, 1958.

19. DAWES, B. The histology of the alimentary tract of the plaice (Pleuronectes platessa). *Quart. J. Microscop. Sci.* 73: 243–274, 1930.

20. DIXON, W. E. The innervation of the frog's stomach. *J. Physiol., London* 28: 57–75, 1902.

21. DOBBEN, W. H. VAN. The food of the cormorant in the Netherlands. *Ardea* 40: 1–63, 1952.

22. DOBREFF, M. Experimentelle Studien über die vergleichende Physiologie der Verdauung. *Arch. Ges. Physiol.* 217: 221–234, 1927.

23. ECKER, A., AND E. GAUPP. *Anatomie des Frosches.* Braunschweig, 1896, 1899, 1904.

24. EGLITIS, I., AND R. A. KNOUFF. A histological and histochemical analysis of the inner lining and glandular epithelium of the chicken gizzard. *Am. J. Anat.* 111: 49–59, 1962.

25. FÁBIÁN G., G. MOLNÁR, AND I. TÖLG. Comparative data and enzyme kinetic calculations on changes caused by temperature in the duration of gastric digestion of some

predatory fishes. *Acta Biol. Acad. Sci. Hung.* 14: 123–129, 1963.

26. FARNER, D. S. *Some Aspects of the Physiology of Digestion in Birds* (Ph.D. Thesis). Univ. of Wisconsin, 1941.

27. FARNER, D. S. The hydrogen ion concentration in avian digestive tracts. *Poultry Sci.* 21: 445–450, 1942.

28. FARNER, D. S. Gastric hydrogen ion concentration and acidity in the domestic fowl. *Poultry Sci.* 22: 79–82, 1943.

29. FARNER, D. S. *Biology and Comparative Physiology of Birds*, edited by A. J. Marshall. New York: Acad. Press, 1960, vol. 1, 411–467.

30. FRIEDMAN, M. H. F. The nervous control of gastric secretion in the frog (Rana esculenta). *J. Cellular Comp. Physiol.* 5: 83–96, 1934.

31. FRIEDMAN, M. H. F. A study of the innervation of the stomach of Necturus by means of drugs. *Trans. Roy. Soc. Canada, Sec. V* 29: 175, 1935.

32. FRIEDMAN, M. H. F. Oesophageal and gastric secretion in the frog. *J. Cellular Comp. Physiol.* 10: 37–50, 1937.

33. FRIEDMAN, M. H. F. Gastric secretion in birds. *J. Cellular Comp. Physiol.* 13: 219–234, 1939.

34. FRIEDMAN, M. H. F. Gastric secretion in Necturus. *J. Cellular Comp. Physiol.* 20: 379-384, 1942.

35. GEILENKIRCHEN, W. L. M., AND P. F. ELBERS. Digestion of edestan and some other protein-substrates by pig stomach extract. *Enzymologia* 14: 304–310, 1951.

36. GOMAZKOV, O. A. Effect of temperature on digestion rate of the burbot (Lota lota L.). *Byul. Inst. Biol. Vodokhranilishch Akad. Nauk. SSSR* 5: 26–28, 1959. (In Russian.)

37. GOMAZKOV, O. A., AND B. V. KRAYUKHIN. The role of the vagus nerve in the regulation of digestion in fish. *Byul. Inst. Biol. Vodokhranilishch Akad. Nauk. SSSR* 8: 124–131, 1963.

38. GRUBER, C. M. The effect of epinephrine on excised strips of frog's digestive tracts. *J. Pharmacol. Exptl. Therap.* 20: 321, 1923.

39. GRÜTZNER, P. Ein Beitrag zum Mechanismus der Magenverdauung. *Arch. Ges. Physiol.* 106: 463–522, 1905.

40. GUNN, M. A study of the enteric plexuses in some amphibians. *Quart. J. Microscop. Sci.* 92: 55–78, 1951.

41. HERPOL, C. Activité protéolytique de l'appareil gastrique des oiseaux granivores et carnivores. *Ann. Biol. Animale Biochim. Biophys.* 4: 239–244, 1964.

42. HERRIOTT, R. M. Transformation of swine pepsinogen into swine pepsin by chicken pepsin. *J. Gen. Physiol.* 21: 575–582, 1938.

43. HEWITT, F. A., AND R. L. SCHELKOPF. pH values and enzymatic activity of the digestive tract of the chicken. *Am. J. Vet. Res.* 16: 576–579, 1955.

44. HOPF, H. Über den hemmenden und erregenden Einfluss des Vagus auf den Magen des Frosches. *Z. Biol.* 55: 409–459, 1911.

45. ISHIDA, J. Distribution of the digestive enzymes in the digestive system of stomachless fishes. *Annotationes Zool. Japon.* 15: 263–284, 1936.

46. ITAGAKI, M. On the innervation of the stomach of the Japanese frog. *Japan. J. Med. Sci.* 1: 105, 1930.

47. JOLY, J. Influence des basses températures sur le cycle alimentaire de quelques tritons français. *Bull. Soc. Zool. France* 83: 128–131, 1958.

48. KAHLE, H. Histologische Untersuchungen über Veränderungen der Magendrüsenzellen bei der Landschildkröte (Testudo graeca) während verschiedener Verdauungsstadien. *Arch. Ges. Physiol.* 152: 129–167, 1913.

49. KEETON, R. W., F. C. KOCH, AND A. B. LUCKHARDT. The response of the stomach mucosa of various animals to gastrin bodies. *Am. J. Physiol.* 51: 454–468, 1920.

50. KENYON, W. A. Digestive enzymes in poikilothermal vertebrates. *Bull. U. S. Bur. Fisheries* 41: 181–200, 1925.

51. KLOK, J. L., AND H. SMIT. Some experiments on gastric acid secretion in the edible frog (Rana esculenta L.). *Comp. Biochem. Physiol.* 7: 251–254, 1962.

52. KRAYUKHIN, B. V. The regulatory mechanism of secretion of digestive juices in fishes. *Tr. Soveshch. Ikhtiol. Komis. Akad. Nauk. SSSR* 8: 179–185, 1958. (In Russian.)

53. KRAYUKHIN, B. V. Effect of food swallowing on the intensity of digestive processes in fishes. *Vopr. Ikhtiol.* 12: 133–137, 1959. (In Russian.)

54. KUNTZ, A. Anatomical and physiological changes in the digestive system during metamorphosis in Rana pipiens and Ambystoma tigrinum. *J. Morphol.* 38: 581–598, 1924.

55. LABARRE J., J. TREMBLAY, L. TROCHU, AND H. P. DUSSAULT. Les enzymes digestives protéolytiques de l'estomac de morue (Gadus calarias). *Rev. Can. Biol.* 10: 140–148, 1951.

56. LANGLEY, J. N. On the histology and physiology of the pepsin-forming glands. *Phil. Trans. Roy. Soc., London, Ser. B* 172: 663–713, 1881.

57. LANGLEY, J. N., AND L. A. ORBELI. Observations on the sympathetic and sacral autonomic system of the frog. *J. Physiol., London* 41: 450–482, 1910–11.

58. LÜDICKE, M. Serpentes. In: *Handbuch Zool.*, edited by W. Kükenthal. Berlin: de Gruyter, 1963, vol. 7, no. 6, 190–201.

59. MACHAN, B. Über Ösophagusdrüsen und Magenhauptdrüsen einheimischer Anuren. *Z. Mikroskop-Anat. Forsch.* 37: 344–372, 1935.

60. MACKAY, M. M. The digestive system of the eel-pout (Zoarces anguillaris). *Biol. Bull.* 56: 8–23, 1929.

61. MENNEGA, A. M. W. *Waterstofionenconcentratie en vertering in de maag van enige vertebraten* (Ph.D. Thesis). Univ. of Utrecht, 1938.

62. MOLNÁR, G., AND I. TÖLG. Relation between water temperature and gastric digestion of largemouth bass (Micropterus salmoides Lacépède). *J. Fish. Res. Bd. Can.* 19: 1005–1012, 1962.

63. MOLNÁR, G., AND I. TÖLG. Experiments concerning gastric digestion of pike perch (Lucioperca l.L.) in relation to water temperature. *Acta Biol. Acad. Sci. Hung.* 13: 231–239, 1962.

64. MORISHITA, T., H. NODA, M. KITAMIKADO, T. TAKAHASHI, AND S. TACHINO. On the activity of the digestive enzymes in cultured fish. *J. Fac. Fisheries, Univ. Mie* 6: 239–246, 1964.

65. NICHOLLS, J. V. V. The influence of temperature on digestion in Fundulus heteroclitus. *Contrib. Can. Biol. Fisheries* 7: 47–55, 1933.

66. NICHOLLS, J. V. V. The effect of temperature variations and of certain drugs upon the gastric motility of elasmobranch fishes. *Contrib. Can. Biol. Fisheries* 7: 447–463, 1933.

67. NICOL, J. A. C. Autonomic nervous systems in lower chordates. *Biol. Rev. Cambridge Phil. Soc.* 27: 1–48, 1952.

68. NICOL, J. A. C. Digestion. In: *The Biology of Marine Animals.* London: Pitman, 1960.

69. NOLF, P. Du rôle des nerfs vague et sympathique dans l'innervation motrice de l'estomac de l'oiseau. *Arch. Intern. Physiol.* 28: 309–428, 1927.

70. NOLF, P. L'appareil nerveux de l'automatisme gastrique de l'oiseau. *Arch. Intern. Physiol.* 46: 1–85, 441–559, 1938.

71. NORRIS, E. R., AND D. W. ELAM. Preparation and properties of crystalline salmon pepsin. *J. Biol. Chem.* 134: 443–454, 1940.

72. NORRIS, E. R., AND J. C. MATHIES. Preparation, properties, and crystallization of tuna pepsin. *J. Biol. Chem.* 204: 673–680, 1953.

73. NORRIS, J. L. The normal histology of the esophageal and gastric mucosae of the frog, Rana pipiens. *J. Exptl. Zool.* 141: 155–175, 1959.

74. NORTHROP, J. H., M. KUNITZ, AND R. M. HERRIOTT. *Crystalline Enzymes.* New York: Columbia Univ. Press, 1948.

75. OPPEL, A. *Lehrb. d. vergleich. mikroskop. Anat. d. Wirbeltiere. I. Der Magen.* Jena: 1896.

76. PATTERSON, T. L. Vagus and splanchnic influence on the gastric hunger movements of the frog. *Am. J. Physiol.* 53: 293–306, 1920.

77. PERNKOPF, E., AND J. LEHNER. In: *Handbuch d. vergleich. Anat. d. Wirbeltiere,* edited by L. Bolk, E. Göppert, E. Kallius, and W. Lubosch. 1937, pt. III, p. 349–476.

78. PJATNITZKIJ, N. P. Vergleichende Untersuchungen über das Pepsin bei Kalt- und Warmblütern. *Z. Physiol. Chem.* 194: 43–52, 1931.

79. PRECHT, H. Anpassungen wechselwarmer Tiere im normalen Temperaturbereich und ihre Ursachen. *Naturw. Rundschau* 17: 438–442, 1964.

80. REEDER, W. G. The digestive system. In: *Physiology of the Amphibia,* edited by J. A. Moore. New York: Acad. Press, 1964, p. 99–149.

81. SARBAHI, D. S. Studies of the digestive tracts and the digestive enzymes of the goldfish, Carassius auratus, and the largemouth bass, Micropterus salmoides. *Biol. Bull.* 100: 244–257, 1951.

82. SCHEURING, L. Beziehungen zwischen Temperatur und Verdauungsgeschwindigkeit bei Fischen. *Z. Fischerei* 26: 231–235, 1928.

83. SCHOLANDER, P. F., W. FLAGG, V. WALTERS, AND L. IRVING. Climatic adaptation in arctic and tropical poikilotherms. *Physiol. Zool.* 26: 67–92, 1953.

84. SCHULTZ, P. Die längsgestreifte Muskulatur der Wirbeltiere. *Arch. Anat. Physiol. Abt.* 307–321, 1897.

85. SCHULZ, H. Histochemische Untersuchungen an den Oesophagus- und Magenhauptdrüsen von Rana esculenta L. *Zool. Anz.* 170: 9–18, 1963.

86. SEASTONE, C. V., AND R. M. HERRIOTT. Immunological studies on pepsin and pepsinogen. *J. Gen. Physiol.* 20: 797–806, 1937.

87. SLIJPER, E. J. Die physiologische Anatomie der Verdauungsorgane bei den Vertebraten. *Tabulae Biol.* 21: 1–81, 1946.

88. SMIRNOFF, A. J. Zur Verdauung bei Kaltblütern. *Ber. Ges. Physiol.* 13: 87, 1922.

89. SMIT, H. *The Regulation of Gastric Secretion in the Edible Frog (Rana esculenta L.)* (Thesis). Leiden: Univ. of Leiden, 1962.

90. SMIT, H. The regulation of pepsin secretion in the edible frog. *Comp. Biochem. Physiol.* 13: 129–141, 1964.

91. SMIT, H. Influence of temperature on the rate of gastric juice secretion in the brown bullhead, Ictalurus nebulosus. *Comp. Biochem. Physiol.* 21: 125–132, 1967.

92. SULLIVAN, M. X. The physiology of the digestive tract of elasmobranchs. *Am. J. Physiol.* 15: 42–45, 1905–06.

93. SWICICKI, H. VON. Untersuchung über die Bildung und Ausscheidung des Pepsins bei den Batrachiern. *Arch. Ges. Physiol.* 13: 444–452, 1876.

94. TAYLOR, W. H. Studies on gastric proteolysis. *Biochem. J.* 71: 73–83, 373–388, 1959.

95. UNGAR G. Perfusion de l'estomac des Sélaciens; étude pharmacodynamique de la sécrétion gastrique. *Compt. Rend. Soc. Biol.* 119: 172–173, 1935.

96. VONK, H. J. Die Verdauung bei den Fischen. *Z. Vergleich. Physiol.* 5: 445–546, 1927.

97. VONK, H. J. Das Pepsin verschiedener Vertebraten. I. Die pH-Optima und die Wasserstoffionenkonzentration des Mageninhaltes. *Z. Vergleich. Physiol.* 9: 685–702, 1929.

98. VONK, H. J. The specificity and collaboration of digestive enzymes in Metazoa. *Biol. Rev. Cambridge Phil. Soc.* 12: 245–284, 1937.

99. VONK, H. J. Die biologische Bedeutung des pH-Optimums der Verdauungsenzyme bei den Vertebraten. *Ergeb. Enzymforsch.* 8: 55, 1939.

100. VONK, H. J. Die Verdauung bei den niederen Vertebraten. In: *Advances in Enzymology.* New York: Interscience, 1941, vol. I, p. 371–417.

101. VONK, H. J. Comparative physiology: nutrition, feeding, and digestion. *Ann. Rev. Physiol.* 17: 483–498, 1955.

102. WALTER, W. G. Bedingte Magensaftsekretion bei der Ente. *Acta Brevia Neerl.* 9: 56–57, 1939.

103. WALTER, W. G. Some experiments on the sense of smell in birds. *Arch. Neerl. Physiol.* 27: 1–72, 1942.

104. WETTSTEIN, O. VON. Crocodilia. In: *Handbuch. Zool.,* edited by W. Kükenthal, 1954, vol. 7, no. 4, p. 343–345.

105. WRIGHT, R. D., H. W. FLOREY, AND A. G. SANDERS. Observations on the gastric mucosa of reptilia. *Quart. J. Exptl. Physiol.* 42: 1–14, 1957.

106. WOLVEKAMP, H. P., AND L. TINBERGEN. Recherches sur la sécrétion de la pepsine par les glandes oesophagéales de la grenouille verte (Rana esculenta L.). *Arch. Neerl. Physiol.* 26: 435–457, 1942.

107. YOUNG, J. Z. The autonomic nervous system of Selachians. *Quart. J. Microscop. Sci.* 75: 571–624, 1933.

108. YOUNG, J. Z. The innervation and reactions to drugs of the viscera of teleostean fish. *Proc. Roy. Soc., London, Ser. B* 120: 303–318, 1936.

109. YÜH, L. On the innervation of the stomach of the Japanese frog. *Japan. J. Med. Sci.* 2: 25, 1931.

CHAPTER 136

Role of indigenous enteric bacteria in intestinal function and disease

R. M. DONALDSON, JR.[1] | *University of Wisconsin Medical School, Madison, Wisconsin*

CHAPTER CONTENTS

DURING THE PAST DECADE several lines of investigation have stimulated a rebirth of interest in the contribution of enteric microorganisms to the host's environment. Dubos and his colleagues (85, 87) have reemphasized the fact that nonsporulating anaerobes, lactobacilli, and anaerobic streptococci dominate the intestinal flora and have pointed out the potential biological significance of these long-neglected bacteria. Furthermore, studies with germ-free animals (192) have indicated the importance of intestinal bacteria to the host in terms of nutrition, resistance to infection, and response to shock, strangulation obstruction of

[1] Present address: Boston University Medical Center, Boston, Mass.

the intestine, and irradiation. Demonstration of the role of enteric bacteria in the pathogenesis of hepatic coma (49) has revived interest in Metchnikoff's (189) concept of intestinal autointoxication resulting from enteric bacterial action on proteins. Interest in intestinal bacteria has been further intensified by the discovery that a bacterial organism appears to play an important role in Whipple's disease and that this disorder, the etiology of which was unknown for over 50 years, is amenable to antibacterial therapy (283). Whatever the reasons, there can be no doubt that the number of investigations concerned with the bacterial populations of the intestine and the role of these microorganisms in intestinal function and disease is rapidly increasing. Several hundred relevant papers have appeared since the subject was extensively reviewed in 1964 (76).

BACTERIAL POPULATIONS OF THE INTESTINE

Description of the kinds of bacteria harbored in the intestine is complicated by the wide variety of microorganisms that may be present and by the diverse and often poorly understood factors that may influence their growth. More than 60 species of bacteria have been isolated from the intestinal tract or feces of apparently healthy animals including man. Many of these are spirochetes, mycobacteria, fusiforms, etc., that predominate in the mouth and respiratory tract and are therefore considered "contaminants" of the intestine. The bacterial species most often isolated from and thought to reside in the intestine of healthy animals including man are listed in Table 1. The morphological, cultural, and biochemical characteristics of these bacteria are summarized in recent reviews (76, 230). It should be emphasized, however, that this listing merely indicates the many different microorganisms that, under a wide variety of circumstances, can be isolated in significant numbers from the intestine or from feces and does not characterize in any way the enteric bacterial population likely to be present at one time in any individual, group, or species. The recent discovery (99) of bizarre helically coiled microorganisms in cecal contents of rats (Fig. 1) emphasizes the fact that by no means have all the microbial inhabitants of the gut been identified.

Relation of Enteric Bacteria to the Host

Definition of the interactions between intestinal microorganisms and the host animal is equally diffi-

TABLE I. *Bacteria Frequently Isolated From Intestinal Tract of Healthy Animals**

Anaerobic or Microaerophilic	Aerobic or Facultatively Anaerobic
Bacteroides	*Enterococcus*
Bacteroides funduliformis	*Streptococcus faecalis*
B. fragilis	*Var. zymogenes*
B. putidus	*Var. liquefaciens*
B. pneumosintes	*S. faecium*
B. serpens	*S. durans*
B. nigrescens	*S. bovis*
	S. lactis
Lactobacillus	
Lactobacillus acidophilus	*Enterobacterium (coli-*
L. bifidus	*aerogenes)*
L. brevis	*Escherichia coli*
L. exilis	*E. freundii*
L. casei	Alkalescens-dispar para-
Boas-Oppler bacillus	colon
	Aerobacteria aerogenes
Clostridium	*A. cloacae*
Clostridium perfringens	*Klebsiella rhinoscleromatis*
Cl. tetani	*K. oxytoca*
Cl. botulinum	
Cl. fibermentans	*Enterobacterium (proteus-*
Cl. sporogenes	*providence)*
	Proteus vulgaris
Bacillus subtilis	*P. morganii*
	P. mirabilis
	P. rettgeri
	Providence group
	Pseudomonas
	Pseudomonas aeruginosa
	Ps. fluorescens
	Ps. ovalis
	Alcaligenes faecalis

* Nomenclature follows that used by Rosebury (230).

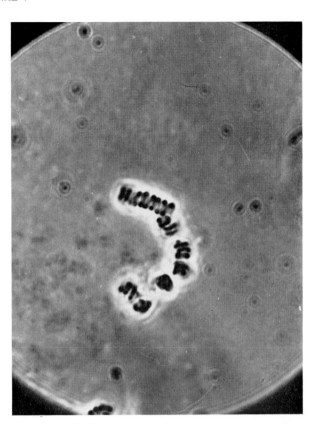

FIG. 1. Phase-contrast micrograph of helically coiled microorganism isolated in pure culture from cecal contents of the rat. The organism is a rod 0.5 × 3 μ in size, and coils consist of many of these rods joined together (99). × 1000. (Photograph kindly supplied by R. J. Fitzgerald.)

cult, and a number of terms have been used to describe this relationship. The bacterial populations found in apparently healthy animals have been called the "normal" or "indigenous" enteric bacteria, but what is considered "normal" may vary greatly depending on the age, species, or environment of the host studied. Dubos et al. (89) propose that certain components of the intestinal flora have, during evolutionary development, become intimately associated and symbiotic with the host; these constitute a true "autochthonous" flora that will persist in the host even when environmental conditions are altered. Other components, however, are ubiquitous in the environment and are transiently acquired by an animal colony because of favorable environmental conditions. The "indigenous" microbiota consists of all microorganisms capable of colonizing the intestine, including the symbiotic, ubiquitous, and pathogenic organisms. The "normal" microbiota is made up of those organisms so ubiquitous in a given animal colony that they become established in practically all members, but unlike the "autochthonous" flora may vary from colony to colony.

The relation between enteric microbiota and host cannot be termed commensal since in no way are the two mutually independent. Certain species cannot exist outside the host, and changes in the intestinal flora are accompanied by altered host characteristics. Indeed, a symbiotic relation is dramatically exemplified by rumen bacteria. It has been demonstrated (285), for example, that even with urea and ammonium salts as the only dietary source of nitrogen, bacteria can thrive in the favorable environment of the rumen, maintain the cow, and even allow for relatively normal milk production. However, the relationship between bacteria and host cannot be dismissed simply as symbiotic since host mechanisms limit intraluminal bacterial growth and since enteric microorganisms may on occasion invade and destroy the host. The complexity of the situation is exemplified by *Escherichia coli* that, under appropriate conditions, may be totally independent of, symbiotic with, or pathogenic for the host animal. Certainly, as Rosebury (230) suggests, the intestine must be considered infected by bacteria if an infection is defined as an interaction that occurs between the host and a smaller self-replicating agent in such a way that both are modified by this interaction.

Development, Character, and Location
of the Enteric Flora

Formerly it was generally accepted that the lumen of the stomach and small intestine was sterile or only sparsely populated with bacteria (76), but several recent studies indicate that in a wide variety of mammalian species the entire gastrointestinal tract harbors an abundant bacterial flora (89, 237, 257, 258). Germ-free techniques provide unequivocal evidence that the intestinal tract of the fetus is sterile and that the intestinal flora is derived exclusively from the environment (192). Although the manner in which the sterile lumen of the newborn rapidly becomes the site of profuse bacterial growth has not been precisely characterized, sufficient data are now available to make some general statements.

When the development of the intestinal flora is studied in young animals of various species, including ox, sheep, pig, dog, cat, rabbit, guinea pig, rat, mouse, chicken, and man (237, 258, 259), some differences but many similarities are found. Colonization of the rat intestine by the major components of the enteric flora is summarized graphically in Figure 2. Similar

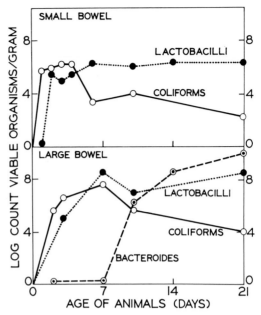

FIG. 2. Development of fecal flora in young rats. [Based on data reported by Smith (258).]

trends may be observed in other host species. The first organisms to colonize the alimentary tract are *E. coli*, *Clostridium welchii*, and streptococci, and these appear within a few hours after birth; *E. coli* appear later and in smaller numbers in mice raised in a clean, but not germ-free, environment (238). During the first day of life, lactobacilli and anaerobic streptococci become established, and in species other than the dog, cat, and rabbit lactobacilli persist in large numbers not only in the colon but also in the small intestine and stomach (237, 258). During the first week there occurs a marked decrease in the numbers of coliforms particularly in the small bowel. In the piglet the flooding of the stomach and small bowel with *E. coli* is particularly striking, and the subsequent abrupt decrease in the numbers of these organisms can be correlated with a lowered pH of gastric contents as gastric secretory function develops (261). The nonsporulating anaerobes, bacteroides, do not become established until later, usually after the tenth day of life. It is of interest that although bacteroides ultimately constitute the major component of the colonic flora in most mammalian species, these organisms uniformly fail to become established in the stomach or small bowel.

It should be pointed out that intestinal bacteria colonize the gut in the oral-to-anal direction and do not infect the intestinal lumen in a "retrograde" fashion from the colon. This is documented by studies in newborn infants with total intestinal obstruction (28). The intestinal lumen proximal to a complete obstruction rapidly becomes the site of bacterial over-growth whereas the distal intestine remains sterile.

Dubos et al. (87) have shown that when mice are raised in a clean but not germ-free environment (NCS mice), an intestinal flora consisting of lactobacilli, anaerobic streptococci, and bacteroides is regularly observed. These microorganisms appear to constitute the true autochthonous microbiota that exerts a pro-found influence on the resistance to infection and to toxins, the efficiency of food utilization, and the rate of growth of these animals (84–87).

If NCS mice are exposed at an early age to an unclean environment, *E. coli* and other bacteria ubiq-uitous in the community readily colonize the intestine (201), but these microorganisms become established at various times, greatly fluctuate in numbers, and, unlike the autochthonous flora, are not constant from one animal colony to another (237). This susceptibility of NCS mice to *E. coli* lasts only 2 weeks, and adult NCS mice consistently resist permanent colonization of coliforms when exposed to these bacteria (201). The consistent qualitative and quantitative character of the autochthonous flora is demonstrated by the observation that when germ-free mice are contami-nated with pure cultures of lactobacilli, anaerobic streptococci (group N), and bacteroides, these or-ganisms rapidly colonize the intestine in the same numbers and locations as are observed in NCS mice (238). Unlike NCS mice, however, germ-free mice exposed to enterococci and coliforms experience mas-sive and persistent growth of these microorganisms throughout the entire intestinal tract. On the other hand, these enterococcal and coliform populations are sharply reduced when previously germ-free mice are subsequently exposed to the autochthonous flora (lac-tobacilli, anaerobic streptococci, and bacteroides) of NCS mice. These results raise the possibility that the autochthonous flora of NCS mice in some way sup-presses growth of other microorganisms and thus promotes stability of the intestinal bacterial popula-tions.

Insufficient experimental data are available to delineate the extent to which these conceptually im-portant findings in NCS and germ-free mice apply to other animal species living under poorly controlled environmental conditions. However, several observa-tions suggest the wide applicability of these concepts. First, many studies indicate that lactobacilli, strepto-cocci, and bacteroides regularly constitute the major and most persistent enteric bacterial flora of many different animal species. Table 2 represents a compila-tion of several investigations that uniformly show these

TABLE 2. *Quantitative Estimation of Bacterial Populations of the Intestine*

Species	Bacteria	Log₁₀ Viable Count/g*		
		Jejunum	Ileum	Colon or Feces
Man	Bacteroides	0	0	10
	Lactobacilli	5	7	8
	Streptococci	3	6	7
	Coliforms	3	6	7
Rat	Bacteroides	0	0	10
	Lactobacilli	7	7	9
	Streptococci	4	5	6
	Coliforms	3	4	5
Mouse	Bacteroides	0	0	9
	Lactobacilli	8	8	9
	Streptococci	5	7	7
	Coliforms	2	4	6
Pig	Bacteroides	0	0	8
	Lactobacilli	7	8	9
	Streptococci	6	7	7
	Coliforms	4	5	7

* Mean values compiled from 9 bacteriologic investiga-tions (35, 89, 116, 157, 170, 258, 259, 261, 312).

microorganisms are regularly isolated in large num-bers from the intestinal tract. Coliforms, though usu-ally present, constitute no more than a few percent of the total microbial population, and a characteristic feature of the enteric microflora is the absence from the small intestine of bacteroides in all mammalian species thus far studied. Second, as shown in Table 2, there is a striking qualitative and quantitative similarity in the major constituents of the intestinal bacterial popu-lations of the pig, rat, mouse, and man. Third, the early development in human infants of a flora domi-nated by lactobacilli was demonstrated by Tissier at the turn of the century, and his observations have been amply confirmed (16, 132, 133). Finally, the stability of the fecal flora has been confirmed in individual human subjects studied over prolonged periods of time (111, 170, 241, 312).

The location of intestinal bacterial populations within the intestinal tract requires comment. When the stomachs of mice, white rats, and swine are cultured for lactobacilli (89), or when the stomach, small bowel, and cecum are cultured for lactobacilli, anaerobic streptococci (group N), and bacteroides (237), the results suggest that these bacteria are closely associated with the gut wall and that large numbers of microorganisms cannot be dislodged from gastric or intestinal tissue even by repeated washings. Frozen sections of the stomach of NCS mice show large numbers of gram-positive rods that look like lacto-bacilli tightly packed and embedded in the mucous layer adherent to the gastric mucosa (89). Thus there is reason to believe that the constant and more important components of the intestinal microbiota are closely associated with the walls of the digestive organs and are probably concentrated in the mucous layer.

An intimate association between certain gut bacteria and the intestinal mucosa is also suggested by the work of Hampton & Rosario (137). Their elegant preparations have revealed attachment of *Streptobacillus moniliformis* to the villous, but not crypt, epithelial cells of mouse ileum (Fig. 3). The significance of this attachment process is not clear. Apparently no harm comes to either the microorganism or the intestinal cell, and there is no evidence that this organism invades lamina propria or other subepithelial layers of the gut. When bacteria grown in tritiated thymidine are studied, bacterial DNA is not observed in intestinal cells. Although Reimann (226) has termed this attachment "microbic phagocytosis by enteric epithelial cells," there is no strong support for the concept that the attachment represents a stage in the phagocytosis and destruction of the microorganism.

Problems of Methodology

Available methods for investigation of intestinal bacterial populations fall short of the ideal, which would provide readily interpretable information concerning the kinds and numbers of intestinal bacteria actually inhabiting various portions of the intestinal tract. Many portions of the gut lumen are relatively inaccessible, and even the collection of material for bacteriological examination poses problems. Feces, though readily available, do not necessarily reflect intestinal bacterial populations, even of the colon, since such vital factors as osmolarity, pH, and redox potential are quite different in feces as opposed to colonic contents. If intestinal contents are aspirated through an open tube, precise localization of the collecting tip may not be possible or specimens may be contaminated by bacteria that have entered the tube from the nasopharynx or from portions of the gut proximal to the area being investigated. Furthermore, misleading results may be obtained if contents remain static within the tube lumen for long periods of time so that overgrowth of one or more bacterial species occurs. Finally, it is often necessary to inject the tube with variable amounts of diluent in order to obtain

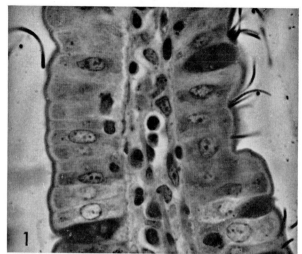
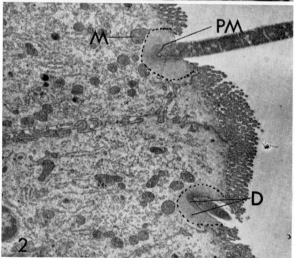

FIG. 3. Attachment of intestinal bacteria to epithelial cells of the ileum as shown in Figs. 1 and 2 of the paper by Hampton & Rosario (137). *Above* is a light micrograph ($\times$ 675) of a villus that shows the attachment of about 10 bacteria to epithelial cells. No cytopathological changes are seen in the involved cells, and the lamina propria shows no inflammatory reaction. The electron micrograph ($\times$ 5475) in the *lower* half of the figure shows portions of 2 epithelial cells with a bacterium attached to each. The attachment zone is outlined by dotted lines and is characterized by thickening of the plasma membrane (*PM*) surrounded by a crescent-shaped area of cytoplasm showing 2 distinct areas of density (*D*). The attachment zone appears to distort an adjacent mitochondrion (*M*). (Photographs kindly supplied by James C. Hampton.)

adequate specimens aspirated from distal segments of bowel.

Collection of intestinal contents in a special capsule that operates in a manner similar to a small-bowel biopsy capsule has been advocated by Shiner (246). Others (140) have described a capsule that is unattached to a tube or wire but can be opened and closed by a high-frequency field whenever collection of a sample is desired. Approaches such as these overcome some but not all the problems outlined above. Direct needle aspiration of gut contents during laparotomy (58) is a method of obtaining samples for bacteriological investigation that has been used by many investigators, but it is of limited value in human subjects since it can only be done on fasting anesthetized patients who for some reason require laparotomy. In general, studies that compare different methods for collecting samples of intestinal contents are lacking, but limited data suggest that direct needle aspiration provides results similar to aspiration of contents through a tube (3) and that the bacterial flora obtained is not different whether samples are collected with a Shiner capsule or via a fine polyethylene tube (157). It should be pointed out that all methods currently used in humans are designed to collect the liquid, and therefore easily removed, contents of the gut lumen.

Recent studies in which intestinal fluid was collected by aspiration tube, needle aspiration, or capsules suggest that the normal human small bowel is sterile or only sparsely contaminated with bacteria (3, 35, 58, 115, 140, 157, 203, 231, 247). Similar results were obtained when the small intestine of experimental animals was flushed with saline (26, 211). On the other hand, large numbers of microorganisms are regularly found in the small bowel of experimental animals when segments of intestine together with their contents are homogenized (237, 259). If it is true that the major components of the intestinal flora are intimately associated with and difficult to dislodge from the mucosal surface (237), then aspiration techniques that obtain only the liquid contents of the gut lumen may not provide accurate information, and homogenization techniques, impractical in man, will be required. In any event, available techniques allow at best only an estimation of the *concentration* of microorganisms in a given sample and provide no information concerning the *total numbers* of bacteria present in the intestine.

Conditions within the intestinal lumen cannot be precisely duplicated by available culture techniques, and it is therefore necessary to culture samples on as many different selective media as feasible so that all of the bacteria present in a sample have a maximum opportunity to grow. In addition, samples must be adequately diluted so that microorganisms that grow well in artificial media do not overgrow others that may be present in large numbers in the sample but do not proliferate rapidly when cultured. At the

TABLE 3. *Fecal Flora of Young and Adult Animals*

	Log_{10} Count Viable Organisms/g*				
	Coliforms	Clostridia	Streptococci	Bacteroides	Lactobacilli
Infants					
Cattle	8	2	7	10	9
Chickens	9	3	7	9	9
Rabbits	8	0	8	9	0
Pigs	8	5	7	8	9
Man	9	3	8	10	10
Adults					
Cattle	4	2	5	0	2
Chickens	7	2	8	0	8
Rabbits	3	0	4	9	0
Pigs	7	4	6	6	8
Man	7	3	5	10	9

* Mean values compiled from data of Smith & Crabb (257–259).

present time adequate bacteriological examination of specimens obtained from the intestinal tract should include serial dilution of the sample to a final dilution of at least 10^9, use of at least 8–10 different selective media, and prompt culture of the diluted samples under strict anaerobic as well as aerobic conditions. Detailed descriptions of this kind of methodological approach are now available (237, 259). Unfortunately, many bacteriological investigations of the gut have not utilized adequate culture methods. Failure to find bacteroides in the colon of dogs (52), for example, is probably due to inadequate dilution of samples rather than actual absence of these microorganisms. A recent study of the microbial populations of the small and large intestine of cattle (181) emphasizes the inadequacy of available bacteriological techniques. These workers found many bacteria not previously described and estimated that they recovered only 1–10 % of the microorganisms present.

When bacteria are cultured by standard techniques, microbial proliferation results in alterations in the nutrient content, pH, and redox potential of the stagnant medium, which in turn must ultimately affect the growth and metabolic activity of the bacteria. In the intestine, however, nutrients are constantly supplied from proximal regions while microorganisms and their metabolites are removed distally. Thus conditions within the intestinal lumen are more closely simulated by continuous-flow than by conventional culture techniques. Indeed, certain interbacterial antagonisms known to occur in the gut lumen can be observed in continuous-flow cultures and yet are not reproduced with conventional techniques (109, 223).

FACTORS AFFECTING ENTERIC BACTERIAL POPULATIONS

From the preceding summary it is apparent that many factors, including the manner in which specimens are collected and cultured, determine the character of the intestinal bacterial flora. Brief consideration of these determinants is necessary, although not all are known and many are poorly understood. During the first few days of life the fecal flora is remarkably similar from one host species to another. However, as shown in Table 3, marked differences, particularly of a quantitative nature, gradually develop in the enteric bacterial populations of the different animal species (258, 259). The species differences observed in adult animals are attributable to the fact that as the animals age increasing dissimilarities develop between species in terms of environs, diet, and habits as well as the structure and function of the alimentary tract. For example, one might expect the ecology of the gut lumen in the suckling calf with an undeveloped rumen to be quite similar to that of the human infant and yet quite different from that of the adult cow possessing a massive rumen and ingesting grasses.

Environmental Factors

Undoubtedly the nature of the enteric flora is to some extent determined by the surroundings in which the host animal exists. Except when this environment is altered by extreme measures, however, it is often difficult to demonstrate a striking effect on bacterial populations. If the host is reared from birth in a germ-free environment, of course the intestinal tract remains sterile (192). Similarly, marked changes in the enteric flora develop when animals are carefully raised in clean quarters and under rigidly controlled conditions to prevent contamination by microorganisms present in the intestinal tract of man and conventionally raised animals (84). Colonization of chick intestine by lactobacilli may be delayed as long as 3 weeks by making no change other than raising the animals in a room not previously housing chickens (17). However, except for these situations in which the degree of "cleanliness" of the environment is deliberately controlled, there is little to suggest that the habitat of the host has any predictable effect on the intestinal bacterial populations. Although often mentioned, no important influence of geography or of climate on the enteric flora of healthy animals including man has yet been documented (230). It has been shown, however, in the guinea pig that *E. coli* is absent from the intestine in winter and present in summer (102).

An environmental factor alleged to influence enteric bacteria is the kind of food available to the host. The large and conflicting literature concerned with the effects of diet on intestinal bacterial populations will not be reviewed here, but the need for further systematic studies (301) should be emphasized. Previous (219) as well as more recent (123, 170, 257, 259) investigations suggest that only extreme, rather unphysiological alterations in diet are accompanied by distinct changes in the enteric flora. Only when very large quantities of lactose are fed is the number of lactobacilli increased, and lactose feeding does not result in complete replacement of the flora by lactobacilli (123, 219, 257, 259, 305). Enteric microbial populations of rabbits fed grasses or cereals are about the same (257).

Although diets extremely high in meat protein (257, 259) or casein are associated with a decreased concentration of lactobacilli and increases in coliforms and enterococci, prolonged fasting or feeding of large quantities of food usually has more effect on the enteric flora than the specific kinds of food ingested (219, 259). A recent detailed study of the fecal flora in human subjects failed to demonstrate any important changes associated with differences in diet (170).

When one considers the nutritional requirements of intestinal bacteria and the various sources of intraluminal nutrients available to these microorganisms, it is not surprising that extreme alterations in diet are necessary to produce relatively minor changes in the enteric flora. Bacteria must compete with the intestinal absorptive cell for nutrients, and since the bulk of the enteric flora is located in the colon, absorbable constituents of the diet are largely unavailable for bacterial utilization. Instead bacterial growth depends on dietary substances that are not digested and absorbed by the host, such as cellulose, or on nutrients supplied directly by the host, which would include desquamated mucosal cells as well as proteins and other substances secreted into the intestinal lumen. Even intestinally excreted waste products such as urea and ammonium can be efficiently utilized by enteric microorganisms (285). Under these circumstances there is little reason to expect that minor or relatively physiological changes in diet would markedly influence intestinal bacterial populations. In special situations, however, the kind of food eaten may have important effects. The poorly developed enteric flora of Antarctic birds (248), for example, can be attributed to antibacterial substances in the algae constituting the major portion of their diet (249).

Bacterial Interactions

Although there is considerable variation in the microbial populations from one host species to another or even from one individual to another, the intestinal flora of a given individual or animal colony remains remarkably constant and tends to resist invasion by new bacterial species (134, 170, 202, 209, 241, 312). The intestinal lumen is infected with a mixture of microorganisms, and the character and stability of the enteric flora are largely determined by the interactions of the various bacterial species present. The mechanisms by which one bacterial species may affect the growth of another are outlined in Table 4. Examples of each mechanism have been described in previous reviews (76, 109, 231). These bacterial interactions are particularly important in any consideration of the pathogenesis of bacterial enteritis.

Competition for available nutrients plays an important role in bacterial interactions. The nutritional requirements of normal intestinal bacterial populations have not been defined, but in the rat it has been indirectly estimated that the enteric flora ultimately utilizes approximately 10% of the host's caloric intake (32). If nutrients were available in excess and there were no mechanisms for limiting bacterial growth of enteric flora, intestinal bacterial proliferation would soon overwhelm the host (264). Thus the limited availability of nutrients is a major factor in checking intestinal bacterial growth and is an important determinant of the kinds of bacteria present (231). Ozawa & Freter (209) have described experiments in continuous-flow cultures and in mouse intestine that show maintenance of a given *E. coli* strain in the intestine depends on the efficiency with which the strain competes for fermentable carbon sources under the prevailing highly reduced conditions. In order to colonize the intestine more or less permanently, a bacterial species must be capable of rapid growth at low concentrations of these carbon sources in a reduced environment.

One bacterial species or strain may antagonize another by altering the pH or the redox potential, by producing a toxic metabolite such as H_2O_2, or by synthesizing more complex antibiotics. It should be emphasized that most investigations of such inter-

TABLE 4. *Interactions of Intestinal Microorganisms*

I. Intermicrobial antagonisms
    A. Competition for available nutrients
    B. Production of harmful conditions
        1. pH
        2. Redox potential
    C. Production of harmful substances
        1. Toxic metabolites (e.g. H_2O_2)
        2. Antibiotics (e.g. colicines)
II. Synergistic interactions
    A. Production of favorable conditions
    B. Production of growth factors
    C. Enzyme-sharing
    D. Transfer of antibiotic resistance

microbial antagonisms have been carried out in vitro in stagnant broth or plate cultures, and similar mechanisms may not necessarily be operative in the intestinal tract. Many reports have indicated that bacterial interactions vary considerably depending on whether they are studied in vitro or in vivo (109, 142, 209, 223), aerobically or anaerobically (272), with solid or liquid mediums (135), or with conventional as opposed to continuous-flow culture techniques (142, 223).

Although many of the complex antibacterial substances produced by microorganisms are poorly understood, considerable information is available concerning colicines, which are powerful antibiotics produced by *E. coli*, salmonella, shigellae, and related bacteria. A similar agent derived from *Pseudomonas aeruginosa* has been termed "pyocine" (147). The striking specificity of colicines is demonstrated by the following (105): *1*) only a few colicines are produced by a given coliform strain, *2*) a colicinogenic strain is never sensitive to the agent that it produces, and *3*) a given colicine inhibits growth of only a few bacterial strains. In general, pathogenic strains of *E. coli* are more likely to be colicinogenic than nonpathogenic strains (212). Transfer of colicinogenic activity from one coliform strain to another or from one species to another has been demonstrated (262). These antibacterial substances are apparently released during bacteriolysis and act at specific receptor sites of sensitive strains. More than 20 colicines with widely differing physical, chemical, and antigenic properties have been isolated. Colicine K isolated from *E. coli* K_{235} has been shown to be a macromolecular complex that is indistinguishable from the O antigen of *E. coli* K_{235} (183). Recently it has been clearly shown that colicine V can be separated from endotoxin by dialysis (38).

There is some indirect evidence that colicines may

be produced in vivo and that these antibacterial substances may contribute to the stability of the enteric flora. Antibacterial substances similar to colicines can be produced in the tissues of mice by subcutaneous and intraperitoneal injections of *E. coli* (38). Halbert (135) showed that children harboring shigella organisms were less likely than uninfected children to have colicinogenic coliform strains in the feces. Recovery from shigellosis in one child was associated with development of an increased number of colicinogenic *E. coli* strains. Studies by Branche et al. (37) in five human volunteers suggested that the ability of *E. coli* strains to maintain themselves in the intestine is associated with their ability to produce colicines. It should be noted, however, that colicine production in these and similar studies is documented by assays performed in vitro rather than in vivo. Indeed, colicines may not be effective within the intestinal lumen of pigs (275) and mice (110, 114). Since, in the absence of serum, endotoxin is able to neutralize the antibacterial activity of colicine, it has been suggested that the combined action of endotoxin and proteolytic enzymes in the intestinal lumen may account for the observed lack of antibiotic effect of colicines in vivo (38).

In some instances intermicrobial antagonisms may actually represent a combination of inhibitory mechanisms. Thus, for example, it has been shown that the bacterial populations of the intestine tend to inhibit the growth of fungi such as *Candida albicans* as a result of competition for foodstuffs (112), production by bacteria of oxidation-reduction potentials unfavorable for fungal growth (210), or bacterial production of an antifungal inhibitory substance (166).

The nature of the enteric flora also depends on the extent to which different bacterial species interact synergistically. Proliferation of aerobic organisms will result in a low redox potential favorable for growth of anaerobes. One bacterial species may synthesize growth factors required by another bacterial species. One bacterial species may promote the growth of another species by allowing the second species to "share" an enzyme system. For example, it has been shown (284) that two strains of *E. coli*, both of which require isoleucine for growth, can thrive when cultured together in an isoleucine-deficient medium. In this case, one bacterial strain is able to synthesize the keto acid for utilization by the second strain. The second strain is unable to synthesize the keto acid but can aminate it to form isoleucine, which then can be utilized for growth by both strains. Mention must also be made of a synergistic interaction that occurs in the

presence of antibiotics. Resistance to one or several antibiotics can be transferred from one species or strain of Enterobacteriaceae to another (294, 295).

Host Factors

The character of the enteric flora is also determined in part by characteristics of the host animal (76). The extent to which gastrointestinal secretions of the host are capable of inhibiting enteric bacterial growth remains uncertain despite numerous investigations (76, 230, 231). Saliva obtained aseptically will actively inhibit growth of various lactobacilli, streptococci, and staphylococci (311) but is also able to serve as the sole nutrient for other organisms such as *S. fecalis* and *B. subtilis* (306). It is not known, however, whether saliva or other factors in the oral cavity have any effect in vivo on the character of the enteric flora.

The effect of gastric acid secretion on the intestinal bacterial populations also remains unsettled. Earlier studies of this subject have been reviewed in recent papers (67, 245). In general, there is a tendency for the numbers of bacteria present in the small intestine to be increased in patients with achlorhydria (57, 67, 245) or after gastric surgery (15, 27, 308) as well as in patients with cirrhosis (182) who often have reduced gastric secretory activity. The reduced gastric acid output that transiently attends gastric freezing is apparently associated with increased bacterial counts in the stomach and small bowel of dogs (139). All investigations concerned with the effects of reduced gastric secretion, however, show that at least some patients with achlorhydria do not have increased small bowel bacterial counts. Lack of any important effect of gastric secretion in vivo is suggested by the work of Dack & Petran (59), who demonstrated that microorganisms placed in the stomach were recovered from the large intestine to the same extent as were microorganisms placed directly in the small bowel of dogs and monkeys.

In general, the antibacterial activity of gastric juice has been attributed to its acidity (21). However, a more complex mechanism may operate in the rabbit. The suckling rabbit differs from other domestic mammals in that the stomach and small bowel are virtually sterile (258). Recent studies (44) suggest that this situation occurs in the rabbit because of: *1*) the high fat content of rabbit milk; *2*) the unique enzyme system of rabbit stomach, which converts the fats in rabbit milk to short-chain fatty acids; and *3*) the pronounced antimicrobial activity of these fatty acids.

There is no evidence that gastrointestinal mucus

has any inhibitory effect on enteric bacteria. Indeed, mucin appears to enhance the virulence of pathogenic microorganisms (256) and to increase survival of lactobacilli and streptococci (251). Similarly, there is no evidence to suggest that intestinal bacteria are adversely affected by the succus entericus, by bile, or by pancreatic juice (59). Secretion of antibodies into the intestinal lumen has recently received considerable attention (266). Antibodies ("coproantibodies") against pathogens such as *V. cholerae* and *Shigella flexneri* (42, 56) have been recovered from feces of infected patients and animals, but gastrointestinal secretion of antibodies active against nonpathogenic microorganisms has not been demonstrated.

Probably the single most important host factor in the control of intestinal bacterial populations is the mechanical cleansing action of intestinal peristalsis. In the relatively stagnant contents of the large bowel, bacterial growth is luxuriant, whereas bacteria are rapidly cleared from the small intestine. Bacteria placed in the small bowel can be quantitatively recovered from the large intestine (59). Furthermore, the rate of removal of bacteria injected into the intestine is not different from that of an inert, poorly absorbed reference substance (71). Thus enteric microorganisms do not appear to be destroyed in the small intestine but are transported intact along its length at a relatively rapid rate. As discussed in detail below, the importance of the cleansing action of peristalsis is emphasized by the fact that whenever normal intestinal peristalsis is for any reason slowed or interrupted, bacterial overgrowth rapidly ensues. A precisely opposite situation exists in the bat (165), which has a markedly reduced bacterial flora, a short small bowel, no colon, and a shortened intestinal transit time.

Florey's (100) classic demonstration that bacteria-sized particles are wrapped in mucus "packets" and carried through the gut lumen suggests that mucus may aid in this mechanical removal of bacteria from the intestine. A role for mucus is further supported by the finding of microorganisms concentrated in the mucous layer that lines the gastrointestinal mucosa (89, 237).

An important influence on enteric bacterial populations is the coprophagy practiced by some host species. However, there is not complete agreement concerning the changes that occur when coprophagy is prevented. It has been shown that if coprophagy is prevented in rats by the use of plastic tail cups a striking decrease occurs in the number of lactobacilli in the cecum or feces (98, 126) and that this alteration is not affected by diet (98). Smith (257), on the other hand, reported that prevention of coprophagy in rabbits, rats, and guinea pigs resulted in reduced numbers of lactobacilli only if the animals were fasted for 24 hours. In another study (172) the lactobacillus populations in the feces and stomach contents of rats were not altered when coprophagy was prevented.

Antibiotics

Consideration of antibiotics as a determinant of the nature of the enteric flora is justified by their widespread use not only in disease states but also in the feeding of domestic animals. Indeed, even the so-called autochthonous flora is disrupted by antibacterial drugs (90). Unfortunately, however, the changes in the enteric flora induced by antibiotics are so variable that an attempt to describe them seems pointless (76). Numerous reviews (64, 176, 177, 184, 302) of the effects of various antibiotics on intestinal bacterial populations emphasize the conflicting results obtained, and it is apparent that the effects of a given antibiotic depend on many variables. These include the dose of the agent as well as the frequency, route, and duration of its administration (177), the species of the host (76, 155), the host's dietary intake (90), the season of the year (43), the extent to which colonic contents are liquefied (177), and the manner in which intestinal contents are collected and cultured (176, 184, 188, 229). Furthermore, the effects of antibiotics on the enteric flora are particularly difficult to evaluate in view of the limitations of available bacteriological methods that estimate the concentrations rather than the total numbers of bacteria present in any portion of the intestinal lumen. Another problem related to antibiotic-induced changes in the enteric flora is raised by the fact that microorganisms may exist in the gut as protoplasts that may respond in an atypical fashion to antibiotics (199). Finally, results will be influenced by development of bacterial resistance to antibiotics, and the situation is further complicated by the fact that resistance to one or several antimicrobial agents can be transferred from one strain or species of Enterobacteriaceae to another (294). This phenomenon is discussed in connection with enteric infections.

Although intestinal microbial populations are undoubtedly influenced by antibacterial substances, the resulting changes are so unpredictable and depend on so many factors difficult to control that experiments in which antibiotics are used to demonstrate the effects of the enteric flora on host function are of limited value. Predictable and reproducible results are more readily obtained when germ-free (192) or pathogen-free (87) animals are purposely contaminated with specific bacterial species and strains under controlled conditions.

EFFECTS OF ENTERIC BACTERIA ON THE INTESTINE

Changes in the bacterial populations of the intestinal tract are associated with alterations in the nutritional status (155, 177) and various other characteristics (87, 192) of the host. It is reasonable to speculate that such alterations may result in part from an effect of the enteric flora on the intestine itself, since considerable experimental evidence suggests that these bacteria influence the structure, cell kinetics, and function of the intestinal mucosa as well as metabolism of various substances within the intestinal lumen.

Morphology

Marked changes occur in the intestinal structure of animals raised in a germ-free environment. In the absence of normal enteric bacteria the intestine is thinner and lighter in weight than in conventionally reared control animals (2, 118, 267). This change has been noted in germ-free guinea pigs, rats, mice, and chicks and appears to be due largely to a marked reduction in the cellular infiltration of the lamina propria and an overall decrease in lymphatic and reticuloendothelial tissue in the intestinal wall.

Sprinz and his colleagues have described in detail the appearance of the intestinal mucosa in germ-free guinea pigs (267, 268) and mice (1), and similar changes occur in rats (47). The principal changes are shown in Figure 4. Since many so-called normal characteristics of the mucosa fail to develop in the absence of a bacterial flora, the intestinal mucosa of conventionally reared germ-free animals can be said to be in a state of "physiological inflammation" (1) when compared to that of germ-free animals. The lamina propria in the germ-free animal consists of a sparse stroma containing only a few lymphocytes and mononuclear cells. Plasma cells are absent. Peyer's patches are reduced in size and number in the germ-free animal and show fewer reactive centers, very small numbers of plasma cells, and little mitotic activity. The relative number of goblet cells appears to be increased (267, 269). Total intestinal mucosal thickness is reduced in the germ-free animal, and there is marked reduction in the depth of mucosal crypts. Villi are more slender and more regular in appearance than in conventional animals. Although the ratio of villus length to crypt depth is increased (1), when measured systematically the absorptive surface area per unit length of intestine is reduced in the germ-free chick (120). The number of mitotic figures in the crypts is significantly reduced.

These morphological alterations, particularly the findings in the crypts, suggest that the rate of regeneration of the intestinal mucosa may be slower in the germ-free state. Indeed, autoradiographic investigations performed after injection of tritiated thymidine into germ-free mice have shown that the rate of cellular transit from crypt to villus tip is significantly reduced in the duodenum (171) and in the ileum (1). In the ileum newly labeled cells reached the extrusion zone at the tip of the villus within 2 days in conventional mice compared with 4 days in germ-free animals. A similar decrease in cell turnover was observed in the lamina propria and in Peyer's patches (1). Experiments must now be designed to determine whether this reduced turnover rate occurs because the presence of bacteria in some way stimulates cellular regeneration or because the proliferative capacity of cells in the germ-free animal is somehow impaired.

The intestinal mucosa rapidly assumes the "normal" appearance observed in conventionally reared animals when the germ-free animal is monocontaminated by cultures of *Cl. welchii* (118), *S. faecalis* (118), or *E. coli* (267) or by mixed bacterial cultures isolated from conventional animals (47). Villi become thicker, crypts deepen, and the lamina propria shows increased numbers of lymphocytes, histiocytes, and macrophages. Also, plasma cells appear. Further support for an effect of enteric bacteria on intestinal mucosal structure is derived from observations made during bacterial overgrowth of the small intestine, but (as discussed in a later section) there is not general agreement concerning these observations.

It should be emphasized that the reduced leukocytic infiltration of the lamina propria observed in the germ-free state may merely represent a diminished capacity to respond to inflammation. At sites distant from the gut, leukocytic infiltration (2) and collagen formation (41) in response to irritants are reduced in germ-free compared with conventional animals.

A striking alteration that occurs in the germ-free intestine is marked dilatation of the cecum. This dilatation is associated with an accumulation of watery fluid in the cecum and has been noted particularly in germ-free guinea pigs (267), mice (1, 238, 253), and rats (92, 149, 171) but not in birds (192). In the

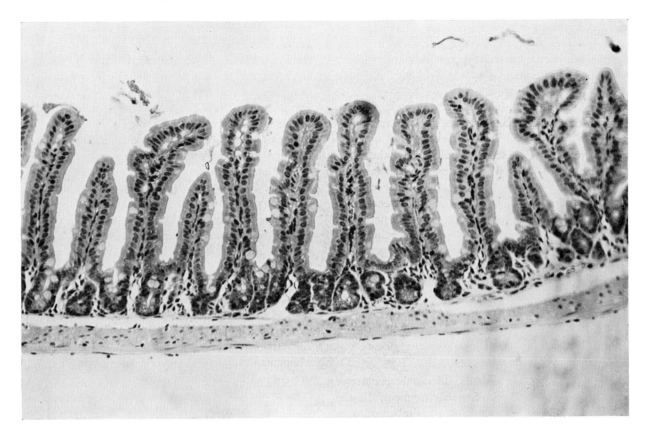

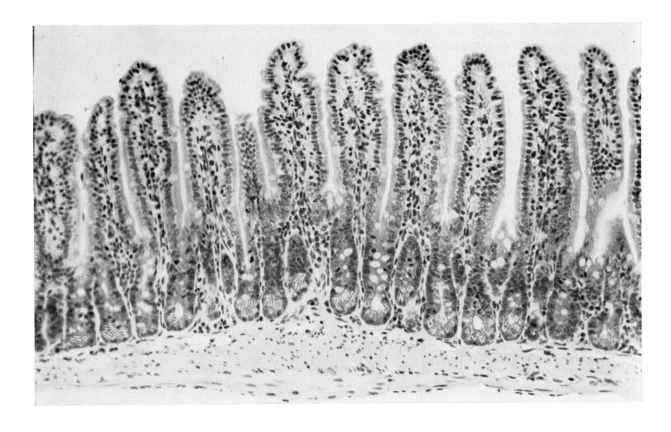

mouse the enlarged cecum on the average accounts for 18% of body weight (253), and in the germ-free guinea pig the cecum may be sufficiently large to account for half the animal's body weight, to interfere with reproduction, and to cause volvulus and subsequent death of the animal (192).

The mechanism responsible for cecal enlargement in animals raised in germ-free environs is not clear. Exposure of germ-free guinea pigs (269), mice (253), or rats (92, 171) to mixed bacterial cultures obtained from conventionally reared animals or from animals grown in a clean, pathogen-free environment (238) results in reduction in cecal size, but in some instances (117) several days must elapse before cecal size approximates that observed in control animals. No reduction in cecal size follows monocontamination of germ-free animals with *E. coli*, *P. vulgaris*, or *L. acidophilus* (117) or exposure to a mixture of aerobic microorganisms (253). On the other hand, reduction in cecal size has been associated with exposure to clostridia or a mixture of two species of bacteroides (253), to an unidentified streptococcus species (149), or to *Salmonella typhimurium* (309).

Recent studies by Gordon (119, 309) attribute cecal enlargement to accumulation of a biologically active substance in the germ-free cecum. This substance is present in greater concentrations in the supernatant fluid of cecal contents obtained from germ-free as compared to conventional mice and rats. After intraperitoneal injection this material causes skeletal muscular paralysis, cardiovascular distress, respiratory failure, and death of the animal. Biological actions parallel those of bradykinin, but, unlike bradykinin, the active compound from cecal contents resists chymotrypsin digestion. Preliminary physical, chemical, and biological assays of this substance suggest that it belongs to the group of hypotensive peptides that include the kinins. When germ-free rats are monocontaminated with *Salmonella typhimurium*, a distinct but transient decrease in cecal size occurs (309). This decrease is associated with reduced concentrations of biologically active substance in cecal contents. When the cecum again becomes enlarged, cecal concentrations of biologically active material are also increased. Thus cecal enlargement is clearly associated with high levels of "bioactive substance," although as yet there is no direct evidence that this substance will in fact cause cecal enlargement. Studies of transport of water and electrolytes by the germ-free cecum and investigation of the effects of Gordon's bioactive substance on intestinal transport might provide information relevant to this problem.

Mucosal Function

In comparison with those concerned with intestinal structure, relatively few studies deal with the effects of enteric microorganisms on intestinal absorption and mucosal function. Since the need for investigation in this area has been obvious for some time, the paucity of relevant data is difficult to explain unless results to date have been negative and therefore unpublished. In any event, there is no evidence to suggest that absorption of sugars or other substances actively transported by the gut is impaired by normal enteric microorganisms of the healthy host. In one study (141) absorption of xylose, as measured both by in vitro and in vivo techniques, was found to be increased in germ-free rats and mice. This increase, although slight, is of interest because according to one report (120) the measured absorptive surface area of the germ-free gut is, if anything, reduced. Antibiotics have been reported to increase absorption of amino acids (46, 82) and calcium (193), but the reported results are not quantitatively impressive, are not necessarily attributable to changes in absorption, and do not exclude a direct effect of the antibiotics themselves on the intestinal mucosa. Recent studies have suggested that alkaline phosphatase (151) and disaccharidase (60, 225) activity of the germ-free intestinal mucosa is increased, but the mechanism for these increases and their significance in relation to absorptive, excretory, and digestive functions of intestinal mucosa remain to be clarified.

Intraluminal Metabolism

Whatever may be their effects on intestinal mucosal function, there can be no doubt that enteric microorganisms play an important role in the metabolism of a wide variety of substances within the intestinal lumen (76). A discussion of all compounds altered by

---

FIG. 4. Ileum of germ-free mouse is shown in *upper* half of figure. The lamina propria is poorly developed, and the crypts are shallow. For comparison the ileum of conventional mouse is shown in the *lower* half of figure. The lamina propria is well developed, the crypts are deeper, and mitotic figures are more numerous. Hematoxylin and eosin; × 144. [Reproduced from Figs. 1 and 2 in the paper by Abrams et al. (1); U.S. Army photograph.]

intestinal bacteria is not possible here, and this section is concerned with bacterial actions of current physiological or clinical interest.

Significant amounts of lipid are recovered from feces of healthy humans or experimental animals ingesting a fat-free diet. Some of this endogenously produced lipid is derived from fat synthesized by enteric microorganisms. There is considerable evidence that fecal fatty acids differ from dietary fatty acids (104, 298). The unusual branched or hydroxylated fatty acids recovered from feces appear to result from bacterial synthesis (8). Although fecal excretion of these unusual fatty acids is markedly reduced in germ-free animals (94), the quantitative significance of bacterially synthesized lipids in normal feces and in steatorrhea is not clear. It has been suggested (154) that standard methods for estimating fecal fat excretion may be in error since hydroxy acids are not extracted. Nevertheless, in one study (78) fecal fat excretion was the same whether or not a method (154) said to extract and measure hydroxylated fatty acids was used.

Of particular importance is the effect of intestinal bacteria on the metabolism of various sterols and steroids (277) including bile acids (220). Some of the transformations of bile acids resulting from bacterial action in the intestine are illustrated in Figure 5. The primary bile acids synthesized by the liver (cholic and chenodeoxycholic acid) are conjugated with taurine or glycine, and these conjugates are excreted in the bile. In a germ-free rat, intestinal hydrolysis of conjugated bile acids does not occur, whereas in the intestine of conventionally reared animals, bacterial conversion of conjugated to free bile acids is complete (125, 130). Hydrolysis of conjugated bile salts has been demonstrated in vitro with pure cultures of *Clostridium* (205), *Enterococcus* (205), and *Bacteroides* (83).

A second major action of enteric microorganisms on bile acids is dehydroxylation of the hydroxy group at C-7 (206). This results in conversion of cholic to deoxycholic acid while chenodeoxycholic is converted to lithocholic acid. Deoxycholic acid is not found in the intestine or bile of germ-free animals (125, 130). Furthermore, mixtures of enteric microorganisms readily cause formation of deoxycholic or lithocholic acid from the primary bile acids in vitro (206). Cholic acid is rapidly converted by intestinal bacteria in vivo to deoxycholic acid, and significant quantities of this bacterial metabolite are reabsorbed and can subsequently be recovered from bile. On the other hand, only trace quantities of lithocholic acid, the major bacterial metabolite of chenodeoxycholate, are found. This difference has been explained by Norman & Shorb (206), who have demonstrated that enteric microorganisms readily attack chenodeoxycholic acid, but the lithocholic acid that is formed, unlike deoxycholic, remains bound to enteric microorganisms and

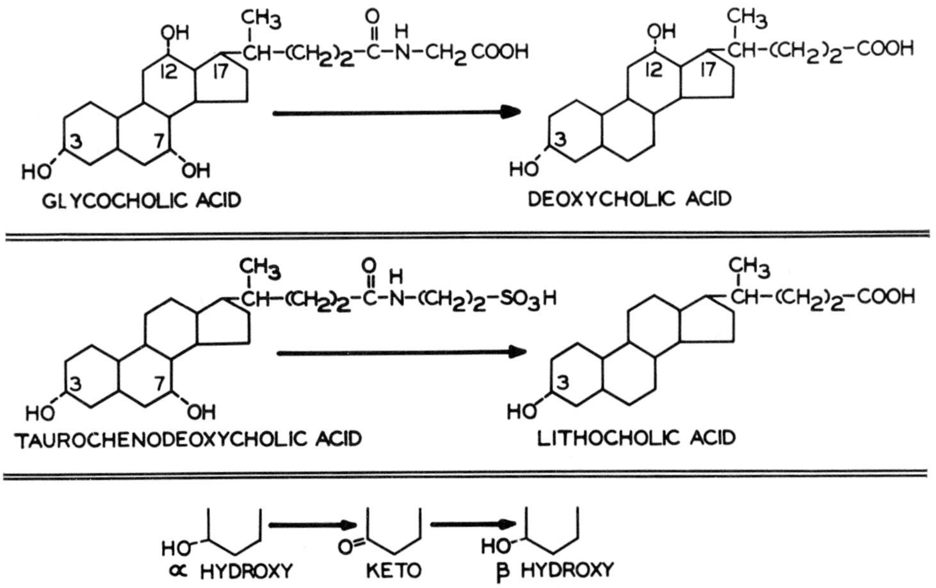

FIG. 5. Effects of enteric bacteria on bile salts. Enteric bacteria are capable of splitting the glycine or taurine conjugates of bile salts and of removing the hydroxyl group at position 7. Oxidation of hydroxyl groups to form keto groups occurs at positions 3, 7 or 12 and is shown in the *lower* portion of the figure.

is not readily reabsorbed. The half-life of ^{14}C-labeled cholic acid is prolonged in the germ-free and antibiotic-treated animal (125, 130). The slow turnover and resulting increased body pool of bile acids in the germ-free state have been attributed to increased intestinal reabsorption and diminished fecal loss (130). In conventional animals, however, bile salt metabolites bind to enteric microorganisms, so that these metabolites are not available for reabsorption (129).

Although 7-dehydroxylation is readily demonstrated in vitro with mixtures of bacteria cultured from the intestine (206), demonstration of this reaction with pure cultures has been difficult (221). Recently, dehydroxylation of chenodeoxycholic acid has been shown with strains of a previously undescribed anaerobic, gram-positive, nonmotile, rod-shaped microorganism isolated in pure culture from rat and human feces (129).

Several other metabolic transformations occur when bile acids are exposed to enteric bacteria, and feces therefore contain an extremely complicated mixture of bacterial metabolites of the primary bile acids (129). In addition to hydrolysis of conjugates and 7-dehydroxylation, oxidation of hydroxyl groups at C-3, C-7, and C-12 also occurs to form keto groups, which can then be reduced to either α- or β-hydroxyl groups. Finally, bacterial action can result in the production of unsaturated derivatives. Thus the potential number of metabolites is large, and indeed seven bacterial metabolites of chenodeoxycholate have already been isolated from man (129).

Degradation of proteins and other nitrogenous compounds by enteric bacteria has important physiological and clinical implications. Some of the substances subjected to bacterial catabolism within the intestinal lumen include pancreatic enzymes (34, 138, 169), bilirubin (128), mucus (175), and urea (216). Ammonia is a major product of protein and urea degradation by bacteria (216), and ammonia levels in the portal vein are markedly reduced in antibiotic-treated (250) or germ-free (290) animals. Little is known about the relative quantitative importance of the various bacterial reactions that result in ammonia production from nitrogenous substrates, but it is apparent that the quantity of ammonia produced depends on the kinds and numbers of microorganisms present and the nature and quantity of substrate available to the enteric flora.

An important source of bacterially produced ammonia is urea, which diffuses freely from the plasma into the gut. More than a fourth of circulating urea is degraded to ammonia and carbon dioxide by urease present in the gastrointestinal tract (288). The extent to which urea catabolism is accomplished by intraluminal as opposed to intramucosal urease has not been established. Although the bacterial origin of intraluminal urease is widely accepted, the origin of urease within the gastric mucosa is debated (53, 167). In any event, an important role for intestinal bacteria in urea catabolism seems certain in view of the marked reduction in the rate of urea degradation observed in germ-free rats (92, 173) and in subjects given broad-spectrum antibiotics (22, 174, 288).

Although the precise role of ammonia remains to be determined, considerable evidence indicates that bacterial catabolism of nitrogenous substrates is important in hepatic coma, and an association is widely recognized between this disorder and enteric microorganisms (49). In recent years several methods for reducing or altering the enteric flora have been reported to benefit patients with hepatic coma. The most widely used approach is the administration of a broad-spectrum, poorly absorbed antibiotic together with cathartics and enemas. When this mode of therapy is ineffective or contraindicated, other approaches are available. Improvement has been reported in patients whose colonic flora has been eliminated by surgical excision or bypass of the colon (9, 69, 153, 185, 227, 287). This approach may be of limited value, however, since ultimately the terminal ileum is likely to dilate and become the site of profuse intestinal growth (50). Other attempts to improve hepatic coma, directed against bacterial urease, include the use of urease antibodies (279) and urease inhibitors (97) as well as feeding of lactobacilli (96, 179, 224) or lactulose (24) to overcome enteric urea-splitting microorganisms.

It should be emphasized that biologically active compounds other than ammonia may result from microbial action within the intestinal lumen. As a result of the findings in hepatic coma and uremia, the possibility originally championed by Metchnikoff (189) must again be entertained, namely, that nitrogenous compounds produced by bacteria within the gut may be harmful to the host, particularly if these substances are allowed to accumulate as a result of inadequate hepatic detoxification or poor renal excretion. It has been suggested that a number of incompletely characterized organic substances that accumulate in the blood of patients with renal failure may be of bacterial origin (168). In the fasting state, nephrectomized germ-free rats survive longer than do control animals contaminated by mixed bacterial flora obtained from conventional rats (92). Whether prolongation of life under these circumstances results from diminished enteric formation of "toxins" remains to be determined, but there is considerable evidence that several aromatic compounds are derived from bacterial metabolism within the intestinal lumen (76).

One source of these aromatic compounds is known to be tryptophan. Bacterial decarboxylation of this amino acid results in the formation of a biologically active amine, tryptamine (303). In the presence of bacterial overgrowth, intraluminal formation of tryptamine is increased (75), but hepatic and intestinal mucosal monoamine oxidase activity causes rapid conversion of the amine to indoleacetic acid (303). Thus even when the small bowel is massively contaminated with microorganisms, tryptamine does not accumulate in the blood or urine although urinary excretion of indoleacetic acid is increased in this situation (75).

One bacterial species, *Chromobacterium violaceum*, has been shown to hydroxylate tryptophan at the 5-position with subsequent formation of a biologically active amine, 5-hydroxytryptamine (serotonin) (198). However, formation of 5-hydroxyindole compounds has not been described in microorganisms usually present in the gut, and urinary excretion of serotonin or its metabolite, 5-hydroxyindole acetic acid (5-HIAA), is not increased in rats with localized small intestinal stasis and bacterial overgrowth (81). Nevertheless, increased blood levels of serotonin and increased urinary excretion of 5-HIAA have recently been reported in dogs and patients with intestinal obstruction and has been attributed to increased intestinal bacterial activity (293). The reasons for these opposing findings are not apparent, nor is it clear why in this last study (293) intestinal stasis resulting from adynamic ileus was not associated with increased production of 5-hydroxyindole compounds.

Certain enteric microorganisms are capable of splitting the side chain of tryptophan to form indole, which is subsequently metabolized by intestinal and hepatic tissue enzymes to form indoxyl sulfate (indican). Increased excretion of a variety of indolic substances including indican is observed in clinical and experimental disorders characterized by small-bowel bacterial overgrowth (81, 156, 271). In addition, indican and other indoles are absent from the urine of germ-free rats (36, 48, 286). Although a significant biological effect of these or similar aromatic compounds has not been directly demonstrated, this possibility deserves further investigation. An important role for histamine produced by intestinal bacteria seems un-

likely, however, since urinary excretion of this amine is similar in germ-free and conventional animals (127).

ROLE OF ENTERIC BACTERIA IN DISORDERS OF THE INTESTINE

Until broad-spectrum antibiotics and practical methods for rearing germ-free animals became available, it was difficult to document the possible influences of normal intestinal microorganisms on gastrointestinal disease. Recent years, however, have witnessed intense investigation and continually changing concepts in this area. Since relevant information is still relatively new and incomplete, this survey is limited to a description of three kinds of intestinal dysfunction in which indigenous enteric bacteria clearly appear to be of importance and in which mechanisms can be discussed with some confidence.

Specific Enteric Infections

There are three generally recognized ways in which normal intestinal bacteria may contribute to the development of specific enteric infections. First, microbial populations of the gut generally tend to remain stable and to resist invasion by pathogenic bacteria. Thus alteration of the "normal" intestinal flora may increase host susceptibility to enteric infections. Second, the normal enteric flora may directly affect the susceptibility of pathogenic microorganisms to antibiotics. Finally, microorganisms commonly present in healthy intestine may under certain circumstances become pathogenic and cause enteritis. Factors other than the indigenous microbiota that affect host susceptibility to enteric infection have been expertly summarized by Formal et al. (103).

Considerable in vitro and in vivo evidence exists to support the concept that normal enteric microorganisms tend to suppress proliferation of enteropathogenic bacteria. For example, salmonella do not ordinarily colonize mouse intestine, but streptomycin-resistant strains of *S. enteriditis* grow readily in the gut of mice pretreated with streptomycin (29). This antibiotic similarly increases susceptibility of mice to infection with *S. typhimurium* (191). Of the changes in bacterial populations of mouse intestine associated with streptomycin treatment, the most consequential was thought to be reduction in the numbers of *Bacteroides* (195), and indeed cultures of these anaerobes isolated from mouse colon inhibited growth of *S. enteriditis* in vitro

(30, 31). In addition, streptomycin-treated mice and guinea pigs are susceptible to infection by *Shigella flexneria* and *Vibrio cholerae*, but this susceptibility is lost when animals are fed streptomycin-resistant strains of *E. coli* (55, 108). A variety of other common enteric microorganisms also antagonize growth of shigella (109, 223). As might be expected, germ-free mice (208) and guinea pigs (102) fed *S. flexneria* develop severe enteritis, whereas the intestine of conventionally reared animals fails to maintain growth of this pathogen. Germ-free guinea pigs monocontaminated with *E. coli* but not with lactobacilli resist shigellosis as readily as do conventional controls (102). Mice pretreated with streptomycin, erythromycin, or mycostatin are capable of maintaining intestinal growth of enteropathogenic strains of *E. coli*, but feeding an antibiotic-resistant, nonpathogenic *E. coli* results in disappearance of the pathogenic strains (6).

Thus the common enteric microorganisms are largely able to prevent or impair establishment of certain pathogenic bacteria in the gut, but how this is accomplished has not been settled. Production of complex antibiotic substances by normal intestinal bacteria does not appear to play an important role, particularly within the intestinal lumen (55, 108, 109, 209, 223). In the case of in vivo suppression of *S. flexneri* by *E. coli*, there is considerable evidence to suggest that the latter microorganism successfully competes for limited fermentable carbon sources in the reduced environment of the gut lumen (109). Studies with continuous-flow culture techniques (209) suggest that this mechanism may operate in other situations and may explain the ability of established, "resident" strains of *E. coli* to prevent successful invasion by a transient "invader" strain of the same species.

However, successful competition for available nutrients does not account for all intermicrobial antagonisms. Growth of salmonella, for example, appears to be suppressed by a very different kind of mechanism (30, 31). It has been clearly shown that the enteric flora prevents proliferation in mouse intestine of *S. typhimurium* (190) and *S. enteriditis* (30, 31) by producing an environment within the intestinal lumen that is unfavorable for growth of the pathogen. The important environmental alterations include accumulation of acetic, butyric, and proprionic acids, together with a lowering of pH and oxidation-reduction potential. Administration of streptomycin markedly reduces the number of viable *Bacteroides* (195), reverses these environmental alterations (30, 31), and permits proliferation of resistant salmonella organisms.

Not always does the normal intestinal flora adversely affect enteric pathogens; in fact, in some instances the presence of these indigenous microorganisms is necessary. *Endamoeba histolytica* is unable to infect the germ-free guinea pig and becomes established only when the germ-free animal is contaminated with *E. coli*, *A. aerogenes*, or *B. subtilis* (217). Similarly, a variety of normal enteric bacteria tend to promote growth of *Trichinella spiralis* in the intestine of mice (270).

The normal microbial flora can also profoundly influence the course of enteric infections by directly affecting the sensitivity of pathogens to antibiotics. Japanese workers were the first to show that resistance to one or several antibiotics may be transferred from one species or strain of Enterobacteriaceae to another. This early work has been reviewed in detail by Watanabe (294). Although mortality due to bacillary dysentery in Japan and elsewhere has diminished in recent years, the number of patients infected has steadily increased (235, 294). This increase is associated with a steady rise in the number of antibiotic-resistant strains of shigella (295), which in turn is readily attributable to infectious drug resistance. Several excellent recent reviews of the problem are available (4, 61, 295).

Resistance to one or several antibiotics is transferred from one enteric microorganism to another by means of self-replicating, extrachromosomal genetic elements that resemble episomes and are called "R factors." The hypothetical portion of the R factor that mediates transfer of drug resistance from one bacterial cell to another is known as the "resistance transfer factor." Intact living cells of both donor and receptor strains are required for transfer to occur. The transfer occurs within minutes and is particularly rapid and complete when the donor cells have themselves repeatedly been infected with R factor. Transferable resistance to penicillin, Ampicillin, streptomycin, tetracycline, chloramphenicol, sulfonamides, furazolidone, kanamycin, and neomycin, or to any combination of these drugs, has been demonstrated. Indeed, transfer of resistance to multiple antibiotics is commonly observed, and an R factor conveying resistance to seven antibiotics, all transferred at one time, has been described (61). Transfer of antibiotic resistance from nonpathogenic coliforms to virulent shigella or salmonella has frequently been reported. Resistance to antibiotics and the capability to transfer resistance survive several serial passages through culture media (260). The phenomenon can be demonstrated not only in vitro but also in the intestine of experimental animals (124, 289).

The importance of infectious drug resistance is emphasized by several facts: *1*) nearly all multiply-resistant strains of pathogens show resistance-transfer capability (45); *2*) infectious drug resistance has now been reported from many parts of the world (254); *3*) infectious spread of antibiotic resistance can be observed not only in microorganisms causing enteric infections but also in Enterobacteriaceae isolated from the urine of patients with urinary tract infections (255); and *4*) multiple drug resistance can be transferred from nonpathogenic enteric microorganisms of domestic animals to bacteria pathogenic for man (5, 260). The last observation clearly indicates that the practice of mixing antibiotics with the feed given to livestock (76) must be carefully re-examined. This formidable defense mechanism that Enterobacteriaceae have developed provides a powerful argument against unwarranted use of antibiotics.

Bacterial species usually considered normal may themselves, under certain circumstances, be pathogenic and cause enteric infections. In domestic animals it has long been known that diarrheal disease may be associated with massive enteric overgrowth of certain strains of *E. coli* (263). In guinea pigs, coliforms normally constitute a minor part of the enteric flora. When these animals are given penicillin, however, rapid proliferation of coliforms in the small intestine follows, associated with a severe and diffuse enteritis (95). Occasionally observed in adults (187), diarrhea due to enteropathogenic strains of *E. coli* is most often observed among infants during the summer months (204). The evidence that has established certain *E. coli* serotypes (particularly types 005:B5, 0111:B4, and 0127:B8) as a cause of diarrhea has been summarized in detail elsewhere (76, 204); it is sufficient to state here that epidemics due to these serotypes have been well documented by fecal cultures, serum antibody titers, and clinical and bacteriological responses to antibiotic therapy. It should be emphasized, however, that enteropathogenic strains of *E. coli* can be isolated from a significant proportion of healthy infants without diarrhea (265). Therefore careful clinical, bacteriological, and serological observations are all necessary before diarrhea is attributed to these microorganisms.

It is not clear why one strain of *E. coli* should be enteropathogenic whereas another is harmless. Enteropathogenic strains are more likely than nonpathogenic strains to produce inflammation and necrosis when injected into isolated small-bowel loops

of rabbits (63, 186, 278), but the mechanism by which this occurs has not been defined. One determinant of pathogenicity may be the ability to proliferate within the small intestine. Deliberate infection of volunteers with enteropathogenic strains of *E. coli* was associated with growth of these bacteria in the small bowel, whereas diarrhea could not be produced when the pathogen was instilled into the colon (310). In addition, acute enteritis due to *E. coli* in calves (263), piglets (261), and guinea pigs (95) is associated with massive overgrowth of coliforms within the lumen of the small bowel. Kent et al. (159) have further documented the association between enteritis and small-bowel proliferation of a pathogen. Enteritis produced in guinea pigs challenged with *S. typhimurium* is more rapidly fatal if the animals are pretreated with opium. Untreated animals rapidly clear salmonella from the small bowel whereas large numbers of these microorganisms can be harvested from the small bowel of opium-treated guinea pigs.

Pathogenicity may also be determined by the capability of a microorganism to invade the intestinal mucosa. Such invasion has been clearly demonstrated with the electron microscope in experimental shigellosis (276). The only difference Formal et al. (103) could detect between virulent *S. flexneri* and a nonpathogenic mutant strain of the same organism was the ability of the former to penetrate bowel mucosa.

Staphylococcus aureus is another microorganism that, although it often contaminates the healthy intestine, may occasionally cause enteric infection. Ordinarily, *E. coli*, lactobacilli, and other enteric microorganisms tend to inhibit growth of staphylococci (93, 273, 304), and their numbers in the intestine are usually small. However, in the antibiotic-treated patient the usual enteric flora may be suppressed while resistant strains of *Staph. aureus* become predominant. This may result in a diffuse enteritis known as pseudomembranous enterocolitis (25, 65, 222). It should be pointed out, however, that neither antibiotics (215) nor staphylococcal proliferation (66) is absolutely necessary for pseudomembranous enterocolitis to develop. Staphylococci apparently cause enteritis as a result of toxin production since feeding of purified staphylococcal enterotoxin to chinchillas results in severe enteritis (292), and since both acute and chronic enteritis can be produced in dogs by instillation of enterotoxin directly into the small intestine (291). Whether the pseudomembranous enterocolitis observed clinically has a similar pathogenetic basis remains to be determined.

Nonspecific Diarrheas

The normal bacterial populations of the intestine may contribute to diarrheas other than those attributed to specific enteric infections. Mere alteration of the normal intestinal flora has frequently been implicated as a cause of acute diarrheas (299); specifically blamed has been overgrowth of the enteric flora with *S. fecalis* (243), *Cl. welchii* (122), and various *Providence* and *Proteus* species (39, 252). However, normal variations in intestinal bacterial populations have not been clearly defined, and the possible secondary effects of diarrhea on these populations have not been explored in detail. It is therefore difficult to determine accurately the clinical significance of alterations in the enteric flora observed in patients with diarrhea.

In general, an altered enteric flora has been most often implicated in those diarrheas that occur at the time of weaning, during travel from one part of the world to another, and during antibiotic therapy. At the time of weaning, a wide variety of microorganisms invades the intestinal tract in contrast to the relatively simple flora present in the breast-fed infant, and the infant at this time is particularly susceptible to diarrhea (121). Since a specific enteropathogenic agent is frequently not found, there is a tendency to attribute diarrhea to a more general alteration in the enteric flora. Similarly, the acute diarrhea that frequently develops in tourists visiting countries with warm climates and relatively poor sanitation cannot usually be ascribed to known pathogens. A possible explanation might be that exposure to a markedly different microbial environment results in extensive change in the bacterial populations of the gut (158). Imbalance of intestinal microorganisms might also explain the nonspecific diarrhea that occurs after antibiotic therapy. Unfortunately, there is insufficient correlation of careful clinical and bacteriological observations to implicate clearly "dysbacteriosis" (299) in the pathogenesis of diarrhea that occurs so frequently in these three situations (76). Badly needed are definitive bacteriological studies to show whether unequivocal and consistent alterations occur in the intestinal bacterial populations of patients with these nonspecific diarrheas.

One mechanism by which intestinal bacteria may contribute to diarrhea involves bacterial catabolism of unabsorbed carbohydrates. In children (300) and adults (91) with deficiency of intestinal mucosal enzymes that hydrolyze various disaccharides, diarrhea occurs when the appropriate sugar is fed. The unhydrolyzed and therefore unabsorbed disaccharide reaches the lower bacteria-rich intestine where microorganisms ferment it to organic acids including lactic, acetic, and formic acids. This results in lowered stool pH, increased serum lactate, and a metabolic acidosis, particularly in infants. The extent to which these organic acids actually cause diarrhea and whether they irritate the intestinal mucosa or merely increase the osmolarity of intestinal contents remain to be determined. In recent studies impaired carbohydrate absorption was conclusively shown in infants with diarrhea (281, 282). Furthermore, diarrhea in these infants was improved and accumulation of organic acids, serum lactate elevation, and metabolic acidosis were all corrected whenever milk feedings were discontinued and replaced by intravenously administered fluids (281). The implication of this work is that the bacterial populations of the gut may be of pathogenetic importance in infant diarrhea and its metabolic consequences.

Appropriate here is brief mention of a possible relation between enteric microorganisms and ulcerative colitis. Broberger & Perlmann (40) demonstrated antibodies to human colon in the sera of patients with ulcerative colitis and suggested that production of these antibodies may have been stimulated by bowel bacteria. This possibility is supported by more recent studies (214) showing that human ulcerative colitis sera that contain antibodies to human colon also react with a polysaccharide antigen obtained from germ-free rat colon, and that this antibody cross-reacts with polysaccharide antigen extracted from certain strains of *E. coli*. Further support is derived from the fact that rabbits injected with dead enteric bacteria produce autoantibodies to gut tissue, including colonic mucosa (7). Whether immune mechanisms are pathogenetically important in human ulcerative colitis remains debatable, but it now seems likely that intestinal microorganisms may provide the antigenic stimulus for the production of the anticolon antibodies found in the sera of some patients with this disease.

Malabsorption

Intestinal malabsorption often results from profuse growth of intestinal microorganisms within the small-bowel lumen. The importance of normal intestinal peristalsis in limiting bacterial growth is em-

TABLE 5. *Causes of Small-Bowel Stasis Associated with Bacterial Overgrowth*

Condition	Species	Authors
Surgical blind loops	Man	Lyall & Parsons (178)
Surgical blind loops	Dog, rat	Bishop (26)
Jejunal diverticula	Man	Doig & Girdwood (73)
Postgastrectomy stasis	Man	Wirts & Goldstein (308)
Intestinal obstruction	Man	Bishop & Anderson (28)
Intestinal obstruction	Dog	Seyderhelmen et al. (242)
Gastrojejunocolic fistula	Man	Atwater et al. (10)
Jejunocolic fistula	Dog	Jew et al. (152)
Scleroderma	Man	Kahn et al. (156)
Vagotomy	Dog	Ballinger et al. (15)
Anticholinergic drug	Rat	Dixon & Paulley (72)

phasized by the fact that intraluminal proliferation of microorganisms accompanies any clinical or experimental condition that causes stasis of intestinal contents. Table 5 lists some examples of this association. Broadly defined, the so-called "blind-loop syndrome" consists of any disorder of the small bowel conducive to intestinal stasis, intraluminal bacterial proliferation, malabsorption of vitamin B_{12}, macrocytic anemia, and steatorrhea (Fig. 6). Barker & Hummel (18) fully documented the major clinical and pathological features of this syndrome in 1939, and, as indicated in recent reviews (11, 73, 79, 200), subsequent studies have served largely to amplify and confirm the basic concepts of these workers.

The microbial flora that proliferates within the small intestine in either the clinical (73, 156, 161, 178, 234, 308) or experimental (26, 211, 297) blind-loop syndrome is complex and tends to resemble the colonic flora. Bishop's (26) extensive study of the bacteriology of the small bowel in rats and dogs with blind loops demonstrated more than 20 different bacterial species. Unfortunately many bacteriological studies performed in patients have not applied the rigorous techniques necessary. For example, numerous reports of the presence of only one species or strain of microorganism in the small-bowel contents

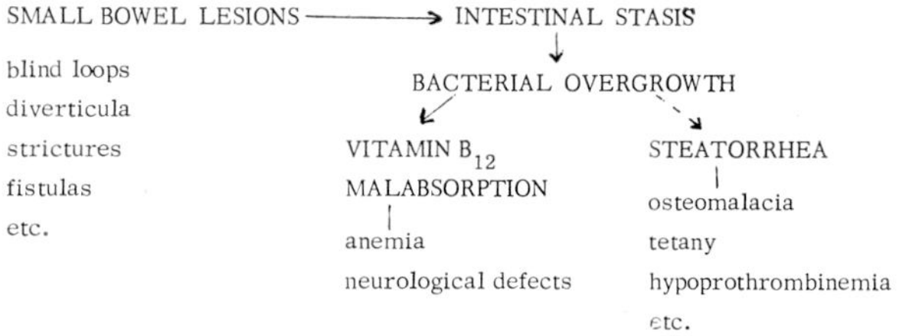

of patients with the blind-loop syndrome more likely reflect inadequate techniques than the actual state of affairs.

The most common clinical feature is a macrocytic anemia associated with megaloblastic bone marrow, low serum vitamin B_{12} levels, and poor absorption of this vitamin. In humans there is little doubt that anemia is due to vitamin B_{12} deficiency. Subacute combined degeneration of the spinal cord, a feature of vitamin B_{12} deficiency, occurs in patients with the blind-loop syndrome, and the anemia responds to physiological doses of vitamin B_{12}. In the experimental animal, however, the cause of the anemia is less certain. Although described as macrocytic (297), the anemia in blind-loop rats occurs too soon to be due to vitamin B_{12} deficiency and is not improved even with massive vitamin B_{12} therapy. A marked reticulocytosis, which incidentally may explain the observed "macrocytosis," further distinguishes anemia in the blind-loop animal from that in patients. A recent study (19) suggests that, unlike the situation in humans, small-bowel bacterial overgrowth in the rat may be associated with significant gastrointestinal blood loss in approximately 20% of the animals. In any event, the only real similarity between the clearly vitamin B_{12}-deficient anemia observed clinically and the unexplained anemia in the experimental state is the fact that both are corrected by broad-spectrum antibiotics (19, 54, 280, 297).

Vitamin B_{12} absorption is decreased in patients (11, 12, 73, 136, 218, 240, 296) or experimental animals (74, 271) with small-bowel bacterial overgrowth. This impaired absorption is clearly not improved by intrinsic factor but can be corrected by antibiotics or, when feasible, by surgical correction of the intestinal stasis (74). The mechanism by which enteric microorganisms impair vitamin B_{12} absorption is not certain, but most of the evidence favors the concept that intestinal bacteria directly compete for dietary vitamin B_{12} and make it unavailable for absorption (73, 74, 80). Experiments designed to demonstrate toxic inhibition of normal vitamin B_{12} absorptive mechanisms have been unrewarding (74, 143). Although vitamin B_{12} bound to viable enteric microorganisms is poorly absorbed (33), it has been argued that simple bacterial uptake may not entirely explain poor absorption of the vitamin since it is well absorbed when bound to dead bacteria (33), and since normal absorption may occur at a time when the small bowel is massively contaminated by enteric bacteria capable of vitamin B_{12} uptake (213).

In any case, a similar direct competitive mecha-

SMALL BOWEL LESIONS ⟶ INTESTINAL STASIS
↓
blind loops   BACTERIAL OVERGROWTH
diverticula   ↙   ↘
strictures   VITAMIN B_{12} STEATORRHEA
fistulas   MALABSORPTION |
etc. | osteomalacia
              anemia   tetany
neurological defects   hypoprothrombinemia
                              etc.

FIG. 6. Pathogenesis of the blind-loop syndrome.

nism does not explain the clinically significant steatorrhea observed in about a third of patients with excessive bacterial proliferation in the small bowel (11) and in experimental animals with intestinal stasis (78, 144, 160, 211). Although bacterial uptake of microgram quantities of vitamin B_{12} seems tenable, the necessary uptake of many grams of lipid by the gut flora is much less likely. Unlike the results observed with vitamin B_{12} (74), only a minute fraction of ^{14}C-labeled lipid fed to animals or a patient with the blind-loop syndrome was found to be bound to enteric microorganisms in the small bowel (78). In addition, recent studies suggest that this form of steatorrhea is not due to increased enteric production of lipid, to severe mucosal injury, or to impaired intraluminal lipolysis (78, 160).

There now exists, however, considerable evidence to suggest that steatorrhea in the blind-loop syndrome results from bacterial metabolism of bile salts (79). The detergent properties of conjugated bile salts normally present in the small-bowel lumen are such that they form mixed micelles with the major products of lipolysis, and it is in this micellar form that these lipid substances are most efficiently absorbed (146). On the other hand, unconjugated or free bile acids are relatively insoluble at the pH of intestinal contents and are therefore unable to contribute to mixed micelle formation (146, 160). Free bile acids may also be ineffective since they are apparently lost from the proximal small-bowel lumen as a result of non-ionic diffusion (70). Furthermore, intestinal mucosal esterification of fatty acids, an essential step in normal lipid absorption, is reportedly stimulated by conjugated bile salts and inhibited by unconjugated or free bile salts, particularly free deoxycholate (62, 236). As outlined earlier, enteric bacteria hydrolyze conjugated bile salts and dehydroxylate cholic acid to form deoxycholic acid. A recent study (83) suggests that several strains of *Bacteroides* isolated from the intestine of blind-loop patients are capable of this hydrolysis, although these results are not entirely consistent with earlier work (205). In any event, an important role for altered bile salt metabolism in the pathogenesis of blind-loop steatorrhea seems likely.

Clinical and experimental observations have provided support for this pathogenetic mechanism. Intestinal contents of blind-loop rats and one patient with the blind-loop syndrome contained free deoxycholate in quantities sufficient to inhibit intestinal esterification of fatty acid in vitro (78). Subsequently, significant quantities of free bile acids were isolated from the small-bowel contents of several patients with intestinal bacterial overgrowth (232, 274) and from dogs with experimentally produced blind-loop steatorrhea (160). A major unanswered question is whether intestinal bacterial action on bile salts produces fat malabsorption because of accumulation of free dihydroxy acids that impair intestinal mucosal function or because of inadequate micelle formation associated with a deficiency of conjugated bile salts. The latter concept is supported by a study in dogs that showed reduced quantities of lipid in micellar form when the gut was overgrown by bacteria (160). Furthermore, feeding these animals conjugated bile salts resulted in reduced fecal fat excretion, suggesting that a deficiency of "good" bile salts rather than accumulation of "bad" bile salts was responsible for steatorrhea. However, it is not known whether these observations can be extended to the clinical situation. Also unknown is whether the concentrations of bacterially produced free bile salts observed in the blind-loop syndrome (78, 274) are sufficient to have any "toxic" effect in vivo. The observed concentrations are apparently capable of deleterious action in vitro (62, 78).

Since excessive growth of microorganisms in the small-bowel lumen is associated with defective absorption of several nutrients, a basic question is whether intestinal mucosal function is generally depressed by the presence of these bacteria or whether all the observed aberrations can be explained on the basis of intraluminal events (77). Although, as outlined above, evidence exists for important effects of bacteria within the lumen, an intracellular effect has not been excluded. If the accumulation of bacteria in small-bowel contents in some way damages the intestinal cell, this effect is apparently sufficiently subtle to escape detection with the light microscope. With the exception of occasional case reports (213, 239), villous architecture and absorptive cells of the intestinal mucosa appear to be quite normal in the clinical (76) and experimental (78, 144, 211) forms of the blind-loop syndrome. The only consistent abnormality noted histologically is increased leukocytic infiltration of the lamina propria. Jejunal mucosa remains undamaged for months after the jejunum has been interposed in the colon and constantly exposed to colonic bacteria (143). Nothing is known, however, about the fine structure of intestinal mucosa exposed to excessive numbers of intraluminal bacteria. Studies of epithelial turnover in the presence of intestinal stasis would also be of interest.

The response of patients and experimental animals

with the blind-loop syndrome to antibiotics raises several important questions. In human subjects tetracycline regularly increases vitamin B_{12} absorption and improves the steatorrhea. Figure 7 clearly demonstrates a consistent response to tetracycline in a patient with surgical blind loops, bacterial overgrowth, macrocytic anemia, and steatorrhea. It is of interest that this patient, as has been true of others (136, 239), showed no objective improvement when treated with neomycin. Since rats with intestinal blind loops (74, 78, 144, 211, 271) show improved vitamin B_{12} absorption and reduced steatorrhea when given neomycin or other poorly absorbed antibiotics, this ineffectiveness of neomycin in the clinical condition is difficult to explain. The following speculations require examination: *1*) neomycin fails to eliminate microorganisms such as *Bacteroides* that may be pathogenetically important in man but not in animals; *2*) neomycin does not come into sufficient contact with those microorganisms close to intestinal mucosa whereas intimate contact is more feasible in the case of antibiotics absorbed and secreted by gut mucosa; or *3*) neomycin itself induces a malabsorptive state (150) in patients but not in rats with intestinal stasis. Recent studies have emphasized the importance

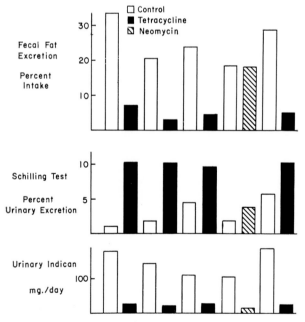

FIG. 7. Studies in a patient with the blind-loop syndrome. Each study period lasted 6 days and was performed after the patient had been treated for at least 2 weeks with tetracycline, with neomycin, or with no antibiotic. Tetracycline consistently reduced fecal fat excretion, improved vitamin B_{12} absorption (Schilling test), and reduced urinary indican excretion. Neomycin, although it reduced indican excretion, did not correct steatorrhea or vitamin B_{12} malabsorption.

of determining the sensitivity of enteric bacteria to antibiotics (156, 234). Why a single brief course of antibiotic therapy will occasionally produce prolonged clinical remission requires clarification.

The question must be raised whether enteric microorganisms contribute in any way to the pathogenesis of absorptive disorders other than the blind-loop syndrome. At one time or another, antibiotics have been reported to be beneficial in nearly every cause of malabsorption (106). Although there is no conclusive evidence that alterations in the enteric flora play a central role in other absorptive disorders, it is possible that bacteria might be important in the pathogenesis of tropical sprue. The inflammatory changes observed in the jejunal mucosa of sprue patients are consistent with a bacterial effect (267, 268), broad-spectrum antibiotics have often been reported to produce clinical remissions in tropical sprue (107, 113, 162, 163, 244), and an epidemic of tropical sprue has been described (13). Bacteriological studies of intestinal contents have generally failed to show any consistent or striking aberrations in patients with tropical sprue (68, 163, 194, 203). Inadequate understanding of the normal enteric flora and inadequate technology rather than a true absence of microbiological alterations may explain this failure. Certainly further investigations of this possibility are in order.

Only when electron-microscopic techniques were applied was the intramucosal presence of bacteria appreciated in patients with malabsorption due to Whipple's disease (51), although in retrospect these microorganisms can be readily seen with the light microscope in properly processed tissue (283). The importance of bacterial invasion in this disease is emphasized by the fact that antibiotic therapy is dramatically beneficial and may be lifesaving. Whether the bacteria found in Whipple's disease are related to the usual enteric flora or are specific pathogens remains to be determined. Also unknown are the host factors that determine susceptibility to this disorder and the mechanisms by which the observed microorganisms alter intestinal mucosal structure and cause malabsorption.

Improved intestinal absorption after antibiotic therapy has been reported in occasional cases (14, 307) in which the cause of malabsorption was not completely understood. In addition, antibiotics appeared to prevent or delay clinical exacerbation when two patients with celiac sprue were exposed to gluten (233). In general, however, there is no convincing evidence that enteric microorganisms are important in gluten-induced enteropathy (celiac sprue) or in other forms of malabsorption except possibly in terms of bacterial metabolism of unabsorbed nutrients.

When a substance is poorly absorbed for any reason, bacterial metabolites of this substance may appear in the feces or urine in increased amounts. Several examples of this phenomenon have been described. Various bacterial metabolites of tryptophan are excreted in increased quantities in the urine of patients with different absorptive disorders (101, 148, 228). Patients with Hartnup disease have impaired renal tubular reabsorption together with poor intestinal absorption of tryptophan. Bacterial conversion of unabsorbed tryptophan results in increased urinary excretion of indican and indoleacetic acid in this disease (197). There may be a similar basis for the indicanuria observed in phenylketonuria (23). Bacterial conversion of poorly absorbed dibasic amino acids may be responsible for the increased quantities of heterocyclic amines in the urine of patients with cystinuria (196). Metabolism or synthesis of lipids by enteric bacteria results in fecal excretion of unusual branched and hydroxylated fatty acids in patients or experimental animals with malabsorption (104, 144, 298). The principal ingredient of castor oil is a hydroxylated fatty acid (ricinoleic acid), and thus it is possible that the diarrhea observed in malabsorption may be due to the cathartic action of bacterially produced lipids. Bacterial metabolism of unabsorbed disaccharides has also been implicated in diarrhea.

Increased bacterial metabolism of intraluminal nutrients observed in various forms of malabsorption could be due either to increased growth of microorganisms in the proximal intestine or to increased quantities of unabsorbed substrate reaching the bacteria-rich distal bowel. The latter mechanism seems more likely since significant bacterial overgrowth within the proximal small bowel has not often been demonstrated in patients with absorptive disorders other than the blind-loop syndrome (3, 180, 247).

Several problems concerning the relation of enteric microorganisms to malabsorption remain entirely unsolved. The question of a possible role for bacterial action on folate metabolism has been frequently raised, since folic acid seems to be particularly important in one kind of antibiotic-responsive malabsorption—namely, tropical sprue. Somewhat low serum folate levels are occasionally observed in patients with bacterial overgrowth of the small bowel (54), and in one such patient macrocytic anemia appeared to be related to folate deficiency (20). Nevertheless, enteric microorganisms are capable of synthesizing large quantities of folic acid and related compounds and of releasing these substances into the incubation medium (73, 163). Furthermore, intestinal absorption of folate is often normal (73), and high rather than low serum folate levels may be present in patients with the blind-loop syndrome (145). Obviously needed are detailed studies of the absorption, catabolism, synthesis, and functional activity of folic acid compounds in the clinical and experimental blind-loop syndromes.

Little is known about carbohydrate absorption in the presence of small-bowel bacterial overgrowth. Absorption of xylose appears to be impaired in some patients but not in others. It has recently been suggested in a preliminary report (114) that intraluminal utilization of xylose by proliferating microorganisms may be responsible for abnormal xylose tolerance tests in the blind-loop syndrome, but further documentation is required. There also exists no adequate explanation for fecal nitrogen loss and low serum proteins present in some patients (12, 218).

The factors that influence host susceptibility to the detrimental effects of small-bowel bacterial overgrowth are poorly understood. Jejunal diverticulosis is a relatively common finding, particularly among older patients, but only a small proportion of patients with multiple jejunal diverticula demonstrate clinically significant malabsorption. On the other hand, an occasional patient with a single large duodenal diverticulum may demonstrate many of the features of the blind-loop syndrome. The need for a better understanding of man's relationship to his enteric flora is obvious.

REFERENCES

1. Abrams, G. D., H. Bauer, and H. Sprinz. Influence of the normal flora on mucosal morphology and cellular renewal in the ileum. A comparison of germ-free and conventional mice. *Lab. Invest.* 12: 355–364, 1963.

2. Abrams, G. D., and J. E. Bishop. Normal flora and leukocyte mobilization. *Arch. Pathol.* 79: 213–217, 1965.

3. Anderson, C. M., and R. F. Langford. Bacterial content of small intestine of children in health, in coeliac disease, and in fibrocystic disease of pancreas. *Brit. Med. J.* 1: 803–806, 1958.

4. Anderson, E. S. Origin of transferable drug-resistance factors in the enterobacteriaceae. *Brit. Med. J.* 2: 1289–1291, 1965.

5. Anderson, E. S., and M. J. Lewis. Drug resistance and

its transfer in *Salmonella typhimurium*. *Nature* 206: 579–583, 1965.

6. ASHBURNER, F. M., AND R. MUSHIN. Experimental intestinal coliform infections in mice. *J. Hyg.* 60: 175–180, 1962.

7. ASHERSON, G. L., AND E. J. HOLBOROW. Autoantibody production in rabbits. VII. Autoantibodies to gut produced by the injection of bacteria. *Immunology* 10: 161–167, 1966.

8. ASSELINEAU, F., AND E. LEDERER. Chemistry and metabolism of bacterial lipides. In: *Lipide Metabolism*, edited by K. Bloch. New York: Wiley, 1960, p. 337–406.

9. ATKINSON, J., AND J. C. GOLIGHER. Recurrent hepatic coma treated by colectomy and ileorectal anastomosis. *Lancet* 1: 461–464, 1960.

10. ATWATER, J. S., H. R. BUTT, AND J. T. PRIESTLEY. Gastrojejunocolic fistulae with special reference to associated nutritional deficiencies and certain surgical aspects. *Ann. Surg.* 117: 414–426, 1943.

11. BADENOCH, J. The blind loop syndrome. In: *Modern Trends in Gastroenterology*, edited by F. A. Jones. New York: Hoeber, 1958, p. 231–242.

12. BADENOCH, J., P. D. BEDFORD, AND J. R. EVANS. Massive diverticulosis of the small intestine with steatorrhea and megaloblastic anemia. *Quart. J. Med.* 24: 321–330, 1955.

13. BAKER, S. J., V. I. MATHAN, AND I. JOSEPH. Epidemic tropical sprue. *Am. J. Digest. Diseases* 7: 959–960, 1962.

14. BALDRIDGE, E. T., AND B. J. HAVERBACK. Unusual malabsorption syndrome (intestinal degradation of pancreatic proteolytic enzymes). *Clin. Res.* 11: 78, 1963.

15. BALLINGER, W. F., J. LIDA, R. T. PADULA, G. E. APORTE, C. W. WIRTS, AND F. GOLDSTEIN. Bacterial inflammation and denervation atrophy of the small intestine. *Surgery* 57: 535–541. 1965.

16. BARBERO, G. J., G. RUNGE, D. FISCHER, M. N. CRAWFORD, F. E. TORES, AND P. GYORGY. Investigations on the bacterial flora, pH, and sugar content in the intestinal tract of infants. *J. Pediat.* 40: 152–163, 1952.

17. BARE, L. N., AND R. F. WISEMAN. Delayed appearance of lactobacilli in the intestines of chicks reared in a "new" environment. *Appl. Microbiol.* 12: 457–459, 1964.

18. BARKER, W. H., AND L. E. HUMMEL. Macrocytic anemia in association with intestinal strictures and anastomoses. *Bull. Johns Hopkins Hosp.* 46: 215–254, 1939.

19. BARRERAS, R., R. DONALDSON, M. MEISS, AND A. MILLER. Gastrointestinal blood loss in the experimental blind-loop syndrome (abstr.). *Clin. Res.* 13: 250, 1965.

20. BARRETT, C. R., AND P. R. HOTT. Postgastrectomy blind loop syndrome: megaloblastic anemia secondary to malabsorption of folic acid. *Am. J. Med.* 41: 629–637, 1966.

21. BARTLE, H. J., AND M. J. HARKINS. The gastric secretion: its bactericidal value to man. *Am. J. Med. Sci.* 169: 373–388, 1925.

22. BELDING, M. D., AND F. KERN, JR. Inhibition of urease by oxytetracycline. *J. Lab. Clin. Med.* 61: 560–566, 1963.

23. BESSMAN, S. P., AND K. TADA. Indicanuria in phenylketonuria. *Metabolism* 9: 377–385, 1960.

24. BIRCHER, J., J. MÜLLER, P. GUGGENHEIM, AND U. P. HAEMMERLI. Treatment of chronic portal systemic encephalopathy with lactulose. *Lancet* 1: 890–893, 1966.

25. BIRNBAUM, D., A. LAUFER, AND M. FREUND. Pseudomembranous enterocolitis. A clinicopathologic study. *Gastroenterology* 41: 345–352, 1961.

26. BISHOP, R. F. Bacterial flora of the small intestine of dogs and rats with intestinal blind loops. *Brit. J. Exptl. Pathol.* 44: 189–196, 1963.

27. BISHOP, R. F. Bacterial flora of stomach and small intestine after gastric surgery. *Ernaehrungsforschung* 10: 417–423, 1965.

28. BISHOP, R. F., AND C. M. ANDERSON. Bacterial flora of stomach and small intestine in children with intestinal obstruction. *Arch. Disease Childhood* 35: 487–491, 1960.

29. BOHNHOFF, M., B. L. DRAKE, AND C. P. MILLER. Effect of streptomycin on susceptibility of intestinal tract to experimental Salmonella infection. *Proc. Soc. Exptl. Biol. Med.* 86: 132–137, 1954.

30. BOHNHOFF, M., C. P. MILLER, AND W. R. MARTIN. Resistance of the mouse's intestinal tract to experimental Salmonella infection. I. Factors which interfere with the initiation of infection by oral inoculation. *J. Exptl. Med.* 120: 805–816, 1964.

31. BOHNHOFF, M., C. P. MILLER, AND W. R. MARTIN. Resistance of the mouse's intestinal tract to experimental Salmonella infection. II. Factors responsible for its loss following streptomycin treatment. *J. Exptl. Med.* 120: 817–828, 1964.

32. BOOTH, A. N. Caloric requirements of rat intestinal microorganisms. *Life Sci.* 3: 215–218, 1963.

33. BOOTH, C. C., AND J. HEATH. The effect of *E. coli* on the absorption of vitamin B_{12}. *Gut* 3: 70–73, 1962.

34. BORGSTRÖM, B., A. DAHLQVIST, B. E. GUSTAFSSON, G. LUNDH, AND J. MALMQUIST. Trypsin, invertase, and amylase content of feces of germfree rats. *Proc. Soc. Exptl. Biol. Med.* 102: 154–155, 1959.

35. BORNSIDE, G. H., AND I. COHN. The normal microbial flora comparative bacterial flora of animals and man. *Am. J. Digest. Diseases* 10: 844–852, 1965.

36. BÖSTROM, H., B. E. GUSTAFSSON, AND B. WENGLE. Studies on ester sulphates. 18. Ester sulphate formation in the germfree rat. *Proc. Soc. Exptl. Biol. Med.* 114: 742–747, 1963.

37. BRANCHE, W. C., JR., V. M. YOUNG, H. G. ROBINET, AND E. D. MASSEY. Effect of colicine production of Escherichia coli in the normal human intestine. *Proc. Soc. Exptl. Biol. Med.* 114: 198–201, 1963.

38. BRAUDE, A. I., AND J. S. SIEMIENSKI. The influence of bacteriocins on resistance to infection by gram-negative bacteria. I. The effect of colicin on bactericidal power of blood. *J. Clin. Invest.* 44: 849–859, 1965.

39. BREIDENBACH, W. C., AND A. MARTIN. Atypical bacterial pathogens in the intestinal tract. *Am. J. Gastroenterol.* 36: 513–520, 1961.

40. BROBERGER, O., AND P. PERLMANN. Autoantibodies in human ulcerative colitis. *J. Exptl. Med.* 110: 657–674, 1959.

41. BRODY, G. L., J. E. BISHOP, AND G. D. ABRAMS. Normal flora and collagen production. *Arch. Pathol.* 81: 258–270, 1966.

42. BURROWS, W., AND L. L. WARE. Studies on immunity to Asiatic cholera. VII. Prophylactic immunity to experimental enteric cholera. *J. Infect. Diseases* 92: 164–174, 1953.

43. CAMPOS, J. V. M., W. HOENER, A. CASTA, L. TRABULSI, AND J. F. PONTES. Changes in intestinal flora under tetracycline. *Gastroenterology* 34: 625–635, 1958.

44. CANANAS, R., AND H. W. SMITH. The identification of the antimicrobial factors of the stomach contents of sucking rabbits. *Biochem. J.* 100: 79–82, 1966.

45. CARPENTER, K. P., AND W. T. DRABBLE. Transferable antibiotic resistance. *Brit. Med. J.* 1: 1553–1554, 1965.

46. CARROLL, R. W., G. W. HENSLEY, C. L. SITTLER, E. L. WILCOX, AND W. R. GRAHAM, JR. Absorption of nitrogen and amino acids from soy bean meal as affected by heat treatment or supplementation with aureomycin or methionine. *Arch. Biochem. Biophys.* 45: 260–269, 1953.

47. CARTER, D., A. EINHEBER, AND H. BAUER. Bacterial colonization of intestine of germ free rats with external esophageal fistula after specific bacterial contamination. *Surg. Forum* 16: 79–80, 1965.

48. CARTER, D., A. EINHEBER, H. BAUER, H. ROSEN, AND W. F. BURNS. The role of the microbial flora in uremia. II. Uremic colitis, cardiovascular lesions and biochemical observations. *J. Exptl. Med.* 123: 251–266, 1966.

49. CHALMERS, T. C. Pathogenesis and treatment of hepatic failure. *New Engl. J. Med.* 263: 23–30, 77–82, 1960.

50. CHAPMAN, M. D., AND H. D. JANOWITZ. Chronic porta-systemic encephalopathy after ileostomy and colonic resection. *Lancet* 1: 1064–1066, 1966.

51. CHEARS, W. C., JR., M. D. HARGROVE, JR., J. V. VERNER, JR., A. G. SMITH, AND J. M. RUFFIN. Whipples disease; a review of 12 patients from one service. *Am. J. Med.* 30: 226–234, 1961.

52. CLAPPER, W. E., AND G. H. MEADE. Normal flora of the nose, throat, and lower intestine of dogs. *J. Bacteriol.* 85: 643–648, 1963.

53. CONWAY, E. J., O. FITZGERALD, K. MCGEENEY, AND F. GEOGHEGAN. The location and origin of gastric urease. *Gastroenterology* 37: 449–456, 1959.

54. COOKE, W. T., E. V. COX, D. J. FONE, M. J. MEYNELL, AND R. GADDIE. The clinical and metabolic significance of jejunal diverticula. *Gut* 4: 115–131, 1963.

55. COOPER, G. N. Experimental shigellosis in mice. I. Chronic infection with *Shigella dysenteriae* type 2. *Australian J. Exptl. Biol. Med. Sci.* 37: 193–200, 1959.

56. COOPER, G. N., AND J. A. PILLOW. Experimental shigellosis in mice. II. Immunological responses to Shigella dysenteric type 2 infections. *Australian J. Exptl. Biol. Med. Sci.* 87: 201–209, 1959.

57. CREGAN, J., E. E. DUNLAP, AND N. J. HAYWARD. The bacterial content of human small intestine in diseases of the stomach. *Brit. Med. J.* 2: 1248–1251, 1953.

58. CREGAN, J., AND N. J. HAYWARD. The bacterial content of the healthy human small intestine. *Brit. Med. J.* 1: 1356–1361, 1953.

59. DACK, G. M., AND E. PETRAN. Bacterial activity in different levels of the intestine and in isolated segments of small and large bowel in monkeys and in dogs. *J. Infect. Diseases* 54: 204–220, 1934.

60. DAHLQVIST, A., B. BULL, AND B. E. GUSTAFSSON. Rat intestinal 6-bromo-2-naphthyl glycosidase and disaccharidase activities. I. Enzymic properties and distribution in the digestive tract of conventional and germ-free animals. *Arch. Biochem.* 109: 150–158, 1965.

61. DATTA, N. Infectious drug resistance. *Brit. Med. Bull.* 21: 254–259, 1965.

62. DAWSON, A. M., AND K. J. ISSELBACHER. Studies on lipid metabolism in the small intestine with observations on the role of bile salts. *J. Clin. Invest.* 39: 730–740, 1960.

63. DE, S. N., K. BHALLACHARYA, AND J. K. SARKAR. A study of the pathogenicity of strains of *Bacterium coli* from acute and chronic enteritis. *J. Pathol. Bacteriol.* 71: 201–209, 1956.

64. DEARING, W. A. Current status of preparation of the intestine for operation. A critical apprasial. *Surg. Clin. N. Am.* 39: 1223–1242, 1959.

65. DEARING, W. H., A. H. BAGGENSTOSS, AND L. A. WEED. Studies on the relationship of staphylococcus aureus to pseudomembranous enteritis and to post antibiotic enteritis. *Gastroenterology* 38: 441–451, 1960.

66. DEARING, W. H., AND F. R. HEILMAN. Micrococcic enteritis as complication of antibiotic therapy: its response to erythromycin. *Proc. Staff Meetings Mayo Clinic* 28: 121–134, 1953.

67. DELLIPIANI, A. W., AND R. H. GIRDWOOD. Bacterial changes in the small intestine in malabsorption states and in pernicious anemia. *Clin. Sci.* 26: 359–374, 1964.

68. DESIA, H. G., D. V. PAREKH, AND K. N. JEEJEEBHOY. Bacteriological study of small intestinal fluid in tropical sprue. *J. Assoc. Physicians India* 14: 203–205, 1966.

69. DIENST, S. G. Treatment of progressive ammonia intoxication by exclusion of the colon. *New Engl. J. Med.* 270: 555–556, 1964.

70. DIETSCHY, J. M., H. S. SOLOMON, AND M. D. SIPERSTEIN. Bile acid metabolism. I. Studies on the mechanisms of intestinal transport. *J. Clin. Invest.* 45: 832–846, 1966.

71. DIXON, J. M. S. The fate of bacteria in the small intestine. *J. Pathol. Bacteriol.* 79: 131–140, 1960.

72. DIXON, J. M., AND J. W. PAULLEY. Bacteriological and histological studies of the small intestine of rats treated with mecamylamin. *Gut* 4: 169–173, 1963.

73. DOIG, A., AND R. G. GIRDWOOD. The absorption of folic acid and labeled cyanocobalamine in intestinal malabsorption with observations on the fecal excretion of fat and nitrogen and the absorption of glucose and xylose. *Quart. J. Med.* 29: 333–374, 1960.

74. DONALDSON, R. M., JR. Malabsorption of Co60-labeled cyanocobalamin in rats with intestinal diverticula. I. Evaluation of possible mechanisms. *Gastroenterology* 43: 271–281, 1962.

75. DONALDSON, R. M., JR. Excretion of tryptamine and indole-3-acetic acid in urine of rats with intestinal diverticula. *Am. J. Physiol.* 202: 289–292, 1962.

76. DONALDSON, R. M., JR. Normal bacterial populations of the intestine and their relation to intestinal function. *New Engl. J. Med.* 270: 938–945, 994–1001, 1050–1056, 1964.

77. DONALDSON, R. M., JR. Malabsorption in the blind loop syndrome. *Gastroenterology* 48: 388–391, 1965.

78. DONALDSON, R. M., JR. Studies on the pathogenesis of steatorrhea in the blind loop syndrome. *J. Clin. Invest.* 44: 1815–1825, 1965.

79. DONALDSON, R. M., JR. Intestinal bacteria and malabsorption. *Ann. Internal Med.* 64: 948–952, 1966.

80. DONALDSON, R. M., JR., H. CORRIGAN, AND G. NATSIOS. Malabsorption of Co60-labeled cyanocobalamin in rats with intestinal diverticula. II. Studies on contents of the diverticula. *Gastroenterology* 43: 282–290, 1962.

81. DONALDSON, R. M., JR., H. A. DOLCINI, AND S. J. GRAY.

Urinary excretion of indolic compounds in rats with intestinal pouches. *Am. J. Physiol.* 200: 794–796, 1961.

82. DRAPER, H. H. Absorption of radiolysine by chick as affected by penicillin administration. *J. Nutr.* 64: 33–42, 1958.

83. DRASAR, B. S., M. J. HILL, AND M. SHINER. The deconjugation of bile salts by human intestinal bacteria. *Lancet* 1: 1237–1238, 1966.

84. DUBOS, R., AND R. W. SCHAEDLER. Some biological effects of the digestive flora. *Trans. Assoc. Am. Physicians* 75: 160–169, 1962.

85. DUBOS, R. J., AND R. W. SCHAEDLER. Some biological effects of the digestive flora. *Am. J. Med. Sci.* 244: 265–271, 1962.

86. DUBOS, R. J., AND R. W. SCHAEDLER. The effect of diet on the fecal bacterial flora of mice and on their resistance to infection. *J. Exptl. Med.* 115: 1161–1172, 1962.

87. DUBOS, R. J., R. W. SCHAEDLER, AND R. COSTELLO. Composition, alteration and effects of the intestinal flora. *Federation Proc.* 22: 1322–1329, 1963.

88. DUBOS, R., R. W. SCHAEDLER, AND R. L. COSTELLO. The effect of antibacterial drugs on the weight of mice. *J. Exptl. Med.* 117: 245–257, 1963.

89. DUBOS, R., R. W. SCHAEDLER, R. COSTELLO, AND P. HOET. Indigenous, normal and autochthonous flora of the gastrointestinal tract. *J. Exptl. Med.* 122: 67–76, 1965.

90. DUBOS, R., R. W. SCHAEDLER, AND M. STEPHENS. The effect of antibacterial drugs on the fecal flora of mice. *J. Exptl. Med.* 117: 231–243, 1963.

91. DUNPHY, J. V., A. LITTMAN, J. B. HAMMOND, G. GORSTNER, A. DAHLQVIST, AND R. K. CRANE. Intestinal lactase deficit in adults. *Gastroenterology* 49: 12–21, 1965.

92. EINHEBER, A., AND D. CARTER. The role of microbial flora in uremia. I. Survival times of germ free, limited flora, and conventionalized rats after bilateral nephrectomy and fasting. *J. Exptl. Med.* 123: 239–250, 1966.

93. EMMANOUILIDOU-ARSENI, A., AND D. SOULTANI. Antibacterial action of candida. *J. Bacteriol.* 80: 137–138, 1960.

94. EVRARD, E., P. P. HOET, AND H. EYSSEN. Faecal lipids in germ-free and conventional rats. *Brit. J. Exptl. Pathol.* 45: 409–414, 1964.

95. FARRAR, W. E., JR., AND T. H. KENT. Enteritis and coliform bacteremia in guinea pigs given penicillin. *Am. J. Pathol.* 47: 629–642, 1965.

96. FENTON, J. C., E. J. KNIGHT, AND F. W. O'GRADY. Treatment of hepatic encephalopathy by alteration of intestinal flora with Lactobacillus acidophilus. *Lancet* 1: 764, 1965.

97. FISHBEIN, W. N., R. P. CARBONE, AND H. D. HOCHSTEIN. Acetohydroxamate: bacterial urease inhibitor with therapeutic potential in hyperammonaemic states. *Nature* 208: 46–48, 1965.

98. FITZGERALD, R. J., B. E. GUSTAFSSON, AND E. G. McDANIEL. Effects of coprophagy prevention on intestinal microflora in rats. *J. Nutr.* 84: 155–160, 1964.

99. FITZGERALD, R. J., J. A. McBRIDE, H. V. JORDAN, AND B. E. GUSTAFSSON. Helically coiled micro-organism from cecum contents of the rat. *Nature* 205: 1133–1134, 1965.

100. FLOREY, H. W. Observations on the function of mucus and the early stages of bacterial invasion of the intestinal mucosa. *J. Pathol. Bacteriol.* 37: 282–289, 1933.

101. FORDTRAN, J. S., W. B. SCROGGIE, AND D. E. POLTER. Colonic absorption of tryptophan metabolites in man. *J. Lab. Clin. Med.* 64: 125–132, 1964.

102. FORMAL, S. B., G. DAMMIN, H. SPRINZ, D. KUNDEL, H. SCHNEIDER, R. E. HOROWITZ, AND M. FORBES. Experimental shigella infections. V. Studies in germ-free guinea pigs. *J. Bacteriol.* 82: 284–287, 1961.

103. FORMAL, S. B., E. H. LABREC, AND H. SCHNEIDER. Pathogenesis of bacillary dysentery in laboratory animals. *Federation Proc.* 24: 29–34, 1965.

104. FRAZER, A. C. Role of lipids in normal metabolism. *Federation Proc.* 20: 146–151, 1961.

105. FREDERICQ, P. Colicins. *Ann. Rev. Microbiol.* 11: 7–22, 1957.

106. FRENCH, J. M. Problems raised by the treatment of steatorrhea with antibacterial drugs. *Postgrad. Med. J.* 37: 259–267, 1961.

107. FRENCH, M. M., R. GADDIE, AND N. M. SMITH. Tropical sprue. A study of seven cases and their response to combined chemotherapy. *Quart. J. Med.* 25: 333–344, 1956.

108. FRETER, R. Experimental enteric shigella and vibrio infections in mice and guinea pigs. *J. Exptl. Med.* 104: 411–418, 1956.

109. FRETER, R. *In vivo* and *in vitro* antagonism of intestinal bacteria against *Shigella flexneri*. *J. Infect. Diseases* 110: 30–46, 1962.

110. FRIEDMAN, D. R., AND S. P. HALBERT. Mixed bacterial infections in relation to antibiotic activities. *J. Immunol.* 84: 11–19, 1960.

111. GAGE, P., C. B. GUNTHER, AND E. H. SPAULDING. Persistence of *E. coli* in the stools of young infants (abstr.). *Bacteriol. Proc.* 117, 1961.

112. GALE, D., AND B. SANDOVAL. Response of mice to the inoculations of both *Candida albicans* and *Escherichia coli*. I. The enhancement phenomenon. *J. Bacteriol.* 73: 616–622, 1957.

113. GARDNER, F. H. Tropical sprue. *New Engl. J. Med.* 258: 791–796, 1958.

114. GOLDSTEIN, F., L. E. CRIDEN, E. R. JENNER, AND C. W. WIRTS. Bacterial utilization of d-xylose. *Gastroenterology* 48: 818–819, 1965.

115. GOLDSTEIN, F., C. W. WIRTS, AND L. JOSEPHS. The bacterial flora of the small intestine. *Gastroenterology* 42: 755–756, 1962.

116. GORBACH, S., R. LEVITAN, L. NAHAS, J. PATTERSON, AND L. WEINSTEIN. Comparison of stool bacterial flora in normal subjects and ileostomy effluent following total colectomy (abstr.). *Gastroenterology* 50: 846, 1966.

117. GORDON, H. A. Morphological and physiological characterization of germ free life. *Ann. N. Y. Acad. Sci.* 78: 208–220, 1959.

118. GORDON, H. A. The germ free animal: its use in the study of "physiologic" effects of the normal microbial flora on the animal host. *Am. J. Digest. Diseases* 5: 841–867, 1960.

119. GORDON, H. A. Demonstration of a bio-active substance in caecal contents of germ-free animals. *Nature* 205: 571–572, 1965.

120. GORDON, H. A., AND E. BRUCKNER-KANDOSE. Effect of normal microbial flora on intestinal surface area. *Am. J. Physiol.* 201: 175–178, 1961.

121. GORDON, J. E., I. D. CHITKARA, AND J. B. WYON. Weanling diarrhea. *Am. J. Med. Sci.* 245: 345–377, 1963.

122. GOUDIE, J. G., AND I. B. DUNCAN. *Clostridium welchii* and neutralizing substances for *Clostridium welchii* alpha toxin in feces. *J. Pathol. Bacteriol.* 72: 381–392, 1956.

123. GRABER, C. D., R. M. O'NEAL, AND E. R. RABIN. Effect

of dietary sodium cholate and lactose on the fecal micro-flora and blood cholesterol of rats. *Gastroenterology* 51: 357–363, 1966.

124. GUINEE, P. A. Transfer of multiple drug resistance from Escherichia coli to Salmonella typhimurium in the mouse intestine. *Antonie van Leeuwenhoek J. Microbiol. Serol.* 31: 314–322, 1965.

125. GUSTAFSSON, B. E., S. BERGSTRÖM, S. LINDSTEDT, AND A. NORMAN. Turnover and nature of fecal bile acids in germfree and infected rats fed cholic acid-24-C¹⁴. *Proc. Soc. Exptl. Biol. Med.* 94: 467–471, 1957.

126. GUSTAFSSON, B. E., AND R. J. FITZGERALD. Alteration in intestinal microbial flora of rats with tail cups to prevent coprophagy. *Proc. Soc. Exptl. Biol. Med.* 104: 319–322, 1960.

127. GUSTAFSSON, B. E., G. KAHLSON, AND E. ROSENGREN. Biogenesis of histamine studied by its distribution and urinary excretion in germ-free reared and not germfree rats fed a histamine free diet. *Acta Physiol. Scand.* 41: 217–228, 1957.

128. GUSTAFSSON, B. E., AND L. S. LANKE. Bilirubin and uro-bilins in germfree, ex-germfree and conventional rats. *J. Exptl. Med.* 112: 975–987, 1960.

129. GUSTAFSSON, B. E., T. MIDTREDT, AND A. NORMAN. Isolated fecal micro-organisms capable of 7 α-dehydrox-ylating bile acids. *J. Exptl. Med.* 123: 412–432, 1966.

130. GUSTAFSSON, B. E., AND A. NORMAN. Comparison of bile acids in intestinal contents of germfree and conventional rats. *Proc. Soc. Exptl. Biol. Med.* 110: 387–389, 1962.

131. GUSTAFSSON, B. E., A. NORMAN, AND J. SJÖVALL. Influence of E. coli infection on tumors and metabolism of cholic acid in germ-free rats. *Arch. Biochem.* 91: 93–100, 1960.

132. GYLLENBERG, H., AND G. CARLBERG. The dominance of a specific nutritional type of Lactobacillus bifidus in breast-fed infants. *Acta Pathol. Microbiol. Scand.* 42: 380–384, 1958.

133. GYORGY, P. A hitherto unrecognized biochemical differ-ence between human milk and cow's milk. *Pediatrics* 11: 98–108, 1953.

134. HAENEL, H. Some rules in the ecology of the intestinal microflora of man. *J. Appl. Bacteriol.* 24: 242–251, 1961.

135. HALBERT, S. P. The antagonism of coliform bacteria against Shigellae. *J. Immunol.* 58: 153–167, 1948.

136. HALSTED, J. A., P. M. LEWIS, AND M. GASSTER. Absorp-tion of radioactive vitamin B₁₂ in the syndrome of megalo-blastic anemia associated with intestinal stricture or anastomosis. *Am. J. Med.* 20: 42–52, 1956.

137. HAMPTON, J. C., AND B. ROSARIO. The attachment of microorganisms to epithelial cells in the distal ileum of the mouse. *Lab. Invest.* 14: 1464–1471, 1965.

138. HAVERBACK, B. J., B. J. DYCE, P. J. GUTENTAG, AND D. W. MONTGOMERY. Measurement of trypsin and chymo-trypsin in stool. A diagnostic test for pancreatic exocrine insufficiency. *Gastroenterology* 44: 588–597, 1963.

139. HEALEY, W. V., R. OLLSTEIN, B. JOHNSON, S. L. WANGEN-STEEN, AND A. B. VOORHEES, JR. Change in the gram-negative enteric flora of dogs undergoing gastric hypo-thermia. *Surg. Forum* 14: 356–357, 1963.

140. HEMMATI, A., AND H. WERNER. A new high frequency-directed capsule for the sampling of the intestinal contents. *Z. Ges. Exptl. Med.* 139: 608–620, 1965.

141. HENEGHAN, J. B. Influence of microbial flora on xylose

absorption in rats and mice. *Am. J. Physiol.* 205: 412–420, 1963.

142. HENTGES, D. J., AND R. FRETER. *In vivo* and *in vitro* antagonism of intestinal bacteria against Shigella flexneri. 1. Correlation between various tests. *J. Infect. Diseases* 110: 38–46, 1962.

143. HERMANN, G., H. K. AXTELL, AND T. E. STARZL. Bacterial contamination of jejunum and vitamin B₁₂ absorption. *Gastroenterology* 47: 61–64, 1964.

144. HOET, P. P., AND H. EYSSEN. Steatorrhea in rats with an intestinal cul-de-sac. *Gut* 5: 309–314, 1964.

145. HOFFBRAND, A. V., S. TABAQCHALI, AND D. L. MOLLIN. High serum-folata levels in intestinal blind-loop syndrome. *Lancet* 1: 1339–1342, 1966.

146. HOFMANN, A. F. Clinical implications of physico-chemical studies on bile salts. *Gastroenterology* 48: 484–494, 1965.

147. HOLLOWAY, B. W. Grouping Pseudomonas aeruginosa by lysogenicity and pyocinogenicity. *J. Pathol. Bacteriol.* 80: 448–449, 1960.

148. HORNING, E. C., AND E. C. DALGLIESH. The association of skatole-forming bacteria in the small intestine with the malabsorption syndrome and certain anaemias. *Biochem. J.* 70: 13P, 1958.

149. HUDSON, J. A., AND T. D. LUCKEY. Bacteria induced mor-phologic changes. *Proc. Soc. Exptl. Biol. Med.* 116: 628–631, 1964.

150. JACOBSON, E. D., R. B. CHODOS, AND W. W. FALOON. An experimental malabsorption syndrome induced by neo-mycin. *Am. J. Med.* 28: 524–533, 1960.

151. JERVIS, H. R., AND D. C. BIGGERS. Mucosal enzymes in the cecum of conventional and germfree mice. *Anat. Record* 148: 591–597, 1964.

152. JEW, E. W., B. S. LEVOWITZ, D. E. GRILLIAN, AND B. FISHER. Alteration of the effects of jejunocolic fistula. An experimental study. *Ann. Surg.* 155: 175–182, 1960.

153. JOHNSTON, G. W., AND H. W. ROGERS. Treatment of ammonia intoxication in rhesus monkeys by total colec-tomy. *Brit. J. Surg.* 52: 304–308, 1965.

154. JOVER, A., AND R. S. GORDON. Procedure for quantitative analysis of feces with special reference to fecal fatty acids. *J. Lab. Clin. Med.* 59: 878–884, 1962.

155. JUKES, T. H. *Antibiotics in Nutrition.* New York: Medical Encyclopedia, 1955, p. 43.

156. KAHN, I. J., G. H. JEFFRIES, AND M. H. SLEISENGER. Mal-absorption in intestinal scleroderma. Correction by anti-biotics. *New Engl. J. Med.* 274: 1339–1344, 1966.

157. KALSER, M. H., R. COHEN, I. ARTEAGA, E. YAWN, L. MAYORAL, W. R. HOFFERT, AND D. FRAZIER. Normal viral and bacterial flora of the human small and large intestine. *New Engl. J. Med.* 274: 500–505, 1966.

158. KEAN, B. H. The diarrhea of travelers to Mexico. Sum-mary of five-year study. *Ann. Internal Med.* 59: 605–614, 1963.

159. KENT, T. H., S. B. FORMAL, AND E. H. LABREC. Acute enteritis due to Salmonella typhimurium in opium-treated guinea pigs. *Arch. Pathol.* 81: 501–508, 1966.

160. KIM, Y. S., N. SPRITZ, M. BLUM, J. TERZ, AND P. SHER-LOCK. The role of altered bile acid metabolism in the steatorrhea of experimental blind loop. *J. Clin. Invest.* 45: 956–962, 1966.

161. KINSELLA, V. J., W. B. HENNESSY, AND E. P. GEORGE. Studies in postgastrectomy malabsorption: the importance

of bacterial contamination of the upper small intestine. *Med. J. Australia* 48: 257–261, 1961.

162. KLIPSTEIN, F. A. Antibiotic therapy in tropical sprue: the role of dietary folic acid in the hematologic remission associated with oral antibiotic therapy. *Ann. Internal Med.* 61: 721, 1964.

163. KLIPSTEIN, F. A., AND I. M. SAMLOFF. Folate synthesis by intestinal bacteria. *Am. J. Clin. Nutr.* 14: 237–246, 1966.

164. KLIPSTEIN, F. A., I. SAMLOFF, AND E. A. SCHENK. Tropical sprue in Haiti. *Ann. Internal Med.* 64: 575–594, 1964.

165. KLITE, P. D. Intestinal bacterial flora and transit time of three neotropical bat species. *J. Bacteriol.* 90: 375–379, 1965.

166. KLITE, P. D., AND G. R. GALE. An antifungal substance from Pseudomonas aeruginosa. *Antibiot. Chemotherapy* 11: 256–260, 1961.

167. KORNBERG, H. L., AND R. E. DAVIES. Gastric urease. *Physiol. Rev.* 35: 169–175, 1955.

168. KRAMER, B., H. SELIGSON, H. BATHUSH, AND D. SELIGSON. The isolation of several aromatic acids from hemodialysis fluids of uremic patients. *Clin. Chim. Acta* 11: 363–371, 1965.

169. LEPKOVSKY, S., M., WAGNER, F. FURUTA, K. OZONE, AND T. KOIKE. Proteases, amylase and lipase of the intestinal contents of germ-free and conventional chickens. *Poultry Sci.* 43: 722–726, 1964.

170. LERNER, P., S. GORBACH, L. NAHAS, AND L. WEINSTEIN. Stability of the normal human intestinal microflora (abstr.). *Clin. Res.* 14: 301, 1966.

171. LESHER, S., H. E. WALBURG, AND G. A. SACHER. Generation cycle in the duodenal crypt cells. *Nature* 202: 884–886, 1964.

172. LEU, M., R. H. ALEXANDER, AND S. M. LEVINSON. Stability of the lactobacillus population in feces and stomach contents of rats prevented from coprophagy. *J. Bacteriol.* 92: 13–16, 1966.

173. LEVENSON, S. M., L. V. CROWLEY, R. E. HOROWITZ, AND O. J. MALM. The metabolism of carbon-labeled urea in the germfree rat. *J. Biol. Chem.* 234: 2071–2062, 1959.

174. LIEBER, C. S., AND A. LEFAVRE. Ammonia as a source of gastric hypoacidity in patients with uremia. *J. Clin. Invest.* 38: 1271–1277, 1959.

175. LINDSTEDT, G., S. LINDSTEDT, AND B. E. GUSTAFSSON. Mucus in intestinal contents of germ free rats. *J. Exptl. Med.* 121: 201–213, 1965.

176. LOH, W. P., AND E. E. BAKER. Fecal flora of man after oral administration of chlortetracycline or oxytetracycline. *Arch. Internal Med.* 94: 74–82, 1955.

177. LUCKEY, T. D. Antibiotics in nutrition. In: *Antibiotics, Their Chemistry and Non-Medical Uses*, edited by H. S. Goldberg. Princeton: Van Nostrand, 1959, p. 174–321.

178. LYALL, I. G., AND P. J. PARSONS. Some aspects of the blind-loop syndrome. *Med. J. Australia* 48: 904–907, 1962.

179. MACBETH, W. A. A. G., E. H. KASS, AND W. V. MCDERMOTT, JR. Treatment of hepatic encephalopathy by alteration of intestinal flora with Lactobacillus acidophilus. *Lancet* 1: 399–403, 1965.

180. MAINGUET, P., AND R. CATTAN. Exploration bacteriologique des diarrhées chroniques par le tubage jejunal protégé. *Arch. Maladies Appart. Digest.* 49: 189–195, 1960.

181. MAKI, L. R., AND K. PICARD. Normal intestinal flora of cattle fed high-roughage rations. *J. Bacteriol.* 89: 1244–1249, 1965.

182. MARTINI, G. A., E. A. PHEAR, B. RUEBNER, AND S. SHERLOCK. Bacterial content of small intestine in normal and cirrhotic subjects: relation to methionine toxicity. *Clin. Sci.* 16: 35–51, 1957.

183. MATSUSHITA, H., M. S. FOX, AND W. F. GOEBEL. Colicine K. IV. The effect of metabolites upon colicine synthesis. *J. Exptl. Med.* 112: 1055–1068, 1960.

184. MCCOY, E. Changes in the host flora induced by chemotherapeutic agents. *Ann. Rev. Microbiol.* 8: 257–272, 1954.

185. MCDERMOTT, W. V., JR., M. VICTOR, AND W. W. POINT. Exclusion of the colon in the treatment of hepatic encephalopathy. *New Engl. J. Med.* 267: 850–854, 1962.

186. MCNAUGHT, W., AND G. B. S. ROBERTS. Enteropathogenic effects of strains of *Bacterium coli* isolated from cases of gastroenteritis. *J. Pathol. Bacteriol.* 76: 155–158, 1958.

187. MCNAUGHT, W., AND J. S. STEVENSON. Coliform "diarrhea" in adult hospital patients. *Brit. Med. J.* 2: 182–184, 1953.

188. MCVAY, L. V., JR. Studies on the concentrations and bacterial effect of aureomycin in different portions of the intestinal tract. *J. Clin. Invest.* 31: 27–34, 1952

189. METCHNIKOFF, E. The nature of man. In: *Studies in Optimistic Philosophy* (English transl.), edited by P. Chalmers Mitchell. New York: Putnam, 1905, p. 309.

190. MEYNELL, G. G. Antibacterial mechanisms of the mouse gut. II. The role of Eh and volatile fatty acids in the normal gut. *Brit. J. Exptl. Pathol.* 44: 209–219, 1963.

191. MEYNELL, G. G., AND T. V. SUBBAIAH. Antibacterial mechanisms of the mouse gut: I. Kinetics of infection by *Salmonella typhimurium* in normal and streptomycin-treated mice studied with abortive transductants. *Brit. J. Exptl. Pathol.* 44: 197–208, 1963.

192. MICKELSEN, O. Nutrition: germfree animal research. *Ann. Rev. Biochem.* 31: 515–548, 1962.

193. MIGICOVSKY, B. B., A. M. NIELSON, M. GLUCK, AND R. BURGESS. Penicillin and calcium absorption. *Arch. Biochem. Biophys.* 34: 479–480, 1951.

194. MILANES, F., F. CURBELO, A. RODRIQUEZ, P. KOURI, AND T. D. SPIES. A note on bacteriological and parasitic studies of the intestinal contents of patients with sprue. *Gastroenterology* 7: 306, 1946.

195. MILLER, C. P., AND M. BOHNHOFF. Changes in the mouse's enteric microflora associated with enhanced susceptibility to Salmonella infection following streptomycin treatment. *J. Infect. Diseases* 113: 59–66, 1963.

196. MILNE, M. D., A. M. ASATOOR, K. D. G. EDWARDS, AND L. W. LOUGHRIDGE. The intestinal absorption defect in cystinuria. *Gut* 2: 323–337, 1961.

197. MILNE, M. D., M. A. CRAWFORD, C. B. GIRAO, AND L. W. LOUGHRIDGE. The metabolic disorder in Hartnup disease. *Quart. J. Med.* 29: 407–421, 1960.

198. MITOMA, C., H. WEISSBACH, AND S. UDENFRIEND. 5-Hydroxytryptophan formation and tryptophan metabolism in *Chromobacterium violaceum.* *Arch. Biochem. Biophys.* 63: 122–130, 1956.

199. MONTGOMERY, J., G. M. KALMANSON, AND L. B. GUZE. The effects of antibiotics on the protoplast and bacterial forms of *Streptococcus fecalis.* *J. Lab. Clin. Med.* 68: 543–551, 1966.

200. MORTIMER, D. E., P. I. REED, M. VIDINLI, AND J. M. FINLAY. The role of upper gastrointestinal flora in the malabsorption syndrome. *Can. Med. Assoc. J.* 90: 559–564, 1964.

201. MUSHIN, R., AND R. DUBOS. Colonization of the mouse intestine with Escherichia coli. *J. Exptl. Med.* 122: 745–757, 1965.

202. MUSHIN, R., AND R. DUBOS. Coliform bacteria in the intestine of mice. *J. Exptl. Med.* 126: 657–463, 1966.

203. NADEL, H., AND F. H. GARDNER. Bacteriological assay of small bowel secretion in tropical sprue. *Am. J. Trop. Med. Hyg.* 5: 686–689, 1956.

204. NETER, E. Enteritis due to enteropathogenic *Escherichia coli*: present day status and unsolved problems. *J. Pediat.* 55: 223–229, 1959.

205. NORMAN, A., AND A. GRUBB. Hydrolysis of conjugated bile acids by *Clostridia* and *Enterococci*. *Acta Pathol. Microbiol.* 36: 537–547, 1955.

206. NORMAN, A., AND M. S. SHORB. *In vitro* formation of deoxycholic and lithocholic acid by human intestinal microorganisms. *Proc. Soc. Exptl. Biol. Med.* 110: 552–555, 1962.

207. NORMAN, A., AND J. SJÖVALL. On the transformation and enterohepatic circulation of cholic acid in the rat. *J. Biol. Chem.* 233: 872–885, 1958.

208. OSAWA, N., S. MITSUHOSHI, Y. UNO, AND M. MIYAKAWA. Infection of germfree mice with Shigella flexneri 3a. *Japan J. Exptl. Med.* 34: 77–80, 1964.

209. OZAWA, A., AND R. FRETER. Ecological mechanism controlling growth of *Escherichia coli* in continuous flow cultures and in the mouse intestine. *J. Infect. Diseases* 114: 235–242, 1964.

210. PAINE, T. F. Inhibitory actions of bacteria on *Candida* growth. *Antibiot. Chemotherapy* 8: 273–281, 1958.

211. PAMOSJ, J. F. Experimental blind loop steatorrhea. *Gastroenterology* 45: 394–399, 1963.

212. PAPARAISILIOU, J. Lysogeny and colicinogeny in *E. coli*. *J. Gen. Microbiol.* 25: 409–413, 1961.

213. PAULK, E. A., JR., AND W. E. FARRAR, JR. Diverticulosis of the small intestine and megaloblastic anemia. *Am. J. Med.* 37: 473–479, 1964.

214. PERLMANN, P., S. HAMMARSTROM, R. LAYERCRAITZ, AND B. S. GUSTAFSSON. Antigen from colon of germ free rats and antibodies in human ulcerative colitis. *Ann. N. Y. Acad. Sci.* 124: 377–394, 1965.

215. PETTET, J. D., A. H. BAGGENSTOSS, W. H. DEARING, AND E. S. JUDD. Postoperative pseudomembranous enterocolitis. *Surg. Gynecol. Obstet.* 98: 546–552, 1954.

216. PHEAR, E. A., AND B. RUEBNER. *In vitro* production of ammonium and amines by intestinal bacteria in relation to nitrogen toxicity as factors in hepatic coma. *Brit. J. Exptl. Pathol.* 37: 253–262, 1956.

217. PHILLIPS, B. P., AND P. A. WOLFE. The use of germ-free guinea pigs in studies on the microbial interrelationships in amoebiasis. *Ann. N. Y. Acad. Sci.* 78: 308–314, 1959.

218. POLACHEK, A. A., W. J. PIJANOWSKI, AND J. M. MILLER. Diverticulosis of the jejunum with macrocytic anemia and steatorrhea. *Ann. Internal Med.* 54: 636–645, 1961.

219. PORTER, J. R., AND L. F. RETTGER. Influence of diet on distribution of bacteria in the stomach, small intestine, and cecum of the white rat. *J. Infect. Diseases* 66: 104–110, 1940.

220. PORTMAN, O. W. Importance of diet, species, and intestinal flora in bile acid metabolism. *Federation Proc.* 21: 896–902, 1962.

221. PORTMAN, O. W., S. SHAH, A. ANTONIS AND B. JORGENSEN. Alteration of bile salts by bacteria. *Proc. Soc. Exptl. Biol. Med.* 109: 959–965, 1962.

222. PROHASKA, J. V., F. MOCK, W. BAKER, AND R. COLLINS. Pseudomembranous enterocolitis. *Surg. Gynecol. Obstet. Intern. Abstr. Surg.* 112: 103–115, 1961.

223. RANSOM, J. P., R. A. FINKELSTEIN, R. E. CEDER, AND S. B. FORMAL. Interactions of vibrio cholerae, Shigella flexner, Enterococci, and Lactobacilli in continuously fed cultures. *Proc. Soc. Exptl. Biol. Med.* 107: 332–336, 1961.

224. READ, A. E., C. F. MCCARTHY, K. W. HEATON, AND J. CAIDLAN. *Lactobacillus acidophilus* (Enpac) in treatment of hepatic encephalopathy. *Brit. Med. J.* 1: 1267–1269, 1966.

225. REDDY, B. S., AND B. S. WORSTMANN. Intestinal disaccharidase activities in growing germfree and conventional rats. *Arch. Biochem. Biophys.* 113: 609–616, 1966.

226. REIMANN, H. A. Microbic phagocytosis by enteric epithelial cells. *J. Am. Med. Assoc.* 192: 100–102, 1965.

227. REYNOLDS, V. H., AND R. E. WILSON. Absence of recurrent ammonia intoxication following right hemicolectomy with anastomosis of the superior mesenteric vein to the inferior vena cava. *Ann. Surg.* 154: 826–832, 1961.

228. RIMINGTON, C. Indigoid pigments derived from a pathological urine. *Biochem. J.* 40: 669–671, 1946.

229. RIVERA, J. A., AND V. M. SBOROV. The effect of terramycin on the intestinal flora. *Gastroenterology* 17: 546–550, 1951.

230. ROSEBURY, T. *Microorganisms Indigenous to Man.* New York: Blakiston, 1962, p. 435.

231. ROSEBURY, T. Bacteria indigenous to man. *Bacterial and Mycotic Infections of Man.* Philadelphia: Lippincott, 1965, p. 326–355.

232. ROSENBERG, I. H., W. G. H. HARDISON, AND D. M. BULL. Jejunal bile salt abnormalities in malabsorption with bacterial stasis (abstr.). *Clin. Res.* 14: 304, 1966.

233. ROUFAIL, W. M., AND J. M. RUFFIN. Effect of antibiotic therapy on gluten-sensitive enteropathy. *Am. J. Digest. Diseases* 11: 587–593, 1966.

234. SALEN, G., F. GOLDSTEIN, AND C. W. WIRTS. Malabsorption in intestinal scleroderma: relation to bacterial flora and treatment with antibiotics. *Ann. Internal Med.* 64: 834–841, 1966.

235. SANDERS, E., P. S. BRACHMAN, E. A. FRIEDMAN, J. GOLSBY, AND C. E. MCCALL. Salmonellosis in the United States: results of nationwide surveillance. *Am. J. Epidemiol.* 81: 370–384, 1965.

236. SAUNDERS, D. R., AND A. H. DAWSON. The absorption of oleic acid in the bile fistula rat. *Gut* 4: 254–260, 1963.

237. SCHAEDLER, R. W., R. DUBOS, AND R. COSTELLO. The development of the bacterial flora in the gastrointestinal tract of mice. *J. Exptl. Med.* 122: 59–66, 1965.

238. SCHAEDLER, R. W., R. DUBOS, AND R. COSTELLO. Association of germfree mice with bacteria isolated from normal mice. *J. Exptl. Med.* 122: 77–82, 1965.

239. SCHIFFER, L. M., W. W. FALOON, R. B. CHODOS, AND E. L. LOZNER. Malabsorption syndrome associated with intestinal diverticulosis. Report of a case with jejunal biopsy. *Gastroenterology* 42: 63–68, 1962.

240. SCUDAMORE, H. H., A. B. HAGEDON, E. E. WOLLAEGER, AND C. A. OWEN. Diverticulosis of the small intestine and macrocytic anemia with report of two cases and studies on absorption of radioactive vitamin B_{12}. *Gastroenterology* 34: 66–82, 1958.

241. SEARS, H. J., I. BROWNLEE, AND J. K. UCHIYAMA. Persistence of individual strains of *Escherichia coli* in the intestinal tract of man. *J. Bacteriol.* 59: 293–301, 1950.

242. SEYDERHELMEN, R., W. LEHMANN, AND P. WICHELS. Experimentelle intestinale pernigiöse Anämie beim Hund. *Klin. Wochschr.* 3: 1439, 1924.

243. SHARPE, M. E. Group D streptococci in the feces of healthy infants and of infants with neonatal diarrhea. *J. Hyg.* 50: 209–228, 1952.

244. SHEEHY, T. W., AND E. PEREZ-SANTIAGO. Antibiotic therapy in tropical sprue. *Gastroenterology* 41: 208–214, 1961.

245. SHERWOOD, W. C., F. GOLDSTEIN, F. I. HAURANI, AND C. W. WIRTS. Studies of the small-intestinal bacterial flora and of intestinal absorption in pernicious anemia. *Am. J. Digest. Diseases* 9: 416–425, 1964.

246. SHINER, M. A capsule for obtaining sterile samples of gastrointestinal fluids. *Lancet* 1: 532–533, 1963.

247. SHINER, M., T. W. WATERS, AND J. D. A. GRAY. Culture studies of the gastrointestinal tract with a newly devised capsule. Results of tests *in vitro* and *in vivo*. *Gastroenterology* 45: 625–632, 1963.

248. SIEBURTH, J. M. Gastrointestinal microflora of Antarctic birds. *J. Bacteriol.* 77: 521–531, 1959.

249. SIEBURTH, J. M. Acrylic acid, an "antibiotic" principle in phaeocystis blooms in Antarctic waters. *Science* 132: 676–677, 1960.

250. SILEN, W., H. A. HARPER, D. L. MAWDSLEY, AND W. L. WEIRICH. Effects of antibacterial agents on ammonia production within the intestine. *Proc. Soc. Exptl. Biol. Med.* 88: 138–140, 1955.

251. SIMS, W. The effect of mucin on the survival of lactobacilli and streptococci. *J. Gen. Microbiol.* 35: 335–340, 1964.

252. SINGER, J. M., J. BAR-HAY, AND R. HOENINGSBERG. The intestinal flora in the etiology of infantile infectious diarrhea. *A.M.A. J. Diseases Children* 89: 531–538, 1955.

253. SKELLY, B. J., P. C. TREXLER, AND J. TANAMI. Effect of clostridium species upon cecal size of gnotobiotic mice. *Proc. Soc. Exptl. Biol. Med.* 110: 455–458, 1962.

254. SMITH, D. H. Salmonella with transferable drug resistance. *New Engl. J. Med.* 275: 625–630, 1966.

255. SMITH, D. H., AND S. ARMOUR. Transferable R. factors in enteric bacteria causing infection of genitourinary tract. *Lancet* 2: 15–18, 1966.

256. SMITH, H. Factors involved in the virulence-enhancing action of mucin. *Proc. Roy. Soc. Med.* 46: 787–790, 1953.

257. SMITH, H. W. Observations on the flora of the alimentary tract of animals and factors affecting its composition. *J. Pathol. Bacteriol.* 89: 95–122, 1965.

258. SMITH, H. W. The development of the flora of the alimentary tract in young animals. *J. Pathol. Bacteriol.* 90: 495–513, 1965.

259. SMITH, H. W., AND W. E. CRABB. The fecal flora of animals and man: its development in the young. *J. Pathol. Bacteriol.* 82: 53–66, 1961.

260. SMITH, H. W., AND S. HALLS. Observations on infective drug resistance in Britain. *Brit. Med. J.* 1: 266–269, 1966.

261. SMITH, H. W., AND J. E. T. JONES. Observations on the alimentary tract and its bacterial flora in healthy and diseased pigs. *J. Pathol. Bacteriol.* 86: 387–412, 1963.

262. SMITH, S. M., AND B. A. D. STOCKE. Colicinogeny and recombination. *Brit. Med. Bull.* 18: 46–51, 1962.

263. SMITH, T., AND M. L. ORCUTT. The bacteriology of the intestinal tract of young calves with special reference to the early diarrhea ("scours"). *J. Exptl. Med.* 41: 89–106, 1925.

264. SMYTHE, P. M. Changes in intestinal bacterial flora and role of infection in kwashiorkor. *Lancet* 2: 724–727, 1958.

265. SOLOMON, P., L. WEINSTEIN, AND S. M. JORESS. Studies of the incidence of enteropathogenic Escherichia coli in a pediatric population. *J. Pediat.* 58: 716–721, 1961.

266. SOUTH, M. A., M. COOPER, F. A. WOLLHEIM, R. HONG, AND R. A. GOOD. The IgA system. 1. Studies of the transport and immunochemistry of IgA in the saliva. *J. Exptl. Med.* 123: 615–627, 1966.

267. SPRINZ, H. Morphological response of intestinal mucosa to enteric bacteria and its implication for sprue and Asiatic cholera. *Federation Proc.* 21: 57–64, 1962.

268. SPRINZ, H. The contribution of germfree research to our understanding of the cellular kinetics and responses of the intestinal mucosa. *Proc. 16th Intern. Congr. Zool.* 3: 155–159, 1963.

269. SPRINZ, H., D. W. KUNDEL, G. J. DAMMIN, R. E. HOROWITZ, H. SCHNEIDER, AND S. B. FORMAL. The response of the germfree guinea pig to oral bacterial challenge with *Escherichia coli* and *Shigella flexneri*. *Am. J. Pathol.* 39: 681–695, 1961.

270. STAFANSKI, W., AND Z. PRZYIALKOWSKI. Effect of alimentary tract microorganisms on the development of *Trichinella spiralis* in mice. *Exptl. Parasitol.* 18: 92–98, 1966.

271. STRAUSS, E. E., R. M. DONALDSON, JR., AND F. H. GARDNER. A relationship between intestinal bacteria and the absorption of vitamin B_{12} in rats with diverticula of the small bowel. *Lancet* 2: 736–738, 1961.

272. STURGEN, N. O., AND L. E. CASIDA, JR. Antibiotic production by anaerobic bacteria. *Appl. Microbiol.* 10: 55–59, 1962.

273. SU, T. L. Micrococcin. An antibacterial substance formed by a strain of micrococcus. *Brit. J. Exptl. Pathol.* 29: 473–478, 1948.

274. TABAQCHALI, S., AND C. C. BOOTH. Jejunal bacteriology and bile salt metabolism in patients with intestinal malabsorption. *Lancet* 2: 12–15, 1965.

275. TADD, A. D., AND A. HURST. The effect of feeding colicinogenic Escherichia coli on the intestinal E. coli of early weaned pigs. *J. Appl. Bacteriol.* 24: 222–228, 1961.

276. TAKEUCHI, A., H. SPRINZ, E. H. LABREC, AND S. B. FORMAL. Experimental bacillary dysentery. An electron microscopic study of the response of the intestinal mucosa to bacterial invasion. *Am. J. Pathol.* 47: 1011–1044, 1965.

277. TALALAY, P. Enzymatic mechanisms in steroid metabolism. *Physiol. Rev.* 37: 362–389, 1957.

278. TAYLOR, J., M. P. WILKINS, AND J. M. PAYNE. Relation of rabbit gut reaction to enteropathogenic Escherichia coli. *Brit. J. Exptl. Pathol.* 42: 43–48, 1961.

279. THOMPSON, A., AND A. W. HOLMES. Immune inhibition of urea breakdown in patients with cirrhosis. *Gastroenterology* 52: 14–17, 1967.

280. TOON, R. W., AND O. H. WANGENSTEEN. Anemia associated with blind intestinal segments and its prevention with aureomycin. *Proc. Soc. Exptl. Biol. Med.* 75: 762–765, 1950.

281. TORRES-PINEDO, R., M. LAUASTIDA, C. L. RIVERS, H. RODRIQUEZ, AND A. ORTEZ. Studies on infant diarrhea. 1.

A comparison of the effects of milk feeding and intravenous therapy upon the composition and volume of the stool and urine. *J. Clin. Invest.* 45: 469–480, 1966.

282. TORRES-PINEDO, R., C. L. RIVERA, AND S. FERNANDEZ. Studies on infant diarrhea. II. Absorption of glucose and net fluxes of water and sodium chloride in a segment of the jejunum. *J. Clin. Invest.* 45: 1916–1922, 1966.

283. TRIER, J. S., P. C. PHELPS, S. EIDELMAN, AND C. E. RUBIN. Whipple's disease: light and electron microscope correlation of jejunal mucosal histology with antibiotic treatment and clinical status. *Gastroenterology* 48: 684–707, 1965.

284. UMBARGER, H. E., AND J. H. MUELLER. Isoleucine and valine metabolism of *E. coli. J. Biol. Chem.* 189: 277–285, 1951.

285. VERTANEN, A. I. Milk production of cows on protein free feed. *Science* 153: 1603–1614, 1966.

286. WAGNER, M. Fecal indol and urinary indican in germ free and conventional (normal stock) animals. *Bacteriol. Proc.* 11: 88, 1958.

287. WALKER, J. G., A. EMLYN-WILLIAMS, A. CRAIGIE, V. M. ROSENOER, J. AGNEW, AND S. SHERLOCK. Treatment of chronic portal-systemic encephalopathy by surgical exclusion of the colon. *Lancet* 2: 861–866, 1965.

288. WALSER, M., AND L. J. BODENLOS. Urea metabolism in man. *J. Clin. Invest.* 38: 1617–1626, 1959.

289. WALTON, J. R. *In vivo* transfer of infectious drug resistance. *Nature* 211: 312–313, 1966.

290. WARREN, K. S., AND W. L. NEWTON. Portal and peripheral blood ammonia concentrations in germ-free and conventional guinea pigs. *Am. J. Physiol.* 197: 717–720, 1959.

291. WARREN, S. E., M. JACOBSON, J. MIRANY, AND J. VAN PROHASKA. Acute and chronic enterotoxin enteritis. *J. Exptl. Med.* 120: 561–568, 1964.

292. WARREN, S. E., H. SUGIYAMA, AND J. V. PROHASKA. Correlation of staphylococcal enterotoxins with experimentally induced enterocolitis. *Surg. Gynecol. Obstet.* 116: 29–33, 1963.

293. WARNER, R. R. P., M. G. FELDMAN, G. M. WARNER, AND I. H. PARNES. Changes in blood serotonin concentrations and urinary 5-hydroxyindoleacetic acid excretion in mechanical obstruction of the small intestine. I. Experimental intestinal obstruction in the dog. II. Findings in patients with intestinal obstruction. *Surgery* 59: 750–757, 758–764, 1966.

294. WATANABE, T. Infective heredity of multiple drug resistance in bacteria. *Bacteriol. Rev.* 27: 87–115, 1963.

295. WATANABE, T. Infectious drug resistance in enteric bacteria. *New Engl. J. Med.* 275: 888–894, 1966.

296. WATKINSON, G., D. B. FEATHER, F. G. W. MARSON, AND J. A. DOSSETT. Massive jejunal diverticulosis with steatorrhea and megaloblastic anemia improved by excision of diverticula. *Brit. Med. J.* 2: 58–62, 1959.

297. WATSON, G. M., AND L. J. WITTS. Intestinal macrocytic anemia. *Brit. Med. J.* 1: 13–17, 1952.

298. WEBB, J. P. W., A. T. JAMES, AND T. D. KELLOCK. The influence of diet on the quality of fecal fat in patients with and without steatorrhea. *Gut* 4: 37–41, 1963.

299. WEIJERS, H. A. Dysbacteriosis as a cause of diarrhea. *Trans. Gastroenterology* 8: 172–175, 1965.

300. WEIJERS, H. A., J. H. VAN DE KAMER, W. K. DICKE, AND J. IJSSELING. Diarrhea caused by a deficiency of sugar-splitting enzymes. *Acta Paediat.* 50: 55–71, 1961.

301. WEINSTEIN, L., R. E. OLSON, T. B. VAN ITALLIE, E. CASO, D. JOHNSON, AND F. J. INGELFINGER. Diet as related to gastrointestinal function. *J. Am. Med. Assoc.* 176: 935–941, 1961.

302. WEINSTEIN, L., C. A. SAMET, AND R. H. MEADE. Effect of paromomycin on the bacterial flora of the human intestine: studies of total numbers and specific components. *J. Am. Med. Assoc.* 178: 891–897, 1961.

303. WEISSBACH, H., W. KING, A. SJOEDSMA, AND S. UDENFRIEND. Formation of indole-3-acetic acid and tryptamine in animals. *J. Biol. Chem.* 234: 81–86, 1959.

304. WHEATER, D. M., A. HIRSCH, AND A. T. R. MATTRICH. Possible identity of "lactobacillin" with hydrogen peroxide produced by lactobacilli. *Nature* 170: 623–624, 1952.

305. WILBUR, R. D., D. V. CATRON, L. Y. QUINN, V. C. SPEER, AND V. W. HAYS. Intestinal flora of the pig as influenced by diet and age. *J. Nutr.* 71: 168–175, 1960.

306. WILLIAMS, N. B., AND D. O. POWLEN. Human parotid saliva as a sole source of nutrient for micro-organisms. *Arch. Oral. Biol.* 1: 48–61, 1959.

307. WIRTS, C. W., AND F. GOLDSTEIN. Effect of antibiotic therapy in a probable case of non-tropical sprue. *Gastroenterology* 39: 628–633, 1960.

308. WIRTS, C. W., AND F. GOLDSTEIN. Studies of the mechanism of postgastrectomy steatorrhea. *Ann. Internal Med.* 58: 25–36, 1963.

309. WISEMAN, R. F., AND H. A. GORDON. Reduced levels of a bioactive substance in the caecal content of gnotobiotic rats mono-associated with Salmonella typhimurium. *Nature* 205: 572–573, 1965.

310. YOUNG, V. M., M. R. SOCHARD, AND H. C. GILLEM. Infectious agents in infant diarrhea. I. A hemagglutination-inhibition procedure for detection of bacterial fractions in infants sera. *Proc. Soc. Exptl. Biol. Med.* 105: 635–638, 1950.

311. ZELDOW, B. J. Studies on the antibacterial action of human saliva. II. Observations of the mode of action of a lactobacillus bactericidin. *J. Dental Res.* 40: 446–453, 1961.

312. ZUBRZYCKI, L., AND E. H. SPAULDING. Studies on stability of normal human fecal flora. *J. Bacteriol.* 83: 968–974, 1962.

CHAPTER 137

Gas in the alimentary canal

DORIS HOWES CALLOWAY | *Department of Nutritional Sciences, University of California, Berkeley, California*

CHAPTER CONTENTS

THE GASTROINTESTINAL TRACT of the fetus contains no gas, but radiographic tracings show gas present in the stomachs of about half of newborn infants examined 30 sec after birth and in all healthy babies within 1 min (16). The gas gradually increases in volume and is seen in all parts of the alimentary canal after 1 or 2 hours (82, 89). This first gas is unquestionably atmospheric air that has entered through the esophagus, because if the esophagus is occluded and there is no fistula communicating with the trachea, gas does not enter the stomach until the obstruction is relieved, and if the duodenum is obstructed, the stomach fills with gas but the small intestine and the colon do not (42). Some of the air may be returned through the esophagus and some passes on, ultimately to be expelled through the anus.

All of the gases found in the alimentary tract of animals and man are known products of bacterial metabolism except nitrogen and oxygen, the only proved source of which is air. Carbon dioxide can also arise by release from endogenous bicarbonate and food carbonates; and it can diffuse inward from the blood and tissues, as can nitrogen, oxygen, and any other gases carried by the blood. Similarly, any gas present in the lumen of the gastrointestinal tract can diffuse into the blood under appropriate circumstances, forming another route for removal of gases from the canal.

A few fishes that do not possess air bladders regularly take air into the stomach where it may function in the same capacity as in the bladder. The swell sharks (*Cephalocyllium* sp.) when captured swallow large volumes of air, the function of which is presumed to be obscurely related to survival. Other than in these exceptional cases, entry of air into the gut is accepted as being a coincidental rather than a purposeful phenomenon.

ATMOSPHERIC AIR

Atmospheric air may be swallowed as such or as a component of air-containing foods; less commonly, it may be aspirated during respiration. It was recognized early that air ingestion can be augmented voluntarily, a case history on the topic of "auto-inflation" appearing in 1813 (51); the fact that ingestion is increased involuntarily during trauma, pain, and anxiety was established experimentally in the early 1900s. The term "aerophagia" (literally, air eating) is applied collectively to these augmented processes.

Entry

The mechanics of normal air swallowing have been elucidated in man by combined auscultatory and fluoroscopic methods with the ingestion of a barium meal (44). Only a diffuse area of light, indicating the presence of gas, can be seen in the fasting stomach. A small bubble of air accompanies each swallow, and a characteristic sound always coincides with passage of the bubble through the cardiac sphincter into the stomach, irrespective of whether the bubble enters with the food or before or after it. With the first swallow a discrete gas mass begins to form that increases with successive swallows until a well-defined air pocket is created. Air entry is reduced by execution of a succession of small swallows, and less air is ingested when the cardiac sphincter is not completely relaxed during the series of deglutitions, so that entry of the bolus is slowed and the esophagus nearly fills with a column of food. More air is swallowed if the subject is supine than if erect (43).

Adults swallow more air with liquids than with solids (43), and patients who have symptoms of excessive gas in the stomach have been observed by fluoroscopy to ingest 2 or 3 times as much air as fluid (3). The infant stomach may increase to 4 or 5 times its usual volume in the course of taking a small liquid feeding from a bottle because of simultaneous swallowing of air (42), although no such influx occurs if the baby is simply sucking on an empty bottle or his fingers (82).

Clinically, aerophagia is more often associated with situations in which swallowing is frequent and the mouth empty. This may be due to hypersalivation, attempts to moisten an overly dry mouth, postnasal drip, and gum chewing. Swallowing to relieve pressure differential in the ears during changes in elevation may also result in unusual air ingestion (3, 72).

Many foods contain air, either as part of the natural structure—an apple contains about 20% of air by volume, for example—or added in preparation or processing, as in ice cream, soufflé, and light breads. Added air volume can be substantial (the volume-to-weight ratio of a beaten egg white is 5 or 6:1), but it is not necessarily all ingested, particularly if the food collapses in the mouth before being swallowed or if it is thoroughly chewed.

The technique for voluntarily swallowing air or belching can be easily learned. Initially, air normally present in the pharynx is forced into the esophagus by elevation of the chin, extension of the neck to pull the larynx forward, and inspiration against a closed glottis. Forced expiration with the glottis closed will then cause rejection of the air, due to increased intrathoracic and intraesophageal pressure , and eructation results. By relaxing instead, or by taking an ordinary swallow, the air mass is propelled into the stomach. This procedure is more easily carried out when recumbent than erect (44).

Direct laryngoscopic examination of subjects performing this act revealed what is apparently a key factor: a small opening appears in the superior esophageal sphincter at the moment of inspiration with the glottis closed (91). This sphincter is normally open only during deglutition, and as the resting pressure of the sphincter is about 15–25 mm Hg above that of the pharynx and esophagus, entry of air is effectively prevented. The attempt to inspire against a closed glottis causes large negative intraesophageal and intragastric pressures to develop (in the order of −30 to −40 mm Hg), and this results in aspiration of large volumes of air through the patent sphincter. Skilled subjects have aspirated as much as 170 ml with a single effort (60). Inspiratory sobs of the crying baby are said to be made with the glottis closed and to contribute significantly to gastric gas on this basis (42).

If the esophagus is first intubated, preventing closure of the sphincter, even the negative intrathoracic pressure of normal respiration is sufficient to carry air into the stomach at a rate of about 40 ml per min in man; with deep respiration the minute volume increases to about 90 ml (60). In animals acute gastric distention can be induced by positioning at the sphincter a tube containing a one-way valve that permits air to enter but not to escape from the lower esophagus. Swallowing movements are rarely seen in the anesthetized animal, indicating that in this case air enters with respiratory effort (55). Air has been seen to accumulate in the stomach of anesthetized patients without apparent swallowing (50) and with only "sighing" movements in a comatose patient having respiratory difficulty (60). Two factors may be involved in these unusual cases: the esophageal sphincter may be somewhat relaxed, and the airway may be partially obstructed.

Data obtained from intubated subjects suggest that the volume of air entering the stomach averages 2–3 ml per swallow and 1 or 2 ml with a single deep breath (50). Extension of these data predicts an hourly volume of 2.5–6.0 liters, but actual volumes of this magnitude have never been reported. About 2.0–3.5 liters of gas have been recovered from adults in 24 hours by constant gastric suction postoperatively (62). The volume of air emitted through a gastrostomy tube from infants is about 1 liter in 6 hours (59) or 160 ml per hour as compared with the adult rate of 90–140 ml per hour. Intubated fasting subjects undergoing pyelography aspirated between 45 and 1,345 ml during the procedure, which lasted from 35 to 68 min. This variance was not related to age or sex, but 3–4 times as much gas was recovered from patients judged by the observer to be nervous as from those who were calm. Maximum volume was 1.2 liters per hour (50).

In view of these data, it is not surprising that atmospheric air is commonly thought to be the dominant component gas in the alimentary canal, and several additional lines of evidence relevant to clinical experience have lent persuasive support to this idea: *1*) During painful procedures in man—ureteral catheterization, for example—large volumes of gas usually appear in the bowel, but this does not occur if patients are intubated and gastric gas is aspirated (50). *2*) In simple obstruction of the gut, large volumes of gas accumulate orad to the obstruction. After experimental obstruction of the ileum of fasted animals, the accumulated volume is reduced if simultaneously an esophagostomy is performed and the distal end of the esophagus is closed (41). If the esophagus is ligated a day in advance of the ileal obstruction, gas accumulation is negligible (32). Little gas is found in completely closed loops (40, 79) and none if care is taken to empty the segment completely of air before the loop is closed (4).

However, in all these cases other normal processes of entry and exchange of gases are impeded and predominance of this single source is made evident by exclusion. Further, when as little as 200–500 ml of gas is introduced into the stomach, the radiographic image is far different from the normal; in fact, gas bubbles as large as 50 ml are exceptional in either the fasting or the food-containing stomach (29). The volume of gas

entering must be less than the amount predicted from gastric tube collections or the air is dissipated rapidly.

Disposition

Depending in part on the position of the subject, air may be returned through the esophagus by eructation or pass through the pylorus into the small intestine. If the subject is erect or prone, gas tends to accumulate in the fundus above the fluid or food mass (Fig. 1) and belching occurs easily when the intragastric tension is appropriately elevated. The fluid-filled fundus prevents escape of gas through the cardia if the subject is supine, lying on his right side, or inverted, in much the same way as a plumbing trap prevents sewage gas from bubbling into a lavatory bowl. In these positions gas accumulates in the antrum and passes through the pylorus. With the subject lying on the left side, gas gathers in both fundus and antrum and their communication may or may not be blocked by the fluid mass. If the stomach is empty, or nearly so, the absence of a fluid barrier permits free passage of air in either direction (42).

The normal small bubble of stomach gas is usually evacuated in a single eructation and even a large accumulation is nearly eliminated in 5 or 6 belches (44). The average volume of a single induced eructation is 20–80 ml (50).

Much of the remaining gas passes into the small bowel, makes its way into the colon, and is finally expelled from the rectum as flatus. Stomach emptying is slower in supine subjects than in those lying on the left side, but intestinal transit time is unaffected by posi-

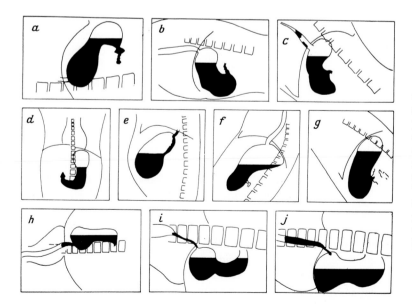

FIG. 1. Drawings from radiographs showing alteration in fluid-air relationships in the stomach with variation in posture. *a*, Lateral projection, supine; *b*, lateral projection, prone; *c*, lateral projection, prone/semierect; *d*, anterior-posterior projection, erect; *e*, lateral projection, erect; *f*, lateral projection, supine/semierect; *g*, lateral projection of infant being "burped"; *h*, anterior-posterior projection, right lateral decubitus; *i*, posterior-anterior projection, left lateral decubitus; *j*, posterior-anterior projection, left lateral decubitus. [From Hood (42).]

tion (53). In the newborn, the natural progression is accomplished within the first 2 hours of life. Gas transit time was confirmed from radiographic studies of the progress of air added to the infant stomach; after 5–30 min most of the 200–300 ml introduced had entered the intestine, and it passed from the rectum in 1–2 hours (82). Emptying time of gas from the adult stomach appears to be the same as that of the infant, but intestinal transit is more rapid. About 30 min is required to empty the stomach of a liter of added gas, but air may be detected radiographically in the cecum within 6–20 min. Passage of flatus begins in 17–36 min, and the intestine empties in as little as 45 min (50, 53). Similar values have been recorded in adults by determining, after intragastric administration of oxygen, the time at which its concentration in collected flatus first reached 18%. The average oxygen transit time 2 hours after a meal was 51 min (range 14–88 min) and in fasting subjects, 33 min (24). The transit time of gas is much shorter than that of liquids and solids.

In the fasting anesthetized cat, peristalsis is stimulated by placing a modest amount of air in the stomach, and this motor activity is postulated to be the means by which gas is swept along the gut (56). Experientially, decreasing ambient barometric pressure is known to precipitate crepitation, and laboratory evidence demonstrates that colonic activity is increased in this situation. As pressure falls, gas present in the gut expands, and the volume is further increased by gases coming out of solution. By means of a pressure transducer attached to a rubber catheter, colonic motility and tone were recorded in subjects after addition of 300 ml of air to the colon before simulated ascent in a decompression chamber (84). Colonic activity was markedly increased (2- to 3-fold) and tone was usually slightly reduced. The colon was more active when subjects breathed oxygen than air and when milk was drunk rather than no food or fluid taken. Increased activity was nearly proportional to the gas expansion factor, comparing ground level with 12,000 and 25,000 feet, but it is not certain that intraluminal pressure was proportionately increased. The elasticity of the gut allows it to accommodate to a broad range of volumes without major change in pressure (66). For instance, rectal pressure rises 10 cm H_2O when 300 ml of air is introduced, but further additions, to 1,500 ml, cause only temporary increase in pressure until the gas is redistributed throughout the colon (9). (However, subjects are distinctly uncomfortable with this amount of colonic gas, and the abdominal circumference is measurably increased.) In

any event, with adequate oxygenation the typical colonic response to the stimulus (pressure or stretch or both) of increased gas volume is motor activity that could accelerate transit of the gas and its expulsion.

Although peristalsis is an infrequent form of motor activity in the colon, the passage of gas is very rapid. A "physiological separator mechanism" that allows gas to travel at a rate far in excess of that of propagation waves in the sigmoid colon has been postulated from cineradiographic studies. Gas was seen to travel through several segments at a time, moving about 10 cm per sec, distending each segment sequentially. The secondary contractions that developed behind the main body of gas appeared to accelerate its progress (71).

Under normal conditions (i.e., without added gas) egestion of flatus accompanies the heightened motor and secretory activity of the gut that follows meals. Egestion begins about 1 hour after the start of a meal and lasts for 20 min or more (2, 46). About 30 ml (from 2 to 100 ml) is passed at a time, in a rhythmic pattern at intervals of 2–4 min. The egested flatus volume is from 8 to 170 ml per hour, depending on the subject, his diet, and the conditions of study. Calculation from data obtained in subjects studied for a minimum of 16 successive hours predicts that normal 24-hour output varies between 200 and 3,700 ml (5, 8, 14, 46).

Most pathological conditions in which there is distention due to gas in the gut are ascribable to interruption of this normal transit and egestion rather than to unusual entry or formation. Transit may be impeded mechanically, as by a bezoar or a tumor, or because of failure of the propulsive activity of the muscle. Any abnormality that interferes with the neurogenic stimuli to the musculature or with responsiveness to the stimuli can lead to failure to pass gas. Obvious neurological bases exist in cases of poliomyelitis and injuries to the cord, and the traumatic and infectious contributors are legion (1, 23). The silent abdomen—when the borborygmus that accompanies transit of gas in the gut cannot be heard—is an ominous sign of the development of ileus.

Possible metabolic causes of defective transit include diminished blood flow, which deprives the tissues of oxygen and nutrients and allows luminal materials to accumulate as well, and deficiency of neuroactive and regulatory substances or their precursors. Many nutrients fall in this category (potassium, calcium, pantothenic acid, thiamine, and niacin, to name a few), and ileus has been induced experimentally by feeding a marginally adequate diet—one low in protein content, high in carbohydrate but devoid of fiber, and borderline with respect to vitamins (13). These observations have led to unwarranted enthusiasm for the potential therapeutic properties of nutritional supplements that can only be of benefit if there is a pre-existing deficiency state and have no relevant pharmacological activity.

Pharmacological compounds that are sometimes effective include cholinergic and anticholinergic and sympatholytic agents; this suggests autonomic imbalance as a possible cause of gas accumulation. Hysterical or neurotic ileus probably represents an air swallower with either a constricted, spastic gut that responds to atropine [the *tympanismus vagotonicus* of the older literature (7)] or a sympathetically affected, atonic tract that evacuates after administration of bethanecol (23).

It is generally necessary to remove the distending gas to effect therapy (or to prevent its accumulation prophylactically by posttrauma decompression) because excessive distention reduces rather than enhances motility. The enlarged organ creates pressure less efficiently (pressure in a cylinder is equal to the circumferential tension in dynes per centimeter divided by the radius), and the lumen is difficult to occlude completely for effective thrust. Contributing to the pathology is the fact that the distended tract becomes shorter, presenting a smaller surface-to-volume ratio for gas absorption; blood flow may be reduced and secretion increased by the distention (1).

GASES PRESENT

All this implies that little gas is retained in the healthy alimentary canal, but quantification of the gas normally contained has proved extremely difficult and the few human data available are widely divergent. There is also much more information about the composition of the gas that leaves the gut than about that present from moment to moment.

Volume

Gas content of rat viscera has been measured by a method based on the differential specific gravity of gas-containing and gas-free tissue. The stomach and intestines were brought to volume in constantly boiling hydrochloric acid and weighed before and after digestion and readjustment of volume. This method, which slightly overestimates volume (to the extent that the mass of carbonate present in the gut is reduced by acid

reaction), indicates that the gas content of the adult rat stomach is about 0.1–0.5 ml during fasting and 0.2–2.5 ml 1–4 hours after feeding. Gas content of the combined small intestine, cecum, and colon varies between 0.7 and 7.0 ml. Volume is greater 4–6 hours after feeding than immediately after a meal or 16–24 hours later. More gas is found when the meal is dried milk or contains free amino acids than when it is a vegetable; smallest volumes accompany casein, meat, and egg meals (36, 37).

The same method was used to measure the gas content of the entire small intestine and colon of two fasting female dogs. One contained 20 ml and the other 55 ml of gas (E. L. Murphy, personal communication). Direct aspiration with a syringe yielded about 3 ml (0–9) of gas from the small intestine of fasting cats (32).

A plethysmographic method based on Boyle's law has been used by two groups of investigators to measure gas content in man. The test is carried out with the subject seated in a small airtight chamber of known volume. As the subject contracts his abdominal muscles maximally, the gastrointestinal gas is compressed; this causes its volume to fall and its pressure to rise. Simultaneously the volume of the surrounding air is increased and air pressure within the chamber falls. The volume of gas has been calculated in two ways: from simultaneous pressure recordings in the stomach and chamber and from a comparison of chamber pressures before and after the addition of a known volume of gas into the stomach or colon. Figure 2 is a schematic drawing of an apparatus used for these determinations.

The two groups of investigators using this apparatus provide estimates of gastrointestinal gas volume that differ by a factor of 10. According to Blair et al. (14), the volume is about 1 liter, based on repeated observations of 16 men. Individual values ranged between extremes of 550 and 2,600 ml but did not vary systematically from day to day or at different times of the day with respect to meals and defecation. The average value for three women was 615 ml. Bedell's group (9) found the volume of 13 normal subjects to be only 115 ± 127 ml and that of 47 patients with lung disease, 116 ± 125 ml.

In both laboratories methods were validated by satisfactory comparison of data obtained by gastric manometry with those of additions of air to the gut. The only perceived methodological difference is that Blair's recordings were made at the end of full expiration and Bedell's at resting lung volume. Bedell's group cites as a possible explanation of the divergent

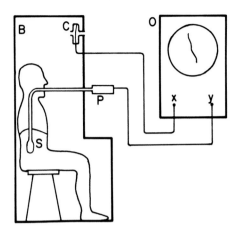

FIG. 2. Diagram of plethysmographic apparatus. The plethysmograph (B) is a chamber with about a 600-liter capacity and an airtight door. The pressure differential between the chamber and the atmosphere is measured by a capacitance manometer (C), the output from which is recorded on the X axis of a cathode-ray oscilloscope (O). The pressure changes in the closed plethysmograph are proportional to volume changes of the air in the plethysmograph, and the manometer is calibrated directly in terms of deflection of the oscilloscope by addition of known volumes of air with the subject seated in the chamber. Stomach pressure is measured by use of an intragastric balloon (S) connected to a capacitance manometer (P) outside the chamber, and the output from this manometer is recorded on the Y axis of the oscilloscope. With the intragastric balloon in place, the subject in the chamber stops breathing at the end of a normal expiration, keeping the airways open, and tenses the abdominal muscles by pushing out against the hands placed firmly on the abdomen, in rapid repeated movements, and raising the pressure in the abdomen. The initial volume of abdominal gas (V) is given by $V = (\Delta V 970/\Delta P)$ ml, where 970 (cm H_2O) is atmospheric pressure minus the pressure of water vapor at 37 C, since water vapor tension in the gastrointestinal tract is presumed constant. The slope of the line traced on the oscilloscope is proportional to $\Delta P/\Delta V$ so that, adding the calibration factors, the equation may be rewritten $V = (970 C_v/C_p \lambda)$ ml where C_v is the calibration of volume change in the plethysmograph, C_p is the calibration pressure change, and λ is the slope of the oscilloscope tracing. [From Bedell et al. (9).]

data the tendency of subjects to compress alveolar air during maximal expiratory effort, which contracts substantially the large thoracic volume and increases the apparent abdominal volume.

Bedell examined his subjects radiographically before and after introduction of 500 ml of air into the stomach or 1,200 ml into the colon. The difference in appearance was thought to be compatible with an initial volume of 0.1 liter rather than 1 liter. Bedell also noted that subjects explosively decompressed (to 17,000 feet in 1 sec) do not experience the amount of distention and discomfort that would be expected if the volume of gut gases were 1 liter and expanded 2.2

times during ascent. However, in more gradual decompression it has been noted that gas immediately adjacent to the ileocecal valve is more likely to cause pain than if it is lower in the colon and that if pain occurs it is relieved by belching and passage of flatus (15). In any case, pain is an unreliable index of gas volume. Much larger volumes are tolerated in the stomach than in the duodenum, which is very sensitive, or the colon; and as the pain is apt to be referred to the chest or back, its source is often misapprehended (69).

Flatus has been collected during simulated ascent and at various altitudes between sea level and 38,000 feet from subjects breathing oxygen (15, 26). The volume (ATSP) of gas collected ranged from 30 to 420 ml, or more than Bedell's estimated content of the entire gut. Separately, the volume of gas contained in the gut has been estimated by the plethysmographic method immediately before and after decompression. Final volumes were found to be increased, decreased, or unchanged and were without relationship to the passage of flatus. The postdecompression average of the group was 94% of initial volume, which is well within the limits of accuracy of the method (15). The preponderance of clinical evidence favors Bedell's conclusion that alimentary gas volume is small; but if this is true, then during decompression gas must be added to the gut at a rate compatible with measured flatus volume.

Composition

In what is probably the earliest record of the composition of colonic gas, samples taken from newly executed individuals were found to include nitrogen, carbon dioxide, and methane (52). Spectacular occurrences—explosions at and within the rectum and facial burns from combustion of eructed gas (35)—prove that inflammable gases may be present in significant volume, and the second combustible gas, hydrogen, was identified soon after methane. Carbon dioxide is always present in gut gases in higher concentration than in atmosphere; the situation is reversed with respect to oxygen. Characteristic odorants of some, but not all, flatus include hydrogen sulfide, volatile amines, and mercaptans.

Data on the composition of alimentary gases are assembled in Tables 1–4. In many studies the concentration of only a few gases was determined; and in all except rare or recent ones, nitrogen concentration was assumed to be the same as the undetermined residuum. The usual collection vessels are syringes in the

TABLE 1. *Composition of Flatus Collected at Reduced Ambient Barometric Pressure from Men Breathing Pure Oxygen**

Description of Sample	Ref.	Number of Tests†	Volume, ml/min‡	Percent by Volume CO₂	Percent by Volume O₂
				CO_2	O_2
Self-selected diet, collected for 10 min after 30 min at:	25				
Ground level		12		10±1	13±1
12,000 ft		8		14±2	11±1
16,000 ft		8		20±2	9±1
25,000 ft		9		24±2	6±1
28,000 ft		8		42±3	4±<1
35,000 ft		10		60±4	2±1
During 10 min at 38,000 ft, subjects fed§	15				
Normal diet		2	3–11		
High-carbohydrate diet		2	12–42	12–36	12–19
High-protein diet		8	7–33	16–50	4–21
After peroral administration of:					
During ascent 0–12,000 ft, 1st 12 min of test	24				
No treatment		4	2.02	8±1	10±4
Hydrochloric acid, 120 ml		8	3.68	12±2	10±2
Aluminum hydroxide gel, 15–30 ml			1.96		
At 35,000 ft, 55–65th min of test					
No treatment		35	4.56	60±3	2±1
Hydrochloric acid		13	3.20	64±4	2±1
Aluminum hydroxide gel		13	4.08	63±4	2±1

* Values are either means and SEMs or the range of reported data.

† Number of tests from which compositional data were derived; number of volume measurements is same or larger.

‡ Measured at ground level or corrected for expansion.

§ Two samples analyzed were found to contain 28% and 4% of combustible gases.

case of gases taken directly from the gut and, in living subjects, tubes connected to fluid-filled glass apparatus or to rubber or plastic bags. Rubber and some plastics are selectively permeable to gut gases, and only modern multi-ply laminated plastics and glass or metal containers adequately preserve specimens for any length of time. Back pressure in collecting systems can impede the passage of flatus, and maintenance of slight negative pressure has the opposite effect of removing gases sooner than they might freely have been expelled. Thus some discordance among experiments is to be expected. Major findings are summarized below from more detailed references cited in the tables.

The oxygen and carbon dioxide percentage composition of stomach gas is interesting in that the data fall into two fairly distinct ranges, perhaps related to method of collection. Sources other than air must be postulated to account for the high carbon dioxide content (up to 34%) of stomach gas obtained directly from rats, dogs, and deceased persons. The much lower proportion of carbon dioxide (4–9%) measured in samples obtained by intubation and aspiration of normal human subjects may result from dilution of the actual composition with air swallowed during intuba-tion or with air entering due to vitiation of sphincter control by intubation. Such an explanation is consist-ent with the high percentage of oxygen in these sam-ples and is supported by the fact that stomach gas col-lected after deliberate air swallowing differs little from air in having only slightly more carbon dioxide and less oxygen.

Hydrogen is reported to be present in the stomach only occasionally and in trace amounts, except in horses and in rats, where it occurs abundantly during the period 4–16 hours after a meal but not so early as 1 or 2 hours after feeding. The stomach of the breast-fed infant is said also to contain hydrogen, but no sup-porting data are given (87).

Methane is an unusual constituent of stomach gases, although it is sometimes found in significant amount in the rat and in pathological human specimens. When methane occurs, hydrogen is present as well and car-bon dioxide content is in the high range of normal values.

Carbon dioxide and hydrogen are present in the small intestine of healthy men, dogs, cattle, and geese, and the proportion of carbon dioxide is said to increase caudally (47a, 48). Values given for the gases found in

TABLE 2. *Composition of Stomach Gases**

Description of Samples	No. of Subjects	Percent by Volume					Volume, ml	Ref.
		CO_2	O_2	H_2	CH_4	Other		
Human								
Fasting	Unknown	3.9–5.3						
Fasting	4	4.7–8.7	15.1–16.4					74
Fasting, deep respiration	1	7.6	17.1					29
Fasting, deliberate air swallowing	1	1.5	19.5					50
2 Hours after eating	Unknown	up to 17.1						50
Various times after eating	5	4.2	17.1					74
Postmortem, unspecified	Unknown	12–20	Present	Trace				44
Various gastrointestinal diseases	22	3–83	0–17					74
								29
Pyloric stenosis	1	9.2	17.4	7.1	0	66		6
Acute gastric dilatation	1	56.0	0	28.0	6.8	9		58
Dog								67
5 Hours after eating								
Meat	1	25.2	6.1					
Vegetables	1	32.9	0.8					
Horse								48
Hay and corn diet	Unknown	75.2	0.2	14.6	0	10		
Rat								36, 37
After eating								
1 Hour	3†	13–18	11–12	0–0.1	0–0.1	72–75	1.2–1.3	
2 Hours	3†	14–17	10–11	0–0.2	0	70–76	1.0–1.4	
4 Hours								
Casein diet	6	22±5	8±2	0.2±0.1	0	69±4	1.3±0.1	
Dry skim milk	6	20±3	4±1	2.6±1.2	0	73±3	1.2±0.2	
Dry beef	6	12±1	9±1	1.4±0.5	0	78±2	2.5±0.2	
Dry cabbage	6	28±8	8±3	4.0±1.8	1.1±1.0	60±9	0.6±0.1	
Dry carrots	6	9±2	9±1	0	0	81±1	0.3±0.1	
Dry beans	6†	11–22	6–11	0.4–13.9	0	63–80	0.8–1.5	
Amino acid diet	6	16±4	12±2	0.6±0.4	5.1±5.0	66±6	1.6±0.2	
6 Hours	3†	16–34	3–7	1.6–11.3	0	64–75	0.7–0.9	
16 Hours	3†	14–19	11–15	1.4–13.0	0	68–74	0.1–0.5	

* Values are either means and SEMs or the range of reported data.

† Values are range of this number of group means, each of which included 6 rats.

the ileum of two presumably fasting dogs indicate that carbon dioxide content is about the same as that of the stomach, but values for oxygen are lower. Animals fed 3 hours previously have much higher levels of carbon dioxide and very little oxygen; hydrogen content varies from 6 to 49 % and is higher with a vegetable diet than when meat or bread are given. No methane is found in the small bowel of men or dogs.

Gases found in the deliberately obstructed small intestine of the dog and cat vary widely in composition, as do human pathological specimens. Hydrogen, hydrogen sulfide, and volatile amines may be absent or present in very high concentration. Methane is found only rarely and then in low concentration (4, 40).

Gas bubbles in the cecum of freshly killed rats contain these same gases and occasionally methane. Small total volumes of bowel gas are associated with relatively higher percentages of nitrogen in the cecum gas and occur with meat and egg diets. With vegetables the dominant gas is carbon dioxide, and high hydrogen concentration is found with milk meals. Both hydrogen and carbon dioxide are present at high levels when the diet contains free amino acids.

Colonic gases of fasting dogs contain more carbon dioxide and less oxygen than do samples obtained from the ileum of the same animals, but there is no remarkable difference between samples taken from the transverse and those from the descending segments. As elsewhere in the alimentary tract, samples from fed animals contain more carbon dioxide than specimens from fasted animals, but the extreme values are over

TABLE 3. *Composition of Intestinal Gases of Animals**

Description of Samples	No. of Subjects	Percent by Volume					Volume, ml	Ref.
		CO₂	O₂	H₂	CH₄	Other		
Dog								
Fasting								
Ileum	2	6–9	4–6					75
Colon	5	7–21	0–2					
5 Hours after eating								
Meat								
Small intestine	1	40	T†	14		46		67
Colon		74	0	1		24		
Vegetables								
Small intestine	1	47	0	49		4		
Colon		65	0	29		6		
Pig								
Colon								
Meat	Unknown	20		5	28	47		48
Milk		66		29	T†	5		
Peas		82		4	13	1		
Cattle								
Cecum and colon	Unknown	36		2	38	23		48
Horse								
Cecum	Unknown	85		2	11	1		48
Rectal catheter		22		3	60	15		
Rat‡								
Cecum, after eating								
1 Hour	3	18–72	1–8	16–33	T–3	9–55	1.1–1.5	36, 37
2 Hours	3	27–73	T–5	10–36	0	6–57	0.9–2.8	
4 Hours	2	25–47	2–10	8–12	0	38–56	0.8–0.9	
Casein diet								
+ Antibiotics	1	10	4	2	0	84	2.5	
Dry skim milk	1	54	T	37	0	8	6.4	
+ Antibiotics	1	21	2	20	0	56	2.7	
Dry red beans	6	52–88	T–2	2–34	0	4–14	2.3–2.8	
+ Antibiotics	1	32	4	35	0	29	3.1	
Dry beef	1	46	2	3	0	48	1.9	
Dry carrots	1	77	T	12	0	11	2.7	
Dry cabbage	1	80	2	4	4	14	2.0	
Amino acid diet	2	52–61	T–1	26–35	1–5	7–11	4.9–5.6	
6 Hours	3	34–70	1–4	9–24	0	12–54	1.2–2.4	
16 Hours	3	28–75	1–4	1–16	0	22–65	0.8–1.7	

* Values are either means and sems or the range of reported data.

† T = trace = less than 1%.

‡ Values are range of this number of group means, each of which included 6 rats.

a much greater range—about 70% and 20%, respectively. Hydrogen and hydrogen sulfide may be present, but methane is usually absent.

Colonic gas of normal persons and pigs differs from that of the dog and rat only in the much more frequent (although not universal) presence of one additional component, methane. (Only the herbivores—cattle, horses, and rabbits—have methane as a regular component gas of the cecum-colon.) Human flatus is composed of 5–80% carbon dioxide, 0–10% oxygen, 0–54% hydrogen and methane, and 17–88% "nitrogen." As in the rat, nitrogen concentration is least when flatus volume is large; concentration of carbon dioxide is high under the same circumstances. When increased flatus production is stimulated by the presence of foods, carbon dioxide and hydrogen or both hydrogen and methane concentrations are elevated and the proportionality patterns with specific foods approximate those of other animals. In response to decreased ambient pressure, carbon dioxide concen-

TABLE 4. *Volume and Composition of Human Colonic Gases**

Description of Samples	No. of Sub-jects	Percent by Volume					Volume Col-lected, ml/min	Ref.
		CO₂	O₂	H₂	CH₄	Other		
Normal								
Collected 0730–1730 hours, schizophrenic patients	3							5
Diet of milk, raws eggs, and sugar		5	T†–1	T–3	T–4	90–92	0.34–0.68	
+ 300 g boiled cabbage		5–7	T–1	0–1	T	91–93	0.32–0.56	
+ 150 g dried green peas, cooked		6–7	1–2	1–4	2–4	86–89	0.38–0.54	
Self-selected diet, rubber bag, 24-hour collection	5	2–10	8–11				0.26–0.45	8
Collected approximately 0800–2400 hours in rubber bags	1							14
Normal diets		12	6	22	8	52	0.20–0.43	
Very-low-protein egg (25 g) diet		17	7	52	2	23	1.39–1.45	
Very-low-protein soybean (25 g) diet		10–43	2–3	39–69	T–2	14–40	1.67–2.56	
Collected 0900–1400 and 1700–2200 hours								46
Normal diet, normal subjects	20	9	4	21	7	59	1.48	
		1–15	0–16	3–32	0–30	40–88	0.36–3.97	
Normal diet without milk, normal subjects	25	10	6	12	3	70	1.45	
Normal diet without milk, colitis patients	22	9	4	7	4	76	0.95	
Normal subjects, no cabbage	10	10	4	19	5	62	1.55	
							0.36–2.74	
+ 300 g each raw and cooked Brussels sprouts		10	7	14	4	64	2.34	
							0.38–4.14	
Colitis patients								
No milk	13	8	5	7	4	76	1.09	
							0.16–4.50	
+ 1 liter milk		8	6	10	4	72	1.08	
							0.18–4.67	
Collection time unknown								73
Normal diet	3	12–54		1–22	9–47	18–45		
Milk diet	2	9–17		44–54	0–1	37–38		
Vegetable diet	3	18–38		0.4	43–56	11–32		
Meat diet	3	8–14		1–3	26–37	46–64		
Collected 2 hours each, 30 min after lunch and dinner								85
High protein (150 g) diet	6	11	3	19	20	47	0.30±0.22	
+ 10 g methylcellulose							0.27±0.20	
27% of diet as canned dry beans		25	2	15	26	32	1.12±0.57	
59% of diet as canned dry beans		31	1	29	16	23	2.12±1.03	
Pathologic								
Ileus	8	5–8	0–4	0–1	0–8	81–95		4
Obstructing carcinoma	4	3–11	1–17	0–8	0–3	69–77		40

* Values are either means and SEMs or the range of reported data.

† T = trace = less than 1%.

tration is elevated. In only a few cases is substantial volume reported with composition fairly closely resembling air.

BACTERIAL GASES

Anaerobic and aerobic bacteria and, more rarely, yeasts and molds isolated from the feces and intestinal tract of normal animals and man utilize a variety of substrates with production of gas. (In fact, most of the information on gas production by enteric organisms derives from studies in which fermentation of selective substrates is used to isolate and identify specific organisms.) These organisms are abundant in the colon and are found at all levels of the small intestine but in decreasing abundance cephalad (17, 35a, 54, 81). In contrast to the normal predominance of gram-negative and anaerobic bacteria found in stool specimens, gram-positive and aerobic strains are more common inhabitants of the jejunum and ileum (17, 35a).

When the stool organisms are predominantly gram-positive forms, in vitro gas production is low, as with specimens from breast-fed infants in which *L. bifidus* and *L. acidophilus* abound. Stools from bottle-fed infants and children and adults on a normal diet have more gram-negative forms—chiefly coliforms, bacteroides, and streptococci—and these evolve larger volumes of gas when incubated in vitro. Gas production may also vary depending on the several types of bacteria present in a mixture, because a second organism often profits from the end products of the metabolism of the first. For example, more gas is generated by a mixed culture of *E. coli* and *A. aerogenes capsulatus* than by *E. coli* in pure culture (39).

Substrates and Products

Enteric organisms are capable of fermenting urea and virtually all the organic substances present in foods: protein and amino acids, fatty acids, sugars, and most of the polysaccharides (lignin is an exception) (20, 32, 39, 54, 80). In a closed intestinal loop, sulfur- and nitrogen-containing compounds are evolved by bacteria even though only sugar is provided as substrate; this indicates that the bacteria can also utilize endogenous proteins of the gut (40). Presumably this would be true of all endogenous energy sources, but the presence of food residues appears to permit more abundant growth. After starvation for only 24 hours, bacterial count is significantly lowered, especially in the upper portions of the intestine, and there is a disproportion of some usually rare forms (81). Fecal bacterial fermentation of cellulose yields carbon dioxide, methane, and hydrogen; and acetic, lactic, butyric, isobutyric, valerianic, formic, propionic, and succinic acids (54). Anaerobic organisms present in human colonic dejecta produce from sugars the same gases and occasionally acetone as well, but cultures from the human ileum produce no methane. Carbon dioxide, hydrogen, and methane are also evolved when amino acids serve as the primary substrate, but relatively more hydrogen and less carbon dioxide are formed than with sugars. Carbon dioxide and hydrogen are also the predominant gases formed from mixed food substrates, but the pattern is variable; for example, more hydrogen is produced from milk than from dried beans (20).

Methane is not formed from beans during in vitro incubation of samples taken from either the small intestine or the colon of the dog (70). This fact coupled with the almost universal absence of methane from gases found in situ suggests that organisms capable of forming methane are not normal inhabitants of the dog bowel or that there is a predominance of organisms that further metabolize methane. In favor of the former hypothesis is the observation that often there is no evidence of digestion of crude fiber (i.e., cellulose, hemicellulose, lignin, cutin, suberin, and pectin) in the dog gut, although occasionally a value as high as that of the rat is recorded. (Only about half of cellulose fed is recovered in rat feces.)

About a fourth (54) of human subjects examined have methane present in high concentration [(47); see Table 4]; in those who do, the concentration varies cyclically, implying alternating overgrowth and subsidence of some strains (19). This variation is often ascribed to variation in inoculum from food and to the diet as a selective culture medium, but idiosyncratic factors must dominate because families and men living in closely confined groups maintain different gas patterns while sharing the same foods and fluids (21).

Among the products of in vitro fermentation are hydrogen sulfide and sometimes methyl mercaptan, but the latter is rarely found in fresh human material. In common with many other products of bacterial metabolism in the gut, the absence of methyl mercaptan may be ascribable to rapid absorption of small amounts formed in vivo or it may not be a customary end product of normal balanced floral populations under conditions in the gut. Pathological specimens, including those from patients with pernicious anemia, marasmus, and steatorrhea, often show high yields of methyl mercaptan, and in these instances it is a persistent, not a transitory, phenomenon (38).

Small amounts of nitrogen are regularly found in cultures grown anaerobically (20). The origin of this nitrogen is uncertain but is presumably bacterial. (It is difficult to exclude dissolved nitrogen completely and, since analysis was carried out by mass spectroscopy, nitrogen cannot be differentiated from carbon monoxide, which is a possible metabolic product and has the same mass.) The older literature refers to the simultaneous production of nitrogen and ammonia by putrefactive organisms, but the statement is unsupported, though nitrogen production from nitrates and nitrites is known (49). Ammonia has not been identified among the gases evolved in vitro by gut organisms, but there is adequate inferential evidence of its usual production in vivo, and it was found in an isolated segment of dog intestine inoculated with a pure culture of *Clostridium welchii*, a normal gut inhabitant (40).

Contribution to Luminal Gas

Calculations of the potential contribution of bacterially generated gas suggest the possibility of prodigious amounts from this source (77). Assuming simple stoichiometry, the 5 g of residual carbohydrates from a diet low in fibrous plant materials could yield 975 ml of carbon dioxide, 375 ml of methane, and 200 ml of hydrogen, or about 1.5 liters of gas at body temperature. Conversion of lactic acid to butyric acid, a known bacterial pathway, could form 2.5 liters each of hydrogen and carbon dioxide from only 10 g of substrate.

The major apparent limitation is one of availability of substrate at the gut level where organisms are profuse. Thus, foods that are digested and absorbed slowly or not at all by the host are most likely to provide a medium for luxuriant growth of bacteria, and the higher in the gut the organisms are able to survive, the better is the opportunity to compete with the host for nutrients useful to both. Clinically, excessive gas production is often associated with maldigestive and malabsorptive syndromes; foods that commonly result in noticeable flatus production have, as one of the probable causes of the effect, a substantial content of essentially nondigestible sugars, such as raffinose and stachyose (61).

Antibiotics have been administered in an attempt to assess the bacterial contribution to alimentary gas, but results have not been definitive. Regrettably, gases from germ-free animals have not been studied. Antibiotics reduce the numbers of organisms present, but the tract is not made sterile; and as antibiotics are selective, and some more so than others, they may alter the balance of flora. The gut itself is also affected by treatment with antibiotics; the wall is thinner and the cecum enlarged, somewhat comparable to that of the axenic animal.

In one test system, substrate was placed in an isolated segment of intestine after pretreatment or during administration of antibiotics. All the sulfa drugs and penicillin reduced gas volume to a tenth of the control value from malted milk, but streptomycin was not consistently effective (78, 80). Iodochlorhydroxyquin and a combination of neomycin and sulfathalidine suppressed gas formation from beans (70).

Dietary supplementation with a mixture of neomycin and nystatin consistently reduced the percentage of carbon dioxide present in the rat cecum, but compared with the respective dietary controls, total volume was increased with the casein diet, decreased if milk was fed, and unchanged in rats given beans (see Table 3). Cecal enlargement was noted (36). The anomaly is resolved if, as is appropriate in the face of a drug-induced side effect, comparison is made properly within drug treatment groups. On this basis it is evident that the antibiotics virtually eliminated the differences in gas volume due to foods, and this points to a microfloral origin of the differences in gas pattern and volume seen normally.

In a single study (25) in which volume of flatus was not measured and the diet was self-selected, carbon dioxide concentration of rectal gas did not vary in response to treatment of normal human subjects with phthalylsulfathiazone (8 g/day). Compared with control tests of bean-induced flatulence, total volume and carbon dioxide content were reduced 45 % the second day of administration of iodochlorhydroxyquin (1.5 g/day) to one subject. Hydrogen virtually disappeared but methane was increased (61).

The opinion was at one time prevalent that organisms cannot survive in the acid medium of the stomach, but modern information indicates that ingested bacteria can and do pass through the stomach and implant in the intestine. This may be because the pH of a bolus of food in the stomach may not fall below 4.0. Thus, bacteria ingested *with* food may not be subjected to extreme acidity, at least until the stomach is empty or nearly so, but it is doubtful if bacteria thrive in the stomach beyond that time. Incubation of stomach contents of 100 unselected patients showed that viable organisms capable of producing gas were present only when hydrochloric acid was deficient (29). In one frankly pathological and very rare case of acute gastric dilatation accompanied by inflammable eructation, the stomach was found to contain yeast and sarcinae, their growth being permitted by high gastric pH (58).

Although supporting data are not available, it seems unlikely that gastric pH is pathologically elevated in human infants and in the large groups of rats in which gases of bacterial origin are found in the stomach in significant concentration. In the rat, coprophagy would continuously seed the stomach with organisms indigenous to the lower bowel, in addition to those present in the food eaten, but no such excessive inoculation can be assumed in the baby. Further, in the rat these gases are found in the stomach 4 hours or more after a meal, at a time when the stomach is virtually empty of food that might serve as substrate. The possibility of bacterial generation in the healthy stomach cannot be ruled out completely, but, alternatively, these gases customary to the intestine might have diffused inward from the blood after having been absorbed lower in the tract or have been refluxed through the pylorus. The resistance of the pyloric sphincter to the reverse passage of fluids is said to preclude reflux as an origin of stomach gas, but since liquids sometimes do reflux it seems likely that gases also sometimes pass in both directions past the sphincter. However, though the question of whether gas may reflux through the pyloric sphincter at pressures present in the gut has not been resolved, hydrogen is probably not evolved orad to the sphincter, yet it is found in the dog stomach whether or not the pylorus has been ligated, so that some gas is brought to the gastric contents by the blood. (74).

There are other, less obvious ways in which the bacterial population of the gut can influence the character and disposition of alimentary gas, none of which has been the subject of systematic study from this point of view. Some of the products of bacterial metabolism can affect the function of the gastrointestinal tract directly or, after absorption, systemically. For example, the short-chain fatty acids evolved are mildly stimulatory to motor activity of the gut and also react with bicarbonate to form additional carbon dioxide. At least two of the amines formed by bacterial decarboxylation of amino acids—histamine from histidine and serotonin from 5-hydroxytryptophan—are known to affect gastrointestinal secretion, blood flow, and responsiveness to distention. Microbially generated amines could thus alter the amount of acid and bicarbonate added to the gut, the capacity for modification by exchange with the blood, and the rate of transit through the bowel.

DIGESTION AND SECRETION

At all levels of the alimentary canal, conditions are suitable for reaction between acid and bicarbonate with the consequent evolution of carbon dioxide. Enormous volumes are available from the gastrointestinal secretions and perhaps smaller amounts from local tissue respiration and from the diet. As illustrations of the latter, the Ewald test meal of tea and soda crackers used for evaluation of gastric function produces 4–5 times its volume of carbon dioxide on acidification to the normal pH of gastric juice (29); and, if drunk rapidly, a 6-oz (170 ml) serving of a cola beverage provides about 500 ml of carbon dioxide (14).

Acids and Bicarbonate

Acidification in the upper tract depends largely on gastric hydrochloric acid although some weak acids are ingested as food. (Among common foods only egg white has a pH above 7.) The daily hydrochloric acid production is variable but amounts to about 0.25–0.35 mole. Acid residues are released during digestion of protein and fat, and acids are produced by bacterial action lower in the gut. Depending on the amount and kind of residual dietary carbohydrate, the 24-hour fecal output of titratable acid is equivalent to 0.1–1.5 moles (90). Since the contents of the gastrointestinal tract are nearly always below pH 7, it may be assumed that acid is not a limiting factor to the evolution of carbon dioxide from bicarbonate.

With the exception of gastric juice, all the secretions of the alimentary canal contain substantial amounts of bicarbonate, and even in the stomach, bicarbonate-rich mucus is formed. Within accepted wide ranges of secretion rate and composition, the amount of bicarbonate available from the various secretions, in millimoles per 24 hours, is: saliva, 60–120; pancreatic juice, 50–325; bile, 15–65; intestinal juice, 700–1600; and colonic fluid, 5–250 (27). The sums of the extreme values are 0.8 and 2.4 moles, discounting mucus. The secreted bicarbonate, if neutralized, is unquestionably the dominant source of carbon dioxide in the gut, with an equivalent daily volume of 18–54 liters of free gas. Enough gastric acid is available to neutralize all the bicarbonate of saliva, pancreatic juice, and bile with evolution of 5.6–7.8 liters of carbon dioxide alone.

The chief questions concern the true volume and composition of the fluids of the ileum and colon, the pH of intestinal contents, and the removal rate of carbon dioxide. It is certain that more bicarbonate is added than is removed across the ileum [although the reverse is true in the jejunum (64)], and the partial pressure of carbon dioxide in the equilibrated gut gases always exceeds that of venous blood (22). At an intestinal pH of 6.1, half the carbon dioxide would be in the form of bicarbonate; a lower pH would shift the equilibrium in favor of carbon dioxide formation, as would rapid removal of carbon dioxide from the gut.

The presence of such high partial pressures of carbon dioxide in the gas of the alimentary canal is entirely consistent with the combination of high bicarbonate concentration in the secretions and relatively low pH of the intestinal contents. In fact, it is only with this combination of high P_{CO_2} that pH can be maintained below 8 with bicarbonate concentration above 60 mEq/per liter; carbon dioxide evolution might be regarded as one of the important contributors to buffering in the gut.

Deliberate manipulation for study of these factors has been limited to addition of acid to the gut and of substances that stimulate gastric and pancreatic secretion. An inhibitor of the enzyme carbonic anhydrase, acetazolamide (Diamox), has been used to control bicarbonate formation, but it has the unfortunate feature, for experimental purposes, of limiting the removal of carbon dioxide from the gut as well as its addition. In one experiment, hydrochloric acid or saline was placed in the jejunum of fed dogs and about 45 min later oxygen was administered intragastrically to stimulate passage of flatus. Carbon dioxide content was 9% in the controls and 31% in those given acid. Fasting human subjects were given histamine and secretin injections or saline, and flatus was collected after a liter of oxygen had been added to the stomach. The spontaneously egested flatus contained 11% carbon dioxide in control trials and 37% with the stimulating agents (25). These experiments confirm the notion that a more brisk secretion rate of acid and bicarbonate will form more carbon dioxide in the gut, and they illustrate that some of the formed gas will be expelled as flatus if there is also sufficient stimulus to the passage of gas.

When decreased ambient pressure is the stimulus to the passage of gas, foreign gas need not be added, and it is possible to capture samples believed to represent more closely the composition high in the gut. Gases collected by rectal catheter from men breathing oxygen during simulated ascent at the rate of 1,000 feet per min or at various altitudes to 35,000 feet contained progressively larger percentages of carbon dioxide as elevation increased [from about 9% (2–20%) at ground level up to 60% (17–82%) at high altitude] (24, 25; see Table 1). This increased concentration of carbon dioxide could result from the absence of other diluting gases or from increased entry of carbon dioxide into the gut from endogenous sources.

Gas present low in the gut would contain some products of bacteria and residues of atmospheric air, and these would be evacuated early. This is more evident in another study in which men were more rapidly decompressed and gas was collected for the duration of the brief (10-min) flight (15). These samples contained substantial amounts of combustible gas and nitrogen and only 32% of carbon dioxide, on the average. Enhanced secretion of bicarbonate has been offered as a possible explanation of the high percentage of carbon dioxide, and adequate gastric secretion may be assumed. [Gastric pH does not rise if subjects are adequately oxygenated, and gastric distention would serve to stimulate, not to impair, secretion (26).] However, neither administration of hydrochloric acid nor the use of aluminum hydroxide gel to reduce acidity affected volume or carbon dioxide content of flatus in altitude studies (24). Varying solubility of the component gases is probably adequate to account for the progressive disproportion as the gases come out of solution with decreasing barometric pressure, particularly as nitrogen was washed out by breathing pure oxygen.

Tissue Metabolism

There is some possibility that carbon dioxide is added to and oxygen removed from the luminal gases because of metabolic activity of the gut, but this is extremely difficult to demonstrate conclusively. The fact that carbon dioxide concentration in the stomach gas is markedly elevated in fed animals is taken as evidence that it is a by-product of secretory activity (30), and some carbon dioxide might well diffuse into the lumen with the elevated P_{CO_2} of the blood during acid production. Alternatively, or additionally, the carbon dioxide may be from bicarbonate of salivary and gastric mucus or it may be regurgitated effervescence from the reaction between gastric acid and pancreatic bicarbonate immediately adjacent to the pylorus (10).

Air introduced into ligated loops of rabbit intestine is enriched with carbon dioxide at a rate of 3.7 ml/cm per hour, and this rate is markedly reduced by poisoning or scalding the epithelium, as is the rate of oxygen uptake from the luminal gases (18). When the blood vessels that drain a segment of cat gut are ligated, oxygen disappears from the lumen at an undiminished or even enhanced rate and carbon dioxide continues to accumulate (57). Except that the conditions of bacterial contamination are unknown, these experiments would appear to establish that the gut tissues profit directly from the oxygen of swallowed air.

DIFFUSION AND ABSORPTION

Unusual gases added to inspired mixtures appear in the lumen of the gut, and gases originating uniquely in the bowel are found in expired air. The composition of air placed in the stomach, colon, or ligated portions of the gut is altered and at a later time it approaches (but does not match exactly) the partial pressures of oxygen and carbon dioxide in blood, oxygen having moved out and carbon dioxide having moved into the lumen. These phenomena conform generally to the physical laws of diffusion. The nearness of fit of the biological data to physical law is remarkable in view of the multiplicity of modes of entry and exit of gases, the complexity of the membrane, and the numerous chemical reactions that produce, remove, and alter gases, all of which occur in the dynamic physiological situation. With very few exceptions, these modifying factors affect primarily the rate, not the direction, of movement of the gases.

Theoretical Considerations

McIver et al. (57) have provided elegant experimental proof of diffusion and the conditions under which it proceeds in the gut. Application of laws governing the diffusion rate of gases in any system yields the following equation descriptive of behavior in the body:

$$\frac{d(xV)}{dt} = \frac{D}{m} S(a - x)$$

where a is the mean tension of the gas in the capillaries of the mucosa measured as a percent of 1 atm; x is the partial pressure of the gas in the lumen of the alimentary canal similarly measured; S is the surface of the viscus in square centimeters; V is the volume in cubic centimeters; m is the effective thickness of the wall in microns; t is time; and D is the diffusion coefficient of the gas, that is, the volume of the gas that will diffuse through 1 cm² under a pressure gradient of 1 atm/1-μ thickness in 1 min. (This diffusion velocity is inversely proportional to the square root of the molecular weight of the given gas.)

This equation is susceptible to experimental validation, assuming that in the course of an experiment a, V, S, and m did not change significantly. In this case

$$\frac{dx}{dt} = \frac{DS}{mV}(a - x)$$

and allowing k to stand for the expression

$$\frac{DS}{mV}$$

substitution and rearrangement yields:

$$k = \frac{1}{t} \log_e \frac{a}{a - x}$$

all of which are easily measured. The k value of carbon dioxide in the stomach of the anesthetized cat was found to be 0.0349 for inward diffusion when air was placed in the stomach and 0.0344 for outward movement when a mixture containing 16.7% of carbon dioxide was introduced.

Calculation of the k value for carbon dioxide removal from the human colon, using an equation derived from the exponential curve of declining percentage of the gas in the lumen, gave a value nearly the same as that computed from McIver's formula; the two values are 0.02884 and 0.03040, respectively. The k for oxygen removal was much smaller, 0.01658 (68).

Comparison of these k values indicates that some factor other than molecular weight must influence the diffusion behavior, for oxygen is the lighter of the two gases yet it is less diffusible. Part of the explanation lies in the fact that gas diffusing from the intestinal lumen does not pass through a single membrane of easily definable composition, but rather must cross alternating layers of lipid-protein membranes and of both extra- and intracellular fluids, which resemble water but also contain various solutes and fat and do not underlie the membrane in a continuous sheet. At 37 C carbon dioxide is 20 times as soluble in water as is oxygen, and the solubility of carbon dioxide in oil is 1.6 times its solubility in water. Oxygen is 5 times as soluble in oil as in water; thus in a lipid system there is not much more than a sevenfold difference between the gases. Nitrogen is much more soluble than is hydrogen in oil and slightly less soluble in water. Neither gas is as soluble as is oxygen in either medium. Diffusion rate of the gases through the fluid layer thus depends on both specific solubility and mass, being directly proportional to the absorption coefficient divided by the square root of the density. The question of kinetics of oxygen and carbon dioxide is further complicated by their chemical combination with blood constituents, which tends to maximize their transportation.

The amount of a given gas that will diffuse per unit time also depends on the difference in its partial pressure on either side of the membrane. Hydrogen, methane, and hydrogen sulfide concentrations are always higher in the lumen of the gut than in the blood; thus these gases are constantly removed, and the amount of each gas that diffuses will be proportional to its individual concentration in the mixture, irrespective of the other components. On the other hand, the partial pressure of nitrogen is high in the tissues and blood and may be nearly equal in the gut lumen, so that there is little pressure differential to promote diffusion. A small increase in intraluminal pressure, not sufficient to initiate motor activity,

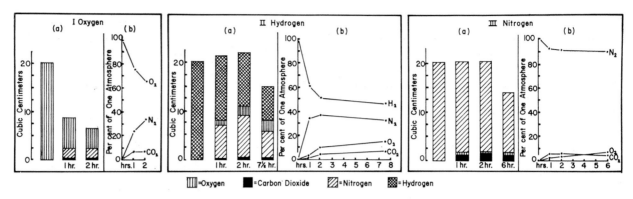

FIG. 3. Course of events after the introduction of pure oxygen (*I*), hydrogen (*II*), and nitrogen (*III*) into an isolated 25-cm loop of small intestine in a cat. The first column in diagram *a* represents the amount of gas injected; the succeeding columns indicate the volumes of component gases found in the total volume withdrawn from the loop after stated intervals of time. The percentage composition is given in diagram *b*. Downward slopes indicate removal of the test gas, and ascending lines show entrance of gases from the blood. [From McIver et al. (57).]

should favor insorption of gas by increasing partial pressures in the contents relative to blood (1).

According to gas laws, diffusion rate varies directly with surface area and inversely with membrane thickness. Because the stomach wall is thicker than that of the small bowel, it should also have a lower potential for diffusion. This has been experimentally validated in that only 6% of a volume of gas placed in a ligated stomach was removed in 24 hours, even though the diffusion gradient was in favor of removal (33). Similarly, irritation or disease could impair transfer rate by causing the membrane to thicken, but often under this condition blood flow is increased and the net effect may be increased rate of resorption (76). The small intestine presents the largest total absorptive surface and has the largest surface-to-volume ratio in the gastrointestinal tract; therefore, it would be expected to have the highest diffusion capacity as well. The distended gut would afford less available surface per unit volume, diminishing the rate at which an entrapped volume of gas would be removed. Diffusion of gas trapped in foam might be impeded because of limited area of membrane contact; this situation occurs in cattle bloat, where plant saponins allow formation of stable bubbles.

Removal of gas from the alimentary canal is affected by perfusion rate not only of the gut, but also of the lungs and perhaps the skin. If the partial pressure is favorable, 80–95% of dissolved gases are usually cleared in a single passage through the lungs. About 5 liters of blood circulates through the lungs each minute, which is several times the rate of gastrointestinal perfusion, so the lungs should not limit gas removal. A gas that appears in expired air in as low a concentration as 100 ppm (0.01%) is disposed of at a rate approximating 40 or 50 ml per hour. When pulmonary and cutaneous perfusion are increased during strenuous exercise, the process of gas exchange is favored in the musculature, but splanchnic blood flow is reduced. Since lung perfusion is not normally limiting, it is unlikely that increased rate and depth of respiration alone can favorably affect intestinal gas removal in the face of reduced intestinal blood flow. Exchange of even the common gases through the skin

FIG. 4. Diagrams on *right* represent volumes of flatus gases collected each 30 min by rectal catheter from 1 subject under 3 conditions: *top*, fasting after the evening meal of the previous day until 8 PM the day of study, when a 900-kcal serving of a bland liquid formula diet was taken; *center*, same formula consumed at regular meal intervals, designated by asterisks; *bottom*, luncheon meal consisting of 100 g dry weight of dried white beans, cooked with enough corn oil and dextrose to equal the formula meal, and an evening meal of formula. Note that the half-hourly flatus volume is above the scale at 3 successive intervals about 5 hours after the bean meal, and carbon dioxide volumes are beyond the scale at 2 of these. *Curves on left* show concentrations in parts per million of hydrogen and methane measured simultaneously. Assuming normal pulmonary ventilation, the scale of breath concentration may be equated with the flatus volumes (i.e., 100 ppm is approximately equal to 30-min pulmonary excretion of 20 ml). When the subject was fasting or consumed only the bland formula, all the hydrogen produced in the gut was removed by diffusion into the blood and out of the lungs and none was found in the small amounts of expelled flatus; but when beans were eaten, a larger amount was produced and appeared in both expired air and flatus. [From Calloway & Murphy (21).]

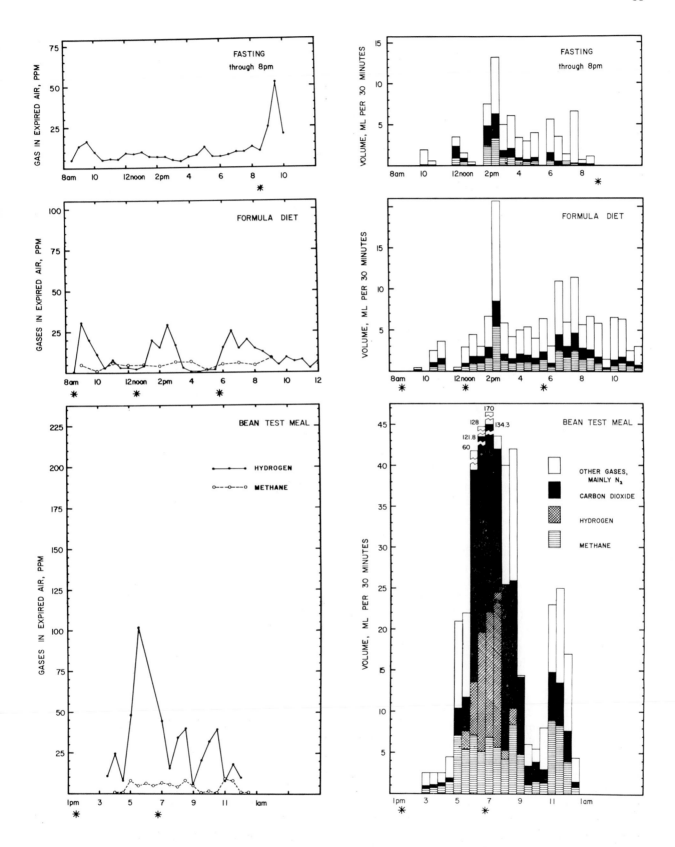

has not been measured with great precision, but the inward diffusion rate of nitrogen through the skin of clothed subjects seated in air and breathing pure oxygen is estimated to be 0.01 ml/kg body wt per min (86). Removal rates would not be expected to be higher.

Blood flow to the gastrointestinal tract is maximal during periods of digestive activity, when the gut processes of addition and formation of gases are probably at a peak. It is known that a high concentration of carbon dioxide in the lumen causes vasodilatation (34) and enhances blood flow (63); and, at least in the colon, motility is depressed when distending gas includes 20% or more of carbon dioxide (25). All these factors favor diffusion.

Experimental Evidence

Diffusion of a number of gases has been studied by placement of single gases or air in ligated portions of dog and cat gut (57, 75). Typical data are portrayed in Figure 3. When oxygen is placed in a loop, its concentration falls rapidly, both by its loss from the loop with reduction in the volume of gas injected and by dilution with nitrogen and carbon dioxide that diffuse into the lumen. With pure hydrogen or nitrogen the rapid counterdiffusion of blood gases and the relatively slow diffusion of the added gut gas cause a temporary increase in the entrapped volume until equilibrium is reestablished. Absorption rates from 20 ml of pure gases placed in 25-cm loops of small intestine of anesthetized cats were found to be (ml/hour): nitrogen, 1.0; methane, 4.3; hydrogen, 7.2; oxygen, 13.7; hydrogen sulfide, 69; and carbon dioxide, 160. The last two rate estimates were computed to 1-hour equivalents from brief periods of measurement, necessitated by the extremely rapid absorption of carbon dioxide and the toxic reaction to hydrogen sulfide (57).

Very early workers demonstrated that a higher proportion of the methane generated in the rabbit gut is found in expired air than is passed rectally (92). In man a trace of methane is nearly always found in expired air, and high concentrations (30–80 ppm) occur in perhaps a quarter of the population (19, 47, 65). Very frequently methane is not detected in expelled flatus (see Table 4); this suggests that at low production rates it is completely cleared by diffusion.

Hydrogen is a regular component of expired air, but it may shift from a low of 1–2 ppm enrichment of room air to values as high as 140 ppm in a single individual in a day (19, 21, 65). The most common

association with its elevation in the breath is consumption of a gas-forming food, such as beans. About 5 or 6 hours after the meal is eaten, breath values rise precipitously, remain elevated for a variable period, and decline slowly to base-line levels (Fig. 4), changes indicating a period of rapid bacterial generation. Depending on the particular subject and the type and amount of food taken, the elevation in breath hydrogen may be the only evidence of increased bacterial action, for apparently the diffusion capacity must be exceeded before hydrogen appears in flatus (19, 21).

When tritium was placed in a dog colon and the rectum tightly sutured, the label was detected in expired air within 5 min and continued to be eliminated during the 6 hours of study, at the end of which 30% of the dose was recovered from the colon (11). This suggests a slow removal rate—slower than is consonant with data from man. The rate may have been affected by the experimental technique, including anesthesia, or the rate may truly differ low in the colon; but, assuredly, the molecular weight of tritium is three times that of hydrogen, so its diffusion rate is lower. The importance of gut location cannot be dismissed from consideration, however. Radioactive krypton, which is 40 times as heavy as hydrogen, is found in expired air within about 2 min if it is put in the duodenum, and peak radioactivity is recorded peripherally at about 15 min; there is no measurable uptake in 30 min if the gas is placed in the colon or stomach (88).

The reverse exchange—of inspired foreign gases—is also very fast and complete. Acetylene given as 80% of respired gas appeared in the dog intestine within 2 min; 6 min after the administration ended, 75% of the dose had been reexcreted through the lungs (75).

Nitrogen from swallowed air tends to remain in the lumen because there are only minor differences in its partial pressure on either side of the membrane. If large volumes of other gases are added to the gut, the partial pressure of nitrogen decreases and the diffusion gradient is favorable to influx of nitrogen from the tissues. Conversely, in order to shift nitrogen out of the gut, it is necessary to increase its partial pressure with respect to the tissues and, therefore, ambient air. This has been accomplished by breathing pure oxygen, which increases threefold the rate of removal of nitrogen from a closed intestinal loop, in comparison with breathing air (33).

In the upper alimentary canal, oxygen usually moves away from the lumen because swallowed air is higher in oxygen content than are the blood and tissues. Lower in the tract the reverse is true, for oxygen has been removed by diffusion and the active processes of the gut and its resident bacteria, and other gases have been added that serve to reduce further the partial pressure of oxygen. The concentration is then below that of the blood and oxygen moves toward the lumen.

Carbon dioxide moves out of the gut at a faster rate than any other gas because of its high absorption coefficient and because it is enzymatically assisted and specifically transported in the blood. Absorption appears to be the most important mechanism for clearing the alimentary canal of its most dominant gas, carbon dioxide. When rats are given ^{14}C-labeled bicarbonate intragastrically, 70% of the label is recovered in the expired air in 2 hours, and its initial appearance is accelerated if hydrochloric acid is given simultaneously (83). Removal from the dog colon is slower, but 30% of $^{14}CO_2$ added to the rectum is found in the expired air within 2.5 hours (16). That diffusion is not the only process involved in its exchange is illustrated by a study of the effect of carbon dioxide on absorption of ethanol from the stomach. It was shown that each is absorbed more rapidly in the presence of the other and that carbon dioxide can be absorbed against a gradient, since its concentration in gastric gas was less than that of blood at the end of the test (31). Participation of carbonic anhydrase in carbon dioxide absorption is demonstrated by accumulation (70) or by decreased rate of removal of carbon dioxide (28) when acetazolamide is placed in the lumen. Data on ethanol effects would be rationalized by a hypothesis that membrane permeability is altered by ethanol but that the enzyme is unaffected. The effect of carbon dioxide on ethanol absorption may be mediated by changes in blood flow.

Many of the foods classed as "gas forming" share a second common feature, besides significant content of nondigestible low-molecular-weight carbohydrates (see above): this is the presence of sulfur-containing compounds that can be degraded into hydrogen sulfide and mercaptans, providing sulfide ion, known to be a potent inhibitor of carbonic anhydrase. Thus the stage is set for maximal bacterial growth and metabolism, with production of gas and metabolites that might transiently reduce intestinal capacity for removal of both bacterial and secreted carbon dioxide, favoring distention and motility with expulsion of abundant, odorous flatus.

The usually small amount of gas passed from the rectum is the residuum of swallowed air from which oxygen has been removed and in which is found the miniscule portion of the carbon dioxide evolved in the gut that escapes absorption. When large volumes of gas are egested, the stimulus appears to be distention caused by increased ingestion or production and decreased absorption or simply by expansion with reduced ambient pressure. The decreased absorption may be due to diminished gut perfusion rate, inhibition of assisted transportation processes, thickening or impaired contact with the gut membranes, and, in the case of swallowed air, insufficient difference between tissues and lumen in partial pressure of the gas. When motility is stimulated, whatever gas is present in the lumen will be swept out even though it might otherwise have been absorbed during longer residence.

The author is indebted to Miss Susan M. Oace for critical editing of the manuscript and to Dr. E. L. Murphy for valuable discussion and assistance.

REFERENCES

1. ADMIRAAL, J. Untersuchungen uber die gasresorption im darm. *Arch. Neerl. Physiol.* 27: 77–117, 1943.

2. ALSTEAD, S., AND J. F. PATTERSON. Assessment of intestinal carminatives. *Lancet* 1: 437–439, 1948.

3. ALVAREZ, W. C. *An Introduction to Gastro-Enterology* (4th ed.). New York: Hoeber, 1948, chapt. XXIX, p. 646–678.

4. ANDERSEN, K., AND A. RINGSTED. Clinical and experimental investigations on ileus with particular reference to the genesis of intestinal gas. *Acta Chir. Scand.* 88: 475–502, 1943.

5. ASKEVOLD, F. Investigations on the influence of diet on the quantity and composition of intestinal gas in humans. *Scand. J. Clin. Lab. Invest.* 8: 87–94, 1956.

6. BASCH, S. The stomach and intestinal gases. *N. Y. Med. J.* 88: 684–689, 738–741, 1908.

7. BAUER, J. Gas in the abdomen: the part played by the nervous system. *Am. J. Gastroenterol.* 29: 78–82, 1958.

8. BEAZELL, J. M., AND A. C. IVY. The quantity of colonic flatus excreted by the "normal" individual. *Am. J. Digest. Diseases* 8: 128–129, 1941.

9. BEDELL, G. N., R. MARSHALL, A. B. DuBois, AND J. H. HARRIS. Measurement of the volume of gas in the gastrointestinal tract. *J. Clin. Invest.* 35: 336–345, 1956.

10. BENEDICT, A. L. Acute formation of gas in the stomach—two types and a theory. *Intern. Clin.* 3 (ser. 9): 149–155, 1899.

11. BERNIMOLIN, J., L. BRULL, J. GOVAERTS, AND M. GUILLAUME. The fate of tritium introduced into the rectum of the dog. *Arch. Intern. Physiol. Biochem.* 66: 448–451, 1958.

12. BERNIMOLIN, J., L. BRULL, J. GOVAERTS, M. GUILLAUME,

AND A. MILET. The fate of $^{14}CO_2$ introduced into the rectum and the blood of the dog. *Arch. Intern. Physiol. Biochem.* 67: 54–58, 1959.

13. BERTÓK, L., AND F. MURÁNYI. Dietetically induced experimental ileus of rats. *Gastroenterologia* 99: 22–29, 1963.

14. BLAIR, H. A., R. J. DERN, AND P. L. BATES. The measurement of volume of gas in the digestive tract. *Am. J. Physiol.* 149: 688–707, 1947.

15. BLAIR, H. A., R. J. DERN, AND V. G. SMITH. Intestinal gas in simulated flights to high altitude. *J. Aviation Med.* 18: 352–366, 1947.

16. BOREADIS, A. G., AND J. GERSHON-COHEN. Aeration of the respiratory and gastrointestinal tracts during the first minute of neonatal life. *Radiology* 67: 407–409, 1956.

17. BORNSIDE, G. H., J. S. WELSH, AND I. COHN, JR. Bacterial flora of the human small intestine. *J. Am. Med. Assoc.* 196: 1125–1127, 1966.

18. BOYCOTT, A. E. Observations on the gaseous metabolism of the small intestine of the rabbit. *J. Physiol., London* 32: 343–357, 1905.

19. CALLOWAY, D. H. Respiratory hydrogen and methane as affected by consumption of gas-forming foods. *Gastroenterology* 51: 383–389, 1966.

20. CALLOWAY, D. H., D. J. COLASITO, AND R. D. MATHEWS. Gases produced by human intestinal microflora. *Nature* 212: 1238–1239, 1966.

21. CALLOWAY, D. H., AND E. L. MURPHY. The use of expired air to measure intestinal gas formation. *Ann. N. Y. Acad. Sci.* 150: 82–95, 1968.

22. CAMPBELL, J. A. Gas tensions in the mucous membrane of the stomach and small intestine. *Quart. J. Exptl. Physiol.* 22: 159–165, 1932.

23. CANTOR, M. O. Ileus. *Hosp. Med.* 2: 16–22, 1966.

24. DANHOF, I. E. *Factors Influencing the Volume and Chemical Composition of Flatus in Man With Simulated Altitude* (Ph.D. Thesis.). Urbana, Ill.: Univ. of Illinois, 1953, Publ. 5226, 304 p. (Univ. Microfilm Order No. A53-719; *Dissertation Abstr.* 13: 1422.)

25. DANHOF, I. E., F. C. DOUGLAS, AND M. O. ROUSE. Mechanisms of intestinal gas formation with reference to carbon dioxide. *Southern Med. J.* 56: 768–776, 1963.

26. DANHOF, I. E., AND F. R. STEGGERDA. Gastric acid secretory responses to distention at simulated altitude. *Aerospace Med.* 32: 520–523, 1961.

27. DAVENPORT, H. W. *Physiology of the Digestive Tract* (2nd ed.). Chicago: Year Book Publ., 1966.

28. DIMMICK, J. F. *The Effects of Diets High in Legumes on the Function of the Gastrointestinal Tract* (Ph.D. Thesis.). Urbana, Ill.: Univ. of Illinois, 1960. (Univ. Microfilm Order No. 61-112, *Dissertation Abstr.* 21: 3137.)

29. DUNN, A. D., AND W. THOMPSON. The carbon dioxid (*sic*) and oxygen content of stomach gas in normal persons. *Arch. Internal Med.* 31: 1–8, 1923.

30. EDKINS, N. Gaseous interchange in the stomach in the anesthetized animal. *J. Physiol., London* 56: 421–425, 1922.

31. EDKINS, N., AND M. M. MURRAY. Influence of CO_2 on the absorption of alcohol by the gastric mucosa. *J. Physiol., London* 59: 271–275, 1924.

32. FINE, J., AND W. S. LEVENSON. Effect of foods on postoperative distention *Am. J. Surg.* 21 (NS): 184–203, 1933.

33. FINE, J., J. B. SEARS, AND B. M. BANKS. The effect of oxygen inhalation on gaseous distention of the stomach and small intestine. *Am. J. Digest. Diseases* 2: 361–367, 1935.

34. FLEISCH, A. La régulation nutritive de la circulation sanguine par l'acide carbonique et les cholates. *Arch. Intern. Physiol.* 40: 385–397, 1935.

35. GALLEY, A. H. Combustible gases generated in the alimentary tract and other hollow viscera and their relationship to explosions occurring during anaesthesia. *Brit. J. Anaesthesia* 26: 189–193, 1954.

35a. GORBACH, S. L., A. G. PLAUT, L. NAHAS, L. WEINSTEIN, G. SPANKNEBEL, AND R. LEVITAN. Studies of intestinal microflora. II. Microorganisms of the small intestine and their relations to oral and fecal flora. *Gastroenterology* 53: 856–867, 1967.

36. HEDIN, P. A. Gastrointestinal gas production in rats as influenced by some animal and vegetable diets, sulfiting, and antibiotic supplementation. *J. Nutr.* 77: 471–476, 1962.

37. HEDIN, P. A., AND R. A. ADACHI. Effect of diet and time of feeding on gastrointestinal gas production in rats. *J. Nutr.* 77: 229–236, 1962.

38. HERTER, C. A. The production of methyl mercaptan by fecal bacteria grown on a peptone medium. *J. Biol. Chem.* 1: 421–424, 1905–06.

39. HERTER, C. A., AND H. C. WARD. On gas production by fecal bacteria grown on a peptone bouillon. *J. Biol. Chem.* 1: 415–419, 1905–06.

40. HIBBARD, J. S. Gaseous distention associated with mechanical obstruction of the small intestine. *Arch. Surg.* 33: 146–167, 1936.

41. HIBBARD, J. S., AND O. H. WANGENSTEEN. Character of the gaseous distension in mechanical obstruction of the small intestine. *Proc. Soc. Exptl. Biol. Med.* 31: 1063–1066, 1934.

42. HOOD, J. H. Effect of posture on the amount and distribution of gas in the intestinal tract of infants. *Lancet* 2: 107–110, 1964.

43. HOOD, J. H. Clinical considerations of intestinal gas. *Ann. Surg.* 163: 359–366, 1966.

44. KANTOR, J. L. A study of atmospheric air in the upper digestive tract. *Am. J. Med. Sci.* 155: 829–856, 1918.

45. KANTOR, J. L., AND J. A. MARKS. A study of intestinal flatulence. *Ann. Internal Med.* 3: 403–422, 1929.

46. KIRK, E. The quantity and composition of human colonic flatus. *Gastroenterology* 12: 782–794, 1949.

47. LEVEY, S., AND O. J. BALCHUM. Studies of metabolic products in expired air. I. Methane. *J. Lab. Clin. Med.* 62: 247–254, 1963.

47a. LEVITT, M. D., AND F. J. INGELFINGER. Hydrogen and methane production in man. *Ann. N. Y. Acad. Sci.* 150:75–81, 1968.

48. LOEWY, A. Die Magen und Darmgase In: *Der Harn*, edited by C. Neuberg. Berlin: Springer, 1911, part II, p. 1318–1321.

49. LUCIANI, L. *Human Physiology*. London: Macmillan, 1913, vol. II, p. 343–348.

50. MADDOCK, W. G., J. L. BELL, AND M. J. TREMAINE. Gastro-intestinal gas. Observations on belching during anaesthesia, operations and pyelography; and rapid passage of gas. *Ann. Surg.* 130: 512–535, 1949.

51. MAGENDIE, F. *Mémoire sur la deglutition de l'air atmosphérique*. Paris: 1813. Cited by Kantor (44).

52. MAGENDIE, M. *Annales de chimie et de physique.* 2: 292, 1816. Cited by Kirk (46).

53. MAGNUSSON, W. On meteorism in pyelography and on the

passage of gas through the small intestine. *Acta Radiol.* 12: 552–561, 1931.

54. MANGOLD, E. The digestion and utilisation of crude fiber. *Nutr. Abstr. Rev.* 3: 647–656, 1934.

55. MCIVER, M. A. Acute dilatation of the stomach occurring under general anaesthesia. *Ann. Surg.* 85: 704–712, 1927.

56. MCIVER, M. A., E. B. BENEDICT, AND J. W. CLINE, JR. Postoperative gaseous distension of the intestine: experimental and clinical study. *Arch. Surg.* 13: 588–604, 1926.

57. MCIVER, M. A., A. C. REDFIELD, AND E. S. BENEDICT. Gaseous exchange between the blood and the lumen of the stomach and intestine. *Am. J. Physiol.* 76: 92–111, 1926.

58. MCNAUGHT, J. A case of dilatation of the stomach accompanied by the eructation of inflammable gas. *Brit. Med. J.* 1: 470–472, 1890.

59. MEEKER, I. A., AND W. H. SNYDER. Gastrostomy for the newborn surgical patient. A report of 140 cases. *Arch. Disease Childhood* 37: 159–166, 1962.

60. MORRIS, C. R., A. C. IVY, AND W. G. MADDOCK. Mechanism of acute abdominal distention. *Arch. Surg.* 55: 101–124, 1947.

61. MURPHY, E. L. Flatus. *Conference on Nutrition in Space and Related Waste Problems, Tampa, Florida, 1964.* NASA Document SP-70, p. 255–259.

62. PAINE, J. R., H. A. CARLSON, AND O. H. WANGENSTEEN. The postoperative control of distension, nausea, and vomiting. *J. Am. Med. Assoc.* 100: 1910–1917, 1933.

63. PALS, D. T., AND F. R. STEGGERDA. Relation of intraintestinal carbon dioxide to intestinal blood flow. *Am. J. Physiol.* 210: 893–896, 1966.

64. PARSONS, D. S. The absorption of bicarbonate saline solutions by the small intestine and colon of the white rat. *Quart. J. Exptl. Physiol.* 41: 410–420, 1956.

65. PARSONS, T. R. The traces of combustible gases in human expired air. *Biochem. J.* 24: 585–588, 1930.

66. PETERSON, E. W., B. S. KENT, AND H. R. RIPLEY. Intestinal gas volumes at altitude. *Can. Med. Assoc. J.* 50: 523–526, 1944.

67. PLANER. Die gase des verdauungsschlauches und ihre beziehungen zum blute. *Sitzber. Wien. Akad. Wiss.* 42: 307–354, 1860.

68. POGRUND, R. S., AND F. R. STEGGERDA. Influence of gaseous transfer between colon and blood stream on percentage gas composition of intestinal flatus in man. *Am. J. Physiol.* 153: 475–482, 1948.

69. POLLAND, W. S., AND A. L. BLOOMFIELD. Experimental referred pain from the gastrointestinal tract. Part II. Stomach, duodenum and colon. *J. Clin. Invest.* 10: 453–473, 1931.

70. RICHARDS, E. A. *Physiological Studies of the Mechanisms Involved in Gaseous Evolution in the Gastrointestinal Tract With Specific Reference to Bacterial Flora* (Ph.D. Thesis.). Urbana, Ill.: Univ. of Illinois, 1965, 181 p. (Univ. Microfilms Order No. 65-11,858; *Dissertation Abstr.* 26: 2839.)

71. RITCHIE, J. A., G. M. ARDRAN, AND S. C. TRUELOVE. Motor activity of sigmoid colon of humans: a combined study by intraluminal pressure recording and cineradiography. *Gastroenterology* 43: 642–668, 1962.

72. ROTH, J. L. A., AND H. L. BOCKUS. Aerophagia: its etiology, syndromes and management. *Med. Clin. N. Am.* 41: 1673–1696, 1957.

73. RUGE, E. Beitrag zur kenntness der darmgase. *Sitzber. Kaiserlicken Akad.* 44: 739–762, 1861.

74. SCHIERBECK, N. P. Ueber kohlensäure im ventrikel. *Skand. Arch. Physiol.* 3: 437, 1892. Cited by Dunn & Thompson (29).

75. SCHOEN, R. Experimentelle untersuchungen über meteorismus. I. Diffusion und resorption der darmgase unter physiologischen bedingungen. *Deut. Arch. Klin Med.* 147: 224–244, 1925.

76. SCHOEN, R. Experimentelle untersuchungen über meteorismus. II. Veranderungen der gastesorption im darm unter pathologischen bedingungen, besonders des kreislaufs und des muskeltonus. *Deut. Arch. Klin. Med.* 148: 86–110, 1925.

77. SCHWARTZ, E. Ueber flatulenz. *Med. Klin.* 5: 1339–1343, 1909.

78. SCHWEINBURG, F., E. FRANK, A. SEGEL, AND J. FINE. Gaseous distention in the obstructed small intestine of cats. *Proc. Soc. Exptl. Biol. Med.* 66: 45–46, 1947.

79. SCOTT, H. G., H. J. DVORAK, C. N. BORMAN, AND O. H. WANGENSTEEN. Comparative study of the quantity of gas in the bowel in simple and closed-loop obstruction. *Proc. Soc. Exptl. Biol. Med.* 28: 902–904, 1931.

80. SEGEL, A., F. SCHWEINBURG, AND J. FINE. Effect of sulfathalidine and sulfamethazine on gaseous distention in the obstructed small intestine of cats. *Proc. Soc. Exptl. Biol. Med.* 63: 17–18, 1946.

81. SISSON, W. R. Experimental studies of the intestinal flora. *Am. J. Diseases Children* 13: 117–127, 1917.

82. SOVERI, V. Der verlauf der luft durch den verdauungskanal des sauglings. *Acta Pediat.* 23, Suppl. 3: 1–60, 1939.

83. STEGGERDA, F. R., AND D. R. ASHER. Elimination of carbon[14]-bicarbonate following its introduction into the stomach of the rat. (abstr.). *Federation Proc.* 15: 179, 1956.

84. STEGGERDA, F. R., W. C. CLARK, AND I. E. DANHOF. Motility and tone of the human colon at various simulated altitudes. *J. Aviation Med.* 26: 189–199, 1955.

85. STEGGERDA, F. R., AND J. F. DIMMICK. Effect of bean diets on concentration of carbon dioxide in flatus. *Am. J. Clin. Nutr.* 19: 120–124, 1966.

86. STEVENS, C. D., H. W. RYDER, E. B. FERRIS, AND M. INATOME. The rate of nitrogen elimination from the body through the lungs. *J. Aviation Med.* 18: 111–132, 168, 1947.

87. TECOZ, R. M. Le meteorisme abdominal. *Gastroenterologia* 66: 130–140, 1941.

88. TOBIAS, C. A., H. B. JONES, J. H. LAWRENCE, AND J. G. HAMILTON. The uptake and elimination of krypton and other inert gases by the human body. *J. Clin. Invest.* 28: 1375–1385, 1949.

89. WASCH, M. G., AND A. MARCK. The radiographic appearance of the gastrointestinal tract during the first day of life. *J. Pediat.* 32: 479–489, 1948.

90. WILLIAMS, R. D., AND W. H. OLMSTED. Manner in which food controls bulk of feces. *Ann. Internal Med.* 10: 717–727, 1936.

91. WYLLIE, J. On gastric flatulence. *Edinburgh Hosp. Rept.* 3: 21, 1895. Cited by Morris (60).

92. ZUNTZ, N., AND B. TACKE. Vortag über die ursachen des meteorismus. *Deut. Med. Wochschr.* 10: 717, 1884. Cited by Hibbard (40).

CHAPTER 138

Cell proliferation[1]

MARTIN LIPKIN

BERTRAND BELL[2]

Department of Medicine, New York Hospital–Cornell University Medical Center, New York City

CHAPTER CONTENTS

INTRODUCTION

THE CONCEPT of rapid renewal and migration of intestinal epithelium emerged during the latter part of the last century. Areas of high mitotic activity were recognized in the intestinal crypts and gastric pits, and were called regeneration zones. Bizzozero (20), in 1888, suggested that cells moved toward the lumen.

[1] This report was prepared during the tenure of Public Health Service Research Career Program Award K3-AM-4468 (Dr. Lipkin). New data were gathered during investigations supported by Project Grants AM-06284 from the National Institute of Arthritis and Metabolic Diseases and CA-08921 from the National Cancer Institute, Bethesda, Md.

[2] Present address: Albert Einstein College of Medicine, The Bronx, New York 10461.

In 1898, Bensley (16) thought that cells arising from mitoses in the gastric pits migrated lumenward to replace "worn out" surface cells and possibly downward to replace chief or mucous cells. Later, in 1945, Friedman "labeled" goblet cells by exposing them to mild radiation which caused them to swell (60), and presented evidence that the swollen goblet cells moved from the crypts onto the villi.

The recent availability of radioactive nucleic acid precursors (59, 190) and the use of high-resolution microautoradiography to determine the morphological localization of the isotopic precursors incorporated into DNA, RNA, and protein (9, 14, 32, 54–57, 100, 108, 118) have stimulated many investigations of the kinetics of cell proliferation. Prior studies by Wright, in 1925 (204), of chick embryo cells grown in tissue culture, set forth a quantitative estimate of the duration of the phases of mitosis. In 1953, Howard & Pelc (81) described the cycle of cell proliferation as a succession of specific phases. Meanwhile, the work of Leblond et al. (110, 134) and Quastler and co-investigators at the Brookhaven National Laboratory (83, 155, 157) amplified the concept of rapid renewal of gastrointestinal cells and prompted new experimental efforts. Additional early studies on various test systems (10, 27, 41, 49, 62, 75, 88, 99, 133, 146) brought new dimensions into the analysis of cell proliferation.

CELLS IN PROLIFERATIVE SYSTEM

Analysis of the kinetics of rapidly proliferating cells has been aided by the definition of relevant parameters. These have usually been oversimplified, and this has led to the development of "ideal proliferative systems" in which the effects of multiple variables are reduced. The manner in which ideally defined systems differ from the true systems now requires study.

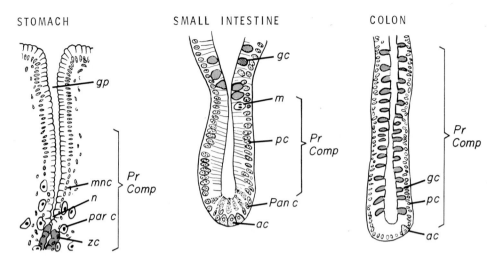

FIG. 1. Diagram of anatomical areas showing the location of cell types in stomach and in small and large intestine. Diagram of stomach shows the surface epithelium and a gastric pit extending into the deeper portion of the glandular area. Diagram of small intestine shows a complete crypt and only the lowest portion of a villus. Diagram of colon shows the lower two-thirds of a colonic crypt. *Pr Comp*, area where proliferating cells are normally found; *ac*, argentaffin cell; *gc*, goblet cell; *gp*, glandular pit; *m*, principal cell in mitosis; *mnc*, mucous neck cell; *n*, neck region; *Pan c*, Paneth cell; *par c*, parietal cell; *pc*, principal cell; *zc*, zymogen cell. In the stomach, the lower portions of gastric pits including neck and isthmus regions contain the proliferating cells. In small intestine, the proliferating cells are located throughout most of the crypt, with the greatest concentration in the central portion. In colon, proliferating cells are located within the lower two-thirds of the crypts. Cells move upward toward the luminal surface of the mucosa, differentiate further, and become mature functional cells. Paneth, argentaffin, zymogen, and parietal cells proliferate more slowly than the principal cells. × approx. 245.

Rapidly renewing gastrointestinal tissues have been considered to contain self-maintaining proliferative cells, maturing cells that may or may not divide, mature cells that do not divide, and reserve cells that move in or out of active proliferation as needed. In the embryo and young animal, the total population is expanding, and in the adult without disease the overall rate of cell gain equals that of cell loss. Whereas the classification of cells in dynamic terms can often be correlated with known morphological characteristics and biochemical activities, biochemical explanations of many of the events occurring during cell proliferation have not been developed.

As cells in the gastrointestinal tract progress along developmental pathways, they may be grouped in a number of ways. For histological purposes, the transitions and stages of development may be defined according to visible anatomical landmarks. Figure 1 shows diagrammatically the locations of cell types in stomach and in small and large intestine.

In small intestine, proliferating cells in the crypts are well separated from mature cells located on the villi. Throughout the crypts, particularly in the upper portion near the villi, proliferating cells go through a transitional stage, differentiate further as they migrate

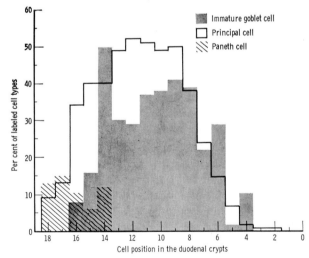

FIG. 2. Distribution of ^{3}H-TdR-labeled principal, goblet, and Paneth cells in crypts of jejunum of rat. The three cell types synthesize DNA and proliferate, and labeled mitoses are subsequently seen. In this diagram, cell position 18 is located at the bottom of the crypt and cell position 1 at the top. [Redrawn from Thrasher & Greulich (192).]

onto the villi, and become mature functional cells, identifiable at each stage by specific microscopic and histochemical criteria (145, 147, 163). Principal, goblet, and Paneth cells in specific crypt areas make new DNA (Fig. 2), following which they can enter into mitosis.

In the stomach and colon, actively proliferating cells are more directly mixed with nonproliferating cells. As the cells move lumenward they differentiate further, cease to proliferate, and become mature functional cells.

For dynamic descriptions, the cell types can be grouped or compartmentalized with additional dimensions, according to their location in or out of the proliferative cycle, and their degree of maturation.

Progenitor Cells (155, 157)

These cells form a compartment of proliferative cells that are self sustaining; in each anatomical area of the gastrointestinal tract these are the cells that give birth to other cells. In the gastrointestinal tract, they are located in the basal layer of the esophagus, the gastric pits, and the crypts of small intestine, colon, and rectum. The probability of daughter cells leaving the progenitor compartment to mature depends on a number of events, including their location in the proliferating column and the need for new cells (28, 117, 125). An illustration of the influence of location is seen in Figure 3, which shows, in the lower two-

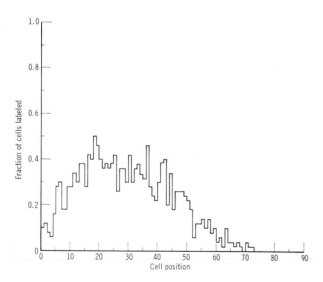

FIG. 3. Fraction of cells synthesizing DNA (labeled with ^{3}H-TdR 2 hours after injection) in normal colonic crypts of a 50-year-old woman who had rectal carcinoma and metastatic disease. Position 1 shows the bottom of the crypt, and position 90 is near and below the luminal surface. The longest crypt contained 101 cell positions. As cells ascend to the luminal surface and move above position 40, fewer synthesize DNA. They cease to proliferate and undergo maturation.

thirds of colonic crypts, the fraction of cells synthesizing DNA at each cell position. In this instance fewer cells were synthesizing DNA as they approached the luminal surface or, more accurately, as they ascended to positions in crypt above position 40. There the cells undergo maturation and cease to proliferate. If more proliferative cells are needed, more cells at these positions make DNA and divide.

It has been estimated that progenitor cells at the base of intestinal crypts in man may undergo 5,000 mitoses over a 60-year period (89), and with shorter duration of cycles (115) some may undergo 10,000. The possibility of immigrant cells functioning as progenitor cells has also been considered (4), but there is no proof of this.

In polyp tissue, in other precancerous lesions, and in normal-appearing tissue near polyps, some cells continue to make new DNA and to divide throughout their ascent to the luminal surface of the mucosa (47). In the abnormality characterized by intestinalization of gastric mucosa, recognizable intestinal cell types perpetuate themselves in the stomach [(167); authors' data submitted for publication].

Reserve Cells

These cells are fertile cells that are not actively proliferating. They may, with appropriate stimuli, reenter the proliferative cell cycle. In the broadest context, they can become fairly well-differentiated functioning cells, which are capable of proliferating. Hepatocytes prior to partial hepatectomy, cells in vaginal epithelium (151), and some stem cells of bone marrow (107) belong to this category. Following mitosis, these reserve cells enter a phase of the cell cycle which has been called G_0 (see glossary below). When recalled into active proliferation they enter the G_1 phase of the proliferative cell cycle, and then S phase (see glossary below and Fig. 6). A kinetic model for the bone marrow stem cell population has been proposed in which the cells can exist in two states: G_1-G_2-S-M, or in G_0, and differentiation occurs primarily from cells in G_0 (106).

Some cells in forestomach of the mouse (203), in pulmonary tissue (178), and in sigmoid colon (117, 120) also remain out of the proliferative cycle for a longer period than their more rapidly dividing counterparts. The duration of their interphase periods before the onset of DNA synthesis varies widely. In forestomach of the mouse, they appear to be recalled into the proliferative cell cycle at random. Exactly why these cells divide much more slowly and what factors determine their ultimate fate are not known. It has been observed that the comparative frequencies of these cells in regions of the gastrointestinal tract can be correlated with the occurrence of carcinomas in the same regions (120). Repeated labeling of the DNA of cells in vaginal epithelium (104), esophagus (109), and stomach (authors' unpublished data) with tritiated thymidine (^{3}H-TdR) reveals that all cells in the proliferative region appear to become labeled in a matter of days. On the basis that all the DNA synthesized is premitotic, this period would prescribe the upper limit of the duration of interphase periods in these populations, and limit the duration of the proliferative cycle of cells considered to be reserve cells.

The phase of the proliferative cell cycle between DNA synthesis and mitosis (the G_2 phase) is characteristically brief, for as a general rule cells move rapidly from DNA synthesis to mitosis. Longer durations of G_2 phase have been suggested in mouse epidermis (65), in esophagus following starvation (29), in osteocytes (144), and in myocardial cells (169). In these instances, polyploid cells, containing at least twice the amount of DNA of the interphase diploid cells, should be observed. Polyploid cells have been found in the liver and other tissues of rodents (85, 184). In epidermis a long G_2 duration has been questioned because cells of ear and dorsal epidermis of the mouse are almost entirely diploid (27, 158), and change in pool size of nucleic acid precursors under some experimental conditions can alter autoradiographic grain count measurements (135). Inhibition of protein synthesis can also lengthen the duration of G_2 (186).

Transitional Cells

These cells develop during the change of proliferative to mature cells. Morphological and histochemical changes take place during the transition. In intestine, undifferentiated cells have a high concentration of ribonucleoprotein, cytochemically detectable as cytoplasmic basophilia, and relatively few membranous components (145). The membranous components enlarge during growth, and there is a decrease in cytoplasmic basophilia. Specific metabolic activities, including greater protein synthesis (118), are carried out in transitional compared to mature functional cells. The microvilli also increase in number and size during this period, and a highly specialized absorptive surface develops. As the cells move up the crypts, and in small intestine reach the crypt-villus junction, further differentiation occurs with, for example, the acquisition of alkaline and acid phosphatase activities by the absorptive cells (145).

Functional Cells

Functional or mature cells may be further compartmentalized according to the specific cell types. They carry out secretory and absorptive functions, which can also be performed to some extent by immature cells. Mature cells, which normally do not proliferate, are located on the small intestinal villi, and mainly in the upper third of gastric and colonic epithelial cell columns. In small intestine, they include approximately two-thirds of all the epithelial cells. Most are principal cells, and a smaller fraction, goblet cells. The Paneth cells form a special population which renew at a slower rate than the principal and goblet cells (192).

In stomach, special cell types also include parietal and zymogen cells, which renew much more slowly than the other epithelial elements. They develop from mucus-containing cells in the neck area of the gastric pits (84, 193). Argentaffin cells are found in all areas and may not be derived from epithelial cells (193). They also proliferate at a slower rate than principal cells and in man appear to be largely replaced by new cells over periods of several months (46).

In sprue, profound structural and chemical alterations have developed in epithelial cells of the jejunum by the time they reach the surface. These include a pronounced cytoplasmic basophilia, reflecting an unusually high concentration of ribonucleoprotein, and decreases in succinic dehydrogenase, esterase, adenosine triphosphate, and acid phosphatase (145, 163).

In terms of cell proliferation kinetics, cells may be classified in other ways—for example, according to age or phase distributions (28, 38, 75) or according to the velocity of movement (28) or whether they migrate (114, 157), and in a two-component system in terms of whether they will continue to proliferate or will mature (28, 142, 143).

The members of the proliferating population can be further delineated in terms of a specific location within the proliferative cell cycle. Here, a glossary of kinetic parameters is very useful (155),[3] and the principal parameters are given below.

[3] The working definitions given here are those presented by Quastler (155).

Glossary

Compartment $(i = G_1, S, C \cdots)$ = any class of cells distinguished from the other cells in the system. Typical compartments of a proliferative system are:

M = cells in mitosis;

S = cells during DNA synthesis, usually equated with cells taking up specific tracers and incorporating them into DNA.

G_1 = postmitotic presynthetic period.

G_2 = postsynthetic premitotic period.

C (for cycle) = $M + G_1 + S + G_2$ = generative compartment.

G_0 = fertile cells not actually proliferating.

Size N_i = number (or mass, etc.) of cells in compartment, usually as fraction of the size of the system.

Transit time (T_i, T_s, T_c) = time elapsed between entering and leaving a compartment, for example, S-time, mitosis time, and cycle time (time for the cells to run through an entire proliferative cycle).

Transit rate $(R_i, R_c \cdots)$ = the inverse of transit time: cells passing compartment per unit time per cell in compartment, for example, cycle rate (preferred to generation rate).

Flux (k_{ij}) = number of cells passing a particular boundary in a particular direction (from i to j) per unit time.

Influx, efflux $(\sum_j k_{ji}, \sum_j k_{ij})$ = total flux, in and out, across all boundaries of a given compartment.

Turnover rate = influx or efflux per cell in compartment.

Proliferative rate (birth rate) = turnover rate for a proliferative system or part of system.

This nomenclature has facilitated estimations of sizes of compartments, transit times (or rates), proliferation and turnover rates, and additional parameters. With the nomenclature given, simplified estimations of these parameters have been made, by using the ratio N_i/T_i (157) for example, as $N_s/T_s = N_m/T_m = N_c/T_c$. However, limitations of this estimate must be noted to compensate for nonsteady-state conditions, for inhomogeneities in the cell cycle, and for compartments that contain varied combinations of parameters (28, 117, 155, 157). The interphase that follows mitosis (M) may therefore be divided into the postmitotic, presynthetic phase (G_1), the DNA synthesis (S) phase, the postsynthetic, premitotic phase (G_2), and the G_0 phase as an extension of G_1 (see diagram of cell cycle phases in Fig. 6).

Decision To Proliferate

Bullough (27) has amplified the description of the phases of the proliferative cell cycle, and particularly the period during which a decision is made for cells to continue to proliferate or mature. He defines an apophase ("moving away from"), a period immediately following mitosis (early G_1). During this period the cell recovers from the previous mitosis and grows in bulk. Following is dichophase, which occupies a period in G_1 during which the cell passes through the decision phase and is committed to specialize either for tissue function or for mitosis. The remainder of the preparation for mitosis occurs during prophase, which extends from the decision phase to the beginning of mitosis. The prophase includes an early period during which enzyme reactions necessary for the mitotic process begin, the period of DNA synthesis itself, and the antephase, extending from the end of DNA synthesis to the beginning of mitosis (i.e., G_2).

Daughter Cell Types

Cell proliferation can also be studied in terms of daughter cell types (28, 142, 143). In these terms, asymmetric divisions of a proliferative cell (P cell) theoretically yield two daughter cells which are different, one remaining a proliferative cell and one becoming nonproliferative (Q cell). Symmetric divisions are of two types, and a proliferative cell yields either two new P cells, or instead two new Q cells which continue to differentiate and mature. Environmental influences may be important in the ultimate fate of P and Q cells (28, 97).

Theoretical models constructed on the basis of symmetric and asymmetric divisions can satisfy necessary requirements of stem cell populations, maintain steady-state conditions observed experimentally, explain regenerative properties of depleted cell populations, and produce differentiated cells on demand. In intestinal epithelium, the probabilities of cells remaining P cells or maturing into Q cells can be estimated by considering the distribution of cells within the proliferative cycle, and the lengths of the respective phases of the cycle. In gastrointestinal tissue, cell divisions in the deep portions of the proliferative columns produce two P cells, balanced under steady-state conditions by cell divisions in the upper part of the crypt and pit columns which produce only Q cells (28). During recovery from stress, when more cells are needed, more cells remain proliferative and the balance is shifted away from Q cells.

BIOCHEMICAL EVENTS IN
PROLIFERATIVE CELL CYCLE

In recent years, important correlates of the proliferative and functional activities of cells have been established, although much essential information is still lacking. Synthetic activities requisite for cell division and growth include DNA as well as RNA and protein syntheses. In mammalian cells, although RNA is synthesized during all of interphase (189), DNA is synthesized during the specific portion designated as S phase. In a number of test systems, enzymes that lead to DNA synthesis are elaborated during G_1 phase (79, 80, 129). DNA synthesis in vitro requires primer DNA, the enzyme DNA polymerase (42, 101), and all of the four deoxynucleoside triphosphates. However, not all of the message sequences within the cell that lead to the elaboration of precursors and enzyme are clear. Of importance is the fact that specific RNAs and proteins are probably produced before DNA synthesis begins (79, 80, 113). In addition, an acceleration of RNA and protein synthesis may occur before the onset of S phase. It has been suggested that the histone content of the nucleus increases before DNA synthesis (68, 86) and contributes to the regulation of DNA function in the chromosomes (2).

As already implied, the nature of all the biochemical processes leading to an irreversible commitment to DNA synthesis and cell division has not been clarified. However, a number of factors are known to correlate with the onset of S phase. Although the development of a critical cell size does not explain the onset of DNA synthesis and generation time (103), a correlation of cell mass with the onset of DNA synthesis has been observed in fibroblast cells (93). Fibroblast cells with low initial masses spent relatively longer periods in G_1 and shorter periods in S and G_2, and mass increased in proportion to the amount of RNA (206). The rate of protein synthesis increased with cellular RNA and mass (207); this implied that the capacity for interphase growth is controlled by the existing number of ribosomes in the cell (94). Previously proposed suggestions (90, 91) that variations in generation time are due to random variations in the rates of the many reactions that prepare a cell for division should thus be modified (102, 103). In *E. coli* B/r, generation times may be influenced by compensatory factors transmitted through the cytoplasm from mother to daughter (103). In leukemic cells undergoing mitosis there is greater variability or error in the distribution of DNA, RNA, and mass to daughter cells (92), and DNA synthesis starts at a higher mass value (63).

In normal fibroblast cells, protein is synthesized in the cytoplasm and transported to the cell nucleus during S phase (205). The increase in cell size that occurs during G_1 is largely cytoplasmic, and nuclear size increases during S and G_2. Since inhibition of protein or RNA synthesis causes an inhibition of DNA synthesis it has been suggested that protein synthesis (71, 127) and more particularly a specific protein (187) are necessary for the initiation of replication. Similarly, an event dependent on amino acid incorporation, occurring at the beginning of S phase, which is not essential for initiation of DNA synthesis, may be essential for its maintenance once it has begun (182). RNA synthesis, which varies during the cell cycle (171, 172, 191, 206), would thus be necessary for the elaboration of DNA (53). RNA essential for mitosis is elaborated at the end of S phase or soon after the cell has entered G_2; however, proteins required for mitosis are made during most of G_2 (98, 186) and before the beginning of prophase (186). In the Chinese hamster cell line (40) the rate of chromosomal and nucleolar RNA synthesis is lowest in G_1, increases continuously through S period concomitantly with the increase in DNA, and then remains constant throughout G_2. The overall rate of RNA synthesis is thus higher in G_2 than G_1 and early S; it drops at the end of prophase, after the disappearance of the nuclear membrane, and synthesis ceases at metaphase.

With the initiation of DNA synthesis, in association with the factors mentioned above, replication of DNA on the chromosomes begins simultaneously at multiple sites. The chromosomes, however, do not duplicate synchronously during the DNA synthesis phase (82, 188). The duration of synthesis of a single chromosome is only a small fraction of the total duration of duplication (S phase) of the genome of the cell (137). In giant Dipteran nuclei, interphase chromosomes appear to be subdivided along their entire lengths into independently operating DNA-containing genetic units of transcription, which may be activated to yield messenger RNA (13). Induction of RNA synthesis at specific chromosomal loci by a hormonal signal has been observed in *Chironomus* salivary gland cells. Additional investigations continue in all of these areas to explain at a molecular biological level the sequence of events leading to cell proliferation and maturation.

IDENTIFICATION OF CELLS
WITHIN PROLIFERATIVE CYCLE

Mitosis

Identification of the biochemical events taking place within the proliferative cell cycle has been aided by the identification of the cell-cycle phases. In both synchronous and asynchronous (49, 75, 95, 159) proliferating populations, cell division has long been used as an important phase marker. Here, the mitotic index (N_m/N_c), as a function of time, has been extensively observed and studied. It must always be kept in mind that when determining the mitotic index it is useful to know the duration of mitosis. The colchicine method permits identification of the number of cells that pass into mitosis per unit time (76). Here, the mitotic rate is equivalent to the rate of accumulation of blocked metaphases after colchicine or Colcemid. In gastrointestinal epithelium, where there is no increase in the population size, the mitotic rate is also an index of the rate both of cell loss and proliferation. Thus, in intestinal epithelium of the rat (17, 76, 110), if 4% of crypt cells are blocked per hour, then 100% can be presumed to be blocked in 25 hours. This can be further clarified by giving colchicine to additional animals every 4 hours and taking measurements around the clock. A mitotic phase index considers cells in prophase, metaphase, anaphase, and telephase as a percent of the total seen in division at a given time (124, 140). The duration of mitosis or its phases can also be estimated (61, 75, 76, 140), for example, by relating the mitotic index to the rate of increase of cells observed after ^{3}H-TdR labeling. In mouse intestine, and many other tissues, the duration of the various phases of mitosis is about 1 hour or less (61, 76). It is important to observe that the generation time cannot directly be inferred from known mitotic indices and known duration of mitosis (177). Similarly, in an exponentially growing population, the percent of cells indicated by a specific marker does not increase directly with the duration spent in the phase (12, 35).

DNA Synthesis

The recent advances in cell proliferation kinetics can largely be traced to the ability of investigators to use radioactively labeled thymidine, the deoxyribonucleoside, incorporated specifically into DNA which is in process of formation at the time of injection (59, 83, 134, 190). Thymidine is converted to its triphosphate derivative, which is incorporated into DNA together with the three additional deoxyribonucleoside triphosphates. Although the incorporation of thymidine into DNA has been useful to cell proliferation studies, thymidine itself does not occur naturally on the main intracellular pathways that lead to DNA synthesis. It is brought into the major pathways by phosphorylation to thymidine monophosphate. The latter may also be formed from pathways that lead from phosphorylated uridine and cytidine derivatives. A complete assessment of DNA synthesis in cells must actually depend on information about all the relevant pathways that lead to the four component deoxyribonucleoside triphosphates.

After either intravenous or intraperitoneal or intramuscular injection, thymidine labeled with tritium (^{3}H-TdR) reaches peak blood levels in minutes and declines to negligible concentrations in the order of one hour, the decline being slightly slower after intramuscular injection (154, 168, 176). Only a small percent of the injected ^{3}H-TdR is incorporated into DNA, mainly in rapidly proliferating intestinal and bone marrow elements and skin (168, 176). The remainder not incorporated is rapidly catabolized to CO_2, tritiated water, and other nonvolatile products including ^{3}H-β-ureidoisobutyric acid and ^{3}H-β-aminoisobutyric acid (154, 168, 176). Adequately prepared microautoradiographs (100) will demonstrate cells synthesizing new DNA heavily labeled with ^{3}H-TdR. When the nucleoside is incorporated into DNA, the decaying tritium atoms emit beta rays which have a range in tissue of about 1 μ. Since the photographic grains produced by the beta rays are closely apposed to the structures labeled, the grains are seen mainly over nuclei. Additional low levels of label, however, will also be seen and must be eliminated from cell counts by simple cutoff levels or more elaborate procedures (23). The additional grains seen on microautoradiographs will be due to background, the absorption of low-range ^{3}H beta rays, short contact between the cells in DNA synthesis and the labeled precursor (176), slow rate of DNA synthesis at ends of S phase, and low concentration of precursor.

Microautoradiographic identification of ^{3}H-TdR incorporation into DNA (150) distinguishes cells in terms of: *a*) those that synthesize at the full rate, double the DNA content, and divide; *b*) those that synthesize at the full rate without rapid cell division (increased G_2 duration); and *c*) cells that do not incorporate the precursor or synthesize DNA. In addition, some cells in slowly dividing or nondividing populations incorporate ^{3}H-TdR at low rates (149, 150) which may indicate additional renewal or repair of DNA in these tissues.

After injection of ^{3}H-TdR, the rate of appearance of grains over cells and their subsequent mitoses are also influenced by factors related to the rate of equilibration, size, and possible dilution of the labeled triphosphate pool. It has been estimated that the conversion time to DNA is short, and local storage of ^{3}H-TdR derivatives is minor (156, 180) after pulse

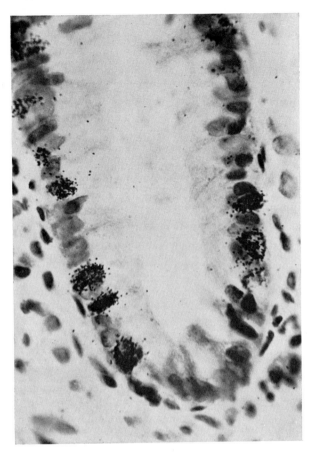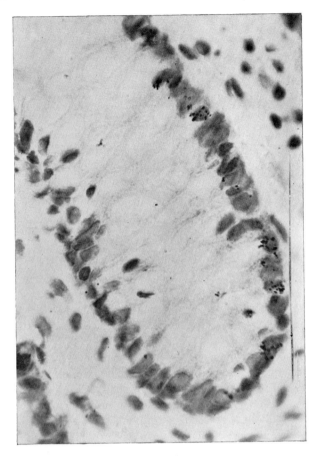

FIG. 4. Microautoradiograph showing newly synthesized labeled DNA in epithelial cells in lower portion of human colonic crypt. A (*left*), 2 hours, and B (*right*), 8 days after injection of ³H-thymidine. Hematoxylin and eosin stain. × 550. [From Lipkin et al. (116).]

injections. However, the acid soluble pool of ³H-TdR derivatives is labile (52), and the pool may be flooded in a number of ways (36, 72), thereby changing the incorporation rate of ³H-TdR. In freshly plucked and synchronized hair follicle cells, a labile intracellular pool of thymidine or thymidine phosphates has been demonstrated which leaches out by usual autoradiographic methods (135).

In comparing data obtained from ³H-TdR and colchicine in rodent gastrointestinal tissues, significant differences in S phase and cell cycle duration were not observed (31, 109). Colchicine and ³H-TdR have also been used simultaneously to mark cells in different portions of the proliferative cell cycle, and can ascertain relative sensitivities of the different parts of the cell cycle to specific agents (195).

While defining the mode of incorporation of ³H-TdR into DNA and the appearance of grains over cells, the point of major importance is that ³H-TdR is incorporated into DNA. This can be observed with microautoradiography as well as with chemical anal-ysis, and the elaboration of new DNA can be studied. Rapidly dividing cells become heavily labeled with ³H-TdR (Fig. 4, A and B). These cells and their subsequently labeled mitoses can be satisfactorily separated from their unlabeled counterparts and quantitatively assessed in informative ways.

Measurements of the spatial distribution of cells labeled with ³H-TdR in normal gastrointestinal epithelium of mouse and man have revealed the cells to be distributed randomly and asynchronously, following statistical Poisson distributions (Fig. 5), or distributed almost randomly (30).

CONTINUOUS LABELING. Continuous labeling with ³H-TdR in vitro has been used to estimate the durations of the phases of the proliferative cell cycle, the frequency distribution of cells within phases, and comparative rates of DNA synthesis (179). Continuous labeling in vivo has demonstrated more rapid replacement of granulocytes than of lymphocytes in peripheral blood (123, 164).

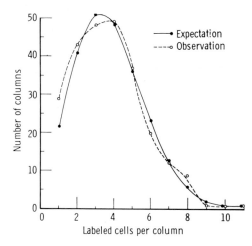

FIG. 5. Distribution of ³H-TdR-labeled cells in gastric pit columns of normal mouse. The distribution observed follows closely the distribution that would be expected if the events occurred randomly. The *solid curve* is the Poisson expectation distributed around the mean of the observed values.

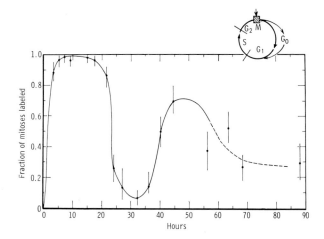

FIG. 6. Fraction of mitoses labeled at various times between labeling and biopsy, in histologically normal colonic tissue of a 50-year-old male patient. Specimens obtained through a colostomy opening. An inoperable adenocarcinoma of the rectum was present distal to the colostomy site. Insert in upper right corner indicates phases of proliferative cell cycle. Cells become labeled during S phase, proceed through G_2 to mitosis (M), then to G_1 or G_0. Following mitosis, cell may also leave the proliferative cycle, and undergo maturation. *Vertical bars* indicate the limits of a 95 % confidence interval.

DOUBLE LABELING. Double labeling with ³H-TdR has also been followed after a short period of time by labeling with ¹⁴C-TdR to estimate the durations of the cell-cycle phases (12, 43, 202). If an asynchronous population in a steady state is pulse-labeled with ³H-TdR and a short time later with ¹⁴C-TdR, cells labeled only with ³H proportional to T_s (synthesis time) will be seen. Between injections, some will have passed out of DNA synthesis, and hence will be labeled only with ³H and not with the subsequently applied ¹⁴C. If no labeled cells have divided, then the value T_s may be obtained from the ratio between the number of singly labeled ³H cells and all the ¹⁴C-labeled cells, where ³H/¹⁴C = T_a/T_s, and T_a is the interval between injections. By increasing the time between the first and second injections, other cell-cycle phases can be estimated (202).

DURATIONS OF INDIVIDUAL PHASES. Duration of individual phases of the proliferative cell cycle and the overall duration of the cell cycle have also been estimated by observing the rate at which mitoses appear labeled with ³H-TdR after injection (10, 62, 115, 119, 133, 155, 157, 203). Figure 6 shows the fraction of mitoses labeled at intervals after the pulse injection of ³H-TdR in the colonic mucosa of a 50-year-old male subject. Estimates of the minimum duration of the G_2 phase can be obtained by noting the time of appearance of the first labeled mitosis; G_2 plus half of the mitosis phase by the midpoint of the ascending wave; the duration of S phase by the interval between the 0.37 points on the first ascending and

descending waves; the length of the entire cell cycle on the basis of the time elapsing between two successive peaks of labeled mitoses; and the duration of the G_1 period by subtracting S, G_2, and M from the duration of the cell cycle. In Figure 6, the G_2 duration is less than 6 hours, S phase is about 20 hours, the average duration of cell cycle is 40 hours, and G_1 is in the order of 14 hours with greater variability. Table 1 summarizes data on the durations of the cell-cycle phases in gastrointestinal and a few other cell types.

In an extension of these analyses, additional insight into the nature of the proliferating cell populations has been obtained by constructing theoretical models to simulate repetitive waves of labeled mitoses (8, 117, 133). One method is shown in Figure 7 (117). In this theoretical model the total population of proliferating cells is divided into subpopulations, with a 20 % spread of cycle durations among the members of the subpopulations. The repetitive labeled mitosis curves of the subpopulations are shown in the lower portion of the diagram. The contribution of each to the total proliferating population is known, as are the repetitive cycle durations of each of the subpopulations. With repetitive mitoses of the cells, the individual labeled mitosis curves shown in the lower portion of the figure become progressively out of step, and the summated curve loses its periodic character and be-

TABLE 1. *Estimated Duration of Proliferative Cell-Cycle Phases*

	Hours				Days	Ref.
	T_S*	T_{G_2}	T_M	T_{G_1}	T_C	
Man						
Esophagus					6	15
Stomach, normal	10	2–4	1		2	15, 115
Stomach, atrophy and intestinalization†	12	2			1	15; Winawer and Lipkin, unpubl.
Duodenum					2	17
Jejunum		1.5			2	15, 173
Ileum	11	2–6	1		2	114, 173
Colon	13–20	1–7	1	10–20	1–2	116, 121, 122
Rectum	10–11	2–6	1		2	121, 173
Carcinoma of colon	11–20	2–6				34; Lipkin, unpubl.
Carcinoma of colon					3	11
Normoblast	9	3		3–6	<1	21
Leukemic blast	22	3	<1	61	2–4	Clarkson, Ohkita, Ota, and Fried, unpubl.
Multiple myeloma					2–6	96
Rodent						
Esophagus	7	3			>2	109
Duodenum‡	8–9	1	1		0.5	62
Jejunum	7	1		9	<1	157, 192
Colon	6	1–3	<1	8	<1	119
Hair follicle	7				0.5	130
Hepatoma	17	2		12	>1	153

* Symbols refer to durations of phases of proliferative cell cycle: T_S (duration of DNA synthesis phase); T_{G_2} (duration of premitotic phase); T_M (duration of mitosis); T_{G_1} (duration of postmitotic phase); T_C (cycle time).

† Includes data on gastric mucous, intestinal columnar, and goblet cells.

‡ Includes data on principal, goblet, and Paneth cells. T_C of Paneth cells estimated to be around 3 days (192).

gins to vary about a steady value on the ordinate, corresponding to the original fraction of cells in *S* phase. In more complex situations the fraction of cells in *S* phase in the individual populations is suggested by the characteristics of the repetitive waves. The reassignment of cycle durations to individual populations can also be studied.

Repetitive waves of labeled mitoses have been studied in the newborn hamster (117) (example shown in Fig. 8). These measurements, together with chemical analysis indicating the rate of removal of tritium from intestine (181), and observation of the rate of removal of cells (117, 120, 134), all indicate that the proliferative rate is fastest in small intestine and slowest in sigmoid colon. In different areas of the same column of proliferating cells, marked changes in duration of cell cycle have not been seen, when cells migrate in the direction of the lumen (Figs. 9–11; data from slides used in reference 117). This is true of all regions of the gastrointestinal tract. As proliferating cells migrate toward the lumen, the decision to stop proliferating appears to be made quite rapidly (28, 117, 157).

VARIABILITY IN PROLIFERATIVE CELL CYCLE

As noted, concepts related to biochemical events in the proliferative cycle, the speed at which cells move into and through the proliferative cycle, and the spatial organization of the cells at different stages of development can be studied by analytical procedures which may be simplified to some degree. These processes can thus be studied in a rather ideal manner, or in greater detail with internal fluctuations more visible. Perturbations can occur in these activities, even though overall steady-state conditions remain unchanged.

A number of systematic and variable perturbations in the proliferative cell cycle have been identified in this manner. In some instances in adult mammals [e.g., cornea (196), epidermis (26), esophagus (48, 134, 152), stomach (33), and rectum (27)], there are systematic diurnal fluctuations in cell-cycle activity. It has been suggested that diurnal inhibition in mitotic activity is related to epinephrine (27) and that mitosis may also be inhibited by glucocorticoid hormones (105, 160) and heparin (160). Involvement of adrenal hormones in the regulation of mitotic activity has been recognized for some time (51, 70).

In general, diurnal mitotic rhythms appear to be present except in tissues which have very high and very low rates of mitotic activity (27); however, exceptions have been observed. Thus, rhythmic mitotic activity was noted in intestine, and was influenced by the time of day that animals were fed (3). Under other conditions, in rodents, diurnal fluctuations in the mitotic activity were not seen in the jejunal crypts (17, 152), but were noted in tongue, esophagus, forestomach (134, 152), and in glandular stomach before and after hypophysectomy (33). Although diurnal rhythms in DNA synthesis have been detected in

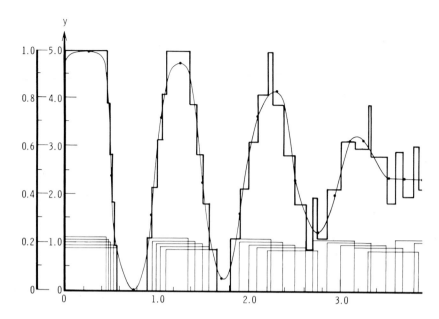

FIG. 7. Repetitive labeled mitosis curves of five theoretical subpopulations (*lower* part of diagram), and summated labeled mitosis curve (*upper* part of diagram) giving the total rate of labeled mitoses. The repetitive redivisions of the subpopulations get progressively out of step, and the summated curve loses its periodic character. The summated curve then settles around an ordinate fraction that corresponds to the original fraction of cells in S phase

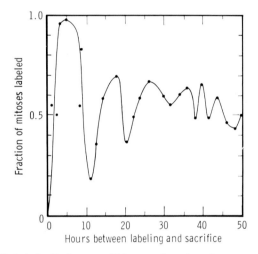

FIG. 8. Labeled mitosis curve of jejunum of newborn hamster, showing repetitive mitoses of ^{3}H-TdR-labeled cells. Peaks and troughs descend and ascend, respectively, as decay of synchronization occurs. More labeled cells redivide in a shorter period in jejunum than in sigmoid colon.

cornea, tongue, esophagus, and forestomach (134, 152), they were not seen in proliferating cells of small intestine (3, 152).

A distinct diurnal variation in mitosis has been seen in human bone marrow cells (128) and some tumors (197), but not in human leukemic blast cells (165). Diurnal variation in the susceptibility of mouse epidermis to a carcinogen was also reported on two occasions (58, 138), suggesting a comparative resistance of the cells to tumor formation when in mitosis and a susceptibility when in DNA synthesis.

Other factors can introduce perturbations in the speed of cell proliferation. Following parasitic and enteric bacterial infection (1, 185), and partial intestinal resection (125), increases in the rate of cell proliferation have been reported. Following corticosteroids, in addition to a decrease in mitosis, inhibition of regrowth of gastric mucosa (139) and liver (69) have been reported. After hypophysectomy, marked involutional changes are also seen in zymogen and parietal cells (6, 39), with diminution in RNA content and oxidative enzyme processes. Zymogenic cells in other organs are also affected. In man, varying degrees of gastric atrophy have been reported in pituitary insufficiency (39).

Ovarian hormones have a direct action on the proliferative cell cycle; they increase the DNA synthesis rate in mammary cells (22) and reduce S and G_1 phases in uterine epithelium (50). In vaginal epithelium, previous action of estrogen or progesterone on basal cells appears to determine whether stratified squamous or mucous epithelium will appear (7).

In intestine, a decrease in the rate of cell proliferation has been observed with aging (112), starvation (24, 77), and after radiation injury (148). Temperature influences all parts of the proliferative cycle of mammalian cells grown in tissue culture. At temperatures below optimum, G_1 and metaphase are most sensitive. Above optimum temperature, metaphase is most sensitive, whereas G_1, S, G_2, and prophase are less sensitive and anaphase least sensitive (174).

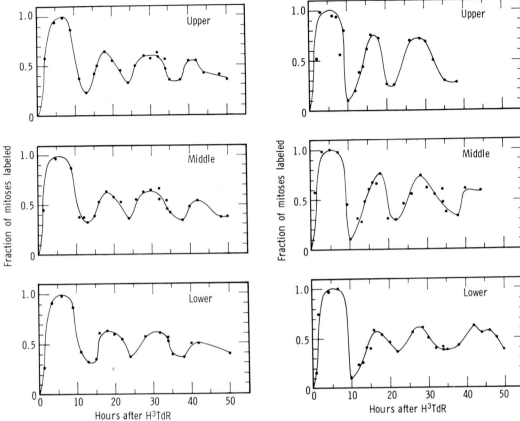

FIG. 9. Fraction of mitoses with ³H-TdR-labeled after pulse injection, plotted against time, in *upper*, *middle*, and *lower* portions of gastric pit columns in newborn hamster.

FIG. 10. Fraction of mitoses labeled with ³H-TdR plotted against time, in *upper*, *middle*, and *lower* crypts of jejunum of newborn hamster.

GASTROINTESTINAL DISEASE

While carrying out their functions in each area, the cells of the gastrointestinal mucosa are thus organized into proliferative, functional, and maturational patterns. These patterns in a broad sense do not change; they remain under "steady-state" conditions, although more or less systematic as well as variable perturbations can occur. In disease states, the previous patterns change and new ones appear. These are either transient and reversible or they evolve as new and permanent expressions of those previously observed. In gastrointestinal disease, both transient and permanent changes can be found, and these can involve either proliferative changes or differences in the development, organization, and function of the cells within the mucosa.

Mucosal Excrescences

In the colon and rectum, as noted previously, cell proliferation takes place in the lower two-thirds of the

crypts, whence maturing cells migrate to the luminal surface of the mucosa and are there extruded. One of the first observations of the spatial distribution of proliferating cells in man (37, 44, 45, 47) demonstrated a difference in patients with multiple polyposis, adenomatous polyps, and villous adenomas. In these lesions, proliferating cells were located in the upper third of the crypts and along the free luminal surface of rectal and colonic mucosa. The same is true in tissue undergoing hyperplasia. In some instances the change appears in tissue that seems completely normal adjacent to mucosal excrescences (47), indicating what may be the earliest sign of hyperplastic activity and future polyp development. This change in the spatial pattern of the proliferating cells supports the concept that mucosal excrescences are derived from surface epithelium. In intestinalized gastric mucosa proliferating cells have also been observed on the luminal surface (authors' data submitted for publication).

In addition to questions of spatial disorganization of DNA-synthesizing cells, the observation raises other important questions about the reasons for DNA syn-

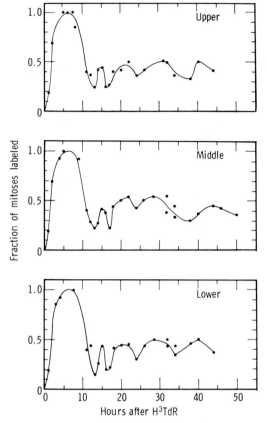

FIG. 11. Fraction of mitoses labeled with ³H-TdR plotted against time, in *upper*, *middle*, and *lower* crypts of sigmoid colon of newborn hamster.

thesis in these cells. This is especially true because villous adenomas, sessile polyps, and intestinalized gastric mucosa have generally been considered to be precancerous lesions. Normally, after intestinal cells divide, daughter cells soon lose their ability to divide. However, in these tissues, some or all cells retain this ability.

Since mitoses are seen on the surface of the mucosa in these abnormal situations, and gram densities in surface and crypt cells are similar, all or most of the DNA synthesized can be presumed to be premitotic DNA. However, the cellular control mechanisms operating here that enable these cells to make DNA during their entire lifespan have not been clarified. The possibility of a greater need for renewal of DNA in these cells must be investigated. This could involve (149) the transfer of information from the DNA to RNA, the action of substances produced in the organism that have found their way into the nucleus, or actual damage induced by ingestion of harmful substances or events such as radiation. There is evidence

for the existence of enzyme systems for repair of damaged DNA. In skin, papilloma-producing virus (162) leads to the production of new DNA in surface cells.

Studies of gastrointestinal carcinoma cells have also demonstrated that the cells proliferate and spread along the surface and edges of the lesions, with rates similar to or slower than those in normal mucosal tissue [(11, 34); authors' unpublished observations]. The proliferation kinetics of normal-appearing tissue adjacent to adenocarcinoma can also be altered. In a single instance the G_2 premitotic portion of the proliferative cell cycle of normal-appearing cells adjacent to a rectal adenocarcinoma was greatly lengthened.

Gastric Atrophy

Rapid proliferation and migration of gastric and intestinal cells in atrophic gastric mucosa have now been documented [(15); authors' additional data submitted for publication]. These include gastric mucous, intestinal principal, goblet, and Paneth cells, all of which have been observed to incorporate ³H-TdR and enter into mitosis. The durations of proliferative cell cycle phases in gastric mucous and intestinal principal cells were similar to those measured in normal stomach and intestine of man. In gastric atrophy, changes may range from a slight reduction in the number of fundic glands to an almost complete disappearance of gastric glands and parietal and peptic cells, and the appearance of intestinal cells in gastric mucosa (167). Often associated with pernicious anemia, the histological lesions of atrophy and intestinalization characteristically do not revert to normal (175).

The factors that lead to a decrease in the number of epithelial cells and to their change to an intestinal type are unknown. It is not clear whether the progenitor cells in gastric mucosa possess total capability to differentiate (totipotential) or whether true stem cells of intestinal type are present (19). If they are totipotential, the distinctive cytodifferentiative changes and dissimilar end product that appear should be the result of specific inductive influences of the environment (19, 136).

In embryonic development the original regional differentiation of gastrointestinal epithelium can be related to adjacent tissues (132). For example, in amphibia, lateral plate mesoderm induces intestine, whereas neural tissue induces pharynx (141), and heart may induce liver (201). Embryonic gastrointestinal tissue may alter the differentiation of the various epithelial derivatives in 5-day chick embryos. Isolated epidermis also shows a dependence on mesenchyme for survival and differentiation and behaves differently depending on the area in stomach to which it may be attached for growth and nourishment (132).

Similar to epidermis, epithelium of the esophagous is plastic (67, 132), and the mucus-secreting epithelium of the 10-day duck embryonic esophagus can be transformed into keratinizing epithelium, even containing feather germs. Adult esophageal epithelium is equally as plastic, and can be transformed to ciliated columnar and mucus-secreting epithelium, whereas normally it is keratinizing in type (78). The alterations so produced are within the epidermal repertory of differentiations. Important factors contributed by mesenchyme have been found to pass through a millipore filter (200) and appear to be intercellular substances (132). Transformations of other adult epithelial cells have also been cited, and these include cell types in epidermis (19) and parenchymal cells of liver (111).

In contrast to the variable behavior cited above, it is believed that a number of visceral tissues, after a given point in embryonic development, reach a stage of relative independence after which their specific differentiations cannot be deflected. The degree to which the differentiation of epithelium becomes fixed varies from extreme stability, as in stomach (131), pancreas (66), and thymus (5), to considerable flexibility, as in epidermis (132). Attempts to shed light on the mode of development of atrophy and intestinalization of the gastric mucosa must therefore be directed to such factors as the hereditary specificity of the germinal cells of these derivatives, the embryonic induction of the cell types, the induction and development of the surrounding mesenchyme itself, the degree to which the differentiation of the induced epithelium becomes fixed and

stable, and the degree of modulation (199) of the gastric cells which may be afforded by all the elements of the surrounding environment under normal and abnormal conditions.

Gastroduodenal Ulceration

The question of whether the proliferative cell cycle has a direct role in ulcer formation has also been considered in the past. As mentioned before, several secretory elements are known to inhibit mitosis, and it has been suggested that chronic stress, accompanied by oversecretion of epinephrine or glucocorticocoid hormones (25), or release of heparin (161), might lead to decreased cell replacement and gastric ulceration. Of equal or greater interest will be the clarification of how other factors, including direct neurogenic stimulation, may influence the cell cycle and the appearance of ulceration.

Direct evidence connecting the proliferative cell cycle and the sequence of events leading to gastric ulceration has now been observed in the case of restraint-stress erosions; cell proliferation was markedly inhibited before and during the early development of these lesions (97). This situation is opposite to the increase in DNA synthesis observed in cells in the precancerous tissues. In the immediate preulcer state, the failure to signal or induce the proliferation of new young cells, despite cell damage and cell loss, contributed to a disproportionate loss of cells from the mucosa and the development of the erosions. Questions critically important to an understanding of how disease processes develop will be clarified as more information becomes available to describe this and related alterations in the proliferating and maturing cells of the mucosa.

REFERENCES

1. ABRAMS, G., D. H. SCHNEIDER, S. B. FORMAL, AND H. SPRINZ. Cellular renewal and mucosal morphology in experimental enteritis. *Lab. Invest.* 12: 1241–1248, 1963.
2. ALLFREY, V. G., V. C. LITTAN, AND A. E. MIRSKY. On the role of histones in regulating ribonucleic acid synthesis in the cell nucleus. *Proc. Natl. Acad. Sci. U.S.* 49: 414–421, 1963.
3. ALOV, I. A. Daily rhythm of mitosis and relationship between cell work and cell division. *Federation Proc.* 22: Trans. Suppl., T 357–362, 1963.
4. ANDREW, W. Lymphocyte transformation in epithelium. *J. Natl. Cancer Inst.* 35: 113–137, 1965.
5. AUERBACH, R. Morphogenetic interactions in the development of the mouse thymus gland. *Develop. Biol.* 2: 271–284, 1960.
6. BAKER, B. L., AND R. H. CLARK. Influence of hypophysectomy on oxidative enzymes and size of parietal cells in gastric mucosa. *Proc. Soc. Exptl. Biol. Med.* 106:65–67, 1961.
7. BARKER, T. E., AND B. E. WALKER. Initiation of irreversible differentiation in vaginal epithelium. *Anat. Record* 154: 149–160, 1966.
8. BARRETT, J. A mathematical model of the mitotic cycle and its application to the interpretation of percentage labeled mitoses data. *J. Natl. Cancer Inst.* 37: 443–450, 1966.
9. BASERGA, R. Effects of histologic and histochemical pro-

cedures on the intensity of the label in the radioautographs of cells labeled with tritiated compounds. *Lab. Invest.* 12: 648–656, 1963.

10. BASERGA, R. The relationship of the cell cycle to tumor growth and control of cell division: A review. *Cancer Res.* 25: 581–595, 1965.

11. BASERGA, R., G. C. HENEGAR, W. E. KISIELESKI, AND H. LISCO. Uptake of tritiated thymidine by human tumors *in vivo. Lab. Invest.* 11: 360–364, 1962.

12. BASERGA, R.. AND K. NEMEROFF. Two-emulsion radioautography. *J. Histochem. Cytochem.* 10: 628–635, 1962.

13. BEERMANN, W. Structure and function of interphase chromosomes. *Proc. Intern. Congr. Genet., 11th*, The Hague, The Netherlands, 1963.

14. BELANGER, L. F., AND C. P. LEBLOND. A method for locating radioactive elements in tissues by covering histological sections with photographic emulsion. *Endocrinology* 39: 8–13, 1946.

15. BELL, B., T. P. ALMY, AND M. LIPKIN. Cell proliferation kinetics in gastrointestinal tract of man. III. Cell renewal in esophagus, stomach and jejunum of a patient with treated pernicious anemia. *J. Natl. Cancer Inst.* 38: 615–623, 1967.

16. BENSLEY, R. R. The structure of the mammalian gastric glands. *Quart. J. Microscop. Sci.* 41: 361–389, 1898.

17. BERTALANFFY, F. D. Mitotic rates and renewal times of the digestive tract epithelia in the rat. *Acta Anat.* 40: 130–148, 1960.

18. BERTALANFFY, F. D. Cell renewal in the gastrointestinal tract of man. *Gastroenterology* 43: 472–475, 1962.

19. BILLINGHAM, R. E., AND W. K. SILVERS. The origin and conservation of epidermal specificities. *New Engl. J. Med.* 268: 539–545, 1963.

20. BIZZOZERO, G. Uber die Regeneration der Elemente der schlauchformigen Drusen und des Epithels des Magendarm Kanals. *Anat. Anz.* 3: 781, 1888.

21. BOND, V. P., T. M. FLIEDNER, E. P. CRONKITE, J. R. RUBINI, AND J. S. ROBERTSON. Cell turnover in blood and blood-forming tissues studied with tritiated thymidine. In: *The Kinetics of Cellular Proliferation*, edited by F. Stohlman, Jr. New York: Grune & Stratton, 1959, p. 188–200.

22. BRESCIANI, F. DNA synthesis in alveolar cells of the mammary gland: acceleration by ovarian hormones. *Science* 146: 653–655, 1964.

23. BRESCIANI, F., AND K. THOMPSON. *Computer Correction of Background in Radioautography With Tritiated Thymidine.* Brookhaven National Laboratories Rept. No. 8360, 1964.

24. BROWN, H. O., M. LEVINE, AND M. LIPKIN. Inhibition of intestinal epithelial cell renewal and migration induced by starvation. *Am. J. Physiol.* 205: 868–872, 1963.

25. BULLOUGH, W. S. The energy relations of mitotic activity. *Biol. Rev.* 27: 133–168, 1952.

26. BULLOUGH, W. S. The control of mitotic activity in adult mammalian tissues. *Biol. Rev.* 37: 307–342, 1962.

27. BULLOUGH, W. S. Mitotic and functional homeostasis: A speculative review. *Cancer Res.* 25: 1683–1727, 1965.

28. CAIRNIE, A. B., L. F. LAMERTON, AND G. G. STEELE. Cell proliferation studies in the intestinal epithelium of the rat. I. Determination of the kinetic parameters *Exptl. Cell Res.* 39: 528–538, 1965.

29. CAMERON, I. L., AND G. CLEFFMANN. Initiation of mitosis in relation to the cell cycle following feeding of starved chickens. *J. Cell Biol.* 21: 169–174, 1964.

30. CAMERON, I. L., D. G. GOSSLEE, AND C. PILGRIM. The spatial distribution of dividing and DNA-synthesizing cells in mouse epithelium. *J. Cellular Comp. Physiol.* 66: 431–35, 1965.

31. CAMERON, I. L., AND R. C. GREULICH. Evidence for an essentially constant duration of DNA synthesis in renewing epithelia of the adult mouse. *J. Cell Biol.* 18: 31–40, 1963.

32. CARNEIRO, J., AND C. P. LEBLOND. Continuous protein synthesis in nuclei, shown by radioautography with H³ labeled amino acids. *Science* 129: 391–392, 1959.

33. CLARK, R. H., AND B. L. BAKER. Effect of hypophysectomy on mitotic proliferation in gastric epithelium. *Am. J. Physiol.* 204: 1018–1022, 1963.

34. CLARKSON, B., K. OTA, T. OKLUTA, AND A. M. O'CONNOR. Kinetics of proliferation of cancer cells in neoplastic effusions in man *in vivo. Clin. Res.* 12: 283, 1964.

35. CLEAVER, J. E. The relationship between the duration of the *S* phase and the fraction of cells which incorporate ³H-thymidine during exponential growth. *Expl. Cell Res.* 39: 697–700, 1965.

36. CLEAVER, J. E., AND R. M. HOLFORD. Investigations into the incorporation of ³H-thymidine into DNA in L-stain cells and the formation of a pool of phosphorylated derivatives during pulse labeling. *Biochim. Biophys. Acta* 103: 654–671, 1965.

37. COLE, J. W., AND A. MCKALEN. Studies on the morphogenesis of adenomatous polyps in the human colon. *Cancer* 16: 998–1002, 1963.

38. COOK, J. R., AND T. W. JAMES. Age distribution of cells in logarithmically growing cell populations In: *Synchrony and Cell Growth*, edited by E. Zeuthen. New York: Interscience, 1964, p. 485–495.

39. CREAN, G. P. The endocrine system and the stomach. *Vitamins Hormones* 21: 215–280, 1963.

40. CRIPPA, M. The rate of RNA synthesis during the cell cycle. *Exptl. Cell Res.* 42: 371–375, 1966.

41. CRONKITE, E. P. The use of tritiated thymidine in the study of DNA synthesis and cell turnover in hemopoietic tissues. *Lab. Invest.* 8: 263–277, 1959.

42. DAVIDSON, J. N. The control of DNA biosynthesis. In: *Molecular Basis of Neoplasia* (M.D. Anderson Hospital). Austin, Texas: Univ. of Texas Press, 1962, p. 420–434.

43. DAVIES, D. R., AND D. E. WIMBER. Studies of radiation-induced changes in cellular proliferation, using a double labelling autoradiographic technique. *Nature* 200: 229–232, 1963.

44. DESCHNER, E. E., C. M. LEWIS, AND M. LIPKIN. *In vitro* study of human rectal epithelial cells. I. *J. Clin. Invest.* 42: 1922–1928, 1963.

45. DESCHNER, E. E., C. M. LEWIS, AND M. LIPKIN. Atypical zone of active DNA synthesis in human rectal mucosa of multiple polyposis. *Clin. Res.* 10: 393, 1962.

46. DESCHNER, E., AND M. LIPKIN. An autoradiographic study of the removal of argentaffin cells in human rectal mucosa. *Exptl. Cell Res.* 43: 661–665, 1966.

47. DESCHNER, E. E., M. LIPKIN, AND C. SOLOMON. Study of human rectal epithelial cells *in vitro*. II. *J. Natl. Cancer Inst.* 36: 849–857, 1966.

48. DOBROKHOTOV, V. N., AND A. G. KURDYUMOVA. 24 hour periodicity of mitotic activity of the epithelium in the

esophagus of albino rats. *Bull. Exptl. Biol. Med.* 53: 81–84, 1962.

49. ENGELBERG, J. Measurement of degrees of synchrony in cell populations. In: *Synchrony in Cell Division and Growth*, edited by E. Zeuthen. New York: Interscience, 1964, p. 497–508.

50. EPIFANOVA, O. I. Mitotic cycles in estrogen-treated mice: a radioautographic study. *Exptl. Cell Res.* 42: 562–577. 1966.

51. EPIFANOVA, O. I. Possible means of hormonal regulation of the mitotic cycle. *Federation Proc.* 22: Transl. Suppl., T 363–368, 1963.

52. FEINENDEGEN, L. E., AND V. P. BOND. Differential uptake of ³H-thymidine into the soluble fraction of single bone marrow cells, determined by autoradiography. *Exptl. Cell Res.* 27: 474–484, 1962.

53. FEINENDEGEN, L. E., V. P. BOND, AND W. L. HUGHES. RNA mediation in DNA synthesis in HeLa cells studied with tritium labeled cytidine and thymidine. *Exptl. Cell Res.* 25: 627–647, 1961.

54. FEINENDEGEN, L. E., V. P. BOND, AND R. B. PAINTER. Studies on the interrelationship of RNA synthesis, DNA synthesis and precursor pool in human tissue culture cells studied with tritiated pyrimidine nucleosides. *Exptl. Cell Res.* 22: 381–405, 1961.

55. FEINENDEGEN, L. E., V. P. BOND, W. W. SHREEVE, AND R. B. PAINTER. RNA and DNA metabolism in human tissue culture cells studied with tritiated cytidine. *Exptl. Cell Res.* 19: 443–459, 1960.

56. FIZGERALD, P. J., M. L. EIDINOFF, J. E. KNOLL, AND E. B. SIMMEL. Tritium in radioautography. *Science* 114: 494–498, 1951.

57. FITZGERALD, P. J., AND K. VINIJCHAIKUL. Nucleic acid metabolism of pancreatic cells as revealed by cytidine-H³ and thymidine-H³. *Lab. Invest.* 8: 319–328, 1959.

58. FREI, J. V., AND A. C. RITCHIE. Diurnal variation in the susceptibility of mouse epidermis to carcinogen and its relationship to DNA synthesis. *J. Natl. Cancer Inst.* 32: 1213–1220, 1964.

59. FRIEDKIN, M., D. TILSON, AND D. ROBERTS. Studies of deoxyribonucleic acid biosynthesis in embryonic tissues with thymidine-C¹⁴. *J. Biol. Chem.* 220: 627, 1956.

60. FRIEDMAN, N. B. Cellular dynamics in the intestinal mucosa: the effect of irradiation on epithelial maturation and migration. *J. Exptl. Med.* 81: 553, 1945.

61. FRY, R. J. M., S. LESHER, AND H. I. KOHN. A method for determining mitotic time. *Exptl. Cell Res.* 25: 469–471, 1961.

62. FRY, R. J. M., S. LESHER, AND H. I. KOHN. Estimation of time of generation of living cells. *Nature* 191: 290–291, 1961.

63. GAHRTON, G., W. HABICHT, AND B. WAHREN. A quantitative cytochemical investigation of DNA, RNA and protein in lymphoid cells from normal, preleukemic and leukemic mice. *Exptl. Cell Res.* 42: 218–229, 1966.

64. GALL, J. G., AND W. W. JOHNSON. Is there "metabolic" DNA in the mouse seminal vesicle? *J. Biophys. Biochem. Cytol.* 7: 657–665, 1960.

65. GELFANT, S. Patterns of epidermal cell division. *Exptl. Cell Res.* 32: 521–528, 1963.

66. GOLOSOW, H., AND C. GROBSTEIN. Epitheliomesenchymal interaction in pancreatic morphogenesis. *Develop. Biol.* 4: 242-255, 1962.

67. GOMOT, L. La culture organotypique. *Colloq. Intern. Centre Natl. Rech. Sci., Paris*, 101: 1961.

68. GURLEY, L. R., J. L. IRWIN, AND D. J. HOLBROOK. Inhibition of DNA polymerase by histones. *Biochem. Biophys. Res. Commun.* 14: 527–532, 1964.

69. GUZEK, J. W. Effect of adrenocortico-trophic hormone and cortisone on the uptake of tritiated thymidine by regenerating liver tissue. *Nature* 201: 930–931, 1964.

70. HALBERG, F., R. E. PETERSON, AND R. H. SILBER. Phase relations of 24 hour periodicities in blood corticosterone, mitoses in cortical adrenal parenchyme and total body activity. *Endocrinology* 64: 222–230, 1959.

71. HANAWALT, P. C., O. MAALØE, D. J. CUMMINGS, AND M. SCHEACHTER. The normal DNA replication cycle. II. *J. Mol. Biol.* 3: 156–165, 1961.

72. HELL, E., R. J. BERRY, AND L. G. LAJTHA. A pitfall in high specific activity tracer studies. *Nature* 185: 47–48, 1960.

73. HIATT, H. H., AND T. B. BOJARSKI. Stimulation of thymidilate kinase activity in rat tissues by thymidine administration. *Biochem. Biophys. Res. Commun.* 2: 35–39, 1960.

74. HINRICHS, H. R., R. O. PETERSEN, AND R. BASERGA. Incorporation of thymidine into DNA of mouse organs. *Arch. Pathol.* 78: 245–253, 1964.

75. HOFFMAN, J. G. *The Size and Growth of Tissue Cells* (American Lecture Series No. 172). Springfield, Ill.: 1953.

76. HOOPER, C. E. S. Use of colchicine for the measurement of mitotic rate in the intestinal epithelium. *Am. J. Anat.* 108: 231–244, 1961.

77. HOOPER, C. S., AND M. BLAIR. The effect of starvation on epithelial renewal in the rat duodenum. *Exptl. Cell Res.* 14: 175, 1958.

78. HOPPER, A. F., AND W. W. MATTHEWS. Metaplasia and other phenomena in some intraocular transplants of adult mouse epithelium. *Anat. Record* 117: 629, 1953.

79. HOTTA, Y. Molecular facets of mitotic regulation. II. Factors underlying the removal of thymidine kinase. *Proc. Natl. Acad. Sci, U.S.* 49: 861–865, 1963.

80. HOTTA, Y., AND H. STERN. Molecular facets of mitotic regulation. I. Synthesis of thymidine kinase. *Proc. Natl. Acad. Sci., U. S.* 49: 648–653, 1963.

81. HOWARD, A., AND S. R. PELC. Synthesis of desoxyribonucleic acid in normal and irradiated cells and its relation to chromosome breakage. *Heredity* 6: Suppl., 261–273, 1953.

82. HSU, T. C. Mammalian chromosomes *in vitro*. XVIII. DNA replication in the Chinese hamster. *J. Cell Biol.* 23: 53–62, 1964.

83. HUGHES, W. L., V. P. BOND, G. BRECHER, E. P. CRONKITE, R. B. PAINTER, H. QUASTLER, AND F. G. SHERMAN. Cellular proliferation in the mouse as revealed by autoradiography with tritiated thymidine. *Proc. Natl. Acad. Sci., U.S.* 44: 476–483, 1958.

84. HUNT, T. E., AND E. A. HUNT. Thymidine-H³ radioautographs of the gastric mucosa of the rat after stimulation with compound 48/80. *Anat. Record* 139: 240–241, 1961.

85. INAMDAR, N. B. Development of polyploidy in mouse liver. *J. Morphol.* 103: 65–90, 1958.

86. IRWIN, J. L., D. J. HOLBROOK, J. H. EVANS., H. C.

McAllister, and E. P. Stiles. Possible role of histones in regulation of nucleic acid synthesis. *Exptl. Cell Res.* Suppl. 9, 1963, p. 359-366.

87. Ives, D. H., P. A. Morse, Jr., and V. R. Potter. Feedback inhibition of thymidine kinase by thymidine triphosphate. *J. Biol. Chem.* 238: 1467-1474, 1963.

88. Johnson, H. A. Some problems associated with the histological study of cell proliferation kinetics. *Cytologia* 26: 32-41, 1961.

89. Kay, H. E. M. How many cell generations? *Lancet* 2: 418-419, 1965.

90. Kelly, C. D., and O. Rahn. The growth rate of individual bacterial cells. *J. Bacteriol.* 23: 147-153, 1932.

91. Kendall, D. G. On the role of variable generation time in the development of a stochastic birth process. *Biometrika* 35: 316-330, 1948.

92. Killander, D. Intercellular variations in generation time and amounts of DNA, RNA and mass in a mouse leukemia population *in vitro*. *Exptl. Cell Res.* 40: 21-31, 1965.

93. Killander, D., and A. Zetterberg. A quantitative cytochemical investigation of the relationship between cell mass and initiation of DNA synthesis in mouse fibroblasts *in vitro*. *Exptl. Cell Res.* 40: 12-20, 1965.

94. Killander, D., and A. Zetterberg. Quantitative cytochemical studies on interphase growth. I. *Exptl. Cell Res.* 38: 272-284, 1965.

95. Killmann, S. A., E. P. Cronkite, T. M. Fliedner, and V. P. Bond. Mitotic indices of human bone marrow cells. I. Number and cytologic distribution of mitoses. *Blood* 19: 743-750, 1962.

96. Killmann, S. A., E. P. Cronkite, T. M. Fliedner, and V. P. Bond. Cell proliferation in multiple myeloma studies with tritiated thymidine *in vivo*. *Lab. Invest.* 11: 845-853, 1962.

97. Kim, Y., R. J. Kerr, and M. Lipkin. Cell proliferation during the development of stress erosions in mouse stomach. *Nature* 215: 1180-1181, 1967.

98. Kishimoto, S., and I. Lieberman. Synthesis of RNA and protein required for the mitosis of mammalian cells. *Exptl. Cell Res.* 36: 92-101, 1964.

99. Koburg, E. The use of grain counts in the study of cell proliferation. In: *Cell Proliferation* (A Guinness Symposium), edited by L. F. Lamerton and R. J. M. Fry. Oxford: Blackwell, 1963, p. 62-76.

100. Kopriwa, B. M., and C. P. Leblond. Improvements in the coating technique of radioautography. *J. Histochem. Cytochem.* 10: 269-284, 1962.

101. Kornberg, A. Biological synthesis of deoxyribonucleic acid. *Science* 131: 1503-1508, 1960.

102. Kubitschek, H. E. Normal distribution of cell generation rate. *Exptl. Cell Res.* 26: 439-450, 1962.

103. Kubitschek, H. E. Generation times: Ancestral dependence and dependence on cell size. Normal distribution of cell generation rates. *Exptl. Cell Res.* 43: 30-38, 1966.

104. Ladinsky, J. L., and B. M. Peckham. The kinetics of the generative compartment of the estrogen dependent vaginal epithelium. *Exptl. Cell Res.* 40: 447-455, 1965.

105. Lahtiharja, A., T. Rasanen, and H. Tier. Inhibition of DNA synthesis in various organs of the mouse following a single corticosteroid injection. *Growth* 28: 221-224, 1964.

106. Lajtha, L. G. Cytokinetics and regulation of progenitor cells. *J. Cellular Physiol.* 67: Suppl. 1, 133-148, 1966.

107. Lajtha, L. G., R. Oliver, and C. W. Gurney. Kinetic model of a bone marrow stem-cell population. *Brit. J. Haematol.* 8: 442-460, 1962.

108. Leblond, C. P., N. B. Everett, and B. Simmons. Sites of protein synthesis as shown by radioautography after administration of S-35-labeled methionine. *Am. J. Anat.* 101: 225-271, 1957.

109. Leblond, C. P., R. C. Greulich, and J. P. M. Pereira. Relationship of cell formation and cell migration in the renewal of stratified squamous epithelia. In: *Advances in Biology of Skin: Wound Healing*, edited by W. Montagna and R. E. Billingham. New York: Pergamon Press, 1964, vol. 5, p. 39-67.

110. Leblond, C. P., and C. E. Stevens. The constant renewal of the intestinal epithelium in the albino rat. *Anat. Record* 100: 357-378, 1948.

111. Leduc, E. H. Cell modulation in liver pathology. *J. Histochem. Cytochem.* 7: 253-255, 1959.

112. Lesher, S., R. J. M. Fry, and H. I. Kohn. Age and the generation time of the mouse duodenal epithelial cell. *Exptl. Cell Res.* 24: 334-343, 1961.

113. Lieberman, I., and P. Ove. Deoxyribonucleic acid synthesis and its inhibition in mammalian cells cultured from the animal. *J. Biol. Chem.* 237: 1634-1642, 1962.

114. Lipkin, M. Cell replication in the gastrointestinal tract of man. *Gastroenterology* 48: 616-624, 1965.

115. Lipkin, M. Cell proliferation in the gastrointestinal tract of man. *Federation Proc.* 24: 10-15, 1965.

116. Lipkin, M., B. Bell, and P. Sherlock. Cell proliferation kinetics in the gastrointestinal tract of man. I. Cell renewal in colon and rectum. *J. Clin. Invest.* 42: 767-776, 1963.

117. Lipkin, M., and E. Deschner. Comparative analysis of cell proliferation in the gastrointestinal tract of newborn hamster. *Exptl. Cell Res.* 49: 1-12, 1968.

118. Lipkin, M., and H. Quastler. Studies of protein metabolism in intestinal epithelial cells. *J. Clin. Invest.* 41: 646-653, 1962.

119. Lipkin, M., and H. Quastler. Cell population kinetics in the colon of the mouse. *J. Clin. Invest.* 41: 141-146, 1966.

120. Lipkin, M., and H. Quastler. Cell retention and incidence of carcinoma in several portions of the gastrointestinal tract. *Nature* 194: 1198-1199, 1962.

121. Lipkin, M., P. Sherlock, and B. Bell. Cell proliferation kinetics in the gastrointestinal tract of man. II. Cell renewal in stomach, ileum, colon, and rectum. *Gastroenterology* 45: 721-729, 1963.

122. Lipkin, M., P. Sherlock, and B. Bell. Generation time of epithelial cells in the human colon. *Nature* 195: 175-177, 1962.

123. Little, J. R., G. Brecher, T. R. Bradley, and S. Rose. Determination of lymphocyte turnover by continuous infusion of H³ thymidine. *Blood* 19: 236-242, 1962.

124. Lopez-Saez, J. F., and E. Fernandez-Gomez. Partial mitotic index and phase indices. *Experientia* xxi/10: 591-592, 1965.

125. Loran, M. R., and T. L. Althansen. Cellular proliferation of intestinal epithelia in the rat two months after

partial resection of the ileum. *J. Biophys. Biochem. Cytol.* 7: 667–671, 1960.

126. LORAN, M. R., AND T. T. CROCKER. Population dynamics of intestinal epithelia in the rat two months after partial resection of the ileum. *J. Cell Biol.* 19: 285–291, 1963.

127. MAALØE, O., AND P. C. HANAWALT. Thymine deficiency and the normal DNA replication cycle. I. *J. Mol. Biol.* 3: 144–155, 1961.

128. MAUER, A. M. Diurnal variation of proliferative activity in the human bone marrow. *Blood* 26: 1–7, 1965.

129. MAZIA, D. Synthetic activities leading to mitosis. *J. Cellular Comp. Physiol.* 62, Suppl. 1: 123–140, 1963.

130. McCARTER, J. A., AND H. QUASTLER. Effect of dimethylbenzanthracine on the cellular proliferation cycle. *Nature* 194: 873, 1962.

131. McLOUGHLIN, C. B. The importance of mesenchymal factors in the differentiation of chick epidermis. II. *J. Embryol. Exptl. Morphol.* 9: 385–409, 1961.

132. McLOUGHLIN, C. B. Mesenchymal influences on epithelial differentiation. *Symp. Soc. Exptl. Biol.* 17: 359–388, 1963.

133. MENDELSOHN, M. L. The kinetics of tumor cell proliferation. In: *Cellular Radiation Biology* (A Symposium). Baltimore: Williams & Wilkins, 1965, p. 498-513.

134. MESSIER, B., AND C. P. LEBLOND. Cell proliferation and migration as revealed by radioautography after injection of thymidine-H³ into rats and mice. *Am. J. Anat.* 106: 247–284, 1960.

135. MOFFAT, G. H., AND S. R. PELC. Delay after plucking of hairs between the appearance of ³H-thymidine in cells and its incorporation into DNA. *Exptl. Cell Res.* 42: 460–466, 1966.

136. MONTAGNA, W. *The Structure and Function of Skin* (2nd ed.). New York: Acad. Press, 1962, p. 425.

137. MOORHEAD, P. S., AND V. DEFENDI. Asynchrony of DNA synthesis in chromosomes of human diploid cells. *J. Cell Biol.* 16: 202–209, 1963.

138. MOTTRAM, J. C. A diurnal variation in the production of tumors. *J. Pathol. Bacteriol.* 57: 265–267, 1945.

139. MYHRE, E. Regeneration of fundic mucosa in rats. V. *Acta Pathol.* 70: 476–485, 1960.

140. ODARTCHENKO, N., H. COTTIER, L. E. FEINENDEGEN, AND V. P. BOND. Evaluation of mitotic time *in vivo*, using tritiated thymidine as a cell marker: successive labeling with time of separate mitotic phases. *Exptl. Cell Res.* 35: 402–411, 1964.

141. OKADA, T. S. The pluripotency of the pharyngeal primordium in urodelan neurulae. *J. Embryol. Exptl. Morphol.* 5: 438–448, 1957.

142. OSGOOD, E. E. A unifying concept of the etiology of the leukemias, lymphomas, and cancers. *J. Natl. Cancer Inst.* 18: 155–166, 1957.

143. OSGOOD, E. E. Radiobiologic observations on human hemic cells *in vivo* and *in vitro*. *Ann. N.Y. Acad. Sci.* 95: 828–838, 1961.

144. OWEN, M., AND S. MACPHERSON. Cell population kinetics of an osteogenic tissue. *J. Cell Biol.* 19: 33–44, 1963.

145. PADYKULA, H. A. Recent functional interpretations of intestinal morphology. *Federation Proc.* 21: 873–879, 1962.

146. PAINTER, R. B., AND R. M. DREW. Studies on deoxyribonucleic acid metabolism in human cancer cell cultures. *Lab. Invest.* 8: 278–285, 1959.

147. PALAY, S. L., AND L. J. KARLIN. An electron microscopic study of the intestinal villus. I. The fasting animal. *J. Biophys. Biochem. Cytol.* 5: 363–372, 1959.

148. PATT, H. M., AND H. QUASTLER. Radiation effects on cell renewal and related systems. *Physiol. Rev.* 43: 357–396, 1963.

149. PELC, S. R. Labelling of DNA and cell division in so called non-dividing tissues. *J. Cell Biol.* 22: 21–28, 1964.

150. PELC, S. R. On the question of renewal of differentiated cells. *Exptl. Cell Res.* 29: 194–198, 1963.

151. PERROTTA, C. A. Initiation of cell proliferation in the vaginal and uterine epithelia of the mouse. *Am. J. Anat.* 111: 195–204, 1962.

152. PILGRIM, C., W. ERB, AND W. MAURER. Diurnal fluctuations in the numbers of DNA synthesizing nuclei in various mouse tissues. *Nature* 199: 863, 1963.

153. POST, J., AND J. HOFFMAN. The replication time and pattern of carcinogen induced hepatoma cells. *J. Cell Biol.* 22: 341–350, 1964.

154. POTTER, V. R. Metabolic products formed from thymidine. In: *The Kinetics of Cellular Proliferation*, edited by F. Stohlman. New York: Grune & Stratton, 1959, p. 104–110.

155. QUASTLER, H. The analysis of cell population kinetics. In: *Cell Proliferation* (A Guiness Symposium), edited by L. F. Lamerton and R. J. M. Fry. Oxford: Blackwell, 1963, p. 18–34.

156. QUASTLER, H. Effects of irradiation on synthesis and loss of DNA. In: *Chemical and Biological Effects of Radiation*, edited by M. Haissinsky. Paris: Masson, 1963, p. 147.

157. QUASTLER, H., AND F. G. SHERMAN. Cell population kinetics in the intestinal epithelium of the mouse. *Exptl. Cell Res.* 17: 420–438, 1959.

158. RADLEY, J. M. Deoxyribonucleic acid content of basal cells of mouse epidermis. *Nature* 205: 594, 1965.

159. RAO, P. N., AND J. ENGELBERG. Effects of temperature on the mitotic cycle of normal and synchronized mammalian cells. In: *Cell Synchrony*, edited by I. L. Cameron and G. M. Padilla. New York: Acad. Press, 1966, p. 332–352.

160. RASANEN, T. Fluctuations in the mitotic frequency of the glandular stomach and intestine of rat under the influence of ACTH, glucocorticoids, stress and heparin. *Acta Physiol. Scand.* 58: 201–210, 1963.

161. RASANEN, T. A., AND E. TASKINEN. The mitotic count in the gastrointestinal epithelium and regenerating liver of heparinized rats. *Gastroenterology* 50: 41–44, 1966.

162. RASHAD, A. L., AND C. A. EVANS. A difference in sites of DNA synthesis in virus induced (shope) and in chemically induced epidermal tumors of rabbit skin. *Cancer Res.* 27: 1639–1647, 1967.

163. RIECKEN, E. O., AND A. G. E. PEARSE. Demonstration of of acid phosphatase activity in the Golgi apparatus of the jejunal epithelium cell in patients with idiopathic steatorrhea. *Histochemie* 5: 182–184, 1965.

164. ROBINSON, S. H., G. BRECHER, I. S. LOURIE, AND J. E. HALEY. Leukocyte labeling in rats during and after continuous infusion of tritiated thymidine: implications for lymphocyte longevity and DNA reutilization. *Blood* 26: 281–295, 1965.

165. ROLL, K., AND S. A. KILLMANN. Lack of diurnal variation in tritiated thymidine labeling index of human leukaemic blast cells. *Nature* 205: 1235–1236, 1965.

166. ROTHERHAM, J., AND W. C. SCHNEIDER. Deoxyribosyl

compound in animal tissues. *J. Biol. Chem.* 232: 853–858, 1958.

167. RUBIN, W., L. L. ROSS, G. H. JEFFRIES, AND M. H. SLEISENGER. Intestinal heterotopia. A fine structural study. *Lab. Invest.* 15: 1024–1049, 1966.

168. RUBINI, J. R., E. CRONKITE, V. BOND, AND T. M. FLIEDNER. The metabolism and fate of tritiated thymidine in man. *J. Clin. Invest.* 39: 909–918, 1960.

169. SANDRITTER, W., AND G. SCOMAZZONI. Deoxyribonucleic acid content (Feulgen photometry) and dry weight (inference microscopy) of normal and hypertrophic heart muscle fibers. *Nature* 202: 101, 1964.

170. SCHNEIDER, W. C., AND L. W. BROWNELL. Deoxyribosidic compounds in regenerating liver. *J. Natl. Cancer Inst.* 18: 579–586, 1957.

171. SEED, J. Studies of biochemistry and physiology of normal and tumour strain cells. *Nature* 198: 147–153, 1963.

172. SEED, J. The relations between DNA, RNA, and protein in normal embryonic cell nuclei and spontaneous tumor cell nuclei. *J. Cell Biol.* 20: 17–23, 1964.

173. SHORTER, R. G., C. G. MOERTEL, J. L. TITUS, AND R. J. REITEMEIER. Cell kinetics in the jejunum and rectum of man. *Am. J. Digest. Diseases* 9: 760–763, 1964.

174. SISKEN, J. E., L. MORASCA, AND S. KIBBY. Effects of temperature on the kinetics of the mitotic cycle of mammalian cells in culture. *Exptl. Cell Res.* 39: 103–116, 1965.

175. SIUROLA, M. Gastric lesion in some megaloblastic anemias. *Acta Med. Scand.* 134: 337–348, 1956.

176. SKOUGAARD, M. *Distribution Kinetics of Tritiated Thymidine in Marmosets.* Brookhaven National Laboratories Rept. No. 8226, 1963.

177. SMITH, C. L., AND P. P. DENDY. Relation between mitotic index, duration of mitosis, generation time and fraction of dividing cells in a cell population. *Nature* 193: 555–556, 1962.

178. SPENCER, H., AND R. G. SHORTER. Cell turnover in pulmonary tissue. *Nature* 194: 880, 1962.

179. STANNERS, C. P., AND J. E. TILL. DNA synthesis in individual L-strain mouse cells. *Biochim. Biophys. Acta* 37: 406–419, 1960.

180. STAROSCIK, R. N., W. H. JENKINS, AND M. L. MENDELSOHN. Availability of tritiated thymidine after intravenous administration. *Nature* 202: 456–458, 1964.

181. STEELE, G. G., AND L. F. LAMERTON. The turnover of tritium from thymidine in tissues of the rat. *Exptl. Cell Res.* 37: 117–131, 1965.

182. STONE, G. E., AND D. M. PRESCOTT. Cell division and DNA synthesis in tetrahymena pyriformis deprived of essential amino acids. *J. Cell Biol.* 21: 275–281, 1964.

183. STRYCKMANS, P., E. P. CRONKITE, J. FACHE, T. M. FLIEDNER, AND J. RAMOS. Deoxyribonucleic acid synthesis time of erythropoietic and granulopoietic cells in human beings. *Nature* 211: 717–720, 1966.

184. SWIFT, H. H. The desoxyribose nucleic acid content of animal nuclei. *Physiol. Zool.* 23: 169–198, 1950.

185. SYMONS, L. E. A., AND D. FAIRBAIRN. Biochemical pathology of the rat jejunum parasitized by the nematode *Nippostrongylus brasiliensis. Exptl. Parasitol.* 13: 284–304, 1963.

186. TAYLOR, E. W. Relation of protein synthesis to the division cycle in mammalian cell cultures. *J. Cell Biol.* 19: 1–18, 1963.

187. TAYLOR, E. W. Control of DNA synthesis in mammalian cells in culture. *Exptl. Cell Res.* 40: 316–332, 1965.

188. TAYLOR, J. H. Asynchronous duplication of chromosomes in cultured cells of Chinese hamster. *J. Biophys. Biochem. Cytol.* 7: 455–464, 1960.

189. TAYLOR, J. H. Nucleic acid synthesis in relation to the cell division cycle. *Ann. N. Y. Acad. Sci.* 90: 409–421, 1960.

190. TAYLOR, J. H., P. S. WOODS, AND W. L. HUGHES. The organization and duplication of chromosomes as revealed by autoradiographic studies using tritium labeled thymidine. *Proc. Natl. Acad. Sci., U. S.* 43: 122–128, 1957.

191. TERASIMA, T., AND L. J. TOLMACH. Growth and nucleic acid synthesis in synchronously dividing populations of HeLa cells. *Exptl. Cell Res.* 30: 344–362, 1963.

192. THRASHER, J. D., AND R. C. GREULICH. The duodenal progenitor population III. *J. Exptl. Zool.* 161: 9–20, 1966.

193. TOWNSEND, S. F. Regeneration of gastric mucosa in rats. *Am. J. Anat.* 109: 133–141, 1961.

194. UMBARGER, H. E. Intracellular regulatory mechanisms. *Science* 145: 674–679, 1964.

195. VAN'T HOF, J., AND Y. HUEN-KUEN. Simultaneous marking of cells in two different segments of the mitotic cycle. *Nature* 202: 981–983, 1964.

196. VASAMA, R., AND R. VASAMA. On the diurnal cycle of mitotic activity in corneal epithelium of mice. *Acta Anat.* 33: 230–237, 1958.

197. VOUTILAINEN, A. Uber die 24-stunden-rhythmik der Mitosenfrequenz in malignen Tumoren. *Acta Pathol. Microbiol. Scand. Suppl.* 99: 1–104, 1953.

198. WATTENBERG, L. W. A histochemical study of five oxidative enzymes in carcinoma of the large intestine in man. *Am. J. Pathol.* 35: 113–138, 1959.

199. WEISS, P. Differential growth. In: *The Chemistry and Physiology of Growth.* New Jersey: Princeton Univ. Press, 1949, p. 135–186.

200. WESSELS, N. K. Tissue interaction during skin histodifferentiation. *Develop. Biol.* 4: 87–107, 1962.

201. WILLIER, B. H., AND M. E. RAWLES. The relation of Hensen's node to the differentiating capacity of whole chick blastoderms as studied in choreoallantoic grafts. *J. Exptl. Zool.* 59: 429–465, 1931.

202. WIMBER, D. E., AND H. QUASTLER. A ^{14}C- and ^{3}H-thymidine double labeling technique in the study of cell proliferation in *tradescantia* root tips. *Exptl. Cell Res.* 30: 8–22, 1963.

203. WOLFSBERG, M. Cell population kinetics in the epithelium of the forestomach of the mouse. *Exptl. Cell Res.* 35: 119–131, 1964.

204. WRIGHT, G. P. The relative duration of the various phases of mitosis in chick fibroblasts cultivated *in vitro. J. Roy. Microscop. Soc.* 414–417, 1925.

205. ZETTERBERG, A. Synthesis and accumulation of nuclear and cytoplasmic proteins during interphase in mouse fibroblasts *in vitro. Exptl. Cell Res.* 42: 500–511, 1966.

206. ZETTERBERG, A., AND D. KILLANDER. Quantitative cytochemical studies on interphase growth. II. *Exptl. Cell Res.* 39: 22–32, 1965.

207. ZETTERBERG, A., AND D. KILLANDER. Quantitative cytophotometric and autoradiographic studies on the rate of protein synthesis during interphase in mouse fibroblasts *in vitro. Exptl. Cell Res.* 40: 1–11, 1965.

CHAPTER 139

A concept of control of gastrointestinal motility[1]

CHARLES F. CODE

JOSEPH H. SZURSZEWSKI

KEITH A. KELLY

Sections of Physiology and Surgery, Mayo Clinic and Mayo Foundation, Rochester, Minnesota

IRVINE B. SMITH | *Burton Upon Trent, Staffordshire, England*

CHAPTER CONTENTS

KNOWLEDGE of the contractions and the electrical activity of the gastrointestinal tract is sufficient to

[1]This article was proposed by the Editorial Committee to the senior author for Volume IV of this *Handbook*. Preparation of the manuscript was delayed, however, until the reviews for all the volumes had been edited. It was then too late for inclusion of the chapter in Volume IV. This investigation was supported in part by Research Grant AM-2015 from the National Institutes of Health, Bethesda, Md.

establish their association and to allow construction of a concept of control of motility by the electrical activity. The main timbers of the structure are firmly established, but some of its outer parts are flimsy. The concept is presented because it offers a hypothesis, a model that may be questioned. Few hypotheses are perfect, many are wrong, but testing them carries knowledge closer to the truth, and that is the objective of this presentation.

CONTRACTILE ELEMENTS

The basic element of motor activity of the alimentary canal is the contraction of a band of circular smooth muscle fibers. The width of the contracting band is variable. It may be 1 or 2 cm in the stomach or small bowel, 10 cm in the lower esophagus, or more than 20 cm during a mass contraction of the large bowel.

The circular contraction may be stationary. Then it is the classic *segmental or segmenting contraction* (type I contraction) of the small bowel. It was so named by Cannon (17) because a series of these contractions, evenly spaced along a length of small bowel, will divide it into segments with the contents compressed into intervening portions between the contractions, to appear in roentgenograms as a row of eggs (Fig. 1).

The band of circular contraction may migrate caudad, becoming the classic *peristaltic contraction*. In the

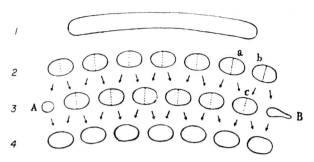

FIG. 1. Diagrammatic representation of simultaneous rhythmic segmentation in the small bowel of the cat. [From Cannon (17).]

alimentary canal, peristalsis is a propagated band of contracting circular muscle fibers moving analward. It is seen most clearly in the esophagus and stomach.

The characteristics and motor effects of contraction of the longitudinal muscle fibers of the canal are not fully understood. Methods have only recently been employed that allow separate and simultaneous recognition of contraction of the longitudinal and circular muscle coats in healthy conscious animals (36).

CONTRACTILE PATTERNS

Definition of contractile patterns has been made in the esophagus, stomach, and the small and large bowel, but observations of associated electrical activity are available only in the small bowel and stomach. This presentation deals therefore only with the patterns of the small bowel and stomach. The motility patterns of the stomach are quite simple. The basic element is a peristaltic contraction, and the patterns are variations around it. These patterns and their control are presented later.

The small bowel has a more complex organization of stationary and mobile contractions. The stationary contractions are represented by bands of contracting circular fibers which do not migrate—the segmental, type I, contractions. They occur in various patterns.

Irregular Contractions

Circular, segmental contractions often occur throughout the small bowel in a random, irregular fashion. No particular order can be identified, and the garbled arrangements offer no clue to the underlying control mechanism.

Rhythmic Contractions

Highly reproducible rhythmic sequences of segmental contractions are recorded from all parts of the small bowel. They often occur at the end of a period of irregular contractions as if to bring it to a close with a burst, a crescendo, of rapid activity (29, 36, 48). The bowel is regularly quiescent for a period following the effort (Fig. 2). The frequency

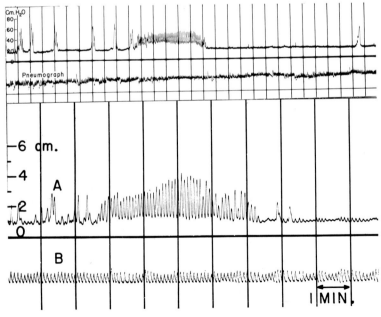

FIG. 2. Two balloon recordings of bursts of rhythmic segmentation terminating a period of irregular activity in upper small bowel of human beings.

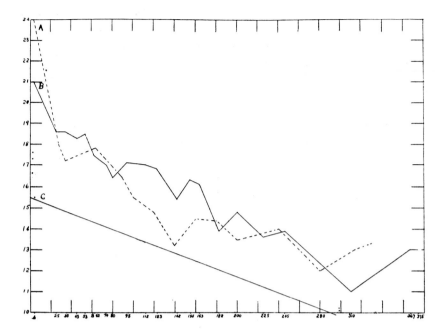

FIG. 3. Frequency of rhythmic segmental contractions in rabbit. *Ordinate* represents contractions per minute and *abscissa* represents distance from pylorus in centimeters. *Line C* obtained from excised segments; *A* represents the average of a single intact animal, and *B* the average from 723 records in a number of animals. [From Alvarez (2).]

of the rhythmic contractions within bursts recorded from a given site is constant or nearly so. These highly reproducible, fixed rhythmic sequences suggest a rigid control system. An important indication of it is that the number of contractions per minute, within a rhythmic sequence, is the maximal frequency at which the bowel at that site can contract.

Frequency Gradient of Rhythmic Segmentation

Alvarez, while working in Cannon's laboratory in 1914 (1), first recognized the rhythmic characteristics of segmental contractions. When he isolated loops of rabbit bowel in a perfusion bath, the rates of rhythmic contraction were slower the more caudad the origin of the segment (Fig. 3). When he studied the rates of rhythmic contraction of intact bowel in anesthetized rabbits, the gradient was present, but the rates of contraction were faster than those of corresponding isolated loops [(2); Fig. 3]. This was the starting point of Alvarez's concept of intestinal gradients. Two important facts were identified: the frequency of rhythmic contractions of rabbit small bowel diminishes caudad, and separation of a segment from continuity within the tract lowers the frequency of its rhythmic contractions.

Years later, Douglas & Mann (28) studied the gradient in trained, healthy, unanesthetized dogs, using Biebl loop preparations, and Douglas later extended the observations (26, 27). The important findings were, first, that a gradient exists in the fre-

quency of rhythmic segmental contractions of the small bowel of healthy unanesthetized dogs, the only difference from the rabbit being that the rates in the dog are slower (Table 1). Second, the frequencies and their gradients are independent of the vagal and sympathetic nerves supplying the bowel. They verified that the frequency of a segment is partly dependent on its continuity with orad bowel, for transection orad to the point of testing reduced the rate but transection caudad did not. Likewise, transposition of a segment to a site lower in the tract decreased its rhythmic frequency. Transposed segments and segments with transections orad still displayed rhythmic contractions, but their frequencies were less. Thus, the gradient of frequency of rhythmic contractions was identified in another species, the dependence of the normal frequency of rhythmic contractions on continuity was reaffirmed, and its independence of external nerves was established.

A gradient has been identified in the frequency of rhythmic segmental (type I) contractions in the small bowel of human beings [(22, 29); Table 1]. These rhythmic contractions occur in man, as they do in dogs, most often in bursts of some minutes' duration, and the bursts often bring to a close a period of irregular motor activity (Fig. 2). The rhythmic rate of contraction in the duodenum of man is 11 per min and in the ileum 8 per min (Table 1).

TABLE 1. *Frequency of Rhythmic Contractions and PSP in Small Bowel*

Species	Conditions	Site	Frequency* (Contractions or Cycles/min)	
			Mechanical	Electrical
Human being	Intact	Duodenum	11 (29)	11.5 (21, 32)
		Ileum	8–9 (22)	9.5 (21)
Dog	Intact	Duodenum	17–20 (9, 10, 28, 33, 36, 49, 53)	17.5–19 (6, 7, 9, 10, 16, 23, 32, 51)
		Ileum	12–14 (20, 33, 49)	12.5–14 (6, 16, 20, 23, 51)
	Ligation or transection at mid-duodenum	Duodenum†	14–15.5 (9, 10)	14–15.5 (9, 10, 16, 23, 45)
		Ileum		14 (16)
Rabbit	Intact	Duodenum	17–22 (4)	17–22 (4) 25–27‡,§
		Ileum	7–11 (4)	7–11 (4) 17–19‡,§
	Isolated	Duodenum	16 (2)	
		Ileum	10 (2)	

* Numbers in parentheses are references.
† Caudad to ligation or transection.
‡ Unanesthetized.
§ J. Szurszewski and C. F. Code (unpublished data).

Arrangements of Segmental Contractions in Rhythmic Sequences

Some years ago Irvine Smith (50) made a detailed study in our laboratory of rhythmic segmental contractions in the small bowel of dogs. The pressure sensors were a series of tiny water-filled balloons arranged in tandem along tubes that conducted the pressure separately from each balloon to a strain-gauge manometer. The detectors were passed into the bowel of unanesthetized, trained animals via cannulas that had been previously placed.

Rhythmic segmental contractions were recorded in two patterns over a length of bowel: occasionally simultaneously (Fig. 4) or, more often, in caudad sequence (Fig. 5). The motor consequence of the simultaneous pattern of contraction is rhythmic segmentation, as described by Cannon (Fig. 1). Cannon's observations have been verified many times in dogs during cineradiographic observations in

our laboratory.[2] The motor consequences of rhythmic segmentation in caudad sequence have not been established, although one of us (Code) has proposed a propulsive as well as a mixing action.

Peristalsis

A classic peristaltic contraction, consisting of a band of contracting circular muscle fibers that migrates caudad, is an unusual occurrence in the small bowel in our experience, but it has been recognized

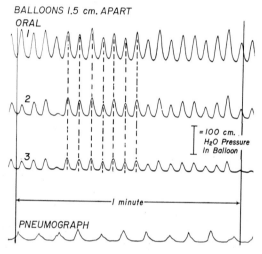

FIG. 4. Simultaneous rhythmic segmental contractions in small bowel of dog.

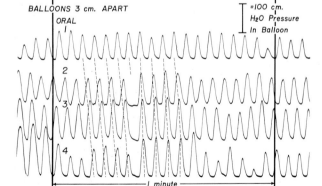

FIG. 5. Rhythmic segmentation in caudad sequence in dog. Recording also illustrates disappearance of a single contraction in the rhythmic sequence—a "dropped beat"—which is one of the causes of the caudad gradient of frequency of rhythmic contractions.

[2] Cineradiograms showing rhythmic segmentation in the small bowel of dogs are available for loan. Address request to: Section of Photography, Mayo Clinic, Rochester, Minnesota 55901.

(30). Its circular component appears to be identical to that of a segmental contraction, but its control mechanisms must differ, for one produces a stationary contraction, the other is propagated.

CONTROL SYSTEMS—VOLUNTARY, REFLEX, AND AUTONOMOUS

The portions of the alimentary canal under voluntary control are its ends. Thus intake and output are, within reasonable limits, controllable. Mastication and the initiation of deglutition—the oral-pharyngeal portion—are entirely voluntary. The motor activity of the esophagus and its lower sphincter cannot be initiated voluntarily except as an in-train sequence to the oral-pharyngeal portion of swallowing. Part of their response—esophageal peristalsis—is reflex, requiring central connections; but part—sphincteric relaxation—is independent of these connections [(43); Chapter 90, Volume IV, this *Handbook*]. Within the stomach, motility becomes even more independent of neural connections, and the small bowel can perform its motor functions with all extrinsic nerves severed.

At the other extremity of the canal, defecation may be initiated and the tone of the anal sphincters influenced by voluntary command. Like deglutition, the act of defecation involves reflex elements requiring central connections. Distention of the rectum, like distention of the esophagus, can initiate motor contractions and changes in sphincter tone which, at both sites, depend in part at least on reflex action (for full discussion of defecation see Chapter 103, Volume IV, this *Handbook*). However, farther within the large bowel, motility becomes largely independent of central connections.

Thus the motor action of the extremities of the canal can be controlled voluntarily. Beyond these are zones of reflex control requiring central connections. But farther within the tract reflex control is soon mixed with mechanisms that are independent of central connections, and still deeper within the canal the independent mechanisms become the major control systems. Through these local mechanisms, the stomach, small bowel, and most of the large bowel can perform their motor functions in the absence of extrinsic nerves. Although their motility may be influenced by autonomic nerves and other factors, their basic control rests with an intrinsic autonomous myogenic control system.

LOCAL AUTONOMOUS MOTOR CONTROL SYSTEM OF THE SMALL BOWEL AND STOMACH

The hypothesis we have developed is that the electrical slow wave provides a mechanism through which the motility of the small bowel and stomach may be regulated. Insufficient data are available from the large bowel to permit construction of concepts. We claim no particular originality in assigning a regulatory role to the slow wave of the small bowel; others have proposed that it has a synchronizing function there (7, 12–14, 24, 40, 41, 46, 54). We have simply extended this concept. In addition, we have demonstrated that the control of motor activity by a slow wave extends over the bowel or stomach for the distance of its wavelength. Once again we make no claim of priority, for Daniel & Chapman (24) first calculated the length of small bowel that would support one slow wave and a segmental contraction. We have also broadened this concept and propose that the wavelength of the slow wave represents a physiological motor segment of small bowel and stomach and that the slow wave controls contraction within this segment.

Small Bowel

ELECTRICAL CORRELATES OF MOTOR ACTIVITY IN THE SMALL BOWEL. Alvarez and Mahoney (3, 4) many years ago first identified electrical activity in the wall of the stomach and small bowel. Studies by many investigators have since established that the electrical activity of these parts has two components (5–7, 12, 15, 23, 35, 45, 54). One is an omnipresent, cyclically recurring, rhythmic, slow fluctuation in potential usually designated as the "slow wave" or the "basic electrical rhythm" (BER) (Fig. 6). It is present when the muscle is at rest or when it is contracting.

The second component consists of a burst of rapid fluctuations in potential superimposed on the slow wave (Fig. 6). They are present when contractions occur (Fig. 7). The fluctuations are usually referred to as "spikes" or "spike potentials," but because they initiate contraction we prefer the term "action potentials" as an appropriate functional designation. They occupy a specific segment of the slow wave, and only one burst of action potentials occurs per slow wave (Figs. 6 and 7).

The best evidence clearly establishes that the slow-wave potential (slow wave) originates in the longitudinal muscle of the small bowel (13, 40). In healthy bowel it is conducted caudad (6, 7, 44) with diminishing velocity (6). It passes as a sleeve along the bowel, with all points on the circumference in the same phase (7). The longitudinal muscle transmits the slow wave to the circular muscle where it is poorly conducted and, if not reinforced by connections with longitudinal fibers, soon will be obliterated (13, 14, 40).

FREQUENCY CONTROL. A major tenet of our hypothesis is that the frequency of the slow wave determines the frequency of contraction of the small bowel. As mentioned, contractions are associated with action potentials (Fig. 7). Action potentials occur in bursts which occupy a specific segment of the slow wave (Figs. 6 and 7). Since only one burst occurs with each slow wave and so only one contraction, the slow-wave frequency of a segment of bowel is also its maximum contractile frequency. Thus, the fre-

quency of the slow wave determines the maximum frequency of contraction; it is the pacesetter. This is why we have adopted the term "pacesetter potential" (PSP) for regular use when referring to the electrical slow wave.

Since the PSP presets maximum frequency of contraction, when its frequency is reduced that of maximum contraction is similarly affected. For example, transection or ligation of the bowel reduces the frequency of the PSP and of contractions in segments caudad to the transection or ligation (9, 10). Also, it has been demonstrated that partial destruction of the intramural plexus reduces both PSP and contractile frequency (52, 53).

Frequency gradient. The gradient of frequency of rhythmic segmentation has already been described. The pacesetter potential also displays a caudad gradient of frequency (16, 51). The frequencies of the PSP and rhythmic segmentation in small bowel have been measured by a number of different investigators in healthy human beings, dogs, and rabbits. The frequencies of the PSP and of rhythmic segmentation are practically identical when determined at the same level of the bowel, in the same species (Table 1). Differences between the two frequencies can be ascribed to differing experimental conditions and to determinations at somewhat different levels in the bowel.

Mechanism of frequency gradient. The mechanisms responsible for the PSP and contractile gradients are not fully understood. Two mechanisms have been identified, however, that reduce the frequency of the PSP, and mechanical correlates of these have been recognized.

We have observed that obliteration of one cycle of the PSP occurs in a random fashion during periods when action potentials are present (Fig. 8). When

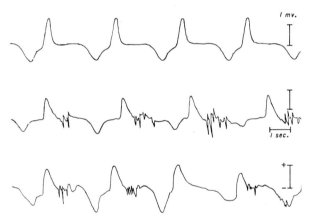

FIG. 6. PSP recorded from canine duodenum. In upper series no action potentials were recorded, in lower series they were present. [From Bass et al. (7).]

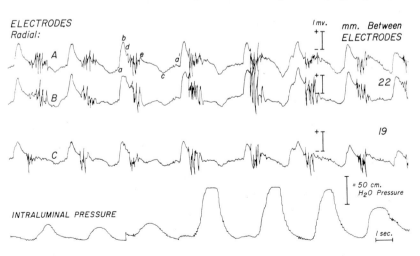

FIG. 7. Simultaneous recording of PSP and intraluminal pressure in canine duodenum following administration of morphine. Note that contractions occur as indicated by an increase of intraluminal pressure with each burst of action potentials and that only one burst of action potentials occurs with each cycle of the PSP.

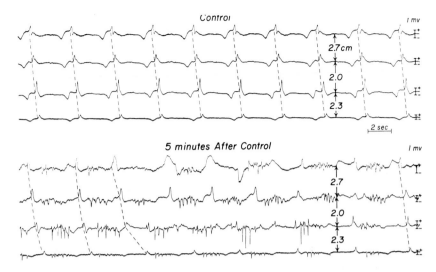

FIG. 8. Loss of one cycle of PSP during occurrence of action potentials. In control (*upper panel*), no action potentials occurred; 5 min after injection of quinidine sulfate (*lower panel*), action potentials were present with each PSP cycle. Lowest recording displays one cycle less between the dotted lines than the uppermost recording, and this was associated with action potential activity at intervening sites.

one cycle of a series of cycles of the PSP is lost in this fashion, the frequency within the sequence is reduced by one cycle per minute, and this reduction in frequency is propagated caudad with the series. If a cycle of the PSP is lost in this way, one contraction of a rhythmic series will be missed. The loss of a contraction, in exactly this fashion, has been recorded and identified as a dropped beat or lost contraction [(50); Fig. 5]. The phenomenon suggests that the action potential of the smooth muscle cell can, under some circumstances, interfere with the acceptance of a PSP or with its generation. This has been recognized previously during abnormally prolonged periods of action potential production (7).

A cycle of the PSP may be lost when competing or overlapping pacemakers of different frequencies are present in an area of bowel (25, 50, 51). Waxing and waning of the amplitude of the PSP may also occur in association with this phenomenon, but its fundamental feature with respect to the gradient is that during the overlapping a cycle of a sequence of PSPs is sometimes lost (Figs. 9 and 10). This loss provides a second mechanism for the production of the gradient of frequency of the PSP and contractions.

Waxing and waning of the amplitude of the PSP have been observed in the absence of competing or overlapping rhythms, and under these circumstances loss of cycles of the PSP has also been observed (25, 51). The mechanical counterpart of this phenomenon has not been identified.

The data presented are in accord with the hypothesis, and we have concluded that the PSP frequency sets the maximum contractile frequency of the small bowel. It also very likely determines, over a period of many hours or days, the number of contrac-

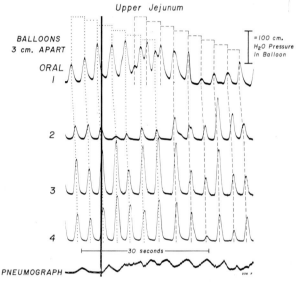

FIG. 9. Upper jejunal motor recording (balloons) from a dog, showing decrease in frequency of rhythmic segmentation as a consequence of overlapping rhythms (superimposition of a new rhythmic sequence).

tions per 24 hours occurring within a segment of healthy bowel. If this is so, the number of contractions per 24 hours will display a gradient of frequency similar to that of the PSP. No counts over such prolonged periods have yet been obtained.

SEGMENTAL CONTROL BY WAVELENGTH. We propose that the wavelength of the PSP defines a physiological segment of the small bowel and that it regulates the motor activity within this segment by limiting the occurrence of action potentials to a restricted portion of the wavelength and so to a restricted portion of the segment.

FIG. 10. Upper jejunal electrical recording from a dog, showing decrease in PSP frequency as a consequence of overlapping pacemaker rhythms. This is seen in the record from electrode 6; two rhythms are present in the center of the recording, and there is some interference of rhythms at electrode 8. PSP cycles are lost as a consequence. The frequency at electrode 5 was 18.8, and at electrode 8, 16.8 cycles per min.

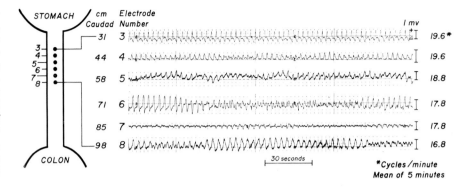

TABLE 2. *Pacesetter Potential: Basic Electrical Rhythm*

Canine Site	Velocity, cm/sec v*	Frequency, cycles/min f*	Wavelength, cm λ*
Duodenum, mid	13	18	44
Jejunum, distal	8	15	32
Ileum, terminal	0.8	13	4
Stomach			
Corpus	0.4	5.4	4.5
Antrum	1.2	5.4	14.0

$* \lambda = v/f.$

As a PSP passes like a sleeve along the longitudinal muscle it is spread out over a length of bowel. The length of spread of a single cycle is given by the formula:

$$\text{wavelength (lambda, } \lambda) = v/f \qquad (1)$$

where v = velocity in centimeters per second and f = frequency in cycles per second. The reciprocal of f is equal to the period of the PSP. An alternative formula is therefore

$$\lambda = v \times p \qquad (2)$$

where p is the period or duration of one cycle of the PSP in seconds. Thus the length of the spread of a cycle of the PSP, its wavelength, depends on its rate of conduction and period. Both velocity and period have caudad gradients, the velocity becoming slower and the period longer. Because the value for v decreases faster than the increase of p, the wavelength of the PSP shortens as it migrates caudad.

The dog is the only animal from which sufficient data have been obtained to calculate the wavelength of the PSP over the full length of the small bowel, and even these estimates must be regarded as preliminary and tentative, for more refined determina-

tions than those now available are necessary for precise definition.

The wavelength of the PSP is longest in the duodenum, where the conduction is fastest. In the dog, current estimates suggest a wavelength of 35–45 cm (Table 2). As estimated velocities of conduction decline from 13 cm per sec in the duodenum to 8 cm per sec in the upper jejunum and 0.8 cm in the terminal ileum, wavelengths shorten from about 40 cm in the duodenum to 30 cm in the upper jejunum and to 4–5 cm in the ileum. Thus the length of a physiological segment displays a caudad gradient.

In an attempt to visualize a physiological segment we have optically expanded one cycle of the PSP, recorded from an electrode on the bowel, to its calculated wavelength. In Figure 11, PSPs recorded from the midduodenum, distal jejunum, and terminal ileum of a dog have been extended in this fashion to their respective wavelengths. If the electrical activity of the bowel could be frozen for an instant, these waves would then occupy the distances of bowel prescribed by their wavelengths and for this moment would appear as standing or stationary.

Vital to the concept is the question, Does the PSP actually spread out over the bowel to its calculated wavelength? Preliminary tests in the small bowel of conscious dogs indicate good agreement between expansion of a PSP by optical means to its theoretical wavelength and the actual definition of the wave as it is spread out over the bowel by simultaneous recordings from multiple electrodes, closely spaced over the calculated distance of the wavelength (Fig. 12).

A vital tenet of the hypothesis is that the PSP controls the motor activity within a physiological segment. Action potentials occur only over a portion of the PSP wavelength (Fig. 13). The period of action potential activity within the wavelength corresponds in position to the circular muscle fibers contracting

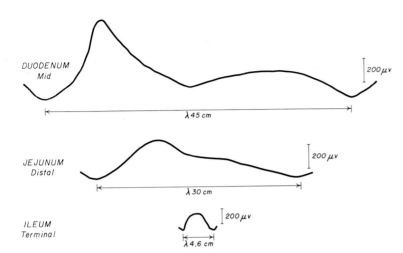

FIG. 11. Wavelength of PSP in small bowel of dog. A cycle of the PSP recorded from one electrode at each site was optically expanded to its calculated wavelength.

within the segment. Thus only a portion of a physiological segment contracts at any one moment. If the duration of the action potential portion of the PSP and the velocity of the PSP are measured, the segment of bowel contracting is given by the formula:

$$LCP = v \times d \qquad (3)$$

where LCP = length of the contracting portion of the segment, v = velocity of the PSP in centimeters per second, and d = duration of the action potential portion of the PSP. Thus according to the hypothesis, at any one instant, only one portion or band of the muscle fibers of a physiological segment contracts, namely that lying beneath the action potential portion of the slow wave (Fig. 13). At this instant the fibers beneath the remaining portions of the wave are not contracting. Thus there can only be one contraction per physiological segment at any one instant. Clearly this prescription requires testing! If the hypothesis can eventually be expressed in mathematical terms as a model, the total number of contractions of which the total length of small bowel is capable per unit of time could be calculated. Re-

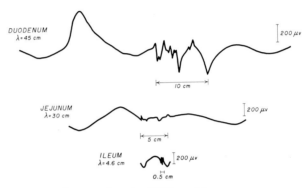

FIG. 13. One wavelength of PSP at different sites of small bowel of a dog, showing examples of length of action potential portion of wavelength.

flection will indicate the complexity of the calculation, but it could have importance in defining species differences and alterations in motility under changing physiological conditions and in disease.

The hypothesis defines a physiological segment of bowel as equal to the wavelength of the PSP. The physiological segment displays a gradient in length, shortening caudad. The hypothesis also states that only one portion of the segment can contract at any instant and that this portion corresponds to the portion of the PSP wavelength occupied by action potentials.

The terminal ileum appears to be exceptional. Here the distribution of action potentials in relation to the PSP does not follow the rigid pattern just described (unpublished observations) for they may occur on any portion of the wave or even cover it. Such arrangements will clearly affect motor activity and will require separate definition, which we have not made.

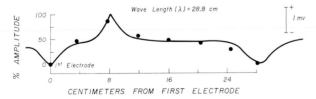

FIG. 12. One cycle of PSP recorded from eight electrodes in upper jejunum of dog showing agreement between visually expanded PSP and its calculated wavelength (*solid line*) and the actual simultaneous recordings from the multiple sites (*solid circles*).

PATTERN CONTROL BY PACESETTER POTENTIAL (PSP). We propose that the slow wave is the instrument through which the motor action of the small bowel and stomach is organized. It does not, however, accomplish this alone. The intramural plexuses apparently provide overall controlling mechanisms, for with their partial or complete destruction the electrical activity loses much of its organization. For example, after prolonged perfusion of loops with saline, conduction of the slow wave loses its unidirectional caudal orientation and PSP frequency is reduced (52). The electrical behavior of the partially or completely deneuronated segment is chaotic rather than organized. Given the framework provided by the plexuses, the PSP is the instrument of the organizational plan, the design of which rests with the plexuses. The plexuses appear to program the motor action of the small bowel and stomach using the slow wave to consummate the program.

The PSP, of course, is not a standing, fixed wave. It migrates caudally and, in doing so, develops its full cycle of potential changes at each point along the bowel. The pattern of motility that will develop during this migration will depend on the excitability of muscle fibers encountered by the action potential portion of the slow wave as it moves caudad. The determinants of the excitability of the smooth muscle clearly do not all rest with the slow wave. For example, epinephrine reduces the incidence of action potentials and cholinergic stimulants increase it. The neural plexuses, vagal and sympathetic nerve impulses, and hormones also have general effects. These effects on excitability might be accomplished by actions in the intramural plexuses or by direct effects on smooth muscle cells or both. But the slow wave appears to have some local responsibility for excitation because it limits contraction to its action potential segment. It may produce local fluctuations in excitability of the smooth muscle as it migrates caudad. The role of the slow wave appears to be local—it sets the pace and maintains organization.

Resting state. No contractions are present when the bowel is at complete rest. Under these circumstances, the hypothesis prescribes that as the PSP passes along the bowel no excitable muscle fibers are encountered and no contractions occur.

Irregular segmentation. If, as the PSP passes caudad, a band of excitable muscle fibers is encountered, a burst of action potentials will occur and the muscle will contract. The pattern of motility that then follows depends on the excitability of the muscle

fibers encountered by the PSP as it progresses past the band which has just contracted.

If the muscle fibers immediately caudal to those contracting are refractory, and if, beyond that, the slow wave encounters excitable fibers distributed in a random fashion, then an irregular pattern of circular contractions will result—rings or bands of contracting fibers occurring irregularly over the bowel. The rings may be of varying width but are not peristaltic—that is, the individual rings do not migrate. This is the pattern of irregular segmentation.

The hypothesis prescribes that the width of the band of contracting fibers will correspond in length to the portion of the PSP wavelength occupied by action potentials (Fig. 13). And according to the hypothesis, the width of contracting bands will be greatest in the duodenum and least in the ileum. This dimension has not been measured accurately.

Rhythmic segmentation. As mentioned, this pattern may possibly occur in two forms: simultaneous rhythmic segmentation (Fig. 4) and rhythmic segmentation in caudad sequence (Fig. 5). Two forms would be expected on the basis of the hypothesis. The first can be depicted best diagrammatically (Fig. 14). In it, a series of PSPs (1, 2, 3, 4, and 5) is identified simultaneously and instantaneously over a length of small bowel (Fig. 14). Action potentials are occurring within the action potential portion of each of the waves, and beneath these, contractions are taking place (Fig. 14). This produces a series of circular contractions dividing the bowel into segments. The contents that occupied the portions contracting are forced into the intervening, noncontracting regions (A_1, B_1, C_1, D_1, E_1, and F_1).

Pacesetter potential 1 is, of course, migrating cau-

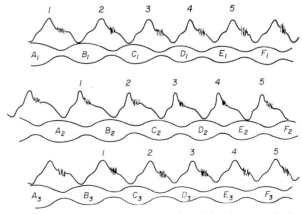

FIG. 14. Diagrammatic representation of simultaneous rhythmic segmentation in small bowel. (For explanation see text.)

dad; all of the other waves—2, 3, 4, and 5—are also. PSP 1 does not encounter excitable fibers until its action potential portion reaches position B_1, which is midway between the action potential portions of PSPs 1 and 2. PSP 2 likewise encounters excitable fibers at position C_1, PSP 3 at D_1, and so on. Each wave then encounters excitable fibers and fires a contraction at the midpoint between previous contractions, the point of previous maximum distention. Half the contents that occupied compartments A_1, B_1, C_1, D_1, E_1, and F_1 are now forced into the intervening, noncontracting compartments (A_2, B_2, C_2, D_2, E_2, and F_2). The third contraction of the rhythmic sequence will occur at sites A_2, B_2, C_2, D_2, E_2, and F_2, which correspond to the sites of the original contractions that were present under the action potential portion of PSPs 1, 2, 3, 4, and 5, respectively. If the sequence continues, the result is a series of simultaneous rhythmic contractions, at the frequency of the PSP and spaced at intervals equal to half the wavelength of the PSP at that site. This is the pattern of simultaneous rhythmic segmentation. This pattern has been recorded in exactly the fashion described by means of balloons placed in the midbowel (Fig. 4). Since the length of segments is relatively long in the duodenum and upper jejunum, rhythmic segmentation, in its classic form, will be best shown by cineradiography in midjejunum and more caudal regions of bowel.

A second program is required to produce rhythmic segmental contractions in caudad sequence. This pattern has not been fully documented in physiological studies. We suspect, as refinements are developed in methods of detecting contractions, that some caudad progress of them within a segment and between contracting segments will be recognized.

The following arrangement offers a possible mechanism for the production of a caudad sequence to the contractions of rhythmic segmentation. If the contractions are rhythmic, the intervals between them can only be prolonged by increasing the relative distance over which the PSP must travel before it encounters excitable tissue. If each succeeding cycle of a series of PSPs is forced, by an unknown mechanism, to travel for a longer time—that is, over a greater distance than it did in its preceding cycle before encountering excitable tissue and so initiating a contraction—then a caudad temporal sequence will be imparted to the contractions. Thus, if each PSP of a series excites a contraction, simultaneous rhythmic segmentation results if the distance traversed is one

wavelength; but if the distance of travel is extended, the contractions will be delayed and the pattern will be that of rhythmic segmentation in caudad sequence. In each of these patterns, each contraction of a rhythmic series is stationary or standing while intervening portions of bowel do not contract. This arrangement differentiates them from peristaltic contractions which are not stationary but migrate caudad.

Peristalsis. If, as the PSP passes along the small bowel, the circular muscle fibers immediately caudal to those that just contracted are excitable and contract when the action potential portion reaches them, then a propagated contraction results. As the process continues, a caudad-migrating band of contraction moving at the velocity of the PSP develops (Fig. 15). This is peristalsis.

Under the conditions described, the band of contracting fibers would move caudad at the velocity of conduction of the PSP, which in the dog is about 16 cm per sec in the duodenum, 8 in the jejunum, and 0.8 in the ileum. The wave of contraction might traverse the gut from duodenum to ileum and would then truly represent what has been described as a "peristaltic rush" (Fig. 15).

Such contractions have been described in agonal states. We have not seen them in healthy animals but have seen contractions that appear to fit their dimensions during cineradiographic observations of dogs' bowels after administration of quinidine sulfate (31). Precise measurements will be needed, however, to determine whether contractions occur that conform to these specifications.

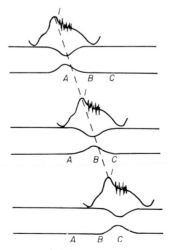

FIG. 15. Diagrammatic representation of mechanisms of production of peristaltic rush—peristalsis propagated caudad at PSP velocity.

A much more slowly migrating peristaltic contraction could result from another program. The sequence is diagramed in Figure 16. In this instance, with the passage of a succession of PSPs, contractions occur with each succeeding wave in the muscle fibers immediately caudal to those that just contracted. The result is a progressive sequence of contractions moving caudad. For example, in the diagram presented in Figure 16, the action potentials of PSP 1 are accompanied by contraction of circular fibers of the bowel at A. The next PSP, 2, excites the fibers at B, which is immediately caudal to A. PSP 3 excites those just caudal to B and so on. A much more slowly migrating peristaltic contraction results. This may have been the type of peristalsis visualized many years ago by Bayliss & Starling (11). The available descriptions of peristalsis in the small bowel do not provide sufficient information to determine whether its dimensions are in accord with the restrictions set by the hypothesis of PSP control.

Stomach

The characteristics of gastric motor and electrical activity are presented fully in Chapters 90 and 96, Volume IV, of this *Handbook*, and the reader is referred to these chapters for detailed descriptions. Only the features of the motor and electrical activities that are clearly related will be identified and summarized here. The application of the concept of PSP control to the stomach is simpler than it is to the small bowel because the motor patterns of the stomach are less complex.

GASTRIC MOTOR ACTIVITY. The major motor contraction of the stomach is the peristaltic wave. Peristaltic contractions often occur in rhythmic sequence [(18); Fig. 17]. Their frequency is then maximal and restricted to a narrow range. For example, in man the frequency of rhythmic peristalsis is 3 per min and the range of variability is small (34, 42); in the dog the range is 4–5 per min (8, 19).

Peristaltic contractions usually start in the orad corpus and sweep in an orderly fashion toward the pylorus. Some appear to pass quickly through the antrum, but most change in character as they enter and traverse it. They cease to be peristaltic and produce simultaneous or very nearly simultaneous contractions of the terminal antrum and pyloric canal. The length of antrum involved in the terminal contraction is not fixed. We propose that it is adjustable.

Typically, contraction of the terminal antrum and

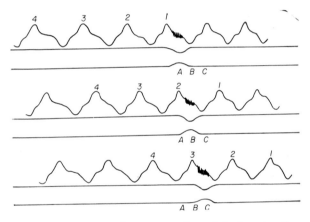

FIG. 16. Diagrammatic representation of slowly migrating peristaltic contraction of small bowel.

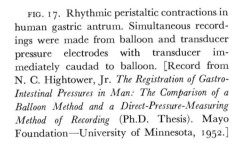

FIG. 17. Rhythmic peristaltic contractions in human gastric antrum. Simultaneous recordings were made from balloon and transducer pressure electrodes with transducer immediately caudad to balloon. [Record from N. C. Hightower, Jr. *The Registration of Gastro-Intestinal Pressures in Man: The Comparison of a Balloon Method and a Direct-Pressure-Measuring Method of Recording* (Ph.D. Thesis). Mayo Foundation—University of Minnesota, 1952.]

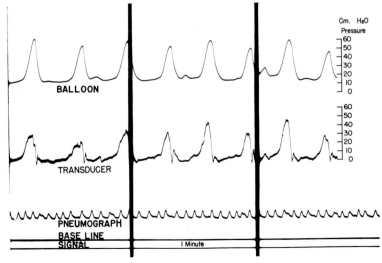

of the pyloric canal starts simultaneously or very nearly so. Since the canal is narrow, it is closed quickly and shuts off the exit from the stomach to the duodenum. The contents in the terminal antrum, as it continues to contract, are then forced back into the corpus of the stomach through the orifice of the peristaltic contraction which initiated the simultaneous contraction. The quantity of contents passed on to the duodenum or retropelled into the corpus depends on the length of the antrum involved in the simultaneous contraction, and this in turn determines how soon in the sequence the pyloric canal is closed. The longer the portion of antrum that contracts simultaneously, the larger is the volume of contents trapped by closure of the pyloric canal and returned to the corpus (see Chapter 90).

GASTRIC ELECTRICAL ACTIVITY. The gastric slow wave, designated by us as the gastric pacesetter potential, or PSP, usually originates in the orad corpus. Its form in the stomach is quite different from that in the small bowel. In the stomach, each cycle consists of two components: a brief initial triphasic oscillation of potential (positive, negative, positive) and a longer isopotential period. The duration of a cycle of the PSP—its period—is customarily measured from the start of one triphasic complex to the start of the next (Figs. 18 and 19).

When the gastric musculature contracts, action potentials are detected. As in the small bowel they occur in bursts, and each burst occupies a definite portion of the PSP. They regularly follow the triphasic complex and occupy about one-fourth to one-half or less of the isopotential phase (Fig. 18).

Sometimes the place of the action potentials is taken by a slow change in potential producing a hump or a dip, or both, in the recording. The amplitude and duration of gastric action potentials have not been correlated with strength and duration measurements of contractions.

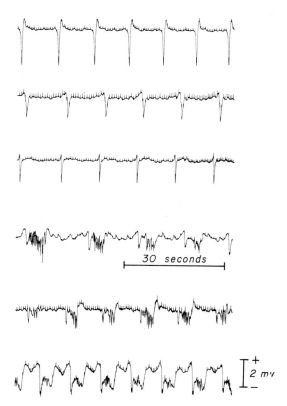

FIG. 18. Pacesetter potentials without (upper three electrodes) and with (lower three electrodes) action potentials

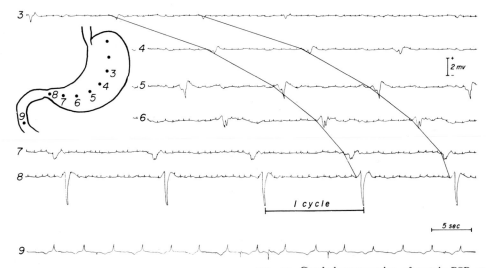

FIG. 19. Caudad propagation of gastric PSP at increasing velocity in a dog.

LOCAL AUTONOMOUS MOTOR CONTROL SYSTEM. Our hypothesis prescribes that the gastric PSP is the frequency regulator and dimension organizer of gastric peristalsis. The PSP sets the frequency of peristaltic contractions, and by controlling the motor activity within a gastric motor segment, defined by the PSP wavelength, it regulates the character of gastric peristalsis.

Motor and electrical correlations. The sites of origin of the PSP and peristaltic contractions are both in the orad corpus. Both are propagated caudad. Their velocities of propagation have not been measured simultaneously, but our impression is, and our hypothesis requires, that they travel together over the stomach. However, no accurate simultaneous measurements have been made.

Frequency control by PSP. The PSP is present whether or not contractions occur. Contractions are initiated by action potentials (8, 19, 24) or by a second slow component which is calcium dependent (47). Only one contraction occurs following a PSP with action potentials or a second slow component. When each cycle of a series of PSPs displays action potentials, peristaltic contractions are present in rhythmic sequence; they occur then at their maximum frequency, and this is also the frequency of the PSP. The frequency of the PSP presets the maximum frequency of gastric peristalsis and predefines when gastric peristaltic contractions may occur. The PSP is thus the frequency regulator of gastric peristalsis.

Pattern control by PSP wavelength. In our hypothesis, the wavelength of the PSP defines a physiological motor segment in the stomach just as it does in the small bowel. Since in the stomach, as in the small bowel, only one burst of action potentials occurs per cycle of the PSP, only one contraction is present within each gastric segment. Thus the PSP wavelength determines the number of peristaltic contractions that can occur simultaneously in the stomach. At any one time, the number of contractions must be equal to the number of wavelengths that can be accommodated in the distance between the orad corpus and the pylorus. This theoretical restriction has not been established experimentally.

The wavelength of the PSP, and so the length of a physiological motor segment, is not fixed in the stomach. The wavelength (λ) is directly related to the velocity of conduction of the PSP and to its frequency ($\lambda = v/f$, equation 1). If velocity becomes faster or frequency slower, wavelength is longer. If velocity is slowed or frequency increased, wavelength is shortened. These parameters are adjustable in the stomach.

The frequency of the PSP does not display a gradient in the stomach as it does in the small bowel. When the frequencies of the PSP in the corpus and antrum are measured simultaneously, they are the same. But we have found recently that the frequency of the gastric PSP may be changed significantly by physiological influences. For example, in healthy, conscious, fasting dogs, the mean frequency of the PSP was 5.4 per min, and this was decreased by about 1 cycle per min by distention of the stomach with water or a balloon and increased by a cycle by the administration of gastrin (37, 39). Although the range of change is small, significant shortening or lengthening of wavelength can result from such shifts in frequency, and these changes in wavelength will alter motor patterns, particularly in the antrum.

The velocity of conduction of the PSP in the stomach displays a gradient, but it is exactly opposite to that in the small bowel. The velocity of the gastric PSP increases as it migrates caudad (Fig. 19) and is faster along the greater curvature than the lesser curvature (47). The speed of conduction is greatest in the antrum (19, 24, 44). As the velocity increases with the caudad spread of the PSP, the wavelength extends. For example, in preliminary experiments done recently in our laboratory, the wavelength in the corpus of the stomach of a dog was 4.5 cm and in the antrum 14 cm (unpublished data, Table 2, and Fig. 20).

Velocity of conduction of the PSP is not fixed, however. We have recently found that it changes with altered physiological conditions. For example, in the corpus of fasting dogs the velocity decreased after fatty meals (37) and increased after insulin administration (38).

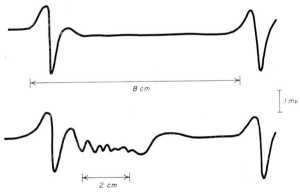

FIG. 20. Wavelength of PSP at gastric corporal-antral junction in a dog. Lower recording also illustrates action potential portion of PSP wavelength.

According to the hypothesis, the length of the action potential portion of the wavelength determines the width of the band of contracting fibers (Fig. 20). Although the length of this portion may vary even when wavelength remains fixed, such changes are small compared with those that may take place if the wavelength is greatly increased or decreased.

The major change in the width of the contracting segment is produced by the increase in the velocity of the PSP as it approaches and traverses the antrum. In the corpus, the PSP velocity is slow, consequently the contracting band is short. As the PSP sweeps down the corpus, its velocity increases gradually and the width of the contracting band broadens. But once the antrum is reached, the PSP velocity is greatly accelerated. This quickly expands the wavelength and the length of its action potential portion. By this means the length of the contracting segment is greatly extended. Sometimes the expansion is sufficient to involve most or all of the antrum and the pyloric canal in a simultaneous or nearly simultaneous contraction. The pyloric canal then closes early in the sequence and much of the antral contents are retropelled; gastric emptying should therefore be prolonged. Sometimes when conduction is slowed and frequency increased, the action potential portion of the PSP wavelength is shortened and the simultaneous or nearly simultaneous contraction involves only the most terminal portion of the antrum. Then closure of the pyloric canal will be late in the sequence, and the volume of retropelled contents may be negligible and gastric emptying may be hastened.

The hypothesis therefore prescribes that the length of the antrum involved in the simultaneous or nearly simultaneous terminal contraction is a function of the wavelength of the PSP. It also presents the proposition that the proportion of the antrum involved in the terminal contraction is a factor in the control of gastric emptying, for the longer the portion of antrum involved the earlier the pyloric canal closes in the peristaltic sequence, and the shorter the period of emptying with each peristaltic contraction.

The hypothesis thus prescribes that the frequency, the rate of propagation, and the width of the band of muscle fibers constituting gastric peristaltic contractions, as well as the length of terminal antral contractions, are all under the control of the PSP. In turn, the PSP is adjustable. The programing of the PSP to deliver different patterns appears to rest with the intramural plexuses, as proposed for the small bowel, but the motility patterns in both regions are changed by extrinsic neural and humoral influences whose site or sites of action, however, have not been established. Clearly, direct effects on smooth muscle cells as well as actions on the neural elements are possible and likely. But wherever the pattern determinant may reside, the PSP is the instrument through which the pattern is consummated.

REFERENCES

1. ALVAREZ, W. C. Functional variations in contractions of different parts of the small intestine. *Am. J. Physiol.* 35: 177–193, 1914.

2. ALVAREZ, W. C. II. Further studies on intestinal rhythm. *Am. J. Physiol.* 37: 267–281, 1915.

3. ALVAREZ, W. C. *An Introduction to Gastro-enterology* (4th ed.). New York: Hoeber, 1948.

4. ALVAREZ, W. C., AND L. J. MAHONEY. Action currents in stomach and intestine. *Am. J. Physiol.* 58: 476–493, 1922.

5. AMBACHE, N. The electrical activity of isolated mammalian intestines. *J. Physiol., London* 106: 139–153, 1947.

6. ARMSTRONG, H. I. O., G. W. MILTON, and A. W. M. SMITH. Electropotential changes of the small intestine. *J. Physiol., London* 131: 147–153, 1956.

7. BASS, P., C. F. CODE, and E. H. LAMBERT. Motor and electric activity of the duodenum. *Am. J. Physiol.* 201: 287–291, 1961.

8. BASS, P., C. F. CODE, and E. H. LAMBERT. Electric activity of gastroduodenal junction. *Am. J. Physiol.* 201: 587–592, 1961.

9. BASS, P., and J. N. WILEY. Electrical and extralumina contractile-force activity in the duodenum of the dog *Am. J. Digest. Diseases* 10: 183–200, 1965.

10. BASS, P., AND J. N. WILEY. Effects of ligation and morphine on electric and motor activity of dog duodenum. *Am. J. Physiol.* 208: 908–913, 1965.

11. BAYLISS, W. M., and E. H. STARLING. The movements and innervation of the small intestine. *J. Physiol., London* 26: 125–138, 1901.

12. BORTOFF, A. Slow potential variations of small intestine. *Am. J. Physiol.* 201: 203–208, 1961.

13. BORTOFF, A. Electrical transmission of slow waves from longitudinal to circular intestinal muscle. *Am. J. Physiol.* 209: 1254–1260, 1965.

14. BORTOFF, A., AND O. H. MULLER. Electrotonic spread of slow waves in circular intestinal muscle. (Abstr.) *Federation Proc.* 26: 383, 1967.

15. BOZLER, E. The action potentials of visceral smooth muscle. *Am. J. Physiol.* 124: 502–510, 1938.

16. BUNKER, C. E., L. P. JOHNSON, and T. S. NELSEN. Chronic

in situ studies of the electrical activity of the small intestine. *Arch. Surg.* 95: 259–268, 1967.

17. CANNON, W. B. *The Mechanical Factors of Digestion.* New York: Longmans, 1911.

18. CARLSON, A. J. *The Control of Hunger in Health and Disease.* Chicago: Univ. of Chicago Press, 1916.

19. CARLSON, H. C., C. F. CODE, AND R. A. NELSON. Motor action of the canine gastroduodenal junction: A cineradiographic, pressure, and electric study. *Am. J. Digest. Diseases* 11: 155–172, 1966.

20. CASTLETON, K. B. An experimental study of the movements of the small intestine. *Am. J. Physiol.* 107: 641–646, 1934.

21. CHRISTENSEN, J., H. P. SCHEDL, AND J. A. CLIFTON. The small intestinal basic electrical rhythm (slow wave) frequency gradient in normal men and in patients with a variety of diseases. *Gastroenterology* 50: 309–315, 1966.

22. CODE, C. F., A. G. ROGERS, J. SCHLEGEL, N. C. HIGHTOWER, JR., AND J. A. BARGEN. Motility patterns in the terminal ileum: Studies on two patients with ulcerative colitis and ileac stomas. *Gastroenterology* 32: 651–665, 1957.

23. DANIEL, E. E., D. R. CARLOW, B. T. WACHTER, W. H. SUTHERLAND, AND A. BOGOCH. Electrical activity of the small intestine. *Gastroenterology* 37: 268–281, 1959.

24. DANIEL, E. E., AND K. M. CHAPMAN. Electrical activity of the gastrointestinal tract as an indication of mechanical activity. *Am. J. Digest. Diseases* 8: 54–102, 1963.

25. DIAMANT, N. E., AND A. BORTOFF. Intestinal slow wave frequency gradient. (Abstr.) *Federation Proc.* 27: 449, 1968.

26. DOUGLAS, D. M. The activity of the duodenum. *J. Physiol., London* 107: 472–478, 1948.

27. DOUGLAS, D. M. The decrease in frequency of contraction of the jejunum after transplantation to the ileum. *J. Physiol., London* 110: 66–75, 1949.

28. DOUGLAS, D. M., AND F. C. MANN. An experimental study of the rhythmic contractions in the small intestine of the dog. *Am. J. Digest. Diseases* 6: 318–322, 1939.

29. FOULK, W. T., C. F. CODE, C. G. MORLOCK, AND J. A. BARGEN. A study of the motility patterns and the basic rhythm in the duodenum and upper part of the jejunum of human beings. *Gastroenterology* 26: 601–611, 1954.

30. FRIEDMAN, G., B. S. WOLF, J. D. WAYE, AND H. D. JANOWITZ. Correlation of cineradiographic and intraluminal pressure changes in the human duodenum: An analysis of the functional significance of monophasic waves. *Gastroenterology* 49: 37–49, 1965.

31. GARRETT, J. M., J. F. SCHLEGEL, AND C. F. CODE. Effect of quinidine on electrical and motor activity of canine small bowel. *Gut* 7: 562–565, 1966.

32. GARRETT, J. M., J. F. SCHLEGEL, AND H. N. HOFFMAN, II. Intraluminal detection of intestinal electrical activity. (Abstr.) *Federation Proc.* 22: 225, 1963.

33. HASSELBRACK, R., AND J. E. THOMAS. Control of intestinal rhythmic contractions by a duodenal pacemaker. *Am. J. Physiol.* 201: 955–960, 1961.

34. HIGHTOWER, N. C., JR., AND C. F. CODE. The quantitative analysis of antral gastric motility records in normal human beings, with a study of the effects of neostigmine. *Proc. Staff Meeting Mayo Clinic* 25: 697–704, 1950.

35. HOLADAY, D. A., H. VOLK, AND J. MANDELL. Electrical

activity of the small intestine with special reference to the origin of rhythmicity. *Am. J. Physiol.* 195: 505–515, 1958.

36. JACOBY, H. I., P. BASS, AND D. R. BENNETT. In vivo extraluminal contractile force transducer for gastrointestinal muscle. *J. Appl. Physiol.* 18: 658–665, 1963.

37. KELLY, K. A., AND C. F. CODE. Myo-electric potentials of the stomach. (Abstr.) *Physiologist* 10: 218, 1967.

38. KELLY, K. A., AND C. F. CODE. Effect of vagotomy on canine gastric myoelectric activity. (Abstr.) *Gastroenterology* 54: 1249, 1968.

39. KELLY, K. A., AND C. F. CODE. The effect of gastrin on gastric myoelectric activity. (Abstr.) *Intern. Congr. Physiol. Sci., 24th, Washington, D.C., 1968.* In press.

40. KOBAYASHI, M., T. NAGAI, AND C. L. PROSSER. Electrical interaction between muscle layers of cat intestine. *Am. J. Physiol.* 211: 1281–1291, 1966.

41. KOBAYASHI, M., C. L. PROSSER, AND T. NAGAI. Electrical properties of intestinal muscle as measured intracellularly and extracellularly. *Am. J. Physiol.* 213: 275–286, 1967.

42. LIND, J. F., H. L. DUTHIE, J. F. SCHLEGEL, AND C. F. CODE. Motility of the gastric fundus. *Am. J. Physiol.* 201: 197–202, 1961.

43. MANN, C. V., J. F. SCHLEGEL, F. H. ELLIS, JR., AND C. F. CODE. Studies of the isolated gastroesophageal sphincter. *Surg. Forum* 13: 248–250, 1962.

44. MCCOY, E. J., AND P. BASS. Chronic electrical activity of gastroduodenal area: effects of food and certain catecholamines. *Am. J. Physiol.* 205: 439–445, 1963.

45. MILTON, G. W., AND A. W. M. SMITH. The pacemaking area of the duodenum. *J. Physiol., London* 132: 100–114, 1956.

46. NAGAI, T., AND C. L. PROSSER. Patterns of conduction in smooth muscle. *Am. J. Physiol.* 204: 910–914, 1963.

47. PAPASOVA, M. P., T. NAGAI, AND C. L. PROSSER. Two-component slow waves in smooth muscle of cat stomach. *Am. J. Physiol.* 214: 695–702, 1968.

48. REINKE, D. A., A. H. ROSENBAUM, AND D. R. BENNETT. Patterns of dog gastrointestinal contractile activity monitored in vivo with extraluminal force transducers. *Am. J. Digest. Diseases* 12: 113–141, 1967.

49. ROSENBAUM, A. H., D. A. REINKE, AND D. R. BENNETT. In-vivo force, frequency, and velocity of dog gastrointestinal contractile activity. *Am. J. Digest. Diseases* 12: 142–153, 1967.

50. SMITH, I. B. *A Study of Small Intestinal Motility in Dogs* (Thesis). Cambridge, England: Univ. of Cambridge, 1959.

51. SZURSZEWSKI, J. H., AND C. F. CODE. Electrical slow wave gradient of canine small intestine. (Abstr.) *Federation Proc.* 27: 449, 1968.

52. SZURSZEWSKI, J., AND F. R. STEGGERDA. The effect of hypoxia on the electrical slow wave of the canine small intestine. *Am. J. Digest. Diseases* 13: 168–177, 1968.

53. SZURSZEWSKI, J., AND F. R. STEGGERDA. The effect of hypoxia on the mechanical activity of the canine small intestine. *Am. J. Digest. Diseases* 13: 178–185, 1968.

54. TAMAI, T., AND C. L. PROSSER. Differentiation of slow potentials and spikes in longitudinal muscle of cat intestine. *Am. J. Physiol.* 210: 452–458, 1966.

INDEX

Index